AVIATION MUSEUMS AND COLLECTIONS OF THE REST OF THE WORLD

(EXCLUDING EUROPE AND NORTH AMERICA)

Bob Ogden

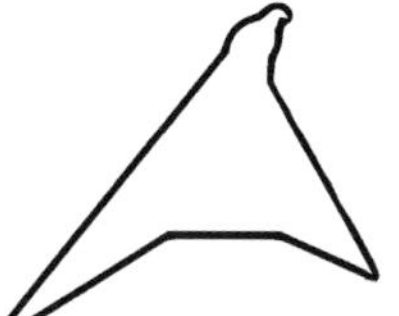

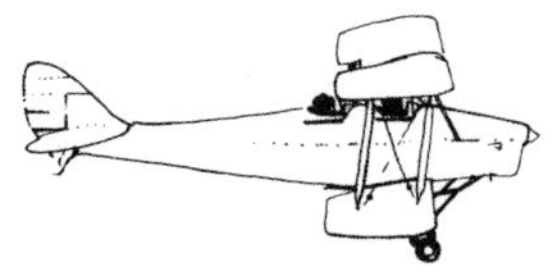

Published by:
Air-Britain (Historians) Ltd

Membership details:
1 Rose Cottages, 179 Penn Road,
Hazlemere, Bucks HP15 7NE
Website:
www.air-britain.co.uk

Sales department:
41 Penhurst Road, Leigh,
Tonbridge, Kent TN11 8HL
Email:
sales@air-britain.co.uk

Correspondence regarding this publication to:
Bob Ogden, 13 Western Avenue,
Woodley, Berkshire RG5 3BJ
Bob.Ogden@air-britain.co.uk

ISBN: 978 0 85130 394 9

Printed by Cromwell Press Ltd,
Aintree Avenue,
White Horse Business Park,
Trowbridge BA14 0XB

Maps and origination by Sue J. Bushell

COVER PHOTOGRAPHS.

Front *The Commonwealth Boomerang of the Temora Aviation Museum is shown on a flight near its New South Wales base. (Temora AM)*

Rear *Very few de Havilland Dragonflies have survived and this example can be seen in the Croydon Aviation Heritage Trust hangar at Mandeville. (Brian Nicholls)*

This colourful Shenyang JJ-5 resides in the vast tunnel at the China Aviation Museum (John Mounce)

CONTENTS

CENTRAL AMERICA

Museums and Collections

SOUTH AMERICA

Museums and Collections

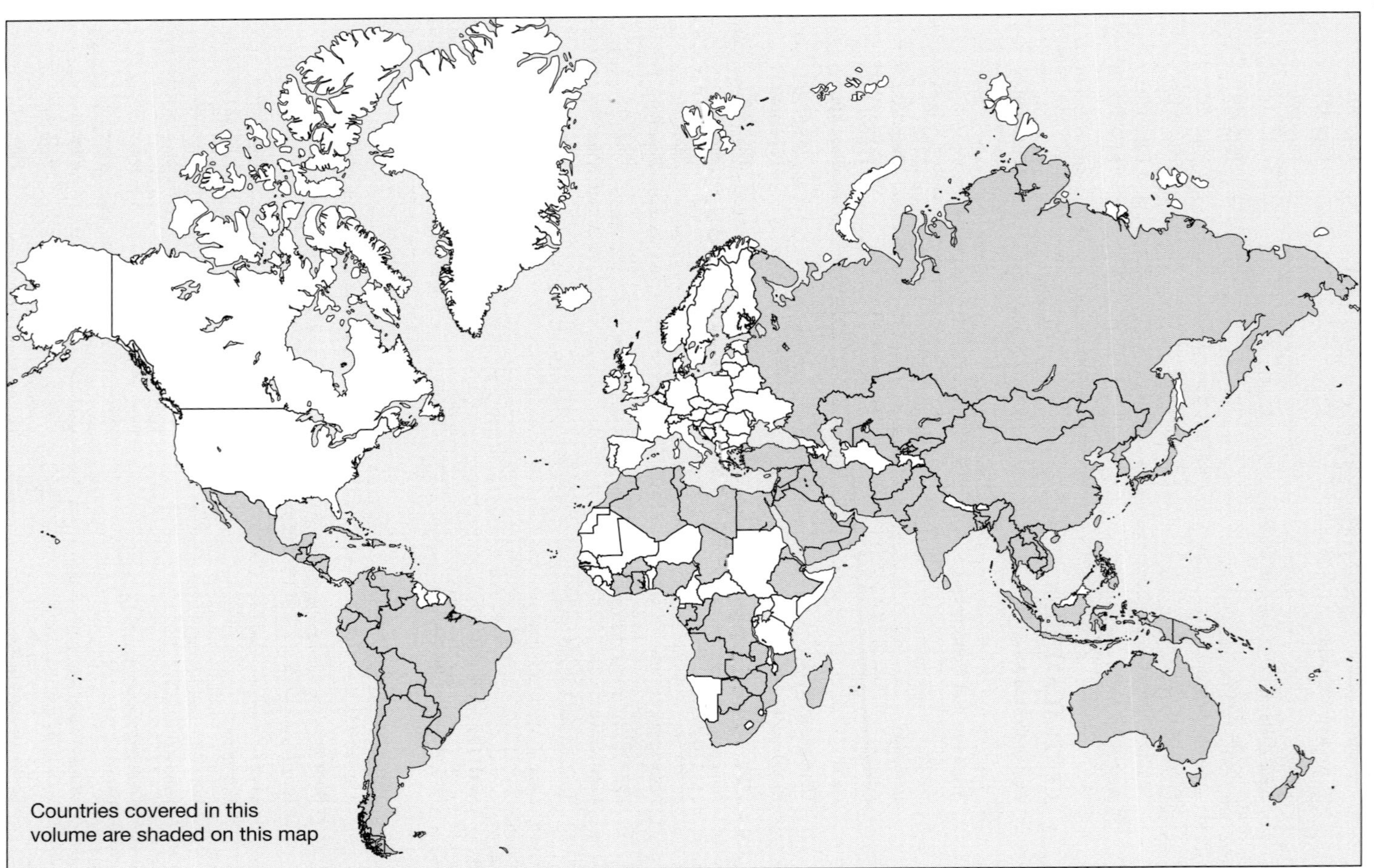
Countries covered in this
volume are shaded on this map

INTRODUCTION

This book covers the areas which were dealt with in Volumes 1, part of 10 and 11 of 'Aircraft Museums and Collections of the World'. Over the last few years much more information has become available and new museums are being set up in many countries. In this volume I have included many single aircraft preserved as monuments at military bases, aero clubs and in cities, towns and villages. Several of my contacts around the world have spent a great deal of time to send me details and I think that these efforts deserve to be put into print. Some of the countries included are difficult to visit because of the current political situation andas a result of this reports may be slightly dated but are included in the hope that more recent details will emerge. Please send me any information however small so that records can be amended. The turbulent conditions in many African countries means that aircraft preservation is very low on the agenda. However, there are a few dedicated individuals who are intent on preserving the heritage of their lands. In Egypt there are a number of small museums and reports of an Air Force collection at Almaza have recently emerged. Morocco has preserved many interesting aircraft at military bases and there are several small collections in other countries. South Africa has some excellent museums and the country boasts a number of flyable propliners as well as the jets at Thunder City.

The vast continent of Asia has large numbers of superb museums as well as preserved aircraft at many military sites and as town memorials. The Middle East area of the continent seems to be in constant turmoil but in Israel there is the large Air Force Museum and a number of base collections. Details of the major museums in China are fairly well documented but a Civil Aviation Museum near the new Beijing Airport was due to open in time for the 2008 Olympic Games. A military collection near a base, which has over five hundred aircraft in store, seems to be open. In India all military bases have small museums and the gate guardians have been designated as part of these. Pakistan has many preserved aircraft around the country and the Air Force Museum near Karachi is expanding. I have been fortunate to be in contact with an enthusiast in Siberia who has toured the area and provided many previously unknown details. Also I have renewed acquaintances with people who have extensive knowledge of the preservation scenes in Japan, South Korea, Taiwan and Thailand. They have again sent me a great deal of information. Turkey was included in 'Aviation Museums and Collections of Mainland Europe' but I have decided to put details in this book as the majority of the country is in Asia and my contact has send new information.

The situation in Australia and New Zealand is vibrant with new museums and collections opened. On the negative side the recent death of Col Pay in a flying accident has cast a shadow over his excellent group of flyable warbirds. The Historical Aircraft Preservation Society has moved into new purpose built premises at Albion Park and the Temora Aviation Museum maintains a number of jets in flying condition. The Australian War Memorial has reorganised their exhibitions and the Fleet Air Arm Museum has changed the emphasis of its displays. New galleries have opened at The RAAF Museum at Point Cook and other museums have gained more aircraft. In New Zealand the highlight has been the opening of the first phase of the Omaka Aviation Heritage Centre. This project has been planned for many years and the dedicated group of enthusiasts now have a superb exhibition ready. A number of interesting aircraft are on the airfield and will be displayed when the next parts of the complex are built. The Croydon Aviation Heritage Trust has built a superb hall to exhibit mainly classic de Havilland types. In Central and South America many aircraft are preserved and there are many excellent museums. Cuba has saved several aircraft and there are collections on a number of military bases. Most Mexican Air Force sites have kept aircraft as monuments and there are a number of interesting museums around the country. Other Air Forces in the region are steadily developing informative museums. On Barbados a superb new hall has been built to exhibit a Concorde. In Argentina there are preserved aircraft around the country and the National Aeronautical Museum has moved into premises at Morón where more aircraft can be shown. The excellent museum opened by the airline TAM in Brazil has many rare types on view with several more in store and under restoration. The Museu Aeroespacial continues to restore and put on show aircraft which have made contributions to the development of aviation in the country. The Chilean national museum is expanding, as is the Air Force Museum in Venezuela. In Uruguay progress is being made following the disastrous 1997 fire which destroyed a number of unique types.

ACKNOWLEDGEMENTS

Special thanks are due to Tony Hancock for his meticulous checking of the aircraft lists. He has added a great deal of new information. I would like to thank all who have sent me reports of their travels, helped with aircraft details and loaned magazines and photographs. Thanks also to the staff and volunteer members of museums who have replied to my requests.

Among the individuals who helped are Carlos Abella, Diego Alvarado, Richard Andrews, Peter R. Arnold, Andy Banthorp, Winston Brent, Tony Broadhurst, Stephan de Bruijn, Eduardo Cardenas, Vito Cedrini, Chris Chatfield, Juan Carlos Cicalesi, Steve Comber, Aidan Curley, Mike Draper, Clarence Fu, Steve Darke, Phil Dunnington, Santiago Flores, Wilman Fuentes, Peter Gerhardt, Darryl Gibbs, Benno Goethals, Paul Harrison, Peter Hellier, Nigel Hitchman, David Holman, Paul Jackson, Peter Knaap, Diego Kusak, Yuval Lapid, Dave Lednicer, Ruud Leeuw, Philippe le Pallec, Chris Lofting, Piet Luijken, Ralph Lunt, Michael Magnusson, Dave McDonald, George Maybury, Gerry Manning, Tony Morris, John Mounce, Eric Munk, Mike Nelson, Iván Nesbit, Brian Nicholls, Gleb Osokin, Jagan Pillarisetti, Nigel Ponsford, Santiago Rivas, Lloyd Robinson, Álvaro Romero, Douglas Rough, Paul Seymour, Sharam Sharifi, Usman Shabbir, Tim Spearman, Renato Spillimbergo, Alan Taylor, Bill Teasdale, Shinsuke Yamamoto and Phil Yeadon.

NOTES

For most museums and collections the following information is stated.

GEOGRAPHY
For each country, state or province a one, two, three or four letter code is allocated. Each museum has been given a number so that the index can be used to trace a particular type of aircraft. The number is also shown on the appropriate map which is normally found after the country heading. Maps are not provided for some countries and all are drawn to different scales.

ADDRESS
The full postal address is given wherever possible. For some voluntary/private organisations the address stated may be that of the owner or an official of the organisation.

TELEPHONE / FAX / E-MAIL
Wherever possible these are given. For some voluntary/private organisations those stated may be that of the owner or an official of the organisation. These details often change so check before making contact. New telephone codes are regularly introduced as more numbers are allocated. Therefore it is advisable to check these. Many Email addresses for museums incorporate the name of an individual. When they leave this is changed.

ADMISSION
The times stated are the latest available and cannot be guaranteed. Intending visitors should check before travelling. The twenty four hour clock has been used and local times stated. For those not familiar with this system – an a.m. time is as follows 8 a.m. is 0800 – noon is 1200: for a p.m. time add 12 hours i.e. 4 p.m. is 1600. Where 'By prior permission Only' is shown the aircraft are on private property or are in restricted areas and normally cannot be seen by the casual caller. Most of the flying collections are based on active airfields and can be seen only with the permission of the airfield operator in addition to that of the owners.

LOCATION
A rough guide to the location of the museum/collection is shown on the map and in the heading. If a museum has aircraft at more than one site a list of these will be given and the number of the location will follow the status symbol.

AIRCRAFT TYPE
Many aircraft have a manufacturers and service number as well as a name. Where known the full manufacturers designation is given with the service number in brackets. For a licence built type which has been given a new designation, the original in the country of design is shown in square brackets.

If the type has been constructed by a number of companies the designing firm is stated.

For homebuilt aircraft and some gliders the designer is named. Shown in brackets after the type name is either its former type if the aircraft has undergone major modifications or the service designations in the order allocated. The symbol (R) denotes a replica which may be an accurate copy built to flying standards. (FSM) denotes a full size model with the correct dimensions.

REGISTRATION / MILITARY SERIAL
The markings normally carried by the aircraft are stated. Many machines are painted in their former markings for display purposes and the serial given may not be a current allocation. False markings are shown in inverted commas i.e. 'A4567'. Some aircraft carry no markings and the current allocation is normally stated.

CONSTRUCTOR'S / MANUFACTURER'S NUMBERS
This is normally the only true way to identify an aircraft and wherever possible this is stated. Some manufacturers do not allocate c/ns – particularly for military aircraft on the assumption that they will keep the same serial for life. In some cases line numbers or fuselage numbers are given. Although not true c/ns they do provide a means of identification. Some registers quote military serials, part numbers etc. as the c/n.

PREVIOUS IDENTITIES / NOTES
These are given in chronological order starting with the initial allocation. Where the country is unclear this is stated in brackets. Reservations which were not taken up are also shown in brackets. Standard abbreviations have been used for many military serials and the civil country identification markings will be found in registers. Additional information may be given here.

STATUS
The system developed by the Smithsonian Institution is used.

- **A** Active – capable of flight and in most cases with a current permit.
- **C** Under restoration or rebuild.
- **D** Derelict or severely damaged – may be restored eventually.
- **PV** On public view – normally in the museum premises.
- **RA** Research accessible – may be seen by serious researchers with prior permission.
- **S** Stored – may be crated or in a restricted area.
- **X** Carries false markings.

Combinations of these may be used. If a number is stated after the codes refer to the location codes for the museum.

AFRICA

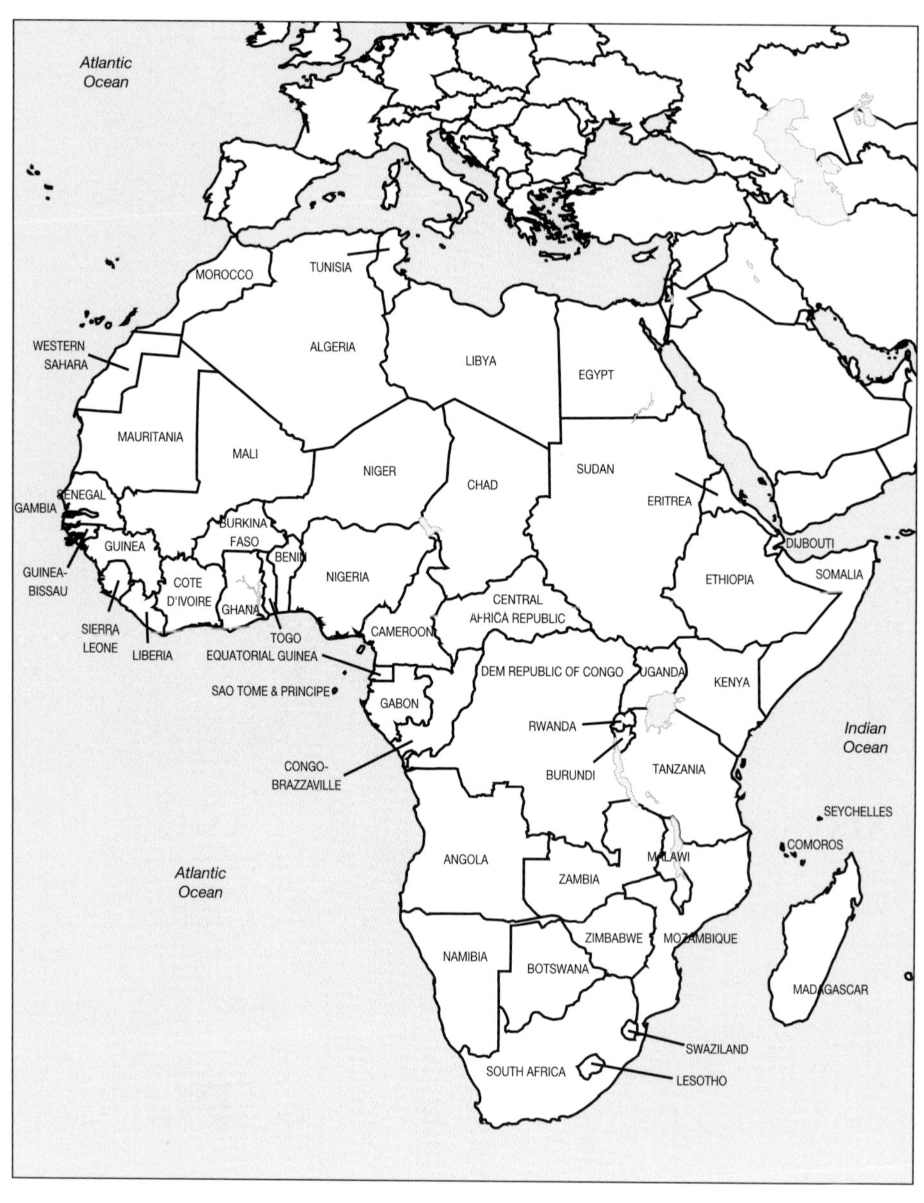
Atlantic Ocean
MOROCCO
TUNISIA
ALGERIA
LIBYA
EGYPT
WESTERN SAHARA
MAURITANIA
MALI
NIGER
CHAD
SUDAN
ERITREA
SENEGAL
GAMBIA
BURKINA FASO
GUINEA
BENIN
NIGERIA
DJIBOUTI
SOMALIA
ETHIOPIA
GUINEA-BISSAU
COTE D'IVOIRE
GHANA
CENTRAL AFRICA REPUBLIC
SIERRA LEONE
LIBERIA
TOGO
CAMEROON
EQUATORIAL GUINEA
DEM REPUBLIC OF CONGO
UGANDA
KENYA
SAO TOME & PRINCIPE
GABON
RWANDA
Indian Ocean
CONGO-BRAZZAVILLE
BURUNDI
TANZANIA
SEYCHELLES
COMOROS
ANGOLA
MALAWI
Atlantic Ocean
ZAMBIA
ZIMBABWE
MOZAMBIQUE
NAMIBIA
BOTSWANA
MADAGASCAR
SWAZILAND
SOUTH AFRICA
LESOTHO

ALGERIA

EXPOSITION DE SÉCURITÉ CIVILE (ALG1)

Address:	Algiers.
Admission:	By prior permission only.
Location:	In the south eastern part of the city.

The organisation is responsible for the security of the county and has posts in all major towns. Two Murphy Rebel aircraft are preserved at the site which is located on the main road to the airport.

TYPE	REG/SER	CON. NO.	PI/NOTES	STATUS
☐ Murphy Rebel	102			RA
☐ Murphy Rebel	103			RA

MONUMENT DE LA BASE AÉRIENNE DE BOU SFER (ALG2)

Address:	Bou Sfer.
Admission:	Aircraft outside base.
Location:	About 2 km north of the town.

This important base was used by French Air Force units before Algeria gained her independence. At the current time it is home to squadrons flying the MiG-29 and Kamov helicopters.

TYPE	REG/SER	CON. NO.	PI/NOTES	STATUS
☐ Mikoyan-Gurevich MiG-21bis				PV

MONUMENT AUX MORTS DE TIZI-OUZOU (ALG3)

Address:	Tizi-Ouzou.
Admission:	On permanent view
Location:	About 150 km east of Algiers.

The monument was set up to honour those who lost their lives in the conflict for independence. The former American and French Texan is the only aircraft on show. There are also guns and military vehicles to he seen.

TYPE	REG/SER	CON. NO.	PI/NOTES	STATUS
☐ North American NA-182 Texan (T-6G)			(USAF), (French AF)	PV

MUSEO DEL POLISARIO (ALG4)

Address:	Tindouf.
Admission:	Hours variable.
Location:	In the northern part of the town.

This western province of Algeria has been claimed by Morocco and wars have taken place between the two countries. The Polisario Front was formed in 1973 with the aim of freeing Western Sahara from the influence of Spain. Guerilla from the movement were involved in actions across the region. The Front set up its main base in Tindouf where they have opened a museum. The wreckage of a Moroccan F-5 is on show. Also to be seen are documents, maps and photographs showing the history of the movement.

TYPE	REG/SER	CON. NO.	PI/NOTES	STATUS
☐ Northrop N-156A Freedom Fighter (F-5A)	69120	N.6224	66-9120 – in Moroccan markings.	PVD

ANGOLA

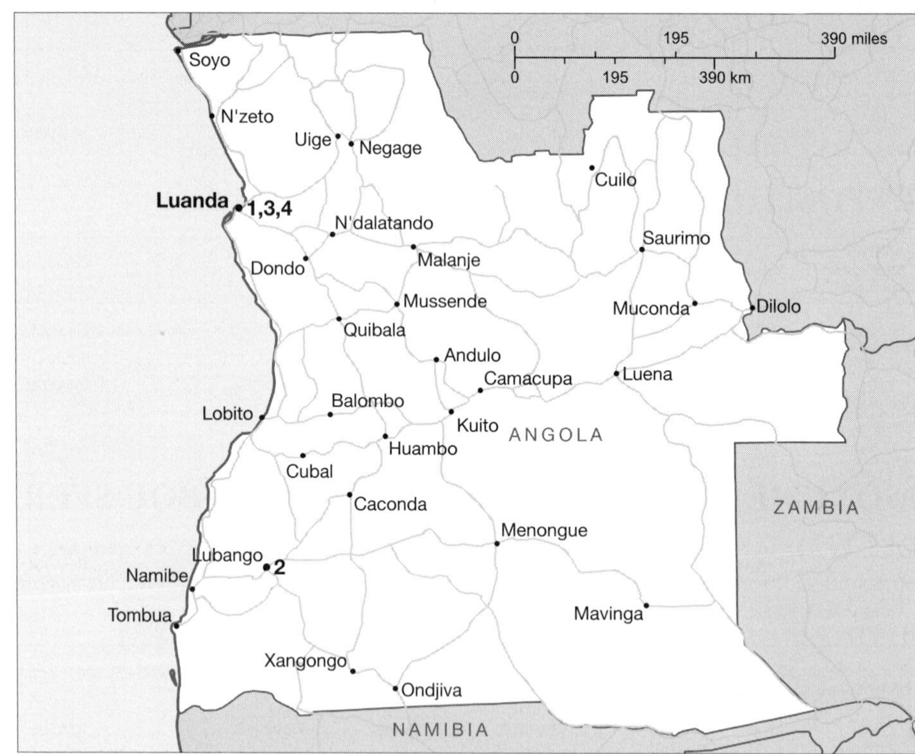

MONUMENTO DE BASE AÉREA DE LUANDA (AN1)

Address:	Luanda
Admission:	By prior permission only.
Location:	In the southern part of the city.

The Air Force has a base at the main airport for the capital city. A MiG-15 UTI was preserved near the main gate but it has not been reported for a few years. There are many derelict military aircraft present.

TYPE	REG/SER	CON. NO.	PI/NOTES	STATUS
☐ Mikoyan-Gurevich MiG-15UTI	C22			RA

MONUMENTO DE BASE AÉREA DE LUBANGO (AN2)

Address:	Lubango.
Admission:	By prior permission only.
Location:	In the southern part of the town.

The airfield serves as the civil airport for the town and the Air Force also has a base on one side of the site. An aircraft preserved as a monument has been reported and is believed to be a MiG-21.

TYPE	REG/SER	CON. NO.	PI/NOTES	STATUS
☐ Mikoyan-Gurevich MiG-21			Possible type.	RA

MUSEU DE GUERRA (AN3)

Address:	Luanda.
Admission:	Unknown
Location:	In the city.

Displays at the museum trace the conflicts which have taken place since independence from Portugal. Two Texans and a number of military vehicles and weapons are on show in the museum grounds.

TYPE	REG/SER	CON. NO.	PI/NOTES	STATUS
☐ North American NA-88 Texan (AT-6D) (Harvard III)	1668	88-10533	42-85112, EX438	PV
☐ North American NA-182 Texan (T-6G)	1685	182-548	51-14861	PVD

SOCIEDADE DE PRESERVAÇÃO (AN4)

Address:	Luanda.
Admission:	By prior permission only.
Location:	In the city.

A group of enthusiasts is trying to set up a museum on the island in the city. Three aircraft are in currently their care. The Woodley-built Gemini operated in the Belgian Congo from 1953 until 1956 before arriving in Angola.

TYPE	REG/SER	CON. NO.	PI/NOTES	STATUS
☐ Fairchild M-62A-4 Cornell (PT-26A)	CR-LBI			RA
☐ Miles M.65 Gemini 1A	CR-LCX	6510	G-AKHS, OO-GAR	RA
☐ Republic F-84G Thunderjet	5158		Possible identity	RA

BOTSWANA

MOLEPOLOLE AIR BASE MONUMENT (BOT1)

Address:	Air Force Base, Molepolole.
Admission:	By prior permission only.
Location:	Just north of the town.

The Botswana Air Force operated thirteen Strikemasters and one has been preserved at Molepolole. This airfield was constructed in the 1990s by an international consortium of firms from around the world.

TYPE	REG/SER	CON. NO.	PI/NOTES	STATUS
☐ British Aircraft Corporation 167 Strikemaster 83	OJ-3	163	G-27-156, ZG810, 115 (Kuwait)	RA

BURKINA FASO

MONUMENT DE LA BASE AÉRIENNE D'OUAGADOUGOU (BUR1)

Address:	Base Aérienne, Ougadougou.
Admission:	By prior permission only.
Location:	In the south eastern part of the town.

Formerly the French colony of Upper Volta, Burkina Faso gained its independence in 1960. Two aircraft were preserved but the Broussard, once parked the main gate, was recently seen stored in a hangar. The SIAI-Marchetti SF.260 is mounted on a pylon near to buildings within the military camp.

TYPE	REG/SER	CON. NO.	PI/NOTES	STATUS
☐ Max Holste MH1521M Broussard	XT-MAC	314	314 (France)	RA
☐ SIAI-Marchetti SF.260W	BF8473			RA

CHAD

MONUMENT DE LA BASE AÉRIENNE DE N'DJAMENA (CHA1)

Address:	Base Aérienne, N'Djamena.
Admission:	By prior permission only.
Location:	In the northern part of the town.

Chad gained its independence from France in 1960 and was presented with a number of aircraft in order to start an Air Force. At least six Broussards joined the service and one has been preserved. This rugged design was ideally suited to the harsh conditions and often carried out missions into unprepared airstrips.

TYPE	REG/SER	CON. NO.	PI/NOTES	STATUS
☐ Max Holste MH.1521M Broussard	TT-KAB	203	203 (France)	RA

CONGO BRAZZAVILLE

COLLECTION DE LA BASE AÉRIENNE DE POINTE NOIRE (CON1)

Address:	Base Aérienne, Point Noire.
Admission:	By prior permission only.
Location:	In the southern suburbs of the city.

This long established airfield was used by Free French aircraft during World War II. From the end of the conflict it was a French Air Force base and also served as the civil airport for the city. Independence was achieved in 1960 and the first aircraft operated by the country were mainly of French origin, but in the mid-1980s the Soviet Union supplied a number fighter and transport types. The MiG-15UTI, one of two delivered, is preserved at the Air Force Headquarters. Four Noratlas transports were supplied by France and these served until at least the late 1970s. One is parked close to the main gate of the base and the other is on the airfield.

TYPE	REG/SER	CON. NO.	PI/NOTES	STATUS
☐ Mikoyan-Gurevich MiG-15UTI		10994819		RA
☐ Nord N.2501F Noratlas	TN-234	130	130 (France)	RA
☐ Nord N.2501F Noratlas	TN-232	138	138 (France)	RA

CÔTE D'IVOIRE

MONUMENT DE LA BASE AÉRIENNE DE ABIDJAN (CTI1)

Address:	Base Aérienne, Abidjan.
Admission:	By prior permission only.
Location:	In the southern part of the town.

The Air Force was formed in 1961 after independence and the initial equipment consisted of a small number of Broussards and Douglas C-47s. One of the former has been preserved at the base.

TYPE	REG/SER	CON. NO.	PI/NOTES	STATUS
☐ Max Holste MH.1521M Broussard				RA

DEMOCRATIC REPUBLIC OF THE CONGO

MONUMENT DE LA BASE AÉRIENNE DE GOMA (DRC1)

Address:	Base Aérienne, Goma.
Admission:	By prior permission only.
Location:	Just north of the town.

The county gained its independence from Belgium in 1960 and since then has operated a variety of aircraft. The former Luftwaffe Dornier Do 27 is parked by the base gate.

TYPE	REG/SER	CON. NO.	PI/NOTES	STATUS
☐ Dornier Do 27A-4	9Q-CIA	492	KD+153, EB+388, D-EKHE	RA

DJIBOUTI

COLLECTION DU DÉTACHMENT AIR 188 (DJ1)

Address:	Base Aérienne 188, Ambouli.
Admission:	By prior permission only.
Location:	In the southern suburbs of the city.

The French Air Force maintains a squadron flying Mirage F.1Cs and a transport unit equipped with Transalls and helicopters at the field. Examples of types operated in the past have been preserved. The Skyraider was widely used in the French colonies in Africa. Djibouti gained its independence from France in 1977 and has a small air force. The Alouette is preserved in their area of the airport.

TYPE	REG/SER	CON. NO.	PI/NOTES	STATUS
☐ Dassault Mirage F.1C	214	214		RA
☐ Dassault Mirage IIIC	82	82		RA
☐ Douglas AD-4NA Skyraider (AD-4N)	125741	7634	Bu125741	RA
☐ North American NA-223 Super Sabre (F-100D)	42293	223-173	54-2293	RA
☐ Sud-Est SE.3130 Alouette II	J2-MAB	1141	75 (France)	RA

EGYPT

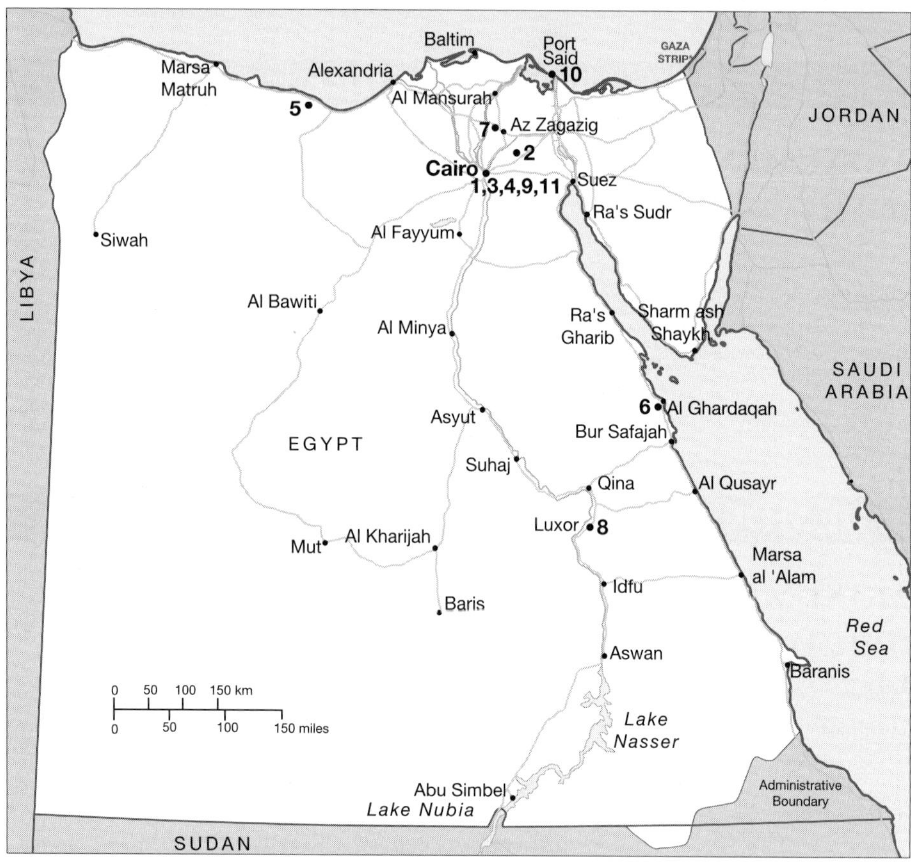

CAIRO WEST AIR BASE MONUMENT (EG1)

Address:	222 Fighter Brigade Headquarters, Cairo West.
Admission:	By prior permission only.
Location:	About 2 km west of the city.

This base houses fighter and helicopter units. The Ilyushin Il-28 has been preserved at the field for many years and is parked close to one of the ramps. The type served with several squadrons.

TYPE	REG/SER	CON. NO.	PI/NOTES	STATUS
☐ Ilyushin Il-28	1772			RA

EGYPTIAN AIR FORCE ACADEMY MONUMENT (EG2)

Address:	Air Force Academy, Bilbeis.
Admission:	By prior permission only.
Location:	In the south eastern suburbs of the town.

The academy was set up by the British in 1938 and was at Almaza Airport near Cairo. The airfield at Bilbeis was operational in World War II and saw use by both British and American aircraft. When the country achieved its independence a move was made to Bilbeis where the air space had less traffic. The Delfin was used for many years for pilot training and an example has been preserved as a monument.

TYPE	REG/SER	CON. NO.	PI/NOTES	STATUS
☐ Aero L-29 Delfin	'2000'			RAX

EGYPTIAN AIR FORCE COLLECTION (EG3)

Address:	Almaza, Cairo.
Admission:	By prior permission only.
Location:	In the north eastern suburbs of the city.

Airline service started at the airfield in the early 1930s by Misr Airlines, the foreunner of the current Egypt Air. The British set up an Air Academy in 1938. During World War II the site was an important military base used by the Royal Air Force. In 1956 Almaza was bombed by British aircraft during the Suez War. A decision was made to develop the ex-American Payne Field as the main international airport for the city eventually led to a reduction in airline operations. The Egyptian Air Force now bases transports, helicopters and trainer at the field. A collection of preserved aircraft has been set up. The first Mirages arrived in Egypt in the mid-1970s and several versions have been flown. A small number of Tupolev Tu-16s were delivered and the bomber remained in service until the late 1980s. Details of the aircraft are sparse and the list is not complete. The majority of the aircraft are parked under shelters to protect them from the sun.

TYPE	REG/SER	CON. NO.	PI/NOTES	STATUS
☐ Dassault Mirage 5				RA
☐ Dassault Mirage F.1				RA
☐ Hiller UH12				RA
☐ Ilyushin Il-14				RA
☐ Mikoyan-Gurevich MiG-15				RA
☐ Mikoyan-Gurevich MiG-21				RA
☐ Mil Mi-4				RA
☐ Mil Mi-6	?01			RA
☐ Sukhoi Su-7BMK				RA
☐ Tupolev Tu-16				RA

EGYPTIAN MILITARY MUSEUM (EG4)

Address:	The Citadel, Salah Salam Street, Cairo.
Tel:	020-511-0955
Admission:	Tuesday-Sunday 0900-1400.
Location:	In the eastern part of the city centre.

The museum is located in the historic citadel area constructed by Saladin in 1183. The building has seen many uses including a period as a harem. The military museum was first set up by the late King Farouk in 1949. On April 20th 1988 President Hosni Mubarak opened the completely refurbished display. The military history of the country is portrayed with models, photographs, documents and uniforms. Components of Israeli aircraft shot down in the various conflicts between the two countries are also on display. Three combat aircraft, the MiG-17F, the MiG-21F-13 and the Sukhoi Su-7, are currently exhibited. These types all served with front line squadrons. The Zlin Trener served with the Air Force from 1957 to 1975 and the Yak-18A from 1958 to 1974. The Polish built Wilga was used on a number of duties including liaison work. Two types formerly on show have not been seen for some time and are presumed scrapped: these were a locally built Goumhouria, a type based on on the classic Bücker Bestmann, and a Campbell Cricket autogyro.

TYPE	REG/SER	CON. NO.	PI/NOTES	STATUS
☐ Mikoyan-Gurevich MiG-17F	2481			PV
☐ Mikoyan-Gurevich MiG-21F-13	5908			PV
☐ Panstwowe Zaklady Lotnicze (PZL) 104 Wilga 35A	254	61144	SP-WEH, SU-AVE	PV
☐ Sukhoi Su-7BMK	7320			PV
☐ Yakovlev Yak-18A	621			PV
☐ Zlin Z-226 Trenér 6				PV

EL ALAMEIN MILITARY MUSEUM (EG5)

Address:	Old Route 1, El Alamein.
Tel:	0349-4100031
Admission:	Daily 0900-1600.
Location:	Just west of the town centre.

In October 1942 a fierce battles took place in the area around the town. The museum has been set up to commemorate this and the North African Campaign. The displays trace the history of the actions with many maps, photographs, uniforms and documents on view. There is an excellent collection of military vehicles, tanks and items of artillery. The Spitfire crashed in the sea on October 10th 1942 whilst taking part in the battle. Parts of the airframe were recovered and put on display in 2000. Over eighty thousand men lost their lives in the area and in the surrounding countryside there are several cemeteries and memorials.

TYPE	REG/SER	CON. NO.	PI/NOTES	STATUS
☐ Supermarine 349 Spitfire F.Vc/Trop)	BR491		Front fuselage and wings only.	PVD

HURGHADA AIR BASE MONUMENT (EG6)

Address:	Hurghada.
Admission:	By prior permission only.
Location:	Just west of the town.

The airfield was used by the Royal Air Force in World War II and was the site of a Maintenance Unit. The Egyptian Air Force based fighter squadrons at field for many years but at the present time no operational aircraft are normally in residence apart from a few helicopters. The site also serves as the civil airport for the region and is being developed for tourist flights to the popular coastal area. The MiG-21PF is mounted on a pole near the main military gate to remind servicemen of the heritage of the base.

TYPE	REG/SER	CON. NO.	PI/NOTES	STATUS
☐ Mikoyan-Gurevich MiG-21PF				RA

INSHAS AIR BASE MONUMENT (EG7)

Address:	Inshas.
Admission:	By prior permission only.
Location:	Just south of Az Zawanil.

This important fighter base houses squadrons of General Dynamics F-16s. For many years MiG-21s were in residence and they took part in many local conflicts including the 1973 October War. About two hundred MiG-21s have been flown by the Egyptian Air Force. For many years they equipped front line squadrons. One example has been preserved as a monument ato those who flew the type from the field.

TYPE	REG/SER	CON. NO.	PI/NOTES	STATUS
☐ Mikoyan-Gurevich MiG-21	54643			RA

LUXOR AIRPORT COLLECTION (EG8)

Address:	Luxor Airport, Luxor.
Tel:	095-237-4655
Fax:	095-232-0825
Email:	info@luxor-airport.com
Admission:	By prior permission only.
Location:	About 6 km east of the city.

Three aircraft formerly operated by the Egyptian Air Force are on show in an area near to the domestic terminal. A MiG-17 which was there for several years has not been seen recently.

TYPE	REG/SER	CON. NO.	PI/NOTES	STATUS
☐ Mikoyan-Gurevich MiG-15UTI	'2357'			RAX
☐ Mikoyan-Gurevich MiG-21PFM	'2358'			RAX
☐ Sukhoi Su-7BMK	'2356'			RAX

MILITARY CAMP DISPLAY (EG9)

Address:	Cairo.
Admission:	By prior permission only.
Location:	In the eastern part of the city.

Four combat jets are preserved at this military installation. They are parked at the corners of a parade ground. Front line squadrons in Egypt have used several variants of both the MiG-21 and The MiG-23. The Presidential Guard have their main barracks on this side of the city and this may well be the location of the aircraft. Egypt ordered at least twenty examples of the variable geometry MiG-23BN and they were flown for a number of years. The two aircraft in the collection are probably from this batch.

TYPE	REG/SER	CON. NO.	PI/NOTES	STATUS
☐ Mikoyan-Gurevich MiG-21				RA
☐ Mikoyan-Gurevich MiG-21				RA
☐ Mikoyan-Gurevich MiG-23BN				RA
☐ Mikoyan-Gurevich MiG-23BN				RA

MILITARY MUSEUM (EG10)

Address:	23 July Street, Port Said.
Tel:	066-224657
Admission:	Winter Saturday-Thursday 0900-1400; Summer Saturday-Thursday 0800-1400; Friday hours variable.
Location:	In the centre of the city.

The city has its origins in an 1850s camp set up to house workers constructing the Suez Canal. Soon an important port was developed. Displays at the museum cover Egyptian military weapons from the early times up to the modern era. Battles in World War II, the conflict against Britain and France in the 1956 Suez campaign and the 1967 and 1973 wars with Israel are all featured. The Cricket is from a batch sold to Kuwait in 1970.

TYPE	REG/SER	CON. NO.	PI/NOTES	STATUS
☐ Campbell Cricket	G-AYBX	CA/331		PV

OCTOBER 1973 WAR PANORAMA MEMORIAL AND MUSEUM (EG11)

Address:	Sharia al-Uruba, Heliopolis, Cairo.
Tel:	020-602317
Admission:	Wednesday-Sunday 0730-1700.
Location:	About 10 km north east of the city centre on the road to the airport.

The Egyptian Air Force was set up in 1932 and from the 1950s to the mid-1970s used almost exclusively Soviet combat aircraft. In the October 1973 War with Israel the Air Force fought with distinction. The museum was established in the late 1980s to honour the contribution of all branches of the Egyptian services to the conflict. In addition to the aircraft, military vehicles, tanks, patrol boats, weapons and armaments can be seen. The three aircraft are all mounted on pedestals and carry a full range of weaponry on the under-side of their wings. About one hundred and twenty five MiG-17s were operated by the force. A panoramic three hundred and sixty degree theatre shows films of the conflict. Nearby is the tomb of the assassinated President Anwar Sadat.

TYPE	REG/SER	CON. NO.	PI/NOTES	STATUS
☐ Mikoyan-Gurevich MiG-17F	2961			PV
☐ Mikoyan-Gurevich MiG-21PFS	8040			PV
☐ Sukhoi Su-20R	7771			PV

ERITREA

EXPO PARK (ER1)

Address:	P.O. Box 5455, Asmara.
Admission:	Daily.
Location:	In the southern suburbs of the city.

This large park houses festivals and trade exhibitions. There are a number of attractions including a steam locomotive. Aircraft are being acquired and put on show around the site.

TYPE	REG/SER	CON. NO.	PI/NOTES	STATUS
☐ Antonov An-12BP	CCCP-12114	402411	Fuselage only.	PV
☐ Boeing 727-25F	5Y-BMW	18255	N8104N, N8104E, N8104N, (N101MU), N8104N – fuselage only.	PV
☐ Douglas DC-3A-456 Skytrain	ET-AJH	19283	42-100820, 5-10 (Iran), 711 (Ethopia) – less wings.	PV
☐ Hughes 500C				PV

ETHIOPIA

DEBRE ZEIT AIR BASE MONUMENT (ET1)

Address:	Debre Zeit.
Admission:	By prior permission only.
Location:	Just south east of the town.

The Ethopian Air Force has used a wide range of aircraft from many countries. Substantial numbers of MiG-21s have been delivered and one is preserved as a monument. There are many wrecked aircraft at the field.

TYPE	REG/SER	CON. NO.	PI/NOTES	STATUS
☐ Mikoyan-Gurevich MiG-21MF				RA

ETHIOPIAN AIRLINES COLLECTION (ET2)

Address:	Bole Airport, Addis Ababa.
Tel:	011-661-5110
Admission:	By prior permission only.
Location:	In the south eastern suburbs of the city.

Ethiopian Airlines was formed in 1946 using DC-3s and this type remained in use until the late 1980s. One has been painted to represent first aircraft flown by the airline: this Dakota crashed at Tippi in January 1962. The DC-6A arrived in the country July 1978 after service with companies in Canada. The four engined airliner was damaged June 1980 at Dire Dawa. The airframe was moved to Addis Ababa in 1985 and is used for training. The airline has a collection of memorabilia in its headquarters and the two aircraft are outside.

TYPE	REG/SER	CON. NO.	PI/NOTES	STATUS
☐ Douglas DC-3A-456 Skytrain (C-47A) (Dakota III)	'ET-T-1'	9628	42-23766, FD906, 6802 (South Africa), ZS-DDV, G-AJXL, G-AMGD, VP-YTT, ZS-EKK, 3D-AAV, ZS-IWL, ET-AIA	RAX
☐ Douglas DC-6A	ET-AGY	45500	CF-CPC, N45500, CF-NWY, C-FNWY	RA

The gate at Molepolole Air Force Base, Botswana, is guarded by this Strikemaster. (Tim Spearman)

Four aircraft, including this Mirage IIIC are preserved at the French Air Force Base in Djibouti. (Philippe le Pallec)

This Shackleton guards the gate at Ysterplaat where the South African Air Force Museum has its Cape Town branch. (Douglas Rough)

GABON

MONUMENT DU BASE AÉRIENNE DE LIBREVILLE (GAB1)

Address:	Aeroport Leon M'ba, Libreville.
Admission:	By prior permission only.
Location:	About 10 km north of the city.

Gabon gained its independence from France in 1960 and the Air Force was set up the following year. The sole Broussard acquired at this time is preserved as a monument near the Air Force Headquarters.

TYPE	REG/SER	CON. NO.	PI/NOTES	STATUS
☐ Max Holste MH.1521M Broussard	TR-KAB	101	101 (France)	RA

GHANA

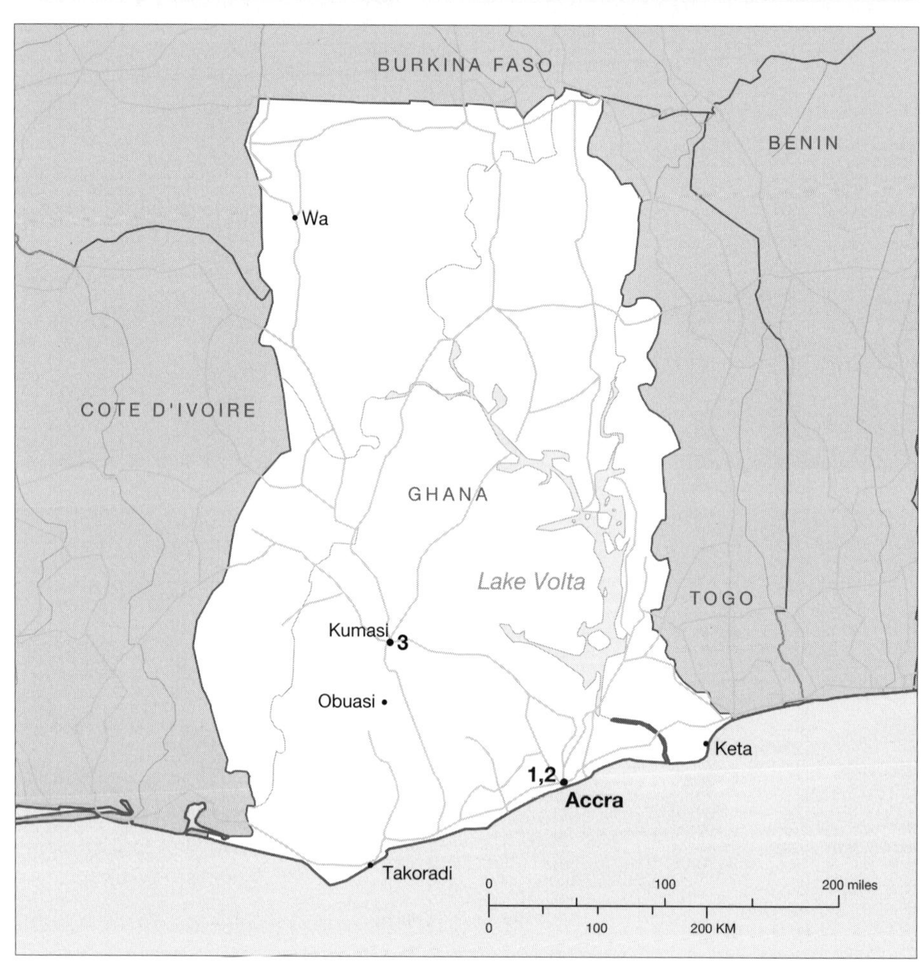

GHANA AIR FORCE COLLECTION (GH1)

Address: Accra Air Force Station,
Kotaka Airport,
Accra.
Admission: By prior permission only.
Location: About 5 km north east of the city.

Ghana became an independent country in March 1957 and the Air Force was formed two years later. Twelve Hindustan HT-2 trainers supplied by India were the initial equipment. In 1960 Britain took over the training of pilots and aircrew and the HT-2s were supplemented by ten former Royal Air Force Chipmunks. Both types were replaced by the Scottish Avaition Bulldogs in the mid-1970s. The first combat type acquired was the Macchi MB.326F, which won an evaluation contest against the British Jet Provost. Seven arrived in 1965 and another pair entered service in 1972 to replace those lost. The type was finally withdrawn in 1989 and replaced by twelve Aero L-29 Delfins obtained from Nigeria. The aircraft are on display at Burma Camp, the Headquarters of the Air Force, and Accra Air Force Station. Currently based at the airfield, which is also the civil airport for the city, are transport squadrons operating a variety of both fixed wing aircraft and helicopters.

TYPE	REG/SER	CON. NO.	PI/NOTES	STATUS
☐ Aermacchi MB.326F	G-700	6318/88	At HQ.	RA
☐ Aermacchi MB.326F	G-705	6323/93		PV
☐ Aermacchi MB.326F	G-706	6324/94	At Burma Camp.	RA

GHANA AIR FORCE SCHOOL OF TECHNICAL TRAINING COLLECTION (GH2)

Address: Kotaka Airport,
Accra
Admission: By prior permission only.
Location: About 5 km north east of the city.

The Air Force maintains a training school at its base at the airport. Airframe and engine fitters learn their skills on a collection of withdrawn aircraft. The collection can be viewed on open days. Ghana operated twelve Scottish Aviation Bulldogs and most were sold in the mid-1990s. Six Skyvans were also used.

TYPE	REG/SER	CON. NO.	PI/NOTES	STATUS
☐ Aermacchi MB.326F	G-702	6320/90		RA
☐ Aermacchi MB.326F	G-708			RA
☐ Aermacchi MB.326KG	G-710	6576/315	I-PAMF	RA
☐ Aero L-29 Delfin	G-960			RA
☐ De Havilland D.H.C.1 Chipmunk T.10	G-162	C1/0535	WG485	RA
☐ Hindustan HT-2				RA
☐ Hindustan HT-2				RA
☐ Hughes 269	G-614	0249		RA
☐ Mil Mi-2	G-660	536824090	(Libya)	RA
☐ Scottish Aviation Bulldog 122	G-101	BH120/225		RA
☐ Short SC.7 Skyvan 3M-400	G-455	SH.1933	G-BCFL	RA

KUMASI FORT AND MILITARY MUSEUM (GH3)

Address: Uaddara Barracks,
Steward Avenue,
Kumasi.
Tel: 051-23103
Admission: Tuesday-Saturday 0800-1700.
Location: In the city.

The first fort was built in the area in 1820 by the Asante people. British forces destroyed it in 1874 during one of the many wars against the local people. Britain had colonised the region in 1820 and set up the Gold Coast. The fort was rebuilt by the British in 1896 and in the fourth and final Asante War in 1900 it was besieged for a time. Over the colonial years the military had collected a number of artefacts and weapons and stored them in their barracks. The fort was converted for exhibition purposes. and the display opened as 'The Gold Coast Regiment Museum' in 1953. Independence was achieved in 1957 and the country became Ghana. The military history of the area is portrayed in detail. The early tribal era and the development of the Asante people is told. The colonial period is well represented and the transition to independence can be followed. The history of the Ghana forces over the last half century is traced. On show are many uniforms, photographs and documents. The British captured a number of enemy weapons in both World War I and World War II and these are on show. Two aircraft used by the Ghanaian Air Force are in the exhibition along with models and components.

TYPE	REG/SER	CON. NO.	PI/NOTES	STATUS
☐ Aermacchi MB.326F	G-707			PV
☐ Mil Mi-2	G-661	536824090		PV

LIBYA

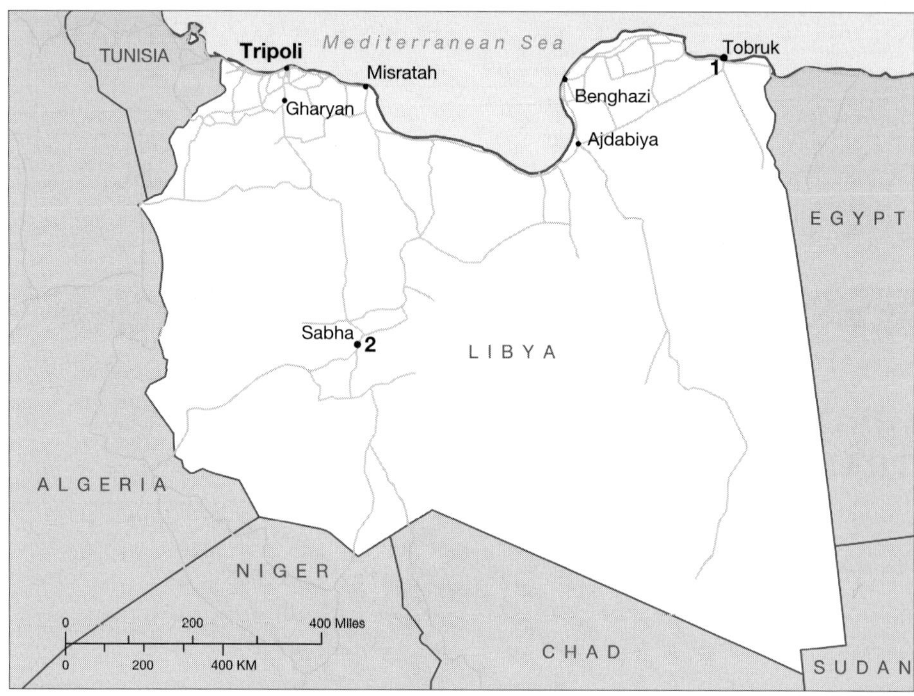

MILITARY MUSEUM (LY1)

Address:	Tobruk.
Admission:	Unknown.
Location:	In the eastern suburbs of the city.

In September 1940 Italian Libyan forces invaded Egypt. They were driven back by the British who seized Tobruk in January 1941. The Germans led by Rommel gained the town a few months later. Tobruk then changed hands a number of times until the Germans finally withdrew in November 1942. On April 5th 1943 the B-24 'Lady Be Good' of the 524th Bombardment Squadron force landed about seven hundred kilometres south of Tobruk. The unit was part of the 376th Bombardment Group of the United States Ninth Air Force. This force was based in Libya from January to early April 1943. The Liberator was discovered almost intact in November 1958 and was recovered in the early 1990s. Currently in store at the army barracks in the town, this aircraft will be restored for display in the museum which commemorates the battles fought in the area during World War II. On show are maps of the campaigns, uniforms, documents, photographs and a variety of weapons. Tours of the battlefields, cemeteries and war memorials in the area regularly take place.

TYPE	REG/SER	CON. NO.	PI/NOTES	STATUS
☐ Consolidated 32 Liberator (B-24D)	41-24301	1096		PVD

SEBHA AIR BASE MONUMENT (LY2)

Address:	Sebha.
Admission:	By prior permission only.
Location:	Just south of Hijarah.

This base in the Sahara region of the country houses fighter squadrons operating MiG-25s. The SIAI-Marchetti SF.260 is preserved as a monument. Large numbers of the type were used and many were assembled in Libya.

TYPE	REG/SER	CON. NO.	PI/NOTES	STATUS
☐ SIAI-Marchetti SF.260WL	1969	414		RA

MADAGASCAR

MONUMENT DE BASE AÉRIENNE D'IVATO (MAD1)

Address:	Antananarivo.
Admission:	By prior permission only.
Location:	About 5 km north of the city.

Formerly a French colony, the country has now achieved independence. The Air Force maintains base at the field which also serves as the international airport for the city. A Broussard has been preserved as a monument.

TYPE	REG/SER	CON. NO.	PI/NOTES	STATUS
☐ Max Holste MH.1521M Broussard	243	243	243 (France)	RA

MOROCCO

BASSATINE AIR BASE COLLECTION (MOR1)

Address:	2 Air Base, Bassantine, Meknes.
Admission:	By prior permission only.
Location:	About 5 km east of the city.

The airfield is one inherited from the French when the country gained its independence in 1956. The base is now home to fighter units operating the Northrop F-5E and F-5F and the General Dynamics F-16. Also in residence is the school for advanced training of fighter pilots which uses Alpha Jets. A Soviet training mission arrived in the country in 1961 and a dozen MiG-17s were put into service.

TYPE	REG/SER	CON. NO.	PI/NOTES	STATUS
☐ Mikoyan-Gurevich MiG-17F	CNA-FE/05	1406029		RA
☐ Mikoyan-Gurevich MiG-17F				RA
☐ North American NA-305 Bronco (OV-10A)	55433	305-44	Bu155433	RA
☐ Northrop N-156A Freedom Fighter (F-5A)	69119	N.6223	66-9119	RA
☐ Northrop N-156A Freedom Fighter (F-5A)	97108	N.6474	69-7108	RA

KENITRA AIR BASE MONUMENT (MOR2)

Address:	3 Air Base, Kenitra.
Admission:	By prior permission only.
Location:	Just north of the town.

The base is home to transport squadrons operating the C-130 Hercules and the CN.235. The C-119 entered Moroccan service in the early 1960s and was flown for about twenty years. One of the aircraft formerly operated from Kenitra has been preserved as a memorial to all crews who flew the rugged freighter.

TYPE	REG/SER	CON. NO.	PI/NOTES	STATUS
☐ Fairchild 110 Flying Boxcar (C-119F)	CNA-MN	10943	22126 (Canada)	RA

MENARA AIR BASE COLLECTION (MOR3)

Address:	Menara, Marrakech.
Admission:	By prior permission only.
Location:	About 7 km south west of the city.

The Air Force Academy is located at this former French airfield. The collection of preserved aircraft is located around the site. In the 1960s Morocco received a pair of MiG-15UTIs to train pilots for the twelve MiG-17Fs supplied but these saw little use and were soon withdrawn and stored. The French Air Force operated the Broussard in Morocco and after independence transferred a few to the new service. In a building there is a display of memorabilia tracing the history of the force.

TYPE	REG/SER	CON. NO.	PI/NOTES	STATUS
☐ Dassault Mirage F.1C	24	24	24 (France) – in training school.	RA
☐ Dassault Mirage F.1C	69	69	69 (France) – in training school.	RA
☐ Dassault Mirage F.1C	80	80	80 (France) – in training school.	RA
☐ Dassault Mirage F.1C			(France) – fuselage only – in training school.	RA
☐ Fairchild 110 Flying Boxcar (C-119G)	862/CNA-MH	11283	53-7862	RA
☐ Fouga CM.170R Magister	212	212	AA+299 – in training school.	RA
☐ Fouga CM.170R Magister				RA
☐ Fouga CM.170R Magister				RA
☐ Fouga CM.170R Magister				RA
☐ Fouga CM.170R Magister				RA
☐ Hawker Fury FB.10				RA
☐ Max Holste MH.1521M Broussard				RA
☐ Mikoyan-Gurevich MiG-15UTI				RA
☐ Mikoyan-Gurevich MiG-17F	CAN-FA/01	1407040		RA
☐ North American NA-182 Texan (T-6G)	78	182-389	51-14702 – in training school.	RA
☐ North American NA-182 Texan (T-6G)				RA
☐ North American NA-182 Texan (T-6G)				RA
☐ North American NA-182 Texan (T-6G)				RA
☐ Northrop N-156A Freedom Fighter (F-5A)	21243	N.6326	67-21243 – in training school.	RA
☐ Northrop N-156A Freedom Fighter (F-5A)	01378	N.6500	70-1378, 01378 (Iran), – in training school.	RA
☐ Sud-Est SE.3130 Alouette II	113	1182	113 (France) – in training school.	RA

MILITARY MUSEUM (MOR4)

Address:	Anfa, Casablanca.
Admission:	By prior permission only.
Location:	In the southern suburbs of the city.

There have been reports of a museum being set up at this airfield which is also the main civil field for the city. This will be a joint venture between Royal Air Maroc and the Air Force The airline has a training school at Anfa with some airframes. The Constellation flew with the airline for several years and has now been restored in period colours. The Air Force has preserved a number of airframes in its area and this collection is growing. Six former United States Broncos were delivered and one is now preserved on the military base. There is the potential for an interesting exhibition as more operational types are withdrawn from service.

TYPE	REG/SER	CON. NO.	PI/NOTES	STATUS
☐ Fouga CM.170R Magister	74	074	AA+104	RA
☐ Fouga CM.170R Magister	97	97	97 (France)	RA
☐ Fouga CM.170R Magister				RA
☐ Fouga CM.170R Magister				RA
☐ Lockheed 749A-79-46 Constellation	CN-CCN	749A-2675	F-BBDT	RA
☐ Max Holste MH.1521M Broussard	47	47	47 (France)	RA
☐ Max Holste MH.1521M Broussard	63	63	63 (France)	RA
☐ Mikoyan-Gurevich MiG-15UTI	07			RA
☐ Mikoyan-Gurevich MiG-17F	CNA-FK/11	1407018		RA
☐ Morane-Saulnier MS.733 Alcyon	39			RA
☐ North American NA-182 Texan (T-6G)	23			RA
☐ North American NA-182 Texan (T-6G)				RA
☐ North American NA-305 Bronco (OV-10A)	55404	305-15	Bu155404	RA
☐ Sud Fennec [North American NA-174 Trojan (T-28A)]	46	174-63	51-3525, 46 (France)	RA

SALE AIR BASE COLLECTION (MOR5)

Address:	Air Base 1, Rabat.
Admission:	By prior permission only.
Location:	About 15 km north east of the city.

The airfield houses helicopter units and the V.I.P. flight. Morocco received a batch of former Iraqi Hawker Fury aircraft and two are preserved along the road from the main gate to the Base Headquarters. The Potez 842 was sold to an American owner in 1978 but it is still parked near the main apron.

TYPE	REG/SER	CON. NO.	PI/NOTES	STATUS
☐ Hawker Fury FB.10				RA
☐ Hawker Fury FB.10				RA
☐ Max Holste MH.1521M Broussard				RA
☐ Potez 842	CN-ALL	4	CN-MBC, CN-ALL, (N9878A)	RA

MOZAMBIQUE

MONUMENTO DE BASE AÉREA DE BEIRA (MOZ1)

Address:	Beira.
Admission:	By prior permission only.
Location:	About 5 km north east of the city.

The country gained its independence from Portugal in 1975 and many aircraft were taken over. Several Dornier Do 27s were acquired and MiG-17s were delivered from both the Soviet Union and East Germany.

TYPE	REG/SER	CON. NO.	PI/NOTES	STATUS
☐ Dornier Do 27A-1	3337	296	PL+403, PJ+304, AC+965, 3337 (Portugal)	RA
☐ Mikoyan-Gurevich MiG-17F				RA

MONUMENTO DE MONTEPUEZ (MOZ2)

Address:	Montepuez.
Admission:	On permanent view.
Location:	In the southern part of the town.

This former Portuguese Air Force Dakota has been preserved in a park in the town. The aircraft is a reminder of the colonial days when it was based in the country. There are some military vehicles on show nearby.

TYPE	REG/SER	CON. NO.	PI/NOTES	STATUS
☐ Douglas DC-3A-456 Skytrain (C-47A)	6172	13140	42-93229, CS-TDG, CR-AGC – in Portuguese markings	PV

NIGERIA

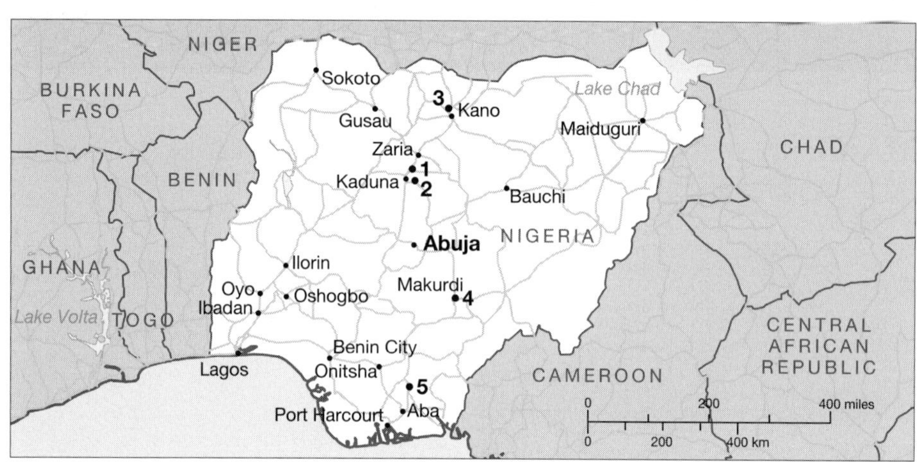

ARMED FORCES COMMAND AND STAFF COLLEGE MONUMENT (NG1)

Address:	Jaji.
Admission:	By prior permission only.
Location:	In the town.

The college was set up in the mid-1970s with British help. Officers from all branches of the services take both military and educational courses. Nigeria obtained at least fourteen former Luftwaffe Piaggio P.149s and one is preserved as a monument along with tanks and items of artillery.

TYPE	REG/SER	CON. NO.	PI/NOTES	STATUS
☐ Piaggio P.149D	NAF203	285	AS+436	RA

KADUNA AIR FORCE BASE COLLECTION (NG2)

Address:	301 Flying Training School, Kaduna.
Admission:	By prior permission only.
Location:	About 5 km north east of the city.

The Nigerian Air Force was formed in 1964 with aid from West Germany. The Primary Flying Training Wing was formed and the present title of 301 Flying Training School was adopted in 1984.

TYPE	REG/SER	CON. NO.	PI/NOTES	STATUS
☐ Dornier Do 27A-4	NAF 153	478	KD+136, GB+371, GC+371	RA
☐ Dornier Do 27A-4	NAF 157	487	KD+148, CC+052	RA
☐ Dornier Do 28D-2 Skyservant	NAF 198	4324	D-ILFH	RA
☐ Dornier Do 28D-2 Skyservant	NAF 177	4350		RA
☐ Mikoyan-Gurevich MiG-17F	NAF 630		At Air Force Club in the town.	PV
☐ Mikoyan-Gurevich MiG-17F	NAF 634			RA
☐ Piaggio P.149D				RA
☐ Scottish Aviation Bulldog 123	NAF 230	BH123/268	G-BBOV	RA
☐ Scottish Aviation Bulldog 123	NAF 233	BH123/271	G-BBPA	RA
☐ Scottish Aviation Bulldog 123	NAF 235	BH123/279	G-BBPR	RA

KANO AIR FORCE BASE MONUMENT (NG3)

Address:	303 Flying Training School, Kano.
Admission:	By prior permission only.
Location:	In the northern suburbs of the city.

The airfield was constructed in the 1930s and was an important stop on airline flights between Europe and Africa. During World War II it was used by the Royal Air Force. The facilities have been improved and airlines operate from the terminal area. The base was established in 1967 as a result of the civil war in the country.

TYPE	REG/SER	CON. NO.	PI/NOTES	STATUS
☐ Aero L-29 Delfin	NAF 409	993330		RA
☐ Mikoyan-Gurevich MiG-17F	NAF 605			RA
☐ Piaggio P.149D	NAF 210	277	AS+428, AC+428	RA

MAKURDI AIR BASE MONUMENT (NG4)

Address:	Makurdi.
Admission:	By prior permission only.
Location:	In the south eastern suburbs of the town.

The Nigerian Air Force acquired several versions of the MiG-21 and one has been preserved as a monument. The base is home to squadrons of the Tactical Air Command and many withdrawn fighters are stored around the field.

TYPE	REG/SER	CON. NO.	PI/NOTES	STATUS
☐ Mikoyan-Gurevich MiG-21				

NATIONAL WAR MUSEUM (NG5)

Address:	Isingwu Amafor, Umuahia.
Admission:	Unknown.
Location:	In the town.

During the conflict between Nigeria and the breakaway state of Biafra in the late 1960s many aircraft arrived in the area in rather dubious circumstances. This museum was set up in the wartime bunker used by the Biafran Army leader Colonel Ojukwu. The number of artefacts increased and a new site was sought. In 1989 a large area of land was acquired and the exhibition moved but the original bunker was retained as an annexe. The aircraft collection includes one of the Ilyushin Il-28s flown by the Nigerian Air Force. Two Dorniers are also on show in this area. The exhibition also includes a number of boats, vehicles, weapons, missiles and pieces of artillery.

TYPE	REG/SER	CON. NO.	PI/NOTES	STATUS
☐ Dornier Do 27A-4	NAF 102	523	GB+373	PV
☐ Dornier Do 28B-1	NAF 170	3093	D-IBUT, N65318	PV
☐ Ilyushin Il-28	NAF 805		NAF209	PV
☐ Malmo Flygindustri MFI-9B Trainer	BB 905	44	SE-EUN – fuselage only.	PVD
☐ Mikoyan-Gurevich MiG-17F	NAF 624			PV

SOUTH AFRICA

BALDING EAGLES (SA1)

Address:	P.O. Box 1189, Halfway House 1685.
Tel:	011-706-2322
Email:	gdell@gonet.co.za
Admission:	By prior permission only.
Location:	About 30 km south east of Pretoria.

The group has an interesting collection of aircraft which regularly appear at shows in southern Africa. The Chipmunk is in the red and white Royal Air Force scheme which was used in their last days of military flying. The Beech 17 is one of the few that has been on the British civil register.

TYPE	REG/SER	CON. NO.	PI/NOTES	STATUS
☐ Beech D17S (UC-43)	ZS-OIX	4922	43-10874, FZ432, G-AJJJ, VH-MJE	RAA
☐ Canadian Car & Foundry Harvard 4 [North American NA-186 (T-6J)]	ZS-WSE/ 'AA+069'	CCF4-543	53-4624, AA+690, 1748 (Portugal), 1748 (Mozambique)	RAA
☐ Classic Aircraft Waco F-5C	ZS-TMS	F5C-073		RAA
☐ De Havilland D.H.C.1 Chipmunk T.10	ZU-AJZ	C1/0202	WB754	RAA
☐ North American NA-200 Trojan (T-28B)	ZU-RCT	200-337	Bu138266, N391W, HB-RCT	RAA
☐ Piper J-3C-65 Cub	ZU-EJM	17326	ZS-BCG, ZS-DTA	RAA

CENTRAL ORGANISATION FOR TRADE TESTING (SA2)

Address:	Old Kempton Park Road, Kempton Park 1665.
Tel:	011-316-2838
Fax:	011-326-4763
Admission:	By prior permission only.
Location:	About 30 km east of Johannesburg.

This organisation has three aircraft which it uses for testing and instructional duties. The Texan is one of thirty remanufactured from older airframes by the South African Air Force in the mid-1950s.

TYPE	REG/SER	CON. NO.	PI/NOTES	STATUS
☐ Atlas-Aermacchi MB.326M Impala I	486	6362/A11		RA
☐ Atlas-Aermacchi MB.326M Impala I	541	A66		RA
☐ North American NA-182 Texan (T-6G)	7716	SA073		RA

DENEL CENTRE FOR LEARNING AND DEVELOPMENT (SA3)

Address:	Atlas Road, Bonaeropark, Kempton Park 1619.
Tel:	011-927-2811
Fax:	011-927-2329
Admission:	By prior permission only.
Location:	About 30 km east of Johannesburg.

Denel is the largest armaments manufacturer and supplier in the country. The company was set up in its present form in 1992 and has factories across South Africa. It undertakes assembly, manufacture and maintenance work on airframes and their systems. The Atlas company was absorbed into Denel and three of its products are in the workshops. The Atlas school was taken over and fitters are trained in a number of skills. Forty Italian designed Bosboks were delivered in the early 1970s and were used on a variety of duties including service during the operations in Angola between 1975 and 1989. Three were ordered by Rwanda but never delivered and all ended up in the Atlas Apprentice School. One of the Harvards is thought to be a composite built up from spares. The Alouette spent a period serving in Rhodesia/Zimbabwe.

TYPE	REG/SER	CON. NO.	PI/NOTES	STATUS
☐ Atlas-Aermacchi AM.3CM Bosbok	'ZS-FRA'	R3	40V03 (Rwanda)	RAX
☐ Atlas-Aermacchi MB.326M Impala I	569	A94		RA
☐ Atlas-Aermacchi MB.326M Impala I	577	102		RA
☐ North American NA-88 Texan (AT-6D) (Harvard III)	7508	88-14959	41-33942, EX335	RA
☐ North American NA-88 Texan (AT-6D) (Harvard III)	'ZS-AIR'		Believed to have been assembled from spares.	RAX
☐ North American NA-88 Texan (AT-6D) (Harvard III)	7570	88-15333	41-34016, EZ143 – possibly c/n 88-12139 41-33618, EX645	RA
☐ Sud-Est SE.3130 Alouette II	20	1470	20, 2000 (Rhodesia/Zimbabwe)	RA

DUNNOTTAR CENTRAL FLYING SCHOOL MEMORIAL (SA4)

Address:	Town Square, Dunnottar 1590.
Admission:	On permanent view.
Location:	In the centre of the town.

The South African Air Force Central Flying School was set up at Swartkop in 1932 operating Avro Avians, de Havilland D.H.9s and Westland Wapitis. The unit changed its name and moved around until being disbanded in February 1945. The following year a new CFS was established at AFS Nigel which was renamed Dunnottar in 1949. Pilots and instructors were trained on Airspeed Oxfords, de Havilland Tiger Moths and North American Harvards. The base closed in 1991 and the unit, now only with Harvards, moved to Langebaanweg. The Harvard which was for many years the gate guardian at the base has moved to the town square as a reminder of the airfield and to serve as a memorial to those who lost their lives serving their country.

TYPE	REG/SER	CON. NO.	PI/NOTES	STATUS
☐ North American NA-88 Texan (AT-6D) (Harvard III)	'7573'			PVX

EDENVALE MOTH SHELLHOLE DISPLAY (SA5)

Address:	115 Dickie Fritz Avenue, Dowerglen, Edenvale 1610.
Tel:	082-848-5368
Email:	dickiefritz@gmal.com
Admission:	On permanent view.
Location:	In the north western part of the town.

The Memorable Order of Tin Hats was formed in May 1927 and there are many branches across South Africa. Their clubhouses are known as 'Shellholes'. The Edenvale site has a display of memorabilia, weapons, and military vehicles. Two aircraft can be seen. South Africa used considerable numbers of the Lockheed Ventura during World War II. The first arrived in 1942 and the type served in the Middle East and the Mediterranean. The Ventura remained in service until 1960. The example on show spent a period at the South African Airways Training School. Sixty nine Pumas were operated from the early 1970s and the type served in Namibia.

TYPE	REG/SER	CON. NO.	PI/NOTES	STATUS
☐ Lockheed 237-27-01 Ventura GR.V (PV-1)	6432	237-5649	Bu34759, FP607, '6432, TS305'	PV
☐ Sud SA.330C Puma	126	1053		PV

FLYING LIONS FORMATION AEROBATIC TEAM (SA6)

Address:	P.O. Box 501, Rand Airport, Germiston 1400.
Tel:	011-827-9220
Fax:	011-827-9221
Email:	info@flyinglions.co.za
Admission:	By prior permission only.
Location:	About 5 km south west of the town.

The Harvard was retired from South African Air Force use in the mid-1990s. Five aircraft were purchased by a private owner at Rand Airport and this led to the formation of the team. Four examples of the classic trainer, in the colours of their sponsors, are now flown at shows throughout the country.

TYPE	REG/SER	CON. NO.	PI/NOTES	STATUS
☐ North American NA-88 Texan (AT-6C) (Harvard IIA)	ZU-BEU	88-10015	41-33345, EX372, 7188	RAA
☐ North American NA-88 Texan (AT-6D)	ZU-BET	88-11622	42-3918, 7695	RAA
☐ North American NA-88 Texan (AT-6D) (Harvard III)	ZU-AYS	88-14716	41-33882, EX909, 7475	RAA
☐ North American NA-88 Texan (AT-6D) (Harvard III)	ZU-BMC	88-15863	41-34109, EZ236, 7609	RAA

HARVARD CLUB OF SOUTH AFRICA (SA7)

Address:	P.O. Box 21173, Valhalla 0137.
Fax:	012-651-3852
Email:	info@theharvardclub.co.za
Admission:	By prior permision only.
Location:	At Swartkop Air Force Base which is on Old Johannesburg Road about 10 km south of Pretoria.

The first Harvards arrived in South Africa in 1942 and the type remained operational with the Air Force for over half a century. Well over seven hundred eventually saw military use in the country. In late 1994 ten examples, one has since crashed, of the famous trainer were allocated to the club. These aircraft were declared national monuments and thus cannot be exported. The club held its first fly-in at Heidelburg on November 5th 1994. The aircraft are now regular performers at shows throughout the country. Two are awaiting rebuild after crashes.

TYPE	REG/SER	CON. NO.	PI/NOTES	STATUS
☐ North American NA-78 Texan (AT-6A)	ZU-AOY	78-4698	41-629, NC61344, 7661	RAA
☐ North American NA-78 Texan (AT-6A)	ZU-AOX	78-7140	41-16762, 7643	RAA
☐ North American NA-88 Texan (AT-6C) (Harvard IIA)	ZU-AOS	88-10008	41-33338, EX365, 7152	RAD
☐ North American NA-88 Texan (AT-6C) (Harvard IIA)	ZU-AOP	88-10536	41-33417, EX444, 7028	RAA
☐ North American NA-88 Texan (AT-6C) (Harvard IIA)	ZU-AOZ	88-10572	41-33250, EX478, 7166, (ZU-AOU), 7166	RAA
☐ North American NA-88 Texan (AT-6C) (Harvard IIA)	ZU-AOV	88-12070	41-33599, EX626, 7306	RAA

TYPE	REG/SER	CON. NO.	PI/NOTES	STATUS
☐ North American NA-88 Texan (AT-6C) (Harvard IIA)	ZU-AOT	88-9922	41-33327, EX354, 7156	RAA
☐ North American NA-88 Texan (AT-6C) (Harvard IIA)	ZU-AOR	88-9283	41-33177, EX204, 7059	RAA
☐ North American NA-88 Texan (AT-6C) (Harvard IIA)	ZU-AOO	88-9958	41-33328, EX355, 7024	RAA
☐ North American NA-88 Texan (AT-6D) (Harvard III)	ZU-AOU	88-15277	41-34005, EZ132, 7569	RAA
☐ North American NA-88 Texan (AT-6D) (Harvard III)	ZU-AOW	88-15777	41-34086, EZ213, 7592 – possibly a composite.	RAD

KIMBERLEY MOTH SHELLHOLE DISPLAY (SA8)

Address:	33 Memorial Road, Kimberley.
Tel:	053-831-5640
Email:	clubsecretary@kimberleyclub.co.za
Admission:	Aircraft on permanent view. Memorabilia display – by appointment.
Location:	In the south western part of the city.

Kimberley was the home to the 21st Air School between 1939 and 1945. The Impala was presented to a local organisation in 1994 to commemorate the contribution of the area to the Air Force. In the clubhouse there are displays of weapons, uniforms and memorabilia along with tanks and pieces of artillery.

TYPE	REG/SER	CON. NO.	PI/NOTES	STATUS
☐ Atlas-Aermacchi MB.326M Impala I	594	119		PV

LANGEBAANWEG AIR FORCE BASE COLLECTION (SA9)

Address:	P.O. Langebaanweg, Langebaanweg 7375,
Tel:	022-706-2911
Admission:	By prior permission only.
Location:	About 20 km east of Saldanha.

The Central Flying School was based at Dunnottar until December 1992 when it replaced combat units at Langebaanweg. A collection of types formerly used by the school, including one Harvard, are preserved. Instructors at the unit operated the five aircraft 'Harvard Aerobatic Team' until 1995.

TYPE	REG/SER	CON. NO.	PI/NOTES	STATUS
☐ Atlas-Aermacchi MB.326M Impala I	576	101		RA
☐ De Havilland D.H.100 Vampire FB.52	235			RA
☐ North American NA-88 Texan (AT-6D) (Harvard III)	7449	88-14483	41-33830, EX857	RA

MAKHADO AIR FORCE BASE DISPLAY (SA10)

Address:	Private Bag X2010, Makhado 0954.
Tel:	015-577-2305
Fax:	015-577-2308
Admission:	By prior permission only.
Location:	About 5 km north west of the town.

The base, known as 'The Fortress of the North', was opened in October 1987. The site was known at Louis Trichardt Air Force Base until November 2003. Squadrons operating the Atlas Cheetah C and D and the British Aerospace Hawk are in residence. The Cheetah C is derived from the Israeli Kfir, itself a developed Dassault Mirage III. The airframes and avionics were supplied by Israel but the engines were under a United Nations embargo so the Atlas company updated the aircraft and fitted them with French Atar motors. The collection of preserved aircraft represents types operated in recent years. South Africa received thirty four Canadair built Sabres and some served in the Korean War. The aircraft in the collection was preserved in Pietersburg for many years. Sixteen Mirage IIICZs were delivered in the 1960s.

TYPE	REG/SER	CON. NO.	PI/NOTES	STATUS
☐ Atlas-Aermacchi MB.326M Impala I	571	A96		RA
☐ Canadair CL-13B Sabre 6 [North American F-86E]	358	1467	23677 (Canada)	RA
☐ Dassault Mirage IIICZ	801	149		RAD
☐ Dassault Mirage IIICZ	804	157		RA

MILITARY MUSEUM (SA11)

Address:	116 Church Street, Bloemfontein 9301.
Tel:	051-447-5478
Fax:	051-447-4359
Email:	mailto:naln@majuba.ofs.gov.sa
Admission:	Monday-Friday 1000-1215 1300-1600; Sunday 1400-1600.
Location:	In the southern part of the town.

The museum is located next to the Old Fort which was completed in 1849 and later used as a gaol. The military history of the region is portrayed in a number of innovative displays. Three aircraft can be seen along with military vehicles, tanks and items of artillery. Inside are many photographs, documents and uniforms.

TYPE	REG/SER	CON. NO.	PI/NOTES	STATUS
☐ Atlas-Aermacchi MB.326K Impala II	1032	33	On loan from SAAFM.	PV
☐ Atlas-Aermacchi MB.326M Impala I	591	116		PV
☐ Dassault Mirage IIIRZ	837	3F3A	On loan from SAAFM.	PV

PIONEERS OF AVIATION MUSEUM (SA12)

Address:	P.O. Box 361, 8300 Kimberley.
Tel:	053-839-2772
Fax:	053-842-1433
Email:	sunet@museumsnc.co.za
Admission:	Monday-Friday 0900-1700.
Location:	At Alexandersfontein which is about 5 km south east of the town.

The first flying school in the country was set up at Kimberley in 1911 by Cecil Compton Paterson. The site, which is part of the McGregor Museum, has been constructed to honour the work carried out by these pioneers. A 1913 style hangar has been reconstructed and this houses a replica of Paterson's Number 2 biplane. This aircraft was built by a volunteer team at the South African Air Force Museum at Lanseria in the early 1980s. The design was similar to Farman types. The original aircraft was quickly destroyed in a crash. Photographs, documents and memorabilia show the work carried out by the school and the early history of flying in the country.

TYPE	REG/SER	CON. NO.	PI/NOTES	STATUS
☐ Paterson No. 2 Biplane (R)				PV

PORT ALFRED AIRFIELD MEMORIAL (SA13)

Address:	43 Air School, Port Alfred 6170.
Tel:	046-624-2433
Fax:	046-624-2432
Email:	fly@43airschool.com
Admission:	On permanent view.
Location:	In the northern suburbs of the town.

No 43 Air School opened at the airfield in 1942 with a fleet of about one hundred Ansons and Oxfords. Navigators, bomb-aimers and gunners received their training at the site. In 1988 a large commercial flying school opened using the original military title. A pleasant garden of remembrance has been constructed near the flightline. A memorial to those who lost their lives and a pole mounted Impala I can be seen.

TYPE	REG/SER	CON. NO.	PI/NOTES	STATUS
☐ Atlas-Aermacchi MB.326M Impala I	466	110/6340		PV

PORT ELIZABETH MUSEUM (SA14)

Address:	P.O. Box 13147, Humewood, Port Elizabeth 6013.
Tel:	041-584-0650
Admission:	Daily 0900-1630
Location:	In the south eastern part of the city.

This museum is part of the Bayworld complex which includes an oceanarium and a snake park – there is a local marine life conservation programme. In 1929 Major Allister Miller, a World War I ace, formed Union Airways. The initial base was at Fairview in Port Elizabeth and the fleet consisted of five de Havilland Gipsy Moths. The company was taken over by the Government in 1934 and became South African Airways. There is a small display at the museum tracing the life of the founder and the airline.

This Vampire FB.5 is mounted at Thunder City at Cape Town. (Douglas Rough)

The Livingstone Museum near the Victoria Falls is home to this Chipmunk. (Nigel Hitchman)

This Spitfire can be seen at the Zimbabwe Military Museum in Gweru. (Winston Brent)

POTCHEFSTROOM MILITARY BASE MEMORIAL (SA15)

Address:	Military Support Base, Potchefstroom 2531.
Tel:	018-289-3355
Admission:	By prior permission only.
Location:	In the north western suburbs of the town.

This large army base houses a number of units and in addition there is a hospital on the site. A memorial has been erected with flags, plaques, pieces of artillery, tanks and the Bosbok on show.

TYPE	REG/SER	CON. NO.	PI/NOTES	STATUS
☐ Atlas-Aermacchi AM.3CM Bosbok	948	2029		RA

RANDFONTEIN MOTH SHELLHOLE DISPLAY (SA16)

Address:	Estate Gold Mine, Randfontein.
Admission:	On permanent view.
Location:	In the south eastern part of the town.

The local branch of the MOTH organisation is responsible for a garden of remembrance dedicated to ex-servicemen. In addition to the Impala a collection of tanks and weapons are on display.

TYPE	REG/SER	CON. NO.	PI/NOTES	STATUS
☐ Atlas-Aermacchi MB.326M Impala I	523	A48		PV

SCI-BONO DISCOVERY CENTRE (SA17)

Address:	1 Miriam Makeeba Street, off Mary Fitzgerald Square, Newtown,
Johannesburg 2167.	
Tel:	011-639-8400
Fax:	011-832-3360
Email:	info@sci-bono.co.za
Admission:	Monday-Friday 0900-1730; Saturday-Sunday 0900-1630
Location:	In the city.

This large complex has displays on many aspects of science and technology. Many of the exhibits are 'hands-on' and are designed to test the skill and knowledge of the visitor. There is a transport section with road and railway items. There are currently two aircraft, from widely different periods, of aviation on show.

TYPE	REG/SER	CON. NO.	PI/NOTES	STATUS
☐ Atlas Cheetah E (Dassault Mirage IIIEZ)	826	450		PV
☐ Paterson No. 2 Biplane (R)				PV

SIR PIERRE VAN RYNEVELD HIGH SCHOOL MEMORIAL (SA18)

Address:	Commissoner Street, Kempton Park 1920.
Admission:	By prior permission only.
Location:	In the town.

Pierre van Ryneveld was a World War I fighter ace. In 1920 he was given the task of setting up the South African Air Force. He flew home in a Vickers Vimy accompanied by Quintin Brand and both were knighted for this epic journey. He commanded the Air Force until 1933 when he was put in charge of all Defence Forces. He held this post until his retirement in 1949. This school is named after him and in the grounds is a Mirage donated by the Air Force. This serves as a memorial to pupils and staff killed during military service.

TYPE	REG/SER	CON. NO.	PI/NOTES	STATUS
☐ Dassault Mirage IIICZ	807	163		RA

SKYCLASS AVIATION (SA19)

Address:	Postnet Suite 007, Private Bag X1037, Germiston 1400.
Tel:	011-827-7860
Fax:	011-827-7865
Email:	enquiries@skyclass.com
Admission:	By prior permission only.
Location:	At Rand Airport which is about 5 km south west of the town.

The company was set up in late 2006 with the assistance of South African Airways. One aim was to offer flights in classic propliners. Three aircraft from the defunct South African Historic Flight are operated on behalf of the South African Airways Museum Society. The three DC-4s were built in 1946/7 for use by South African Airways. ZS-BMH was the last of the twelve hundred and forty five examples of the four engined transport. One of the DC-4s is owned by the Dutch Dakota Association and is on a long term lease. Rand Airport was built in the 1920s as the main field for Johannesburg.

TYPE	REG/SER	CON. NO.	PI/NOTES	STATUS
☐ Douglas DC-3A-456 Skytrain (C-47A) (Dakota III)	ZS-BXF	12107	42-92320, FZ572, 6821, ZS-BXF, 6888 – operated for SAA Museum Society.	RAC
☐ Douglas DC-3A-456 Skytrain (C-47A) (Dakota III)	ZS-CAI	13541	42-93610, KG674, 6838	RAA
☐ Douglas DC-4-1009 Skymaster	ZS-AUA	42934	ZS-AUA, 6901, ZS-NUR, PH-DDS – leased from Dutch Dakota Association.	RAA
☐ Douglas DC-4-1009 Skymaster	ZS-AUB	42984	ZS-AUB, 6905, ZS-AUB, 6905 – operated for SAA Museum Society.	RAA
☐ Douglas DC-4-1009 Skymaster	ZS-BMH	43157	ZS-BMH, 6904, ZS-BMH, 6904 – operated for SAA Museum Society.	RAA

SOUTH AFRICA MILITARY ACADEMY MEMORIAL (SA20)

Address:	Private Bag X2, Saldanha 7395.
Tel:	022-702-7395
Email:	arina@ma2.sun.ac.sa
Admission:	By prior permission only.
Location:	About 2 km south west of the town.

The Academy was set up in 1950 at Pretoria and the first entry soon followed. In 1953 a site at Saldanha was chosen where new buildings would be constructed. This complex was ready in 1957 and the first students took up residence. All aspects of military training are carried out and many academic subjects are studied. The Impala is mounted near the parade ground as part of a memorial dedicated to past students.

TYPE	REG/SER	CON. NO.	PI/NOTES	STATUS
☐ Atlas-Aermacchi MB.326M Impala I	586	111		RA

SOUTH AFRICAN AIR FORCE 68 AIR SCHOOL (SA21)

Address:	Trichardt Road, P.O. Box 15088, Lyttelton 0140.
Tel:	012-672-5000
Fax:	012-672-5293
Admission:	By prior permission only.
Location:	In the western part of the town.

The school was set up at Voortrekkerhootge in 1936 and took up its present title four years later. The premises were too small and a move was made to Lyttleton in October 1942. The students undertake courses in a variety of mechanical and technical subjects. The collection of airframes can be seen on open days.

TYPE	REG/SER	CON. NO.	PI/NOTES	STATUS
☐ Atlas-Aermacchi MB.326K Impala II	1025	26		RA
☐ Atlas-Aermacchi MB.326K Impala II	1044	45		RA
☐ Atlas-Aermacchi MB.326K Impala II	1065	66		RA

☐ Atlas-Aermacchi MB.326K Impala II	1066	67		RA
☐ Atlas-Aermacchi MB.326M Impala I	514	A39		RA
☐ Atlas-Aermacchi MB.326M Impala I	559	A84		RA
☐ Atlas-Aermacchi MB.326M Impala I	562	A87		RA
☐ Atlas-Aermacchi MB.326M Impala I	583	108		RA
☐ North American NA-88 Texan (AT-6C) (Harvard IIA)	7360	88-12332	41-33639, EX666	RA
☐ North American NA-88 Texan (AT-6D) (Harvard III)	7488	88-14877	41-33905, EX932	RA
☐ Pilatus PC-7 Mk.II	'ATTD2'			RAX
☐ Sud-Est SE.3160 Alouette III	72	1492		RA
☐ Sud-Est SE.3160 Alouette III	622	1711	N6823	RA

SOUTH AFRICAN AIR FORCE MUSEUM (SA22)

Address: P.O. Box 21084, Valhalla 0137.
Tel: 012-351-2290
Fax: 012-351-2346
Email: saafrmuseum@telkom
Admission: Monday-Friday 0900-1600; Saturday 1000-1600
Location: At Swartkop Air Force Base which is on Old Johannesburg Road about 10 km south of Pretoria.

The first military flights in the country took place in 1912 and in the same year Compton Paterson set up a flying school at Kimberley. Prior to World War I a Union Defence Force was formed and ten officers were trained by Mr. Paterson. In 1915 the South African Aviation Corps was established with the main aim of serving in the campaign against German South West Africa. This force was disbanded at the end of the conflict and on February 1st 1920 the South African Air Force was formed. Up to the outbreak of World War II almost all the aircraft used were of British origin. From 1940 to 1946 over thirty three thousand British and South African aircrew were trained in the country. In this period American types were added to the inventory and South African units served in North and East Africa and the Mediterranean. In the latter stages of the war the squadrons moved into Europe. In addition, many South Africans joined the Royal Air Force. A fighter squadron later served with distinction in the Korean War. During the 1960s and 1970s the country set up its own aircraft industry and combat machines were obtained from France and Italy. With this varied tradition the potential for a museum was evident. The initial suggestion was made in 1944 and after a long campaign the museum was formally established on October 26th 1973. The first aircraft, a Lockheed Ventura once used by General Smuts, arrived two days later. Airframes and artefacts were steadily acquired and the search for a permanent site began. Initially storage facilities at Snake Valley were used and in 1976 the majority of the collection moved to a hangar at Lanseria. The plans finally came to fruition on May 14th 1993 when the exhibition opened in some of the 1920s historic hangars and associated buildings at Swartkop. A comprehensive display tracing the history and traditions of military flying in the country has been staged. On show are uniforms, photographs and memorabilia. A wide range of aircraft can be seen and several more are under restoration in the workshops. Products of the local industry feature prominently. Some of the aircraft are maintained in flying condition and often appear at shows around the country. The displays act as a memorial to all who have served with the Air Force.

TYPE	REG/SER	CON. NO.	PI/NOTES	STATUS
☐ Atlas AH-2 Rooivalk			Due soon.	–
☐ Atlas C.4M Kudu	968	18		RAD
☐ Atlas C.4M Kudu	ZU-CWZ	19	969	PV
☐ Atlas C.4M Kudu	972	22	Contains parts of c/n 23 982.	PV
☐ Atlas C.4M Kudu	987	29		RA
☐ Atlas Cheetah C (Israeli Aircraft Industries Kfir C2)	342			PV
☐ Atlas Cheetah D (Dassault Mirage IIID2Z)	844	200		RA
☐ Atlas Cheetah E (Dassault Mirage IIIEZ)	842	17F		PV
☐ Atlas Cheetah R (Dassault Mirage IIR2Z)	855			RA
☐ Atlas XH-1 Alpha		001		PV
☐ Atlas-Aermacchi AM.3CM Bosbok	959/ZU-CXA	2040		PVA
☐ Atlas-Aermacchi MB.326K Impala II	1000	6555//296/001		PV
☐ Atlas-Aermacchi MB.326M Impala I	519	A44		RA
☐ Atlas-Aermacchi MB.326M Impala I	524	A49	At Air Force HQ.	RA
☐ Atlas-Aermacchi MB.326M Impala I	532	A57		PV
☐ Atlas-Aermacchi MB.326M Impala I	589	114		PV
☐ Avro 652A Anson I	3209		DG819 – fuselage frame and centre section only.	PVC
☐ Avro 696 Shackleton MR.3	1721	1531		PV
☐ Bensen B-8 Gyroglider				PV
☐ Blackburn B-103 Buccaneer S.50	414	B3-14-63/SA4	G-2-4	RA
☐ Blackburn B-103 Buccaneer S.50	421	B3-06-64/SA11	G-2-11	PV
☐ Boeing 707-328C	1419	19917	F-BLCL, (ZS-LSK)	PV
☐ Canadair CL-13B Sabre 6 [North American F-86E]	361	1470	23680 (Canada)	PV
☐ Canadair CL-13B Sabre 6 [North American F-86E]	367	1476	23686 (Canada)	PV
☐ Canadair CL-13B Sabre 6 [North American F-86E]	372	1481	23691 (Canada)	RA
☐ Cessna 185			Due soon.	–
☐ Cessna 185			Due soon.	–
☐ Dassault Mirage IIIBZ	816	228		PV
☐ Dassault Mirage IIIBZ	817	229	817, ZU-DMD	RAA
☐ Dassault Mirage IIIBZ	818	230		PV
☐ Dassault Mirage IIICZ	800	149	800, ZU-DME	RAA
☐ Dassault Mirage IIICZ	805	158		PV

☐ Dassault Mirage IIICZ	809	168		RA
☐ Dassault Mirage IIIRZ	835	1F-1A		PV
☐ Dassault Mirage IIIRZ	838	4F-4A		PV
☐ Dassault Mirage F.1AZ	235	143		PV
☐ Dassault Mirage F.1CZ	213	14F-14A		RA
☐ Dassault Mirage F.1CZ	202	62	At Air Force HQ.	RA
☐ Dassault Mirage F.1CZ	204	64		RA
☐ Dassault Mirage F.1CZ-200	203	63		PV
☐ De Havilland D.H.6	G-EAML		C9449 – parts only.	PVD
☐ De Havilland D.H.82A Tiger Moth	2341	DHA.568	DX491, 2341, ZS-BCN	RAA
☐ De Havilland D.H.87B Hornet Moth	2007	8121	ZS-ALA, 2007, ZS-ALA	PVA
☐ De Havilland D.H.89A Dragon Rapide	ZS-DLS	6773	NR674, G-AGZU – wings and tail only.	PV
☐ De Havilland D.H.100 Vampire FB.52	227	V.0567	Gate guard SAAF College.	–
☐ De Havilland D.H.100 Vampire FB.52	229	V.0581		RA
☐ De Havilland D.H.100 Vampire FB.52	253	V.0689		RAD
☐ De Havilland D.H.100 Vampire FB.52	254	V.0697	254, R1388 (Rhodesia) – fuselage pod only.	RA
☐ De Havilland D.H.115 Vampire T.11	R4032	15392	XE823, SR119, RRAF403	RA
☐ De Havilland D.H.115 Vampire T.55	257	15431		RA
☐ De Havilland D.H.115 Vampire T.55	276	15497		RAA
☐ De Havilland D.H.115 Vampire T.55	ZU-DFH	15498	277, R4152 (Zimbabwe), 277	RAA
☐ De Havilland D.H.C.1 Chipmunk 22 (T.10)	WG354	C1/0441	WG354, ZS-DIU	PVA
☐ Dornier Do 27Q-1	ZS-CMA	2034	ZS-ABE	RA
☐ Dornier Do 27Q-4	'5430'	2035	VQ-ZBK, 7P-ZBK, ZS-FAH	RACX
☐ Douglas A-26B Invader	ZS-CVD	27846	44-34567, N9412Z – (On Mark Marksman)	RA
☐ Douglas DC-3A-456 Skytrain (C-47A) (Dakota III)	6859	12586	42-92751, KG474	PV
☐ Douglas DC-4-1009 Skymaster	6902	43155	ZS-BMF	PV
☐ Edgar Percival E.P.9	'XM797'	36	ZS-CHZ	RAAX
☐ English Electric EA.1 Canberra T.4	457	EEP71543	WJ991 – modified to B.2.	PV
☐ Fairchild 24R9 Forwarder (UC-61K) (Argus III)	KK476	R9-1094	44-83133, KK476, ZS-DEY	PVA
☐ Fiat CR.32			Small parts only.	RA
☐ Fieseler Fi 156C-7 Storch	VD+TD	475099	VD+TD, AM.99, 200 (SAAF)	PVA
☐ Lockheed 18-08-01 Lodestar	'245'	18-2058	ZS-ATL, (249), ZS-ATL – at Lanseria.	RAX
☐ Lockheed 37-21-01 Ventura I	6066	37-4184	AE841	RAD
☐ Lockheed 137-27-01 Ventura II	6112	137-4642	AJ504	RA
☐ Lockheed 137-27-01 Ventura II	6120	137-4646	AJ508	RA
☐ Lockheed 237-27-01 Ventura GR.V (PV-1)	'6453'	237-6011	Bu48775, JS956, 6534	RAX
☐ Lockheed 237-27-01 Ventura GR.V (PV-1)	6487	237-6219	Bu49403, JT861	RA
☐ Lockheed 237-27-01 Ventura GR.V (PV-1)	'TS306'	237-6290	Bu49474, JT867, 6498	PVX
☐ Mikoyan-Gurevich MiG-21bis	C-340	75091800	In Angolan markings.	PV
☐ Mil Mi-24V	2034		In Algerian markings.	PV
☐ North American NA-77 Texan (AT-6A)	ZU-CXX	77-4547	41-0508, 7675	RA
☐ North American NA-88 Texan (AT-6C) (Harvard IIA)	7111	88-9684	41-33241, EX268	PVA
☐ North American NA-88 Texan (AT-6C) (Harvard IIA)	7072	88-9868	41-33308, EX335	PVA
☐ North American NA-88 Texan (AT-6C) (Harvard IIA)	'7570'	88-12139	41-33618, EX645, 7356	RAA
☐ North American NA-88 Texan (AT-6D) (Harvard III)	7506	88-14950	41-33933, EX960	RADX
☐ North American NA-88 Texan (AT-6D) (Harvard III)	7573	88-15336	41-34019, EZ146 – front fuselage only.	PV
☐ North American NA-88 Texan (AT-6D) (Harvard III)	7001	88-15683	41-34052, EZ179, 7559	PVA
☐ North American NA-88 Texan (AT-6D) (Harvard III)	7731	88-15774	41-34083, EZ210, 7605, EZ210, H-19 (Belgium)	RA
☐ North American NA-122 Mustang (P-51D)	'325'	122-38661	44-72202, Fv26112, 1917 (Dominican)	PVA
☐ Patchen TSA-2C Explorer	2000	1	N1EX, ZS-UGF	PV
☐ Piaggio P.166S Albatross	ZU-DFI	417	881	PV
☐ Sikorsky S-51 Dragonfly	A-1	51102	A-1, ZS-HBT	PV
☐ Sikorsky S-55C	A-4	55959	A-4, ZS-HCO, CR-ALO, (C9-ALO), 'ZS-O', ZS-HCO	PVC
☐ Sikorsky S-55D Whirlwind HAS.22 (HO4S-3)	WV203	55475	Bu133743, WV203, ZS-HDO	RA
☐ Sikorsky S-55D Whirlwind HAS.22 (HO4S-3)	WV224	55499	Bu133752	RAD
☐ Sud SA.321L Super Frelon	309	129		PV
☐ Sud SA.330C Puma	129	1070		PV
☐ Sud SA.330C Puma	133	1089	At Pretoria Zoo.	PV
☐ Sud SA.330H Puma	175	1468		PV
☐ Sud-Est SE.3130 Alouette II	22/ZU-CXW	1280	VQ-ZBJ, 22, 2200	PVA
☐ Sud-Est SE.3130 Alouette II	15	1452		RA
☐ Sud-Est SE.3130 Alouette II	18	1455	1800, 18 (Rhodesia)	PVA
☐ Sud-Est SE.3130 Alouette II	19	1469		RA
☐ Sud-Est SE.3130 Alouette II	40	1893	Cabin only.	RA
☐ Sud-Est SE.3160 Alouette III	51	1049		RAC
☐ Sud-Est SE.3160 Alouette III	29	1478		PV
☐ Supermarine 361 Spitfire HF.IXe	'5553'		TE213, 5518, 'W5581', 'W5518'	RADX
☐ Transall C-160Z	337	Z-4		PV
☐ Westland Wasp HAS.1	90	F9559		RA
☐ Westland Wasp HAS.1	96	F9764		PV

SOUTH AFRICAN AIR FORCE MUSEUM – CAPE TOWN (SA23)

Address:	AFB Ysterplaat, Private Bag X4, Ysterplaat 7425.
Tel:	021-508-6576
Fax:	021-508-6134
Email:	cteale@saafmuseum.org.sa
Admission:	Monday-Friday 0700-1500; Saturday 0830-1230.
Location:	About 5 km north of Cape Town.

This interesting collection is housed in a hangar relocated to the domestic area of the base. In addition to the aircraft, artefacts, photographs, documents, uniforms and models can be seen tracing the history of the Air Force and the base. The oldest aircraft on show is the superbly restored Lockheed Ventura. This type served on patrol duties from the early 1940s up to 1960. Two of the recently retired Harvards have been allocated to Ysterplaat and are maintained in flying condition. The other airworthy aircraft are kept at the nearby D.F. Malan civil airport. Eight Shackletons were ordered in the late 1950s and they gave excellent service for almost twenty years. Twenty Piaggio P.166s were delivered to the Air Force with the first arriving by sea in 1969. The type was used on coastal patrol duties for a quarter of a century. More aircraft are expected.

TYPE	REG/SER	CON. NO.	PI/NOTES	STATUS
☐ Atlas-Aermacchi MB.326M Impala I	460	102/6332		RA
☐ Atlas-Aermacchi MB.326M Impala I	480	6356/A5	Front fuselage only.	PV
☐ Atlas-Aermacchi MB.326M Impala I	502	6397/A27	Front fuselage only.	RA
☐ Atlas-Aermacchi MB.326M Impala I	531	A56		PV
☐ Avro 696 Shackleton MR.3	'1717'	1530	1720 – gate guard at base.	PVX
☐ Avro 696 Shackleton MR.3	1722	1532		RAA
☐ Blackburn B-103 Buccaneer S.50	416	B3-01-64/SA6	G-2-6	RA
☐ Canadair CL-13B Sabre 6 [North American F-86E]	372	1481	23691 (Canada)	RA
☐ Dassault Mirage F.1AZ	216	47		RA
☐ Dassault Mirage F.1CZ	213	14F-14A		RA
☐ Dassault Mirage F.1CZ	204	64		RA
☐ De Havilland D.H.100 Vampire FB.5	208	EEP42917		PV
☐ De Havilland D.H.100 Vampire FB.52	241	V.0657	On loan to Stellenbosch F.C.	PV
☐ Douglas DC-3A-456 Skytrain (C-47A) (Dakota III)	6832	12478	42-108863, KG443	RAC
☐ Lockheed 237-27-01 Ventura GR.V (PV-1)	6447	237-5855	Bu34965, FP682, 6447, TS303	PV
☐ North American NA-88 Texan (AT-6C) (Harvard IIA)	7293	88-10642	41-33522, EX549	RAA
☐ North American NA-88 Texan (AT-6C) (Harvard IIA)	7231	88-10663	41-33543, EX570	RAA
☐ Piaggio P.166S Albatross	896	458	.	RAA
☐ Sikorsky S-55D Whirlwind HAS.22 (HO4S-3)	WV204	55476	Bu133744, WV204, ZS-HDN	PVC
☐ Sud SA.316B Alouette III	611	1629	N9835, (Southern Rhodesia)	RAA
☐ Sud SA.321L Super Frelon	314	140	F-ZKBK	PV
☐ Westland Wasp HAS.1	93	F9755		RA
☐ Westland Wasp HAS.1	95	F9763		RA

SOUTH AFRICAN AIR FORCE MUSEUM – PORT ELIZABETH (SA24)

Address:	AFS Port Elizabeth, Private Bag X6016 Port Elizabeth 8000.
Tel:	041-505-1442
Fax:	041-505-1295
Admission:	Monday-Friday 0800-1530.
Location:	On the south side of the airport which is in the south western suburbs of the town.

The airfield was an active base up to the 1990s and now has no operational units. The runways are also used by civilian traffic. The local branch of the Friends of the South African Air Force Museum assist with the running of this collection. In the early 1970s the country placed the first export order for the Mirage F.1CZ. Shrouded in secrecy, the first pair arrived in the country in April 1975. The type gave excellent service for almost two decades. A fleet of Wasps served with the Navy from the mid-1960s. The Oxford, a type which served in South Africa, is being rebuilt to original military configuration. Work is proceeding well on the airframe and engines. After its military days were over the aircraft served at Hamble and Perth training airline pilots before joining the R.A.F. Museum in 1970. All branches of the services are honoured and military vehicles can also be seen. A display of photographs, memorabilia, uniforms and components has also been set up.

TYPE	REG/SER	CON. NO.	PI/NOTES	STATUS
☐ Airspeed AS.40 Oxford I (AS.10)	G-AITF		ED290	PVC
☐ Atlas-Aermacchi AM.3CM Bosbok	920	2001	I-TAAA	PV
☐ Atlas-Aermacchi MB.326K Impala II	1037	38		PV
☐ Dassault Mirage F.1CZ	201	58		PV

TYPE	REG/SER	CON. NO.	PI/NOTES	STATUS
☐ De Havilland D.H.100 Vampire FB.5	205	EEP42784		PV
☐ North American NA-88 Texan (AT-6C) (Harvard IIA)	7289	88-10646	41-33526, EX553	PVA
☐ North American NA-88 Texan (AT-6D) (Harvard III)	ZU-DML	88-14725	41-33891, EX918, 7480 – with parts from c/n 88-14725 41-33891, EX918	PVA
☐ Sud SA.319B Alouette III	632	2287		PV
☐ Sud SA.330C Puma	123	1030		PV
☐ Westland Scout AH.1	GT	F9619	G-17-2, BSP-1 (Bahrain)	PV
☐ Westland-Bell 47G-3B-1 Sioux AH.1	XT562	WA.451	XT562, ZS-HHA – incorporates parts of Bell 47G-3 c/n 7593 N6229N, ZS-HCS.	PV

SOUTH AFRICAN AIRWAYS APPRENTICE SCHOOL COLLECTION (SA25)

Address:	Private Bag 12, 1627 Oliver Tambo International Airport, Kempton Park 1620.
Admission:	By prior permission only.
Location:	About 10 km north east of Johannesburg.

The airline has trained apprentice technicians for many years and a number of aircraft now preserved in museums around the country once served as instructional airframes at the school. Six survivors of the vast fleet of South African Air Force Harvards are currently at the site. Two are Canadian built and served with the Luftwaffe and the Portuguese Air Force before arriving in the country. One of these and one of the American aircraft are maintained in flying condition. Two locally built Impalas joined the school in the summer of 1993.

TYPE	REG/SER	CON. NO.	PI/NOTES	STATUS
☐ Atlas-Aermacchi MB.326M Impala I	546	A71		RA
☐ Atlas-Aermacchi MB.326M Impala I	567	A92		RA
☐ Canadian Car & Foundry Harvard 4 [North American NA-186 (T-6J)]	ZS-WLU	CCF4-425	52-8504, AA+638, 1727 (Portugal), 1727 (Mozambique)	RA
☐ Canadian Car & Foundry Harvard 4 [North American NA-186 (T-6J)]	ZS-WLR	CCF4-448	52-8527, AA+658, 1731 (Portugal), 1731 (Mozambique)	RAA
☐ Canadian Car & Foundry Harvard 4 [North American NA-186 (T-6J)]	ZS-WLS	CCF4-451	52-8530, AA+660, 1751 (Portugal), 1751 (Mozambique)	RA
☐ North American NA-88 Texan (AT-6D) (Harvard III)	ZS-WLQ	88-15069	41-33962, EX989, 7530, E (Gabon), '7700'	RA
☐ North American NA-88 Texan (AT-6D) (Harvard III)	ZS-WLP	88-15698	41-34067, EZ194, 7601, G (Gabon), 7601	RAA
☐ North American NA-88 Texan (AT-6D) (Harvard III)	ZS-WLT	88-16235	42-84454, EZ310, 7625, H-15 (Belgium), 7729, ZS-WLR	RA

SOUTH AFRICAN AIRWAYS MUSEUM SOCIETY (SA26)

Address:	Rand Airport, Germiston 1400.
Tel:	011-978-5625
Email:	enquiry@historicflight.co.za
Admission:	By prior permission only.
Location:	About 5 km south west of the town.

South African Airways was formed on February 1st 1934 when It took over Union Airways and their fleet of two de Havilland Gipsy Moths, one Puss Moth, three Junkers F 13s and a W 34. The first Junkers Ju 52/3m was delivered in November 1934 and eventually fifteen were operated. In the late 1970s a decision was made to collect aircraft types which had once been operated by the airline. The first to arrive was the Lodestar, which was soon restored to the colours it wore when flown in the 1940s and 1950s. Two Doves were used between 1947 and 1952. Eight Vikings were operated at the same period and the example in the collection was retrieved, in 1987, from the roof of Vic's Viking Garage near Johannesburg where it had spent many years advertising the business. The fourth static aircraft is the Starliner which was once leased from Trek Airways. In 1980 the airline bought a Spanish built Junkers Ju 52/3m from England with the aim of restoring it to airworthy condition for the fiftieth anniversary of the company. This aircraft continued to fly for a period on charter flights and special occasions and is painted in period SAA colours. The fleet has now grown with the addition of a DC-3 and two DC-4s. In 1966 most of S.A.A.'s DC-4 fleet was sold to the South African Air Force who used the type until the early 1990s. The first example to join the collection arrived in 1993 and since then has flown to the U.S.A. to visit the E.A.A. Convention at Oshkosh in 1994 and to take part in the fiftieth anniversary celebrations at London's Heathrow Airport in 1996. The second DC-4 was chartered to Swissair in 1997 and for three months flew in their colours. Two retired Boeing 747s have recently joined the collection. One is a SP model which was derived from the 747-100 series and featured a shortened fuselage and extra fuel capacity to give it a longer range. SAA ordered six during the Apartheid era when they were banned from overflying other African countries. The example on show flew into Rand in September 2006 after three years in store. An impressive collection of memorabilia has also been assembled. This is on show in the

Transvaal Aero Club buildings. On display are uniforms, aircraft models, instruments and timetables. The history of the company and its aircraft is portrayed. Guided tours of the aircraft at Rand can be booked. The airline is to be commended on preserving so many delightful propliners. There have been a number of organisational changes and the airworthy types are currently flown by Skyclass. Three of the aircraft are still at Oliver Tambo IAP.

TYPE	REG/SER	CON. NO.	PI/NOTES	STATUS
☐ Boeing 747-244B	ZS-SAN	20239		RA
☐ Boeing 747SP-44	ZS-SPC	21134	N8297V, ZS-SPC, 3B-NAG	RA
☐ Construcciones Aeronáuticas (CASA) 352L [Junkers Ju 52/3m]	ZS-AFA	164	T.2B-273, G-BFHE, ZS-UYU – at Tambo IAP.	RAA
☐ De Havilland D.H.104 Dove 6 (1) (2)	ZS-BCC	04079	(G-AJOU), ZS-BCC, VP-RCL, VP-YLX, 9J-RHX, G-AWFM	RA
☐ Douglas DC-3A-456 Skytrain (C-47A) (Dakota III)	ZS-BXF	12107	42-92320, FZ572, 6821, ZS-BXF, 6888 – operated by Skyclass.	RAA
☐ Douglas DC-4 Skymaster (C-54D)	ZS-PAJ	22192	43-17242, N-242 (Denmark), N4988V, C-GRYY, C9-ATS, EL-AWX, 3D-AWX	RA
☐ Douglas DC-4-1009 Skymaster	ZS-AUB	42984	ZS-AUB, 6905, ZS-AUB, 6905 – operated by Skyclass.	RAA
☐ Douglas DC-4-1009 Skymaster	ZS-BMH	43157	ZS-BMH, 6904, ZS-BMH, 6904 – operated by Skyclass.	RAA
☐ Lockheed 1649A-98-17 Starliner	ZS-DVJ	1649A-1042	D-ALOL, N45520, ZS-DVJ, LX-LGX – at Tambo IAP.	RA
☐ Lockheed 18-08-01 Lodestar	ZS-ASN	18-2026	ZS-ASN, 1372	RA
☐ Vickers 498 Viking 1A	ZS-DKH	121	G-AHOT, XD635, G-AHOT – at Tambo IAP.	RA

SOUTH AFRICAN NATIONAL MUSEUM OF MILITARY HISTORY (SA27)

Address:	Post Office Box 52090, Erswold Way, Saxonwold, Gauteng 2132.
Tel:	011-646-5513
Fax:	011-646-5256
Email:	milmus@iccn.co.sa
Admission:	Daily 0900-1630.
Location:	About 8 km north west of Johannesburg city centre near the zoo.

The idea of this museum was put forward in July 1941 by the official historian of the South African Defence Force, Captain J. Agar-Hamilton. The plans were approved by General Smuts and an exhibition was held at Zoo Lake in Johannesburg the following year during the Liberty Cavalcade. Aircraft were collected but unfortunately two civil types – a Junkers F 13 and a de Havilland D.H.66 Hercules – were turned down and subsequently scrapped. A number of military machines an Avro Tutor, a Hawker Fury, a Junkers Ju 52/3m, a Junkers Ju 88 and a Westland Wapiti were acquired but due to lack of space these were also destroyed. The official opening of the collection, then known as the South African War Museum, at Saxonwold was carried out by General Smuts on August 29th 1947. A comprehensive range of artefacts, photographs, documents, uniforms and models complements the military hardware on view. The aircraft collection still contains a number of rare machines. The earliest two, the DH.9 and the S.E.5A, are from the batch of one hundred and ten presented to the country by Great Britain in the early 1920s. The D.H.9 served with the Air Force until 1936 and after being on the civil register from 1938 to 1940 was impressed for instructional use. The Hawker Hartbees is a development of the Audax adapted for ground attack duties in tropical conditions. Four of the type were built by the parent company in England and a further sixty five by the Aircraft and Artillery Depot of the S.A.A.F. at Roberts Heights near Pretoria from 1937. The Hartbees on show is believed to have taken part in the mass raid on Italian positions at Banda and Moyale on the Kenya-Ethiopia border on June 11th 1940. Very few examples of the classic Hawker biplanes of the inter-war period have survived. Four German and three British aircraft from the World War II period are exhibited. Two of the former Luftwaffe aircraft were among those tested at Farnborough in England at the end of the conflict. Three recently retired jets which have flown in regional conflicts have been added to the display.

TYPE	REG/SER	CON. NO.	PI/NOTES	STATUS
☐ Atlas C.4M Kudu	990	32	Fuselage only.	PVD
☐ Atlas-Aermacchi MB.326K Impala II	1045	46	85	PV
☐ Blackburn B-103 Buccaneer S.50	422	B3-07-64/SA12	G-2-12	PV
☐ Dassault Mirage IIICZ	813	178		PV
☐ De Havilland D.H.9			(South Africa), ZS-AOI, 2005, IS-8	PV
☐ De Havilland D.H.98 Mosquito PR.IX	LR480			PV
☐ Focke-Wulf Fw 190A-6/R6	'RN+LU'	550214	550214, AM.10	PV
☐ Hawker Hartbees	851			PV
☐ Hawker Hurricane IIC	5285		LD619	PV
☐ Messerschmitt Bf 109E-3	'2'	1289	SH+FA	PV
☐ Messerschmitt Bf 109F-4/trop	'6'	31010 (?)	'6', 777	PV
☐ Messerschmitt Me 262B-1a/U1	110305	110305	110305, AM.50	PV
☐ Royal Aircraft Factory S.E.5A	'D6856'	683/204	F7781 or F7783 (?), 320	PVX
☐ Supermarine 359 Spitfire HF.VIIIc	5501	6S.238666	JF294	PV

SOUTH AFRICAN NAVAL MUSEUM (SA28)

Address:	Private Bag X1, Simon's Town 7895.
Tel:	021-787-4686
Fax:	021-787-4606
Email:	navpro@telkomsa.net
Admission:	Daily 1000-1600.
Location:	In the centre of the town.

The museum is located in the former dockyard magazine and storehouse constructed in 1743/4 at the historic Simon's Town yard. When the Royal Navy moved its headquarters to Cape Town in 1810 the building was extended and subsequently used for a variety of tasks. Control of the British base was passed over to South Africa in 1955. The museum traces the maritime history of the nation with a number of innovative displays. Life-size replicas of a ship's bridge and a submarine operational control room have been constructed. On show are a variety of weapons, mines, mine sweeping equipment, small boats, models, documents, photographs and uniforms. The Wasp is one of the batch flown from the decks of naval ships.

TYPE	REG/SER	CON. NO.	PI/NOTES	STATUS
☐ Westland Wasp HAS.1	85	F9554	On loan from SAAFM.	PV

SPRINGBOK FLYING SAFARIS (SA29)

Address:	Hangar 5, Rand Airport, Germiston 1400.
Admission:	By prior permission only.
Location:	About 5 km south west of the town.

The company offers tours of Africa in its fleet of classic propliners. One DC-3 and a DC-6 are currently airworthy and the latter is leased from Namibian Commercial Aviation. It was the last DC-6 to be built and was delivered to JAT in Yugoslavia in 1958. Over the next few years it spent period with the Yugoslav Air Force and Adria Airlines before being donated to Zambia in 1975. Three DC-3s are under restoration. The earliest was delivered to United Airlines in America in April 1938 and flew on their routes for sixteen years. Two of these are former South African air force machines. The SAAF received its first Dakota during World War II and about one hundred served with the force. A few, re-engined with turboprops, are still operational at Ysterplaat.

TYPE	REG/SER	CON. NO.	PI/NOTES	STATUS
☐ Douglas DC-3A-197B	ZS-KEX	2008	NC18942, N92C, N80R, N8044	RAC
☐ Douglas DC-3A-456 Skytrain (C-47A)	ZS-GPL	9581	42-23719, NC47573, ZS-GPL, A2-ACH	RAA
☐ Douglas DC-3A-456 Skytrain (C-47A) (Dakota III)	ZS-NTE	11926	42-92157, FL565, 6873	RAC
☐ Douglas DC-3A-456 Skytrain (C-47A) (Dakota III)	ZS-BXJ	12413	42-92595, KG383, 6829	RAC
☐ Douglas DC-6B	V5-NCG	45564	YU-AFB, 7452 (Yugoslavia), 73102 (Yugoslavia), YU-AFB, 73102 (Yugoslavia), 7512 (Yugoslavia), GBM112 (Zambia)	RAA

THUNDER CITY (SA30)

Address:	Site 10 Tower Road, Cape Town International Airport, Cape Town 7525.
Tel:	021-934-8007
Fax:	021-934-8003
Email:	info@thundercity.com
Admission:	Daily 1000-1700.
Location:	About 5 km north east of the city.

This private collection of former military aircraft was started in 1994 by Mike Beachy-Head. Two Hunters and a Canberra were flown to South Africa from England in early 1995. The Canberra was sadly destroyed in a crash soon after its arrival. Four Lightnings arrived soon afterwards. Restoration work soon started with the first of the two seaters flying in 1999 and a single seater in 2001. These impressive jets are at the current time the only airworthy examples of their type. The South African Air Force ordered sixteen Blackburn Buccaneers which were delivered during 1965/66. Eight were ferried by air to the country and one was lost on this flight. The second batch arrived by sea. Five survived to be preserved in museums. The collection now includes three former Royal Air Force machines. These all flew on M.O.D work at Boscombe Down before arriving in South Africa. This trio are once again the last operational examples of the type. The fleet includes several Hawker Hunters. One single-seater was formerly flown by the Swiss Air Force and spent time in Swaziland before arriving at the site. Thunder City is currently the only organisation in the world to offer supersonic flights to members of the public. Several privately owned aircraft are based in the hangars and these include two Delfins which were once part of an aerobatic team. Along the road to the hangar is a display of former military types. The Javelin served as a gate guard at the Royal air Force stations at Yatesbury and Stanmore Park before being sold at auction when the latter closed.

TYPE	REG/SER	CON. NO.	PI/NOTES	STATUS
☐ Aero L-29 Delfin	ZU-CYH	294898	112 (Bulgaria)	RAA
☐ Aero L-29 Delfin	ZU-AUX	591707	(Soviet), RA-1707	RAA
☐ Blackburn B-103 Buccaneer S.2B	ZU-NIP	B3-01-72	XW986	PVA
☐ Blackburn B-103 Buccaneer S.2B	ZU-BCR	B3-02-72	XW987	PVA
☐ Blackburn B-103 Buccaneer S.2B	ZU-AVI	B3-03-72	XW988	PVA
☐ Blackburn B-103 Buccaneer S.50			Front fuselage only.	PV
☐ British Aircraft Corporation 167 Strikemaster 83	ZU-PER	161	G-27-154, ZG808, 113 (Kuwait), OJ6 (Botswana), G-BXFW	PVA
☐ De Havilland D.H.100 Vampire FB.5	242	V.0636		PV
☐ English Electric P.26 Lightning F.6	ZU-BEW	95238	XR773, G-OPIB	PVA
☐ English Electric P.26 Lightning F.6 (F.3) (F.3A)	ZU-BEY	95116	XP693, G-FSIX	PV
☐ English Electric P.27 Lightning T.5	ZU-BEX	B1/95011	XS451, 8503M, G-LTNG	PVA
☐ English Electric P.27 Lightning T.5	ZU-BBD	B1/95012	XS452, G-BPFE	PVA
☐ Gloster Javelin FAW.1	XA553		XA553, 7470M	PV
☐ Hawker P.1099 Hunter F.6A (F.6)	ZU-AUJ	41H/679991	XE653, 8829M, G-BVWV	PVA
☐ Hawker P.1101 Hunter T.68 (P.1067 Hunter F.4)	ZU-HUN	HABL 003119	XF951, 7947M, G-9-389, J-4202 (Switzerland)	PVA
☐ Hawker P.1101 Hunter T.7A (T.7)	ZU-LEE	41H/695347	XL613, G-BVMB	PVA
☐ Hawker P.1101 Hunter T.8B (P.1067 Hunter F.4)	ZU-CTN	41H/695343	XF967, (9182M), 9186M – composite with parts from XL609, 8866M G-BZRI	PVA
☐ Hawker P.1101 Hunter T.8C (T.8)	ZU-ATH	41H/693836	XL598, G-BVWG	PVA
☐ Hawker P.1067 Hunter GA.11 (F.4)	G-BZRH	HABL 003097	XF368	PVA
☐ Hawker P.1099 Hunter F.58	ZU-AVC	41H/697426	J-4059 (Switzerland), ZU-AVC, 3D-HUN	PVA
☐ Hiller UH12E Raven (H-23G) (OH-23G)		1605	63-12890	PV
☐ North American NA-77 Texan (SNJ-3)	ZU-BAK	77-4454	Bu6806, 7679	PVA
☐ Piaggio P.166S Albatross	ZS-NJY	445	883, ZU-ADO	PVA
☐ Piaggio P.166S Albatross	ZS-NJU	452	890	PVA
☐ Piper PA-23-250 Aztec	ZS-NKF	27-7654017		PVA
☐ Sikorsky S-62A	ZS-HHK	62062	N2512M, N92867, CF-JOK, 5B-CBW, A7-HAC, ZS-HHK, 3D-HAE, N2516M, 3D-HAE	PV
☐ Sud SA.330H Puma	ZU-PUM	1405	157	PVC
☐ Westland-Bell 47B-3B-1 Sioux AH.1	ZS-HLW	WA.360	XT201	RAA

WARRIORS GATE MOTH MUSEUM OF MILITARIA (SA31)

Address:	1 NMR Avenue, Old Fort Road, Durban 4001.
Tel:	031-307-3337
Email:	may@hixnet.co.xa
Admission:	Tuesday-Friday 1100-1500; Saturday 1000-1200; Sunday 1100-1500.
Location:	In the centre of the city.

This museum is located in the grounds of the Old Fort which in 1824 was the refuge for the British population of the city during a month long siege. This earthwork was improved and buildings added in the 1850s. The site was used by troops until the end of the nineteenth century.The display has been set up by the local branch of the Memorable Order of Tin Hats and features South Africa's contribution to the two World Wars. On show is a large collection of medals, uniforms, documents, photographs and weapons. The contribution of the South African Air Force during the inter-war period and the 1939/45 conflict is portrayed in the informative exhibition. The contribution of many local servicemen is highlighted in a series of poignant displays.

WATERKLOOF BASE COLLECTION (SA32)

Address:	Private Bag X1001, Centurion 0140.
Tel:	012-672-4911
Admission:	By prior permission only.
Location:	Just east of the town on Hans Strijom Drive.

The base, opened in August 1938 housed combat squadrons for many years. The airfield was upgraded during World War II. At the current time it houses transport squadrons operating a variety of types from the Lockheed Hercules to single engined Cessnas. Waterkloof is also home to the Presidential Flight and is the busiest military airfield in the country. Three types which served at the field have been preserved around the site. Their squadrons were all disbanded in the early 1990s as part of a round of defence cuts. South Africa ordered three Canberra T.4s and these were delivered in 1964. The other two were sold to Peru.

TYPE	REG/SER	CON. NO.	PI/NOTES	STATUS
☐ Blackburn B-103 Buccaneer S.50	412	B3-12-63/SA2		RA
☐ Canadair CL-13B Sabre 6 [North American F-86E]	369	1478	23688	RA
☐ English Electric EA.1 Canberra T.4	459	EEP71546	WJ617	RA

TUNISIA

GAFSA AIR BASE MONUMENT (TUN1)

Address:	Ksar, Gafsa.
Admission:	By prior pemission only.
Location:	Just east of the town.

The base is home to squadrons operating the Czech designed L-159 and helicopters. In the late 1960s twelve F-86F Sabres were supplied by the United States and one is preserved as a monument.

TYPE	REG/SER	CON. NO.	PI/NOTES	STATUS
☐ North American NA-227 Sabre (F-86F)				RA

SIDI AHMED BASE MEMORIAL (TUN2)

Address:	Bizerte.
Admission:	By prior permission only.
Location:	About 5 km west of the town.

The airfield was used by the French Air Force before independence. Now combat types are in residence. A Flamant is preserved near one of the ramps. At least three served with the Tunisian Air Force.

TYPE	REG/SER	CON. NO.	PI/NOTES	STATUS
☐ Dassault MD-315 Flamant				RA

SOUSSE AIR FORCE BASE MEMORIAL (TUN3)

Address:	Sousse.
Admission:	By prior permission only.
Location:	In the town.

The Air Force base a detachment of helicopters at the barracks in the town. Just after independence Tunisia sent several officers to Sweden for pilot training. Fifteen SAAB Safirs were ordered and served in this role at Bizerte for many years. One has been preserved as a memorial inside the camp.

TYPE	REG/SER	CON. NO.	PI/NOTES	STATUS
☐ Svenska Aeroplan Aktiebolaget (SAAB) 91D Safir	Y31006	91423		RA

TUNIS-CARTHAGE AIR BASE MEMORIAL (TUN4)

Address:	Carthage, Tunis.
Admission:	By prior permission only.
Location:	In the north eastern part of the city.

The Air Force maintain a base at the main international airport for the city. The Safir is preserved in this area and the Texan is mounted on a pole near to the old terminal building complex.

TYPE	REG/SER	CON. NO.	PI/NOTES	STATUS
☐ North American NA-182 Texan (T-6G)				PV
☐ Svenska Aeroplan Aktiebolaget (SAAB) 91D Safir				RA

ZAMBIA

LIVINGSTONE MUSEUM (ZA1)

Address:	Mosi-ao-Tunya Road, P.O. Box 60498, Livingstone.
Tel:	03-324427.
Fax:	03-320991
Admission:	Daily 0830-1600.
Location:	In the centre of the town which is near the Victoria Falls.

Zambia, formerly Northern Rhodesia, became an independent country in 1964. The famous explorer David Livingstone discovered the nearby Victoria Falls on his 1852–1856 expedition which followed the Zambesi River. His work features prominently in the exhibition at the National Museum of Zambia which carries his name. The displays also trace the history of the region and its people. The only aircraft on display is the Chipmunk which is one six former Royal Air Force machines bought in 1966. The type was used for initial pilot training until 1970 when it was replaced by the SIAI-Marchetti SF.260.

TYPE	REG/SER	CON. NO.	PI/NOTES	STATUS
☐ De Havilland D.H.C.1 Chipmunk T.10	AF-506	C1/0502	WG428	PV

ZAMBIAN AIR FORCE MEMORIAL (ZA2)

Address:	Lusaka City Airport, Lusaka.
Admission:	On permanent view.
Location:	In the eastern suburbs of the city.

The Zambian Air Force came into being when the country gained its independence in 1964. Two aircraft have been preserved as memorials at the airport. One is believed to a Shenyang F-6. China presented the country with a dozen examples in 1978. The other type has not been positively identified.

TYPE	REG/SER	CON. NO.	PI/NOTES	STATUS
☐ Shenyang F-6 [Mikoyan-Gurevich MiG-19SF]				PV
☐ Unknown Type				RA

ZIMBABWE

ZIMBABWE AIR FORCE HEADQUARTERS MEMORIAL (ZI1)

Address:	Borrowdale Road, Harare.
Admission:	By prior permission only.
Location:	In the north eastern part of the city.

The Zimbabwe Air Force operated Hawker Hunters with the first arriving in what was then Southern Rhodesia in 1962. One is mounted outside the Headquarters Building to serve as a memorial.

TYPE	REG/SER	CON. NO.	PI/NOTES	STATUS
☐ Hawker P.1099 Hunter FGA.9 (F.6)	1088		XG155	RA

ZIMBABWE MILITARY MUSEUM (ZI2)

Address:	Lobengula Avenue, P.O. Box 1300, Gweru.
Tel:	054-222816
Admission:	Daily 1000-1700.
Location:	On the south eastern side of the Civic Centre.

The museum was formed as a result of the efforts of Thornhill Air Force Base and the then School of Defence. The initial plan was for collections to be set at both establishments but this was changed and the museum was located at the latter site. The display opened to the public in January 1974. Zimbabwe, formerly Southern Rhodesia, gained its independence on April 18th 1980. The Southern Rhodesia Air Force was formed on November 28th 1947 and over the last fifty years has operated a variety of types. Displays at this museum trace the history of the Army, Air Force and Police. In addition to the aircraft, engines, photographs, uniforms and artefacts can also be seen. The Australian built Tiger Moth was delivered to the Rhodesian Air Training Group in 1941 and served until 1955. Over seven thousand six hundred pilots and two thousand three hundred navigators were trained in Rhodesia during World War II. A special display honours the work of the R.A.T.G. In the mid-1950s the Provost was chosen to replace the Tiger Moth and sixteen were delivered. In addition several more were acquired during the period of sanctions in the late 1960s and one of this batch is on view. Over fifty Vampires have served in the country and three are exhibited. The Spitfire was delivered to Southern Rhodesia in 1951; the Canberra entered service in Rhodesia in 1959 and served until at least the mid-1980s. The first batch of twelve Hunter FGA.9s were flown to Rhodesia in December 1962 and ten more arrived the following year, seeing combat in the struggle against insurgent forces and also carried out cross-border strikes into Mozambique. The Pou-du-Ciel was built by Aston Redrup in Bulawayo. The Viscount was the first of five ordered by Central African Airways in 1966. It flew until 1985 and arrived at the museum in August 1986.

TYPE	REG/SER	CON. NO.	PI/NOTES	STATUS
☐ Agusta-Bell 205A-1				PV
☐ De Havilland D.H.100 Vampire FB.9	1380	V.0679	234 (South Africa)	PV
☐ De Havilland D.H.100 Vampire FB.9	RRAF112	V.0988	WR199, SR112	PV
☐ De Havilland D.H.100 Vampire FB.9			At Gweru Air Force Base.	RA
☐ De Havilland D.H.115 Vampire T.11	4220	15375	XE819, SR122, RRAF406	PV
☐ De Havilland D.H.82A Tiger Moth	SR26	DHA.746	DX658	PV
☐ English Electric EA.1 Canberra B.2	R2504	EEP71173	WH707, RRAF163, RRAF204	PV
☐ Hawker P.1099 Hunter FGA.9 (F.6)	'1188'			PVX
☐ Mignet HM-14 Pou-du-Ciel				PV
☐ North American NA-88 Texan (AT-6C) (Harvard IIA)	SR48	88-13194	41-33722, EX749, 7397 (South Africa)	PV
☐ Percival P.56 Provost T.1	3614	P.56/285	XF554, G-AWTD	PV
☐ Supermarine 356 Spitfire F.22	PK355	CBAF.44	PK355, SR65, RRAF65	PV
☐ Vickers 748D Viscount	Z-YNA	98	VP-YNA, 7Q-YDK, VP-YNA	PV

Makhado Air Force Base is assembling a collection. This Mirage IIICZ will soon be put on display. (Winston Brent)

This Atlas Impala I is preserved outside the Military Museum in Bloemfontein. (Winston Brent)

INDEX

All aircraft are listed alphabetically by manufacturer or designer (in the case of some gliders and homebuilt aircraft) followed by the type. Each country is denoted by a two/three letter code and each museum/collection a number e.g. SA10 is tenth museum/collection in alphabetical order in South Africa.

Country codes are as follows:-
ALG Algeria; **AN** Angola; **BOT** Botswana**; BUR** Burkina Faso**; CHA** Chad**; CON** Congo-Brazzaville; **CTI** Cote D'Ivoire **DRC** Democratic Republic of the Congo; **DJ** Djibouti; **EG** Egypt; **ER** Eritrea; **ET** Ethopia; **GAB** Gabon; **GH** Ghana; **LY** Libya; **MAD** Madagascar; **MOR** Morocco; **MOZ** Mozambique; **NG** Nigeria; **SA** South Africa; **TUN** Tunisia; **ZA** Zambia; **ZI** Zimbabwe.

The October 1973 War Panorama Memorial and Museum in Cairo has this MiG-21PFS and Sukhoi Su-20 on show (Ralph Lunt)

ASIA

Norwegian Sea
Arctic Ocean
Bering Sea
RUSSIA
TURKEY
GEORGIA
ARMENIA
LEBANON
ISRAEL
SYRIA
IRAQ
JORDAN
AZERBAIJAN
KAZAKHSTAN
UZBEKISTAN
TURKMENISTAN
MONGOLIA
NORTH KOREA
SOUTH KOREA
JAPAN
Pacific Ocean
KYRGYZSTAN
TAJIKISTAN
IRAN
KUWAIT
BAHRAIN
QATAR
AFGHANISTAN
CHINA
SAUDI ARABIA
PAKISTAN
NEPAL
BHUTAN
U.A.E.
YEMEN
OMAN
MYANMAR
INDIA
PHILIPPINES
LAOS
PALAU
BANGLADESH
THAILAND
VIETNAM
SRI LANKA
CAMBODIA
BRUNEI
MALAYSIA
MALAYSIA
Indian Ocean
SINGAPORE
INDONESIA

AFGHANISTAN

HERAT CITY WAR MEMORIAL (AF1)

Address: Herat
Admission: Airfield by prior permission only.
Location: The memorial is in the town.
The airfield is south of the town.

Two former Soviet helicopters are located at this memorial in the town. Guns, military vehicles and items of equipment are also to be seen. There are plaques honouring the personnel killed. The Sukhoi is at the airport which was a major air base for Soviet forces during their stay in the country.

TYPE	REG/SER	CON. NO.	PI/NOTES	STATUS
☐ Mil Mi-17	669			PV
☐ Mil Mi-24D	25		43 (Soviet)	PV
☐ Sukhoi Su-7BMK	060			RA

KABUL INTERNATIONAL AIRPORT MEMORIAL (AF2)

Address: Kabul.
Admission: On permanent view.
Location: About 10 km north east of the city.

Two jets are preserved near the airport. Both types flew in the country during the period when Soviet forces were in residence. They serve as memorials to the military personnel killed in the conflict.

TYPE	REG/SER	CON. NO.	PI/NOTES	STATUS
☐ Mikoyan-Gurevich MiG-15UTI				PV
☐ Sukhoi Su-22M4				PV

KANDAHAR AIR BASE MEMORIAL (AF3)

Address: Kandahar
Admission: By prior permission only.
Location: South of the town.

The area around Kandahar has seen many conflicts in recent years. The Soviet Air Force used the airfield for a number of years and the MiG is a memorial to this turbulent period.

TYPE	REG/SER	CON. NO.	PI/NOTES	STATUS
☐ Mikoyan-Gurevich MiG-21bis				RA

KUNDUZ AIR BASE MEMORIAL (AF4)

Address: Kunduz.
Admission: On permanent view.
Location: Just south east of the town.

The Soviet Air Force based helicopters at the field during their time in Afghanistan. A Mil-24 which was flown from the site was mounted as a monument but a recent photograph shows it to have been damaged.

TYPE	REG/SER	CON. NO.	PI/NOTES	STATUS
☐ Mil Mi-24D	03			PVD

ORGANISATION FOR MINE CLEARANCE AND AFGHAN REHABILITATION MUSEUM (AF5)

Address: Kabul.
Tel: 0521-814599
Fax: 0521-812085
Admission: By prior permission only.
Location: In the city.

This collection is displayed at a compound operated by the organisation. A number of derelict airframes which were located around the city and on local airfields have been moved for display. Some restoration work has been carried out. The Mil-24 was on show at the Armed Forces Museum which existed in the 1980s. As the other four then at the site are not in the new collection they have presumably been destroyed or badly damaged. The types represent those flown by the Soviet Air Force in Afghanistan during their period of occupation.

TYPE	REG/SER	CON. NO.	PI/NOTES	STATUS
☐ Aero L-39C Albatros	0017	232417		RA
☐ Antonov An-2	224			RA
☐ Ilyushin Il-28U	003			RA
☐ Mikoyan-Gurevich MiG-17	43			RA
☐ Mikoyan-Gurevich MiG-21MF	924			RA
☐ Mikoyan-Gurevich MiG-21SPS	352			RA
☐ Mikoyan-Gurevich MiG-21U-400	578	661719		RA
☐ Mil Mi-8T	271	9710813		RA
☐ Mil Mi-24A	344	808764		RA
☐ Sukhoi Su-7BKL				RA
☐ Yakovlev Yak-11	35			RA
☐ Yakovlev Yak-40	RA-87255	9311226	CCCP-87255	RA

This Yak-11 is preserved at the Organisation for Mine Clearance Museum in Kabul. (Skillet)

Several aircraft are stored at Tejgaon Air Force Base near Dhaka for the Bangladesh Air Force Museum. Among them is this MiG-21MF (Tim Spearman)

This colourful Fouga Magister is at Matiur Rehman Air Force Base near Jessore in Bangladesh. (Tim Spearman)

BANGLADESH

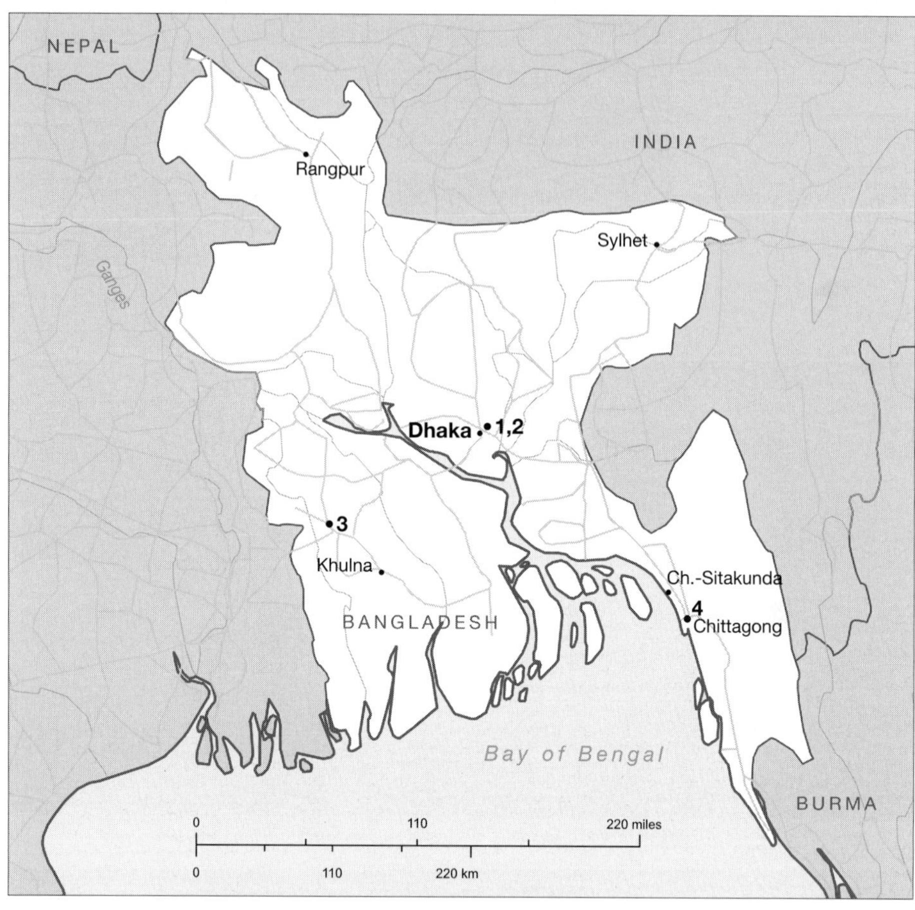

BANGLADESH AIR FORCE MUSEUM (BA1)

Address:	Tejgaon Air Force Base, Dhaka.
Tel:	02-884-524
Admission:	By prior permission only.
Location:	In the north eastern part of the city.

Formerly East Pakistan, Bangladesh became independent in 1971 with assistance from India. The Air Force was set up in India on September 28th 1971 as 'Kilo Flight'. The aim was to assist the freedom fighters in their homeland. Several Bengali pilots and ground crew were in the Pakistan Air Force so there was the potential for an operational unit. Among the first aircraft flown were two or three Sabres and a small number of T-33s captured from Pakistan. India donated a Dakota, a Caribou and a few Alouette IIIs. After a visit to Moscow in 1972 by the Prime Minister the Soviet Union supplied a number of combat aircraft. China delivered two dozen Shenyang F-6s in the late 1970s along with a several trainers. For a number of years a Sabre was on show at the Armed Forces Museum in the city but this display closed a number of years ago. The Air Force has preserved and stored several machines at Tejgaon and a small display tracing the history of the service has been set up in one of the buildings. This site is part of the large Bashar Air Force base which has two sites. Tejgaon is the old international airport which is now surrounded by buildings. The airfield is currently used by helicopter units. A short distance north is the Zia International Airport which shares its runway with Kurmitola Air Force Base, a home to major fighter units and a transport squadron. The types operated include the Nanchang A-5, Shenyang F-6, Chengdu F-7 and MiG-29. The Hunter and Ajeet were donated by India and are believed to be stored at Tejgaon. More aircraft will join the collection as they are withdrawn from service. M.K. Bashar was a local commander during the Liberation War and he later rose to the rank of Air Vice Marshal. A display honouring his life and military career is a prominent part of the informative indoor exhibition.

TYPE	REG/SER	CON. NO.	PI/NOTES	STATUS
☐ Aero Engine Services T6/24 Airtourer	S3-AAK	B-580	ZK-DKV	RA
☐ Antonov An-24RV	0001	27308304		RA
☐ Antonov An-32	1702	1702	S3-ACB	RA
☐ Canadair CL-13B Sabre 6 [North American F-86E]	1802	1802	JB+255 – identity doubtful.	RA
☐ De Havilland D.H.C.3 Otter	B721	211	IM1713	RA
☐ Fouga CM.170R Magister	061	061	(AA+161), 5V-MAT	RA
☐ Hawker P.1099 Hunter F.56A (F.6)	A463	8757	IF-13 (Belgium), G-9-128 – in Indian markings.	RA
☐ Hindustan Ajeet [Folland Fo.141 Gnat 2]				RA
☐ Mikoyan-Gurevich MiG-15UTI				RA
☐ Mikoyan-Gurevich MiG-21F	'1736'		In Indian markings.	RA
☐ Mikoyan-Gurevich MiG-21MF	7006			RA
☐ Mikoyan-Gurevich MiG-21MF	7007		On main base.	RA
☐ Mikoyan-Gurevich MiG-21MF	7009		At Air Force HQ.	RA
☐ Mikoyan-Gurevich MiG-21UM	036			RA
☐ Mil Mi-4	02			RA
☐ Mil Mi-8T	401			RA
☐ Mil Mi-8T	402			RA
☐ Mil Mi-8T	410			RA
☐ Mil Mi-8T	412			RA
☐ Mil Mi-8T	3037			RA
☐ Nanchang Q-5-IIIA	56908			RA
☐ Shenyang F-6C [Mikoyan-Gurevich MiG-19SF]	3917			RA
☐ Shenyang F-6C [Mikoyan-Gurevich MiG-19SF]	4125		In Pakistani markings.	RA
☐ Shenyang F-6C [Mikoyan-Gurevich MiG-19SF]	5359		On main base.	RA
☐ Shenyang F-6C [Mikoyan-Gurevich MiG-19SF]	8632		At Bijoy Sarani Roundabout close to airport.	RA
☐ Shenyang FT-6 [Mikoyan-Gurevich MiG-19U]	10937	48-10937	In Pakistani markings.	RA
☐ Shenyang JJ-5	723	551723		RA

LIBERATION WAR MUSEUM (BA2)

Address:	5 Segun Bagicha, Dhaka 1000.
Tel:	02-955-9091
Fax:	02-955-9092
Email:	mukti@citecho.net
Admission:	Summer Monday-Saturday 1000-1800. Winter Monday-Saturday 1000-1700.
Location:	In the northern part of the city centre.

For a number of years there was an Armed Forces Museum in the city but this has closed. The Liberation War Museum was established in 1996 and its impressive displays trace the military history of the region from early times. The struggles against the British Raj by the Bengali people are portrayed in detail. The area became East Pakistan in 1947 and was separated from the main government by the vast country of India. Conflicts between Pakistan and India often made communications difficult. On March 26th 1971 the people declared that they were independent and established the new state of Bangladesh. A civil war erupted between locals in the Pakistani forces and West Pakistanis stationed in the Bengal region. India supported the new country and this led to yet another war in the sub-continent. The struggle for independence is told in great detail and the horrific acts of genocide and the discovery of mass graves can be seen in the exhibition.

TYPE	REG/SER	CON. NO.	PI/NOTES	STATUS
☐ Mikoyan-Gurevich MiG-21M				PV

MATIUR RAHMAN AIR FORCE BASE MEMORIAL (BA3)

Address:	Air Force Academy, Jessore.
Admission:	By prior permission only.
Location:	In the western suburbs of the town.

The military side of the airfield houses the Air Force Academy where pilot and officer training are carried out. Currently in use are Cessna T-37Bs and Bell 206Ls. The Fouga Magister was formerly operated and an example has been preserved on the base. Matiur Rahman was born in Dhaka in 1945 and later joined the Pakistan Air Force. On August 20th 1971 whilst on a training mission in a Lockheed T-33 he attempted to fly the aircraft from Karachi across India to Bangladesh. The other pilot resisted this and the aircraft crashed at Thatta near the Pakistan/India border. Rahman was buried at Masroor Air Force Base and after more than thirty years his body was returned to Bangladesh and interned with full military honours. A room at the academy traces the story of his life and air force career. Also preserved is a Shenyang F-6 supplied by China.

TYPE	REG/SER	CON. NO.	PI/NOTES	STATUS
☐ Fouga CM.170R Magister	070			RA
☐ Shenyang F-6 [Mikoyan-Gurevich MiG-19SF]	1014			RA

ZAHURAL HAQUE AIR FORCE BASE COLLECTION (BA4)

Address:	Zahural Haque Air Force Base, Chittagong.
Admission:	By prior permission only.
Location:	In the western suburbs of the city.

This base is home to a school where training of technicians is carried out. There are several instructional airframes in the workshops. The base is named after Sergeant Zahural Haque who was killed in detention in the late 1960s. The New Zealand built Airtourer was used for primary training.

TYPE	REG/SER	CON. NO.	PI/NOTES	STATUS
☐ Aero Engine Services T6/24 Airtourer	S3-AAH	B-575	(ZK-DKT), 575, G-BAFO, ZK-DKT	RA
☐ Canadair CL-13B Sabre 6 [North American F-86E]	'606'		(Germany), (Pakistan)	RAX
☐ Mikoyan-Gurevich MiG-17	3812			RA
☐ Mil Mi-8	406		In Technical School	RA
☐ Mil Mi-8	407		In Technical School	RA
☐ Mil Mi-8	3024		In Technical School	RA
☐ Shenyang F-6 [Mikoyan-Gurevich MiG-19SF]	108		In Technical School	RA
☐ Shenyang F-6 [Mikoyan-Gurevich MiG-19SF]	0911			RA
☐ Shenyang F-6 [Mikoyan-Gurevich MiG-19SF]	1015		In Technical School	RA
☐ Shenyang F-6 [Mikoyan-Gurevich MiG-19SF]	1421		In Technical School	RA
☐ Shenyang F-6 [Mikoyan-Gurevich MiG-19SF]	7104		In Technical School	RA
☐ Shenyang F-6 [Mikoyan-Gurevich MiG-19SF]	8626			RA
☐ Shenyang F-6 [Mikoyan-Gurevich MiG-19SF]	8627		In Technical School	RA

BRUNEI

BRUNEI AIR FORCE MEMORIAL (BRU1)

Address:	Brunei International Airport Bandar Seri Bagawan.
Admission:	On permanent view.
Location:	In the western part of the city.

The first miltary aviation in the Sultanate came into being in the mid-1960s. The Air Force became a separate entity in October 1991. A small fleet of helicopters, transports and combat types fly from the field.

TYPE	REG/SER	CON. NO.	PI/NOTES	STATUS
☐ Bell 205A-1	AMDB-100	30057		PV

CAMBODIA

WAR MUSEUM (C1)

Address:	Kasekam Village, Sra Nge Commune, Siem Riep.
Tel:	012-873666
Admission:	Daily 0800-1730.
Location:	To the west of the town on Route 6.

Displays at this museum trace the complex military history of the country from early times. The period of French rule from 1863 until 1953 is featured. The country became the Khmer Republic in 1970 and Kampuchea from 1975 until 1989. In the early 1970s a small number of Chinese built MiG-19s were supplied and used against the Vietnamese invasion of 1977. The two aircraft were on show at a museum in Phnom Penh for a period but this display closed and the exhibition was moved to the new site on the main tourist routes.

TYPE	REG/SER	CON. NO.	PI/NOTES	STATUS
☐ Mil Mi-8T	XU-814	22903		PV
☐ Shenyang F-6 [Mikoyan-Gurevich MiG-19S]	30-950	F6-8837		PV

CHINA

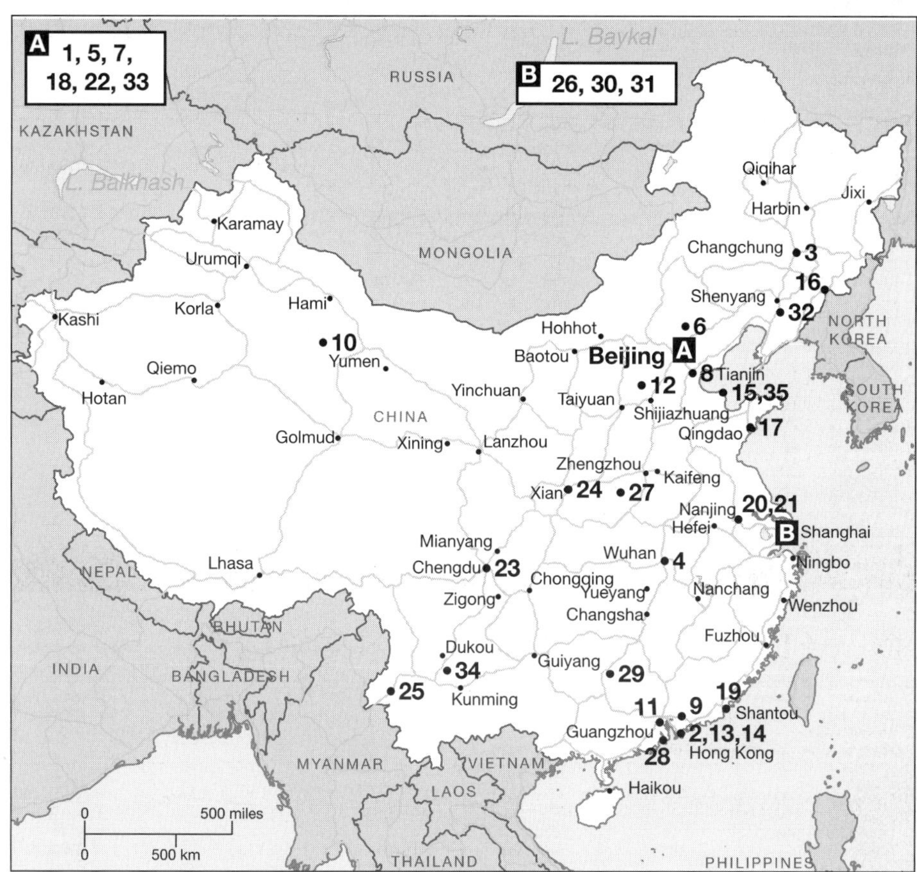

BEIJING AVIATION MUSEUM (CHI1)

Address:	Beijing Aeronautical Institute, 37 Xue Yuan Lu, Beijing 100083.
Tel:	010-8231-7658
Fax:	010-8223-8180
Email:	webmaster@buaa.edu.cn
Admission:	Tuesday-Sunday 0830-2000 1400-1700.
Location:	In the northern suburbs of the city.

This interesting collection is housed at the institute which trains many aeronautical engineers. The museum was set up in 1985 and there are two exhibition halls. The inside display traces the development of the technical side of aviation with many photographs, models, engines and components on view. Missiles and satellites can also be seen. Graduates of the institute who have made significant contributions to Chinese Aviation are also featured. A number of locally built microlights are exhibited in this area. The majority of the aircraft are parked behind the museum building. The star exhibit is the Northrop Black Widow. Only three complete examples of this twin boom aircraft are known to survive. Another recovered from New Guinea is under restoration in the U.S.A. P-61s were based in China at the end of World War II and the aircraft on show was donated to the Chengdu Institute of Aeronautical Engineering in 1947. Seven years later it was transported to its new home. One complete airframe and the fuselage of a Thunderbolt can also be seen. Another rarity is the Beijing NR-1 twin engined feeder liner. This was designed and built at the institute but only one flight was made. The test airframe and three incomplete fuselages are also on show. China ordered fifty Ryan STMs in late 1939 and the aircraft arrived in the country during 1940 and 1941. There are many Soviet designed aircraft displayed, including some from the 1940s plus several versions developed and built in China.

TYPE	REG/SER	CON. NO.	PI/NOTES	STATUS
☐ Aero 45	'7508'			PVX
☐ Aero L-60 Brigadyr	'7100-24'	650055		RAX
☐ Beijing Mifeng 2				PV
☐ Beijing Mifeng 3				RA
☐ Beijing Mifeng 3C				PVD
☐ Beijing Mifeng 4				RAD
☐ Beijing NR-1	001			PV
☐ Beijing NR-1			Fuselage only.	RA
☐ Beijing NR-1			Fuselage only.	RAD
☐ Beijing NR-1			Unfinished fuselage.	RAD
☐ Chengdu J-7 I [Mikoyan-Gurevich MiG-21F-13]	7311			RA
☐ Chengdu J-7 I [Mikoyan-Gurevich MiG-21F-13]	'86102'	10003	0003, '7311'	PV
☐ Douglas DC-3A-467 Skytrain (C-47B) (Dakota IV)	102		(USAAF), (RAF)	PV
☐ Harbin H-5 [Ilyushin Il-28]	0851	4149		PV
☐ Harbin Z-5 [Mil Mi-4]	'86103'		3709	PVX
☐ Hawker-Siddeley P.1127 Harrier GR.3	XZ965	41H/712201	XZ965, 9184M	PV
☐ Ilyushin Il-10	6		'7100-25'	PV
☐ Ilyushin Il-10				RA
☐ Ilyushin Il-14P	666	14803050	DM-ZZV	PV
☐ Lavochkin La-11	09		'7505', 03	PV
☐ Lockheed 580 (T-33A)			Rear fuselage and wing only.	RAD
☐ Mikoyan-Gurevich MiG-9	'86104'		'7503', 6201'	PV
☐ Mikoyan-Gurevich MiG-9			Fuselage only.	RAD
☐ Mikoyan-Gurevich MiG-15bis	'86101'		4649, '7502'	PVX
☐ Mikoyan-Gurevich MiG-15bis	'86105'		'7501'	PVX
☐ Mil Mi-17	LH94736			PV
☐ Mraz M-1D Sokol	03			RA
☐ Nanchang CJ-5 [Yakovlev Yak-18]			Fuselage only.	PVD
☐ Nanchang CJ-6A				RA
☐ Nanchang CJ-6A	08		61664	PV
☐ Nanchang Q-5	'86106'		10067, 1172'	PVX
☐ Nanchang Y-5 [Antonov An-2]			Fuselage only.	PV
☐ Noorduyn Harvard IIB [North American NA-77 (AT-16)]		14-233	42-696, FE499	PV
☐ North American NA-88 Texan (AT-6D) (Harvard III)	'7506'	88-14960	41-33933, EX960	RAX
☐ Northrop NS-8C Black Widow (P-61A)	'25171'	N.1234	42-39715, '7602'	PVX
☐ Polikarpov Po-2				RA
☐ Republic P-47D Thunderbolt	'7601'		(USAAF)	PVX
☐ Republic P-47N Thunderbolt		499-6808	Fuselage only	RA
☐ Ryan STM-2E	9R	364		RA
☐ Shenyang J-5 [Mikoyan-Gurevich MiG-17F]	018			RA
☐ Shenyang J-6 [Mikoyan-Gurevich MiG-19SF]	0004			PV
☐ Shenyang J-6 [Mikoyan-Gurevich MiG-19SF]	727			RA
☐ Shenyang J-6 [Mikoyan-Gurevich MiG-19SF]	'7703'		Fuselage only	PVX
☐ Shenyang J-6 II [Mikoyan-Gurevich MiG-19PM] (FSM)	'14025'	'650733'	Contains some original parts.	PVX
☐ Shenyang J-8II	8300			PV
☐ Shenyang JJ-5	5727			RAD
☐ Shenyang JJ-6 [Mikoyan-Gurevich MiG-19U]				RA
☐ Shijiazhuang SY-5S				PV
☐ Tachikawa Ki-54a	10351			PVD
☐ Tupolev Tu-2S	'7100-18'	1098751		PVX
☐ Yakovlev Yak-11	07			PV
☐ Yakovlev Yak-11	'7506'			RAX
☐ Yakovlev Yak-18				RA

CATHAY PACIFIC AIRWAYS DISPLAY (CHI2)

Address:	Cathay City, 5F South Tower, 8 Scenic Road, Hong Kong International Airport, Lantau Island.
Tel:	0852-2747-1234
Admission:	On permanent view.
Location:	At Chep Lap Kok Airport which is on the northern part of the island.

Cathay Pacific Airways was founded in September 1946 and its first aircraft was a single DC-3 which was flown on local routes for seven years. This aircraft is now on show in the Hong Kong Science Museum. The airline grew steadily and acquired its first jet, a Convair 880, in the 1960s. Now a fleet of modern jets is operated on services around the world. To coincide with its sixtieth anniversary the airline purchased a DC-3 in the Philippines and flew it to Chep Lak Kok Airport. The aircraft now resides outside the headquarters building and is resplendent in the colours of one operated in the early days of the company.

TYPE	REG/SER	CON. NO.	PI/NOTES	STATUS
☐ Douglas DC-3A-456 Skytrain (C-47A)	'VR-HDA'	9525	42-23663, 223663 (Philippines), RP-534, RP-C-1101	PVX

The Beijing Aviation Museum is home to this Harrier GR.3. (John Mounce)

The Technical School at Guangzhou has several interesting airframes including this Trident which is pictured at the old location. (Gerry Manning)

This Kamov Ka-50 is on show at the Kiev Military Theme Park near Tianjin. (Clarence Fu)

CHANGCHUN FILM THEME PARK (CHI3)

Address:	28 Huxiku, Changchun Lu 100111
Tel:	0431-8877-8704
Admission:	Daily 0800-1630
Location:	About 5 km south east of Changchun railway station.

The city has been home to one of the major film studios in the country for more than sixty years. A theme park tracing the development of the company and its movies has been set up. The MiG-15 is preserved by the studios.

TYPE	REG/SER	CON. NO.	PI/NOTES	STATUS
☐ Mikoyan-Gurevich MiG-15				PV

CHILDREN'S MILITARY MUSEUM (CHI4)

Address:	Wuhan 430070.
Admission:	Daily 0900-1800.
Location:	In the town.

A report mentioned that a Chinese built MiG-19 was preserved in Wuhan. There is a Children's Museum in the city so they may be the same place. Further information would be welcome.

TYPE	REG/SER	CON. NO.	PI/NOTES	STATUS
☐ Shenyang J-6 [Mikoyan-Gurevich MiG-19SF]				PV

CHINA AGRICULTURAL MUSEUM (CHI5)

Address:	16 Dongsanhuan Road, Chaoyang, Beijing 100026.
Tel:	010-650-18877
Admission:	Tuesday-Saturday 0900-1600.
Location:	In the northern part of the city.

Agriculture has played an important part in this populous country and displays at the museum trace the development of machinery and scientific progress. There are many interesting items on view including tractors. The Ilyushin Il-18 was flown on airline routes in China for many years. The aircraft was serving as a restaurant but was reported missing in 2005. However, the museum website shows it as still being there.

TYPE	REG/SER	CON. NO.	PI/NOTES	STATUS
☐ Ilyushin Il-18D	B-228	185008702	50855 – not seen Sep 2007 ?>	PV

CHINA AVIATION MUSEUM (CHI6)

Address:	P.O.Box 5806, Xiaotanzhanzen, Changping, Beijing 102211.
Tel:	010-69784882
Admission:	Daily 0800-1730.
Location:	About 40km north of Beijing.

Work on collecting aircraft for this museum started in 1986 and the exhibition officially opened on November 11th 1989, the fortieth anniversary of the formation of the People's Liberation Army Air Force. The site chosen was at a former air force installation near Chiangping. In the late 1960s a vast underground tunnel had been driven through an isolated hill about 5 km from Shahe Air Force Base. Measuring almost two thousand feet by one hundred and thirty feet the hangar was designed to house over one hundred fighters in the event of an attack. The complex was connected to the airfield by a taxiway which could also serve as a runway. The tunnel, which had been unused for some time, was cleared out and an entrance hall constructed at one end. Aircraft were moved to the site from Air Force bases, technical schools and municipal parks around the country. When the museum opened there were about one hundred and twenty aircraft on show and over the last few years this number has steadily increased. There are plans for developing the site to include leisure facilities and a sports airfield. Dominating the entrance hall is a vast diorama depicting the PLA flypast over Beijing in 1949. Just inside the tunnel is the MiG-15 flown in the Korean War by Wang Hai, who was commander of the PLA when the museum opened. Along each side of the hall are lines of aircraft. A number of replicas of early types have been constructed. On September 21st 1909 Feng Rue, who was living in the U.S.A., built and flew an aircraft of his own design. He returned home in 1911 with two aircraft and was appointed air force leader of the Guangdong Military Government. He was killed in a flying accident on August 25th 1912. In 1918 Yang Xianyi was recalled to China by Dr. Sun Yat Sen to set up an aviation section in the Guangdong Revolutionary

Government. He was in charge of the production of a two seat biplane which was named 'Rosamunde'. This was the student name of the wife of Sun Yat Sen. In 1930 a Vought Corsair belonging to the Kuomintan Air Force landed at Xuan Huadin in Hubei Province. The pilot was persuaded to join the Red Army and the aircraft flew a number of missions. Nearby is a replica of a Mosquito. About two hundred were given to the Nationalist Government in the late 1940s. An outer wing panel was discovered in a poor condition and the remainder of the airframe has been built around this. A number of types from the World War II period can be seen and these include several of Soviet origin. One of the Antonov An-2's has its wings bedecked with flowers. This aircraft was used to scatter the ashes of the former Premier Zhou en lai. China has supplied several Shenyang fighters to Pakistan and a Canadian built Sabre has been donated to the museum. Two aircraft have arrived from Africa. These are a Provost from Zimbabwe and a former Luftwaffe Piaggio P.149 from Tanzania. A few machines from the Taiwanese Air Force which have force landed on mainland China since the Communist take over in 1948 can also be seen. Many developments of post-war Soviet types are on view along with indigenous designs. The first type to be constructed in China in the Communist era was the Nanchang CJ-5, a licence built Yakovlev Yak-18. The airframe was later developed into the CJ-6 and almost two thousand examples of this model were built. The Nangchang Q-5 is an attack aircraft based on the MiG-19 airframe. Work on the project began in 1958 but the programme was abandoned two years later. The design was revived and the prototype flew in June 1965. Over one thousand Q-5s have been built in several versions and some have been sold to Bangladesh, North Korea and Pakistan. The large outside area also houses a considerable number of aircraft. A line of transports now includes two Curtiss Commandos, a DC-3 and several licence built Lisunov Li-2s, a Convair 240, a Viscount and three Tridents. At the end of World War II the Nationalists took over a substantial number of C-46s and many were left on the mainland when they moved to Taiwan. Two of the Li-2s were used by Mao Tse Tung and Zhou en lai on their travels around the vast country. The Convair 240, still in its original colours, was delivered to Central Air Transport in early 1949. The aircraft was seized in December of that year and stored in the Beijing area. Six Viscounts were ordered by the Civil Aviation Administration in the early 1960s. All were flown to Hong Kong by British crews in 1963/4 where they were handed over. In July 1944 a Boeing B-29 of the 58th Bomb Wing of the U.S.A.A.F. ran out of fuel and force landed near Vladivostock. Two more landed the following year and the Tupolev Design Bureau copied the aircraft which went into production as the Tu-4. Over one thousand were completed with about four hundred going to China. Two Tu-4s modified by the Chinese to take the Zhuzhou WJ5 turboprop are among the highlights. One was used as a drone carrier and the other has a large radome mounted above the fuselage. There are also many weapons, pieces of radar equipment and vehicles displayed. In early 2008 a Curtiss C-46 and one of the Li-2s moved to to the new Civil Aviation Museum in the city. Some of the aircraft denoted by 'RA' are believed to be in store at Shahe Air Base. Several markings have faded and this often makes identification difficult and this list has been the subject of much discussion.

TYPE	REG/SER	CON. NO.	PI/NOTES	STATUS
☐ Aero L-29 Delfin	103	792639		PV
☐ Aero L-29 Delfin	102	792640		PV
☐ Antonov An-12BP	B-1059	7345307	1059	PV
☐ Antonov An-12BP	1151	8345308		PV
☐ Antonov An-24	07104	17307104	71291	RA
☐ Antonov An-24	71291	17307104		PV
☐ Antonov An-24	50954	67302201		PV
☐ Antonov An-24RV	B-4060	47309501		PV
☐ Barnett J4B2	N2071Y	222		PV
☐ Beijing Keyuan AD-200 Blue Eagle				PV
☐ Bell 33 Kingcobra (P-63A)	13???		Possibly a replica.	PV
☐ Bell 205 Iroquois (UH-1H)	'95690'	11864	69-15576, 95690 (Vietnam), 576 (Vietnam)	PVX
☐ Beriev Be-6P	'9886'		98706	PVX
☐ Canadair CL-13B Sabre 6 [North American F-86E]	1783	1783	BB+178, JB+124 – in Pakistani markings.	PV
☐ Cessna 172	N5981A	28581		RA
☐ Chengdu J-7 I [Mikoyan-Gurevich MiG-21F-13]		0302		RA
☐ Chengdu J-7 I [Mikoyan-Gurevich MiG-21F-13]	'3487'	70004	11343	PVX
☐ Chengdu J-7 I [Mikoyan-Gurevich MiG-21F-13]	'1238'	70703	12381	PVX
☐ Chengdu J-7 I [Mikoyan-Gurevich MiG-21F-13]	12284	70705		RA
☐ Chengdu J-7 I [Mikoyan-Gurevich MiG-21F-13]	11244	714611		RA
☐ Chengdu J-7 I [Mikoyan-Gurevich MiG-21F-13]		714618		RA
☐ Chengdu J-7 I [Mikoyan-Gurevich MiG-21F-13]	11447	714619		PV
☐ Chengdu J-7 I [Mikoyan-Gurevich MiG-21F-13]	01			PV
☐ Chengdu J-7 I [Mikoyan-Gurevich MiG-21F-13]	F-0107			RA
☐ Chengdu J-7 I [Mikoyan-Gurevich MiG-21F-13]	70162			PV
☐ Chengdu J-7 I [Mikoyan-Gurevich MiG-21F-13]	89119			RA
☐ Chengdu J-7 I [Mikoyan-Gurevich MiG-21F-13]	98071			PV
☐ Convair 240-14	XT-610	131	(N8305C), 401	PV
☐ Curtiss 68B Hawk III (FSM)	'IV/1'			PVX
☐ Curtiss H81-B Warhawk (P-40B) (FSM)	'77'			PVX
☐ Curtiss-Wright CW-20B Commando (C-46A)	36044		Or 36047	PV
☐ Curtiss-Wright CW-20B Commando (C-46A)	36045		Or 36047	PV
☐ Dashatou Rosamonde 1 (R)				PV
☐ De Havilland D.H.121 Trident 1E-103	50051	2130	G-ATNA, AP-ATK, 232	PV
☐ De Havilland D.H.C.2 Beaver	981	1610	AP-AVB	PV
☐ De Havilland D.H.98 Mosquito FB.26	'6691'		Partial replica	PVX
☐ Douglas DC-3A-467 Skytrain (C-47B)	4766		(USAAF), 97042	PV
☐ Douglas DC-8-21 (DC-8-11) (DC-8-12)	N220RB	45280	N8038D, N8003U	PV
☐ Fairchild M-62A Cornell (PT-19A)				PV
☐ Feng Ru 2 (FSM)				PV
☐ Harbin EB-5 [Ilyushin Il-28]				PV
☐ Harbin H-5 [Ilyushin Il-28]	11264	54120		RA
☐ Harbin H-5 [Ilyushin Il-28]	10198	H501305		PV
☐ Harbin HD-5 [Ilyushin Il-28]	21112			PV
☐ Harbin HJ-5 [Ilyushin Il-28U]	10692	87211		PV
☐ Harbin HZ-5 [Ilyushin Il-28R]	44690	H502608		PV
☐ Harbin Y-11	351	Y110101		PV
☐ Harbin Y-11	'3884'	Y110210	B-3384	PVX
☐ Harbin Z-5 [Mil Mi-4]	5512	2510405		RA

☐ Harbin Z-5 [Mil Mi-4]	65567	2512207		PV
☐ Harbin Z-5 [Mil Mi-4]		2514009		PV
☐ Harbin Z-5 [Mil Mi-4]	3112			RA
☐ Harbin Z-5 [Mil Mi-4]	3529			PV
☐ Harbin Z-5 [Mil Mi-4]	3685			PV
☐ Harbin Z-5 [Mil Mi-4]	3889			PV
☐ Harbin Z-5 [Mil Mi-4]	5251			RA
☐ Harbin Z-5 [Mil Mi-4]	5361			RA
☐ Harbin Z-5 [Mil Mi-4]	5381			RA
☐ Harbin Z-5 [Mil Mi-4]	5551			RA
☐ Harbin Z-5 [Mil Mi-4]	5651			RA
☐ Harbin Z-5 [Mil Mi-4]	7272			PV
☐ Harbin Z-5 [Mil Mi-4]	8673			PV
☐ Harbin Z-5 [Mil Mi-4]	8919			PV
☐ Harbin Z-5 [Mil Mi-4]	9218			RA
☐ Harbin Z-6	26			PV
☐ Harbin Z-701 [Bell 47G]	701	L-701001		PV
☐ Hawker-Siddeley H.S.121 Trident 2E-107	B-2202	2158	G-AZFU, 240	PV
☐ Hawker-Siddeley H.S.121 Trident 2E-108	50055	2188	G-BBWG, B-269	PV
☐ Hughes 77 Apache (AH-64A) (FSM)				PV
☐ Ilyushin Il-10	23			RAD
☐ Ilyushin Il-10	28			PV
☐ Ilyushin Il-10	33			PV
☐ Ilyushin Il-10	56		Fuselage only.	RA
☐ Ilyushin Il-10	80		23 – fuselage only.	RAD
☐ Ilyushin Il-10	83		24, 25 – fuselage only.	RAD
☐ Ilyushin Il-10	96		23 – fuselage only.	RAD
☐ Ilyushin Il-10	1219			PV
☐ Ilyushin Il-10UTI	10			PV
■ Ilyushin Il-12B	35141	275		PV
☐ Ilyushin Il-12B	'5116'	2505	35140	PVX
☐ Ilyushin Il-12B	35048			RA
■ Ilyushin Il-12B	'35046'		35240	PVX
■ Ilyushin Il-14P	4202	6341010		PV
■ Ilyushin Il-18D	'208'	187009703	B-224	PVX
■ Ilyushin Il-18D	B-226	187009902	50856	PV
■ Ilyushin Il-18V	'232'	184007605	50851, B-230	PVX
■ Ilyushin Il-62	B-2024	11101	2024	PV
☐ Jiefang 5		77-43-88		RA
☐ Jiefang 5	03	77-45-123		RAD
☐ Jiefang 5	102	78-10		RA
☐ Jiefang 5	171	78-46-171		RA
☐ Jiefang 5	101	78-9		RA
☐ Jiefang 5	58			RA
☐ Jiefang 5	62			RA
☐ Jiefang 5	63			RA
☐ Jiefang 9	11	78-11		PV
☐ Jiefang 9	12	78-12		RA
☐ Jiefang 9	13	78-13		RA
☐ Jiefang 9	101	78-9		RA
☐ Jiefang 9	49	79-49		RAD
☐ Jiefang 9	50	79-50		RA
☐ Jiefang 9	54	79-54		RA
☐ Jiefang 9		79-58		RA
☐ Jiefang 9	58	79-58		RA
☐ Jiefang 9	59	79-59		RA
☐ Kawasaki Ki-48	308		Partial replica.	PV
☐ Lavochkin La-11	24		'7504'	PV
☐ Lavochkin La-9	06			RA
☐ Lavochkin La-9UTI				RA
■ Lisunov Li-2 [Douglas DC-3 modified]	'311'	18439703	15	PVX
■ Lisunov Li-2 [Douglas DC-3 modified]	8205	18439709		PV
■ Lisunov Li-2 [Douglas DC-3 modified]	3019	18439903		PV
■ Lisunov Li-2 [Douglas DC-3 modified]	5070	18440106		PV
■ Lisunov Li-2 [Douglas DC-3 modified]	'4227'	18440204	3049	PVX
■ Lisunov Li-2 [Douglas DC-3 modified]	'XT-115'	5006266 ?	C/n quoted as 5006266	PVX
☐ Lisunov Li-2 [Douglas DC-3 modified]	3018			PV
■ Lisunov Li-2 [Douglas DC-3 modified]	3029			PV
☐ Lockheed 683-10-19 Starfighter (F-104S) (F-104S/ASA)	MM6795	683-6795		PV
☐ Mikoyan-Gurevich MiG-9	30	108005		PV
☐ Mikoyan-Gurevich MiG-15		51538		RA
☐ Mikoyan-Gurevich MiG-15		180611		RA
☐ Mikoyan-Gurevich MiG-15	35	515394	In North Korean markings.	PV
☐ Mikoyan-Gurevich MiG-15	008	111010	In North Korean markings.	PV
☐ Mikoyan-Gurevich MiG-15	08	111019	In North Korean markings.	PV
☐ Mikoyan-Gurevich MiG-15	03		In North Korean markings.	PV
☐ Mikoyan-Gurevich MiG-15	13		In North Korean markings.	PV
☐ Mikoyan-Gurevich MiG-15	15		In North Korean markings.	RA
☐ Mikoyan-Gurevich MiG-15	25		In North Korean markings.	PV
☐ Mikoyan-Gurevich MiG-15	1481			PV
☐ Mikoyan-Gurevich MiG-15	4169			PV
☐ Mikoyan-Gurevich MiG-15	63364			RA
☐ Mikoyan-Gurevich MiG-15	84681			RA
☐ Mikoyan-Gurevich MiG-15bis	63862	4011		RA

☐ Mikoyan-Gurevich MiG-15bis	4060	5932		RA
☐ Mikoyan-Gurevich MiG-15bis	'8064'	5936	4068	PVX
☐ Mikoyan-Gurevich MiG-15bis	0081	13173		PV
☐ Mikoyan-Gurevich MiG-15bis	4169	1264906		RA
☐ Mikoyan-Gurevich MiG-15bis	32	179081	In North Korean markings.	RA
☐ Mikoyan-Gurevich MiG-15bis			6006	PV
☐ Mikoyan-Gurevich MiG-15bis	2249		In North Korean markings.	PV
☐ Mikoyan-Gurevich MiG-15bis	3137			RA
☐ Mikoyan-Gurevich MiG-15bis	3218		In North Korean markings.	RA
☐ Mikoyan-Gurevich MiG-15bis	3747			PV
☐ Mikoyan-Gurevich MiG-15bis	6273			RA
☐ Mikoyan-Gurevich MiG-15bis	13651			RA
☐ Mikoyan-Gurevich MiG-15UTI	2348	0849	63883	PV
☐ Mikoyan-Gurevich MiG-15UTI	63138	3213		PV
☐ Mikoyan-Gurevich MiG-15UTI	63635	3604		PV
☐ Mikoyan-Gurevich MiG-15UTI	1991	4141		PV
☐ Mikoyan-Gurevich MiG-15UTI	'86081/18048'	11418	86481	PVX
☐ Mikoyan-Gurevich MiG-15UTI	6717	550108		RA
☐ Mikoyan-Gurevich MiG-15UTI	63	712170		RA
☐ Mikoyan-Gurevich MiG-15UTI	63833	722545	63633	PV
☐ Mikoyan-Gurevich MiG-15UTI	42741	722561		PV
☐ Mikoyan-Gurevich MiG-15UTI	63638/83636	7416		PV
☐ Mikoyan-Gurevich MiG-15UTI	63364			PV
☐ Mikoyan-Gurevich MiG-15UTI	63639			RA
☐ Mikoyan-Gurevich MiG-15UTI	63663			RA
☐ Mikoyan-Gurevich MiG-17F	6691	7627		PV
☐ Mikoyan-Gurevich MiG-17F	19867			PV
☐ Mikoyan-Gurevich MiG-21F				RAD
☐ Mikoyan-Gurevich MiG-21F				RAD
☐ Mikoyan-Gurevich MiG-21F-13	'98071'	1623		PV
☐ Mikoyan-Gurevich MiG-21FL	C1116		In Indian markings.	PVD
☐ Mil Mi-1				RAD
☐ Mil Mi-8P		1222		RA
☐ Mil Mi-8P	756	20203		PV
☐ Mil Mi-8P	762	20206		PV
☐ Mil Mi-8P	770	20210		PV
☐ Mil Mi-8P	790	20220	790, B-7810	RA
☐ Mil Mi-8P			Possibly 50338	RA
☐ Mil Mi-8T	26			RA
☐ Mil Mi-24D	5806			PV
☐ Mitsubishi A6M2 Zero Sen Model 21 (FSM)				RAX
☐ Mraz M-1C Sokol	04			RA
☐ Nanchang CJ-5 [Yakovlev Yak-18]	04	1232014		PV
☐ Nanchang CJ-5 [Yakovlev Yak-18]	05	1332010		RA
☐ Nanchang CJ-5 [Yakovlev Yak-18]	7610	1332023		PV
☐ Nanchang CJ-5 [Yakovlev Yak-18]	01	1432029	In brown scheme	PV
☐ Nanchang CJ-5 [Yakovlev Yak-18]	03	1532011		PV
☐ Nanchang CJ-5 [Yakovlev Yak-18]	02	1532033		RA
☐ Nanchang CJ-5 [Yakovlev Yak-18]	01	932008		PV
☐ Nanchang CJ-5 [Yakovlev Yak-18]		932025		PV
☐ Nanchang CJ-5 [Yakovlev Yak-18]	01			PV
☐ Nanchang CJ-5 [Yakovlev Yak-18]	7608			RA
☐ Nanchang CJ-6A	62233	1232032		RA
☐ Nanchang CJ-6A	61767	2751242		RA
☐ Nanchang CJ-6A	102	2951244		PV
☐ Nanchang CJ-6A	61137			RA
☐ Nanchang CJ-6A	61568			PV
☐ Nanchang CJ-6A	61968			PV
☐ Nanchang CJ-6A	62135			RA
☐ Nanchang CJ-6A	62339			RA
☐ Nanchang CJ-6A	62430			RA
☐ Nanchang CJ-6A	62438			RA
☐ Nanchang CJ-6A	64354			
☐ Nanchang CJ-6A	67651			PV
☐ Nanchang J-12	01	132001		PV
☐ Nanchang J-12	02	132002		PV
☐ Nanchang Q-5	0064			PV
☐ Nanchang Q-5	10262			PV
☐ Nanchang Q-5	21368	'G24-32003'		PV
☐ Nanchang Q-5I-A	10769	05-015		RA
☐ Nanchang Q-5I-A	11262	432008		RA
☐ Nanchang Q-5I-A	11264	432010		PV
☐ Nanchang Q-5I-A	11265	432011		RA
☐ Nanchang Q-5I-A	12306			RA
☐ Nanchang Q-5I-B	31124	732006		PV
☐ Nanchang Y-5 [Antonov An-2]	3129	1050347		PV
☐ Nanchang Y-5 [Antonov An-2]	10996	1432030		PV
☐ Nanchang Y-5 [Antonov An-2]	921			RA
☐ Nanchang Y-5 [Antonov An-2]	3139			PV
☐ Nanchang Y-5 [Antonov An-2]	7225			PV
☐ Nanchang Y-5 [Antonov An-2]	10553			RA
☐ Nanchang Y-5 [Antonov An-2]	10953			RA
☐ Nanchang Y-5 [Antonov An-2]	10997			RA
☐ Nanchang Y-5 [Antonov An-2]	60066			PV
☐ Nanchuan C-0101 (FSM)	'C-0101'			PV

☐ North American NA-111 Mustang (P-51K)	03	111-30591	44-12458, (Korea), 3003 (China)	PV
☐ North American NA-174 Trojan (T-28A)	216	174-660	51-7807	RA
☐ North American NA-200 Trojan (T-28B)	Bu138149	200-220	Bu138149, N391NA	PV
☐ Northrop N-311 Tiger II (F-5E)	5120	V.1020	74-0977 – in Taiwanese markings.	PVD
☐ Orlican L-40 Meta-Sokol	3018			PV
☐ Percival P.56 Provost T.52 (T.1)	R3605	P.56/358	In Zimbabwean markings.	PV
☐ Piaggio FWP.149D	JWTZ 205	012	DA+394, 106 (Tanzania), JW 9205 (Tanzania)	PV
☐ Polikarpov I-16 tip 10 (FSM)	'5806'			PVX
☐ Polikarpov Po-2 (FSM)	'6691'			RAX
☐ Shenyang Dong Feng 102 (MiG-19 modified)	5619	0307		PV
☐ Shenyang J-5 [Mikoyan-Gurevich MiG-17F]	0101	0101		PV
☐ Shenyang J-5 [Mikoyan-Gurevich MiG-17F]	2579	1504	21183	PV
☐ Shenyang J-5 [Mikoyan-Gurevich MiG-17F]	31489	1838		PV
☐ Shenyang J-5 [Mikoyan-Gurevich MiG-17F]	3837	2231		PV
☐ Shenyang J-5 [Mikoyan-Gurevich MiG-17F]	51230	5006		PV
☐ Shenyang J-5 [Mikoyan-Gurevich MiG-17F]	31481	5706		PV
☐ Shenyang J-5 [Mikoyan-Gurevich MiG-17F]	3839	5708		PV
☐ Shenyang J-5 [Mikoyan-Gurevich MiG-17F]	31685	5713		PV
☐ Shenyang J-5 [Mikoyan-Gurevich MiG-17F]	31682	5734		PV
☐ Shenyang J-5 [Mikoyan-Gurevich MiG-17F]	31482	5735		RA
☐ Shenyang J-5 [Mikoyan-Gurevich MiG-17F]	31581	5738		PV
☐ Shenyang J-5 [Mikoyan-Gurevich MiG-17F]	31584	5753		PV
☐ Shenyang J-5 [Mikoyan-Gurevich MiG-17F]	31586	58?6		PV
☐ Shenyang J-5 [Mikoyan-Gurevich MiG-17F]	31580	5821		PV
☐ Shenyang J-5 [Mikoyan-Gurevich MiG-17F]	1488	5825		RA
☐ Shenyang J-5 [Mikoyan-Gurevich MiG-17F]	8679	5826		RA
☐ Shenyang J-5 [Mikoyan-Gurevich MiG-17F]	3637	5827		RA
☐ Shenyang J-5 [Mikoyan-Gurevich MiG-17F]	31681	5835		PV
☐ Shenyang J-5 [Mikoyan-Gurevich MiG-17F]		5836		RA
☐ Shenyang J-5 [Mikoyan-Gurevich MiG-17F]	31583	5846		RA
☐ Shenyang J-5 [Mikoyan-Gurevich MiG-17F]	0879			RA
☐ Shenyang J-5 [Mikoyan-Gurevich MiG-17F]	31487			PV
☐ Shenyang J-5 [Mikoyan-Gurevich MiG-17F]	31582			RA
☐ Shenyang J-5A [Mikoyan-Gurevich MiG-17PF]	2074	1507		PV
☐ Shenyang J-5A [Mikoyan-Gurevich MiG-17PF]	2424	2533		RA
☐ Shenyang J-6 [Mikoyan-Gurevich MiG-19SF]	40004	0035		RA
☐ Shenyang J-6 [Mikoyan-Gurevich MiG-19SF]		10504		RA
☐ Shenyang J-6 [Mikoyan-Gurevich MiG-19SF]	20708	5614		PV
☐ Shenyang J-6 [Mikoyan-Gurevich MiG-19SF]	51312	5905		RA
☐ Shenyang J-6 [Mikoyan-Gurevich MiG-19SF]	9214			PV
☐ Shenyang J-6 [Mikoyan-Gurevich MiG-19SF]	70403			RA
☐ Shenyang J-6 I [Mikoyan-Gurevich MiG-19PF]				PV
☐ Shenyang J-6 I [Mikoyan-Gurevich MiG-19PF]	0001	0001		PV
☐ Shenyang J-6 I [Mikoyan-Gurevich MiG-19PF]	2207	0101		PV
☐ Shenyang J-6 I [Mikoyan-Gurevich MiG-19PF]	0201	0201		PV
☐ Shenyang J-6 II [Mikoyan-Gurevich MiG-19PM]	40403	3031		PV
☐ Shenyang J-6 II [Mikoyan-Gurevich MiG-19PM]	40404	6-2-3032		PV
☐ Shenyang J-6 II [Mikoyan-Gurevich MiG-19PM]	14121	650640		PV
☐ Shenyang J-6 II [Mikoyan-Gurevich MiG-19PM]	10425	650737		RA
☐ Shenyang J-6 III [Mikoyan-Gurevich MiG-19PM]	51209			PV
☐ Shenyang J-6 III [Mikoyan-Gurevich MiG-19PM]	11323	4730		PV
☐ Shenyang J-6 III [Mikoyan-Gurevich MiG-19PM]	51208	5025		PV
☐ Shenyang J-6 IV [Mikoyan-Gurevich MiG-19R]	20158	346-4702		PV
☐ Shenyang J-6B [Mikoyan-Gurevich MiG-19R]	14025			PV
☐ Shenyang J-8I	20852			PV
☐ Shenyang J-8I	72061	18-8061		PV
☐ Shenyang J-8II	0001	J8II-0102		PV
☐ Shenyang J-8II	20255	J8II-0203	Tail from c/n J8II-0208.	PV
☐ Shenyang JJ-1	0101	103		PV
☐ Shenyang JJ-5	6717	550108		RA
☐ Shenyang JJ-5	2216	550216		PV
☐ Shenyang JJ-5		550420		PV
☐ Shenyang JJ-5	507	550423		PV
☐ Shenyang JJ-6 [Mikoyan-Gurevich MiG-19U]	56002	7810		PV
☐ Shenyang JJ-6 [Mikoyan-Gurevich MiG-19U]	41483	8008		PV
☐ Shenyang JZ-6	51312	5905		PV
☐ Shenyang Qian Jin	33			PV
☐ Shijiazhuang W-5	W5-11			PV
☐ Shijiazhuang W-5A	199771			RA
☐ Shijiazhuang W-5A	W5A-18			PV
☐ Stinson V-76 Sentinel (L-5B)	15	76-3524	(USAAF)	PV
☐ Sud-Est SE.3160 Alouette III	753			PV
☐ Tachikawa Ki-36	'102/3'			PV
☐ Tupolev Tu-2S	20			PV
☐ Tupolev Tu-2S	0093			PVD

☐ Tupolev Tu-2S	0462			PV
☐ Tupolev Tu-2S	20562			PV
☐ Tupolev Tu-2S	20608			PV
☐ Tupolev Tu-2S	20661			PV
☐ Tupolev Tu-2S	41562			PV
☐ Tupolev Tu-4	4134	225008		PV
☐ Tupolev Tu-4	4114	2806501		PV
☐ Tupolev Tu-104A			Fuselage only.	PV
☐ Tupolev Tu-124	50256	5351808		PV
☐ Tupolev Tu-124	50257	5351809		PV
☐ Vickers 843 Viscount	50258	453	G-ASDS, 84303, 406, B-406	PV
☐ Vought V-65C Corsair (O2U-4) (FSM)				PVX
☐ Vought V-393 Crusader (F8U-1P) (RF-8A)			Rear fuselage only.	RAD
☐ Vultee V-54D Valiant (BT-13)	40-0977	54-368		PVD
☐ Wright Flyer (R)				PV
☐ Xian H-6D [Tupolev Tu-16]	10794	052408		PV
☐ Xian H-6E [Tupolev Tu-16]	'4251'	222000154	50671	PVX
☐ Yakovlev Yak-11	'488'		4589	PVX
☐ Yakovlev Yak-11	*-127			PV
☐ Yakovlev Yak-11	351			PV
☐ Yakovlev Yak-12				RA
☐ Yakovlev Yak-17UTI	12			PV
☐ Yakovlev Yak-18		3105	Fuselage frame only.	RAD
☐ Yakovlev Yak-18		5712		RAD
☐ Yakovlev Yak-18		3100228		RAD
☐ Yakovlev Yak-18		3205310		RAD
☐ Yakovlev Yak-18	40	332011		RA
☐ Yakovlev Yak-52	67651			RA

CHINA CIVIL AVIATION MUSEUM (CHI7)

Address: Minhang 200,
Jichangfu Road,
Chaoyang District,
Beijing.
Admission: Opening in July 2008.
Location: In the north eastern part of the city.

The Civil Aviation Administration of China was set up on November 2nd 1949 to manage all non-military flying in the country. Up until 1980 it was run by by the People's Liberation Army Air Force and then it became under direct control of the state. An airline network was operated around the country using a large fleet of aircraft. Plans were put forward in 2005 and the museum was formally established on April 11th 2007. A site near the new international airport is being developed and aircraft are joining the collection. A Curtiss C-46 and a Lisunov Li-2 have been from the China Aviation Museum. The Ilyushin Il-14 flew in considerable numbers in the country from the mid-1950s. The example in the collection was built at Tashkent and after withdrawal in December 1991 was preserved at Zhongyuan. Two recently retired jets have now arrived. The Airbus was delivered to China in 1985 and flown by China Eastern until withdrawn in September 2006. The British Aerospace 146 arrived in the country in 1986 and flew for two decades. The history of civil flying in the country will be portrayed and more aircraft should arrive before the opening in July 2008.

TYPE	REG/SER	CON. NO.	PI/NOTES	STATUS
☐ Airbus A310-222	B-2301	311	F-WZEJ	PV
☐ Boeing B&W (R)				RAC
☐ British Aerospace 146 Series 100	B-2701	E1019	G-5-019, G-5-523, G-5-019, G-XIAN	PV
☐ Curtiss-Wright CW-20B Commando (C-46A)			36045 or 36046 or 36047	PV
☐ De Havilland D.H.121 Trident 1E-103	'B-2207-	2133	AP-AUG, 50152	PVX
☐ Ilyushin Il-14P	B-4208	6341504		PV
☐ Lisunov Li-2 [Douglas DC-3 modified]			From CAM	PV
☐ Lisunov Li-2 [Douglas DC-3 modified]	324			PV
☐ Nanchang Y-5 [Antonov An-2]	8404			PV
☐ Xian Y-7-100 [Antonov An-24]				PV

CIVIL AVIATION ADMINISTRATION OF CHINA AERONAUTICAL INSTITUTION COLLECTION (CHI8)

Address: 10 Xiangyun West Street,
Binhai Airport,
Tianjin 300300.
Tel: 022-2496-0647
Admission: By prior permission only.
Location: In the eastern suburbs of the town.

This large training school was set up in the early 1990s and all the aircraft are used for both training and exhibition purposes. Associated displays trace the history of aviation in the country. Transport types, including a former Pan American Boeing 707, feature prominently. The Harbin Y-11 twin engined light transport first flew in 1990 and over forty of the initial version were built. A Chinese version of the successful Antonov An-24 can be compared with the original Soviet design. In 1966 the Chinese Government obtained a licence to build the An-24. The first example flew in 1970 and the type has seen service with many airlines in the country and with the Air Force. A special cargo version has also been produced.

TYPE	REG/SER	CON. NO.	PI/NOTES	STATUS
□ Antonov An-12BP	B-3152	8345303	203, B-203	RA
□ Antonov An-24B	B-3409	27308201	B-436	RA
□ Boeing 707-321B	N893PA	20030		RA
□ Boeing 737-2T4/Adv	B-2516	23447	N5573B	RA
□ Harbin Y-11	352	Y11-0102	352, B-3874	RA
□ Harbin Z-5 [Mil Mi-4]	713			RA
□ Hawker-Siddeley H.S.121 Trident 2E-108	B-2204	2175	G-BBVS, B-280	RA
□ Ilyushin Il-12B	503			RA
□ Ilyushin Il-18V	B-210	184007602	210	RA
□ Lisunov Li-2 [Douglas DC-3 modified]	301	18433601	301, B-301	RA
□ Lisunov Li-2 [Douglas DC-3 modified]	305	18440206		RA
□ Mikoyan-Gurevich MiG-17	31585			RA
□ Nanchang CJ-5 [Yakovlev Yak-18]	11			RA
□ Nanchang CJ-6A	07			RA
□ Nanchang Y-5 [Antonov An-2]	B-8073	832027	8073	RA
□ Nanchang Y-5 [Antonov An-2]	B-8452	1732006	8452	RA
□ Shenyang J-5 [Mikoyan-Gurevich MiG-17F]				RA
□ Shijiazhuang Y-5 [Antonov An-2]	B-8034	4705505	8034	RA
□ Shijiazhuang Y-5 [Antonov An-2]	B-8036	4705512	8036	RA
□ Shijiazhuang Y-5 [Antonov An-2]	B-8052			RA
□ Xian Y-7-100 [Antonov An-24]	B-3453	02704		RA

DONGHU PARK (CHI9)

Address:	Luoho District, Shenzhen.
Admission:	Daily 0700-1800.
Location:	In the north eastern part of the city.

This large park, situated near a major reservoir, has many attractions including an amusement area with a giant roller coaster. One area is dedicated to children and there are a number of transport attractions. The only aircraft is an all silver MiG-15UTI mounted on pylons. The aircraft served as a trainer for many years.

TYPE	REG/SER	CON. NO.	PI/NOTES	STATUS
□ Mikoyan-Gurevich MiG-15UTI	64707			PV

DUNHUANG CITY MUNICIPAL MUSEUM (CHI10)

Address:	Dongdajie, Dunhuang, Gansusheng 736200.
Tel:	0937-8822981
Admission:	Summer daily 0830-1830; Winter daily 0800-1200 1430-1800.
Location:	In the southern part of the city centre.

The displays at this museum trace the history of the area from the early times. There are many interesting artefacts to be seen. The city was once an important place on the 'Silk Road' and this period is highlighted. There is a section devoted to local military exploits and sole aircraft on show is the MiG-15.

TYPE	REG/SER	CON. NO.	PI/NOTES	STATUS
□ Mikoyan-Gurevich MiG-15				PV

GUANGZHOU CIVIL AVIATION COLLEGE MUSEUM (CHI11)

Address:	2360 Jinhai Road, Pudong 201209.
Tel:	021-5021-6813
Email:	master@sspu.cn
Admission:	By prior permission only.
Location:	At the airport.

The school has recently moved to new premises at the recently opened international airport. At the old airfield there was a museum in a small building and these artefacts have been transferred to the new site. Some of the airframes have not yet made the journey to their new home but they may be transported.

TYPE	REG/SER	CON. NO.	PI/NOTES	STATUS
☐ Antonov An-28RV	B-3414	37309003	B-446 – at old airport.	RA
☐ Hawker-Siddeley H.S.121 Trident 2E-107	B-2219	2160	G-AZFW, 246	RA
☐ Hawker-Siddeley H.S.121 Trident 2E-107	B-2216	2177	G-BBVU, B-284 – at old airport.	RA
☐ Hawker-Siddeley H.S.121 Trident 2E-107	B-2217	2179	G-BBVW, B-288 – at old airport.	RA
☐ Ilyushin Il-14	622	6341503	Dismantled.	RA
☐ Ilyushin Il-14G	611	148001941	At old airport.	RA
☐ Mil Mi-8	B-7805	20215		RA
☐ Mil Mi-8	B-7806	20216		RA
☐ Nanchang CJ-6A				RA
☐ Nanchang CJ-6A				RA
☐ Nanchang Y-5 [Antonov An-2]	8419		At old airport.	RA
☐ Shenyang J-6 [Mikoyan-Gurevich MiG-19SF]	10901			RA
☐ Shenyang J-6 [Mikoyan-Gurevich MiG-19SF]	81084			RA
☐ Shenyang J-6 [Mikoyan-Gurevich MiG-19SF]	81088			RA
☐ Shenyang J-6 [Mikoyan-Gurevich MiG-19SF]	81089			RA
☐ Shenyang J-6 [Mikoyan-Gurevich MiG-19SF]				RA
☐ Shenyang JJ-6 [Mikoyan-Gurevich MiG-19U]				RA
☐ Xian Y-7 [Antonov An-24]	B-3457	3704		RA
☐ Xian Y-7-100C [Antonov An-24]	B-3468	5703		RA
☐ Xian Y-7-100C [Antonov An-24]	B-3486	7705		RA
☐ Xian Y-7-100C [Antonov An-24]	B-3488	7707		RA

HEBEI MILITARY SCHOOL MEMORIAL (CHI12)

Address: Hebei.
Admission: By prior permission only.
Location: In the city.

This long established military school has trained personnel for all branches of the service. In the grounds there are a number of plaques honouring past students. The J-5 is displayed along with weapons.

TYPE	REG/SER	CON. NO.	PI/NOTES	STATUS
☐ Shenyang J-5 [Mikoyan-Gurevich MiG-17F]	63248			RA

HONG KONG HISTORIC AVIATION ASSOCIATION (CHI13)

Address: Apartment 4,
The Elegance,
60 Tai Hang Road,
Hong Kong.
Tel: 0852-2895-2434
Admission: By prior permission only.
Location: At Chep Lap Kok Airport which is on the northern part of Lantau Island.

On March 18th 1911 Charles van den Born made the first powered flight in the territory of Hong Kong using a modified Farman biplane. The association decided to build a replica of this historic machine and it was constructed in Texas by Vintage Aviation Services. The aircraft was flown in the U.S.A. before shipment to Hong Kong where it again took to the air. The historic flight was re-enacted on March 18th 1977 at the then incomplete new airport. The original location at Shatin is now covered by housing. The biplane is displayed in the terminal building of the new airport along with photographs, models and items of memorabilia.

TYPE	REG/SER	CON. NO.	PI/NOTES	STATUS
☐ Van den Born Farman (R)	B-HMB		N7498Y – in airport terminal.	PV

HONG KONG SCIENCE MUSEUM (CHI14)

Address: 2 Science Museum Road,
Tsimshatsui East,
Kowloon.
Tel: 0852-2732-3232
Fax: 0852-2311-2248
Email: enquiries@hk.science.museum
Admission: Monday-Wednesday, Friday 1300-2100; Saturday-Sunday 1000-2100.
Location: In the centre of Kowloon.

The museum has eighteen galleries on four floors. These cover a wide range of topics including Life Science, Weather, Telecommunications and the dreaded 'Occupational Health and Safety'. There is also a major section designed especially for children. On show in the Transportation area is the Cathay Pacific DC-3 'Betsy'. In 1945 two American pilots who were flying for the China National Aviation Corporation bought an ex-U.S.A.A.F. C-47 in Georgia. They flew it on charters from Shanghai but were forced to move to Hong Kong where they set up Cathay Pacific Airways on September 24th 1946. The C-47 was sold in August 1953 and flew in New Guinea and Australia. In September 1983 the airline bought back the historic machine and it was eventually put on show in the museum. Also here is an informative display on the science of yachting.

TYPE	REG/SER	CON. NO.	PI/NOTES	STATUS
☐ Douglas DC-3A-360 Skytrain (C-47)	VR-HDB	4423	41-18385, NC58093, VR-HDB, VH-MAL	PV

KIEV MILITARY THEME PARK (CHI15)

Address:	Haifang Road, Tanggu 300450.
Tel:	022-2531-9020.
Admission:	Daily 0900-1700.
Location:	About 40 km south east of Tianjin.

The Soviet aircraft carrier 'Kiev' was laid down at the Nikolayev yard in 1970 and launched two years later. The ship entered service in December 1975 and served mainly with the Northern Fleet. In the mid-1980s the carrier was extensively modified so that she could be equipped with the VTOL Yakovkev Yak-38. Kamov anti-submarine helicopters were also based aboard. The 'Kiev' was retired in June 1993 and three years later was sold to a Chinese group. A long journey to Tianjin followed and on May 1st 2004 the ship was opened to the public. Visitors can tour large areas of the carrier and view the conditions encountered by the crew on their long periods at sea. The aircraft are mainly positioned on the deck area. The Chengdu J-10 is believed to have made its maiden flight in 1996 after years of development. The fighter finally entered service in 2004 and export orders are being negotiated. Two types which recently joined the display are the Kamov Ka-50 helicopter and the Sukhoi Su-27. Both of these are believed to be genuine aircraft and not full scale mock-ups.

TYPE	REG/SER	CON. NO.	PI/NOTES	STATUS
☐ Chengdu J-10 (FSM)	'1068'			PVX
☐ Kamov Ka-50	078			PV
☐ Mil Mi-8	'K-001'			PVX
☐ Nanchang Q-5	'K-01'			PVX
☐ Nanchang Q-5	'K-02'			PVX
☐ Nanchang Q-5	'K-03'			PVX
☐ Nanchang Q-5	'X-04'			PVX
☐ Nanchang Q-5	'X-05'			PVX
☐ Shenyang J-6 [Mikoyan-Gurevich MiG-19SF]	82275			PV
☐ Shenyang J-6 [Mikoyan-Gurevich MiG-19SF]	82379			PV
☐ Shenyang J-6 [Mikoyan-Gurevich MiG-19SF]	82381			PV
☐ Shenyang J-6 [Mikoyan-Gurevich MiG-19SF]	88278			PV
☐ Shenyang J-6 [Mikoyan-Gurevich MiG-19SF]				PV
☐ Shenyang J-6 [Mikoyan-Gurevich MiG-19SF]				PV
☐ Shenyang J-6 [Mikoyan-Gurevich MiG-19SF]				PV
☐ Shenyang J-6 [Mikoyan-Gurevich MiG-19SF]				PV
☐ Shenyang J-6 [Mikoyan-Gurevich MiG-19SF]				PV
☐ Shenyang J-6 [Mikoyan-Gurevich MiG-19SF]				PV
☐ Shenyang J-6 [Mikoyan-Gurevich MiG-19SF]				PV
☐ Sukhoi Su-27	27			PV

KOREAN WAR MEMORIAL MUSEUM (CHI16)

Address:	Dandong City, Liaoning. 188134.
Tel:	0415-2150510
Admission:	Summer daily 0800-1600; Winter daily 0830-1530.
Location:	In the north western part of the town,

The displays at this museum highlight the Chinese contribution to the Korean War which lasted between June 1950 and July 1953. Korea was divided in 1948 and the Communist forces of the North tried to unify the country. Chinese forces aided the North and behind the museum is a graveyard containing about ten thousand dead. Dandong is on the Yalu River which is the border between China and North Korea so the town is an appropriate site for the museum. The large building contains nine halls highlighting aspects of the conflict. The aircraft are located in an outside park along with military vehicles and weapons.

TYPE	REG/SER	CON. NO.	PI/NOTES	STATUS
☐ Mikoyan-Gurevich MiG-15	'08'			PVX
☐ Mikoyan-Gurevich MiG-15	'25'			PVX
☐ Shijiazhuang Y-5 [Antonov An-2]	516?			PV
☐ Tupolev Tu-2S				PV

This Tupolev Tu-2 is on show at the Korean War Memorial Museum in Dandong. (Phil Dunnington)

Above: The Chinese Maritime Museum at Quindao is home to this Harbin H-5. (Shinsuke Yamamoto)

Right: The unique Yin An is at the Northwest Polytechnic University Museum in Xian.

MARITIME MUSEUM (CHI17)

Address:	8 Laiyanglu, Quingdao 266100.
Tel:	0532-2866784
Admission:	Daily 0800-1600.
Location:	In the southern part of the town.

The Chinese Navy established a flying school in 1916 and since then the service has always had an aviation branch. At the current time it operates a range of helicopters and fixed wing aircraft on maritime reconnaissance and coastal defence work. This museum traces the history of the Chinese Navy from the early days with many relics on show. A number of ships including two destroyers, one Russian built, and a pair of frigates are amongst those moored at a series of jetties. Several smaller craft are also on show. On land there is a collection of missiles, ships guns and vehicles. The indoor display includes, uniforms, photographs and documents along with personal items. The aircraft collection includes types used by the force in recent years. The Beriev Be-6 flying boat made its maiden flight in 1949 and over two hundred left the Taganrog lines. A range of licence built Soviet types is in this interesting exhibition.

TYPE	REG/SER	CON. NO.	PI/NOTES	STATUS
☐ Beriev Be-6				PV
☐ Chengdu J-7 I [Mikoyan-Gurevich MiG-21F-13]	81890			PV
☐ Harbin H-5 [Ilyushin Il-28]	80002			PV
☐ Harbin HR-5 [Ilyushin Il-28R]	82025			PV
☐ Harbin Z-5 [Mil Mi-4]	94000			PV
☐ Ilyushin Il-14	9232			PV
☐ Nanchang CJ-5 [Yakovlev Yak-18]				PV
☐ Nanchang CJ-6A				PV
☐ Nanchang Q-5	81802			PV
☐ Nanchang Q-5	82357			PV
☐ Shenyang J-5 [Mikoyan-Gurevich MiG-17F]	81044			PV
☐ Shenyang J-5 [Mikoyan-Gurevich MiG-17F]	81254			PV
☐ Shenyang J-5 [Mikoyan-Gurevich MiG-17F]	7514			PV
☐ Shenyang JJ-5	82960			PV
☐ Shenyang JJ-5	83969			PV
☐ Shenyang J-6 I [Mikoyan-Gurevich MiG-19PF]	84053			PV
☐ Shijiazhuang Y-5 [Antonov An-2]	9206			PV

MILITARY MUSEUM OF THE PEOPLE'S REPUBLIC OF CHINA (CHI18)

Address:	9 Fuxing Lu, Haidan District, Beijing 100038.
Tel:	010-6681-7161
Admission:	Daily 0900-1700.
Location:	About 7 km west of the city centre.

This museum commemorates the Communist Revolution which took the party into power in 1948. The exhibits cover the history of the country from early times up to the present day. Displays in the main building trace the lives of people who have made major contributions in the struggle. Photographs, uniforms, personal items and excerpts from their writings can be seen. There are also many weapons, military vehicles and tanks on show. The political history of the country with particular reference to the part played by the military is highlighted along with the philosophy of the Communist Party. The aircraft collection changed in the early 1990s with the opening of the China Aviation Museum. From the 1950s up to the Cultural Revolution a number of U.S. aircraft – including two Mitchells, a Kaydet and a Hoverfly – which served with the Nationalist forces were displayed but these have since disappeared. A Mustang remains from this era and the Beaver, Sabre and T-33 were 'captured' from the Taiwanese forces. For many years a Zero was stored at this museum. A partial replica has now been put on show at the China Aviation Museum and this may have used some parts from the original aircraft.

TYPE	REG/SER	CON. NO.	PI/NOTES	STATUS
☐ Chengdu J-7 I [Mikoyan-Gurevich MiG-21F-13]	31130			PV
☐ De Havilland D.H.C.2 Beaver (L-20A) (U-6A)	8018	875	54-1725 – in Taiwanese markings.	PV
☐ Lockheed 580 (T-33A)	T-33024	580-8202	52-9971 – in Taiwanese markings.	PV
☐ Lockheed U-2B	3512	358	56-6691 – in Taiwanese markings.	PVD
☐ Mikoyan-Gurevich MiG-15	079	119079	In North Korean markings.	PV
☐ Mikoyan-Gurevich MiG-15bis	70209			RA
☐ Mikoyan-Gurevich MiG-15UTI	67973			PV
☐ Mikoyan-Gurevich MiG-17	30474			PV
☐ Mitsubishi A6M5 Zero Sen Model 52			May possibly be incorporated in the replica at China Aviation Museum.	RA
☐ Nanchang Q-5	33027			PV
☐ Nanchang Y-5 [Antonov An-2]	8209			RA
☐ North American NA-122 Mustang (P-51D)	03	122-40460	44-73920	PV

TYPE	REG/SER	CON. NO.	PI/NOTES	STATUS
☐ North American NA-191 Sabre (F-86F])	F-86272	191-137	52-4441 – in Taiwanese markings.	PV
☐ Shenyang J-6 I [Mikoyan-Gurevich MiG-19PF]				PV
☐ Shenyang J-6 I [Mikoyan-Gurevich MiG-19PF]	025	6-4701		PV
☐ Shenyang J-8I	053			PV
☐ Tachikawa Ki-55	103/2		02	PV
☐ Tupolev Tu-2S	44792			PV

MINSK WORLD (CHI19)

Address: Dapeng Bay,
Shatoujiao,
Shenzhen 518081.
Tel: 0755-2525141
Fax: 0755-2521480
Email: minsk@minskworld.com
Admission: Daily 0930-1930.
Location: In the eastern part of the city.

The carrier was built in the mid-1970s as part of the Soviet Navy Pacific Fleet. At the time it was the fifth largest carrier in the world. The ship was sold to a Chinese group who opened it as a theme park in May 2000. An area on the shore displays military equipment, including some of the aircraft, and from here a bridge to the carrier has been constructed. There is also an exhibition hall which includes a cinema. Many areas of the ship are now open and visitors can see displays tracing the history of the Minsk and of naval operations in the area. The aircraft have all been painted with false serials and their origins are unknown. The Nanchang Q-5 is a Chinese development of the MiG-19 for ground attack duties. The air intakes were moved to the side of the fuselage and the wings were of larger area with a greater degree of sweep. About one thousand were produced with some being exported to Bangladesh, North Korea and Pakistan. Another successful licence built type is the Chengdu J-7. Well over a thousand were constructed in China and many were sold abroad.

TYPE	REG/SER	CON. NO.	PI/NOTES	STATUS
☐ Chengdu J-7 I [Mikoyan-Gurevich MiG-21F-13]	'M601'			PVX
☐ Chengdu J-7 I [Mikoyan-Gurevich MiG-21F-13]	'M602'			PVX
☐ Chengdu J-7 I [Mikoyan-Gurevich MiG-21F-13]	'M603'			PVX
☐ Mikoyan-Gurevich MiG-23B	'28'			PVX
☐ Mikoyan-Gurevich MiG-23UB	'26'			PVX
☐ Mil Mi-8P				PV
☐ Mil Mi-24D	'98'			PVX
☐ Mil Mi-24D	'99'			PVX
☐ Nanchang Q-5	'M501'			PVX
☐ Nanchang Q-5	'M502'			PVX
☐ Nanchang Q-5	'M503'			PVX
☐ Nanchang Q-5	'M504'			PVX

NANJING AIRPORT MEMORIAL (CHI20)

Address: Nanjing.
Admission: By prior permission only.
Location: South east of the city.

A report has been received that an example of the Lisunov Li-2 has been preserved as a memorial at the airport. The aircraft is in a restricted area and can only be visited with an authorised guide.

TYPE	REG/SER	CON. NO.	PI/NOTES	STATUS
☐ Lisunov Li-2 [Douglas DC-3 modified]				RA

NANJING UNIVERSITY OF AERONAUTICS AND ASTRONAUTICS (CHI21)

Address: 29 Yudao Street,
Nanjing 210016.
Tel: 025-8489-2440
Fax: 025-8449-8069
Email: icedao@nuaa.edu.cn
Admission: By prior permission only.
Location: In the south eastern suburbs of the city.

This aeronautical institute maintains a collection of mainly military aircraft for both instructional and display purposes. Before the split with Russia, China acquired and assembled large numbers of MiG-15s. When supplies were halted the Shenyang company developed the later MiG-17 into the J-5 during the early 1960s. The Harbin factory has also built Soviet types in considerable numbers with several being exported as well as a number of original designs for both civil and military use. A small display of components, engines, photographs and models has been assembled in and around the workshops.

TYPE	REG/SER	CON. NO.	PI/NOTES	STATUS
☐ Antonov An-24RV	B-3425	47309309	B-478	RA
☐ Harbin H-5 [Ilyushin Il-28]				RA
☐ Harbin Z-5 [Mil Mi-4]				RA
☐ Hawker-Siddeley H.S.121 Trident 2E-108	B-2210	2178	G-BBVV, B-286	RA
☐ Mikoyan-Gurevich MiG-15bis	25		In North Korean markings.	RA
☐ Mikoyan-Gurevich MiG-15bis				RA
☐ Mil Mi-8	B-7808	20218	786	RA
☐ Shenyang J-5 [Mikoyan-Gurevich MiG-17F]				RA
☐ Shenyang J-5 [Mikoyan-Gurevich MiG-17F]				RA

NANYUAN AIRPORT COLLECTION (CHI22)

Address: Nanyuan Airport,
Beijing.
Tel: 010-6799-2139
Admission: By prior permission only.
Location: About 15 km south of the city.

The airport is a former military field which has been developed as an airport, China United Airlines was set up in 1986 as part of the transport wing of the People's Liberation Army. Services were operated to cities around the country. The law was changed in 2003 and the airline is now a civilian carrier although it still flies into military airports which are normally closed to commercial traffic. The collection of preserved aircraft is at two nearby sites. Some are used by the airline for instructional duties and the others are near a military installation.

TYPE	REG/SER	CON. NO.	PI/NOTES	STATUS
☐ Antonov An-12	1058			
☐ Antonov An-24B	4066			RA
☐ Antonov An-24B	CUA-50959	97305209	50959	RA
☐ Harbin Y-5 [Antonov An-2]	10995			
☐ Ilyushin Il-18	50853	187009704	Fuselage only.	RA
☐ Mikoyan-Gurevich MiG-15	63561			RA
☐ Mil Mi-8	4210			RA
☐ Mil Mi-8	4211			RA
☐ Nanchang CJ-6A				RA
☐ Nanchang CJ-6A				RA
☐ Shenyang J-6 [Mikoyan-Gurevich MiG-19SF]				RA
☐ Shenyang J-6 [Mikoyan-Gurevich MiG-19SF]				RA
☐ Shenyang J-6 [Mikoyan-Gurevich MiG-19SF]				RA

NATIONAL DEFENCE PARK (CHI23)

Address: 17 Xin Yuan da Dao Road,
Chengdu 610500.
Tel: 028-8531-1888
Admission: Daily 0800-1700.
Location: In the city.

The city is home to one of the factories producing military aircraft for the country and overseas forces. Several indigenous designs have appeared in recent years. The park which contains a full size mock up of part of an aircraft carrier has been set up to honour the work of the Chinese aviation industry and the Air Force.

TYPE	REG/SER	CON. NO.	PI/NOTES	STATUS
☐ Chengdu J-7 I [Mikoyan-Gurevich MiG-21F-13]	'9957'			PVX
☐ Harbin H-5 [Ilyushin Il-28]	'9959'			PVX
☐ Harbin Z-5 [Mil Mi-4]	'8188'			PVX
☐ Ilyushin Il-14P	602	4340602	Nearby.	PV
☐ Nanchang Q-5	'9956'			PVX
☐ Shenyang J-5 [Mikoyan-Gurevich MiG-17F]	'9958'			PVX
☐ Shenyang J-6 [Mikoyan-Gurevich MiG-19SF]	'9955'			PVX

NORTHWEST POLYTECHNIC UNIVERSITY MUSEUM (CHI24)

Address: 127 Youy Xilu,
X'ian 710072,
Tel: 029-8849-2583
Email: aedmar@nwpu.edu.cn
Admission: Term time 0830-1600.
Location: In the south western suburbs of the city

Xian is normally associated with the famous Terracotta Army but the Polytechnic University has an interesting aviation collection. A large hangar houses models, components, photographs and some of the airframes. In the late 1950s the college designed and built the Yin An. This high wing four seat utility aircraft powered by a 260 h.p. Ivchenko radial made its maiden flight in 1959. The static test airframe of the Y-10 jet airliner can also be seen. The first of two prototypes of this design made its maiden flight on September 26th 1980.

TYPE	REG/SER	CON. NO.	PI/NOTES	STATUS
☐ Chengdu J-7 I [Mikoyan-Gurevich MiG-21F-13]	016			PV
☐ Chengdu J-7 I [Mikoyan-Gurevich MiG-21F-13]		70301		PV
☐ Harbin H-5 [Ilyushin Il-28]	84103	54335		PV
☐ Harbin Z-5 [Mil Mi-4]	4940	2515109		PV
☐ Lockheed U-2C	3511		In Taiwanese markings.	PVD
☐ McDonnell M.36CM Voodoo (F-101C)	56-0022	181	Possible identity.	PVD
☐ Mikoyan-Guervich MiG-15bis	2875	238		PV
☐ Nanchang CJ-6A	5131	2332034		PV
☐ North West Yin An	01			PV
☐ Shenyang J-6 [Mikoyan-Gurevich MiG-19SF]		0216		PV
☐ Shenyang J-6 [Mikoyan-Gurevich MiG-19SF]			Fuselage only.	PV
☐ Shenyang J-6 [Mikoyan-Gurevich MiG-19SF]		0218		PV
☐ Shenyang J-8I	052			PV
☐ Shanghai Y-10		B00002	Static test airframe.	PV

NUJIANG MEMORIAL HALL OF THE HUMP ROUTE (CHI25)

Address:	Pienma, Nujiang 673200.
Tel:	0886-388-1017
Admission:	Open twenty four hours.
Location:	In the centre of the town.

In March 1943 three aircraft took off from Kunming in China to fly over the mountains to India. The weather deteriorated and one crashed. A group of Americans searched for years for the wreck and they came across it in 1996. The remnants were brought down and the C-53 was rebuilt with the addition of components from other aircraft. A hall has been erected and the displays trace the history of the 'Hump Route'. There are many photographs and documents to be seen. The centrepiece is the restored transport in CNAC markings.

TYPE	REG/SER	CON. NO.	PI/NOTES	STATUS
☐ Douglas DC-3A-405 Skytrooper (C-53)	53	4904	41-20134	PV

ORIENTAL GREEN BOAT PARK (CHI26)

Address:	6888 Hu Quin Ping Expressway, 2101713 Shanghai.
Tel:	021-5923-3000
Email:	dflz@ogb.com.ch
Admission:	Daily 0830-1630
Location:	In the western part of the city.

This large park contains several distinct areas including national defence, science education and a variety of sports facilities. A large mock-up of an aircraft carrier has been constructed and several aircraft are parked on its deck. The remainder are in an area nearby. The Xian H-6 is a development of the successful Tupolev Tu-16. This long range jet bomber entered Soviet service in the early 1950s and about one hundred were constructed in China from the late 1960s. Some of the fighter aircraft may be full size replicas.

TYPE	REG/SER	CON. NO.	PI/NOTES	STATUS
☐ Antonov An-24RV	B-4062	47309502	B-496	PV
☐ Chengdu J-7 I [Mikoyan-Gurevich MiG-21F-13]				PV
☐ Chengdu J-7 I [Mikoyan-Gurevich MiG-21F-13]				PV
☐ Harbin H-5 [Ilyushin Il-28]				PV
☐ Mikoyan-Gurevich MiG-15	64803			PV
☐ Mil Mi-8P	814			PV
☐ Mil Mi-8P	820			PV
☐ Nanchang CJ-6A				PV
☐ Nanchang Q-5				PV
☐ Nanchang Q-5				PV
☐ Nanchang Q-5				PV
☐ Nanchang Q-5				PV
☐ Nanchang Q-5				PV
☐ Nanchang Q-5				PV
☐ Nanchang Y-5 [Antonov An-2]				PV
☐ Shenyang J-5 [Mikoyan-Gurevich MiG-17F]	80138			PV
☐ Shenyang J-5A [Mikoyan-Gurevich MiG-17PF]	88801			PV

TYPE	REG/SER	CON. NO.	PI/NOTES	STATUS
☐ Shenyang J-6 [Mikoyan-Gurevich MiG-19SF]	38801			PV
☐ Shenyang JJ-5	31088			
☐ Shenyang JJ-6 [Mikoyan-Gurevich MiG-19U]				PV
☐ Shenyang JJ-6 [Mikoyan-Gurevich MiG-19U]				PV
☐ Xian H-6 [Tupolev Tu-16]	30312	042408		PV

RANGHE AVIATION EXHIBITION HALL (CHI27)

Address:	Pingdingshan City, Henan, Lushan County.
Admission:	Daily 0900-1700.
Location:	South of Luyang Air Base which is about 5 km south of Lushan.

The airfield at is used for storage purposes and at the current time over five hundred aircraft, mainly fighters, are there. A museum has been set up on either side of a taxiway which leads from the main base to a large hangar excavated into a hill. The stars of the collection are the two Curtiss Commandos, one painted in a special colour scheme. China acquired several examples of the transport in the period immediately after World War II. When the Communist Government took over the country some of the airlines joined up with their new rulers. The C-46s flew on routes in the country and some were taken over by the Air Force. Also on show are pieces of radar, anti aircraft weapons and airfield equipment. Only one of the MiG fighters has been positively identified.

TYPE	REG/SER	CON. NO.	PI/NOTES	STATUS
☐ Antonov An-12BP				PV
☐ Curtiss-Wright CW-20B Commando (C-46A)				PV
☐ Curtiss-Wright CW-20B Commando (C-46A)				PV
☐ Harbin H-5 [Ilyushin Il-28]				PV
☐ Harbin H-5 [Ilyushin Il-28]				PV
☐ Harbin H-5 [Ilyushin Il-28]				PV
☐ Harbin Z-5 [Mil Mi-4]				PV
☐ Mikoyan-Gurevich MiG-15	70008			PV
☐ Mil Mi-8				PV
☐ Mil Mi-8				PV
☐ Mil Mi-8				PV
☐ Mil Mi-8				PV
☐ Nanchang CJ-6A				PV
☐ Nanchang CJ-6A				PV
☐ Nanchang Y-5 [Antonov An-2]				PV
☐ Shenyang J-5 [Mikoyan-Gurevich MiG-17F]			May be MiG-15.	PV
☐ Shenyang J-5 [Mikoyan-Gurevich MiG-17F]			May be MiG-15.	PV
☐ Shenyang J-5 [Mikoyan-Gurevich MiG-17F]			May be MiG-15.	PV
☐ Shenyang J-5 [Mikoyan-Gurevich MiG-17F]			May be MiG-15.	PV
☐ Shenyang J-5 [Mikoyan-Gurevich MiG-17F]			May be MiG-15.	PV
☐ Shenyang J-5 [Mikoyan-Gurevich MiG-17F]			May be MiG-15.	PV
☐ Shenyang J-5 [Mikoyan-Gurevich MiG-17F]			May be MiG-15.	PV
☐ Shenyang J-5 [Mikoyan-Gurevich MiG-17F]			May be MiG-15.	PV
☐ Shenyang J-5 [Mikoyan-Gurevich MiG-17F]			May be MiG-15.	PV
☐ Shenyang J-5 [Mikoyan-Gurevich MiG-17F]			May be MiG-15.	PV
☐ Shenyang J-5 [Mikoyan-Gurevich MiG-17F]			May be MiG-15.	PV
☐ Shenyang J-5 [Mikoyan-Gurevich MiG-17F]			May be MiG-15.	PV
☐ Shenyang J-5 [Mikoyan-Gurevich MiG-17F]			May be MiG-15.	PV
☐ Shenyang J-5 [Mikoyan-Gurevich MiG-17F]			May be MiG-15.	PV
☐ Shenyang J-5 [Mikoyan-Gurevich MiG-17F]			May be MiG-15.	PV
☐ Shenyang J-6 [Mikoyan-Gurevich MiG-19SF]				PV

SANZAO ZHUHAI MUSEUM (CHI28)

Address:	Sanzao, Zhuhai.
Admission:	Unknown.
Location:	Presumed by the airport which is about 40 km west of Zhuhai.

Sanzao, the new airport for Zhuhai, opened in 1995 and replaced the much smaller field located in the coastal area of the city. A report of the Shenyang J-5A appeared in a magazine but no further details were given.

TYPE	REG/SER	CON. NO.	PI/NOTES	STATUS
☐ Shenyang J-5A [Mikoyan-Gurevich MiG-17PF]	'87-12'			PVX

SEVEN STARS PARK (CHI29)

Address:	Guilin.
Admission:	Daily 0800-1700.
Location:	In the south western part of the city.

This large park has many attractions designed to suit people of all ages. There is an area devoted to transport and one dedicated to the military. The only aircraft on show is the Shenyang J-5.

TYPE	REG/SER	CON. NO.	PI/NOTES	STATUS
☐ Shenyang J-5 [Mikoyan-Gurevich MiG-17F]	80584			PV

SHANGHAI AVIATION ENTHUSIASTS CENTRE (CHI30)

Address: 6700 Humin Road,
Shanghai.
Admission: Daily 1000-1800.
Location: In south western part of the city.

An interesting collection has been built up over recent years by this enthusiastic group. A small display building containing models, documents, photographs, engines and components can be seen. The largest aircraft on view is the former Japan Air Lines DC-8 which overshot the runway at Shanghai in September 1982. Among the former PLA aircraft are an Ilyushin Il-14 and several fighters. A number of microlights and gliders were on show but were not seen on a recent visit and are believed to be stored.

TYPE	REG/SER	CON. NO.	PI/NOTES	STATUS
☐ Douglas DC-8-61	JA8048	46160		PV
☐ Harbin Z-5 [Mil Mi-4]	9328			PV
☐ Ilyushin Il 14M	652	146001102		PV
☐ Mikoyan-Gurevich MiG-15UTI	1204	5308	In nearby park.	PV
☐ Mikoyan-Gurevich MiG-15UTI	8761			PV
☐ Mikoyan-Gurevich MiG-15UTI	12347			PV
☐ Mikoyan-Gurevich MiG-15UTI	81467	2915392	In nearby park	PV
☐ Nanchang CJ-6A	80	3732024		PV
☐ Nanchang Q-5	10405			PV
☐ Quickie Aircraft Quickie 1 (Rutan 54)				PV
☐ Shenyang J-5 [Mikoyan-Gurevich MiG-17F]	12641	5847		PV
☐ Shenyang J-5 [Mikoyan-Gurevich MiG-17F]	10406			PV
☐ Shenyang J-6 [Mikoyan-Gurevich MiG-19SF]	30733	5655		PV
☐ Shenyang J-6 II [Mikoyan-Gurevich MiG-19PM]	2996	0114		PV
☐ Shenyang Liberation 7				RA
☐ Shenyang Liberation 9				RA
☐ TPAY Microlight				RA
☐ Weedhopper JC-24				RA

SHANGHAI VOCATIONAL SCHOOL COLLECTION (CHI31)

Address: Longhua Airport,
Shanghai 200232.
Admission: By prior permission only.
Location: In the eastern part of the city.

An area at the almost closed Longhua Airport is used by the school. Three airframes painted in special colours are parked on an apron. The Ilyushin Il-14 is one of the eighty built at Dresden in East Germany and first flew in 1958. The airliner was withdrawn from use in 1985 and joined the school soon afterwards. Well over one thousand Antonov An-2s were built at two factories in China between 1957 and 1992.

TYPE	REG/SER	CON. NO.	PI/NOTES	STATUS
☐ Antonov An-24B	'SVS-001'	17307105	B-430, B-3406	RAX
☐ Ilyushin Il-14P	'SVS-002'	14803052	DM-ZZR, 674 (China)	RAX
☐ Nanchang Y-5 [Antonov An-2]	'SVS-003'	232008	8100, B-8100	RAX

SHENFEI AIRCRAFT CORPORATION MUSEUM (CHI32)

Address: 1 Linfbei Street,
Shenyang City,
Liaoning 110034.
Tel: 024-8569-9602
Admission: Tuesday-Sunday 0830-1630.
Location: In the north eastern part of the city.

The Shenyang Aircraft Corporation was founded in 1953 and is part of the giant Shenfei Group. Their first work was the assembly of MiG-15s but following the breakdown of relations with the Soviet Union they started work on developing the designs. The J-5 based on the successful MiG-17 was the first to enter production and this was further modified. Indigenous two seat versions of the designs appeared. The exhibition has been set up to trace the work of the factory which has produced and exported many aircraft. The history of the aviation industry in the country is highlighted in the display which is still being developed. The J-8 was designed in the turbulent times of the 1960s and did not enter service until the early 1980s. The type was the first truly indigenous jet fighter produced in the country. Over three hundred have been produced in several versions.

TYPE	REG/SER	CON. NO.	PI/NOTES	STATUS
☐ Chengdu J-7 I [Mikoyan-Gurevich MiG-21F-13]	66117			PV
☐ Nanchang Q-5	33526			PV
☐ Nanchang Y-5 [Antonov An-2]	3238			PV
☐ Shenyang J-5 [Mikoyan-Gurevich MiG-17F]	56719		'11201'	PV
☐ Shenyang J-6 I [Mikoyan-Gurevich MiG-19PF]	??24	2309 (?)	At nearby company technical school.	PV
☐ Shenyang J-6 I [Mikoyan-Gurevich MiG-19PF]	11250		Front fuselage only.	PV
☐ Shenyang J-6 I [Mikoyan-Gurevich MiG-19PF]	69930		'11202'	PV
☐ Shenyang J-6 III [Mikoyan-Gurevich MiG-19PM]	69805	J6-7616	'11204'	PV
☐ Shenyang JJ-6 [Mikoyan-Gurevich MiG-19U]	70116		'11203'	PV
☐ Shenyang J-8I	69705		'11206'	PV
☐ Shenyang J-8II	84612	J8B-0101	'11207'	PV

WORLD PARK (CHI33)

Address:	158 Dabotai, Huaxiang Township, Fentai District, Beijing 100071.
Tel:	010-8361-3685
Admission:	Daily 0900-1800.
Location:	In the south western part of the city.

This large site contains scale replicas of over one hundred famous buildings and attractions from more than fifty countries. The lawns are home to many models and copies of well known statues. There is also an area where groups from around the world perform plays, dance and music. The only aircraft is the Ilyushin Il-62. The four engined airliner served in China for many years and also operated on international routes.

TYPE	REG/SER	CON. NO.	PI/NOTES	STATUS
☐ Ilyushin Il-62	B-2028	21202	2028	PV

YAKOU MEMORIAL (CHI34)

Address:	Yakou.
Admission:	On permanent view.
Location:	On the outskirts of the village.

The fighter has been preserved as a memorial to local pilots who have lost their lives in flying accidents. The Shenyang J-6 is surrounded by flags and plaques giving their details.

TYPE	REG/SER	CON. NO.	PI/NOTES	STATUS
☐ Shenyang J-6 [Mikoyan-Gurevich MiG-19SF]	'2000'			PVX

ZHOU EN-LAI AND DENG YINGCHAO MEMORIAL HALL (CHI35)

Address:	Shuishan Gongyuan Road, Tianjian 300000.
Tel:	022-2352-9257
Admission:	Tuesday-Sunday 0830-1700.
Location:	In the southern part of the city.

This museum honours the life and achievements of the former prime minister of the country. On show are many personal items and documents relating to his early years and his time in government. The life of his wife is also highlighted. Zhou En-lai attended a school in Tianjin in the years just before World War I. The only aircraft is the Ilyushin Il-14 he used on many journeys around China. The airliner moved to the museum in 1997.

TYPE	REG/SER	CON. NO.	PI/NOTES	STATUS
☐ Ilyushin Il-14P	678	147001513		PV

This C-53 was recovered from a crash site and is now on show in Pienma. (Diego Kusak)

A line up at the Ranghe Aviation Exhibition Hall.

The largest aircraft at the Shanghai Aviation Enthusiasts Centre is this former Japanese DC-8. (Lloyd Robinson)

A line up at the Shenyang Company Museum. (Shinsuke Yamamoto)

This J-8 is part of the Shenyang collection. (Shinsuke Yamamoto)

INDIA

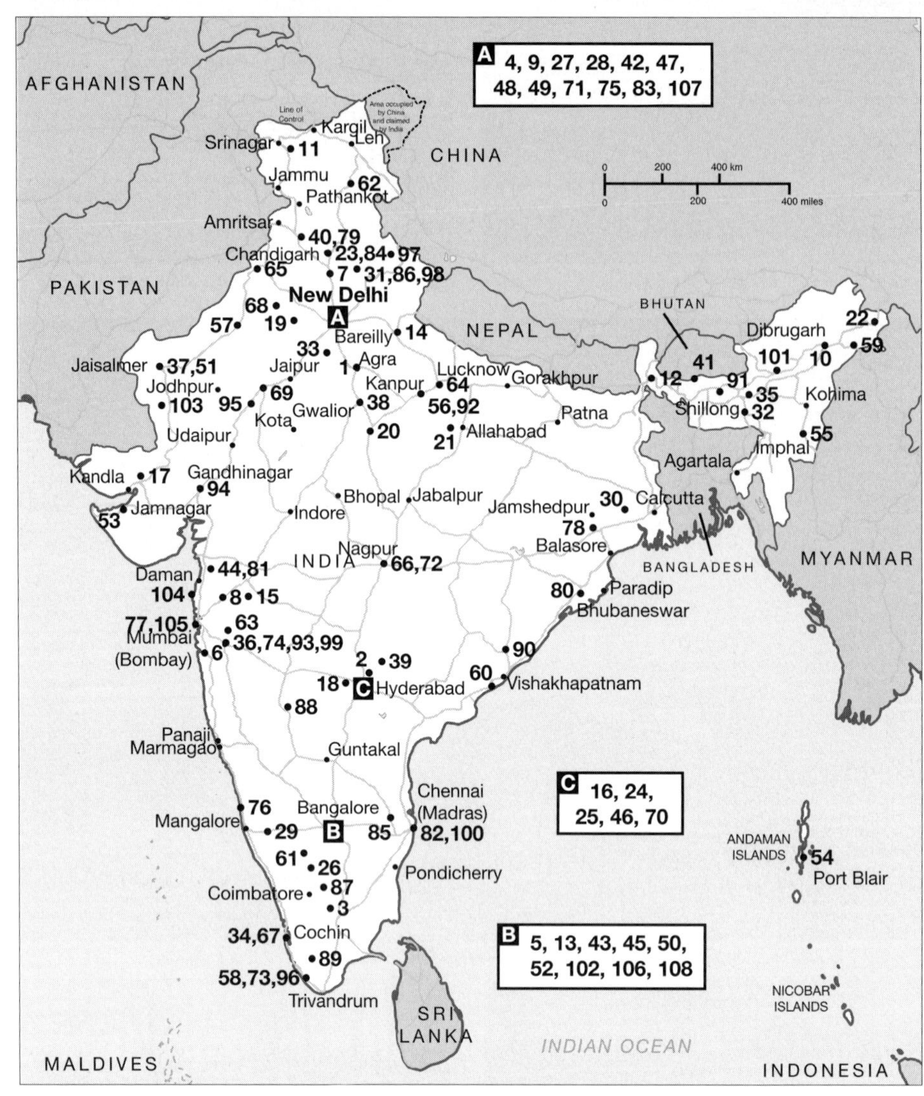

AGRA AIR FORCE STATION MUSEUM (IDA1)

Address:	Agra, Uttar Pradesh 282001.
Admission:	By prior permission only.
Location:	About 8 km south west of the city.

The base opened in August 1947 and since then has housed mainly transport units. Types flown from the field include the famous Douglas C-47, the Fairchild C-119 and in recent years the Antonov An-32 and Ilyushin Il-76. In addition a squadron operating various marks of the English Electric Canberra was in residence. The small museum traces the history of the airfield and its units. On show are photographs, documents, uniforms and trophies. The preserved aircraft are located around the vast site. The C-119 and Super Constellation were here for many years but have not been seen recently and may have moved on.

TYPE	REG/SER	CON. NO.	PI/NOTES	STATUS
☐ Dassault Mystère IVA			May still be here.	RA
☐ Douglas DC-3A-467 Skytrain (C-47B)	HJ905		Less wings.	RA
☐ English Electric EA.1 Canberra B(I).58				RA
☐ English Electric EA.1 Canberra B(I).58				RA
☐ Fairchild 110 Flying Boxcar (C-119G)	IK455	11286	53-4651 may be c/n 11310 53-4659 IK463 – current location not known.	–
☐ Hindustan HF-24 Marut 1	D1277			RA
☐ Lockheed 1049G-82-106 Super Constellation	BG583	1049G-4686	VT-DJW – stored for IAF Museum – current location not known.	–
☐ Mil Mi-4				RA

AIR FORCE ACADEMY MUSEUM (IDA2)

Address:	Dundigal, Hyderabad, Andhra Pradesh 500043.
Tel:	040-2330-7430
Admission:	By prior permission only.
Location:	About 30 km north of the city off road NH7.

Prior to independence many Indian officers received their training in England at R.A.F. Cranwell. This work was moved to Ambala and later Begumpet, but the need for a purpose built college gained momentum. A site at Dundigal was chosen and the impressive buildings opened in 1970. Three of the aircraft preserved are examples of trainers used at the field. One hundred and forty Tiger Moths were flown between 1939 and 1957 when many survivors were passed to flying clubs. A similar number of Texans was also used. This advanced trainer was in use between 1942 and 1975. Just inside the gate is the Toofani Triangle where the Ouragan, Mystère IV and Sukhoi Su-7 are displayed in the middle of a roundabout. The Ouragan was called the Toofani in the Air Force. The remainder of the preserved aircraft are dispersed around the site. The Tiger Moth is located in the museum building where the informative displays trace the story of the Air Force and the Academy. Many personal items are on show. Some aircraft are in the technical training school.

TYPE	REG/SER	CON. NO.	PI/NOTES	STATUS
☐ Dassault MD-450 Ouragan	IC578	272		RA
☐ Dassault Mystère IVA	IA938	254		RA
☐ De Havilland D.H.82A Tiger Moth	'HU358'	83750	T5852, G-AKGU, HU720, VT-DBK, 'HU838', 'AFA-1975'	RAX
☐ De Havilland D.H.100 Vampire FB.52	IB1638			RA
☐ English Electric EA.1 Canberra PR.57			May be PR.67.	RA
☐ Folland Fo.141 Gnat F.1	E355		By ramp.	RA
☐ Hindustan HT-2	IX718			RA
☐ Hindustan HJT-16 Kiran 1	U328			RA
☐ Hindustan HJT-16 Kiran 1	U718		Cutaway airframe.	RA
☐ Hindustan HJT-16 Kiran 1	U752		Front fuselage only.	RA
☐ Hindustan HF-24 Marut 1T	D1691			RA
☐ Hindustan HPT-32 Deepak	X3254		Fuselage only.	RA
☐ Hindustan HPT-32 Deepak			Fuselage only.	RA
☐ Mikoyan-Gurevich MiG-21FL	C1167		By Air Cadets Mess.	RA
☐ Mikoyan-Gurevich MiG-25U	DS362			RA
☐ North American NA-88 Texan (AT-6C)	IT365			RA
☐ Panstwowe Zaklady Lotnicze (PZL) TS-11 Iskra 200bisC	W1741	2H 09-03	0903 (Poland), 903 (Poland)	RA
☐ Panstwowe Zaklady Lotnicze (PZL) TS-11 Iskra 200bisD	W1772	3H 19-12	1912 (Poland)	RA
☐ Panstwowe Zaklady Lotnicze (PZL) TS-11 Iskra 200bisD	W1755	3H 19-15	1915 (Poland)	RA
☐ Sukhoi Su-7BMK	B784			RA

AIR FORCE ADMINISTRATIVE COLLEGE MUSEUM (IDA3)

Address:	Redfields, Coimbatore, Tamil Nadu 641018.
Tel:	0422-222-2611
Admission:	By prior permission only.
Location:	In the suburbs of the town.

The college is one of the oldest in the Indian Air Force and trains officers for all three services as well as some from foreign countries. A small display tracing the history of organisation has been set up.

TYPE	REG/SER	CON. NO.	PI/NOTES	STATUS
☐ Hindustan HT-2				RA

AIR FORCE BAL BHARATI SCHOOL DISPLAY (IDA4)

Address:	Lochi Road, New Delhi 110001.
Tel:	011-2461-6220
Admission:	By prior permission only.
Location:	In the central area of the city.

The school was set up in 1955 to initially cater for preparatory pupils but has now takes all ages. Students are trained in all subjects as well as military matters. A Folland Gnat is displayed at the site.

TYPE	REG/SER	CON. NO.	PI/NOTES	STATUS
☐ Folland Fo.141 Gnat F.1				RA

AIRCRAFT SYSTEMS AND TESTING ESTABLISHMENT MUSEUM (IDA5)

Address:	Yelahanka Air Force Station, Bangalore, Karnatka 560063.
Tel:	080-2847-8029
Admission:	By prior permission only.
Location:	About 10 km north of the city.

The base is home to a number of units and a training school. The Test Pilots School has set up a small museum tracing their history and showing the work carried out. A Marut is displayed outside their building. This aircraft is one of the eighteen two seat versions of the indigenous jet built for training duties.

TYPE	REG/SER	CON. NO.	PI/NOTES	STATUS
☐ Hindustan HF-24 Marut 1T	D1696			

ALIBAUG MOTOR MUSEUM (IDA6)

Address:	Alibaug, Maharastra 402201.
Admission:	Unknown.
Location:	In the town.

A Stinson Sentinel is reported as being on show in a car museum at this tourist resort. After World War II several examples of the type were allocated to flying clubs around the country.

TYPE	REG/SER	CON. NO.	PI/NOTES	STATUS
☐ Stinson V-76 Sentinel (L-5)	VT-CBT	76-1653	42-99412	PV (?)

AMBALA AIR FORCE STATION WAR MEMORIAL (IDA7)

Address:	Ambala Air Force Station, Ambala Cantonment, Haryana 133001
Tel:	0171-263-1818
Admission:	By prior permission only.
Location:	Just east of the town off Road NH1.

The airfield was taken over from the Royal Air Force after India achieved its independence and initially housed training units but has been a front line base for many years. No. 1 Air Force Academy was set up in 1949 and remained here until the site at Dundigal was built. The airfield now houses squadrons flying the Jaguar and the MiG-21 and was attacked by Pakistani aircraft in both 1966 and 1971. The Gnat is at the 'Frozen Tear' War Memorial which commemorates all those who lost their lives flying from the base and those killed on the ground in the attacks. Around the base of the monument are plaques giving their names. The wreckage of the Spitfire was found in a local river in 2003. The aircraft was stored at a number of Royal Air Force Maintenance Units in the United Kingdom before being sent to India in 1944 where it was struck off charge in June 1947. Station personnel recovered the remains and they are now in one of the hangars. Some conservation work has been carried out and the aircraft will hopefully be put on show. The museum in one of the buildings traces the history of the airfield and its units.

TYPE	REG/SER	CON. NO.	PI/NOTES	STATUS
☐ Folland Fo.141 Gnat F.1	E1051			RA
☐ Hawker P.1099 Hunter F.56				RA
☐ Hawker P.1099 Hunter F.56				RA
☐ Supermarine 359 Spitfire LF.VIII	MV459			RA

ARMY MUSEUM (IDA8)

Address: 665 AOP Squadron, Artillery Centre, Nashik Road, Deolali, Maharastra 422101.
Admission: By prior permission only.
Location: About 8 km south east of the town off Road NH50.

During the latter stages of World War II Indian A.O.P. pilots flew with the Royal Air Force. The Auster A.O.P.5, which was on show at the Air Force Museum at Palam, moved to Mahrastra in the late 1980s for display in this collection which portrays the history of the Indian Army. There is an excellent collection of uniforms, weapons and military vehicles to be seen. The MiG-21 is parked outside the nearby School of Artillery.

TYPE	REG/SER	CON. NO.	PI/NOTES	STATUS
☐ Auster J AOP.5	IN959	1358	TJ268, IN959, VT-COG	RA
☐ Mikoyan-Gurevich MiG-21FL				RA

ARMY PUBLIC SCHOOL MARTYR'S GALLERY (IDA9)

Address: Ridge Road, Dhaula Kuan, New Delhi 110010.
Admission: By prior permission only.
Location: In the south eastern part of the city.

The school was set up in 1953 to provide education for the children of Army families. Many former pupils have joined the services and several have lost their lives whilst on duty. A Martyr's Gallery has been set up to honour these people and photographs and details of their service careers can be viewed.

TYPE	REG/SER	CON. NO.	PI/NOTES	STATUS
☐ Sukhoi Su-7BMK	B909	7212		RA

ASSAM RIFLES DISPLAY (IDA10)

Address: Mohabari, Dibrugarh, Assam 786001.
Admission: By prior permission only.
Location: In the southern part of the town.

The regiment was set up during the British Colonial period and is now a para-military force with over forty battalions. The unit at Dibrugarh has set up a small display and among the items on show is the Mil Mi-4.

TYPE	REG/SER	CON. NO.	PI/NOTES	STATUS
☐ Mil Mi-4				RA

AWANTIPUR AIR FORCE STATION MUSEUM (IDA11)

Address: Awantipur, Jammu and Kashmir 655516.
Tel: 01933-286909
Admission: By prior permission only.
Location: About 15 km south east of Srinagar.

The base is in the disputed area of Kashmir. For many years it has housed units on detachment from other airfields. The museum traces the history of the site and the units which have been in residence.

TYPE	REG/SER	CON. NO.	PI/NOTES	STATUS
☐ Folland Fo.141 Gnat F.1				RA
☐ Sukhoi Su-7BMK				RA

BAGDOGRA AIR FORCE STATION MUSEUM (IDA12)

Address:	Bagdogra, Darjeeling, West Bengal 734421.
Tel:	0353-255-1088
Admission:	By prior permission only.
Location:	About 5 km south of the town on road NH31.

The airfield is home to a wing flying the MiG-21 and in addition a detatchment of helicopters is in residence. The Gnat is located by the gate and the preserved Sukhoi Su-7s are inside the camp. The airfield saw a great deal of use during the various conflicts with Pakistan. A small museum has been set up in one of the buildings.

TYPE	REG/SER	CON. NO.	PI/NOTES	STATUS
☐ Folland Fo.141 Gnat F.1				RA
☐ Sukhoi Su-7BMK				RA
☐ Sukhoi Su-7BMK				RA

BANGALORE MILITARY SCHOOL MEMORIAL (IDA13)

Address:	PB 2500 Museum Road, Hosur Road, Bangalore, Karnatka 560025.
Tel:	080-2555-4972
Admission:	By prior permission only.
Location:	In the eastern part of the city.

This long established school trains students of military personnel. Many former pupils have joined the services and several have been killed on duty. The Hindustan HT-2 trainer honours these people.

TYPE	REG/SER	CON. NO.	PI/NOTES	STATUS
☐ Hindustan HT-2	IX752			RA

BAREILLY AIR FORCE STATION MUSEUM (IDA14)

Address:	Bareilly, Uttar Pradesh 243002.
Admission:	By prior permission only.
Location:	About 8 km north of the town off road NH94.

The field is currently home to squadrons flying the Sukhoi Su-30 and has been home to front line units for many years On May 1st 2006 a ceremony was held to commemorate the withdrawal of the MiG-25R. A small number was acquired by the Indian Air Force and Bareilly was their home for almost a quarter of a century. Four of the five airworthy survivors were flown to other bases for preservation. The museum traces the history of the site with a display of models, photographs, documents and uniforms.

TYPE	REG/SER	CON. NO.	PI/NOTES	STATUS
☐ English Electric EA.1 Canberra B(I).58				RA
☐ Folland Fo.141 Gnat F.1				RA
☐ Mikoyan-Gurevich MiG-25R				RA
☐ Sukhoi Su-7BMK				RA

BARNES SCHOOL MEMORIAL (IDA15)

Address:	Deolali, Maharasthra 422401.
Tel:	0253-249253
Email:	barnesschool@sanchet.in
Admission:	By prior permission only.
Location:	In the northern part of the town.

The school was founded in 1925 and many of its former pupils have served with distinction in the armed forces. An Indian built MiG-21 has been preserved as a memorial.

TYPE	REG/SER	CON. NO.	PI/NOTES	STATUS
☐ Mikoyan-Gurevich MiG-21				RA

BEGUMPET AIR FORCE STATION MUSEUM (IDA16)

Address:	Bowenpally, Hyderabad, Anddhra Pradesh 500019.
Tel:	040-2371-0426
Admission:	By prior permission only.
Location:	In the north eastern suburbs of the city off road NH9.

The airfield was constructed in the 1930s for use by the Hyderabad Aero Club. The field also housed the Nizam of Hyderabad's personal aircraft. A terminal building and control tower were built and these still survive. During World War II the Royal Air Force used the site for pilot training and many Tiger Moths were in residence. At the end of the conflict the field returned to civilian control. No. 1 Air Force Academy moved in from Ambala in October 1951 and stayed for several years. In recent years transport aircraft of the Indian Air Force have been in residence. The museum opened in August 2004 and its displays trace the history of the airfield. Many personal items from people who served at Begumpet have been acquired. There is an excellent collection of photographs from the pre-war era and uniforms and models can also be seen. The Iskra is parked outside the building.

TYPE	REG/SER	CON. NO.	PI/NOTES	STATUS
☐ Panstwowe Zaklady Lotnicze (PZL) TS-11 Iskra 200bisD	W1769	3H 15-09		RA

BHUJ AIR FORCE STATION MUSEUM (IDA17)

Address:	Bhuj, Gujarat 370001
Tel:	02832-22900
Admission:	By prior permission only.
Location:	About 3 km north of the town.

The airfield was constructed in 1968 in the aftermath of the 1965 war with Pakistan. The site was put into Care and Maintenance but saw some operational use in the 1971 conflict and was bombed a number of times. The first based squadron arrived in 1979 and now MiG-21bis fighters are in residence. In 2001 a violent earthquake caused considerable damage at the airfield and in the locality. The runway fortunately remained open.

TYPE	REG/SER	CON. NO.	PI/NOTES	STATUS
☐ English Electric EA.1 Canberra B(I).58	'F971'	EEP.71618	IF971	RAX
☐ Hawker P.1099 Hunter F.56				RA
☐ Sukhoi Su-7BMK	B911			RA
☐ Sukhoi Su-7BMK	B912			RA

BIDAR AIR FORCE STATION MUSEUM (IDA18)

Address:	VSV Area, Bidar, Karnataka 585401.
Tel:	08482-220215
Admission:	By prior permission only.
Location:	about 3 km west of the town.

The airfield was constructed by the Nizam of Hyderabad between 1943 and 1947 as tensions in the area increased prior to the partition of the country. The site was disused until 1963 when a jet training wing moved in. This unit was disbanded in 1965 and the airfield was vacant for a year. Another training unit arrived and the field still serves in this role. Currently in use is the indigenous Hindustan HJT-16 Kiran. The Surya Kiran aerobatic team was formed in 1996 and has twelve aircraft painted in a distinctive red and white scheme. Nine are normally flown at displays around the country. The team is successor to the 'Thunderbirds' which made its debut in 1982 and flew Hawker Hunters until it was disbanded in 1989. The small, yet informative, museum traces the history of the site with many photographs and documents. The only aircraft preserved is a Hindustan HT-2 piston engined trainer.

TYPE	REG/SER	CON. NO.	PI/NOTES	STATUS
☐ Hindustan HT-2				RA

Above: The collection at Agra Air Force Station includes this Hindustan Marut 1.

Left: The Indian Air Force Academy at Dundigal is home to this T-6 (Via Jagan Pilarisetti)

Left: The Iskra has recently been withdrawn from Indian service and several examples of the trainer have been preserved. This one is at Begumpet Air Force Station. (Via Jagan Pilarisetti)

BIRLA INSTITUTE OF SCIENCE AND TECHNOLOGY MUSEUM (IDA19)

Address:	Vidhya Vihar Campus, Pilani, Rajasthan 333031.
Tel:	01596-245073
Fax:	01596-244183
Admission:	Tuesday-Saturday 1000-1600.
Location:	In the southern suburbs of the town.

A DC-3 has recently been put on display at this institute which trains aeronautical engineers. A small exhibition of models, photographs and components is housed in one of the buildings. The aircraft was used by the American forces in India at the end of World War II and sold to the Maharjah of Patalia in September 1948. After several other owners it was withdrawn from service in 1985 and presented to the museum a few years later.

TYPE	REG/SER	CON. NO.	PI/NOTES	STATUS
☐ Douglas DC-3A-467 Skytrain (C-47B)	VT-CYT	16244/32992	44-76660	PV

BORDER SECURITY FORCES ACADEMY DISPLAY (IDA20)

Address:	P.O. Tekanpur, Madhya Pradesh 475005.
Tel:	075-2427-4180
Email:	acy@dsf.delhi.nic.in
Admission:	By prior permission only.
Location:	In the northern part of the town.

India has a long border with several neighbouring countries and over the years there have been many disputes. The academy was set up to train members of the force in all aspects of security work. A small display has been set up in the picturesque grounds of the academy and this includes the C-47.

TYPE	REG/SER	CON. NO.	PI/NOTES	STATUS
☐ Douglas DC-3A-456 Skytrain (C-47A) (Dakota III)				RA

CENTRAL AIR COMMAND HEADQUARTERS MUSEUM (IDA21)

Address:	Bamrauli, Allahabad, Uttar Pradesh 211012.
Tel:	0532-229-6928
Admission:	By prior permission only.
Location:	North of the airfield which is about 12 km west of the city off road NH2.

Central Air Command was established in 1962 at Rani Kuthee near Calcutta. Owing to increased tension along the borders with Nepal and Tibet a move was made to Allahabad four years later. Now six active bases are under its control. A museum tracing the history of the command has been set up in the buildings. Four jet fighters and an Iskra trainer have been put on show in the grounds of the complex.

TYPE	REG/SER	CON. NO.	PI/NOTES	STATUS
☐ Folland Fo.141 Gnat F.1				RA
☐ Hawker P.1099 Hunter F.56	BA360			RA
☐ Mikoyan-Gurevich MiG-21M	C1959			RA
☐ Panstwowe Zaklady Lotnicze (PZL) TS-11 Iskra 200bisD	W1792	3H 15-12	W1772	
☐ Sukhoi Su-7BMK				RA

CHABUA AIR FORCE STATION MUSEUM (IDA22)

Address:	Chabua, Assam 786102.
Admission:	By prior permission only.
Location:	About 5 km south west of the town off road NH37.

The airfield was built in 1939 and was the second Allied Air Forces Station in India. When Japan invaded Burma and cut the road to the east transport flights to supply Chiang Kai-Shek's forces in China were initiated. These operations became known as 'Flying the Hump'. The Indian Air Force reopened the airfield in the early 1960s and fighters and transports moved in. At the current time MiG-21s are operated. The museum traces the interesting history of the airfield. On show are photographs and documents from the early period. The only aircraft is a Hunter, painted in 'Thunderbirds' aerobatic team, colours.

TYPE	REG/SER	CON. NO.	PI/NOTES	STATUS
☐ Hawker P.1099 Hunter F.56				RA

CHANDIGARH AIR FORCE STATION MUSEUM (IDA23)

Address:	Air Force Station 12, Chandigarh, Haryana 160019.
Tel:	0172-264-1151
Admission:	By prior permission only.
Location:	In the southern suburbs of the town off road NH21.

This long established airfield is home to a maintenance base which overhauls helicopters and two fighter squadrons flying MiG-21s. Ilyushin Il-76 transports also operate from the station. In the past Antonov An-12s flew the important route to Leh taking supplies into the north east region of Kashmir and this airlift continues. The base was turned over to the Indian Air Force in 1941 by the Royal Air Force.

TYPE	REG/SER	CON. NO.	PI/NOTES	STATUS
☐ Folland Fo.141 Gnat F.1				RA
☐ Hindustan HF-24 Marut 1				RA
☐ Mikoyan-Gurevich MiG-21bis				RA
☐ Mikoyan-Gurevich MiG-21bis				RA
☐ Mil Mi-4				RA
☐ Mil Mi-8				RA
☐ Mil Mi-8				RA

COLLEGE OF AIR WARFARE MUSEUM (IDA24)

Address:	2 Sardar Patel Road, Secunderabad, Andhra Pradesh 500003.
Admission:	By prior permission only.
Location:	About 2 km east of Begumpet Air Force Base.

The college was initially set up in Delhi but soon moved to its present location. The courses are designed primarily for Air Force officers although students from other services do attend. A separate unit is responsible for the publication of books tracing the history of the Indian Air Force and its units. There is a small museum which highlights the history and development of the college and outside is preserved a Hawker Hunter.

TYPE	REG/SER	CON. NO.	PI/NOTES	STATUS
☐ Hawker P.1099 Hunter F.56	BA313			RA

COLLEGE OF DEFENCE MANAGEMENT MEMORIAL (IDA25)

Address:	Bolaram Post, Secunderabad, Andhra Pradesh 500010.
Tel:	040-862259
Email:	cdm@ap.nic.in
Admission:	By prior permission only.
Location:	In the eastern part of the town.

The need for modern management training became apparent after the 1965 war with Pakistan. The organisation was set up in 1970 and took up its present name a decade later. Personnel from all services attend the college. A two seat MiG-21U is parked in the grounds to serve as a memorial. About seventy examples of this two seat version were acquired from the Soviet Union and a few more arrived from Bulgaria and Hungary.

TYPE	REG/SER	CON. NO.	PI/NOTES	STATUS
☐ Mikoyan-Gurevich MiG-21U	U660			RA

DEFENCE SERVICES STAFF COLLEGE DISPLAY (IDA26)

Address:	Wellington, Tamil Nadu 643241.
Tel:	0423-228-2429
Admission:	By prior permission only.
Location:	About 5 km north of Coonor.

The college was originally set up at Deolali in 1905 and moved to Quetta, now in Pakistan, two years later. After partition a site at Wellington came into use. A display of military equipment is located in the grounds.

TYPE	REG/SER	CON. NO.	PI/NOTES	STATUS
□ Hindustan Ajeet [Folland Fo.141 Gnat 2]	E1049			RA

DELHI FLYING CLUB DISPLAY (IDA27)

Address:	Safdarjung Airport, New Delhi 110003.
Tel:	011-463-5080
Email:	nfo@delhiflyingclub.org
Admission:	By prior permission only.
Location:	In the southern part of the city.

The club was formed in May 1928 to train civilian pilots. In 1931 a club aircraft carried out the first air mail service in India. At the present time both pilots and mechanics are trained. J.R.D. Tata obtained the first pilots licence awarded in India in 1929. Tata Airlines was formed in 1932 and the founder made the first scheduled flight from Karachi to Mumbai on October 15th in a de Havilland Puss Moth. Forty years later he re-enacted the flight in a Leopard Moth. The aircraft had been delivered to India in 1938 and survived the war. The aircraft was restored in England by Cliff Lovell in Hampshire before the flight and the Moth is now preserved at the club The airline operated several types prior to World War II and these included de Havilland D.H.86s and D.H.89 Dragon Rapides. After the end of the conflict the company developed in to the national airline 'Air India'.

TYPE	REG/SER	CON. NO.	PI/NOTES	STATUS
□ De Havilland D.H.85 Leopard Moth	VT-AKH	7052	G-ACRJ	RA

DELHI PUBLIC SCHOOL – GHAZIABAD MEMORIAL (IDA28)

Address:	Ghaziabad, Uttar Pradesh 201010.
Email:	dpsghaziabad@fastmail.fm
Admission:	By prior permission only.
Location:	In the town.

The school was set up in 1980 and moved into a purpose built complex a few years later. Many students have gone on to serve in the armed forces and a Mystère has been preserved as a memorial

TYPE	REG/SER	CON. NO.	PI/NOTES	STATUS
□ Dassault Mystère IVA	IA1012			RA

DHARMASTHALA TOWN MUSEUM (IDA29)

Address:	Dharmasthala, Karnataka 574216.
Admission:	Daily 0800-1100 1600-1800.
Location:	About 75 km east of Mangalore.

The DC-3 saw military service with both the U.S.A.A.F. and the R.A.F. before embarking on a long civil career in India. This included seven years airline use with Bharat Airways and sixteen with Indian Airlines Corporation before a well deserved retirement. Shelters have been constructed over the pair to protect them from the sun and rain. Also in the town is another museum with an excellent collection of vintage cars.

TYPE	REG/SER	CON. NO.	PI/NOTES	STATUS
□ Douglas DC-3A-456 Skytrain (C-47A) (Dakota III)	VT-CGQ	13573	42-93639, KG706	PV
□ Hindustan HT-2	'10'			PVX

DIAMOND JUBILEE MUSEUM (IDA30)

Address:	Kalaikunda Air Force Base, Midnapur, West Bengal 721303.
Tel:	0322-232005
Admission:	By prior permission only.
Location:	About 15 km west of Kharagpur off road NH6.

The airfield was constructed during World War II and was re-activated in 1955. Since then Mystère IVs, Vampires, Hunters, Canberras, MiG-21s, Su-7s and currently MiG-27s have been flown by the resident squadrons. The last Hunters in the service were withdrawn from use by No. 2 Target Tug Flight in 2001. The museum was opened to commemorate the sixtieth anniversary of the base. The display includes many photographs and documents along with uniforms and trophies and badges. The aircraft collection is dispersed around the site. Three are by the museum buildings and the others are with squadrons, by the control tower, on the parade ground and by the main gate. India operated well over one hundred Antonov An-32s with the first arriving from the Kiev factory in July 1984. The type replaced the Fairchild C-119 with transport squadrons. The example with the museum was written off at the airfield after a heavy landing. The Otter was the only single engined transport operated by the Indian Air Force and was selected for its rugged construction and its ability to fly into unprepared airstrips. The example in the collection was flown by the de Havilland company in England.

TYPE	REG/SER	CON. NO.	PI/NOTES	STATUS
☐ Antonov An-32	K2688	0303		RA
☐ De Havilland D.H.C.3 Otter	'DJ32'	17	G-ANCM, IM1057	RAX
☐ Folland Fo.141 Gnat F.1	'DJ1992'			RAX
☐ Folland Fo.141 Gnat F.1	E232	GT.071		RA
☐ Hawker P.1099 Hunter F.56				RA
☐ Hawker P.1099 Hunter F.56			On gate.	PV
☐ Hawker P.1099 Hunter F.56 (F.6)	BA207		(XK163)	RA
☐ Hawker P.1099 Hunter F.56A (F.6)	A968	41H/688063	XJ646, G-9-275	RA
☐ Hindustan Ajeet [Folland Fo.141 Gnat 2]	E1956			RA
☐ Mikoyan-Gurevich MiG-25R				RA

DOON SCHOOL MEMORIAL (IDA31)

Address:	The Mall, Dehradun, Uttar Pradesh 248001.
Tel:	0135-2526400
Email:	hmdsco@sancharnet.in
Admission:	By prior permission only.
Location:	In the town.

The idea of the school was put forward in 1929 and it opened six years later in sixty nine acre grounds. The Ajeet serves as a memorial to former pupils who have lost their lives on military service.

TYPE	REG/SER	CON. NO.	PI/NOTES	STATUS
☐ Hindustan Ajeet [Folland Fo.141 Gnat 2]	IE1241			RA

EASTERN AIR COMMAND HEADQUARTERS MUSEUM (IDA32)

Address:	MES T/42, Cantonment, Shillong, Meghalaya 793001.
Tel:	0304-222-4300
Admission:	By prior permission only.
Location:	In the town.

The 1st Operational Group was set up in Calcutta in 1958. When tensions along the border with China increased the decision was made to move the unit to Shillong and rename it as Eastern Air Command. There are many important bases in this area and the museum traces their history and that of the command. A large new headquarters was built in the 1980s and the aircraft are displayed in the grounds,

TYPE	REG/SER	CON. NO.	PI/NOTES	STATUS
☐ De Havilland D.H.C.4 Caribou	BM772	137		RA
☐ Hindustan Ajeet [Folland Fo.141 Gnat 2]				RA
☐ Mikoyan-Gurevich MiG-21FL	C1106			RA
☐ Mil Mi-4	Z317			RA
☐ Panstwowe Zaklady Lotnicze (PZL) TS-11 Iskra 200bisD	W1784	3H 15-24		RA

FARIDABAD WAR MEMORIAL (IDA33)

Address:	Town Square, Fariadbad, Haryana 121004.
Admission:	On permanent view.
Location:	In the centre of the town.

The town has commemorated those who have lost their lives in the service of their country. Recent border conflicts are also remembered. The Hunter is the centrepiece of the memorial.

TYPE	REG/SER	CON. NO.	PI/NOTES	STATUS
☐ Hawker P.1099 Hunter F.56	BA219		(XK159)	PV

GARUDA NAVAL AIR STATION MUSEUM (IDA34)

Address:	Kochi, Kerala 682011.
Admission:	By prior permission only.
Location:	In the northern part of the town.

The Royal Air Force set up the airfield which opened in 1941. Soon a Royal Navy Aircraft Repair Yard was in residence. The Indian Navy took over the field in 1953 and it now houses both rotary and fixed wing types. A museum has been set up to trace the history of the airfield and its units with items of memorabilia and photographs.

TYPE	REG/SER	CON. NO.	PI/NOTES	STATUS
☐ Breguet 1050 Alizé	IN204	67	67 (France)	RA

GAUHATI AIR FORCE STATION MUSEUM (IDA35)

Address:	Post Borjhor, Gauhati, Assam 781015.
Admission:	By prior permission only.
Location:	About 15 km south west of the town off road NH37.

This airfield is now home to transport units operating a variety of types. For many years de Havilland Caribous were flown from the base. The only aircraft on show is the Hawker Hunter.

TYPE	REG/SER	CON. NO.	PI/NOTES	STATUS
☐ Hawker P.1099 Hunter F.56				RA

GOVERNMENT GLIDING CENTRE COLLECTION (IDA36)

Address:	Hadapsar, Pune, Maharastra 411028.
Admission:	Sunday-Thursday 0900-1800 – by appointment.
Location:	Just south of the town which is about 12 km east of Pune.

The airfield is located on a plateau with several ranges of hills nearby. A collection of types formerly used has been preserved in the hangars. These include several indigenous designs which were produced in some numbers for use by clubs around India. The ITG-3 is a modified Grunau Baby and considerable numbers were constructed in the 1960s. The prototype KS-I Kartik made its maiden flight in March 1963 and the KS-II followed two years later. The design is a high performance wooden sailplane with a monocoque fuselage. The HS-2 is a standard class design which first took to the air in April 1973 and the second prototype flew four years later. Hopefully a museum can be set up to display these interesting Indian designs.

TYPE	REG/SER	CON. NO.	PI/NOTES	STATUS
☐ Aeronautical Services ITG-3				RA
☐ Aeronautical Services ITG-3	VT-GAJ	AS-1024		RA
☐ Government Technical Centre HS-2 Mrigasheer	VT-GEG	TC-61		RA
☐ Government Technical Centre HS-2 Mrigasheer	VT-GEH	TC-62		RA
☐ Government Technical Centre KS-II Kartik	VT-GEF	TC-49		RA
☐ Kerestesi MG-1	VT-GMB	TG-301		RA
☐ Schleicher Ka-6 Rhönsegler	VT-GAQ	348		RA
☐ Slingsby T-21B	VT-GAN	638		RA

GOVERNMENT MUSEUM (IDA37)

Address:	Sam Road, Jaisalmer, Rajasthan 345001.
Admission:	Saturday-Thursday 1000-1630.
Location:	In the western suburbs of the town.

This museum was set up in 1984 and houses many fossils found in the local desert. There is also an excellent collection of wood samples from the many trees which grow in the area. The geological history of the region is highlighted in the informative displays. The Marut fighter is parked outside the building.

TYPE	REG/SER	CON. NO.	PI/NOTES	STATUS
☐ Hindustan HF-24 Marut 1	D1237			PV

GWALIOR AIR FORCE STATION MUSEUM (IDA38)

Address:	c/o P.O. Box 99, Post Borjhar, Guwahati, Madhya Pradesh 781017.
Tel:	0361-184-0978
Admission:	By prior permission only.
Location:	About 25 km south west of the town off road NH3.

This important airfield is one of the oldest Indian Air bases in the country. At the current time it is home to fighter squadrons flying the Dassault Mirage 2000 and the MiG-27. In addition there is a transport unit in residence. The small museum traces the history of the site. The informative display contains photographs, documents, trophies and models along with uniforms. The Su-7 is parked nearby.

TYPE	REG/SER	CON. NO.	PI/NOTES	STATUS
☐ Sukhoi Su-7BMK	B802			RA

HAKIMPET AIR FORCE STATION MUSEUM (IDA39)

Address:	FT21, Hasmathpet, Andhra Pradesh 500015.
Tel:	040-2779-3564
Admission:	By prior permission only.
Location:	North of Hyderabad near Shamirpet Lake

The airfield was built in the early days of World War II and the Indian Air Force took over the site in 1951. Initially it was home to a conversion and training unit. A Fighter Training Wing arrived later and operated the Iskra for a quarter of a century. Now HJT-16 Kirans are flown and there is also a helicopter training school on the field. A museum tracing the history of the airfield was opened in the summer of 2001. On show are display boards, models, photographs, documents and uniforms along with weapons and survival equipment.

TYPE	REG/SER	CON. NO.	PI/NOTES	STATUS
☐ De Havilland D.H.113 Vampire FB.52	'FTW1971'		IB1618	RAX
☐ Hindustan HSA.316B Chetak [Sud SA.316B Alouette III]				RA
☐ Panstwowe Zaklady Lotnicze (PZL) TS-11 Iskra 200bisC	W1746	2H 09-05	0905 (Poland), 905 (Poland)	RA
☐ Panstwowe Zaklady Lotnicze (PZL) TS-11 Iskra 200bisD	W1786	3H 16-01		RA
☐ Panstwowe Zaklady Lotnicze (PZL) TS-11 Iskra 200bisD	W1744	3H 19-07	1907 (Poland)	RA
☐ Panstwowe Zaklady Lotnicze (PZL) TS-11 Iskra 200bisD	W1748	3H 20-15	2015 (Poland)	RA

HALWARA AIR FORCE STATION WAR MEMORIAL (IDA40)

Address:	Halwara, Punjab 141001.
Tel:	0161-276523
Admission:	By prior permission only.
Location:	Just north of the town which is about 15 km south west of Ludhiana.

An impressive memorial honouring pilots and aircrew who have lost their lives in both peace and war. Obelisks, connected by pathways, give the names of the dead. These are surrounded by pleasant gardens, Behind these are two aircraft. Hunters flew many missions the 1965 war against Pakistan and the Sukhoi achieved some success in the 1971 conflict. India ordered considerable numbers of MiG-23s and one is preserved by the Officers' Mess. The resident squadrons currently operate the MiG-23 and MiG-27.

TYPE	REG/SER	CON. NO.	PI/NOTES	STATUS
☐ Hawker P.1099 Hunter F.56	BA233	41H/679912	XE537	RA
☐ Mikoyan-Gurevich MiG-23BN	SM276		By Officer's Mess.	RA
☐ Sukhoi Su-7BMK	B785			RA

HASIMARA AIR FORCE STATION MUSEUM (IDA41)

Address:	Hasimara, West Bengal 735215.
Admission:	By prior permission only.
Location:	About 6 km south of the town.

The airfield has been an important fighter base since the early 1960s. Three types which flew with resident squadrons over the years have been preserved. A small museum tracing the history of the field has been set up.

TYPE	REG/SER	CON. NO.	PI/NOTES	STATUS
☐ Dassault MD-450 Ouragan	'IC867'			RAX
☐ Folland Fo.141 Gnat F.1	E1046			
☐ Hawker P.1099 Hunter F.56				RA

HINDON AIR FORCE STATION MUSEUM (IDA42)

Address:	Hindon, Ghaziabad, Delhi 201004.
Tel:	0120-289-9401
Admission:	By prior permission only.
Location:	In the north eastern suburbs of the city.

Hindon was a fighter station for many years but these units moved out in the late 1990s and were replaced by transport and squadrons. Now only helicopters are flown. The museum opened in October 2002 and displays many items of memorabilia and photographs. Two aircraft are preserved on the base.

TYPE	REG/SER	CON. NO.	PI/NOTES	STATUS
☐ Mikoyan-Gurevich MiG-25R				RA
☐ Sukhoi Su-7BMK	'B747'			RAX

HINDUSTAN AEROSPACE HERITAGE CENTER AND AEROSPACE MUSEUM (IDA43)

Address:	Airport Service Road C, Bangalore, Karnataka 560037.
Tel:	080-2522-8341
Admission:	Tuesday-Sunday 0900-1700.
Location:	In the eastern suburbs of the city.

Hindustan Aircraft was established in in December 1940. The first type produced was the Harlow PC-5A and this was soon followed by the Curtiss Hawk 75A-5 and the Vultee V-12-D. The first original design was a nine-seat troop carrying glider which took to the air in August 1941. At the current time it has factories across the country with aircraft production facilities at Bangalore, Kanpur and Nasik. Over two thousand five hundred aircraft have been produced including many indigenous designs. Licence production of many types such as the de Havilland Vampire, Folland Gnat, Avro 748, Sepecat Jaguar and MiG-21 has ensured a steady supply of modern types to the services. The company has set up a Heritage Center close to its Bangalore Headquarters which traces the history of the company and its products. The display opened on August 30th 2001 in a building formerly used as a cinema. A mock-up control tower has been added and the visitor can view the airport and runway. In addition to the aircraft a range of models, photographs and components can be seen.

TYPE	REG/SER	CON. NO.	PI/NOTES	STATUS
☐ De Havilland D.H.104 Devon C.1	HW201	04074		PV
☐ English Electric EA.1 Canberra T.4	Q1793	EEP.71445	WT485	RA
☐ English Electric EA.1 Canberra B(I).58	BF597			PV
☐ Hindustan Advanced Light Helicopter (FSM)	'IN701'			PVX

TYPE	REG/SER	CON. NO.	PI/NOTES	STATUS
☐ Hindustan HT-2L (HT-2)	IX480	T.017		PV
☐ Hindustan HJT-16 Kiran II	U784			PV
☐ Hindustan HF-24 Marut 1T	D1695			PV
☐ Hindustan HUL-26 Pushpak	VT-DZF	PK143		PV
☐ Hindustan HA-31 Basant II	VT-ECV	HA-010		PV
☐ Hindustan HJT-36	S3446			RA
☐ Hindustan HJT-36 (FSM)				PV
☐ Hindustan HSA.316B Chetak [Sud SA.316B Alouette III]	Z1897			PV
☐ Hindustan Light Combat Aircraft (FSM)				PV
☐ Mikoyan-Gurevich MiG-21U-400	U2974			PV
☐ National Aerospace Laboratories Hansa II	VT-XIW			PV
☐ Westland-Sikorsky WS-61 Sea King 42A (42)	IN504	WA.736		PV

HINDUSTAN AEROSPACE PRAGATHI AEROSPACE MUSEUM (IDA44)

Address: Ojhar Township P.O.,
Nasik,
Maharastra 422201.
Tel: 02550-275333
Fax: 02550-275825
Email: haltx_nsh@sandharet.in
Admission: Sunday 1000-1400.
Location: About 10 km north of the town.

This factory has produced many combat aircraft in recent years. The company has opened a museum tracing the history of the site and and the types built. On show are photographs, documents, components, engines and models. The three aircraft, all constructed at the factory, are parked outside the building.

TYPE	REG/SER	CON. NO.	PI/NOTES	STATUS
☐ Mikoyan-Gurevich MiG-21bis C	C2836			PV
☐ Mikoyan-Gurevich MiG-21FL	C1175			PV
☐ Mikoyan-Gurevich MiG-27ML	TS539			PV

HINDUSTAN AEROSPACE WAR MEMORIAL PARK (IDA45)

Address: 151/1 Cubbon Road,
Bangalore,
Karnataka 560001.
Tel: 080-2286-6701
Fax: 080-2286-7533
Email: cmc@hal-india.com
Admission: On permanent view.
Location: In the centre of the city.

The company has set up a memorial to honour those who lost their lives in the service of India. In 1997 an Ajeet was mounted on a plinth and nearby is a memorial to those who died.

TYPE	REG/SER	CON. NO.	PI/NOTES	STATUS
☐ Hindustan Ajeet [Folland Fo.141 Gnat 2]	E1083			PV

HYDERABAD PUBLIC SCHOOL DISPLAY (IDA46)

Address: Begumpet,
Hyderabad,
Andhra Pradesh 500016.
Tel: 040-2776-1546
Fax: 040-2776-5613
Admission: By prior permission only.
Location: In the north eastern suburbs of the city off road NH9.

The school was founded in 1923 to educate the children of the Indian aristocracy and became one of the most prestigious public schools in the country. Many of its pupils have gone on to positions in government, the professions and the services. The Canadian built Chipmunk is preserved in the grounds.

TYPE	REG/SER	CON. NO.	PI/NOTES	STATUS
☐ De Havilland D.H.C.1 Chipmunk 1B				RA

Right: This Hindustan HT-2 is at the Indian Air Force Technical College on the outskirts of Bangalore (Via Jagan Pilarisetti)

Right: The Hindustan company has set up a museum at Bangalore and among the exhibits are this Basant and Pushpak. (Stephen Wolf)

Below: The National Aeronautical Laboratories Hansa has been put on show at the Hindustan company exhibition in Bangalore. (Stephen Wolf)

INDIAN AIR FORCE HEADQUARTERS DISPLAY (IDA47)

Address:	Vayu Bhawan, Delhi 110011.
Tel:	011-2301-0231
Fax:	011-2301-2870
Email:	webmaster@iaf.nic.in
Admission:	By prior permission only.
Location:	In the southern suburbs of the city.

India ordered twenty three Folland Gnats in the late 1950s and the type was built under licence in Bangalore in the 1960s. Over two hundred were constructed and gave excellent service for many years. An improved version, the Ajeet, was developed in India and eighty nine were built. The three aircraft are displayed outside the building and are mounted on poles in a simulated flying formation. The Hunter can be found in the grounds of an Army facility nearby. This site is close to the Hyatt Regency hotel.

TYPE	REG/SER	CON. NO.	PI/NOTES	STATUS
☐ Folland Fo.141 Gnat F.1	IE1205	GT.021		PV
☐ Folland Fo.141 Gnat F.1	IE1246	GT.062		PV
☐ Hawker P.1099 Hunter F.56A (F.6)	A1012	8956	N-274 (Netherlands), G-9-279 – in nearby Army complex.	PV
☐ Hindustan Ajeet [Folland Fo.141 Gnat 2]	E1975			PV
☐ Mikoyan-Gurevich MiG-21bis	C2284		At nearby Officer's Mess.	RA
☐ Mikoyan-Gurevich MiG-23BN	SM287		At nearby Officer's Mess.	RA

INDIAN AIR FORCE HISTORIC FLIGHT (IDA48)

Address:	Air Force Station Palam, Delhi 110010.
Admission:	By prior permission only.
Location:	At the IAF base which about 15 km south west of the city.

The flight is housed in the hangar next to the Air Force Museum. The Spitfire, built at Keevil in 1944, was shipped to India for R.A.F. use in early 1945 and transferred to the Indian Air Force on December 31st 1947. In 1967 it joined the Air Force Museum and in the early 1980s a decision was made to rebuilt it to flying condition for the 1982 Golden Jubilee of the I.A.F. The Spitfire is flown rarely, usually on the Annual Air Force Day. The Tiger Moth and Harvard also spent a long time on show in the museum before joining the flight. Many Indian pilots were trained on these types and both served with The I.A.F. for many years. The first Dakotas were acquired by the service in 1946 and between 1949 and 1951 Hindustan Aircraft converted over one hundred former U.S.A.A.F. C-47s which had been left at a depot in India. The type was the backbone of the transport fleet until the early 1970s. The HT-2 trainer made its maiden flight on August 5th 1951 and was the first indigenous type operated by the I.A.F. One hundred and sixty nine were built for civil and military use between 1952 and 1959. Hindustan Aircraft constructed almost three hundred single seat Vampires and sixty two seaters. In addition twenty nine Vampire night fighters were delivered from England in the early 1950s and served for ten years. The Gnat gave excellent service for many years and saw operational use in the conflicts with Pakistan. More types will possibly be added as they are withdrawn from active use.

TYPE	REG/SER	CON. NO.	PI/NOTES	STATUS
☐ Bell 47G			Reported on web site but may be incorrect.	RAA
☐ De Havilland D.H.82A Tiger Moth	HU512	85778	DE893, 2492 (South Africa), HU512, VT-DPK	RAA
☐ De Havilland D.H.113 Vampire FB.52	IB799			RAA
☐ Douglas DC-3A-467 Skytrain (C-47B)	IJ302		(USAAF)	RAA
☐ Folland Fo.141 Gnat F.1	E265			RAA
☐ Hindustan HT-2	IX732			RAA
☐ Noorduyn Harvard IIB [North American NA-77 (AT-16)]	HT291	14A-927	43-12628, FS787	RAA
☐ Supermarine 359 Spitfire LF.VIIIc	NH631	6S.326987		RAA

INDIAN AIR FORCE MUSEUM (IDA49)

Address:	Air Force Station Palam, Delhi 110010.
Tel:	011-2569-7551
Admission:	Wednesday-Sunday 1000-1700.
Location:	At the IAF base which is about 15 km south west of the city.

Located in a former Royal Air Force hangar, this excellent museum traces the history of military flying in India over eighty years. The R.A.F. based aircraft in the country from 1913 and the Royal Indian Air Force was formed in 1932. Displays in the entrance hall show the history of the R.A.F. in the sub-continent prior to independence in 1947 and the subsequent development of the I.A.F. A large number of photographs, models, memorabilia, uniforms, weapons, engines and components can be seen. The history of each squadron is also portrayed. The first aircraft used by the R.I.A.F. were four Westland Wapitis transferred from the R.A.F. One airframe was found in a derelict condition and restored to display condition; this is the only survivor of the type. A number of other British designs are also on show. Hurricanes were first supplied to the R.I.A.F. in the spring of 1942 and the one on show flew against the Japanese. Nearby is another classic Sydney Camm aircraft – the Tempest, over two hundred examples of which served with the I.A.F. from 1947. Also on show are two Hunters which were used operationally in conflicts with Pakistan. The Lysander was obtained in Canada and the Prentice was built under licence by Hindustan Aircraft. Parked outside is a Liberator which was flown until 1958 but is now lacking a nosewheel undercarriage leg. Aircraft from France, the Soviet Union and the U.S.A. can also be seen. Examples of the Dassault Ouragan and Mystère, which gave excellent service for many years, are in the hangar. Three indigenous designs produced by Hindustan Aircraft show the progress made by the Indian aviation industry. The high wing Krishak first flew in 1965 and over sixty were delivered for A.O.P. duties. The Indian Air Force has flown many Soviet types in recent years. Hindustan Aerospace have produced MiG fighters under licence and four of the classic Russian fighters can be seen. A fairly recent addition to the collection is one of three Tupolev Tu-124s acquired in 1966 for use as V.I.P. transport duties. The Antonov An-12 is another new arrival and the C-119 is normally parked behind the hangar. This area is not always open to visitors and also some of the collection is stored in the hangar used by the Historic Flight. Close to the Liberator are remains of Pakistani aircraft shot down in the numerous border conflicts which have flared up since partition. Plans have been approved for a purpose built complex on land nearby and work is expected to start in the near future. The building will include display halls, a library and archive and a cinema. The latest audio-visual techniques will also feature.

TYPE	REG/SER	CON. NO.	PI/NOTES	STATUS
☐ Antonov An-12A	BL727	2401205	L727	PV
☐ Consolidated 32 Liberator (B-24J) (B.VII)	HE924	1508	44-44213, KH342	PV
☐ Dassault MD-450 Ouragan	IC554	245	IC564 (?)	PV
☐ Dassault Mystère IVA	IA1329	401		PV
☐ De Havilland D.H.113 Vampire NF.54 (NF.10)	ID606	13085	WV690	PV
☐ De Havilland D.H.C.4 Caribou	BM774	146	Composite.	PV
☐ Douglas DC-3A-467 Skytrain (C-47B)	IJ817		(USAAF)	PV
☐ English Electric EA.1 Canberra B(I).58 (B(I).8)	IF907	EEP71548	XH237	PV
☐ Fairchild 110 Flying Boxcar (C-119G)	IK450	11262	53-4646	PV
☐ Folland Fo.141 Gnat F.1	IE1059	FL-7	(XK768), G-39-3	PV
☐ Folland Fo.141 Gnat F.1	IE1205	GT.021		RA
☐ Folland Fo.141 Gnat F.1	IE1246	GT.062		RA
☐ Hawker Hurricane IIB	'AB832'		V6846 (?), 'AP832'	PVX
☐ Hawker Tempest II	HA623		MW848	PV
☐ Hawker P.1099 Hunter F.56	BA263			PV
☐ Hawker P.1099 Hunter F.56 (F.6)	A941	41H/680011	XG186, G-9-237	PV
☐ Hawker P.1099 Hunter F.56A (F.6)	A467	8843	IF-85 (Belgium), G-9-139	PV
☐ Hindustan Ajeet [Folland Fo.141 Gnat 2]	IE1975			PV
☐ Hindustan Ajeet [Folland Fo.141 Gnat 2]	E2016			PV
☐ Hindustan HT-2	IX737			PV
☐ Hindustan HF-24 Marut 1	D1274			RA
☐ Hindustan HF-24 Marut 1	D1205			PV
☐ Hindustan HAOP-27 Krishak	N949		N943 (?)	RA
☐ Ilyushin Il-14	IL860			RA
☐ Indian Air Force Kanpur II				PV
☐ Lockheed 1049G-82-106 Super Constellation	BG583	1049G-4686	VT-DJW – at Agra.	–
☐ Martin 272B Canberra (B-57B)			(USAF) – in Pakistani markings	PVD
☐ Mikoyan-Gurevich MiG-21bis				RA
☐ Mikoyan-Gurevich MiG-21FL	C499			PV
☐ Mikoyan-Gurevich MiG-23MF	SK434			PV
☐ Mikoyan-Gurevich MiG-25R	KP355	20563		PV
☐ Mil Mi-4	BZ900			PV
☐ North American NA-176 Sabre (F-86F)	51-13386	176-317	In Pakistani markings.	PVD
☐ North American NA-191 Sabre (F-86F)	52-5248	191-944	In Pakistani markings – tail only.	PVD
☐ Panstwowe Zaklady Lotnicze (PZL) TS-11 Iskra 200bisD	W1758	3H 19-08	1908 (Poland)	PV
☐ Panstwowe Zaklady Lotnicze (PZL) TS-11 Iskra 200bisD	W1757	3H 19-16	1916 (Poland)	PV
☐ Percival P.40 Prentice T.1	'IV3368'		IV336	PVX
☐ Sikorsky S-55C	IZ1590	551077		PV
☐ Sukhoi Su-7BMK	B888			PV
☐ Sukhoi Su-7BMK	8909	7212	Rear fuselage only	PVD
☐ Supermarine 394 Spitfire F.XVIIIe	HS986	6S.699526	SM986	PV
☐ Tupolev Tu-124K	V644	6351903	(CCCP-45098)	PV
☐ Westland Wapiti IIA	'K813'		K163	PVX
☐ Westland Lysander III	'1589'		V9415, 1531 (Canada)	PVX
☐ Yokosuka MXY-7 Ohka 11				PV

INDIAN AIR FORCE TECHNICAL COLLEGE COLLECTION (IDA50)

Address:	Jalahalli West Road, Bangalore, Karnataka 560015.
Tel:	080-2372-3254
Admission:	By prior permission only.
Location:	In the western part of the town.

Set up as the Technical Training College in 1949, the institution became almost entirely an Air Force site in 1957. The first course passed out in 1951 and since then many students have been in residence. Aeronautical engineers specialising in a number of disciplines are trained to degree standard. The students work on a collection of airframes which can be seen by the public on the regular open days.

TYPE	REG/SER	CON. NO.	PI/NOTES	STATUS
☐ De Havilland D.H.100 Vampire F.3	HB546		VV211, VT-CXJ/HB546, 'T-27'	RA
☐ Folland Fo.141 Gnat F.1				RA
☐ Folland Fo.141 Gnat F.1	E323			RA
☐ Hindustan HT-2	IX472			RA
☐ Hindustan HT-2	IX502			RA
☐ Hindustan HT-2	IX506			RA
☐ Hindustan HPT-32 Deepak	'X2517'		X2542 – possible identity.	RAX
☐ Mikoyan-Gurevich MiG-21F-13	BC817		Possible identity.	RA
☐ Mikoyan-Gurevich MiG-21FL	C589			RA
☐ Mikoyan-Gurevich MiG-21FL	C590			RA
☐ Mikoyan-Gurevich MiG-23MF	SK440			RA
☐ Panstwowe Zaklady Lotnicze (PZL) TS-11 Iskra 200bisD	W1776	3H 15-16	1516 (Poland)	RA
☐ Panstwowe Zaklady Lotnicze (PZL) TS-11 Iskra 200bisD	W1767	3H 19-03	1903 (Poland)	RA
☐ Sud SA.316B Alouette III	Z406	1701		RA

JAISALMER WAR MEMORIAL (IDA51)

Address:	Jaisalmer Air Base, Jaisalmer, Rajasthan 345001.
Tel:	02992-252370
Admission:	By prior permission only.
Location:	About 5 km south west of the town.

This important base near the border with Pakistan was constructed in 1970 when tensions were high. A small detachment of Hunters moved in the following year and flew combat missions in the conflict. The preserved aircraft is located by the 'Victory Pillar' on the airfield. The exploits in the aerial battles are commemorated and the names of those who lost their lives can be seen. Currently in residence is a MiG-21bis unit.

TYPE	REG/SER	CON. NO.	PI/NOTES	STATUS
☐ Hawker P.1099 Hunter F.56 (F.6)	BA237	41H/679922	XE547	RA

JALAHALLI AIR FORCE STATION COLLECTION (IDA52)

Address:	14 Jalzhalli, Jalahalli, Karnataka 560000.
Tel:	080-2839-6746
Admission:	By prior permission only.
Location:	In the western part of Bangalore.

The Air Force Technical College is located close to this base. The two Iskras arrived in 2005. The aircraft are parked around the site with one of the HT-2s located by the main gate to the airfield.

TYPE	REG/SER	CON. NO.	PI/NOTES	STATUS
☐ Hindustan HT-2	IX492			RA
☐ Hindustan HT-2	IX712			RA
☐ Panstwowe Zaklady Lotnicze (PZL) TS-11 Iskra 200bisD	W1743	3H 14-18		RA
☐ Panstwowe Zaklady Lotnicze (PZL) TS-11 Iskra 200bisD	W1760	3H 20-14	2014 (Poland)	RA
☐ Sukhoi Su-7BMK	B811			RA
☐ Sukhoi Su-7BMK	B825			RA

JAMNAGAR AIR BASE MUSEUM (IDA53)

Address:	Jamnagar, Gujarat 361006.
Tel:	0288-271-1552
Admission:	By prior permission only.
Location:	About 5 km west of the town.

This important fighter base is home to No. 33 Wing which operates a variety of MiG fighters. One of the recently withdrawn MiG-23s is preserved. The small museum traces the history of the field.

TYPE	REG/SER	CON. NO.	PI/NOTES	STATUS
☐ Mikoyan-Gurevich MiG-23MF				RA

JARAWA NAVAL MUSEUM (IDA54)

Address:	Port Blair, Andaman Islands.
Admission:	By prior permission only.
Location:	About 3 km north of the town.

A Mitsubishi Zero on floats is reported to be at this military museum which is not normally open to the public. The islands were badly hit by the 2004 Tsunami but it is believed that the aircraft still exists.

TYPE	REG/SER	CON. NO.	PI/NOTES	STATUS
☐ Mitsubishi A6M2-N Zero Sen Model 21				RA

KANGLA FORT (IDA55)

Address:	Imphal, Manipur 795004.
Admission:	Daily.
Location:	In the centre of the town.

This historic fort was constructed in the early part of the seventeenth century and has been the site of many conflicts over the years. Substantial parts of the buildings still remain and a major programme of restoration is underway. An Ajeet is parked by the main gate.

TYPE	REG/SER	CON. NO.	PI/NOTES	STATUS
☐ Hindustan Ajeet [Folland Fo.141 Gnat 2]				PV

KANPUR AIR FORCE STATION MUSEUM (IDA56)

Address:	Nathu Singh Road, Cantonment 4, Kanpur, Uttar Pradesh 208001.
Tel:	0512-238-0529
Admission:	By prior permission only.
Location:	In the south eastern suburbs of the city off road NH91.

The nearby airfield was an important base in World War II and was from 1945 to 1966 the site of an unofficial museum. Some of the aircraft then moved to the new museum at Palam. The base now houses maintenance units and military schools. An example of the classic Hunter has been preserved.

TYPE	REG/SER	CON. NO.	PI/NOTES	STATUS
☐ Hawker P.1099 Hunter F.56	BA312A			RA

KARN MAHAL (IDA57)

Address:	Junagarh Fort, Bikaner, Rajasthan 334061.
Tel:	0151-2270840
Admission:	Saturday-Thursday 1000-1630.
Location:	In the north eastern part of the town centre.

Three dismantled D.H.9s were discovered in the basement of this museum in the late 1960s. The aircraft had been acquired by the local ruler in the 1920s and their engines were used to power water pumps in the area. Two have since been sold and will be restored in England. There are many displays tracing the history of the fort and the palaces within the complex. The military history of the area can also be traced.

TYPE	REG/SER	CON. NO.	PI/NOTES	STATUS
☐ De Havilland D.H.9				PV

KERALA STATE SCIENCE AND TECHNOLOGY MUSEUM (IDA58)

Address:	Vikasbhvan P.O., Thiruvananthapuran, Kerala 695033.
Tel:	0471-2306976
Fax:	0471-2304286
Admission:	Tuesday-Sunday 10001-700.
Location:	In the centre of the town.

Set up in 1984 this museum has galleries which concentrate on many aspects of engineering and science. In all areas there are many innovative displays. The history and development of computers also features.

TYPE	REG/SER	CON. NO.	PI/NOTES	STATUS
☐ Folland Fo.141 Gnat F.1				PV

KENDRIYA VIDHYALAYA JORHAT MEMORIAL (IDA59)

Address:	Air Force Station, Jorhat, Assam 785005.
Tel:	0376-231-1310
Email:	info@kvafsjorhat.org
Admission:	By prior permission only.
Location:	In the south western part of the town.

This military school is was established in 1966 and is located in a picturesque mountainous region. The pupils take part in many activities and the Mil Mi-4 is preserved as a memorial to those who have joined the services.

TYPE	REG/SER	CON. NO.	PI/NOTES	STATUS
☐ Hawker P.1101 Hunter T.66	BS488		In nearby park.	RA
☐ Mil Mi-4	Z331			RA

KURSURA MUSEUM / VICTORY AT SEA MEMORIAL (IDA60)

Address:	Ramakrishna Road, Vizag Andhra Pradesh 530016.
Admission:	Daily 1000-1600.
Location:	In the eastern part of the town on the coast.

A Sea Hawk is on show at this museum on the beach in Vizag. Also to be seen is a T-55 tank and other military items. The Navy flew over seventy Sea Hawks until the arrival of the Sea Harrier in the mid-1980s. Close by is the submarine 'Kursara' and there is also a town museum with some military items.

TYPE	REG/SER	CON. NO.	PI/NOTES	STATUS
☐ Hawker P.1040 Sea Hawk 101	IN240	6719	RB+375	PV

LAWRENCE SCHOOL MEMORIAL (IDA61)

Address:	Lovedale, Tamil Nadu 643003.
Tel:	0423-52552
Admission:	By prior permission only.
Location:	In the north western part of the town.

The school was established in September 1858 and named after Major General Henry Lawrence. Before the independence of India its pupils were mainly the children of serving or ex-members of the British Army. In 1949 it was taken over by the Indian Government as a state school. The Gnat is preserved in the grounds.

TYPE	REG/SER	CON. NO.	PI/NOTES	STATUS
☐ Folland Fo.141 Gnat F.1				RA

LEH AIR FORCE STATION MUSEUM (IDA62)

Address:	Leh, Jammu and Kashmir 194101.
Tel:	01982-260501
Admission:	By prior permission only.
Location:	About 8 km south west of the town.

This base, in a disputed region of the sub-continent, currently houses MiG-29 squadrons. A museum tracing the history of the base has been set up. Also personnel of 114 Helicopter Squadron have their own small display in two rooms on the base. The airfield also handles civil flights to the region.

TYPE	REG/SER	CON. NO.	PI/NOTES	STATUS
☐ Hawker P.1099 Hunter F.56	BA317			RA

LOHEGAON AIR FORCE STATION MUSEUM (IDA63)

Address:	AFIS 120, Lohegaon, Pune, Maharastra 411032.
Tel:	020-2669-5258
Admission:	By prior permission only.
Location:	About 12 km north east of the city.

The site is one of the oldest Indian Air Force bases. Over the years it has housed squadrons operating Vampires, Super Constellations, Canberras and MiG-21s. A number of the Liberators flown to museums around the world in the early 1970s took off from here. A small display tracing the history of the base and its units is housed in one of the buildings. Photographs, documents and uniforms can be seen.

TYPE	REG/SER	CON. NO.	PI/NOTES	STATUS
☐ English Electric EA.1 Canberra T.4	IQ994		XK647	RA
☐ English Electric EA.1 Canberra B(I).58 (B(I).8)	'F910'	EEP.71588	XH240, IF910	RAX
☐ Mikoyan-Gurevich MiG-21bis	C2098			RA
☐ Mikoyan-Gurevich MiG-27	SK425			RA
☐ Mikoyan-Gurevich MiG-29	KB741			RA

LUCKNOW CITY MUSEUM (IDA64)

Address:	Banarsibagh, Lucknow, Uttar Pradesh 226001.
Tel:	0522-220-6158
Admission:	Tuesday-Sunday 1000-1630.
Location:	On the eastern outskirts of the city

The displays at this museum, located close to Lucknow Zoo, trace the history and culture of the city and the surrounding area with many interesting displays. The Tupolev Tu-124 is the only aircraft on show.

TYPE	REG/SER	CON. NO.	PI/NOTES	STATUS
☐ Tupolev Tu-124K	V642	6351901		PV

MAHARAJA KHEWALJI TRUST (IDA65)

Address:	Faridkot, Punjab 151203.
Admission:	By prior permission only.
Location:	In the town.

The late Maharaja had a collection of vintage cars and armoured vehicles. Before he died he set up a trust. Three derelict aircraft were later discovered in one of his buildings. None have been identified.

TYPE	REG/SER	CON. NO.	PI/NOTES	STATUS
☐ Fairchild 24W41A Forwarder (C-61A) (UC-61A) (Argus III)				RAD
☐ Percival P.44 Proctor 5				RAD
☐ Stinson V-76 Sentinel (L-5G)				RAD

MAINTENANCE COMMAND HEADQUARTERS DISPLAY (IDA66)

Address:	Vayusena Nagar, Nagpur, Maharastra 440007.
Tel:	071-2251-2601
Admission:	By prior permission only.
Location:	About 6 km north east of the city off road NH7.

Kanpur was an important overhaul and repair base before independence. Maintenance Command was set up in January 1945 to co-ordinate this work at all sites across the country. A move was made to Nagpur in the mid-1960s where a new building had been constructed. The museum highlights the history of the command.

TYPE	REG/SER	CON. NO.	PI/NOTES	STATUS
☐ Breguet / British Aircraft Corporation Jaguar S				RA
☐ Folland Fo.141 Gnat F.1	E261			RA
☐ Mikoyan-Gurevich MiG-23BN	SM262			RA
☐ Mikoyan-Gurevich MiG-29	KB3298			RA

MARITIME HERITAGE MUSEUM (IDA67)

Address:	INS Dronacharya, Fort Kochi, Cochin, Kerala 682001.
Tel:	0484-228341
Admission:	Daily 0930-1300 1400-1800.
Location:	In the northern part of the city.

The displays at this informative museum highlight many aspects of the maritime history of the country. The development of the Indian Navy from the seventeenth century up to modern times is portrayed. On show are documents, models, uniforms and photographs. A sound and light show can be seen. The work of the modern navy in peace and war are both featured. The conflicts with Pakistan and the liberation of Goa are traced. India has a long tradition of ship construction and a fascinating display of models shows this aspect of Indian life.

TYPE	REG/SER	CON. NO.	PI/NOTES	STATUS
☐ Westland-Sikorsky WS-61 Sea King 42	IN502	WA.734		PV

MARTYR'S MEMORIAL (IDA68)

Address:	Dharamsala, Haryana 176200.
Admission:	Daily 0800-2000.
Location:	About 3 km south west of the town.

On show at this memorial to the local war dead is one of the original batch of Gnats supplied to India in the late 1950s. The aircraft is painted in the colours of No. 2 Squadron which was originally formed at Peshawar in 1939. Also in the pleasant wooded park are a tank and some items of artillery.

TYPE	REG/SER	CON. NO.	PI/NOTES	STATUS
☐ Folland Fo.141 Gnat F.1	IE1062	FL-10		PV

MAYO COLLEGE MEMORIAL (IDA69)

Address:	Srinagar Road, Ajmer, Rajasthan 305008.
Tel:	0145-266-1697
Admission:	By prior permission only.
Location:	Just north of the town.

The school was founded in 1875 and named after the Earl of Mayo who was Viceroy of India between 1869 and 1872. An impressive building beneath the Aravali Hill Range dominates the local area. Many pupils have gone on to serve with Indian military forces. A Folland Gnat has been preserved to remember these ex-students.

TYPE	REG/SER	CON. NO.	PI/NOTES	STATUS
☐ Folland Fo.141 Gnat F.1	E1059			RA

MILITARY COLLEGE OF ELECTRICAL AND MECHANICAL ENGINEERING (IDA70)

Address:	Secunderabad, Hyderabad, Andhra Pradesh 500015.
Tel:	040-862551
Admission:	By prior permission only.
Location:	In the northern part of the town.

Three aircraft are displayed at this college. The Ajeet is mounted outside the main building. The Chetak, a licence built Alouette III, and one built in France are also on show. Approximately two hundred and eighty were constructed in India. One sectioned airframe is on pedestals near the main gate and the other is also used for instruction. The college trains students in many trades so that they can serve in all the services.

TYPE	REG/SER	CON. NO.	PI/NOTES	STATUS
☐ Hindustan Ajeet [Folland Fo.141 Gnat 2]	E1979			RA
☐ Hindustan HSA.316B Chetak [Sud SA.316B Alouette III]	Z968			RA
☐ Sud SA.316B Alouette III	Z396	1689		RA

MODERN SCHOOL MEMORIAL (IDA71)

Address:	Barakhamba Road, Connaught Palce, New Delhi 110011.
Tel:	011-2311-1610
Email:	reception@modernschool.net
Admission:	By prior permission only.
Location:	In the northern part of the city centre.

The school was founded in 1920 with the aim of educating pupils in academic, cultural and sporting subjects. The Hunter which initially flew in India with No. 27 Squadron at Ambala has been preserved as a memorial. The aircraft was stored in England before returning to the manufacturers for conversion for Indian use.

TYPE	REG/SER	CON. NO.	PI/NOTES	STATUS
☐ Hawker P.1099 Hunter F.56 (F.6)	BA241	S 4U 3340	XF463	RA

NAGDA MUSEUM (IDA72)

Address:	Nagda, Madhya Pradesh 456331
Admission:	By prior permission only
Location:	Just east of the town.

The last DC-3 owned by the Birla Group is currently parked at the local airfield. Reports that it would move to the town museum have been seen but this has not occurred and the aircraft is now in poor condition. The aircraft was operated by the Americans at Karachi and it was then purchased by Tata and Sons. The C-47 then flew with a number of airlines in India before being withdrawn in the mid-1990s. Many historic buildings can be seen in Nagda and the local museum has an exhibition tracing the development of the area.

TYPE	REG/SER	CON. NO.	PI/NOTES	STATUS
☐ Douglas DC-3A-456 Skytrain (C-47A)	VT-AUM	18905	42-100442	PV

NAPIER MUSEUM (IDA73)

Address:	Trivandrum, Kerala 695033.
Admission:	Tuesday, Thursday-Sunday 1000-1645; Monday-Wednesday 1300-1645.
Location:	In the centre of the city.

The original museum opened in 1855 but twenty years later the building was demolished and the collection moved to a purpose built complex. The collection is named after Lord Napier, who was Govenor of Madras for a period. Parked nearby is the Sea Hawk which is believed to be part of the exhibition.

TYPE	REG/SER	CON. NO.	PI/NOTES	STATUS
☐ Hawker P.1040 Sea Hawk FB.5	IN174		(Great Britain)	PV

NATIONAL DEFENCE ACADEMY (IDA74)

Address:	Khadakwasla, Pune, Maharastra 411023.
Tel:	094-2300-3898
Email:	comdt@nda.pune.org
Admission:	By prior permission only.
Location:	In the south western part of the city.

The decision to set up the academy was made soon after India gained its independence. The foundation stone was laid by Prime Minister Nehru in October 1949 and basic training soon commenced. The college was fully operational by 1955. Officers from all branches of the services train at the Academy. The collection of preserved aircraft are located in the grounds of the impressive domed building. Military vehicles, including some captured Pakistani tanks, can also be seen. The Sea Hawk is displayed with folded wings.

TYPE	REG/SER	CON. NO.	PI/NOTES	STATUS
☐ Dassault MD-450 Ouragan	IC585			RA
☐ Dassault Mystère IVA	IA1022	347		RA
☐ English Electric EA.1 Canberra B(I).58 (B(I).8)	IF906	EEP.71493	WT338	RA
☐ Folland Fo.141 Gnat F.1	E247			RA
☐ Hawker P.1040 Sea Hawk 101				RA
☐ Mikoyan-Gurevich MiG-21FL				RA
☐ Mikoyan-Gurevich MiG-25R	KP351			RA

NATIONAL CADET CORPS HEADQUARTERS DISPLAY (IDA75)

Address:	Old Sectt, New Delhi 110054.
Tel:	011-2389-0146
Email:	dirnccdel@hub.nic.in
Admission:	On permanent view.
Location:	In the centre of the city.

The National Cadet Corps was formed in 1948 and was the successor to the University Officer Training Units set up by the British. The headquarters are in Delhi and there are units around the country. Mounted outside the building is a Hunter. The aircraft was built by Fokker in the Netherlands in the late 1950s. Hawker-Siddeley Aviation bought the fighter in 1968 and converted it to FGA.9 standards for Indian use.

TYPE	REG/SER	CON. NO.	PI/NOTES	STATUS
☐ Hawker P.1099 Hunter F.56A (F.6)	A1012		N-274 (Netherlands),G-9-279	PV

NAVAL AVIATION MUSEUM (IDA76)

Address:	Bogmalo Road, Dabolim, Goa 403801
Tel:	0832- 510183 ext.5525
Admission:	Tuesday-Sunday 1000-1600.
Location:	About 6 km south east of Vasco da Gama.

The Naval Air Arm was formed as a separate entity in 1961 and currently has two shore bases at Cochin and Dabolim. The first aircraft to join the new service were Sea Hawks and Alizés. More than seventy Sea Hawks were delivered from both England and Germany and served for over twenty years. The Navy ordered the Sea Harrier in the 1980s to replace the Sea Hawk. Both single- and two-seat versions of the VTOL aircraft were flown. Five ex-Air Force Super Constellations were used in the maritime patrol role and the one that dominates the aircraft park was first used by Air India. Very few Sealands survive and the Navy operated ten examples of the amphibian. The first was flown from Rochester to Cochin in January 1953. Five ex Royal Navy Firefly FR.1s were converted at Hamble for target towing duties. Sadly none of these survived and a replica has been built. Hopefully more aircraft will be added to the display when they are withdrawn. A number of interesting types are still in use and examples of these would greatly enhance the collection. The museum opened in October 1998 and presents a fascinating picture of the service. The indoor displays include photographs, models, components, uniforms and engines. The history of all squadrons is portrayed along with the aircraft they flew. There are large scale replicas of the carriers 'Vikrant' and Viraat'. There is an excellent display of weapons carried by naval aircraft. These include torpedoes, cannons bombs and sensors.

TYPE	REG/SER	CON. NO.	PI/NOTES	STATUS
☐ Breguet 1050 Alizé	IN202	63	63 (France)	PV
☐ De Havilland D.H.104 Dove 6	IN124			PV
☐ De Havilland D.H.115 Vampire T.55	IN149			PV
☐ Fairey Firefly TT.1 (FSM)	'INS112'			PVX

TYPE	REG/SER	CON. NO.	PI/NOTES	STATUS
□ Hawker P.1040 Sea Hawk 101	IN234	6666	VA+233	PV
□ Hawker-Siddeley P.1184 Sea Harrier FRS.51	IN621	B15	ZH239	PV
□ Hindustan HSA.316B Chetak [Sud SA.316B Alouette III]	IN475	AH290		PV
□ Hindustan HT-2	BX748			PV
□ Hughes 269B	IN083			PV
□ Lockheed 1049G-02-82 Super Constellation (1049E-55-87) (1049E-55-106)	IN315	1049E-4614	VT-DHM, BG575 (India)	PV
□ Short SA.6 Sealand 1	IN106	SH.1763		PV
□ Westland-Sikorsky WS-61 Sea King 42	IN505	WA.737		PV

NEHRU SCIENCE CENTRE (IDA77)

Address: Dr. E. Moses Road,
Worli,
Mumbai 400018.
Tel: 022-2492-0482
Fax: 022-2493-2668
Email: nscm@mtnl.net.in
Admission: Tuesday-Sunday 1100-1700.
Location: In the southern part of the city.

The exhibits at this museum include a number of 'hands-on' displays showing the latest developments in science and technology. An Aerospace Hall was constructed a few years ago. The Marut in the collection was the second prototype and is the oldest in existence. A Tiger Moth and a Shadow ultralight can also be seen. The Royal Air Force used large numbers of Tiger Moths in India before, during and after World War II. When the British left many airframes were abandoned at former Care and Maintenance Units. The Indian Air Force sent many of these to the Hindustan factory at Bangalore and almost one hundred were reconditioned. The biplane served with the Air Force Auxiliary squadrons until 1957. Many of the survivors were then passed on to civilian flying clubs. The displays trace the development of aeronautical science and a large model of the Wright Flyer can be seen along with components, engines, instruments and photographs.

TYPE	REG/SER	CON. NO.	PI/NOTES	STATUS
□ Cook Flying Machines Shadow BD	VT-UME	083		PV
□ De Havilland D.H.82A Tiger Moth				RA
□ Hindustan HF-24 Marut 1	BR463	HF.002		PV

NEHRU TECHNOLOGY MUSEUM (IDA78)

Address: Hijli Shaheed Building,
Indian Institute of Technology,
Kharagpur,
West Bengal 721302.
Tel: 032-2225-5221
Fax: 032-2225-5303
Admission: Tuesday-Sunday 1000-1700.
Location: In the town.

This museum is housed in the former Hijli Detention Centre. The building was constructed by the British in the 1930s to imprison local freedom fighters. On show are exhibitions tracing all aspects of technology with particular emphasis on local industries. Many working pieces of machinery are on show. The Hunter, which was transported from Kalaikunda Air Force Base, is on show outside the building.

TYPE	REG/SER	CON. NO.	PI/NOTES	STATUS
□ Hawker P.1099 Hunter F.56	BA335			PV

NIRMAL JIT SINGH SEKHON MEMORIAL (IDA79)

Address: Sekhon Chowk,
Ludhiana,
Punjab.
Admission: On permanent view.
Location: In the town.

Flying Officer Nirmal Sekhon was posthumously awarded India's highest military honour, the Param Vir Chakra, in December 1971. He lost his life in defending Srinigar Air Base when it was attacked by Pakistani Air Force Sabres. Flying alone in a Folland Gnat he fought off the Sabres but was killed when his aircraft crashed. He was born in the Ludhiana district and a memorial to his exploits has been erected outside the District Collectors Office. This consists of a statue on a plinth and an example of the Gnat in pleasant gardens.

TYPE	REG/SER	CON. NO.	PI/NOTES	STATUS
□ Folland Fo.141 Gnat F.1				PV

The sole remaining Westland Wapiti can be seen at the Indian Air Force Museum. (Via Jagan Pilarisetti)

Above: This de Havilland D.H.9 is exhibited in the Karn Mahal.

Left: The carrier Vikrant is now a museum in Mumbai. Several aircraft can be seen on the deck including this Westland Sea King and Breguet Alizé.

No. 9 AIRMEN SELECTION CENTRE MEMORIAL (IDA80)

Address:	Near Aerodrome Gate, Bhubaneshwar, Orissa 751020.
Tel:	0674-591736
Admission:	On permanent view.
Location:	In the south western suburbs of the town.

The Air Force has Selection Centres at many sites around the country where applicants undergo medical and aptitude tests. A Folland Gnat has been put on display as a memorial.

TYPE	REG/SER	CON. NO.	PI/NOTES	STATUS
☐ Folland Fo.141 Gnat F.1	IE1071	FL-30	IE1071, G-45-3	RA

OZHAR AIR FORCE STATION MUSEUM (IDA81)

Address:	Dindon Road, Nasik, Maharastra 422004.
Tel:	0253-253-4878
Admission:	By prior permission only.
Location:	About 10 km north of the town.

The airfield is home to a major overhaul depot which works on MiG-21s, MiG-23s, MiG-27s and MiG-29s. Hindustan Aeronautics has a factory on the site with its own museum. Five fighters have been preserved at the base which has a small exhibition in a building tracing its history and the work carried out. In recent years India has been a major operator of Soviet designed aircraft and the majority have been constructed in the country.

TYPE	REG/SER	CON. NO.	PI/NOTES	STATUS
☐ Dassault MD-450 Ouragan	'IC867'		IC667 (?)	RAX
☐ Mikoyan-Gurevich MiG-21FL	C585			RA
☐ Mikoyan-Gurevich MiG-23MF	SK408			RA
☐ Mikoyan-Gurevich MiG-29	KB732			RA
☐ Sukhoi Su-7U	U877			RA

PERIYAR TECHNOLOGY CENTER (IDA82)

Address:	Gandhi Mandapam Road, Chennai, Tamil Nadu 600025.
Tel:	044-2441-6751
Fax:	044-2440-2893
Admission:	Tuesday-Saturday 1000-1745.
Location:	In the southern part of the city.

Work on the centre started in 1983 and there are now exhibition halls covering many aspects of science and technology. The exhibition is named after a well known Tamil social reformer who saw the importance of science in improving the lives of the people. One area deals with transport and communications. A modern planetarium is among the highlights. Another area is designed to interest children in scientific topics.

TYPE	REG/SER	CON. NO.	PI/NOTES	STATUS
☐ Hindustan HT-2	IX741			PV
☐ Hindustan HF-24 Marut 1T	BD888			PV

PRAGATHI MAIDAN DEFENCE EXHIBITION (IDA83)

Address:	Pragathi Maidan, New Delhi 110001.
Admission:	Daily 1000-1700.
Location:	In the eastern part of the city.

This major exhibition centre was opened in 1982 to coincide with the Asian Games. The site has eighteen halls and twenty two pavilions. There are a number of permanent exhibitions and trade fairs are held regularly. The Defence Exhibition highlights the progress India has made in producing military hardware.

TYPE	REG/SER	CON. NO.	PI/NOTES	STATUS
☐ Folland Fo.141 Gnat F.1	E254			PV
☐ Mikoyan-Gurevich MiG-21FL	C1168			PV

PUSHPA GUJRAL SCIENCE CITY (IDA84)

Address:	SCO 60-61 Kapurthala, Chandigarh, West Bengal 160022.
Tel:	0172-260183
Email:	dg@pgsciencecity.org
Admission:	Daily 0900-1700.
Location:	In the western suburbs of the city.

Work on this large complex started in October 1997 when the foundation stone was laid. The first stage of the exhibition on the large landscaped site opened in March 2005. There is a major section devoted to the use and conservation of energy. A planetarium has also been constructed. The development of the extensive Indian railway network is highlighted. A flight simulator is in one of the buildings.

TYPE	REG/SER	CON. NO.	PI/NOTES	STATUS
☐ Mikoyan-Gurevich MiG-23MF				PV

RAJALI NAVAL AIR STATION MUSEUM (IDA85)

Address:	Arakkonam, Tamil Nadu.
Admission:	By prior permission only.
Location:	About 5 km sourh east of the town.

The base opened on March 11th 1992 and is home to helicopter training units. Maritime patrol aircraft also fly from the long runway. A display of memorabilia is located in one of the buildings. There are photographs, models and documents on view along with details of the aircraft which have flown from the field.

TYPE	REG/SER	CON. NO.	PI/NOTES	STATUS
☐ Breguet 1050 Alizé	IN201	62	62 (France)	RA

RASHTRIYA INDIAN MILITARY COLLEGE MEMORIAL (IDA86)

Address:	Dehradun, Uttar Pradesh 248008.
Tel:	0135-275-2083
Email:	info@rimc.org
Admission;	By prior permission only.
Location:	In the town.

Set up in 1923 as the Prince of Wales Military College this institution has trained many students over the years. Several have subsequently lost their lives in the service of their country. The buildings occupy a magnificent one hundred and thirty acre site on the edge of the town and have landscaped gardens. The Hunter serves as a memorial to them. Built in at Kingston specifically for India, the aircraft was delivered by the well known test pilot David Lockspeiser in November 1960 and was one of the last of the batch of one hundred and sixty.

TYPE	REG/SER	CON. NO.	PI/NOTES	STATUS
☐ Hawker P.1099 Hunter F.56	BA357			RA

SAINIK SCHOOL AMARVATHINAGAR MEMORIAL (IDA87)

Address:	Udumalpet Taluk, Amaravathinagar, Tamil Nadu 642102.
Tel:	04252-256296
Admission:	By prior permission only.
Location:	In the town.

Sainik Schools have been set up in every Indian State with the aim of training students for the National Defence Academy. This one in Tamil Nadu was established in 1962 and has the Texan as a memorial.

TYPE	REG/SER	CON. NO.	PI/NOTES	STATUS
☐ North American NA-88 Texan (AT-6C)				RA

SAINIK SCHOOL BIJAPUR MEMORIAL (IDA88)

Address:	Bijapur, Karnatka 586102.
Tel:	08352-270638
Email:	ssbj@sainikschoolbijapur.org
Admission:	By prior permission only.
Location:	In the centre of the town.

This school was the thirteenth to be set up in the Sainik system and opened in temporary premises in 1963. The foundation stone was laid by the late Indira Gandhi. A move to the new site took place in 1966.

TYPE	REG/SER	CON. NO.	PI/NOTES	STATUS
☐ North American NA-88 Texan (AT-6C)				RA

SAINIK SCHOOL KAZHAKOOTAM DISPLAY (IDA89)

Address:	Sainik School PO, Kazhakootam, Trivandrum 695585.
Tel:	0471-241-8245
Email:	pplesa@sainikschooltvm.org
Admission:	By prior permission only.
Location:	About 20 km north of the city.

This school was formed in barracks in Pagode in 1961 and three years later moved to a new complex. Two aircraft and a number of military vehicles are parked in the grounds to serve as memorials.

TYPE	REG/SER	CON. NO.	PI/NOTES	STATUS
☐ Hindustan HF-24 Marut 1	D1227			PV
☐ North American NA-88 Texan (AT-6C)				RA

SAINIK SCHOOL KORUKONDA MEMORIAL (IDA90)

Address:	Korukonda, Vizianagaram, Andhra Pradesh 531214.
Tel:	08922-46128.
Admission:	By prior permission only.
Location:	In the town.

The Sainik School in the state of Andhra Pradesh was established in 1961 and has trained many students over the years. Two training aircraft are preserved as memorials in the landscaped grounds. The Hindustan HT-2 was the first indigenous design to serve with the Indian Air Force. The prototype made its maiden flight in August 1951. One hundred and sixty nine were completed for both military and civil use and small numbers were exported. Students at the Air Force Academy carried out primary training on the type.

TYPE	REG/SER	CON. NO.	PI/NOTES	STATUS
☐ Hindustan HT-2				RA
☐ North American NA-88 Texan (AT-6C)				RA

SAINIK SCHOOL MOARI MEMORIAL (IDA91)

Address:	Moari, Assam.
Admission:	By prior permission only.
Location:	In the town.

The Indian Air Force received many Harvards/Texans and were mainly used for advanced pilot training. A few were fitted with guns and bomb racks and took part in counter insurgency work.

TYPE	REG/SER	CON. NO.	PI/NOTES	STATUS
☐ North American NA-88 Texan (AT-6C)				

SAINIK SCHOOL SAROJINAGAR DISPLAY (IDA92)

Address: Sarojinagar,
Uttar Pradesh 226008.
Tel: 0522-243-9155
Admission: By prior permission only.
Location: In the town.

This school was set up in 1960 and soon moved to purpose built premises at Sarojinagar. The Indian Air Force operated over seventy Ouragan fighters and an example is preserved in the grounds as a monument.

TYPE	REG/SER	CON. NO.	PI/NOTES	STATUS
☐ Dassault MD-450 Ouragan	IC567			RA

SHRI SHIVAJI PREPARATORY MILITARY SCHOOL DISPLAY (IDA93)

Address: Kennedi Road,
Pune,
411001.
Admission: By prior permission only.
Location: IKn the city.

The school was set up in 1932 to train young students for future military service. Many have gone on to serve India and a Canberra has been preserved in the grounds as a memorial to those who have died.

TYPE	REG/SER	CON. NO.	PI/NOTES	STATUS
☐ English Electric EA.1 Canberra B(I).58 (B(I).8)	IF908		XH238	RA

SOUTH WESTERN AIR COMMAND HEADQUARTERS DISPLAY (IDA94)

Address: Sector 9 Gandhinagar,
Gujarat 382020.
Tel: 079-2686-8006
Admission: By prior permission only.
Location: In the town.

Established as No. 1 Operational Group in Jodhpur in September 1972, the command took up its present title in 1980. A move to a new complex in Gandhinagar was made in 1988. Now more than twelve airfields are under its control. A display of fighter aircraft can be seen in the grounds of the headquarters.

TYPE	REG/SER	CON. NO.	PI/NOTES	STATUS
☐ Hawker P.1099 Hunter F.56A (F.6)	A492	8780	IF-36 (Belgium), G-9-141	RA
☐ Hindustan HF-24 Marut 1				RA
☐ Mikoyan-Gurevich MiG-23BN			.	PV
☐ Mikoyan-Gurevich MiG-23MF	SK412		At nearby roundabout	RA

SOUTH WESTERN AIR COMMAND HERITAGE MUSEUM (IDA95)

Address: Air Force Station,
Jodhpur,
Rajasthan 342005.
Tel: 0291-263-6168
Admission: By prior permission only.
Location: In the south eastern part of the city.

This museum opened in September 2001 in the former Command House. The South Western Air Command moved to Gandhinagar on May 1st 1998 and the building became vacant. The history of aviation in Jodhpur from 1931 to the present day is portrayed in the displays. There are five main sections – Bygone Era, Present Era, Aviation Era, 1971 Era and Gandhinagar Era. An aero club was formed in the city in 1931 and this led to the setting up of the Air Force Station which trained many pilots up to 1965. The story of aviation in the area from the Tiger Moth up to the Sukhoi Su-30 is told in detail. Momentos of the combat squadrons based in the region can be seen along with photographs, weapons and flying equipment. On the verandah is a collage of unservicable aircraft parts. The Marut and Sukhoi are parked by the entrance along with a Russian missile system. The HT-2 can be seen on the rear lawn. The recently withdrawn MiG-25 is a fairly new arrival at the museum. Another Marut is by the gate of the Air Force Station. This base now houses combat units operating MiG-23s and MiG-27s. In addition helicopter squadrons fly Mil Mi-8s and Mi-17s along with Chetaks.

TYPE	REG/SER	CON. NO.	PI/NOTES	STATUS
☐ Hindustan HT-2				RA
☐ Hindustan HF-24 Marut 1				RA
☐ Hindustan HF-24 Marut 1	D1198			RA
☐ Mikoyan-Gurevich MiG-25R				RA
☐ Mikoyan-Gurevich MiG-27				RA
☐ Sukhoi Su-7BKL				RA

SOUTHERN AIR COMMAND HEADQUARTERS MUSEUM (IDA96)

Address:	Akkulam, Trivandrum, Kerala 695011.
Tel:	0471-244-1498
Email:	pubri@edata.in
Admission:	By prior permission only.
Location:	In the northern part of Trivandrum.

The command was set up in the mid-1980s to cover the increased tension in the Indian Ocean and the political problems in Sri Lanka. A purpose built complex was soon built in the picturesque area of Akkulam. A small display in the buildings traces the history of the organisation. The Gnat is parked outside.

TYPE	REG/SER	CON. NO.	PI/NOTES	STATUS
☐ Folland Fo.141 Gnat F.1				RA

ST. GEORGE'S COLLEGE MEMORIAL (IDA97)

Address:	Barlowgani, Mussoorie, Uttaranchal 248122.
Tel:	0135-263-2591
Email:	contact@st_georges.info
Admission:	By prior permission only.
Location:	Just south of the town.

The school was established in 1853 and is housed in impressive buildings. An Iskra has been put on show to honour those who have served and lost their lives with the Indian Armed Forces.

TYPE	REG/SER	CON. NO.	PI/NOTES	STATUS
☐ Panstwowe Zaklady Lotnicze (PZL) TS-11 Iskra 200bisD	W1792	3H 15-12	W1772	RA

ST. JOSEPH'S ACADEMY MEMORIAL (IDA98)

Address:	10 Rajpur Road, Dehradun, Uttaranchal 248001.
Tel:	0135-271-2071
Admission:	By prior permission only.
Location:	In the north eastern part of the town.

This school was founded in 1932 and many former students have served with the military. On show as a memorial is a Fokker built Hunter which was converted to a two seater in England before delivery to India.

TYPE	REG/SER	CON. NO.	PI/NOTES	STATUS
☐ Hawker P.1101 Hunter T.66D (P.1099 Hunter F.6)	S580	8839	N-218 (Netherlands), G-9-184	RA

ST. MARY'S SCHOOL MEMORIAL (IDA99)

Address:	5-B General Bhagat Marge, Pune, Maharastra 411001.
Tel:	020-2635-6282
Email:	st_sms@dataone.in
Admission:	By prior permission only.
Location:	In the south eastern part of the town.

The school was established in 1866 and is one of the oldest in the country. On show in the grounds is a Hindustan Ajeet. This small jet fighter was developed from the Folland Gnat.

TYPE	REG/SER	CON. NO.	PI/NOTES	STATUS
☐ Hindustan Ajeet [Folland Fo.141 Gnat 2]	'E1972'		E1973	RAx

TAMBARAM AIR FORCE STATION MUSEUM (IDA100)

Address:	Tambaram, Chennai, Tamil Nadu 600046
Tel:	044-237-5556
Admission:	By prior permission only.
Location:	Just south of the town off Road NH45.

The airfield was built for use by the Royal Air Force and then transferred for Indian use. The airfield is home to the Flying Instructors School which currently uses the HPT-32 Deepak and the HJT-16 Kiran. The unit was formed at Ambala in 1948 and moved to Tambaram six years later. Among the types previously used by the school are the Harvard, Prentice, Vampire and HT-2. A museum tracing the history of the airfield and the school has been set up in the buildings. On show are many interesting photographs and items of memorabilia.

TYPE	REG/SER	CON. NO.	PI/NOTES	STATUS
☐ Folland Fo.141 Gnat F.1	IE-1078	GT.008		RA
☐ Mikoyan-Gurevich MiG-21FL				

TEZPUR AIR FORCE BASE MUSEUM (IDA101)

Address:	P.O. Balonibari, Tezpur, Assam 784001.
Tel:	0371-258001
Admission:	By prior permission only.
Location:	About 8 km north of the town off road NH52.

Tezpur has been a fighter base for many years. In recent times the site has been home to squadrons flying versions of the MiG-21. The Operational Flying Training Unit for the type was located at the field. The type first arrived at the field in 1968 and in the autumn of 2007 the last one flew out. The field is being upgraded and Sukhoi Su-30s are expected to move in during 2008. Two complete MiG-21s have been preserved with one located in the town. The museum, in one of the buildings, exhibits photographs, documents and uniforms.

TYPE	REG/SER	CON. NO.	PI/NOTES	STATUS
☐ Mikoyan-Gurevich MiG-21FL	C599		Wings only.	RA
☐ Mikoyan-Gurevich MiG-21U	'CS112'		CS-117 in nearby town.	PVX
☐ Mikoyan-Gurevich MiG-21U	U3004	664220	4220 (?)	RA
☐ Sukhoi Su-7U	U1356			RA

TRAINING COMMAND HEADQUARTERS DISPLAY (IDA102)

Address:	JC Nagpur Post, Bellary Road, Bangalore, Karnatka 560006.
Tel:	080-2341-1061
Admission:	By prior permission only.
Location:	In the southern part of the city,

The command is responsible for all aspects of technical training in the Air Force. Two aircraft have been preserved at the Headquarters complex in the city and another is located at the Officer's Mess.

TYPE	REG/SER	CON. NO.	PI/NOTES	STATUS
☐ Hindustan HT-2	'T-64'		At nearby Officer's Mess	RAX
☐ Hindustan HT-2	IX743			RA
☐ Panstwowe Zaklady Lotnicze (PZL) TS-11 Iskra 200bisD	W1773	3H 15-13		

UTTARLAI AIR FORCE BASE WAR MEMORIAL (IDA103)

Address:	Uttarlai, Rajasthan 344001.
Admission:	By prior permission only.
Location:	About 12 km north east of Barmer.

Utterlai was constructed in the early 1970s and housed fighter squadrons for many years. Types based at the field included the Hunter, Gnat, Marut and MiG-21. At the current time no operational units are in residence. The preserved Hunter is part of a memorial to Flight Lieutenant P.V. Apte of No. 221 Squadron who lost his life in the 1971 war with Pakistan. The Marut is located in another part of the airfield.

TYPE	REG/SER	CON. NO.	PI/NOTES	STATUS
☐ Hawker P.1099 Hunter F.56				RA
☐ Hindustan HF-24 Marut 1				RA

VIJAYPAT SINGHANIA DISPLAY (IDA104)

Address:	Pokhran Road 2, Thane, Navi Mumbai, Maharastra 400601.
Admission :	Aircraft on permanent view.
Location:	In the western part of the town.

Vijay Singhania is a well known aviator and industrialist. Among his achievements are flying a microlight aircraft from England to India in 1998 and setting a hot air balloon altitude record of over sixty nine thousand feet in November 2005. On show in Thane is a DC-3 which after service with the United States Army Air Force was used on airline work in India. Mr. Singhania's companies used the aircraft as an executive transport until it was retired in the early 1990s. The C-47 was put on show at Singhania Hospital which was funded by the industrial group. In August 2001 a local political leader died in the hospital which was subsequently destroyed by local rioters. The aircraft was slightly damaged when petrol was poured on a propeller and ignited. Mr Singhania's original intention was to leave the Dakota in its damaged condition to serve as a reminder of the destruction of the much needed medical services. However the aircraft has been restored and carries Safari Airlines titles.

TYPE	REG/SER	CON. NO.	PI/NOTES	STATUS
☐ Douglas DC-3A-467 Skytrain (C-47B)	VT-CEB	15046/26491	43-49230	PV

VIKRANT MARITIME MUSEUM (IDA105)

Address:	Western Command Headquarters, Indian Navy, Mumbai, Maharastra 400086.
Tel:	022-268-7200
Admission:	Daily 0900-1730
Location:	In the harbour near the Gate to India.

The Vikrant was India's first aircraft carrier and saw service from 1961 to 1997. The ship was originally built by Vickers-Armstrongs on the Tyne as H.M.S. Hercules in 1943 and launched in 1945. The carrier was moved to Belfast for completion but was not required and laid up; Short and Harland completed the ship before sale to India. The first aircraft to serve on the carrier were Sea Hawks and Alizés. In 1965 Pakistan claimed that the Vikrant has been sunk but actually the ship was in dry dock at the time. In the early 1980s a major refit took place and a 'ski-jump' ramp was fitted for Sea Harrier operations. On retirement the Vikrant moved to Mumbai where it is now berthed. Conversion for museum use took place and during Navy Week in December 2001 the vessel was open to the public. Visitors can tour large areas of the ship and see the workings of an aircraft carrier. Aircraft are being acquired for the display with a number in action dioramas. Currently on show are types which flew from the ship during their service life. India operated fifteen Alizés on anti submarine work. This type made its maiden flight in France and entered service three years later. The Indian Navy examples saw combat use against Pakistan and one was shot down by a Starfighter in one conflict. The Sea King replaced the Alizé on some duties and over forty were ordered. The informative displays are still being developed.

TYPE	REG/SER	CON. NO.	PI/NOTES	STATUS
☐ Breguet 1050 Alizé	IN209	82	82 (France)	PV
☐ Breguet 1050 Alizé	IN212	85	85 (France)	PV
☐ Hawker P.1040 Sea Hawk 101	IN244	6711	RB+256	PV
☐ Hawker P.1040 Sea Hawk 101	IN246	6716	RB+372	PV
☐ Hawker P.1040 Sea Hawk FGA.6 (FGA.4)	IN188	6122	WV907	PV
☐ Hindustan HSA.316B Chetak [Sud SA.316B Alouette III]	IN464			PV
☐ Westland-Sikorsky WS-61 Sea King 42A	IN510	WA.779		PV
☐ Westland-Sikorsky WS-61 Sea King 42A	IN511	WA.780		PV

VISVESVARAYA INDUSTRIAL AND TECHNICAL MUSEUM (IDA106)

Address:	Kasturba Road, Bangalore, Karnakata 560001.
Tel:	080-2286-4563
Email:	vitm@vsnl.com
Admission:	Tuesday-Sunday 1000-1730.
Location:	In the centre of the city near Cubbon Park.

Displays at this museum, which opened in 1962, trace the development of local industry and its associated technology. On show are examples of machinery from the early days up to modern computer operated designs. Several 'hands-on' exhibits are located in the galleries. Outside is an example of the locally produced Marut fighter developed by a team headed by the famous Focke Wulf designer Kurt Tank. The prototype Marut first flew on June 17th 1961. The Wright Flyer was built to commemorate the centenary of powered flight.

TYPE	REG/SER	CON. NO.	PI/NOTES	STATUS
☐ Hindustan HF-24 Marut 1R	BD884			PV
☐ Wright Flyer (R)				PV

WESTERN AIR COMMAND HEADQUARTERS DISPLAY (IDA107)

Address:	Gurgaon Road, Subroto Park, Delhi 110010.
Admission:	By prior permission only.
Location:	In the south western part of the city.

In July 1949 No. 1 Operational Group was set up and this evolved into Western Air Command which took up the name in June 1963. The group is responsible for over two hundred sites which includes sixteen operational airfields. Displayed outside the building are the two aircraft and a number of military vehicles.

TYPE	REG/SER	CON. NO.	PI/NOTES	STATUS
☐ Dassault Mystère IVA	IA1016	341		RA
☐ De Havilland D.H.113 Vampire NF.54			(RAF) – at nearby Air Force School.	RA

YELANANKA AIR FORCE STATION MUSEUM (IDA108)

Address:	Yelahanka, Karnatka 560063.
Tel:	080-2847-8029
Admission:	By prior permission only.
Location:	In the northern suburbs of the town.

This long established airfield is used for the instruction of transport pilots and also houses training command units. One of the recently withdrawn Iskras has been preserved.

TYPE	REG/SER	CON. NO.	PI/NOTES	STATUS
☐ Douglas DC-3A-456 Skytrain (C-47A) (Dakota III)	VT-CYX	13543	42-93612, KG676 – with Border Security Force.	RA
☐ Panstwowe Zaklady Lotnicze (PZL) TS-11 Iskra 200bisDA	W1759	3H 20-10	2010 (Poland)	R

INDONESIA

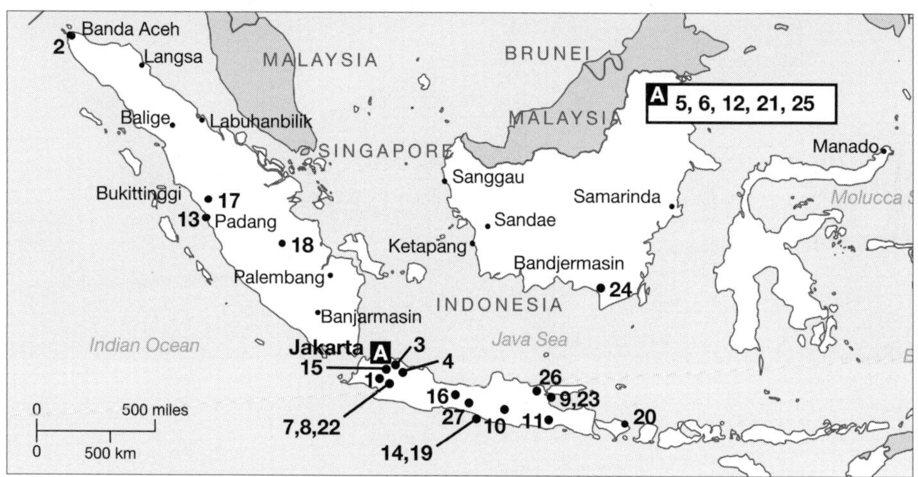

ATANG SENJAYA AIR BASE MONUMENT (IND1)

Address:	Bogor, Java.
Admission:	On permanent view.
Location:	North of the town.

The grass airfield is home to units operating a variety of helicopters. A Polish built SM-1 is preserved as a monument close to the base and by the side of the main road from Bogor to Jakarta.

TYPE	REG/SER	CON. NO.	PI/NOTES	STATUS
☐ Wytwornia Sprzetu Komunikacyjnego (WSK) SM-1 [Mil Mi-1]	H-121			PV

BANDA ACEH SEULAWAH STRUGGLE MONUMENT (IND2)

Address:	Blang Padang Square, Banda Aceh, Sumatra.
Admission:	On permanent view.
Location:	In the centre of the town.

The citizens of the town purchased the DC-3 as a reminder of their struggle against the Dutch forces in the period before independence. Plaques commemorate significant events in the conflicts.

TYPE	REG/SER	CON. NO.	PI/NOTES	STATUS
☐ Douglas DC-3A-456 Skytrain (C-47A)	'RI-001'			PVX

GEDUNG JUANG 45 – NGANJUK (IND3)

Address:	Nganjuk, Java.
Admission:	Daily.
Location:	In the town.

The museum commemorates the struggle for independence which started again after the end of World War II. The work of the local fighters is highlighted in the informative displays of memorabilia.

TYPE	REG/SER	CON. NO.	PI/NOTES	STATUS
☐ Mikoyan-Gurevich MiG-15UTI	J-759			PV

A fairly new addition to the collection at Halim Air Base is this British Aerospace Hawk. 209 (Aidan Curley)

The only known surviving Mansyu Ki-79 is on show in the Museum Abri Satriamandala in Jakarta.

This Mitsubishi Ki-51 was recovered from the Jungle and restored for display in the Indonesian Air Force Museum.

GEDUNG JUANG 45 – SUBANG (IND4)

Address:	Subang, Java.
Admission:	Unknown.
Location:	In the town.

The museum commemorates the independence fighters who fought against the Dutch in the years after World War II. A Vultee Valiant was preserved outside but there have been no recent reports.

TYPE	REG/SER	CON. NO.	PI/NOTES	STATUS
☐ Vultee V-74 Valiant (BT-13A)	B-610			PV

HALIM PERDANAKUSUMA AIR BASE COLLECTION (IND5)

Address:	Jakarta 13650, Java.
Admission:	By prior permission only.
Location:	About 10 km south east of the city centre.

The site served as the main civil airport for the city until the mid-1980s. Local flights still operate from the old terminal. The Air Force maintains a base on the field where transport aircraft reside.

TYPE	REG/SER	CON. NO.	PI/NOTES	STATUS
☐ British Aerospace Hawk 209	TT-1209	IS005	(ZJ145)	RA
☐ Commonwealth CA-27 Sabre 32 [North American F-86F]	TS-8603		(Australia)	RA
☐ Douglas DC-3A-456 Skytrain (C-47A)	AT-4752	13207	42-93310, DT-952/VHREF, PK-REF, T-452, A-4752, AT-4752	RA
☐ Douglas DC-3A-456 Skytrain (C-47A)	'RI-001'	13503	42-93576, Q-8/W-8/VHPAH, T-475, AT-4775	RAX
☐ Douglas DC-3A-456 Skytrain (C-47A) (Dakota III)	T-459	9551	42-23689, FD898, DT-959/ VHREM, PK-REM, T-459, PK-VDM – at nearby hospital.	RA
☐ Lockheed 1329 JetStar 6	A-1645	1329-5059	T-1645	RA
☐ Mikoyan-Guervich MiG-15UTI	J-185			RA
☐ Mikoyan-Gurevich MiG-21F-13	F-2167	742117		RA
☐ North American NA-122 Mustang (P-51D)	F-303			RA

INDONESIAN AIR FORCE HEADQUARTERS (IND6)

Address:	Jalan Gatot Subroto II, Jakarta, Java.
Admission:	By prior permission only.
Location:	In the south eastern part of the city.

The Indonesian Air Force acquired several examples of the P-51 from the departing Netherlands East Indies Air Force. Six Cavalier Mustangs were later purchased. Two aircraft are mounted outside the building.

TYPE	REG/SER	CON. NO.	PI/NOTES	STATUS
☐ Cavalier Mustang II (F-51D) [North American NA-122]	F-338			RA
☐ North American NA-122 Mustang (P-51D)	F-362	122-40769	44-74229	RA

INDUSTRI PESARAT TERBANG NUSANTARA MONUMENT (IND7)

Address:	JI Pajaran 154, Bandung 40173, Java.
Tel:	0622-604-3277
Admission:	By prior permission only.
Location:	Just north of the city.

The company produces a number of types under licence and has also manufactured some original designs. The NU-200 built by the Air Force Technical unit in the mid-1950s is preserved by the main gate.

TYPE	REG/SER	CON. NO.	PI/NOTES	STATUS
☐ Nurtanio NU-200 Sikumbang	01			RA

LEMBANG POLISI UDARA MONUMENT (IND8)

Address:	Lembang, Java.
Admission:	On permanent view.
Location:	In the town.

The Indonesian Police use a number of helicopters and fixed wing types on their work around the country. One of their fleet of BO 105s has been preserved outside their Lembang Station.

TYPE	REG/SER	CON. NO.	PI/NOTES	STATUS
☐ Bölkow BO 105C	P-4004	S-374		PV

LOKA JALA SRANA MUSEUM (IND9)

Address:	Morokrembangan, Surabaya 60178, Java.
Admission:	Daily 0800-1400.
Location:	In the northern part of the city.

This museum was set up in 1969 and four years later became the official museum of the Indonesian Navy and is situated in the grounds of the Naval Academy. The inside displays trace the maritime history of the region from early times. Outside in the landscaped ground is a collection of ship's guns, missiles and the aircraft. The Indonesia Navy operated a small number of Mil Mi-4 helicopters and one is on show.

TYPE	REG/SER	CON. NO.	PI/NOTES	STATUS
☐ Fairey Gannet AS.4 (AS.1)	'S-105'			PVX
☐ Mil Mi-4	V-408			PV

MADIUN ISHWAHYUDI AIR BASE COLLECTION (IND10)

Address:	Madiun.
Admission:	By prior permission only.
Location:	In the western part of the town.

The base houses fighter units operating the Northrop F-5 Tiger II, the General Dynamics F-16 and the British Aerospace Hawk. A collection of preserved aircraft has been assembled.

TYPE	REG/SER	CON. NO.	PI/NOTES	STATUS
☐ Commonwealth CA-27 Sabre 32 [North American F-86F]	TS-8621		(Australia)	RA
☐ Lockheed 580 (T-33A)	'TS-3326'		(USAF) – near main gate.	PVX
☐ Mikoyan-Gurevich MiG-17F	F-1103			RA
☐ Mikoyan-Gurevich MiG-17F	F-1110		In town square.	PV
☐ Wytwornia Sprzetu Komunikacyjnego (WSK) Lim-5 [MiG-17F]	F-1162			RA

MALANG AIR FORCE BASE COLLECTION (IND11)

Address:	Abdulrachman Saleh, Malang, Java.
Admission:	By prior permission only.
Location:	About 5 km east of the city.

This base is home to a transport squadrons operating a variety of types including the C-130 Hercules. A unit flying the Bronco is also in residence. A collection of preserved aircraft is located on the field. A number of MiG-21s were preserved at several locations around the town but these have not been reported for some time.

TYPE	REG/SER	CON. NO.	PI/NOTES	STATUS
☐ Douglas A-26B Invader	M-264		(USAAF)	RA
☐ North American NA-108 Mitchell (B-25J)	M-434		(USAAF)	RA
☐ North American NA-122 Mustang (P-51D)	F-363		(USAAF)	RA

MUSEUM ABRI SATRIAMANDALA (IND12)

Address:	Jalan Gatot Subroto 14, Jakarta – Selantan 10260, Java.
Tel:	021-522-7949
Admission:	Tuesday-Sunday 0900-1600.
Location:	On the main road from Jakarta to Halim Airport.

Indonesia waged a long and bitter struggle against the Dutch to gain independence, which was finally achieved on December 27th 1949. The indoor exhibition traces the history of the islands with a series of vivid dioramas depicting scenes from early times, through the colonial period, the Japanese occupation and the setting up of the Republic. A new building, opened in the late 1980s, portrays the often turbulent period from independence. On show are photographs, documents, uniforms and flags. Displayed outside are military vehicles, weapons and the aircraft collection. After VJ Day in 1945 an aviation section of the People's Security Force was established with about fifty aircraft recovered from a dump near Jakarta. These were often used in raids on Dutch positions. The first flight was made in a Tachikawa Ki-9 biplane by Augustion Adisutjipo from Maguwo airfield near Yogyakarta. The Air Force Museum is now located here and the airfield is named after him. A Japanese survivor is the one of the few remaining examples of the Mansyu Ki-79 Otsu. This type is a trainer version of the Nakajima Ki-27 which was the first monoplane fighter flown by the Japanese Army. Over thirteen hundred Ki-79s were built in four slightly different versions. The first Indonesian aircraft to fly was the Wiweko WEL-1 high wing monoplane which took to the air in 1948. In the 1970s three replicas, two static and one flyable, were built and one of the former is on show. Another indigenous design is the Nurtanio Kunang which set a number of class records. This type made its maiden flight in the late 1950s but was not put into production. Military types from four countries complete this impressive exhibition.

TYPE	REG/SER	CON. NO.	PI/NOTES	STATUS
☐ Agusta-Bell 204B	H-2068	3170		PV
☐ Douglas DC-3A-467 Skytrain (C-47B)	'RI-001'		(USAAF.	PVX
☐ Fairey Gannet AS.4 (AS.1)	AS-00	F9127	WN355	PV
☐ Lipnur Gelatik 32 [PZL 104 Wilga 32]	'ST-1410'		ST-1421	PVX
☐ Mansyu Ki-79b Otsu	01			PV
☐ Mikoyan-Gurevich MiG-21F-13	F-2164	742114		PV
☐ Mil Mi-4	HA-5007			PV
☐ Noorduyn Harvard IIB [North American NA-77 (AT-16)]	B-416		(Canada)	PV
☐ North American NA-108 Mitchell (B-25J)	M-458	108-33674	44-30399, N5-258 (KNIL)	PV
☐ North American NA-122 Mustang (P-51D)	F-347		(USAAF)	PV
☐ Nurtanio NU-25 Kunang	04			PV
☐ Piper J-3C-65 Cub (L-4J)	R-344	13766	45-5026	PV
☐ Wiweko WEL-1 (R)	'RI-X'			PVX
☐ Yokosuka K5Y	62			PV

MUSEUM ADITYAWARMAN (IND13)

Address:	Diponegro J.L. Permudo, Padang, Sumatra.
Tel:	0752-31523
Admission:	Tuesday-Sunday 0800-1600.
Location:	In the centre of the town which is on the west coast of Sumatra.

The museum has impressive displays relating to local history and culture. Indonesia was supplied with a number of Harvards in the early 1950s and they served as trainers for many years. The military airfield at Tabang outside the city has played an important role since the first days of independence.

TYPE	REG/SER	CON. NO.	PI/NOTES	STATUS
☐ Noorduyn Harvard IIB [North American NA-77 (AT-16)]	B-424	14-547	42-12300, FE813	PV

MUSEUM AKADEMI ANGKATAN UDARA (IND14)

Address:	c/o Pangkalan Adisutjipto, Yogyakarta 55002, Java.
Email:	pullahta@aau.ac.id
Admission:	By prior permission only.
Location:	At the south eastern side of the air base.

The non-flying element of the Air Force Academy has a small museum in one of its buildings so that cadets can learn about the history and traditions of the service. On show are uniforms, documents, photographs and personal items. The development of aviation in the region is portrayed with the colonial period and the Japanese occupation featuring. Courses are offered in academic subjects and officers undergo full military training. The aircraft are displayed around the grounds of the site. Among the types acquired from the Dutch were the Mitchell and the Skytrain. A number of Texans were soon purchased for training and Invaders for attack use. Twenty Commonwealth built Avon powered Sabres were delivered in March 1973 and served for a decade. Some of the aircraft were not seen on a recent visit and may be in store around the academy or on the airfield.

TYPE	REG/SER	CON. NO.	PI/NOTES	STATUS
☐ Commonwealth CA-27 Sabre 32 [North American F-86F]	TS-8615	CA27-88	A94-988, F-8615	RA
☐ Douglas A-26B Invader	M-263		(USAAF)	RA
☐ Mikoyan-Gurevich MiG-17F	F-1161			RA
☐ Mikoyan-Gurevich MiG-17F	F-1712			RA
☐ Mikoyan-Gurevich MiG-19S	F-1903			RA
☐ Noorduyn Harvard IIB [North American NA-77 (AT-16)]	B-440		(RCAF)	RA
☐ Noorduyn Harvard IIB [North American NA-77 (AT-16)]	B-442		(RCAF)	RA
☐ North American NA-108 Mitchell (B-25J)	M-433	108-32297	44-29022, N5-233 (KNIL)	RA
☐ Vultee V-74 Valiant (BT-13A)	B-605		(USAAF)	RA
☐ Vultee V-74 Valiant (BT-13A)	B-616		(USAAF)	RA

MUSEUM HIDUP DIRGANTARA MANDALA (IND15)

Address:	Suryadarma Air Base, Kalijati, Java.
Admission:	By prior permission only.
Location:	In the south western suburbs of the town.

The base is currently home to squadrons flying SIAI-Marchetti SF.260s and helicopters. A museum tracing the history of the airfield and its units opened in 1979. On show are photographs, documents, models and uniforms. The aircraft are stored in hangars on the field and some, including the Lockheed 12, may move to the Air Force Museum at Yogyakarta. The classic twin was delivered to the Netherlands Training School at Jackson in Missouri in 1942. The aircraft was transferred to Indonesia in 1950 and served until about 1971. The Goose is probably one of the batch obtained from the Shell company in the late 1950s. A small number were flown on oil prospecting and survey general duties by the firm. The Indonesian Navy operated the amphibians on coastal patrols. The Polish designed Wilga first flew in 1963 and a batch was sold to Indonesia. The Lipnur company obtained a licence to build the high wing utility monoplane and about forty were delivered to the military. The Vultee Valiant trainer was built in large numbers and after World War II America supplied several to the fledgling force.

TYPE	REG/SER	CON. NO.	PI/NOTES	STATUS
☐ Cessna 180B	L-185			RA
☐ Cessna 207A	L-2071	2070142		RA
☐ Glider	G-116			RA
☐ Grumman G-21A Goose	PB-521			RA
☐ Lipnur Gelatik 32 [PZL 104 Wilga 32]	IN-012		ST-1412	RA
☐ Lockheed 12-26 Electra Junior	T-303	1308	L2-40 (Netherlands), L2-103 (Netherlands), E-8463	RA
☐ Piper J-3C-65 Cub (L-4J)	R-370	13816	45-5076, R-370, PK-SAG	RA
☐ Schweizer SGU.2-22C	G-111			RA
☐ Vultee V-54D Valiant (BT-13)	B-604			RA

MUSEUM PALAGAN (IND16)

Address:	Ambarawa, Java.
Admission:	Tuesday-Sunday 1000-1700.
Location:	About 40 km south of Semarang on the road to Magelang.

During World War II over fifteen thousand Europeans were detained by the Japanese occupiers in a camp at Ambarawa. In November 1945 British forces were attacked by local freedom fighters as they tried to free the prisoners. Another battle took place on July 29th 1947 when Dutch forces attacked the local militia. The displays at this museum commemorate these conflicts and the struggle for independence. On show are many photographs, documents, weapons and items of memorabilia. The Indonesian Air Force flew Mustangs from 1950 until the mid-1980s. An example of this classic fighter is on show at this museum. The aircraft has recently been restored in period markings and now resides under a canopy so that it is protected from the elements. There is an excellent railway museum nearby where several historic locomotives can be seen. The history of transport in the region is portrayed. Ambarawa was an important railway down and a branch employing a cog-drive went into the central mountain range. This line closed down in 1977.

TYPE	REG/SER	CON. NO.	PI/NOTES	STATUS
☐ North American NA-122 Mustang (P-51D)	'F-354'		(USAAF), (Switzerland)	PVX

MUSEUM PERJUANGAN (IND17)

Address:	Jelan Panorama, Bukittinggi 26115. Sumatra.
Admission:	Sunday-Thursday 0800-1700, Friday 0800-1100 1300-1700.
Location:	In the south western part of the town near the Japanese Channel.

Displays at this museum trace the history of the Japanese occupation in World War II, the independence struggle against the Dutch colonial authorities, the communist revolution in 1965 and the conflict against the Frelitin guerillas. The Harvard served in the training role for many years and honours the work of the Air Force. One highlight is a panorama depicting the large complex of caves built by slave labour in World War II. There is also a section of the display devoted to the early history of the region and many interesting items can be seen. The Anson replica is mounted as a memorial near the site of the old airfield which was used by the Air Force.

TYPE	REG/SER	CON. NO.	PI/NOTES	STATUS
☐ Avro 652A Anson I (R)	'RI-003'			PVX
☐ Noorduyn Harvard IIB [North American NA-77 (AT-16)]	B-419		(Canada)	PV

MUSEUM PERJUANGAN RAKYAT JAMBI (IND18)

Address:	Jambi, Sumatra 360???.
Admission:	Daily
Location:	In the town.

In December 1948 a Catalina crashed in the Batanghai River. The airframe remained for many years and in the 1990s it was removed. A plan to rebuild it was initiated but there was serious corrosion in the airframe and a full size replica incorporating some parts from the wrecked aircraft was constructed. The aircraft now resides on the lawn in front of the museum which has exhibits tracing the culture and history of the region. The award winning building was designed by an Indonesian architect in the traditional local style.

TYPE	REG/SER	CON. NO.	PI/NOTES	STATUS
☐ Consolidated 28-5A Catalina (R)	'RI-005'/'VH-BDP'			PVX

MUSEUM PUSAT TNI-AU (IND19)

Address:	Dirgantara Mandala, Lanud Adisutjipto, Yogyakarta 55002. Java.
Tel:	0274-564465
Admission:	Daily 0800-1500.
Location:	On the airbase which is about 5 km east of the town.

Indonesia declared its independence of August 17th 1945 but Dutch forces returned to try and regain their colony. A four-year struggle ensued before the country achieved its aim. The Air Force came into being in 1950 and was assisted by a Dutch military mission. The Netherlands Indies Air Force was disbanded on June 21st 1950 and all its aircraft and airfields were handed over to Indonesia. In 1958 there was a rebellion in Sumatra and MiG-15UTIs, MiG-17s, Il-14s and Il-28s were obtained through Czechoslovakia. The establishment of Malaysia brought the country into conflict with Great Britain and supplies of western arms ceased. The Soviet Union stepped in and delivered MiG-19s, MiG-21s and Tu-16s. With the fall of President Sukarno arms agreements were signed with Australia and the U.S.A. and the majority of the Eastern Bloc aircraft were withdrawn. The Air Force Museum was set up in Jakarta in 1969 and moved nine years later to the Academy in Yogyakarta before opening at its present location on July 29th 1984. A modern entrance hall has been added to a 'T'-shaped hangar. A mural depicting all types flown by the service, command flags and squadron badges are on show in the foyer. The history of each unit is told with models, photographs and uniforms in the main exhibition room. Also here is the flyable WEL-1 replica which was once damaged by communist guerillas during a show at the airfield. Three Japanese aircraft found derelict in West Irian and restored at Bandung are parked close to the hangar entrance. The Mitsubishi Ki-51 ground attack monoplane is believed to be the only complete survivor of the almost two and a half thousand produced. Indonesia bought its first jet aircraft, eight Vampire T.55s, in 1955 but none survived. The example on show was exchanged for a Mustang with the Royal New Zealand Air Force. A range of MiG fighters can be seen along with a modified Lavochkin La-11. Two locally built Kampret gliders are suspended from the roof. A pair of arrivals in the late 1990s were the Tu-16, which spent many years stored at Bandung, and the Catalina painted to represent one flown in the early 1950.

TYPE	REG/SER	CON. NO.	PI/NOTES	STATUS
☐ Aero L-29 Delfin	'LL-2902'			PVX
☐ Aero L-29 Delfin	'LL-2918'		Near base gate.	PVX
☐ Auster E AOP.3	'R-62'		(RAF), (KNIL), R-58	PVX
☐ Beech A45 Mentor (T-34A)	LD-3481		(USAF), B-681 (?)	RA
☐ Boeing-Stearman E75 Kaydet (PT-13D)	'TAL-OA'	75-5648	42-17485, N4812N	PVX

TYPE	REG/SER	CON. NO.	PI/NOTES	STATUS
☐ Cessna R172F Mescalero (T-41D)	LM-4188		On main road near museum entrance.	PV
☐ Commonwealth CA-27 Sabre 32 [North American F-86F]	TS-8618	CA27-???	(RAAF)	PV
☐ Consolidated 28-5A Catalina (PBY-5A)	'PB-505'	1903	Bu46539, N1563M	PVX
☐ De Havilland D.H.115 Vampire T.11	'J-701'	15580	XH266, NZ5708, INST204	PVX
☐ Douglas DC-3A-456 Skytrain (C-47A) (Dakota III)	'T-482'	12719	42-92870, DT985/VHRCC, N1-474 (KNIL), PK-DPE, PK-GDT, T-474, PK-GDT	PVX
☐ Douglas DC-3A-467 Skytrain (C-47B)	'VT-CLA'		Original VT-CLA was c/n 15471/26916 43-49655 – rear fuselage only.	PVDX
☐ Douglas A-26B Invader	M-265		(USAAF)	PV
☐ Grumman G-64 Albatross (SA-16A) (HU-16A)	IR-0117	G-436		PV
☐ Hiller UH12B	H-101			PV
☐ Kampret Glider	G-002			PV
☐ Kampret Glider	GX-001			PV
☐ Lavochkin La-11	F-911			PV
☐ Lembaga Industri Penerbangan Nurtanio LT-200 [Pazmany PL-2]	IN-202			PV
☐ Lipnur Gelatik 32 [PZL 104 Wilga 32]	ST-1419			PV
☐ Lockheed 580 (T-33A) (TV-2) (T-33B)	TS-3334	580-9609	55-3068, Bu141553 – may be c/n 580-8407 53-5068.	PV
☐ Lockheed 1329 JetStar 6	A-9446	1329-5046	N9282R, PK-IJS, T-9446	PV
☐ Mansyu Ki-79b Otsu (R)				PV
☐ Mikoyan-Gurevich MiG-15UTI	J-754		On base	PV
☐ Mikoyan-Gurevich MiG-15UTI	J-767			PV
☐ Mikoyan-Gurevich MiG-19S	F-1904			PV
☐ Mikoyan-Gurevich MiG-21F-13	F-2160	742110		PV
☐ Mil Mi-4	H-200		H-251 (?)	PV
☐ Mitsubishi A6M5 Zero Sen Model 52	30-1153			PV
☐ Mitsubishi Ki-51	G32			PV
☐ Nakajima Ki-43-II Hayabusa	H45			PV
☐ Noorduyn Harvard IIB [North American NA-77 (AT-16)]	B-427		(USAAF)	PVD
☐ Noorduyn Harvard IIB [North American NA-77 (AT-16)]	B-448		(USAAF)	PV
☐ North American NA-108 Mitchell (B-25J)	M-439	108-32307	44-29032, N5-239 (KNIL)	PV
☐ North American NA-122 Mustang (P-51D)	F-338		(USAAF)	PV
☐ Panstwowe Zaklady Lotnicze (PZL) TS-8 Bies	'STUPA 01'		Possibly c/n 1e 05-06	PVX
☐ Piper J-3C-65 Cub (L-4J)	R-371	13817	45-5077	PV
☐ Piper J-3C-65 Cub (L-4J)			(USAAF)	RAC
☐ Sikorsky S-58 Seahorse (HUS-1) (UH-34D)	H-5802	581173	Bu148060, H-3404	PV
☐ Star-lite SL-1 Star-lite	PK-SLX			PV
☐ Tupolev Tu-16KS-1	M-1625	7203427		PV
☐ Vultee V-74 Valiant (BT-13A)	B-633		(USAAF)	PV
☐ Wiweko WEL-1 (R)	'RI-X'			PVX
☐ Wiweko WEL-1 (R)	'RI-X'			PVX
☐ Wytwornia Sprzetu Komunikacyjnego (WSK) Lim-5 [MiG-17F]	F-1160			PV
☐ Yokosuka K5Y1 (R)	'TJ'			PVX

NGURAH RAI AIRPORT MEMORIAL (IND20)

Address:	Denpasar, Bali.
Admission:	On permanent view.
Location:	Just south of Kuta.

With the rise in tourist traffic the airport now handles flight from around the region. In the past Indonesian Air Force aircraft have used the field. The Vultee Valiant is mounted by the approach road to the terminal.

TYPE	REG/SER	CON. NO.	PI/NOTES	STATUS
☐ Vultee V-74 Valiant (BT-13A)	'B-427'			PVX

SATUAN UDARA FEDERASI AERO SPORT INDONESIA (IND21)

Address:	c/o Air Force Headquarters, Jakarta, Java.
Admission:	By prior permission only.
Location:	At a number of airfields around the country.

The organisation was set up in January 1972 to assist sport aviation in the country including parachuting and aeromodelling. Several former Air Force types are flown from a number of fields. Some current aircraft also take part in the varied activities. The local Air Force Commanders serve as presidents of the branches around the country. There are active aeromodelling branches in many towns and these organise many competitions. The fleet includes a number of gliders based at both civil and military airfields but I have no details of these. The list of aircraft is far from complete and any additions and identities would be most welcome.

TYPE	REG/SER	CON. NO.	PI/NOTES	STATUS
☐ Aero Commander 500A	P-2002	1049-44	Monument at Pondok Cabe Air Base.	RA
☐ Antonov An-2				RAA
☐ Antonov An-2				RAA
☐ Aviat A-1 Husky				RAA
☐ Beech A45 Mentor (T-34A)				RAA
☐ Beech A45 Mentor (T-34A)				RAA
☐ Canadian Car & Foundry Harvard 4 [North American NA-186]	B-475			RAA
☐ Cessna 150	L-1501			RAA
☐ Cessna 185E	L-1810			RAA
☐ Cessna 401A				RAA
☐ Douglas DC-3A-456 Skytrain (C-47A) (Dakota III)	AF-4776	13334	42-93424, KG603, PH-TCT, PH-DAT, JZ-PDF, PK-GDP, PK-NDF, PK-VTO	RAA
☐ Douglas DC-3A-456 Skytrain (C-47A) (Dakota III)	AF-4777	9281	42-23419, DT-951/VHREE, PK-REE, T-451, PK-GDA, PK-NDK, PK-MVD, PK-VTM	RA
☐ Douglas DC-3A-456 Skytrain (C-47A) (Dakota III)	AF-4790			RA
☐ Flug und Fahrzeugwerke (FFA) AS.202/15 Bravo				RAA
☐ Flug und Fahrzeugwerke (FFA) AS.202/15 Bravo				RAA
☐ Grumman G-64 Albatross (SA-16A) (HU-16A)				RA
☐ Lipnur Gelatik 32 [PZL 104 Wilga 32]	IN-025			RA
☐ Lipnur Gelatik 32 [PZL 104 Wilga 32]	IN-039			RAA
☐ Lipnur Gelatik 32 [PZL 104 Wilga 32]				RAA
☐ Lipnur Gelatik 32 [PZL 104 Wilga 32]				RAA
☐ Lipnur Gelatik 32 [PZL 104 Wilga 32]				RAA
☐ Noorduyn Harvard IIB [North American NA-77 (AT-16)]	B-423		(USAAF)	RAA
☐ Noorduyn Harvard IIB [North American NA-77 (AT-16)]	B-475		(USAAF)	RAA
☐ Piper J-3C-65 Cub (L-4J)	PK-SLR	13772	44-5032, R-350	RA
☐ Piper J-3C-65 Cub (L-4J)	R-379	13883	45-5143	RAA
☐ Piper PA-23-250 Apache				RAA
☐ Piper PA-32-300 Cherokee Six	L-3201	32-7540162		RAA
☐ Piper PA-34-200 Seneca				RAA
☐ Schweizer SGU.2-22C				RAA
☐ Schweizer SGU.2-22C				RAA
☐ Schweizer SGU.2-22M				RAA
☐ Schweizer SGS.1-23				RAA
☐ Schweizer SGU.1-26B				RAA
☐ Schweizer SGU.1-26B				RAA
☐ Short SC.7 Skyvan 3M-400	AF-0702	SH.1881	G-14-53, T-702	RAA

SEKOLAH STAF DAN KOMANDO ANGKATAN DARAT MONUMENT (IND22)

Address:	Bandung.
Admission:	By prior permission only.
Location:	In the town.

The college is responsible for the training of Army officers and runs a variety of educational and military courses. A Lockheed T-33 has been moved from Madiun to serve as a monument.

TYPE	REG/SER	CON. NO.	PI/NOTES	STATUS
☐ Lockheed 580 (T-33A)	TS-3333		(USAF)	RA

SURABAYA NAVAL AIR BASE COLLECTION (IND23)

Address:	Juanda Naval Air Base, Surabaya, Java.
Admission:	By prior permission only.
Location:	The airfield is in the western suburbs of the city.

The Indonesian Naval Air Arm (Tentara Nasional Indonesia-Angkatan Laut) was established in 1958 with a fleet of eighteen Gannets. In the mid-1960s the service was expanded to include fighter squadrons with MiG-19s and MiG-21Fs along with a few Ilyushin Il-28 bombers. Five aircraft are currently in the collection and the Gannet, is displayed in the centre of a roundabout near the base. An exhibition was planned for the base but a change in plans resulted in the establishment of the Loka Jala Srana Museum.

TYPE	REG/SER	CON. NO.	PI/NOTES	STATUS
☐ Fairey Gannet AS.4 (AS.1)	'AS-00'	F0139	WN367, AS-07	PVX
☐ Government Aircraft Factory N.22SL Nomad	P-814	N22SL-111		RA
☐ Ilyushin Il-28	510			RA
☐ Mikoyan-Gurevich MiG-17F	F-1105			RA
☐ Westland Wasp HAS.1	HS-434	F9688	243 (Netherlands), G-17-1	RA

SYAMSUDDIN AIR BASE MEMORIAL (IND24)

Address: Banjarmasin
Admission: By prior permission only.
Location: About 25 km south east of the town.

The airfield is the main civil airport for the region and handles flights from many cities. The Indonesian Air Force has a base at the site and the MiG-17 is preserved as a memorial.

TYPE	REG/SER	CON. NO.	PI/NOTES	STATUS
☐ Mikoyan-Gurevich MiG-17F	F-1108			RA

TAMAN MINI INDONESIA MUSEUM TRANSPORTASI (IND25)

Address: Jagorawi Toll Road,
Kampung Rambutan,
Jakarta,
Java.
Tel: 021-840-9214
Fax: 021-840-0709
Email: Info@tamanmini.com
Admission: Daily 0800-1700.
Location: About 18 km south east of the city centre.

This complex which aims to show the whole country in one park opened in 1975. There are representative houses from each of the twenty seven provinces in Indonesia, museums, theatres, gardens and wildlife to be seen. Replica buildings and monuments have also been constructed. A small transport exhibition has been set up in one area of the vast site. On show are several vehicles, railway engines and rolling stock. Four aircraft are currently displayed. The C-47 is one of many in the country painted in the colours of the first one flown by Indonesian Airways. The identity of this aircraft is not known at the present time. The DC-9 was operated by Garuda, mainly on local flights, from 1979 until it was withdrawn from service. Two light aircraft are in the collection. Both types were popular with flying clubs and private owners.

TYPE	REG/SER	CON. NO.	PI/NOTES	STATUS
☐ Aero Engine Services T6/24 Airtrainer	PK-ATV	B.567	ZK-DDO	PV
☐ Beech B19 Musketeer Sport	PK-ATK	MB-523	N711GM	PV
☐ Douglas DC-3A-456 Skytrain (C-47A)			Front fuselage only.	PVD
☐ Douglas DC-3A-467 Skytrain (C-47B)	'RI-001'		(USAAF) – original RI-001 was c/n 15458/26903 43-49642, VH-HEC.	PVX
☐ Douglas DC-9-32	PK-GNT	47790		PV

WAR MEMORIAL – JOMBANG (IND26)

Address: Jombang,
Java.
Admission: On permanent view.
Location: About 30 km south west of Surabaya.

Sixteen Broncos were acquired in 1976 to replace the P-51 Mustang and one has been put on show at this memorial which honours local people who have lost their lives in combat duties. Close air support for ground troops was used in World War II and to a greater degree in the Korean conflict. In the mid-1960s a Joint Services Committee in the U.S.A. was set up to investigate designs and from these studies came the OV-10.

TYPE	REG/SER	CON. NO.	PI/NOTES	STATUS
☐ North American NA-397 Bronco (OV-10F)	TT-1006	397-6	Bu160221, S-106	PV

This Grumman Goose is preserved at the museum at Kalijati Air Base. (Phil Dunnington)

This former Garuda DC-9 is at the Taman Mini-Indonesia Transport Museum in Jakarta. (Steve Darke)

This former Royal Air Force Chipmunk is on show at Iranian Aerospace Exhibition Centre in Tehran (Sharam Shafiri)

This Piper Aztec can be seen at the Iranian Aerospace Exhibition Centre in Tehran (Sharam Shafiri)

WAR MEMORIAL – MELATI (IND27)

Address:	Melati, Java.
Admission:	On permanent view.
Location:	About 10 km north of Yogyakarta.

China supplied two dozen Lavochkin La-11s to Indonesia in the late 1950s. The piston engined fighter saw little service in the country. One is displayed as a memorial to the local people killed in conflict. The prototype of the design first flew in 1946 and was a long range version of the La-9. The type was first known in the west when a defecting pilot crash landed his La-11 at Tullinge in Sweden on May 18th 1949.

TYPE	REG/SER	CON. NO.	PI/NOTES	STATUS
☐ Lavochkin La-11			With parts from a T-6.	PV

IRAN

IRANIAN AEROSPACE EXHIBITION CENTRE (IR1)

Address:	Tenran-Kiraj Expressway Km.4, Tehran.
Tel:	021-6600-9328
Admission:	Daily 0800-1900.
Location:	On the north west side of Mehrabbad Airport.

This privately owned collection has been assembled over the last few years. The exhibition area includes landscaped gardens and paths. Dominating the site is the Boeing 707 parked on a man-made hill. This airliner also serves as a restaurant. Many of the civil aircraft were damaged in the revolution in 1979. Several versions of the Aero Commander can be seen in both civil and military markings. The prototype of this twin-engined high wing monoplane designed by Ted Smith was built in Oklahoma in the late 1940s. The Commander was improved over the years and many versions were put into production. Over three thousand examples powered by both piston and turboprop engines were built. The Sparrow Commander is one of a pair acquired by the Ministry of Agriculture in 1969. The aircraft is a development of the Callair series of monoplanes, several of which were adapted for agricultural use. Rockwell took over the design but only built a few before selling all stocks and proction rights to a company in Mexico. Six former R.A.F. Chipmunks were overhauled at Leavesden in 1956 and shipped to Iran for the state Aero Club. The Invader was abandoned on an airfield in the country and transported by road to the museum. This aircraft was never delivered to the United States military and was immediately put up for civilian disposal. In 1947, piloted by Bill Odom, it made two round the world flights. On the second, a solo journey, he broke Howard Hughes record. The Invader arrived in Iran in 1977 but saw little use. During the rule of the Shah, America supplied many aircraft to Iran and the several Texans were delivered in the early 1950s. A number of withdrawn airliners are parked in a section of the Iran Air maintenance base close to the exhibition area. Useually at least one of these is open to the public and guided tours take place. The Glass Goose amphibian is a improved version of the Sea Hawk, later Sea Hawker, designed by Gary LeGare in the early 1980s. Little is known of the history of this example of the American design. The C-47 served in Europe in the latter days of World War II. The aircraft then became and executive transport. Purchased by the Power and Water Company it moved to Iran in 1971 and was operated for just under ten years. After a number of years in store at the airport it moved to the museum. Some aircraft have left the exhibition in recent years.

TYPE	REG/SER	CON. NO.	PI/NOTES	STATUS
☐ Aero Commander 500	EP-ABD	836-94	N8492C – Incomplete.	PV
☐ Aero Commander 500S	5-2502	3141		PV
☐ Aero Commander 500S	5-2503	3142		PV
☐ Aero Commander 500S	5-2504	3143		PV
☐ Aero Commander 680FLP	EP-AHU	1509-21	EP-PSP	PV
☐ Aero Commander 681B	EP-AGU	6012	Front fuselage only.	PV
☐ Aero Commander 681B	EP-AKA	6065	N10C	PV
☐ Aero Commander 681B	EP-AKB	6067	N10C	PV
☐ Aero Commander 681B	5-282	6072	5-8903	PV
☐ Aero Commander 690	5-2501	11076		PV
☐ Boeing 707-321B	EP-IRJ	18958	N416PA – possible identity.	PV
☐ Boeing 727-30	EP-PLN	18363	D-ABIF, N16768, (N44CR), EP-SHP	
☐ Boeing 727-81	EP-GDS	19557	JA8321, N329K, EP-MRP	PV
☐ Boeing 737-270C	EP-IGA			PV
☐ Boeing 737-286Adv	EP-IRF	20498		
☐ Boeing 737-286Adv	EP-IRH	20500		PV
☐ Boeing 737-286CAdv	EP-IRI	20740		PV
☐ Boeing 747-2J9F	EP-ICC	21514	N8277V, 5-8115	PV
☐ Cessna 185A Skywagon	1114			RA
☐ Cessna 305A Bird Dog (L-19A) (O-1A)	51-12245	22559		RA
☐ Cessna T310Q	EP-JBA	310Q0011	N7511Q, EP-BRJ	PV
☐ Cessna 414	EP-KID	4140074	HB-LFM	PV
☐ De Havilland D.H.C.1 Chipmunk 22 (T.10)	EP-AFN	C1/0140	WB692	PV
☐ De Havilland D.H.C.2 Beaver (L-20A) (U-6A)	6-9701	566	53-7784	PV
☐ De Havilland D.H.C.4A Caribou	5-?552			PV

TYPE	REG/SER	CON. NO.	PI/NOTES	STATUS
☐ Douglas A-26B Invader	N956R	28038	44-34759, NX67834, N67834,N28W, N956	PV
☐ Douglas DC-3A-456 Skytrain (C-47A)	EP-TWB	12680	42-92835, NC49952, N78SR	PV
☐ Fairchild-Hiller FH-227D (FH-227)	EP-SNA	524	N701U, EP-AMI	PV
☐ Fokker F.27 Friendship 600	'5-4101'			PVX
☐ Fokker F.28-4000 Fellowship	EP-ASE	11144	PH-EXS, 5N-ANV, F-GDUZ	PV
☐ Kaman K-600-3 Huskie (H-43B) (HH-43B)	HH43-9411		(USAF)	PV
☐ Lockheed L-1011-100 TriStar	9L-LDC	1231	N7035T	PV
☐ North American NA-168 Texan (T-6G)	03-546	168-590 (?)	49-3456 (?)	PV
☐ North American NA-168 Texan (T-6G)			At CAA HQ.	RA
☐ North American NA-176 Sabre (F-86F)	3-118	176-110	51-13179	PV
☐ North American NA-176 Sabre (F-86F)			(USAF) – at nearby college.	RA
☐ North American NA-182 Texan (T-6G)	114-815	182-502	51-14815	PV
☐ Piper PA-18-135 Super Cub			Incomplete.	PVD
☐ Piper PA-23-250 Aztec E	EP-PAH	27-7305151	N40388	PV
☐ Piper PA-31-350 Navajo Chieftain	EP-PAJ	31-7552057	5-2214 (Iran)	PV
☐ Quikkit Glass Goose				PV
☐ Rockwell A-9B Commander A-9B	EP-AHH	1460		PV
☐ Sikorsky S-55A				PV

IRANIAN AIR FORCE MUSEUM (IR2)

Address:	Iranian Air Force Headquarters, Doshan-Tappeh Airport, Tehran.
Admission:	Currently closed.
Location:	In the north eastern suburbs of the city.

Military aviation came to Iran in 1922 when the army acquired a Junkers F-13. The following year a Czechoslovakian Aero A-30 was purchased by subscription and a hangar was erected at Galeh-Morghi. In 1924 more Junkers F-13s, plus de Havilland D.H.4s and DH.9s along with several Breguet, Potez and SPAD biplanes arrived. Pilots were sent to France and Russia for training and more airfields were constructed. British types were bought in the 1930s. After World War II American aircraft were acquired under the Mutual Assistance Program. Large numbers of modern American designswere supplied and are still in use along with Russian and Chinese types. The museum, which has been closed for some time, was set up in 1972 at the airport. A large hall was constructed along with an outside display area. The airfield is used by units of the Revolutionary Guard so a decision was made not to allow visitors. I have managed to obtain details of some of the types which were on show and also those in store. This is far from complete and any information would be appreciated. Thirty two Hawker Audax biplanes were delivered between 1933 and 1935. Also the Shabaz works at Doshan-Tappeh acquired a licence to produce the type but none were made. One of my sources told me that the Hurricane in store is a two seater. If so the aircraft was KZ232 first flown at Hamble in September 1946. One Ilyushin Il-14 was delivered to Iran in the spring of 1957 and this is believed to be the outside the building.

TYPE	REG/SER	CON. NO.	PI/NOTES	STATUS
☐ Cessna 185A Skywagon				RA
☐ Douglas DC-3A-456 Skytrain (C-47A)				RA
☐ Hawker Audax				RA
☐ Hawker Hurricane IIc	2-31		KZ232 – possible identity.	RA
☐ Ilyushin Il-14M	5-55	1470012041	EP-HMI – possible identity.	RA
☐ Lockheed 580 (T-33A)				RA
☐ Mikoyan-Gurevich MiG-23ML			Possible type.	RA
☐ North American NA-191 Sabre (F-86F)				RA
☐ Republic P-47D Thunderbolt				RA
☐ Republic F-84G Thunderjet	RA			RA
☐ Shenyang F-6C [Mikoyan-Gurevich MiG-19SF]			Possible type.	RA

MILITARY MUSEUM (IR3)

Address:	Shahid Taheri Street, Shahid Fallahi Avenue, Vali-e-Asr, Tajrish, Tehran.
Tel:	021-228-2031
Fax:	021-228-2079
Admission:	Saturday-Thursday 0900-1800.
Location:	In the northern part of the city.

Work on this vast complex of houses and palaces started in the nineteenth century. From 1920 until the overthrow of the Shah in 1979 it was home to members of the royal family. Now the site houses a number of museums tracing aspects of the history of Iran. Exhibitions of minatures, paintings and calligraphy can be seen in some of the buildings. Other palaces show the furniture and fittings of the Imperial period. The military museum is housed in the Sharham Castle. The complex history of the region is portrayed in the informative displays. The four aircraft are displayed in the picturesque grounds. The Sabre is painted in the colours of the 'Golden

Crown' aerobatic team which was formed in 1958 with F-84G Thunderjets. F-86F Sabres were flown from 1960 until 1970. The Beaver is in Imperial markings. The Mil-24 was captured during the bitter war between Iran and Iraq which occurred between September 1980 and August 1988. Over one hundred Iraqi aircraft were flown to Iran during the conflict and others may well be stored for future exhibition at this museum.

TYPE	REG/SER	CON. NO.	PI/NOTES	STATUS
☐ De Havilland D.H.C.2 Beaver	6-9704			PV
☐ Mil Mi-24A	3128		In Iraqi markings.	PV
☐ North American NA-191 Sabre (F-86F)	3-121			PV
☐ Republic F-84G Thunderjet	2-148			PV

IRAQ

BAGHDAD MUSEUM (IQ1)

Address:	Baghdad.
Admission:	Unknown.
Location:	In the centre of the city.

A collection of aircraft has been assembled in the 'Green Zone' of the city. Information is sparse and hopefully this exhibition will be developed. The Dove and the Heron moved from the former military museum.

TYPE	REG/SER	CON. NO.	PI/NOTES	STATUS
☐ Aero L-29 Delfin				RA
☐ De Havilland D.H.104 Dove 5				RA
☐ De Havilland D.H.114 Heron 2C	393	14105	G-5-18 – probable identity.	RA
☐ Mikoyan-Gurevich MiG-17				RA
☐ Mikoyan-Gurevich MiG-21F				RA
☐ Sukhoi Su-7BMK				RA
☐ Zlin Z-526 Trenér Master				

MILITARY MUSEUM (IQ2)

Address:	Muthenna Airfield, Baghdad.
Admission:	No longer exists but aircraft listed in the hope information will emerge.
Location:	In the eastern suburbs of the city – also at Al Abeid racing circuit.

The aircraft are no longer at the circuit and some hangars at Muthenna were bombed. Two aircraft, a Dove and a Heron are now preserved in the city and the others may well have been scrapped or destroyed.

TYPE	REG/SER	CON. NO.	PI/NOTES	STATUS
☐ Aero L-39ZO Albatros				RA
☐ Antonov An-2	533			RA
☐ Bristol 170 Freighter 31M				RA
☐ Cessna 305A Bird Dog (L-19A) (O-1A)				RA
☐ De Havilland D.H.100 Vampire FB.52				RA
☐ De Havilland D.H.100 Vampire FB.52	370			RA
☐ De Havilland D.H.115 Vampire T.55				RA
☐ De Havilland D.H.C.1 Chipmunk T.20				RA
☐ Hawker Fury FB.10				RA
☐ Hawker Fury FB.10				RA
☐ Hawker Nisr				RA
☐ Hawker P.1099 Hunter FGA.59 (F.6)				RA
☐ Hunting-Percival P.84 Jet Provost T.52				RA
☐ Mikoyan-Gurevich MiG-15bis	1093			RA
☐ Mikoyan-Gurevich MiG-15UTI	543			RA
☐ Mikoyan-Gurevich MiG-17F	471			RA
☐ Mikoyan-Gurevich MiG-17PF	458			RA
☐ Mikoyan-Gurevich MiG-21F-13	706			RA
☐ Mikoyan-Gurevich MiG-21MF			8008 (Poland)	PVX
☐ Mikoyan-Gurevich MiG-21MF				RA
☐ Mil Mi-4			(Cubaa)	RA
☐ Mil Mi-8T				RA
☐ Northrop N-311 Tiger II (F-5E)	3-7047	U.1035	73-0967 – in Iranian markings.	RA
☐ Northrop N-311 Tiger II (F-5E)	3-7090	U.1087	74-1390 – in Iranian markings.	RA
☐ Percival P.56 Provost T.53				RA
☐ Piaggio P.166DL2				RA
☐ Westland-Sikorsky WS-58 Wessex 52				RA

This Polish built Wilga is preserved outside the Military Museum in Cairo. [EG4] (Gerry Manning)

This Dornier Skyservant is preserved outside the National War Museum at Umuahia in Nigeria. [NG5] (Mike Draper)

Two aircraft are outside the M.O.T.H. Shellhole at Edenvale. One is this Lockheed Ventura. [SA5] (Chris Chatfield)

The unique Patchen Explorer is on show at The South African Air Force Museum. [SA22] (Chris Chatfield)

Above: The South African Airways Museum Society owns this Lockheed Lodestar. [SA26] (Ruud Leeuw)

Left: This Messerschmitt Bf 109E is displayed at the South African National Museum of Military History at Saxonwold. [SA27] (Chris Chatfield)

Right: This MiG-17 is preserved at the Organisation for Mine Clearance Museum in Kabul. [AF5] (Skillet)

Below: This Canadair Sabre is parked near the gate of Zahural Haque Air Force Base near Chittagong. [BA4] (Tim Spearman)

The War Museum at Siem Reip contains this Mil Mi-8T. [C1] (Peter R. Arnold)

This Beriev Be-6P can be seen at the China Aviation Museum. [CHI6] (John Mounce)

This Xian H-6 can be seen at the Oriental Boat Park. [CHI26] (Lloyd Robinson)

The Naval Aviation Museum at Dabolim is home to this Short Sealand. Behind is a Hawker Sea Hawk..

This Percival Prentice can be seen in the Indian Air Force Museum. [IDA49] (Lloyd Robinson)

Above: One of the gate guardians at Lohegaon Air Force Station is this MiG-21bis. [IDA63]

Right: The Indonesian Air Force Museum at Yogyakarta is home to two replicas of the Wiweko WEL-1. One is shown here. [IND19]

Above: This Spitfire once flown by Ezer Weizman is in the Israeli Air Force Museum at Hatzerim. (Aidan Curley)

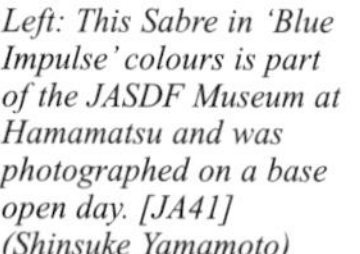

Left: This Sabre in 'Blue Impulse' colours is part of the JASDF Museum at Hamamatsu and was photographed on a base open day. [JA41] (Shinsuke Yamamoto)

The Shin Meiwa company modified this Grumman Albatross for flying boat research. The aircraft is on show at the Kakamigahara Aerospace Museum. [JA48] (Shinsuke Yamamoto)

Above: The Tokorozawa Aviation Museum has several helicopters on view including this Vertol V.44A. [JA126]

Right: The Lebanese Air Force is establishing a museum at Rayak Air Force Base. The collection includes this Alouette II. [LEB1] (Piet Luijken)

The Royal Malaysian Air Force Museum is home to this Percival Provost. [MALA13] (Aidan Curley)

Left: A view of part of the main hall of the Defence Services Museum in Yangon. In the foreground is a Spitfire LF.IXe, behind a Seafire F.XV and at the end of the row a Provost T.53. To the left is a C-47B. [MY1] (Peter R. Arnold)

The Victorious Fatherland Liberation War Museum in Pyongyang has this Yak-18 on show. [NK3] (Phil Dunnington)

On outside display at the Pakistan Air Force Museum are this MiG-15UTI and Martin B-57B Canberra. [PAK28] (Via Usman Shabbir)

This Shenyang F-6C is spectacularly mounted at Sargodha Air Force Base. [PAK41] (Paul Harrison Photography).

Above: A rare exhibit at the new Philippine Air Force Museum is this Temco Super Pinto.[PH7] (Lloyd Robinson)

Right: This Yakovlev Yak-9 is preserved in Novosibirsk. [RUS24] (Gleb Osokin)

This impressive line up is at Salekhard Airport. [RUS43] (Marek Chojnowski)

This Temco Buckaroo is housed in the Royal Saudi Air Force Museum. [SAU4] (Lloyd Robinson)

The Singapore Air Force Museum is home to this SIAI-Marchetti SF.260MS. [SI3] (Douglas Rough)

The impressive War Memorial Museum in Seoul has on show this example of the indigenous KTX-1. [SKO49] (John Mounce)

The Sri Lankan Air Force operated a small number of Chipmunks and this example is in their museum. [SR2] (Tim Spearman)

On show in the War Museum in Damascus is this MiG-21PFM. [SY4] (Piet Luijken)

Above: *This Grumman Albatross is parked outside the main hall of the Taiwan Taoyuan International Airport Museum. [TA59] (Chris Chatfield)*

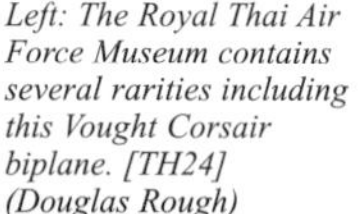

Left: The Royal Thai Air Force Museum contains several rarities including this Vought Corsair biplane. [TH24] (Douglas Rough)

This Cessna A-37B Dragonfly can be seen at the War Remants Museum in Ho Chi Minh City. (Lloyd Robinson)

Above: This Messerschmitt Bf 109G is on show in the Australian War Memorial. [AUS1] (Nigel Hitchman)

Right: The second Harley Newman Gyrocopter can be seen in the Australian Aviation Museum at Bankstown. [AUS3] (Nigel Hitchman)

Below: The only complete Vultee Vengeance is in the Camden Museum of Aviation. [AUS7] (Nigel Hitchman)

Above: The Historical Aviation Restoration Society operates this de Havilland Drover. [AUS15] (Nigel Hitchman)

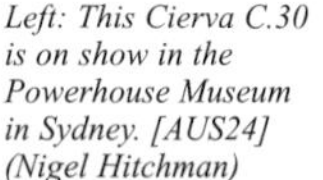

Left: This Cierva C.30 is on show in the Powerhouse Museum in Sydney. [AUS24] (Nigel Hitchman)

The Central Australian Aviation Museum at Alice Springs is home to this Commonwealth Wackett. [AUS41] (Eric Munk)

The only aircraft at the Katherine Museum is a D.H.60M Moth used by the pioneering doctor Clyde Fenton. [AUS42]

Above: The collection of the Queensland Air Museum includes this Piaggio P.166A [AUS62] (Eric Munk)

Right: The Avro Baby flown by Bert Hinkler is on show in the Queensland Museum.[AUS63] (Eric Munk)

Above: The only genuine Bristol M.1C resides in the Captain Harry Butler Memorial at Minlaton. [AUS73]

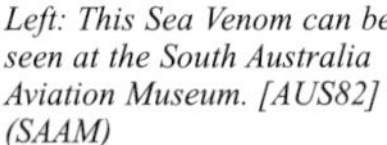

Left: This Sea Venom can be seen at the South Australia Aviation Museum. [AUS82] (SAAM)

This Catalina is displayed at the Lake Boga Flying Boat Museum. [AUS99]

ISRAEL

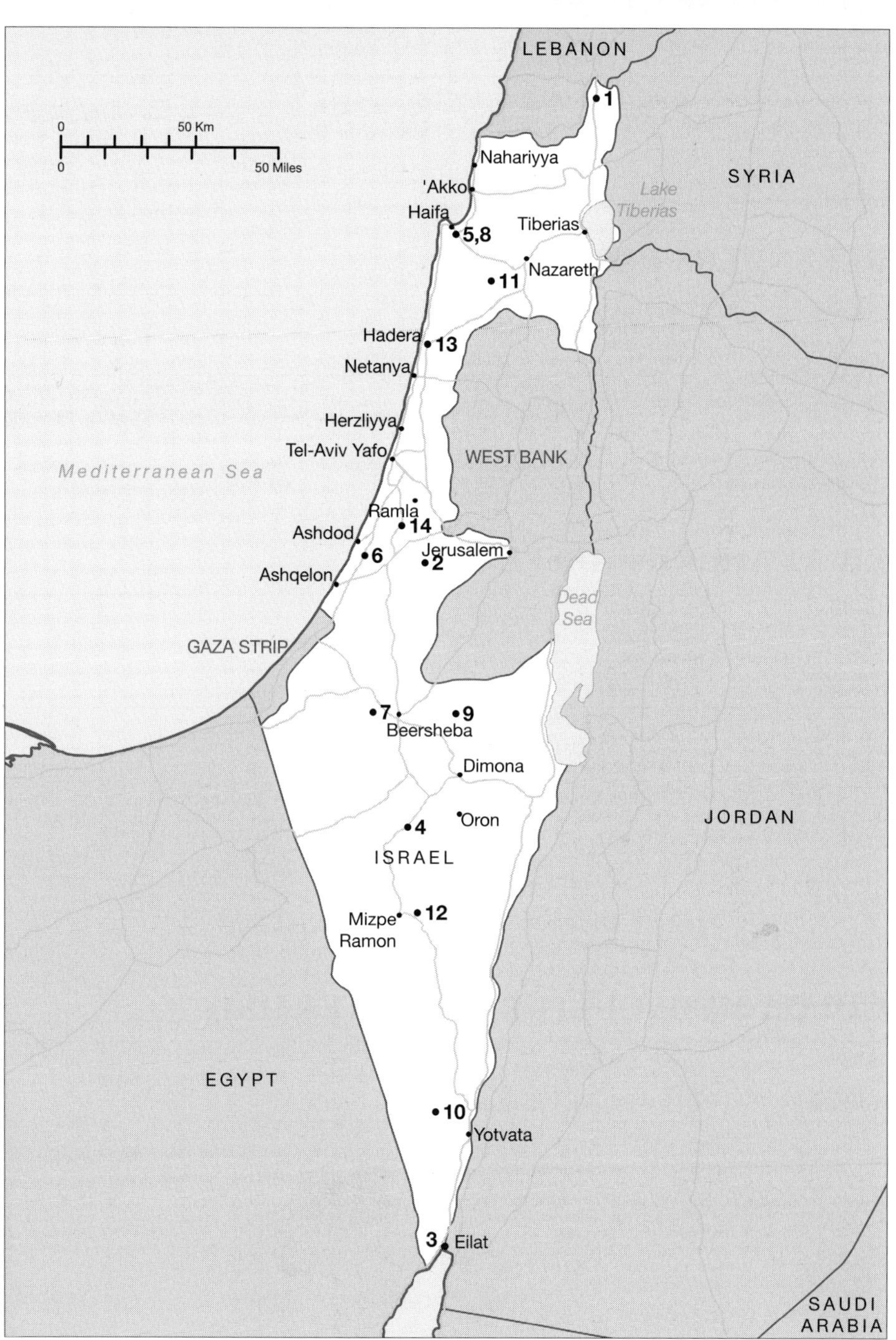
LEBANON
SYRIA
0
50 Km
0
50 Miles
Nahariyya
'Akko
Haifa
5,8
Tiberias
Lake Tiberias
Nazareth
11
Hadera
13
Netanya
Herzliyya
Tel-Aviv Yafo
WEST BANK
Mediterranean Sea
Ramla
14
Ashdod
6
Jerusalem
2
Ashqelon
Dead Sea
GAZA STRIP
7
9
Beersheba
Dimona
Oron
4
JORDAN
ISRAEL
Mizpe Ramon
12
EGYPT
10
Yotvata
3
Eilat
SAUDI ARABIA
1

BEIT HASHOMER MUSEUM (IS1)

Address:	Kfar Giladi 12210.
Tel:	04-694-1565
Admission:	Sunday-Thursday 0800-1530; Friday 08001-200;Saturday 0900-1200.
Location:	North east of Misgav'Am.

This museum located on the Kfar Giladi Kibbutz traces the history of the region and the setting up of the commune. A Vautour IIA is a recent addition to the collection. Twenty five of the thirty IIAs built were acquired by Israel in the mid-1950s and they were operated for several years.

TYPE	REG/SER	CON. NO.	PI/NOTES	STATUS
☐ Sud-Ouest SO-4050 Vautour IIA	29	8	8 (France)	PV

DEFENDERS PARK (IS2)

Address:	Kibbutz Nahshon, Nachshon Junction 99760.
Admission:	On permanent view
Location:	About 5 km south west of Latrun.

This park honours the contribution of Israelis in the defence of their country. The German built Noratlas is on show along with a number of military vehicles and tanks. The area has seen fighting in the many wars with insurgents. Also on display are military vehicles, tanks and items of artillery.

TYPE	REG/SER	CON. NO.	PI/NOTES	STATUS
☐ Nord N.2501D Noratlas	072/4X-FAW	089	GB+251	PV

EILAT AIRPORT DISPLAY (IS3)

Address:	Arava Road, Eilat 88000.
Tel:	08-636-3838
Fax:	08-636-3829
Admission:	On permanent view.
Location:	In the eastern part of the town.

The airport was built in 1949 for use by the Israeli Air Force and for civil flights around the country. In 1950 Arkia Airlines became the largest airline at the field and started regular flights to many cities. The company was formed in 1949 as Israel Inland Airlines with a fleet of de Havilland Dragon Rapides. DC-3s were soon acquired to cope with the increased demand. A former Israeli Air Force aircraft has been put on show to honour the pioneering era of Arkia. The aicraft has painted in the colours of one of the first used by the company. The airliner was put on show with a display board in the spring of 2004. The airport, which is very close to the town, is scheduled to close in 2010 so hopefully the DC-3 will be saved and preserved elsewhere.

TYPE	REG/SER	CON. NO.	PI/NOTES	STATUS
☐ Douglas DC-3A-360 Skytrain (C-47) (Dakota I)	'4X-AES'	6223	42-5635, FD769, G-AGFX, ZS-DAI, G-AGFX, 4X-FAG/04, U-401 (Uganda), 4X-DCF, 4X-FMF/04, N473DK	PVX

GOLDA MEIR CULTURAL CENTER (IS4)

Address:	Kibbutz Revivim, Doar-Na-Halutza 85515.
Admission:	Daily.
Location:	About 40 km south of Beersheba.

Kibbutz living is an essential part of Israeli culture and many such establishments have played an important role in the defence of the country. Revivim set up a museum to show its history in the 1948 conflict which followed the creation of Israel. The display includes photographs, models, documents and personal items. On show is a collection of period armoured cars and weapons along with two aircraft. The first three C-47s used by the Israeli Air Force were acquired from South Africa and by the mid-1960s around thirty were in use. The Piper Super Cub has been used for liaison, airborne observation and training duties for many years. A cultural complex dedicated to Golda Meir is at the site. She was born in Russia in 1898 and after serving in a number of ministerial roles she became Prime Minister in 1969. She resigned in 1974 and died four years later.

TYPE	REG/SER	CON. NO.	PI/NOTES	STATUS
☐ Douglas DC-3A-456 Skytrain (C-47A)	026/4X-FNS		(USAAF)	PV
☐ Piper PA-18-150 Super Cub	13			PV

HAIFA AIR FORCE BASE COLLECTION (IS5)

Address:	Haifa Airport, Military Section, Doar-Tzvai, 02148 Tel Aviv. – Attn P.R. Officer.
Admission:	By prior permission only.
Location:	On the southern outskirts of the city.

Haifa airport was the first airfield in Palestine to have concrete runways. Constructed in 1934 for use by the Iraq Petroleum Company, the field saw limited use for a number of years. Egyptian and Italian airlines operated services for periods up to the outbreak of World War II. The Royal Air Force took over the site in 1941 and Hurricanes were based there until 1942. Civilian flying resumed in the late 1940s but it was not until the mid-1980s that international flights resumed. In the late 1950s the Israeli Air Force opened a technical school in the former Royal Air Force area. In the mid-1980s a decision was taken to set up a collection to complement the Air Force Museum at Hatzerim. The outdoor display shows a range of types which have served with the force over recent years. The oldest aircraft on show is the C-47 which flew in the 1948 war. The Mystère '30' has been at Haifa since 1965 – nine years earlier it shot down an Egyptian MiG-15 during the conflict which followed the nationalisation of the Suez Canal by Egypt. The Kfir carries a Syrian roundel below its cockpit which indicates it gained a victory in one of the battles which have taken place in the region. France has supplied many aircraft to Israel and a large proportion of the collection come from this country. The Magister was delivered to Israel in 1961 and modified by Israeli Aircraft Industries in 1984. The I.A.F. operated thirty nine Fokker Instructor trainers. There is also an Air Force Technical Training School on the base where several instructional airframes are in use. These are listed along with some stored for possible future preservation.

TYPE	REG/SER	CON. NO.	PI/NOTES	STATUS
☐ Bell 209 Huey Cobra (AH-1G) (AH-1Q)	130			RA
☐ Bell 209 Huey Cobra (AH-1G) (AH-1S)	667		(USAF) – stored.	RA
☐ Boeing-Stearman A75N1 Kaydet (PT-17)	'55'	75-1846	41-8287, 2713, 13	RAX
☐ Dassault MD-450 Ouragan	'68'		(France), 60	RAX
☐ Dassault Mystère IVA	37		(France), 4537	RA
☐ Dassault Mystère IVA	52	165	165 (France), 6652, 4552	PV
☐ Dassault Mystère IVA	30	223	223 (France), 6648, 4530	RA
☐ Dornier Do 27B-1	039	204	PE+107, PE+104, LA+151, AC+919, 55+64, N9536	RA
☐ Douglas A-4H Skyhawk	215		(USN)	RA
☐ Douglas A-4N Skyhawk	341		(USN) -stored.	RA
☐ Douglas DC-3A-456 Skytrain (C-47A)	005/4X-FNB	19420	42-100957, F-BAXN, 1405 (Israel) 860 (Israel)	RA
☐ Fokker S.11.2 Instructor (S.11)	'22'	6223	PH-NEK, X-24, 12	RAX
☐ Ford Philco RPV				RA
☐ General Dynamics 401 Fighter Falcon (F-16A)	750	61-132	79-0347 – front fuselage only – in Technical School.	RA
☐ General Dynamics 401 Fighter Falcon (F-16A)	791		In Technical School.	RA
☐ Israeli Aircraft Industries Kfir C.2	821	44		RA
☐ Israeli Aircraft Industries Kurnass 2000 [McDonnell M.98HO Phantom II (F-4E)]	001		(USAF), 304	RA
☐ Israeli Aircraft Industries Tsukit [Fouga CM.170]	647	170	170 (French)	RA
☐ McDonnell M.199-1A Eagle (F-15A)	393	A027	73-0093	RA
☐ McDonnell M.199-1A Eagle (F-15A)	622		(USAF) – in Technical School.	RA
☐ McDonnell M.98HO Phantom II (F-4E)	001		(USAF)	RA
☐ Nord N.2501D Noratlas	056/4X-FAH	167	KA+178, GB+237, 307 (Nigeria) (ntu)	PV
☐ North American NA-78 Texan ((SNJ-3)	10	78-6169	Bu6932, NC58412	RA
☐ North American NA-111 Mustang (P-51K)	'01'	111-29944	44-11811	RAX
☐ Piper PA-18-135 Super Cub (L-21B)	'07'	18-5128	58	RAX
☐ Sikorsky S-65A Sea Stallion (CH-53A)	873		Bu154870	RA
☐ Sud SA.321K Super Frelon	008	110		RA
☐ Sud-Est SE.3130 Alouette II	'021'	1963	12, 010 may be c/n 1884 or 1887.	RAX
☐ Sud-Ouest SO-4050 Vautour IIA	12	36	17 (France)	RA

HATZOR AIR FORCE BASE COLLECTION (IS6)

Address:	Hatzor 79630.
Admission:	By prior permission only.
Location:	About 10 km south east of Ashdod.

Hatzor is a former Royal Air Force base and since the creation of Israel has served as an important fighter station. For many years an Avia CS.199 (Czechoslakian-built Messerschmitt Bf 109) was housed at the site but this moved to Hatzerim in the 1980s. A collection of fighters has been assembled to show the role of the base over the years. The former Egyptian Air Force MiG-15 was the first of the type captured by Israel. The Skyhawk was never flown in Israel and came from the U.S.A. for instructional use. Four examples of the range of fighters produced by the Dassault company in France can be seen. The Ouragan first flew in 1949 and seventy five were supplied to Israel. The swept wing Mystère IVA made its maiden flight in 1952 and sixty one were delivered to the I.A.F. The Super Mystère B2 was the first European production type capable of achieving supersonic speed in level flight and two dozen were supplied. The classic delta wing Mirage III flew in prototype form in 1958 and served with distinction in more than a dozen nations. Seventy two were delivered with the first pair arriving at Hatzor in April 1962 for operation by No. 101 Squadron. The F-16 is a recent addition to the collection.

Left: The Military Museum in Tehran has on show this F-84G Thunderjet. (Sharam Shafiri)

Below: Ramat David Air Force Base in Israel has a collection of preserved aircraft which includes this Meteor FR.9. (Ofer Zidan via Steve Comber)

The collection at Tel Nof Air Force Base includes this Super Frelon. (Steve Comber)

TYPE	REG/SER	CON. NO.	PI/NOTES	STATUS
☐ Dassault MD-450 Ouragan	70		(France)	RAX
☐ Dassault Mirage IIICJ	'101'		(French), 144	RAX
☐ Dassault Mystère IVA	'80'			RAX
☐ Dassault Super Mystère B2	60	141	141 (France)	RA
☐ Douglas A-4E Skyhawk (A4D-5)	'01'			RAX
☐ General Dynamics 401 Fighting Falcon (F-16A)	765			RA
☐ Israeli Aircraft Industries Kfir C.2	869			RA
☐ McDonnell M.98HO Phantom II (F-4E)	202		(USAF)	RA
☐ Mikoyan-Gurevich MiG-15			(Egypt)	RA

ISRAELI AIR FORCE MUSEUM (IS7)

Address:	APO 2832, Hatzerim Air Force Base.
Tel:	08-990-6853
Admission:	Sunday-Thursday 0900-1600; Friday 0900-1300.
Location:	About 20 km west of Beersheba.

Israel came into existence on May 14th 1948 and on that day was attacked by five Arab countries. Prior to this a small military air service had flown a number of lightplanes, mainly Austers, painted in Palestine civil colours. Two Egyptian Air Force Spitfires entered Israeli airspace the following day and the search for combat aircraft started. A small number of Mosquitos and Spitfires were built up from airframes left behind on dumps by the Royal Air Force and aircraft were acquired from sympathetic European countries. Over the next decade supplies came from France, Sweden and the U.S.A. The force became renowned for its combat prowess and is now one of the most modern in the region. This museum was established at Hatzerim in 1978 and has grown rapidly. A Society of Friends has helped in the construction of exhibition areas, a lecture theatre, a cinema and an administration block. Photographs, documents, uniforms, engines and components are exhibited. Aircraft have been acquired from around the world to fill gaps in the inventory. In one deal a Hunter from Chile was exchanged for a Mystère IV. Three aircraft were bought in the United Kingdom, an Auster, a Dragon Rapide and a Harvard. A Vampire trainer came from Venezuela, a Venom from Switzerland and a Fouga Magister from Belgium. The famous black Spitfire once flown by Ezer Weizman is still in airworthy condition. The CS. 199 was formerly on show at Hatzor and this has been superbly restored. Nine Meteors of four different marks can be seen. Eleven F.8s and four T.7s were supplied by Gloster in 1953 and were joined from Belgium by two T.7s with F.8 tail units. Flight Refuelling converted seven former R.A.F. FR.9s the following year. Six ex-R.A.F. NF.13s were delivered in 1956 with the first two arriving just in time for the Suez conflict. From the same period are a number of Ouragans and Mystères. Four Beaufighters were flown to Palestine in 1948 ostensibly for use by a film company. The remains of one of these has been found and put on show. Israeli Aircraft Industries products feature prominently. The Tsukit is an updated Fouga Magister, the Saar is a modified Super Mystère and the Nesher and Kfir are improved Mirage 5s. The Lavi was designed to serve as a multi-role combat aircraft. The first prototype flew on December 31st 1986 and the second three months later. The original plans called for over three hundred to be produced but the programme was cancelled in August 1987. Small numbers of Slingsby gliders were ordered for club use in the 1950s and some of these have survived. The largest aircraft on show are the pair of Boeing Stratofreighters, the two 707s and the 720. A batch of Phantoms arrived in the late 1990s and these along with many other withdrawn aircraft are stored in revetments close to the museum site. More types are expected in the near future. This excellent collection traces the history of the Israeli Air Force which for many years had been shrouded in secrecy.

TYPE	REG/SER	CON. NO.	PI/NOTES	STATUS
☐ Aero Jet Commander 1121	4X-COA	1121-71	N1500M, N150CM, N150CT, N150HR, N71JC, N721GB	PV
☐ Agusta-Bell 204B	135			RA
☐ Agusta-Bell 205A	002	4020		PV
☐ Agusta-Bell 206B Jet Ranger	040	8538	OE-DXL	PV
☐ Auster E AOP.3				RAD
☐ Auster J AOP.5			Front fuselage only.	PV
☐ Auster J/1 Autocrat	13	1956	G-AHAY, 'VQ-PAS', 1948	PVA
☐ Avia CS-199 [Messerschmitt Bf 109G-12]	'D-112'	782358	'04'	PVX
☐ Beech 65-B80 Queen Air	104	LD-481		PV
☐ Beech 65-B80 Queen Air	109	LD-489		PV
☐ Bell 209 Huey Cobra (AH-1G) (AH-1F)	115	20710	68-15176	PV
☐ Bell 209 Huey Cobra (AH-1G) (AH-1F)	'444'		021	PVX
☐ Bell 212	026	32227		PV
☐ Boeing 367-76-66 Stratofreighter (KC-97G)	039/4X-FPN	16767	52-2736	PV
☐ Boeing 367-76-66 Stratofreighter (KC-97G)	035/4X-FPQ	16830	52-2799	PV
☐ Boeing 707-131F (131)	008/4X-JYD	17667	N740TW, (4X-BYH), 4X-BYD, 4X-JYD, 4X-BYD	PV
☐ Boeing 707-328	'103'	17617	F-BHSE, 4X-BYW, 116/4X-JYW	PVX
☐ Boeing 720-023B	4X-JYG/010	18013	N7527A, G-BCBB, 6O-SAU, C9-ARG, G-BCBB, 4R-ACS, G-BCBB, 4X-BMB	RA
☐ Boeing-Stearman A75N1 Kaydet (PT-17)	'32'	75-3015	41-25508, N60015, 4X-AII	RADX
☐ Boeing-Stearman A75N1 Kaydet (PT-17)	022	75-4291	42-16128	RAD
☐ Boeing-Stearman A75N1 Kaydet (PT-17)	2752	75-5096	41-25357, N1148N, 4X-AIK c/n 5096 is 42-16933 – 41-25357 is c/n 75-2852	RAA
☐ Boeing-Stearman A75N1 Kaydet (PT-17)	'02'			PVX
☐ Boeing-Stearman E75 Kaydet (PT-13D)	'31'	75-5777	42-17614, N?????, N4991T, 2745, 4X-ACH	PVAX
☐ Bristol 156 Beaufighter TT.10 (TF.X)	171		RD448, G-AJMC	PVD
☐ Britten-Norman BN-2A Islander	001/4X-FMA	107	G-51-40, 4X-AYW, 006	RA
☐ Britten-Norman BN-2A-2 Islander	004/4X-FMD	285	G-51-285, G-AZBV, (EI-AVO), 4X-AYK, 4X-FNP	PVA
☐ Cessna U206D Super Skywagon	031	U2061313	N1698C	RAD

☐ Cessna U206D Super Skywagon	059	U2061536		PV
☐ Consolidated 28-6A Catalina (PBY-6A)	N285RA	2087	Bu64017, N2864D, N555H, F-ZBAV, CF-HNH, C-FHNH, N212DM, G-BPFY, N212DM, G-BPFY, N212DM	RA
☐ Dassault MD-450 Ouragan	69	204	204 (France)	RA
☐ Dassault MD-450 Ouragan	80	218	218 (France)	PV
☐ Dassault MD-450 Ouragan	'113'	233	233 (France), 108	RAX
☐ Dassault MD-450 Ouragan	82	241	241 (France)	RA
☐ Dassault MD-450 Ouragan	94	328	328 (France)	RA
☐ Dassault MD-450 Ouragan	49	332	332 (France), 49	PVX
☐ Dassault Mystère IVA	'007'	71	71 (France)	PVX
☐ Dassault Mystère IVA	41	152	152 (France), 6641, 4541	RA
☐ Dassault Mystère IVA	60	173	173 (France), 6642, 4560 – also reported as c/n 172.	PV
☐ Dassault Mystère IVA	09	176	176 (France), 6646, 4564	PV
☐ Dassault Mystère IVA	'11'	214	214 (France), 4X-FWA, 4510	RAX
☐ Dassault Mystère IVA	10	216	216 (France), 4X-FWB, 4510	RA
☐ Dassault Mystère IVA	92	225	225 (France)	RA
☐ Dassault Mystère IVA	30	233	233 (France)	RA
☐ Dassault Mystère IVA	82	241	241 (France), 4580	RA
☐ Dassault Mirage IIIBJ Barak	988		88, 288 – Kfir TC.1 conversion.	PV
☐ Dassault Mirage IIICJ	'158'	6	111, '159'	PVX
☐ Dassault Mirage IIICJ	'159'	CJ-42	C-713 (Argentina)	PV
☐ De Havilland D.H.82A Tiger Moth	'VQ-PAU'		Composite.	PVX
☐ De Havilland D.H.89A Dragon Rapide (D.H.89B Dominie I)	'VQ-PAR'	6952	RL981, G-AKRS, 4X-970, '002'	PVX
☐ De Havilland D.H.98 Mosquito FB.VI			Wings and engines only.	PVD
☐ De Havilland D.H.100 Vampire FB.5	'L158'	V.0699	255 (South Africa), R1839 – in false Lebanese Markings.	PVX
☐ De Havilland D.H.112 Venom FB.1	'353'	726	J-1516 (Switzerland) – in false Iraqi markings.	PVX
☐ De Havilland D.H.115 Vampire T.55	'0053'	15809	2E35 (Venezuela) – in false Egyptian markings.	PVX
☐ Dornier Do 27A-4	033/4X-FIH	474	KD+132, EA+386, 57+43, D-EERI	PV
☐ Dornier Do 27A-4 (A-1)	019	258	PH+106, PC+106, AC+963, 19	PVD
☐ Dornier Do 27Q-1	036			RA
☐ Dornier Do 27Q-1	025	2015	D-ELON, N8323	RAD
☐ Dornier Do 27Q-1	'100'	2016	D-EMYS, D-EMAM, F-OBOV, 027	PVX
☐ Dornier Do 28B-1	005/4X-FTI	3113	N8933, L-613, 4X-FIJ	PV
☐ Douglas A-4E Skyhawk (A4D-5)	891	13017	Bu149964	RA
☐ Douglas A-4E Skyhawk (A4D-5)	814	13309	Bu151139	RA
☐ Douglas A-4E Skyhawk (A4D-5)	885	13349	Bu151179	RA
☐ Douglas A-4E Skyhawk (A4D-5)	854	13438	Bu152050	RA
☐ Douglas A-4E Skyhawk (A4D-5)	844	13481	Bu152099	RA
☐ Douglas A-4E Skyhawk (A4D-5)	884	13485	Bu152097	RA
☐ Douglas A-4F Skyhawk	611	13782	Bu155010	PV
☐ Douglas A-4H Skyhawk	222	13948	Bu155254	RA
☐ Douglas A-4H Skyhawk	229	13963	Bu155269	RA
☐ Douglas A-4H Skyhawk	230	13965	Bu155271	RA
☐ Douglas A-4H Skyhawk	261	13981	Bu155287	RA
☐ Douglas A-4H Skyhawk	270	13983	Bu155289	PV
☐ Douglas A-4H Skyhawk	232		(USN)	PV
☐ Douglas A-4N Skyhawk	379	14515	Bu159816	RA
☐ Douglas A-4N Skyhawk	307		(USN)	RA
☐ Douglas A-4N Skyhawk	314		(USN)	PV
☐ Douglas A-4N Skyhawk	316		(USN) rear fuselage	RA
☐ Douglas A-4N Skyhawk	337		(USN)	RA
☐ Douglas A-4N Skyhawk	339		(USN)	RA
☐ Douglas A-4N Skyhawk	340		(USN)	RA
☐ Douglas A-4N Skyhawk	357		(USN)	PV
☐ Douglas A-4N Skyhawk	359		(USN)	RA
☐ Douglas A-4N Skyhawk	364		(USN)	RA
☐ Douglas A-4N Skyhawk	365		(USN)	RA
☐ Douglas A-4N Skyhawk	367		(USN)	RA
☐ Douglas A-4N Skyhawk	368		(USN)	RA
☐ Douglas A-4N Skyhawk	371		(USN)	RA
☐ Douglas A-4N Skyhawk	377		(USN)	RA
☐ Douglas A-4N Skyhawk	385		(USN)	RA
☐ Douglas A-4N Skyhawk	393		(USN)	RA
☐ Douglas A-4N Skyhawk	397		(USN) rear fuselage	RA
☐ Douglas A-4N Skyhawk	399		(USN)	RA
☐ Douglas A-4N Skyhawk	407		(USN)	RA
☐ Douglas DC-3A-456 Skytrain (C-47A) (Dakota III)	004/4X-FNL	12486	42-92661, KG451, G-AIYT, ZS-BCJ, 1404	RA
☐ Douglas DC-3A-467 Skytrain (C-47B)	038/4X-FNZ	16559/33307	44-76975, 476975 (French), 76975 (French), (Israel), (Uganda) – c/n 16559/33307 also reported as 029/4X-FNT.	PV
☐ Douglas DC-3A-467 Skytrain (C-47B) (Dakota IV)	042/4X-FNJ	16283/33031	44-76699, KN503, 476699 (French), 037/4X-FNW, 4X-DCB	PV
☐ Fokker S.11.2 Instructor (S.11)	3139	6232	X-33, 4X-ADM	RAD
☐ Fokker S.11.2 Instructor (S.11)	3140	6235	X-36, 4X-ANB	RAD

☐ Fokker S.11.2 Instructor (S.11)	'05'	6256	PH-NFV, X-57, 4X-ANC, 3137	PVX
☐ Ford Philco RPV				PVA
☐ Ford Philco RPV				RA
☐ Fouga CM.170R Magister				PV
☐ Fouga CM.170R Magister	214	214		RAD
☐ Fouga CM.170R Magister	'212'	278	MT-21 (Belgium), 184	PVX
☐ Gloster Meteor T.7	15		(RAF), G-7-107, 2164	PV
☐ Gloster Meteor T.7	18		WL466, G-7-132, 2171, 112	PV
☐ Gloster Meteor T.7/8	21		(RAF)	RAC
☐ Gloster Meteor F.8	40		WA905	PV
☐ Gloster Meteor F.8	06		(RAF), G-7-117, 2173	PV
☐ Gloster Meteor FR.9	37		WL259, G-7-125, 212	RAD
☐ Gloster Meteor NF.13	50/4X-FND	5571	WM309, 2159	RA
☐ Gloster Meteor NF.13	157/4X-FNE	5582	WM320, 2160, 4X-FNE, BK801, 4X-BET	PVA
☐ Gloster Meteor NF.13	51	5600	WM334, 2157, 4X-FNB	PV
☐ Grumman G-40 Avenger (TBM-3) (TBM-3E)	'34'	2094	Bu69355, N7850C – in false RAF markings.	PVX
☐ Grumman G-40 Avenger (TBM-3) (TBM-3U)	'829'	4646	Bu91741, N6829C	RA
☐ Grumman G-123 Hawkeye (E-2C)	944	A44	Bu160773	PV
☐ Hawker P.1099 Hunter FGA.71 (F.6)		S4U 3276	XF376, J-747 (Chile) – in false Jordanian markings.	PVX
☐ Hiller UH12A	3301	105	N8105H – parts only.	RAD
☐ Hughes 500MD Defender	204	89-0550D		PV
☐ Hughes 500MD Defender	203			RA
☐ Hughes 500MD Defender	206			RA
☐ Hughes 500MD Defender	209			RA
☐ Hughes 500MD Defender	212			PV
☐ Hughes 500MD Defender	215			RA
☐ Hughes 500MD Defender	217			RA
☐ Hughes 500MD Defender	218			RA
☐ Hughes 500MD Defender	221			RA
☐ Hughes 500MD Defender	222			RA
☐ Hughes 500MD Defender	225			RA
☐ Hughes 500MD Defender	242			RA
☐ Hughes 500MD Defender	254			RA
☐ Hughes 500MD Defender	282			RA
☐ Israeli Aircraft Industries IAI.202 Arava	203/4X-JUB	101		PV
☐ Israeli Aircraft Industries Kfir C.1 (F-21A)	703		703, Bu999703	S
☐ Israeli Aircraft Industries Kfir C.1 (F-21A)	724		724, Bu999724	S
☐ Israeli Aircraft Industries Kfir C.1 (F-21A)	725		725, Bu999725	RA
☐ Israeli Aircraft Industries Kfir C.1 (F-21A)	764	29	764, Bu999764	PV
☐ Israeli Aircraft Industries Kfir C.1 (Nesher A)	712	01		PV
☐ Israeli Aircraft Industries Kfir C.1R	419		719	RA
☐ Israeli Aircraft Industries Kfir C.2	874	74		PV
☐ Israeli Aircraft Industries Kfir C.2	664			S
☐ Israeli Aircraft Industries Kfir C.2	826			RA
☐ Israeli Aircraft Industries Kfir C.2	853			RA
☐ Israeli Aircraft Industries Kfir C.2	886			RA
☐ Israeli Aircraft Industries Kfir C.2	895			RA
☐ Israeli Aircraft Industries Kfir C.7 (C.2)	514			RA
☐ Israeli Aircraft Industries Kfir C.7 (C.2)	529	178		PV
☐ Israeli Aircraft Industries Kfir RF	451	47	725 – c/n may be 34.	PV
☐ Israeli Aircraft Industries Kfir TC.2	310			PV
☐ Israeli Aircraft Industries Kfir TC.2	988		Prototype	PV
☐ Israeli Aircraft Industries Kurnass 2000 [McDonnell M.98HO Phantom II (F-4E)]	4X-JPA/229	2594	66-0327, 334	PV
☐ Israeli Aircraft Industries Kurnass 2000 [McDonnell M.98HO Phantom II (F-4E)]	614			PV
☐ Israeli Aircraft Industries Lavi	B-2			PV
☐ Israeli Aircraft Industries Nesher A [Dassault Mirage 5J]	501	01	Original c/n 586.	PVA
☐ Israeli Aircraft Industries Saar (Dassault Super Mystère B2)	096	06	06 (French)	PV
☐ Israeli Aircraft Industries Tsukit [Fouga CM.170]	603	03		RA
☐ Israeli Aircraft Industries Tsukit [Fouga CM.170]	607	07		RA
☐ Israeli Aircraft Industries Tsukit [Fouga CM.170]	623	23		RA
☐ Israeli Aircraft Industries Tsukit [Fouga CM.170]	528	28	Original c/n 008 serial 272.	RA
☐ Israeli Aircraft Industries Tsukit [Fouga CM.170]	629	29		RA
☐ Israeli Aircraft Industries Tsukit [Fouga CM.170]	630	30	Original c/n 152 serial 181.	PV
☐ Israeli Aircraft Industries Tsukit [Fouga CM.170]	634	34	Original c/n 132, 109, 634, '689' – on base gate.	RAX
☐ Israeli Aircraft Industries Tsukit [Fouga CM.170]	635	35	Original c/n 087 serial 022.	PV
☐ Israeli Aircraft Industries Tsukit [Fouga CM.170]	639	39		RA
☐ Israeli Aircraft Industries Tsukit [Fouga CM.170]	540	40	Original c/n 016 serial 280.	RA
☐ Israeli Aircraft Industries Tsukit [Fouga CM.170]	645	45	Original c/n 190 serial 153.	PV
☐ Israeli Aircraft Industries Tsukit [Fouga CM.170]	652	52	Original c/n 071 serial 045.	RA
☐ Israeli Aircraft Industries Tsukit [Fouga CM.170]	555	55	Original c/n 002 serial 216.	RA
☐ Israeli Aircraft Industries Tsukit [Fouga CM.170]	659	59	Original c/n 111, 102, 659, '689' – on base gate.	RA
☐ Israeli Aircraft Industries Tsukit [Fouga CM.170]	670	70	Original c/n 188 or 138 serial 197.	RA
☐ Israeli Aircraft Industries Tsukit [Fouga CM.170]	673	73		RA
☐ Israeli Aircraft Industries Tsukit [Fouga CM.170]	677	77	Original c/n 111 serial 153.	PV
☐ Israeli Aircraft Industries Tsukit [Fouga CM.170]	584	84	Original c/n 004 serial 218.	RA

☐ Israeli Aircraft Industries Tsukit [Fouga CM.170]	685	85		RA
☐ McDonnell M.98DF Phantom II (RF-4C)	141	3634	68-0602	PV
☐ McDonnell M.98HO Phantom II (F-4E)	327	3203	67-0346	RA
☐ McDonnell M.98HO Phantom II (F-4E)	333	3250	67-0368	RA
☐ McDonnell M.98HO Phantom II (F-4E)	326	3281	67-0383	RA
☐ McDonnell M.98HO Phantom II (F-4E)	323	3461	68-0380	PV
☐ McDonnell M.98HO Phantom II (F-4E)	108	3494	68-0398	RA
☐ McDonnell M.98HO Phantom II (F-4E)	122	3529	68-0417	RA
☐ McDonnell M.98HO Phantom II (F-4E)	134	3682	68-0499	RA
☐ McDonnell M.98HO Phantom II (F-4E)	321	3686	68-0502	RA
☐ McDonnell M.98HO Phantom II (F-4E)	171	3721	68-0524	RA
☐ McDonnell M.98HO Phantom II (F-4E)	178	3744	68-0540	RA
☐ McDonnell M.98HO Phantom II (F-4E)	187	3751	68-0544	RA
☐ McDonnell M.98HO Phantom II (F-4E)	141	3834	69-0294	RA
☐ McDonnell M.98HO Phantom II (F-4E)	193	3837	69-0296	RA
☐ McDonnell M.98HO Phantom II (F-4E)	111	3840	69-0299	RA
☐ McDonnell M.98HO Phantom II (F-4E)	124	3887	69-7224, 624	RA
☐ McDonnell M.98HO Phantom II (F-4E)	127	3890	69-7226	RA
☐ McDonnell M.98HO Phantom II (F-4E)	131	3908	69-7237	RA
☐ McDonnell M.98HO Phantom II (F-4E)	153	3915	69-7243	RA
☐ McDonnell M.98HO Phantom II (F-4E)	152	3918	69-7244	RA
☐ McDonnell M.98HO Phantom II (F-4E)	156	3920	69-7245	PV
☐ McDonnell M.98HO Phantom II (F-4E)	159	3998	69-7553	RA
☐ McDonnell M.98HO Phantom II (F-4E)	148	4021	69-7569	RA
☐ McDonnell M.98HO Phantom II (F-4E)	328	4032	69-7577	RA
☐ McDonnell M.98HO Phantom II (F-4E)	170	4213	71-0227	RA
☐ McDonnell M.98HO Phantom II (F-4E)	189	4223	71-0235	RA
☐ McDonnell M.98HO Phantom II (F-4E)	314	4243	71-1074	RA
☐ McDonnell M.98HO Phantom II (F-4E)	208	4263	71-1090	RA
☐ McDonnell M.98HO Phantom II (F-4E)	210	4267	71-1093	RA
☐ McDonnell M.98HO Phantom II (F-4E)	317	4272	71-1394	RA
☐ McDonnell M.98HO Phantom II (F-4E)	225	4280	71-1402	RA
☐ McDonnell M.98HO Phantom II (F-4E)	261	4354	71-1791	RA
☐ McDonnell M.98HO Phantom II (F-4E)	266	4361	71-1792	RA
☐ McDonnell M.98HO Phantom II (F-4E)	277	4505	72-1495	RA
☐ McDonnell M.98HO Phantom II (F-4E)	295	4817	74-1014	RA
☐ McDonnell M.98HO Phantom II (F-4E)	297	4822	74-1015	PV
☐ McDonnell M.98HO Phantom II (F-4E)	149	4862	74-1018	RA
☐ McDonnell M.98HO Phantom II (F-4E)	223	4885	74-1027	RA
☐ McDonnell M.98HO Phantom II (F-4E)	322		(USAF)	RA
☐ McDonnell M.98HO Phantom II (F-4E)	332		(USAF)	RA
☐ McDonnell M.98LG Phantom II (RF-4E)	'496'	4023	69-7567, 498	PVX
☐ McDonnell M.98LG Phantom II (RF-4E)	189	4223	71-0235	
☐ McDonnell M.98LG Phantom II (RF-4E)	485		(USAF)	PV
☐ McDonnell M.98LG Phantom II (RF-4E)	488		(USAF)	RA
☐ McDonnell M.199-1A Eagle (F-15A)	'695'	A032	73-0098, 398 (Israel)	PVX
☐ McDonnell M.199-1A Eagle (F-15A)	669	IA006	76-1510 – front fuselage only.	PV
☐ Mikoyan-Gurevich MiG-17F	'1033'		513 – in false Syrian markings.	PVX
☐ Mikoyan-Gurevich MiG-19S			Egyptian Air Force – tail section only.	PVD
☐ Mikoyan-Gurevich MiG-21F-13	007		534 (Iraq)	PV
☐ Mikoyan-Gurevich MiG-23MLD	2786	0390324522	In Syrian markings.	PV
☐ Mil Mi-8T			(Egypt)	PVA
☐ Nederlandse Helicopter Industrie (NHI) H-3 Kolibrie	N88983	3006	PH-YMP, (4X-BDC), N88983, 4X-BEA	PVA
☐ Noorduyn Harvard IIB [North American NA-77 (AT-16)]	'1/1'	14-660	42-12413, FE926	RAD
☐ Noorduyn Norseman VI (C-64A) (UC-64A)	4X-ARS	769	44-70504	RAD
☐ Nord N.2501D Noratlas	043/4X-FAC	134	GC+124, GB+245, KA+145,	RA
☐ Nord N.2501D Noratlas	045/4X-FAE	151	KA+162, AS+558, GC+234,	PV
☐ Nord N.2501D Noratlas	055/4X-FAG	165	GB+235, KA+176, 305 (Nigerian), 4X-AOS	RA
☐ North American NA-77 Texan (AT-6A)	54	77-4576	41-0537	PV
☐ North American NA-77 Texan (AT-6A)	08	77-4613	41-0534 – c/n 77-4613 is 41-0654 – 41-0534 has c/n 77-4493.	PV
☐ North American NA-78 Texan (AT-6A)	'3/5'	78-6821	41-16443	RADX
☐ North American NA-78 Texan (AT-6A)	'1/3'	78-6920	41-16542	RADX
☐ North American NA-78 Texan (AT-6A)	'/2'	78-7074	41-16696	RADX
☐ North American NA-78 Texan (AT-6A)	102	78-7247	41-16869	RA
☐ North American NA-84 Texan (AT-6B)	'14'	84-7666	41-17288, NC5552, 1114	PVX
☐ North American NA-88 Texan (AT-6D)				RA
☐ North American NA-88 Texan (AT-6D)			(USAAF)	RAD
☐ North American NA-88 Texan (AT-6D)			(USAAF)	RAD
☐ North American NA-88 Texan (AT-6D)				RA
☐ North American NA-88 Texan (AT-6D)	1124		(USAAF)	RAD
☐ North American NA-88 Texan (AT-6D)	39		(USAAF)	RA
☐ North American NA-88 Texan (AT-6D)	48		(USAAF)	RA
☐ North American NA-88 Texan (AT-6D)	92		(USAAF)	RA
☐ North American NA-88 Texan (AT-6D)	25	88-17025	42-85244, 1125, 4X-ARC, 1125	PVA
☐ North American NA-111 Mustang (P-51K) (F-6K)	39	111-36126	44-12843	RAD
☐ North American NA-122 Mustang (P-51D)	41		(USAAF)	PV
☐ North American NA-122 Mustang (P-51D)	'39'		(USAAF)	RAX
☐ North American NA-122 Mustang (P-51D)	'53'		73, '008' – composite.	PVX
☐ North American NA-122 Mustang (P-51D)	01		(USAAF)	PVD

TYPE	REG/SER	CON. NO.	PI/NOTES	STATUS
☐ North American NA-122 Mustang (P-51D)	57		(USAAF)	RA
☐ North American NA-122 Mustang (P-51D)	38	122-31590	44-63864, 18 (?)	PV
☐ North American NA-182 Texan (T-6G)	'001'	182-720	51-15033, G-BDZZ	PVA
☐ Pilatus PC.6/B1-H2 Turbo-Porter	006	646	HB-FCV, 06, 006/4X-SVY	PV
☐ Piper PA-18-150 Super Cub	068	18-5240		PVA
☐ Piper PA-18-150 Super Cub	099	18-7760		PV
☐ Piper PA-18-150 Super Cub	087	18-7887		RAD
☐ Piper PA-18-150 Super Cub	114	18-8209024		PVC
☐ Piper PA-18-150 Super Cub	030	18-8574		PVC
☐ Republic RC-3 Seabee	'B-61'	834	NC6564K, N6564K	PVX
☐ Sikorsky S-55C	03	55992	41	PV
☐ Sikorsky S-58 Seahorse (HUS-1) (CH-34G)	07	581595	Bu150776, N9F	PV
☐ Sikorsky S-65A Sea Stallion (CH-53A)	471		Bu153307	PV
☐ Slingsby T.30B Prefect	4X-GEB			RA
☐ Slingsby T.30B Prefect	90			RA
☐ Slingsby T.30B Prefect	15	04	4X-GFH	RAD
☐ Slingsby T.30B Prefect	4X-GFB	06	4X-106	RA
☐ Slingsby T.30B Prefect	4X-GEM	08	19	RA
☐ Slingsby T.30B Prefect	25	14	4X-GEK	RAD
☐ Slingsby T.31B Tandem Tutor	010			RAD
☐ Slingsby T.31B Tandem Tutor	19	08	4X-GEM	RA
☐ Slingsby T.31B Tandem Tutor	4X-GEJ	10	21	PV
☐ SOCATA TB.20 Trinidad	334	1694		PV
☐ Sud SA.318C Alouette II	01			PV
☐ Sud SA.321K Super Frelon	002	104	F-WMHH	PV
☐ Sud SA.321K Super Frelon	009	114		RA
☐ Sud SA.321K Super Frelon	010	125		PV
☐ Sud SA.321K Super Frelon	015	130		RA
☐ Sud SA.321K Super Frelon	018	136		RA
☐ Sud SA.321K Super Frelon	020	138		PV
☐ Sud SA.321K Super Frelon	021	146		RA
☐ Sud SA.342L Gazelle	907	1788	1222 (Syria)	PVX
☐ Sud-Est SE.3130 Alouette II	'030'		05	PVX
☐ Sud-Est SE.3130 Alouette II	19			PV
☐ Sud-Est SE.3130 Alouette II	007	1055	F-WIEA, F-BIEA	PV
☐ Sud-Est SE.3130 Alouette II	003	1063		PV
☐ Sud-Est SE.3130 Alouette II	17	1099		RA
☐ Sud-Est SE.3130 Alouette II	'03'	1969	12	RAX
☐ Sud-Ouest SO-4050 Vautour IIA	109	30	15 (France), 09	PV
☐ Sud-Ouest SO-4050 Vautour IIBR	33	95	624 (France)	PV
☐ Sud-Ouest SO-4050 Vautour IIBW (IIN)	70	60	329 (France)	PV
☐ Sukhoi Su-7BMK		7724	Rear fuselage only – in Egyptian markings.	PVD
☐ Supermarine 361 Spitfire LF.IXc	78	6S.240837	EN145, MM4116, 105, 2078	PV
☐ Supermarine 361 Spitfire LF.IXe	57/4X-FOG	CBAF-11394	TE554, A708 (Czechoslovakia), 20-57,	PVA
☐ Supermarine 361 Spitfire LF.IXe	'26'	CBAF-IX-578	TE578, (UB425), 105, 2028	PVX
☐ Taylorcraft A	'VQ-PAH'	627		PVX
☐ Warsztaty Szybowcowe Wrona bis	13			PV
☐ Wytwornia Sprzetu Komunikacyjnego (WSK) SBLim-2 [MiG-15UTI]	307	3507	In Polish markings.	PV

NATIONAL MUSEUM OF SCIENCE, TECHNOLOGY AND SPACE (IS8)

Address:	25 Shmariyahu Levin Street, Hadar Hacarmel, P.O. Box 44927, Haifa 31448.
Tel:	04-861-4444
Fax:	04-867-9103
Admission:	September-June Sunday, Monday, Wednesday, Thursday 0900-1600, Tuesday 0900-1930; Friday 1000-1400, Saturday 1000-1800; July-August Sunday, Monday, Wednesday, Thursday 1000-1800, Tuesday 0900-1930; Friday 1000-1400, Saturday 1000-1800.
Location:	In the city centre.

This is the main technical museum in the country and its displays show the development of industry in the country. The only aircraft on show is the Kfir which is a design developed from the Dassault Mirage.

TYPE	REG/SER	CON. NO.	PI/NOTES	STATUS
☐ Israeli Aircraft Industries Kfir C.1P (C.1)	742	35		PV

NEVATIM AIR FORCE BASE COLLECTION (IS9)

Address:	Nevatim 85540.
Admission:	By prior permission only.
Location:	About 30 kim east of Beersheba.

Haganah was a Jewish para-military organisation established in British run Palestine in the interwar period. In 1947 an aviation wing, Sherut Air was set up, intially using aircraft from Aviron. This Jewish airline was formed in 1936. When Israel achieved its independence in 1948 the fleet numbered around twenty five aircraft. The first airfield to be built at Nevatim was constructed in 1947 and Sherut Airplanes were based at the site. The runways were unpaved and facilities were limited and the airfield saw little use. With the withdrawal of the Israeli Air Force from occupied Sinai after the Camp David Agreement the United States and Israel funded the modernisation of Nevatim. A fighter base with appropriate facilities was built and the site is now home to squadrons flying the General Dynamics F-16. When the military base at Tel Aviv closes in a few years time transport squadrons operating a number of types will move to Nevatim.

TYPE	REG/SER	CON. NO.	PI/NOTES	STATUS
☐ Dassault Mystère IVA	'92'		(France)	RAX
☐ Dassault Mystère IVA	50	164	164 (France)	RA
☐ Douglas A-4H Skyhawk	211		Composite.	RA

OVDA AIR FORCE BASE MUSEUM (IS10)

Address:	Mobile Post 'Arava', Ovda.
Admission:	By prior permission only.
Location:	About 10 km west of Gerofit.

The airfield was built by the Americans in 1981 to house units withdrawing from bases in occupied Sinai. Combat squadrons operating General Dynamics F-16s are in residence along with an attack helicopter unit flying the Bell AH-1 Huey Cobra. Located in the Negev Desert, this remote base is used to store withdrawn aircraft and large numbers are usually present. The site is also believed to house top-secret units. A small museum has been set up to trace the history of the field. The history of the airfield and its units are told in the informative displays. Some of the preserved aircraft are parked by the museum building, others are near the gate and some are located by the fire station. In 1982 civil flights started into Ovda and a modern terminal was built. Eilat Airport, located in the centre of the town, was too small to accommodate wide-bodied airliners bringing tourists to the area.

TYPE	REG/SER	CON. NO.	PI/NOTES	STATUS
☐ Douglas A-4E Skyhawk (A4D-5)	886		(USN)	RA
☐ Douglas A-4N Skyhawk	338			RA
☐ Israeli Aircraft Industries Kfir C.1	'944'		747	RAX
☐ Israeli Aircraft Industries Kfir C.7	517			RA
☐ McDonnell M.199-1A Eagle (F-15A)	314			RA
☐ McDonnell M.199-1A Eagle (F-15A)				RA
☐ McDonnell M.98HO Phantom II (F-4E)			(USAF)	RA
☐ McDonnell M.98HO Phantom II (F-4E)	102		(USAF)	RA
☐ McDonnell M.98HO Phantom II (F-4E)	133		(USAF)	RA
☐ McDonnell M.98HO Phantom II (F-4E)	686			RA
☐ McDonnell M.98HO Phantom II (F-4E)	165	4029	69-7575	RA

RAMAT DAVID AIR FORCE BASE COLLECTION (IS11)

Address:	Ramat David 36587.
Admission:	By prior permission only.
Location:	About 15 km south east of Haifa.

Constructed in the early days of World War II, this airfield housed Royal Air Force units from July 1942 until April 1948 although British aircraft stayed longer to assist with the evacuation of forces. During World War II the base housed fighter, transport and communication squadrons. Also in 1942 it assisted in the maintenance of U.S.A.A.F. B-24 Liberators stationed in Palestine. On May 15th 1948 the airfield was attacked by Egyptian Spitfires and two R.A.F. Spitfires were destroyed and seven damaged. The Egyptians later apologised for this raid. The Israeli Air Force moved in soon after and since then fighter units have been in residence. The first I.A.F.squadron flying jets was established at the base. This unit, the 117th, flew Gloster Meteor T.7s, F.8s and FR.9s. Two versions of this classic early jet have been saved. General Dynamics F-16s and Hughes 500MDs are now in residence.

TYPE	REG/SER	CON. NO.	PI/NOTES	STATUS
☐ Bell 209 Huey Cobra (AH-1G)	'669'		126	RAX
☐ Dassault Mystère IVA				RA
☐ Dassault Mystère IVA				RA
☐ Dassault Mystère IVA	04			RA
☐ Douglas A-4E Skyhawk (A4D-5)	310			RA
☐ Douglas A-4H Skyhawk	241		(USN) – at nearby school.	PV
☐ Douglas A-4N Skyhawk	328		(USN)	RA
☐ Gloster Meteor T.7	13		2162	RA
☐ Gloster Meteor FR.9	31		WX975, G-7-128, 215	RA
☐ Hughes 500MD Defender	202			RA
☐ Hughes 500MD Defender	210	109-0571D		RA
☐ Israeli Aircraft Industries Kfir C.2	814			RA

TYPE	REG/SER	CON. NO.	PI/NOTES	STATUS
☐ McDonnell M.98HO Phantom II (F-4E)	112		(USAF)	RA
☐ McDonnell M.98HO Phantom II (F-4E)	144		(USAF)	RA
☐ Sud-Ouest SO-4050 Vautour IIA	26	61	26 (France)	RA

RAMON AIR FORCE BASE COLLECTION (IS12)

Address: Ramon
Admission: By prior permission only.
Location: South west of Avdat.

Originally known as Matred, the airfield is yet another constructed with the help of American funds following the Israeli withdrawal from Sinai. There is also a small civil terminal which handles occasional Arkia flights. The base is now home to squadrons operating the General Dynamics F-16I. This is a version of the two seat F-16D specifically modified for the Israeli Air Force. Also in residence are units flying the Hughes AH-64 attack helicopter. Three aircraft have been preserved on the base including two Kfir C.1Ps.

TYPE	REG/SER	CON. NO.	PI/NOTES	STATUS
☐ Dassault Mystère IVA	711		(France)	RA
☐ Douglas A-4F Skyhawk	603		(USN)	RA
☐ Hughes 500MD Defender	299	100-0723D		RA
☐ Israeli Aircraft Industries Kfir C.1P (C.1)	622			RA
☐ Israeli Aircraft Industries Kfir C.1P (C.1)	703			RA
☐ McDonnell M.98HO Phantom II (F-4E)	'119'	2528	66-0313, 331	RAX

TECHNODA CENTER FOR SCIENCE AND TECHNOLOGY EDUCATION (IS13)

Address: 2 Harav Nisom Street,
P.O. Box 1144,
Givat Olga,
Hadera 38110.
Tel: 04-633-3505
Fax: 04-633-7595
Admission: Daily
Location: In the centre of the town

This centre runs many courses in all aspects of science and technology. These are designed to interest children of all ages. The complex contains a large observatory. Technoda has proved to be so popular that there are plans for new buildings on a nearby site. The only aircraft on show is the Kfir which highlights the work of the Israeli aircraft industry. The aeronautical section traces the development of flight. There are many working models in the exhibition along with photographs showing how aircraft have changed over the years.

TYPE	REG/SER	CON. NO.	PI/NOTES	STATUS
☐ Israeli Aircraft Industries Kfir C.2	'004'	88	875 – possible identity.	PVX

TEL NOF AIR FORCE BASE COLLECTION (IS14)

Address: Tel Nof 70710.
Admission: By prior permission only.
Location: About 5 km south of Rehovot.

The airfield opened in 1941 and was known as R.A.F. Aqir. Designed to house two bomber squadrons it soon became used for a variety of roles. Repair facilities were set up and it was also used for ammunition storage. During and just after World War II the site was home to many squadrons using a variety of types. In the period of tension between Arab and Jewish areas of Palestine British paratroopers were stationed in the area and Dakotas and Halifaxes were based at Aqir. Also the Army trained glider pilots, flying Horsas, at the field. The site was turned over to Israel in 1948 and is now an important base. Fighter units operating the F-15 Eagle and the IAE F-4E-2000 Kurnass are in residence. A heavy helicopter transport squadron using Sikorsky CH-53s is also based at Tel Nof. The Air Force bases a fleet of gliders at the field for basic training and sport flying.

TYPE	REG/SER	CON. NO.	PI/NOTES	STATUS
☐ Gloster Meteor NF.13	'119'		55 or 52	RAX
☐ Israeli Aircraft Industries Kurnas 2000 [McDonnell M.98HO Phantom II (F-4E)]	630			RA
☐ McDonnell M.98HO Phantom II (F-4E)	169		(USAF) – in training school.	RA
☐ McDonnell M.199-1A Eagle (F-15A)	'133'	A021	73-0087 – in training school.	RA
☐ McDonnell M.199-1A Eagle (F-15A)	'695'	A032	73-0098, 398 (Israel)	RAX
☐ McDonnell M.199-1A Eagle (F-15A)	'008'	A041	73-0107, 307 (Israel)	RAX
☐ Sud SA.321K Super Frelon	'669'	108	06	RAX

JAPAN

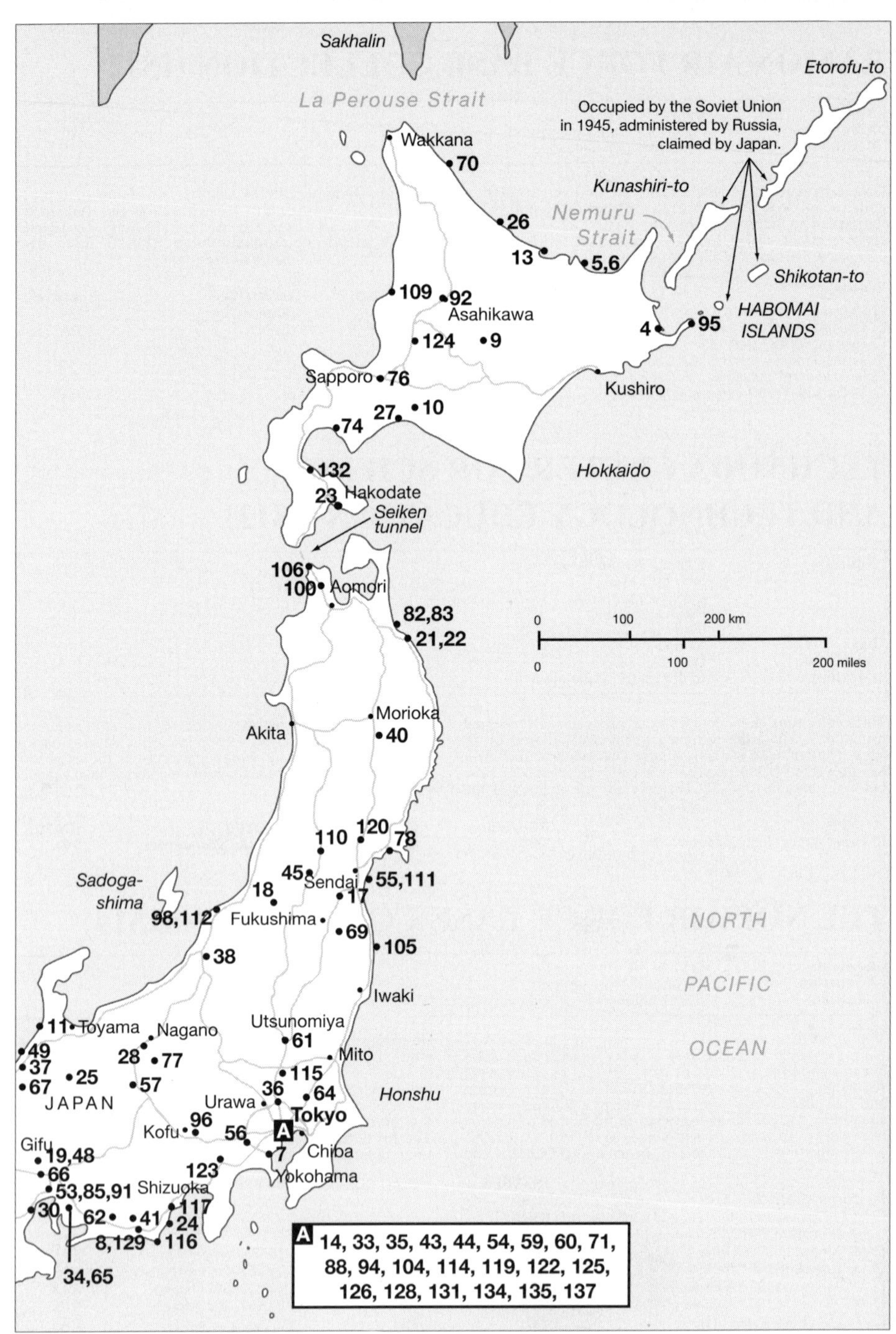

Sakhalin
La Perouse Strait
Etorofu-to
Occupied by the Soviet Union in 1945, administered by Russia, claimed by Japan.
Kunashiri-to
Nemuru Strait
Shikotan-to
HABOMAI ISLANDS
Wakkana
70
26
13
5,6
109
92
Asahikawa
124
9
4
95
Sapporo
76
Kushiro
27
10
74
132
Hokkaido
23
Hakodate
Seiken tunnel
106
100
Aomori
82,83
21,22
0
100
200 km
0
100
200 miles
Morioka
Akita
40
110
120
78
45
Sendai
55,111
Sadoga-shima
18
17
98,112
Fukushima
69
105
NORTH
PACIFIC
OCEAN
38
Iwaki
11
Toyama
Nagano
Utsunomiya
61
49
37
28
77
Mito
67
25
57
115
JAPAN
36
64
Urawa
Honshu
Tokyo
Kofu
96
56
A
Gifu
19,48
7
Chiba
66
123
Yokohama
53,85,91
Shizuoka
30
117
62
41
24
8,129
116
34,65
A 14, 33, 35, 43, 44, 54, 59, 60, 71, 88, 94, 104, 114, 119, 122, 125, 126, 128, 131, 134, 135, 137

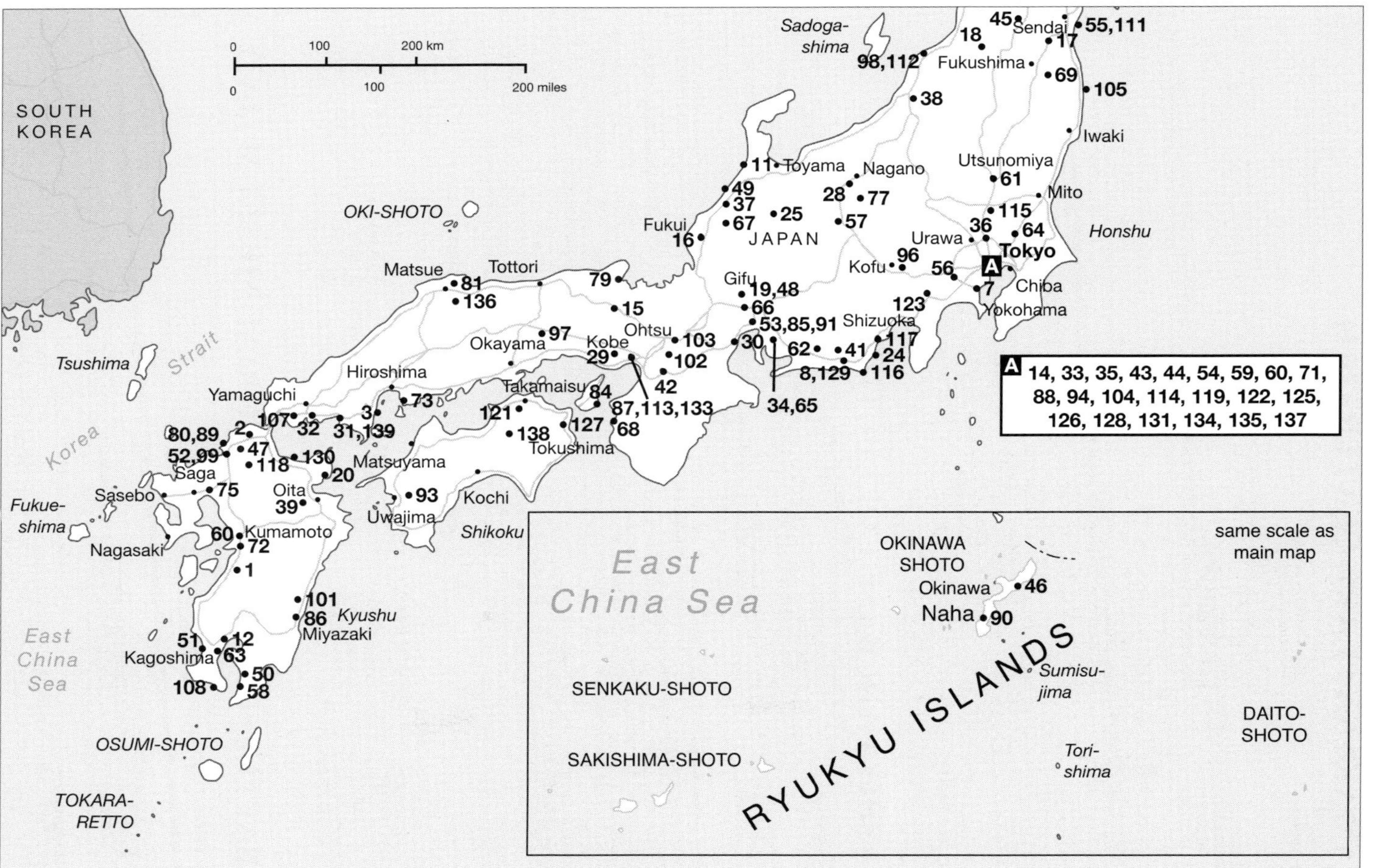
SOUTH KOREA
0 100 200 km
0 100 200 miles
OKI-SHOTO
Tsushima
Korea Strait
Fukue-shima
Sasebo
Nagasaki
Saga
Yamaguchi
Hiroshima
Matsue
Tottori
Okayama
Kobe
Ohtsu
Takamatsu
Tokushima
Matsuyama
Uwajima
Kochi
Shikoku
Oita
Kumamoto
Kyushu
Miyazaki
Kagoshima
East China Sea
OSUMI-SHOTO
TOKARA-RETTO
Fukui
JAPAN
Gifu
Toyama
Nagano
Kofu
Shizuoka
Urawa
Tokyo
Chiba
Yokohama
Utsunomiya
Mito
Honshu
Iwaki
Fukushima
Sendai
Sadoga-shima
A 14, 33, 35, 43, 44, 54, 59, 60, 71, 88, 94, 104, 114, 119, 122, 125, 126, 128, 131, 134, 135, 137
East China Sea
SENKAKU-SHOTO
SAKISHIMA-SHOTO
RYUKYU ISLANDS
OKINAWA SHOTO
Okinawa
Naha
Sumisu-jima
Tori-shima
DAITO-SHOTO
same scale as main map

AMAKUSA PEARL CENTER (JA1)

Address:	6225-8 Aitsu, Matsushima-machi, Kami Amakusa-shi, Kumamoto pref. 861-6100.
Tel:	0969-56-1155
Email:	office@amakusapearl.com
Admission:	Daily 0900-1700.
Location:	About 35 km south west of Kumamoto city.

The area is home to a vibrant pearl industry. The centre traces the history of the region with many historic artefacts on show. The story of the industry is portrayed in detail and many items of jewellery produced by local craftsmen can be seen. The exhibition traces the development of pearl diving. The Shin Meiwa PS-1 was put on display in the late 1990s. The Kawanishi company had built several flying boats during World War II and in 1949 the firm was re-established as Shin Meiwa. Initially they only carried out overhaul work on American aircraft but as flying was allowed in Japan they maintained both civil and military types. They soon turned to flying boat work and modified a Grumman Albatross, supplied by the United States, to investigate new concepts in design. This aircraft survived and can be seen in the Kakamighara Aerospace Museum. An original model the PX-S made its maiden flight in October 1967 and was developed into the PS-1. Twenty one were built and they served in the maritime reconnaissance role until replaced by Lockheed P-3 Orions.

TYPE	REG/SER	CON. NO.	PI/NOTES	STATUS
☐ Shin Meiwa PS-1	5810	1010		PV

ASHIYA AIR BASE COLLECTION (JA2)

Address:	Ashiya-machi, Onga-gun, Fukuoka pref. 807-0192.
Tel:	093-223-0981
Admission:	By prior permission only.
Location:	About 40 km north east of Fukuoka city off Route 3.

The airfield was in use during World War II and for many years after the conflict ended American squadrons were in residence. The site was handed back to Japan in the late 1950s. Now units housed at the base include a technical training school and a flying training squadron using Kawasaki T-4s. An air-sea rescue detachment is also in residence and this operates Sikorsky UH-60Js and Raytheon U-125s. The display of preserved aircraft, located in an area close to the main gate, includes training types which have been operated from the field. In the late 1950s four Sikorsky S-55s were imported from America and then the type was put into production by the Mitsubishi company for use by all three services. The JASDF received seventeen licence built examples which served until 1971. Japan operated many Texans and the first were ten AT-6D models. The example in the collection was the second delivered and entered service in 1955. Two versions of the classic Sabre are also in the collection. The prototype of this famous fighter took to the air at Muroc Army Air Field (now Edwards Air Force Base) in California on October 1st 1947. The type became one of the classic early swept wing fighters and almost ten thousand, including the naval Fury, were built. The last operational models were withdrawn in Bolivia in 1994. The type was also modified and built under licence in Australia and Canada. These fighters can be compared with more modern designs in the collection. The Starfighter acquired a certain notoriety in European service but was successful with many Air Forces around the world.

TYPE	REG/SER	CON. NO.	PI/NOTES	STATUS
☐ Fuji T-1A	05-5812			RA
☐ Lockheed 580 (T-33A)	51-5610	580-8712	53-5373	RA
☐ Lockheed 683-07-14 Starfighter (F-104J)	56-8663	683B-3163		RA
☐ Mitsubishi F-1	80-8219	75		RA
☐ North American NA-88 Texan (AT-6D)	52-0002		(USAAF)	RA
☐ North American NA-173 Sabre (F-86D)	84-8106	173-101	51-5957	RA
☐ North American NA-191 Sabre (F-86F)	52-7406	191-541	52-4845	RA
☐ Sikorsky S-55B (H-19C)	'91-4777'	M55-003	91-4707	RAX

BATTLESHIP MUTSU MEMORIAL MUSEUM (JA3)

Address:	Ibota, Sun-Ohshima-cho, Oshima-gun, Yamaguchi pref. 742-2601.
Tel:	0820-75-0042
Admission:	Daily 0900-1630.
Location:	About 50 km south of Hiroshima city.

The battleship Mutsu was laid down in 1918, launched in 1920 and entered service the following year. On June 8th 1943 there was a large explosion in one of the ammunition magazines and the ship sank with the loss of many lives. The official ruling of a Navy investigation was 'human circumstances'. Over eleven hundred men were killed and around three hundred and fifty saved. The wreck was untouched until 1970 and over the next few years a portion of the bow, a turret and some artefacts were raised. The informative displays at this museum trace the history and service life of the ship and the personnel who served on her. On show are excellent displays of photographs, documents, and uniforms and items of memorabilia. A memorial to the ship and its crew has been erected. The only aircraft displayed is the Shin Meiwa PS-1 flying boat. This example was delivered to the Navy in March 1977 and served at Iwakuni for over twenty years.

TYPE	REG/SER	CON. NO.	PI/NOTES	STATUS
☐ Shin Meiwa PS-1	5818	1018		PV

BEKKAI ARMY BASE MONUMENT (JA4)

Address:	42-1 Nishishunbetsu, Bekkai-cho, Notsuke-gun, Hokkaido pref. 088-2592.
Tel:	0153-77-2231
Admission:	By prior permission only.
Location:	On the east coast of the island.

A Kawasaki built Hughes helicopter is preserved as a monument at this Army Camp. Over one hundred of the OH-6J model were delivered between 1969 and 1979 and flew from bases around the country. The prototype Hughes 369 flew in February 1963 and was the winner of a United States Army competition for a light observation helicopter. Over seven hundred were delivered and the type saw service in the latter stages of the Vietnam war Kawasaki took up licence production and delivered both civil and military models.

TYPE	REG/SER	CON. NO.	PI/NOTES	STATUS
☐ Kawasaki-Hughes 369M (OH-6J)	31043	6346		RA

BIHORO ARMY AIR BASE COLLECTION (JA5)

Address:	Bihoro-cho, Abashiri-gun, Hokkaido pref. 092-8501.
Tel:	0152-73-2114
Admission:	By prior permission only.
Location:	About 20 km south of Abashiri city off Route 39.

No aircraft are normally based at this small military airfield. Five helicopters formerly flown by the service have been preserved around the site. Thirty eight American built Hughes TH-55Js were delivered to the Army between 1971 and 1975. The type served with the basic rotary wing trainer at the main flying school at Akeno and the detachments at Kasumiguara and Utsunomiya for almost twenty years.

TYPE	REG/SER	CON. NO.	PI/NOTES	STATUS
☐ Fuji-Bell 204B-2 Iroquois (HU-1B)	41543	MH-44		RA
☐ Hughes 269B (TH-55J)	61322	0231		RA
☐ Kawasaki-Hughes 369M (OH-6J)	31055	6358		RA
☐ Kawasaki-Vertol KV-107-II-4	51701	4015		RA
☐ Kawasaki-Vertol KV-107-II-4	51741	4074		RA

BIHORO AVIATION PARK (JA6)

Address:	343-7 Akinno Bihoro-cho, Abashiri-gun, Hokkaido pref. 092-0006.
Tel:	0152-73-0289
Admission:	Daily 0900-1800.
Location:	About 20 km south of Abashiri city off Route 39.

An aviation park has been set up by the town of Bihoro near the local army airfield. A pair of former Air Force trainers, the T-6 and the T-34 can be seen. Nine Fuji built Beech Mentors were transferred from the Air Force to the Army in 1964 and used at Iwanuma and Utsunomiya. Two Vertol V.44A twin rotor helicopters were delivered in 1959 and they served until replaced by the KV-107 in the early 1970s. The example on show was formerly preserved at the Army airfield at Okadama. A display tracing the local aviation history has been set up.

TYPE	REG/SER	CON. NO.	PI/NOTES	STATUS
☐ Beech A45 Mentor (T-34A)	60505	KD.28	51-0338	PV
☐ Fuji-Bell 204B-2 Iroquois (HU-1B)	41583	MH-84		PV
☐ Lockheed 580 (T-33A)	81-5387	1187		PV
☐ North American NA-182 Texan (T-6G)	52-0076			PV
☐ Vertol V.44A	50001	42.19		PV

CAFE AVION (JA7)

Address:	1-25-5 Kirigaoka, Mihori-ku, Yokohama-shi, Kanagawa pref. 226-0016.
Tel:	045-921-8048
Admission:	Friday-Wednesday 0900-1800.
Location:	Near Tokaichiba Station in the suburbs of Yokohama city.

Three fighters are displayed as an attraction at this establishment. Japan received one hundred and eighty F-86F Sabres between 1955 and 1957. The last forty five delivered were never used because of a shortage of pilots and were returned to the U.S.A. in 1959. Mitsubishi built another three hundred under licence. The single seat and two seat Starfighters were both constructed by Mitsubishi at Komaki.

TYPE	REG/SER	CON. NO.	PI/NOTES	STATUS
☐ Lockheed 583-10-17 Starfighter (F-104DJ)	36-5011	583B-5411	16-5011	PV
☐ Lockheed 683-07-14 Starfighter (F-104J)	46-8654	683B-3154	Front fuselage only.	PV
☐ North American NA-256 Sabre (F-86F)	92-7913	256-33	57-6370 – fuselage only.	PV

CAFE HIKOHJYO (JA8)

Address:	4702-16 Irinocho, Nishi-ku, Hamamatsu-shi, Shizuoka 432-8061.
Tel:	053-448-5679
Admission:	Thursday-Tuesday 1100-2000.
Location:	About 4 km west of Hamamatsu just south of Lake Sanari.

This private collection has been set up just south of Lake Sanari. Several former JASDF aircraft and one ex-JMSDF helicopter have been acquired. One of the Starfighters carries the same serial as one at Chiden and it is not known which is marked correctly. The fin of another F-104 can also be seen. The Mitsubishi MU-2 flew in prototype form in September 1963 and subsequently over seven hundred were built in both Japan and the United States. Many were delivered to civilian owners around the world. The Air Force operated twenty seven MU-2Ss in the search and rescue role. In addition four MU-2Js were flown on calibration duties. The MU-2S on show was the first delivered and entered service in August 1967. The Fuji T-1B and the Mitsubishi F-1 arrived in the late 1990s. The Mitsubishi F-1, developed from the T-2 trainer, made its maiden flight at Komaki in June 1977. The type was in service until 2006. Well over one hundred Sea Kings were built by the Mitsubishi company and the first was delivered to the Navy in the spring of 1964. For many years this ubiquitous helicopter was a familiar sight around the coast of the country flying on ASW patrols.

TYPE	REG/SER	CON. NO.	PI/NOTES	STATUS
☐ Fuji T-1B	25-5852		Fuselage only.	PV
☐ Fuji T-1B	25-5855			PV
☐ Lockheed 580 (T-33A)	51-5623		(USAF)	PV
☐ Lockheed 683-07-14 Starfighter (F-104J)	'26-5506'			PVX
☐ Lockheed 683-07-14 Starfighter (F-104J)	36-8536	683B-3036	Front fuselage only.	PV
☐ Lockheed 683-07-14 Starfighter (F-104J)	46-8604	683B-3104	Front fuselage only.	PV
☐ Lockheed 683-07-14 Starfighter (F-104J)	46-8617	683B-3117	Fuselage only.	PV
☐ Mitsubishi F-1	80-8212	58	Front fuselage only.	PV
☐ Mitsubishi MU-2S	73-3201	901		PV
☐ North American NA-173 Sabre (F-86D)	04-8164	173-344	51-6200 – front fuselage and tail only.	PV
☐ Sikorsky S-61 Sea King (HSS-2A)	8067	M61-073		PV

CHIPPUBETSU FAMILY SPORTS PARK COLLECTION (JA9)

Address:	2-1 Chippubetsu, Chippubetsu-cho, Uryu-gun, Hokkaido.
Admission:	Daily.
Location:	In the town.

Several sporting facilities are located in this picturesque park. There is a small military display to be seen. On show are a Mitsubishi built Starfighter and an example of the all-weather F-86D Sabre.

TYPE	REG/SER	CON. NO.	PI/NOTES	STATUS
☐ Lockheed 683-07-14 Starfighter (F-104J)	36-8552	683B-3052		PV
☐ North American NA-173 Sabre (F-86D)	84-8119	173-276	51-6132	PV

CHITOSE AIR BASE COLLECTION (JA10)

Address:	Heiwa, Chitose, Hokkaido pref. 066-8510.
Tel:	0123-23-3101 ext 212
Admission:	By prior permission only.
Location:	About 50 km south east of Sapporo off Route 36.

An airfield opened at Chithose in 1926 and the first landing was made by a Hokkai 1 owned by the OTARU newspaper. In 1939 a naval flight was established and the field saw extensive use during World War II. From October 1945 to June 1958 American Air Force units were in residence. A civil terminal for the town was built in late 1951. A new airport was ready in 1988 and all airline operations moved to this field. The 2nd Air Wing moved to the field from Hamamatsu in August 1957 and has operated F-86Ds, F-104Js and F-4EJs. The current equipment is the F-15J Eagle and the Kawasaki T-4. In addition a search and rescue detachment is in residence along with government operated Boeing 747s. The collection of preserved aircraft, parked close to the main gate, represents types used by the wing and trainers flown by their pilots.

TYPE	REG/SER	CON. NO.	PI/NOTES	STATUS
☐ Beech A45 Mentor (T-34A)	71-0416	FM.56		RA
☐ Lockheed 580 (T-33A)	71-5303	1103		RA
☐ Lockheed 683-07-14 Starfighter (F-104J)	46-8574	683B-3074	36-8574	RA
☐ Lockheed 683-07-14 Starfighter (F-104J)	46-8642	683B-3142		RA
☐ Lockheed 683-07-14 Starfighter (F-104J)	76-8689	683B-3189		RA
☐ North American NA-190 Sabre (F-86D)	04-8199	190-508	52-4105	RA
☐ North American NA-191 Sabre (F-86F)	62-7415	191-612	52-4916 – c/n given by base as 191-613 which is ex 52-4917.	RA

CROSSLAND OYABE DISPLAY (JA11)

Address:	10 Washigashima, Oyabe-shi, Toyama pref.
Tel:	0766-68-0932
Admission:	On permanent view except Wednesday.
Location:	About 15 km north west of Kanazawa city.

The town is home to an annual Helicopter and Disaster Prevention Festival. The military forces send a variety of types and rides are offered. A Kawasaki built Vertol 107 is permanently displayed at the site.

TYPE	REG/SER	CON. NO.	PI/NOTES	STATUS
☐ Kawasaki-Vertol KV-107-IIA-4	51818			PV

DAI-ICHI KOGYO DAIGAKU COLLECTION (JA12)

Address:	1-10-2 Kokubu-chuo, Kirishima-shi, Kagoshima pref. 899-4395.
Tel:	0995-45-0640
Admission:	By prior permission only.
Location:	About 25 km north east of Kagoshima city

Four aircraft are displayed at this technical university. There are two versions of the classic Texan, one in Navy and one in Air Force colours. Well over two hundred served as the standard basic trainer with both forces from the mid 1950s up to 1970. The Sikorsky S-55 is one of forty five built by Mitsubishi at Komaki. Kawasaki constructed just over one hundred Bell 47s under licence with all but eight serving with the Army.

TYPE	REG/SER	CON. NO.	PI/NOTES	STATUS
☐ Kawasaki-Bell 47G-2 (H-13H)	30124	154		RA
☐ North American NA-88 Texan (AT-6D) (SNJ-5)	6192		(USAAF), (USN)	RA
☐ North American NA-182 Texan (T-6G)	52-0118		(USAF)	RA
☐ Sikorsky S-55B (H-19C)	01-4710	M55-009		RA

ENGARU ARMY BASE MONUMENT (JA13)

Address:	272 Engaru, Engaru-cho, Monbetsu-gun, Hokkaido 099-0497
Admission:	By prior permission only.
Location:	In the town.

Helicopters are regular visitors to this army camp. The Fuji factory built ninety HU-1B versions of the Bell Iroquois for the Japanese Army and they were delivered between 1962 and 1971.

TYPE	REG/SER	CON. NO.	PI/NOTES	STATUS
☐ Fuji-Bell 204B-2 Iroquois (HU-1B)	41558	MH-59		RA

FIRE MUSEUM (JA14)

Address:	Yotsuya 3-10, Shinjuku-ku, Tokyo 160-0004.
Tel:	03-3353-9119
Admission:	Tuesday-Sunday 0930-1700.
Location:	In the centre of the city near Yotsuya 3chome metro station.

This fascinating museum, set up by the Tokyo Fire Department, traces the development of fire fighting in the country. The first organised fire brigades were established in the seventeenth century and the history of the service is portrayed in vivid detail. Apparatus from this period up to modern times has been collected. Films are shown to complement the story. Fire engines dating from early manual machines, through horse drawn vehicles up to modern equipment can be seen. Two helicopters used in the Tokyo region are on view.

TYPE	REG/SER	CON. NO.	PI/NOTES	STATUS
☐ Sud SA.316B Alouette III	JA9071	1877		PV
☐ Sud-Est SE.3160 Alouette III	JA9020	1376		PV

FUKUCHIYAMA ARMY CAMP MONUMENT (JA15)

Address:	Amada Fukuchiyama-shi, Kyoto pref 620-5802.
Tel:	0773-22-4141
Admission:	By prior permission only.
Location:	In the town.

As the Fuji built Bell Iroquois helicopters are withdrawn from active service examples are being allocated to Army camps to serve as monuments. The one here came from Kasumigaura. Several units are based at the site and they operate a variety of military vehicles. Some older models are displayed around the camp.

TYPE	REG/SER	CON. NO.	PI/NOTES	STATUS
☐ Fuji-Bell 205 Iroquois (HU-1H)	41649	49		RA

FUKUI UNIVERSITY OF TECHNOLOGY DISPLAY (JA16)

Address:	3-9-1 Gakuen, Fukui-shi, Fukui pref. 910-8505.
Tel:	0776-29-7864
Admission:	By prior permission only.
Location:	In the western part of the city.

The university was founded in 1873 and has twice been badly destroyed. Once in a bombing in World War II and again in an earthquake. Courses in a variety of technical subjects are offered and many graduates have subsequently joined the aviation industry or the armed forces. The Starfighter is displayed on a roof.

TYPE	REG/SER	CON. NO.	PI/NOTES	STATUS
☐ Lockheed 683-07-14 Starfighter (F-104J)	46-8607	683B-3107		RA

FUKUSHIMA ARMY CAMP COLLECTION (JA17)

Address:	Arai, Fukushima-chi, Fukushima pref. 960-2192.
Tel:	0245-593-1212
Admission:	By prior permission only.
Location:	About 60 km south west of Sendai city.

This small heliport, with no resident units, serves the nearby army camp. The site is under the control of the North Eastern Army Aviation Group which has its headquarters at Kasuminome. Two helicopters formerly used by the Army have been preserved along with an ex-Air Force Texan.

TYPE	REG/SER	CON. NO.	PI/NOTES	STATUS
☐ Fuji-Bell 204B-2 Iroquois (HU-1B)	41586	MH-87		RA
☐ Kawasaki-Hughes 369M (OH-6J)	31031	6332		RA
☐ North American NA-182 Texan (T-6G)	52-0071		(USAF)	RA

FUNAOKA ARMY CAMP COLLECTION (JA18)

Address:	1-1 Ohnumabata, Funoaka, Shibata-machi, Shibata-gun, Miyagi pref. 989-1694.
Tel:	0224-55-2301
Admission:	By prior permission only
Location:	In the town.

Three helicopters are displayed at this camp which has several regiments of ground troops in residence. All of the types have served in considerable numbers with the service for many years.

TYPE	REG/SER	CON. NO.	PI/NOTES	STATUS
☐ Fuji-Bell 205 Iroquois (HU-1H)	61612	12		RA
☐ Kawasaki-Hughes 369M (OH-6D)	31127			RA
☐ Kawasaki-Vertol KV-107-IIA-4	51812	4106		RA

GIFU AIR BASE MUSEUM (JA19)

Address:	Naka, Kakamigahara-shi, Gifu pref 504-8701.
Tel:	0583-82-1101
Admission:	By prior permission only.
Location:	About 40 km north of Nagoya.

The airfield was in use during World War II and in the latter stages of the conflict was used for Kamikaze missions. This site is home to the Air Proving Wing which over the years has operated a variety of aircraft. Currently operated are several fighter, trainer and transport types. The Kawasaki company has a factory located at the site and also an Air Force storage unit is in residence. One World War II aircraft has been recovered from a crash site. The Aichi E13A1 'Jake' reconnaissance floatplane flew in late 1938 and over fourteen hundred were built. The fuselage and one wing have been acquired and the aircraft is exhibited in the condition in which it was found. There is an exhibition in a building on the camp where the history of the field is portrayed in detail. On show are uniforms, models, documents, photographs, components, engines and trophies.

TYPE	REG/SER	CON. NO.	PI/NOTES	STATUS
☐ Aichi E13A1		41116		RAD
☐ Beech A45 Mentor (T-34A)	61-0406	FM.46		RA
☐ Curtiss-Wright CW-20B Commando (C-46A)	91-1141	27053	42-107366, (China), (Taiwan)	RA
☐ Fuji T-3	11-5538	038		RA
☐ Fuji T-3	11-5543	043		RA
☐ Fuji T-3	11-5547	047		RA
☐ Kawasaki-Vertol KV-107-II-5	74-4801	4027		RA
☐ Lockheed 580 (T-33A)	51-5663		(USAF)	RA
☐ Lockheed 580 (T-33A)	61-5201	1001		RA
☐ Lockheed 683-07-14 Starfighter (F-104J)	36-8540	683B-3040		PV
☐ Mitsubishi T-2 (CCV)	29-5102	02		RA
☐ North American NA-182 Texan (T-6G)	52-0100		(USAF)	PV
☐ North American NA-190 Sabre (F-86D)	'04-8182'	190-725	52-10000, '04-8209'	RAX
☐ North American NA-191 Sabre (F-86F)	'82-7780'	191-605	52-4909, 62-7427, '92-7897'	RAX
☐ North American NA-231 Sabre (F-86F)	72-7723	231-23	55-5070 – front fuselage only.	RA
☐ Piasecki PD-22 Work Horse (H-21B) (CH-21B)	02-4759	B.160	54-4007	RA

HACHIMENZAN PEACE PARK (JA20)

Address:	Sankoh-Taguchi, Nakatsu-shi, Ohita pref.
Tel:	0979-43-2050
Admission:	On permanent view.
Location:	About 10 km south of Nakatsu town.

This local park, which houses a number of events each year, is dedicated to the peace which has existed in Japan for over half a century. The only aircraft on show is the Sabre. Around the site are monuments and flags along with display boards tracing the post-World War II history of the country.

TYPE	REG/SER	CON. NO.	PI/NOTES	STATUS
☐ North American NA-256 Sabre (F-86F)	92-7888	256-8	57-6345	PV

HACHINOHE AIR BASE COLLECTION (JA21)

Address:	Kikyono, Ichikawa-machi, Hachinohe-shi, Aomori pref. 039-2295.
Tel:	0178-28-3111
Admission:	By prior permission only.
Location:	About 80 km south east of Aomori city.

The Army maintains a detachment at this primarily Navy base. A number of types which have given excellent service have been preserved. The only Army fixed wing aircraft is the Fuji built updated version of the Bird Dog. The company completed fourteen L-19E-1s and eight L-19E-2 instrument trainers. The Hughes OH-6J replaced the Bird Dog and the Bell 47 in the observation role. The KV-107 was chosen as the standard medium helicopter for all three services. Sixty served with the Army in this role and a small number are still in use. Also almost forty KV-107s were used by the Air Force with the first being delivered in late 1967. Some were used as support aircraft for the radar sites dotted around the country and others served with the rescue detachments located at most major bases. The Hughes TH-55J was used in the training role for many years. The Navy have put on show one of the King Airs used for instrument training from the mid-1970s. Currently the Navy fly Lockheed P-3 Orions and Sikorsky UH-60s whilst the Army operate AH-1s and OH-6s from the base.

TYPE	REG/SER	CON. NO.	PI/NOTES	STATUS
☐ Beech TC90 King Air	6803	LJ-599	N1847W –in Navy area.	RA
☐ Cessna 305C Bird Dog (L-19E-1)	11206			RA
☐ Fuji-Bell 204B-2 Iroquois (HU-1B)	41556	57		RA
☐ Fuji-Bell 205 Iroquois (HU-1H)	41663	63		RA
☐ Hughes 269B (TH-55J)	61336	0345		RA
☐ Kawasaki-Hughes 369M (OH-6J)	31087	6391		RA
☐ Kawasaki-Hughes 369M (OH-6J)	31178		Composite with tail boom from 31201.	RA
☐ Kawasaki-Vertol KV-107-II-4	51714	4032		RA

HACHINOHE CHILDRENS PARK DISPLAY (JA22)

Address:	33-2 Tenma, Tohkaichi, Hachinohe-shi Aomori pref. 900-1700.
Tel:	0178-96-3409.
Admission:	Tuesday-Sunday 0900-1700
Location:	About 5 km south of the Hachinohe town.

There are many attractions for local children in this municipal park. A military area contains two aircraft, information boards and vehicles. Both types were formerly flown by the Navy. The Queens Airs replaced the Beech 18 in the 1960s and the majority were flown on communications duties by the service.

TYPE	REG/SER	CON. NO.	PI/NOTES	STATUS
☐ Beech A65 Queen Air	6724	LC-324		PV
☐ Sikorsky S-61 Sea King (HSS-2B)	8146	M61-165		PV

HAKODATE ARMY CAMP MONUMENT (JA23)

Address:	6-18 Hirono-cho, Hakodate -shi, Hokkaido 042-8567.
Tel:	0138-51-9171
Admission:	By prior permission only.
Location:	In the town.

Preserved as a monument at this army camp is a Fuji built Iroquois helicopter. The type was one of the mainstays of the Japanese Army helicopter force for many years. Some military vehicles are also displayed.

TYPE	REG/SER	CON. NO.	PI/NOTES	STATUS
☐ Fuji-Bell 204B-2 Iroquois (HU-1B)	41589	MH-90 (?)		RA

HASEGAWA CORPORATION DISPLAY (JA24)

Address:	3-1-2 Yagusu, Yaizu-shi, Shizuoka pref. 425-8711.
Tel:	054-628-8241
Admission:	By prior permission only.
Location:	In the town.

The company was formed in 1941 as a manufacturer of wooden teaching materials. Their first plastic glider was produced in the early 1960s and the firm soon moved into making scale plastic kits of aircraft, cars, ships, railway engines and carriages. Their products are available throughout the world.

TYPE	REG/SER	CON. NO.	PI/NOTES	STATUS
☐ Fuji T-3	91-5514	014		RA
☐ Lockheed 683-07-14 Starfighter (F-104J)	76-8706	683B-3206		RA

HIDA AIR PARK COLLECTION (JA25)

Address:	2635-7 Kitagata, Nyukawa-mura, Ohno-gun, Gifu pref.
Admission:	On permanent view.
Location:	About 10 km north east of Takayama city.

A collection is being assembled at the airfield. At the current time two former navy aircraft have arrived. There are plans to add more types to the display. The Fuji KM-2 is a development of the Beech T-34A Mentor and the type was first delivered in 1961 and over sixty were operated in the primary training role. The Sea King entered service in Japan in 1964 and was used on Air Sea Rescue duties around the country.

TYPE	REG/SER	CON. NO.	PI/NOTES	STATUS
☐ Fuji KM-2	6277	TM.47		PV
☐ Sikorsky S-61 Sea King (HSS-2B)	8114			PV

HIDAKA ARMY CAMP MONUMENT (JA26)

Address:	75-Chisaka, Hidaka-cho, Saru-gun, Hokkaido 079-2314.
Tel:	01457-6-2241
Admission:	By prior permission only.
Location:	In the eastern suburbs of the town.

Helicopters have been an essential part of army operations for over half a century. Most camps have a landing area and Hidaka is no exception. A Japanese built Hughes is preserved as a monument.

TYPE	REG/SER	CON. NO.	PI/NOTES	STATUS
☐ Kawasaki-Hughes 369M (OH-6J)	31097			RA

HIGASHI-CHITOSE ARMY AIR BASE COLLECTION (JA27)

Address:	1016 Syukubai, Chitose-shi, Hakkaido pref 066-8577.
Tel:	0123-23-5131
Admission:	By prior permission only.
Location:	Just north east of Chitose Air Base.

This small airfield with a hard runway is used by the Army but normally there are no aircraft based at the site. The T-34 was one of eight transferred from the Air Force to the Army in 1964.

TYPE	REG/SER	CON. NO.	PI/NOTES	STATUS
☐ Beech A45 Mentor (T-34A)	60501	KD.2	41-0312	RA
☐ Kawasaki-Hughes 369M (OH-6J)	31037	6338		RA
☐ North American NA-182 Texan (T-6G)	52-0078		(USAF)	RA

HIJIRI MUSEUM (JA28)

Address:	Sarugabamba, Omi Village, Higashi-Chikuma-gun, Nagano pref. 399-7700.
Tel:	0263-67-2210
Admission:	Daily 0900-1700.
Location:	About 30 km south west of Nagano city off Route 19.

This privately run museum has on show a number of transport and military items. Outside the building the visitor can see a steam locomotive, and several vehicles. There is a large collection of weapons including a number of ships' guns. A collection of cars is also on view along with associated items, engines and items of memorabilia. Inside the building are aero engines, components, models and photographs.

TYPE	REG/SER	CON. NO.	PI/NOTES	STATUS
☐ Beech A45 Mentor (T-34A)	51-0337	KD.27		PV
☐ Curtiss-Wright CW-20B Commando (C-46A)	91-1144	296	43-47225, (China), (Taiwan)	PV
☐ Lockheed 683-07-14 Starfighter (F-104J)	46-8608	683B-3108		PV
☐ North American NA-173 Sabre (F-86D)	94-8146	173-167	51-6023	PV
☐ North American NA-238 Sabre (F-86F)	82-7865	238-95	56-2867	PV

HIMEJI ARMY CAMP MONUMENT (JA29)

Address:	1-70 Hounan-cho, Himeji-shi, Hyogo pref. 680-8580
Tel:	0792-22-4001
Admission:	By prior permission only.
Location:	In the northern part of the town.

Two aircraft are preserved at this camp. One is an example of the Hughes OH-6J which was flown in numbers by the Army. The other is a F-86F Sabre once operated by the Air Force. Also displayed are military vehicles, weapons and tanks along with flags and a number of memorials.

TYPE	REG/SER	CON. NO.	PI/NOTES	STATUS
☐ Kawasaki-Hughes 369M (OH-6J)	31108		Possible identity.	RA
☐ North American NA-256 Sabre (F-86F)	02-7956	256-76	57-6413	RA

HISAI ARMY CAMP MONUMENT (JA30)

Address:	975 Shinmachi, Hisai-shi, Mie pref. 514-1118
Tel:	059-255-3133
Admission:	By prior permission only.
Location:	About 60 km south west of Nagoya.

Two licence built helicopters are displayed as monuments at this camp. The Vertol KV-107 was formerly flown at the Army Aviation School at Kasumigaura before being withdrawn from use.

TYPE	REG/SER	CON. NO.	PI/NOTES	STATUS
☐ Fuji-Bell 205 Iroquois (HU-1H)	41667	67		RA
☐ Kawasaki-Vertol KV-107-IIA-4	51811	4105		RA

HISTORY MUSEUM AIR STATION IWAKUNI (JA31)

Address:	Fleet Air Wing 31, JMSDF, 2-Misumi-cho, Iwakuni-shi, Yamaguchi pref. 740-0025.
Tel:	0827-22-3181 ext.583.
Admission:	By prior permission only. Due to close and aircraft will be scrapped.
Location:	About 40 km south west of Hiroshima off Route 2.

Iwakuni was built as an Imperial Navy base just before the outbreak of World War II. After the end of the conflict R.A.F., R.A.A.F., U.S.A.A.F, U.S.N. and U.S.M.C. units operated from the field. The U.S. Marines are still in residence (see Zero Hangar Visitor Center). The JMSDF moved in during 1957 and the field is home to Fleet Air Wing 31 using the Shin Meiwa US-1, the EP-3D Orion and the U-36 Lear Jet. Helicopter Squadron 111 flies the Sikorsky MH-53E in the mine-sweeping role. A small museum tracing the history of maritime aviation and the base has been set up. On show are models, uniforms, photographs, documents, components and weapons. The aircraft park now contains just two types.

TYPE	REG/SER	CON. NO.	PI/NOTES	STATUS
☐ Beech A65 Queen Air	6725	LC-325		PV
☐ Shin Meiwa PS-1	5813	1013		PV

HOFU AIR BASE COLLECTION (JA32)

Address:	Tajima, Hofu-shi, Yamaguchi pref. 747-8567.
Tel:	0835-22-1950
Admission:	By prior permission only.
Location:	About 120 km south west of Hiroshima City off Route 2.

Hofu is a primary training base whose resident unit flies the Fuji T-7, which is a turbo-prop development of the Beech Mentor. Some of the aircraft are preserved inside the gate of the North Base and the others are displayed along the fence of the South site. Two standard Beech Mentors are on view.

TYPE	REG/SER	CON. NO.	PI/NOTES	STATUS
☐ Beech A45 Mentor (T-34A)	41-0309	CG.42	On North Base.	RA
☐ Beech A45 Mentor (T-34A)	61-0391	FM.31	On South Base.	RA
☐ Fuji T-1A	15-5816		On North Base.	RA
☐ Fuji T-3	81-5506	006	On North Base.	RA
☐ Lockheed 580 (T-33A)	51-5632		(USAF) – on North Base.	RA
☐ Lockheed 683-07-14 Starfighter (F-104J)	36-8537	683B-3037	On North Base.	RA
☐ Lockheed 683-07-14 Starfighter (F-104J)	46-8636	683B-3136	On South Base.	RA
☐ Mitsubishi F-1	10-8256	119	On North Base.	RA
☐ North American NA-173 Sabre (F-86D)	84-8127	173-111	51-5967 – on South Base.	RA
☐ North American NA-190 Sabre (F-86D)	04-8203	190-704	52-4301 – on North Base.	RA
☐ North American NA-191 Sabre (F-86F)	52-7403	191-314	52-4618 – on South Base.	RA

HYAKURI AIR BASE COLLECTION (JA33)

Address:	170 Hyakuri, Omitama-shi, Ibaraki pref. 311-3494.
Tel:	0299-52-1331
Admission:	By prior permission only.
Location:	About 60 km north east of Tokyo off Route 6.

This base is under control of the Central Air Defence Force which has its headquarters at Iruma. The based wing currently operates the F-15 Eagle, the Kawasaki and F-4E, R-4E, F-4EJ Phantoms In addition an Air Rescue Group detachment are also in residence. The collection of preserved aircraft is near the main gate.

TYPE	REG/SER	CON. NO.	PI/NOTES	STATUS
☐ Lockheed 580 (T-33A)	51-5629		(USAF)	RA
☐ Lockheed 580 (T-33A)	81-5373	1173	May still be here.	RA
☐ Lockheed 683-07-14 Starfighter (F-104J)	46-8630	683B-3130		RA
☐ Mitsubishi F-1	60-8274			RA
☐ Mitsubishi T-2(K)	29-5175	134		RA
☐ North American NA-190 Sabre (F-86D)	04-8197	190-474	52-4071	RA
☐ North American NA-256 Sabre (F-86F)	92-7885	256-5	57-6342	RA

ICEBREAKER FUJI MUSEUM (JA34)

Address:	1-9 Minato-Machi, Minato-ku, Nagoya-shi,, Aichi Pref. 455-0033
Tel:	052-652-1111
Admission:	Daily 0930-1700.
Location:	In the port area of the city.

The port authority has set up a museum in its headquarters building. The local maritime history of the region is portrayed in the informative displays. The icebreaker 'Fuji' is moored nearby and visitors can tour the ship. The Mitsubishi built Sikorsky S-61A on show is one of four which operated from the vessel.

TYPE	REG/SER	CON. NO.	PI/NOTES	STATUS
☐ Sikorsky S-61A	8181	M61.008		PV

INAGE CIVIL AVIATION COMMEMORATION CENTER (JA35)

Address:	2-2 Takahama 7-chome, Mihama-ku, Chiba-shi, Chiba pref. 261-0003.
Tel:	043-277-9000
Admission:	Tuesday-Sunday 0900-1700.
Location:	On the sea front in Inage which is about 30 km east of Tokyo and south of Route 14.

Sanji Narahara was born in December 1876 and built his first aircraft in 1910. His fourth design, a biplane, appeared the following year. The aircraft flew successfully before the Crown Prince in May 1911. These demonstrations resulted in Narahara receiving the first Imperial Award in the country for someone involved in civil aviation. Restrictions at Tokorozawa forced him to find a new site and he moved to the beach at Inage. The museum was built in the mid-1990s and highlights the work of the pioneers who used the site. Large models of significant types in the development of Japanese aviation have been constructed. There are photographs, documents and press cuttings on view. A replica of the Ohtori, containing some original parts, was built in October 1988 and can be seen along with a glider. This is one of many primary designs constructed in Japan.

TYPE	REG/SER	CON. NO.	PI/NOTES	STATUS
☐ Narahara Type 4 Ohtori (R)				PV
☐ Primary Glider	C-5131			PV

IRUMA AIR BASE COLLECTION (JA36)

Address:	4-942 Irumagawa, Sayama-shi, Saitama pref. 350-1305.
Tel:	0429-53-6131
Admission:	Monday-Friday 0800-1700 (by appointment)
Location:	About 50 km north west of Tokyo off Route 17.

This important base houses a variety of units including the Headquarters of the Central Air Defence Force, a transport wing, the Air Traffic Control and Weather Wing, an air sea rescue detachment and missile squadrons. Among the types operated is the Kawasaki C-1 jet transport. The prototype made its maiden flight in November 1970 and the type entered service the following year. An EC-1 serves as an electronic warfare trainer. The majority of the preserved aircraft are located in a park inside the base. Thirty six Curtiss Commandos were supplied under the MDAP programme in the 1950s and a further twelve were obtained from China. The Mitsubishi F-1 fighter is displayed close to the main gate. This design is a single seat strike fighter version of the T-2 supersonic trainer and first flew in June 1977. The Ohka rocket powered suicide aircraft was developed in 1944 by a team headed by transport pilot Mitsuo Ohta. Construction of unmanned prototypes took place within a short period and the first piloted flight was carried out in late 1944. The Ohka was carried aloft in the bomb bay of a Mitsubishi G4M 'Betty'. Over eight hundred and fifty were constructed.

TYPE	REG/SER	CON. NO.	PI/NOTES	STATUS
☐ Beech A45 Mentor (T-34A)	71-0419	FM.59		RA
☐ Curtiss-Wright CW-20B Commando (C-46A)	91-1145	399	43-47328, (China)	RA
☐ Lockheed 580 (T-33A)	51-5620		(USAF)	RA
☐ Lockheed 683-07-14 Starfighter (F-104J)	56-8666	683B-3166		RA
☐ Mitsubishi F-1	72-8201	47		RA
☐ North American NA-238 Sabre (F-86F)	82-7807	238-37	56-2809	RA
☐ Yokosuka MXY-7 Ohka 11				RA

ISHIKAWA AVIATION PLAZA (JA37)

Address:	92 Atakashimmachi, Komatsu-shi, Isikawa pref 923-0995.
Tel:	0761-23-4811
Admission:	Tuesday-Sunday 0900-1700
Location:	At Komatsu Airport which is about 40 km south west of Kanazawa city.

This impressive museum near Komatsu Airport opened in a modern purpose built structure on November 17th 1995. The history and development of aviation is told in the displays which make use of the latest computer techniques. Many models, photographs, engines, components and documents can be seen along with radar screens from control towers and flight simulators. The story of the air force base which shares the runways is also shown in detail. The site is home to fighter units which have flown the Starfighter and the T-33 in the past. Currently in use are McDonnell F-15s, Kawasaki T-4s and a search and rescue unit with Sikorsky UH-60s and Raytheon U-125s. Aircraft from all three services and civil machines can be seen. Jet trainers on show include a Kawasaki built Lockheed T-33 and a Mitsubishi built T-2. A Mitsubishi constructed Starfighter can also be seen. The Beech E33 Bonanza is a developed Debonair and a number were imported into the country and used for training civilian pilots. A replica of the first Japanese man-powered aircraft, which built in 1983 by Chuhachi Ninomiya, has been constructed and is on show on the upper floor of the main building. The Evans VP-1 was assembled by a local amateur constructor and was flown for a short time. The Pilatus Turbo-Porter arrived in Japan in 1979 and was used mainly for Arctic survey work. The Dornier Do 28 is a comparatively rare exhibit. The prototype of this twin engined design developed from the Do 27 and first flew in 1959. Around one hundred and twenty were built. The designation was used again on the Skyservant which was of similar configuration but was in essence a completely new design. Three helicopters, one civilian, are also on display. A hang glider and the Quad City Challenger microlight, designed in the U.S.A. and powered by a Rotax engine, are suspended in the foyer. The associated displays trace the history of aviation with special reference to the local area. On show are posters, components, engines, photographs, maps, items of memorabilia, models, documents and uniforms.

TYPE	REG/SER	CON. NO.	PI/NOTES	STATUS
☐ Beech E33 Bonanza	JA3442	CD-1198	N7619N	PV
☐ Dornier Do 28A-1	JA5115	3033	D-INAB	PV
☐ Evans VP-1 Volksplane	'001'			PVX
☐ Fuji KM-2	6288	TM.58		PV
☐ Hang Glider				PV
☐ Hashnata W-1-1	JR0467			PV
☐ Hughes 269B (TH-55J)	61324	0291		PV
☐ Kawasaki-Bell 47G-2	JA7316	220		PV
☐ Kawasaki-Hughes 369M (OH-6J)	31093	6397		PV
☐ Lockheed 580 (T-33A)	71-5321	1121		PV
☐ Lockheed 683-07-14 Starfighter (F-104J)	46-8539	683B-3039		PV
☐ Mitsubishi T-2(K)	99-5163	89		PV
☐ Ninomiya Man Powered Aircraft (R)				PV
☐ Pilatus PC.6/B2-H2 Turbo-Porter	JA8221	800		PV
☐ Quad City Ultralights Challenger				PV
☐ Sikorsky S-61 Sea King (HSS-2B)	8101	M61-113		PV

ISOROKU YAMAMOTO MEMORIAL HALL AND MUSEUM (JA38)

Address:	1-4-1Gofukum-machi, Nagaoka-shi, Niigata pref. 940-0056.
Tel:	0258-37-8001
Admission:	Daily 1000-1700
Location:	Just north of Nagaoka railway station.

Isoroku Takano was born in the town in 1884. He was later adopted by the Yamamoto family and took their name. He joined the Imperial Japanese Navy and studied both in his home country and at Harvard University in the U.S.A. He rose to be Commander in Chief of the Combined Fleet in World War II. During a tour of forward positions in the Solomon Islands the Mitsubishi G4M in which he was flying was shot down by a Lockheed P-38 Lightning on April 18th 1943. The wreck of the aircraft still survives in the Papua New Guinea jungle and local islanders take tourists to the site. This involves quite a long trek along a path hacked out through the bushes and scrub. The left wing and his seat were brought to Japan in 1989 and displayed this small memorial hall. There are photos and items of memorabilia tracing his early life and his military career is portrayed in detail. The story of his contribution to World War II can be followed with many maps and documents.

TYPE	REG/SER	CON. NO.	PI/NOTES	STATUS
☐ Mitsubishi G4M1	T1-323	2656	Port wing Admiral's seat and other small components.	PVD

IWASHITA COLLECTION (JA39)

Address:	645-6 Kawakita, Yufuin-cho, Yufu-shi, Ohita pref.
Tel:	0977-28-8900
Admission:	Daily 0900-1700
Location:	In the town.

Housed in a two story building this private collection contains many interesting items. On the ground floor are household items, photographs, pieces of machinery, toys and a collection of old telephones. There is an area honouring Steve McQueen which includes a motor-cycle sidecar. The fuselage of a former Air Force Sabre is exhibited in this area. Upstairs is a superb display of about one hundred and fifty classic motor cycles. There are several Harley-Davidson and Indian models along with Japanese types. A car museum, run by another organisation, is located a short distance away and here many machines are on show.

TYPE	REG/SER	CON. NO.	PI/NOTES	STATUS
☐ North American NA-256 Sabre (F-86F)	'32369'	256-25	57-6362, 92-7905 – fuselage on show other parts in store.	PV

IWATE ARMY CAMP MONUMENT (JA40)

Address:	Takazawi-mura, Iwati-gun, Iwake-pref 020-0173.
Tel:	019-688-4311
Admission:	By prior permission only.
Location:	In the village.

The camp houses armoured units with a variety of specialist vehicles. A former Air Force Texan has been preserved as a monument to all who have served the military at the base. One hundred and eighty examples of the famous trainer served with the JASDF from the mid-1950s. The last were withdrawn from use in the spring of 1970. Also parked in the grounds are a number of vehicles and pieces of artillery.

TYPE	REG/SER	CON. NO.	PI/NOTES	STATUS
☐ North American NA-182 Texan (T-6G)	72-0147			RA

JAPAN AIR SELF-DEFENCE FORCE MUSEUM (JA41)

Address:	Nishiyama-cho, Nishi-ku, Hamamatsu-shi, Shizuoka pref 432-8001.
Tel:	053-472-1111
Admission:	Tuesday-Sunday 0900-1600
Location:	About 15 km north west of the city.

The Japanese Air Self-Defence Force was formed in 1954 when military flying was allowed again after World War II. Over the last half century the service has developed into one of the major air arms in the region operating a variety of indigenous and American types. The idea of a museum tracing the history of JASDF was put forward several years ago and the collection opened to the public in a purpose built structure in April 1999. For many years a large collection of preserved aircraft had been displayed around the site and the majority of these have joined the museum. This history and traditions of the force are portrayed in the displays with many photographs, models, engines and uniforms on view. The replica Ansaldo SVA-9 was formerly on show in a transport museum in Osaka. In January 1956 the Air Proving Group acquired a single Vampire Trainer which was flown on trials until September 1960 but no orders were placed. The Zero was recovered from Guam in 1963 and rebuilt for the display. A fairly new addition to the display is the single seat prototype Mitsubishi XF-2A. This design was developed in conjunction with the Lockheed-Martin company in the U.S.A. The prototype made its maiden flight in July 1995 and parts were made in both countries with final assembly in Japan.

TYPE	REG/SER	CON. NO.	PI/NOTES	STATUS
☐ Ansaldo SVA 9 (R)	'13148'			PVX
☐ Beech A45 Mentor (T-34A)	51-0382	FM.22		PV
☐ Beech A45 Mentor (T-34A)	41-0322	KD.12		RA
☐ Beech 65 Queen Air	03-3094	LC-334	6728 (Japan)	PV
☐ Curtiss-Wright CW-20B Commando (C-46A)	91-1138	30553	42-101098, (China), (Taiwan)	PV
☐ De Havilland D.H.115 Vampire T.55	63-5571	15752		PV
☐ Fuji T-1A	15-5825			PV
☐ Fuji T-3	91-5517	017		PV
☐ Kawasaki-Vertol KV-107-IIA-5	24-4832	4136		PV
☐ Lockheed 580 (T-33A)	61-5207	1007		RA
☐ Lockheed 580 (T-33A)	71-5239	1039		PV
☐ Lockheed 580 (T-33A)	71-5254	1054		RA
☐ Lockheed 580 (T-33A)	71-5323	1123		PV
☐ Lockheed 683-07-14 Starfighter (F-104J)	46-8571	683B-3071		RA
☐ Lockheed 683-07-14 Starfighter (F-104J)	76-8693	683B-3193		PV
☐ Lockheed 683-07-14 Starfighter (F-104J)	76-8698	683B-3198		PV
☐ Mitsubishi A6M5 Zero Sen Model 52	43-188	4685		PV
☐ Mitsubishi F-1	90-8225	81		PV
☐ Mitsubishi F-1	90-8227	90		PV
☐ Mitsubishi MU-2S	13-3209	909		PV
☐ Mitsubishi T-2(Z)	59-5111	11		PV
☐ Mitsubishi T-2(Z)	59-5114	14	Front fuselage only.	PV
☐ Mitsubishi XF-2A	63-8501			PV
☐ North American NA-88 Texan (AT-6D)	52-0010		(USAAF)	PV
☐ North American NA-182 Texan (T-6G)	52-0074		(USAF)	RA
☐ North American NA-190 Sabre (F-86D)	84-8104	190-445	52-4042	PV
☐ North American NA-218 Trojan (T-28B)	63-0581	218-1	JA3096	PV
☐ North American NA-256 Sabre (F-86F)	'12-7984'	256-49	57-6386, 92-7929	RAX
☐ North American NA-256 Sabre (F-86F)	02-7960	256-80	57-6417	PV
☐ North American NA-256 Sabre (F-86F)	02-7966	256-86	57-6423	PV
☐ Piasecki PD-22 Work Horse (H-21B) (CH-21B)	02-4756	B.148	53-4398	PV
☐ Sikorsky S-55B (H-19C)	91-4709	M55-006		RA
☐ Sikorsky S-62J	53-4774	M62-011		PV

This Shin Meiwa PS-1 is on show at the Iwakuni History Museum. Sadly this maginificent aircraft will soon be scrapped. (Shinsuke Yamamoto)

The Fuji KM-2 evolved from the Beech Mentor. This example is at the Kohta City Museum. (Shinsuke Yamamoto)

This Sikorsky S-62J is part of the collection at Komaki Air Force Base. (Shinsuke Yamamoto)

JAPAN AIR SELF-DEFENCE FORCE OFFICER CANDIDATE SCHOOL COLLECTION (JA42)

Address:	1578 Hokkeji-cho, Nara-shi, Nara-ken 630-8001.
Tel:	0742-33-3951 ext 313.
Admission:	By prior permission only.
Location:	In the northern part of Nara city which is about 50 km east of Osaka.

The Japanese Air Self Defence Force set up an education centre for officer training at Hamamatsu Air Base in December 1954. An Officer Candidate School was established at Hofu in September 1955. United States forces moved out of Nara in March 1957 and the new combined unit moved to its current home. A display of aircraft has been set up to inform students of the heritage of the service. The earliest is the Texan which was one of the first types supplied when military flying was allowed after World War II. Many of the first pilots in the JASDF earned their wings on the T-6. The T-34 and its Japanese derivatives took over the basic flying instruction role. The T-33 was used for advanced jet training for many years and served at almost all bases in the country. Examples of fighters flown by operational squadrons can also be seen.

TYPE	REG/SER	CON. NO.	PI/NOTES	STATUS
☐ Beech A45 Mentor (T-34A)	51-0331	KD.21		RA
☐ Lockheed 580 (T-33A)	51-5601		(USAF)	RA
☐ Lockheed 580 (T-33A)	81-5348	1148		RA
☐ Lockheed 683-07-14 Starfighter (F-104J)	56-8653	683B-3153		RA
☐ North American NA-173 Sabre (F-86D)	'84-8100'		(USAF)	RAX
☐ North American NA-182 Texan (T-6G)	52-0075		(USAF)	RA
☐ North American NA-227 Sabre (F-86F)	62-7527	227-114	55-3929	RA

JAPAN GROUND SELF-DEFENCE FORCE PUBLIC INFORMATION CENTRE (JA43)

Address:	Oizumigahen-cho, Nerima-ku, Wakashi-shi, Saitama pref. 178-8501
Tel:	03-3924-4176
Admission:	Tuesday-Sunday 1000-1700.
Location:	In the northern outskirts of Tokyo.

A display has been set up at the centre which also serves as a recruiting office. The history of the Army is portrayed in the indoor exhibition which contains many photographs, documents and models. A number of military vehicles and tanks are on show. Two helicopters are displayed outside the building along with some tanks and vehicles. The Bell AH-1 was developed from the experimental Bell 207 Sioux Scout and was soon put into production for use in the Vietnam war. This fearsome attack helicopter has been steadily developed over the last four decades. The example on show was the first delivered to the JGSDF and entered service in the summer of 1979. A fairly new arrival is one of the experimental helicopters developed by the Fuji company.

TYPE	REG/SER	CON. NO.	PI/NOTES	STATUS
☐ Bell 209 Huey Cobra (AH-1S)	73401	21507		PV
☐ Fuji Battlefield Surveillance Helicopter				PV

JAPANESE AERONAUTIC ASSOCIATION (JA44)

Address:	1-18-1 Shimbashi, Minato-ku, Tokyo 105-004.
Tel:	03-3502-1201
Admission:	By prior permission only.
Location:	In the store of the National Science Museum at Tsukuba which is about 40 km north east of Tokyo.

This society owns the sole remaining example of the Nakajima Ki-115 special attack aircraft. Intended for suicide missions the Tsurugi prototype flew in March 1945. Designed and built in three months the low wing monoplane had a simple structure and was intended to be built by semi-skilled workers. One hundred and five were constructed but none were used operationally. The survivor was found at Yokota when the Americans occupied the base in 1945 and was parked outside a barrack block for several years. After this the aircraft was stored at many locations and is currently dismantled in a crate at the National Science Museum store. There are long term plans to restore the airframe and put it on show in a museum.

TYPE	REG/SER	CON. NO.	PI/NOTES	STATUS
☐ Nakajima Ki-115 Tsurugi				RA

JINMACHI ARMY CAMP MONUMENT (JA45)

Address:	3-1-1 Jinmachi-Minami Higashine-shi, Yamagata pref 999-3797.
Tel:	0237-48-1151
Admission:	By prior permission only.
Location:	About 1 km east of Yamagata Airport.

The Army has a base close to the airport for the area. A training school has a number of airframes which are also used for display purposes. A former Air Force Sabre is preserved as a monument.

TYPE	REG/SER	CON. NO.	PI/NOTES	STATUS
☐ Fuji-Bell 205 Iroquois (HU-1H)	41639	39	In Technical School.	RA
☐ Kawasaki-Hughes 369M (OH-6J)	31117		In Technical School.	RA
☐ Kawasaki-Vertol KV-107-II-4	51717	4035	In Technical School.	RA
☐ Kawasaki-Vertol KV-107-II-4	51730	4056	In Technical School.	RA
☐ North American NA-173 Sabre (F-86D)	84-8126	173-157	51-6013	RA

KADENA UNITED STATES AIR FORCE BASE COLLECTION (JA46)

Address:	Kadena-cho, Nakagami-gun, Okinawa pref. 904-0203.
Tel:	098-939-7812.
Admission:	By prior permission only.
Location:	About 10 km north west of Okinawa city.

This important American base houses fighter, tanker, reconnaissance and rescue squadrons. A collection of preserved fighter aircraft highlights this role and several classic types have been preserved.

TYPE	REG/SER	CON. NO.	PI/NOTES	STATUS
☐ Lockheed 580 (T-33A)	'53-5612'			RAX
☐ McDonnell M.98DJ Phantom II (F-4C)	'37433'	1372	64-0913	RAX
☐ McDonnell M.199-1A Eagle (F-15A)	74-0088	A049		RA
☐ North American NA-191 Sabre (F-86F)	52-4341	191-37		RA
☐ North American NA-192 Super Sabre (F-100A)	52-5756	192-1	52-5756, '58-617'	RA
☐ North American NA-276 Sabreliner (T-39A) (CT-39A)	62-4484	276-37		RA
☐ Republic F-105F Thunderchief	62-4418	F-7		RA

KAIZUKA TRANSPORT PARK (JA47)

Address:	7-8-33 Hakozaki, Higashi-ku, Fukuoka-shi, Fukouka pref. 812-0053.
Tel:	092-651-6907
Admission:	Daily 0900-1800.
Location:	About 5 km north east of Fukuoka city.

The only aircraft at the transport section of this large public park is the Heron. This type was quite popular in Japan and in the 1960s many of the former Garuda Indonesian Airlines fleet were purchased by C. Itoh and Company. The example on show was delivered to Indonesia in February 1954 and arrived in Japan in 1960. Cars, commercial vehicles and railway engines are also on show at the site.

TYPE	REG/SER	CON. NO.	PI/NOTES	STATUS
☐ De Havilland D.H.114 Heron 1B	JA6159	14027	PK-GHK	PV

KAKAMIGAHARA AEROSPACE MUSEUM (JA48)

Address:	5-1 Shimogiri-cho, Kakamigahara-shi, Gifu pref. 504-0924.
Tel:	0583-86-8500
Admission:	Museum – daily 0930-1630 (Closes at 1730 July-August). Outside park – daily 0900- 1700 (Closes at 1800 July-August).
Location:	Near Gifu Air Force base about 20 km north of Nagoya city off Route 41.

In 1912 plans were put forward for an airfield near Kakamigahara. The site at Gifu was completed in 1917 and the first pilot to land was Captain Tokugawa who arrived from Tokorozawa in a Morane-Saulnier biplane. A French mission was in residence for a period in 1919 and trained Japanese personnel in flight operations and aircraft maintenance. Two years later the local branch of the Kawasaki Dockyard Company produced a licence built version of the Salmson 2A-2, called the Otsu 1. The airfield became the test centre for many companies including Aichi, Kawanishi, Kawasaki and Mitsubishi up to 1945. When the Allies allowed aircraft manufacture to resume in the early 1950s Kawasaki soon flew the prototype of the KAL-1 and the first of two hundred and ten locally built T-33s. The site was a natural choice for a museum and the impressive structure opened on March 23rd 1966. The main aim of the collection is to feature Japanese designed types and a wide range can be seen. The local aircraft industry is portrayed in detail with a section devoted to Takeo Doi who joined Kawasaki in 1927 and was still designing aircraft thirty years later. Examples of his work include the KAT-1, P-2J Neptune and the YS-11 airliner. A local group built a replica of the Salmson 2A-2 for the museum in 1995. The front fuselage of a Kawasaki built original is on loan from the National Science Museum in Tokyo. The development of flight from the early days is shown with many models, posters, engines and components on view. Space flight also features prominently. Six flight simulators are available for visitors to try out their skills in a variety of simulated flying conditions. Kawasaki constructed a wooden mock up of their XOH-1 for engineering studies but the type was not built. The BK 117 on show is the strength test airframe. One of the OH-6Js was once used in a research programme for an advanced rotor system and was then converted back to original configuration. Work in the restoration shop can be viewed through a large glass window. The main hall and outside area contain many types which have been tested at the airfield. Two flying boats from the Shin Meiwa factory are on view. The UF-XS is a Grumman Albatross modified for STOL research in the early 1960s. The PS-1 patrol type first flew in 1967 and twenty three were delivered to the Navy. Ten of the US-1 search and rescue version followed in the late 1970s and early 1980s. The Asuka STOL jet was modified from a Kawasaki C-1 transport and made its first flight on October 28th 1985 and its last on March 30th 1989. Other STOL machines are modified versions of the Fuji FA-200 and the SAAB Safir. The standard FA-200 was used to demonstrate basic flight control systems. Several other products from this company are in the exhibition. A range of locally built light aircraft and gliders are on view along with modern civil and military types. The Naito YURI-1 made the first man-powered hovering flight in the world on December 5th 1993. Nihon University students lead by Hidemasa Kimura developed an STOL wing. This was tested on the Nihon N-58 which was based on a Piper Tri-Pacer airframe. The aircraft was built by the Itoh company who developed the N-62. The prototype made its maiden flight in August 1964 and ambitious production plans were put forward. Only three examples are believed to have been completed and the second is on show in the museum. Gliding has been an important sport in Japan since the 1920s. Several examples of indigenous designs can be seen. At least sixty Kirigamine Hato K-14 primaries were produced and many Japanese pilots made their first flights in the type. The Hagiwara company produced several designs in the 1950s and 1960s. These were all secondary sailplanes and used for more advanced training. The Mita 3-1 dates from the mid-1960s and about fifty were completed over the next few years This excellent museum contains several unique designs and the associated displays are well presented. On show are many models, photographs, documents, engines and components along with uniforms.

TYPE	REG/SER	CON. NO.	PI/NOTES	STATUS
☐ Fuji FA-200-180 Aero Subaru	JA3483	51		PV
☐ Fuji FA-200kai	JA3263	KAI-1		PV
☐ Fuji KM-2	6255	TM.25		PV
☐ Fuji Mokko SK21DC	JA0147	211		S
☐ Fuji T-1B (T-1A)	05-5810			PV
☐ Grade Eindekker (R)				PV
☐ Hagiwara H-22B-3	JA0170	41		S
☐ Hagiwara H-23BA-2	JA2023	23		S
☐ Hagiwara H-23C-2	JA2077	88		S
☐ Hinon Hikouki X1G1B [SAAB 91B Safir mod]	TX-7101	91201	Fv50001, SE-BWB, JA3055, Gi-101	PV
☐ Kawasaki Automatic Landing Test Vehicle				PV
☐ Kawasaki KAT-1	JA3084	2002		PVC
☐ Kawasaki P-2J [Lockheed 726]	4782	7081		PV
☐ Kawasaki XOH-1 (Mock up)				PV
☐ Kawasaki-Bell 47G-3B-KH4	JA7110	2193		PV
☐ Kawasaki-Hughes 369M (OH-6J)	31058	6361	Was modified for research but now returned to normal configuration.	PV
☐ Kawasaki-Hughes 369M (OH-6J)	31081	6385		PV
☐ Kawasaki-Messerschmitt-Bölkow-Blohm BK 117	02			PV
☐ Kawasaki-Vertol KV-107-IIA-4	51804	4089		PV
☐ Keihikoki SS-2	JA2114	69-23		PV
☐ KHR-1	2500			PV
☐ Kirigamine Hato K-14			Composite of at least three airframes.	PVC
☐ KoToNo Hyper Chick				PV
☐ Lockheed 580 (T-33A)	61-5221	1021		PV
☐ Lockheed 683-07-14 Starfighter (F-104J)	36-8515	683B-3015		PV
☐ Mansyu Ki-79 Otsu 1			Fuselage frame only.	PVD
☐ Mansyu Ki-79 Otsu 1 (FSM)	1001			PVX
☐ Mita 3-1 Kai	JA2080	66-2		S
☐ Mita 3-1 Kai	JA2091	67-7		PV
☐ Mita 3-1 Kai	JA2176	74-48		S
☐ Mitsubishi T-2B(K)	19-5173	132		PV
☐ Naito YURI-1				PV
☐ National Aerospace Laboratories Asuka [Kawasaki C-1]	JQ8501	8501		PV
☐ National Aerospace Laboratories VTOL Flying Test Bed		0001		PV
☐ National Defence Academy B-5Kai-1	B5-1	1		PVC
☐ Nichidai N70 Cygnus				PV
☐ Nihon Kokuki Seizo Kabushiki Kaisha (NAMC) YS-11A-500R (YS-11A-213)	JA8731	2099		PV
☐ Nihon N-62 Eaglet	JA3521	0101		PV

TYPE	REG/SER	CON. NO.	PI/NOTES	STATUS
☐ Salmson 2A2			Front fuselage only – on loan from NSM.	PVD
☐ Salmson 2A2 (FSM)	'1001'			PVX
☐ Shin Meiwa UF-XS	9911		Converted from Grumman G.64 Albatross (PF-1) (UF-1) c/n G-153 Bu149822.	PV
☐ Shin Meiwa US-1A (US-1)	9078	2008		PV
☐ Sud SA.319B Alouette III	JA9093	1988		PV

KANAZAWA ARMY CAMP MONUMENT (JA49)

Address: 1-8 Nodamachi, Kanazawa-shi, Ishikawa pref. 921-8520
Tel: 076-241-2171
Admission: By prior permission only.
Location: About 5 km south east of the town.

This important camp on the outskirts of the town is home to a number of units. A Japanese built Iroquois has been preserved as a monument to those who have served at the site which has a helicopter landing area. Also displayed is a collection of military vehicles along with a number of weapons and pieces of artillery.

TYPE	REG/SER	CON. NO.	PI/NOTES	STATUS
☐ Fuji-Bell 205 Iroquois (HU-1H)	41656	56		RA

KANOYA BASE AVIATION MUSEUM (JA50)

Address: 3-11-2 Nishihara 3, Kanoya-shi, Kagoshima pref. 893-8510.
Tel: 0994-43-3111
Admission: Daily 0900-1630.
Location: About 30 km south east of Kagoshima city.

The first post-war Japanese Naval Air Service was formed as a Maritime Guard in April 1952 and took up its present title in July 1954. Kanoya, opened on December 1st 1953, was the second naval air station in post-war Japan. On August 15th 1972 a museum was set up to trace the history of the base. Aircraft and artefacts were steadily gathered and in the early 1990s a new modern building was erected with a large park surrounding it. This new display opened in July 1993. The history of naval aviation in the country is portrayed from the formation of the service in 1913. On show in the building are photographs, documents, uniforms, models, engines and components. A number of memorials from the old Imperial Navy period have been moved to the museum. A star exhibit is the only surviving Kawanishi H8K2 'Emily' four engined flying boat. The prototype first flew in 1941 and one hundred and sixty were built. The example on show was found by the Americans on Shikoku Island and eventually flown to the U.S.A. for trials. The aircraft was then stored at Norfolk in Virginia before being returned to Japan in 1979. For many years it was outside the Museum of Maritime Sciences in Tokyo. When the JMSDF was established in the early 1950s the majority of types in use were American. The C-47 is the only example of this classic type preserved in Japan. Sixty Grumman Trackers were acquired by the service in the late 1950s and the type remained operational until 1984. Two were converted for use as utility transports and four for target towing duties. A Lockheed built Neptune can be compared with two of the eighty two developed versions produced by Kawasaki. This version featured turbo-prop engines, a lightened airframe, a longer fuselage and improved electronics. Japan has been one of the few countries to use flying boats designed after World War II and an example of the Shin Meiwa US-1 flown on search and rescue duties can be seen. The prototype made its maiden flight in October 1974 and the first deliveries took place the following year. This excellent museum traces the history of the service and as types are withdrawn they will join the display.

TYPE	REG/SER	CON. NO.	PI/NOTES	STATUS
☐ Beech D18S Expeditor (C18S) (C-45F) (UC-45F) (JRB-4)	6434	7964	44-47556, Bu85125	PV
☐ Beech A45 Mentor (T-34A)	9012	FM.26	51-0386	PV
☐ Beech B45 Mentor (T-34A)	9006	CG-38	7101, 9006, 7141	RA
☐ Beech 65 Queen Air	6714	LC-220		PV
☐ Bell 47G-2A	8753	528		PV
☐ Douglas DC-3A-467 Skytrain (C-47B) (R4D-7) (R4D-6Q)	9023	16347/33095	44-76763, Bu99824	PV
☐ Fuji KM-2	6263	TM.33		PV
☐ Grumman G-89 Tracker (S2F-1) (S-2A)	4131	631	Bu136722	PV
☐ Kawanishi H8K2		426		PV
☐ Kawasaki Ki-61 Hien				PVD
☐ Kawasaki P-2J [Lockheed 726]	4770	7069	Front fuselage only.	PV
☐ Kawasaki P-2J [Lockheed 726]	4771	7070		PV
☐ Kawasaki P-2J [Lockheed 726]	4783	7082		PV
☐ Kawasaki-Bell 47G-2A	8753	528		PV
☐ Kawasaki-Hughes 369M (OH-6J)	8763	6343		PV
☐ Kawasaki-Vertol KV-107-IIA-3A	8608	4096		PV
☐ Lockheed 726-45-14 Neptune (P2V-7) (P-2H)	4618	726-2002	(Bu149090)	PV
☐ Mitsubishi A6M5 Zero Sen Model 52		22383	Composite of two.	PV

TYPE	REG/SER	CON. NO.	PI/NOTES	STATUS
☐ North American NA-88 Texan (SNJ-5)	6180	88-15252	Bu52039	PV
☐ Shin Meiwa US-1A (US-1)	9076	2006		PV
☐ Sikorsky S-61 Sea King (HSS-2)	8041	M61-045	Front fuselage only.	PV
☐ Sikorsky S-61 Sea King (HSS-2A)	8074	M61-082		PV
☐ Sikorsky S-61AH	8941	M61-072		PV

KASEDA PEACE MUSEUM (JA51)

Address:	1955-3 Takahashi, Kaseda-shi, Kagoshima pref. 897-1123.
Tel:	0993-52-3979
Admission:	Daily 0900-1630.
Location:	About 30 km south west of Kagoshima city.

The displays at this museum trace the story of conflicts which have involved Japanese forces in recent years. The theme of peace following these wars is highlighted throughout the exhibition. On show are many documents, models, photographs and uniforms as well as weapons. The only aircraft exhibited is the Aichi E13A 'Jake' reconnaissance floatplane. Over one thousand four hundred were built with the prototype making its maiden flight in late 1938. The example on show was recovered from a crash site and lacks the floats.

TYPE	REG/SER	CON. NO.	PI/NOTES	STATUS
☐ Aichi E13A1		41116		RAD

KASUGA AIR BASE COLLECTION (JA52)

Address:	3-1-1 Hara-machi, Kasuga-shi, Fukuoka pref. 816-0804.
Tel:	092-581-4031
Admission:	By prior permission only.
Location:	About 3 km south west of Fukuoka International Airport off Route 3.

This base is home to the Headquarters of the Western Air Defence Force which controls the wings at Nyutabaru and Tsuiki. A unit flying the Kawasaki T-4 and a helicopter squadron operating Vertol CH-47Js are currently in residence. The CH-47 is used on transport duties and the fleet is dispersed around the country.

TYPE	REG/SER	CON. NO.	PI/NOTES	STATUS
☐ Lockheed 683-07-14 Starfighter (F-104J)	46-8603	683B-3103		RA
☐ Mitsubishi F-1	90-8234	97		RA
☐ North American NA-238 Sabre (F-86F)	82-7777	238-7	56-2779	RA

KASUGAI ARMY CAMP MONUMENT (JA53)

Address:	Nishiyama-cho, Kasugai-shi, Aichi pref. 786-8550.
Tel:	0568-81-7183
Admission:	By prior permission only.
Location:	About 15 km north east of Nagoya station.

A large military arsenal was established in the area prior to the outbreak of World War II. The majority of this land has now been converted for industrial use with factories and office buildings in use by many companies. An army camp remains and the Iroquois in preserved as a monument to all who have served at the site.

TYPE	REG/SER	CON. NO.	PI/NOTES	STATUS
☐ Fuji-Bell 205 Iroquois (HU-1H)	41623	23		RA

KASUMIGAURA ARMY AIR BASE MUSEUM (JA54)

Address:	2410 Migamomi, Tsuchiura-shi, Ibaraki pref. 300-8619.
Tel:	029-842-1211
Admission:	By prior permission only.
Location:	About 40 km north east of Tokyo off Route 6.

A unit of the Army Aviation School is housed at this busy airfield, Currently operated are the Bell UH-1 Iroquois, the Bell AH-1S Cobra, the Hughes OH-6D and the Boeing-Vertol CH-47 Chinook. Also in use are small numbers of Mitsubishi LR-1s along with its successor the Beech LR-2. A collection of types previously used for training has been assembled. Two versions of the famous Huey can be compared, both were built by Fuji. Twenty Mitsubishi MU-2Cs were acquired for liaison and reconnaissance duties.

TYPE	REG/SER	CON. NO.	PI/NOTES	STATUS
☐ Fuji-Bell 205 Iroquois (HU-1H)	41609	09		PV
☐ Fuji-Bell 205 Iroquois (HU-1H)	41644	44		RA
☐ Fuji-Bell 205 Iroquois (HU-1H)	41655	55		RA
☐ Fuji-Bell 205 Iroquois (HU-1H)	41662	62		RA
☐ Fuji-Bell 209 Huey Cobra (AH-1F) (AH-1S)	73402			RA
☐ Hughes 269B (TH-55J)	61326	0235 (?)		PV
☐ Kawasaki-Hughes 369M (OH-6D)	31125	6426		RA
☐ Kawasaki-Hughes 369M (OH-6D)	31126	6427		RA
☐ Kawasaki-Hughes 369M (OH-6D)	31128	6429		RA
☐ Kawasaki-Hughes 369M (OH-6D)	31131	6432		RA
☐ Kawasaki-Hughes 369M (OH-6J)	31001	6301		RA
☐ Kawasaki-Hughes 369M (OH-6J)	'31038'	6302	31002 – believed correct.	RAX
☐ Kawasaki-Hughes 369M (OH-6J)	31082	6382		PV
☐ Kawasaki-Hughes 369M (OH-6J)	31094	6398		RA
☐ Kawasaki-Vertol KV-107-IIA-4	51815			PV
☐ Mitsubishi MU-2C (LR-1)	22001	801		RA

KASUMINOME ARMY AIR BASE COLLECTION (JA55)

Address:	1-1-1 Kasuminome Wakabayashi-ku, Sendai-shi, Miyagi pref. 984-8580.
Tel:	022-286-3101
Admission:	By prior permission only.
Location:	About 4 km south east of Sendai city off Route 4.

Several helicopter squadrons, operating Bell UH-1H and UH-1J versions along with Hughes OH-6Ds, and a unit flying the Mitsubishi MU-2C (LR-1) are in residence at the field. There is also a technical school, with a number of instructional airframes, on the site. Three aircraft have been preserved on the airfield and the Japanese built Iroquois is displayed in the main camp across the road from this site.

TYPE	REG/SER	CON. NO.	PI/NOTES	STATUS
☐ Fuji-Bell 204B-2 Iroquois (HU-1B)	41569	MH-70		RA
☐ Kawasaki-Hughes 369M (OH-6D)	31137			RA
☐ Kawasaki-Hughes 369M (OH-6D)	31138			RA
☐ Mitsubishi MU-2C (LR-1)	22008	808		RA

KAWAGUCHIKO MOTOR MUSEUM / HARADA AIR PARK (JA56)

Address:	Fuji-sakurakougen, Narusawa Village, Minami-Tsuru-gun, Yamanashi pref. 401-0322.
Tel:	0555-86-3511
Fax:	0555-86-3511
Email:	racing@big.or.jp
Admission:	April-December Friday-Wednesday 0900-1700.
Location:	About 80 km west of Tokyo south of Route 412.

Situated in a beautiful setting under Mount Fuji this museum has around seventy five cars dating from the 1920s on show. The development of motoring is portrayed with a display of engines, components, models and photographs. The earliest vehicle on show is an 1886 Benz and classic designs from many companies around the world can be seen. In addition there is a collection of motor cycles with the examples on show dating from the earliest years of the twentieth century. The collection is owned by racing driver and car restorer Nobuo Harada. Three wrecked Zero fighters were recovered several years ago and one has been restored to airworthy standards. This aircraft has been temporarily exhibited at a number of other locations. The Commando is parked in the outside yard and many of the other aircraft are currently in store. The Kawasaki Ki-61 was produced in large numbers during World War II. The prototype first flew in December 1941 and just over three thousand were completed. The type differed from most Japanese fighters as it used a liquid-cooled in-line engine rather than the favoured air-cooled radial. The Allies first encountered the Hien in New Guinea in 1943 and many pilots initially believed it to be a derivative of the classic Messerschmitt Bf 109. No complete Mitsubishi G4M 'Betty' bombers survive. There are a number of components recovered from wrecks in collections. The museum has in store the rear fuselage of one obtained from a crash site. A replica has been built of a

Yokosuka K5Y1 known to the Allies as 'Willow'. The prototype of this biplane first flew in late 1933 and was the standard primary trainer for the Japanese Navy for many years. The sole civil aircraft in the collection is the N-58 built by students at Nihon University. This high wing monoplane used some Piper Tri-Pacer parts and first flew on November 28th 1960. Only one was built and was used as a development machine for the N-62.

TYPE	REG/SER	CON. NO.	PI/NOTES	STATUS
☐ Cessna 305C Bird Dog (L-19E-1)	11204			RA
☐ Curtiss-Wright CW-20B-2 Commando (C-46D)	61-1127	33255	44-77859	PV
☐ Kawasaki Ki-61 Hien				PVD
☐ Lockheed 580 (T-33A)	51-5639		(USAF)	PV
☐ Lockheed 583-10-17 Starfighter (F-104DJ)	26-5007	583B-5407	16-5007	PV
☐ Mitsubishi A6M2 Zero Sen Model 21		91518		PV
☐ Mitsubishi A6M2 Zero Sen Model 21		92717		SD
☐ Mitsubishi A6M5 Zero Sen Model 52		1493		SD
☐ Mitsubishi G4M2			Rear fuselage only.	S
☐ Nihon University N-58	JA3133	1		RA
☐ North American NA-256 Sabre (F-86F)	'02-7960'			PVX
☐ North American NA-256 Sabre (F-86F)	02-7962	256-82	57-6419	RA
☐ Piper PA-18-135 Super Cub (L-21B)	12045			PV
☐ Sikorsky S-55B (H-19C)	40012	551133		RA
☐ Yokosuka K5Y1 (R)	'?-753'			PV

KIRIGAMINE GLIDING MUSEUM (JA57)

Address:	13338-1, Kamisuwa, Suwa-shi, Nagano pref 392-0003.
Tel:	0266-57-2811
Admission:	May-November daily 0900-1700.
Location:	About 15 km northwest of Lake Suwa.

The site has been used for gliding since before World War II and the Japan Soaring Society has plans to build a National Gliding Museum. Several clubs and private owners have promised types for the exhibition. In addition a large collection of memorabilia is in store. At the current time three locally designed machines are displayed in the main hangar. The Hato primary was built in reasonable numbers both before and after World War II. The Taka and Tobi made their maiden flights in the mid-1930s and saw use by many clubs across the country. There are a number of classic types flying from the field and some of these may eventually join the collection. A workshop restoring sailplanes was here for many years but the owner recently died and the majority of his personal types have moved to other fields where enthusiasts are completing their rebuilds.

TYPE	REG/SER	CON. NO.	PI/NOTES	STATUS
☐ Kirigamine Hato K-14	JA0068	14		PV
☐ Kirigamine Taka 7	JA2011	18		PV
☐ Kirigamine Tobi 1	JA0141	039		PV

KIRISHIMAGOKA KOEN COLLECTION (JA58)

Address:	Kaoya-shi, Kagoshima pref. 893.
Admission:	Daily 0900-1800.
Location:	About 6 km south of Kanoya Airbase.

This private collection consists of three former Navy aircraft displayed in a park. Sixty two Fuji KM-2s were flown by the Navy for primary training and several remain in use at Ozuki. The Sikorsky HSS-2 was built under licence by the Mitsubishi company. One hundred and twenty seven were operated on ASW duties. The OH-6Js were delivered in 1973/4 to replace Bell 47s used for training at Kanoya. These were later replaced by the improved OH-6D which was also built in Japan by the Kawasaki company.

TYPE	REG/SER	CON. NO.	PI/NOTES	STATUS
☐ Fuji KM-2	6266	TM.36		PV
☐ Kawasaki-Hughes 369M (OH-6J)	8762	6342		PV
☐ Sikorsky S-61 Sea King (HSS-2A)	8081	M61-089		PV

KISARAZU AIR BASE COLLECTION (JA59)

Address:	1-4-1 Iwane, Kisarazu-shi, Chiba pref. 292-0061.
Tel:	0438-41-1111
Admission:	By prior permission only.
Location:	About 3 km north of Kisarazu railway station.

The Army bases helicopters and fixed wing aircraft at this field and they have a Vertol on show in a hangar. A short distance away there is an Air Force depot where three aircraft are preserved.

TYPE	REG/SER	CON. NO.	PI/NOTES	STATUS
☐ Fuji T-1B	35-5867			RA
☐ Kawasaki-Vertol KV-107-II-4	51736	4065		RA
☐ Lockheed 580 (T-33A)	51-5604		(USAF)	RA
☐ Lockheed 683-07-14 Starfighter (F-104J)	36-8532	683B-3032		RA

KITA-KUMAMOTO ARMY BASE COLLECTION (JA60)

Address:	2-17-1 Hakkeimizutani, Kumamoto-shi, Kumamoto pref. 861-8529.
Tel:	096-343-3141
Admission:	By prior permission only.
Location:	In the northern part of Kumamoto city.

No flying units are based at this heliport which serves the nearby Army camp. Helicopters are regular visitors to the site. Two rotary wing types, both of which have given excellent service with the Army, have been put on show along with a former Air Force F-86D Sabre which was flown in the 1950s and 1960s. The Army flew the Mitubishi LR-1 on liaison and photo reconnaissance duties. Thc first example for the service was delivered in 1967 but only ten of the twenty ordered were in use by the spring of 1979.

TYPE	REG/SER	CON. NO.	PI/NOTES	STATUS
☐ Fuji-Bell 205 Iroquois (HU-1H)	41646	46		RA
☐ Kawasaki-Hughes 369M (OH-6D)	31132			RA
☐ Mitsubishi MU-2C (LR-1)	22013	813		RA
☐ North American NA-173 Sabre (F-86D)	94-8138	173-117	51-5973	RA

KITA-UTSUNOMIYA ARMY AIR BASE COLLECTION (JA61)

Address:	1360 Kamiyokota-machi, Utsounomiya-shi, Tochigi pref 321-1016.
Tel:	028-658-2151
Admission:	By prior permission only.
Location:	About 100 km north of Tokyo off Route 4.

Helicopter units of the Eastern Army, which has its aviation headquarters at Tachkawa, are based at this field which has in the past been used by the other two services. An aviation school also operates from the site. A large collection of preserved aircraft has been assembled at the airfield. One of the first helicopters to be used by the Army was the Bell 47. Six American built examples were delivered in 1954 and these were followed by seventy five Kawasaki constructed aircraft between 1957 and 1964. Many of these remained in service until 1970 when they were replaced by the Hughes OH-6J. The F-86D represents the brief use of the field by all-weather squadrons of the JASDF in the late 1950s and early 1960s. A Fuji T-1A is preserved in the Fuji factory area which is located close by. Forty six T-1As, powered by the Orpheus engine, were built at Utsonomiya in the late 1950s and early 1960s. Twenty improved T-1Bs, with a locally designed engine, followed.

TYPE	REG/SER	CON. NO.	PI/NOTES	STATUS
☐ Beech A45 Mentor (T-34A)	60506	KD.33	51-0343 (JASDF)	RA
☐ Cessna 305C Bird Dog (L-19E-2)	11366			RA
☐ Fuji KM-2	6291		At Fuji Heavy Industries factory area.	RA
☐ Fuji T-1A	25-5841		At Fuji Heavy Industries factory area.	RA
☐ Fuji T-3	11-5546		At Fuji Heavy Industries factory area.	RA
☐ Fuji-Bell 204B-2 Iroquois (HU-1B)	41571	MH-72		RA
☐ Fuji-Bell 205 Iroquois (HU-1H)	'41601'		41701	RAX
☐ Fuji-Bell 205 Iroquois (HU-1H)	41630	30		RA
☐ Fuji-Bell 205 Iroquois (HU-1H)	41637	37		RA
☐ Fuji-Bell 205 Iroquois (HU-1H)	41681	81		RA
☐ Hughes 269B (TH-55J)	61304	0139		RA
☐ Hughes 269B (TH-55J)	61321	0230		RA
☐ Hughes 269B (TH-55J)	61335	0344		RA
☐ Kawasaki-Bell 47G-2 (H-13H)	30166	262		RA
☐ Kawasaki-Hughes 369M (OH-6D)	31121			RA
☐ Kawasaki-Hughes 369M (OH-6D)	31124			RA
☐ Kawasaki-Hughes 369M (OH-6D)	31141			RA
☐ Kawasaki-Hughes 369M (OH-6J)	'31019'	6314	31013	RAX
☐ Kawasaki-Hughes 369M (OH-6J)	31053	6356		RA
☐ Kawasaki-Hughes 369M (OH-6J)	31061	6365	At Fuji Heavy Industries factory area.	RA

☐ Kawasaki-Hughes 369M (OH-6J)	31115	6419		RA
☐ Mitsubishi MU-2C (LR-1)	22006	806		RA
☐ North American NA-256 Sabre (F-86F)	'82-7818'	256-3	57-6340, 92-7883	RAX
☐ Sikorsky S-55B (H-19C)	40014	551145		RA

KOHTA CITY MUSEUM (JA62)

Address:	36-1 Fukouzu-shimizu, Kohta-cho, Nukata-gun, Aichi pref. 444-0124.
Tel:	0564-62-6682
Admission:	Tuesday,Wednesday, Friday-Sunday 1000-1700.
Location:	About 45 km south east of Nagoya.

Displays at this museum trace the history and culture of the city. There are many interesting items to be seen. The Army is represented by a Kawasaki built Bell 47 which was delivered in September 1959. Resplendent in an all yellow scheme is the Fuji KM-2 in the markings of the 201st Kyoiku Kokutia which operated the type at Kanoya and later Ozuki. The Sabre carries a false serial and is painted to represent an 8th Hikotai aircraft.

TYPE	REG/SER	CON. NO.	PI/NOTES	STATUS
☐ Fuji KM-2	6247	TM.17		PV
☐ Kawasaki-Bell 47G-2 (H-13H)	30120	148		PV
☐ North American NA-231 Sabre (F-86F)	'92-7910'	231-43 (?)	55-5090, 72-7743 – possible identity.	PVX

KOKOBU ARMY CAMP COLLECTION (JA63)

Address:	2-14-4Kokobu-Fukushima, Kirishima-shi, Kagoshima pref. 899-4392.
Tel:	0995-46-0350
Admission:	By prior permission only.
Location:	About 10 km south east of Kagoshima airport.

Three helicopters are part of a display at this army camp. All served in considerable numbers with the Japanese Army. The Vertol featured a sealed fuselage which enabled it to land on water. The type was selected for use by all three Japanese services and was produced at Kawasaki's Gifu factory.

TYPE	REG/SER	CON. NO.	PI/NOTES	STATUS
☐ Fuji-Bell 205 Iroquois (HU-1H)	41652	52		RA
☐ Kawasaki-Hughes 369M (OH-6D)	31062	6366		RA
☐ Kawasaki-Vertol KV-107-II-4	51711	4025		RA

KOKUDO CHIRI-IN (JA64)

Address:	1 Katasato Tsukuba-shi, Ibaraki pref. 305-0811.
Tel:	02975-64-1111
Admission:	Monday-Friday 0900-1700.
Location:	About 60 km north east of Tokyo.

The National Geographic Laboratory has used aircraft for survey work for many years. Inside the building is a display of the work carried out. The Queen Air can be seen in the grounds of the centre.

TYPE	REG/SER	CON. NO.	PI/NOTES	STATUS
☐ Beech 65 Queen Air	9101	L-2	N820B, JA5061	PV

KOKUKAN BOON (JA65)

Address:	120-1 Aoyama-aza-Shinmei, Toyoyama-cho, Aichi pref 480-0201.
Tel:	0568-29-0036
Admission:	Tuesday-Sunday 0900-1600.
Location:	About 2 km north of Nagoya airport.

For many years the viewing area at Nagoya Airport housed an Air and Space Museum. This exhibition closed in 2004. A collection is being set up at the new International Airport and two aircraft are now on site.

TYPE	REG/SER	CON. NO.	PI/NOTES	STATUS
☐ Kawasaki-Hughes 369HS	JA9053	6608		PV
☐ Mitsubishi MU-2A	JA8626	003		PV

KOMAKI AIR BASE COLLECTION (JA66)

Address: 1-1 Kasuganji,
Komaki-shi,
Aichi pref. 485-8652.
Tel: 0568-76-2191
Admission: By prior permission only.
Location: About 15 km north of Nagoya city centre off Route 41.

A transport squadron operating the several types and a technical school with a flying element of Kawasaki T-4s reside at this base. The collection of preserved aircraft is parked just inside the main gate.

TYPE	REG/SER	CON. NO.	PI/NOTES	STATUS
☐ Fuji T-1B	35-5866			RA
☐ Lockheed 580 (T-33A)	51-5645		(USAF)	RA
☐ North American NA-173 Sabre (F-86D)	'84-8111'		(USAF)	RAX
☐ North American NA-238 Sabre (F-86F)	82-7778	238-8	56-2780	RA
☐ Sikorsky S-62J	53-4775	M62-012		RA

KOMATSU AIR BASE COLLECTION (JA67)

Address: Mukaimoto-ori-machi,
Komatsu-shi,
Ishikawa pref. 923-8586.
Tel: 0761-22-2101
Admission: By prior permission only.
Location: Just south west of Komatsu city.

The airfield was in use during World War II and was later occupied by American forces. Front line squadrons of the Central Air Defence Force flying F-15 Eagles and Kawasaki T-4s now operate from this base. In addition an air-sea rescue detachment is in residence. This unit uses the Sikorsky UH-60J and the Raytheon U-125A. A collection of types formerly flown from the site has been assembled. Apart from the Texan they are parked near the main gate to the site. This trainer is located in a bunker close to the airfield.

TYPE	REG/SER	CON. NO.	PI/NOTES	STATUS
☐ Beech A45 Mentor (T-34A)	61-0402	FM.42		RA
☐ Lockheed 580 (T-33A)	81-5379	1179		RA
☐ Lockheed 683-07-14 Starfighter (F-104J)	46-8638	683B-3138		RA
☐ Lockheed 683-07-14 Starfighter (F-104J)	46-8646	683B-3146		RA
☐ North American NA-176 Sabre (F-86F)	52-7408	176-307	51-13376	RA
☐ North American NA-182 Texan (T-6G)	52-0082		(USAF)	RA
☐ North American NA-190 Sabre (F-86D)	14-8217	190-369	52-3966	RA

KOMATSUSHIMA NAVAL AIR STATION MONUMENT (JA68)

Address: 4-3 Subana,
Wadajima-cho,
Komatsushima-shi,
Tokushima pref. 773-0025.
Tel: 08853-7-2111
Admission: By prior permission only.
Location: About 10 km south east of Tokushima city.

The base houses a helicopter unit carrying out search and rescue and coastal patrol duties. Currently in use is the Sikorsky UH-60J. This type is a version of the Sikorsky S-70A and was built under licence by Mitsubishi. Two aircraft are preserved near the main gate to serve as monuments to those who flew from the site. A second Sea King which was on show for many years is no longer on show and has probably been scrapped.

TYPE	REG/SER	CON. NO.	PI/NOTES	STATUS
☐ Beech A45 Mentor (T-34A)	9010	FM.3	51-0363	RA
☐ Sikorsky S-61 Sea King (HSS-2B)	8161	M61-180		RA

KORIYAMA ARMY CAMP MONUMENT (JA69)

Address:	Ohtsuki-machi, Koriyama -shi, Fukushima pref 963-0292.
Tel:	024-951-0225
Admission:	By prior permission only.
Location:	About 5 km west of Koriyama station.

A Kawasaki built Hughes helicopter has been preserved as a monument at this camp which has seen frequent use by visiting helicopters. A Bell 47 which was on show has not been seen for some time and is likely to have been scrapped or put in store. Also displayed are military vehicles and pieces of artillery.

TYPE	REG/SER	CON. NO.	PI/NOTES	STATUS
☐ Kawasaki-Hughes 369M (OH-6J)	30130	6431		RA

KOTOBUKI PARK DISPLAY (JA70)

Address:	Nakatonbetsu, Hokkaido.
Admission:	Daily.
Location:	In the town.

This small park has a number of attractions which are designed to interest people of all ages. There are many items for children including rides and sporting facilities. Among the items on show are a steam locomotive and a Starfighter. Also to be seen are a small number of vehicles and display boards.

TYPE	REG/SER	CON. NO.	PI/NOTES	STATUS
☐ Lockheed 683-07-14 Starfighter (F-104J)	46-8568	683B-3068		PV

KUMAGAYA AIR FORCE TECHNICAL SCHOOL COLLECTION (JA71)

Address:	4th Technical School, 839 Jyurokken, Kumagaya-shi, Saitama pref. 360-8586.
Tel:	0485-32-3554
Admission:	By prior permission only.
Location:	About 60 km north west of Tokyo on Route 17.

Kumagaya is home to the 4th. Technical School which trains personnel in a variety of trades. The five aircraft displayed in the grounds are there to show students types that have served at operational bases. There are a number of engines and components exhibited in one of the buildings along with other material.

TYPE	REG/SER	CON. NO.	PI/NOTES	STATUS
☐ Lockheed 580 (T-33A)	51-5609		(USAF)	RA
☐ Lockheed 683-07-14 Starfighter (F-104J)	76-8704	683B-3204		RA
☐ North American NA-173 Sabre (F-86D)	84-8128	173-133	51-5989	RA
☐ North American NA-182 Texan (T-6G)	52-0128		(USAF)	RA
☐ North American NA-238 Sabre (F-86F)	82-7849	238-79	56-2851	RA

KUMAMOTO CITY MUSEUM (JA72)

Address:	3-2 Kokyoh cho, Kumamoto-shi, Kumamaota pref 860.
Tel:	096-324-3500
Admission:	Tuesday-Sunday 0900-1700
Location:	In the centre of the city.

Three aircraft are on show in this municipal science and local history museum. There is a section devoted to local wildlife and plants with many interesting items on show. The progress of technology and industry are portrayed in the exhibition with particular emphasis on the region. Another attraction is a planetarium. The aeronautical section includes a J-47 jet engine, models, components and photographs. The Robinson R-22 two seat helicopter first flew on August 28th 1975 and production examples were ready four years later. Since then well eight thousand R-22s and the four seat R-44 have been constructed in California and many exported around the world. The classic Beech 18 was imported from the U.S.A. in late 1962 for use by the Maritime Safety Agency and was normally based at Kagoshima although it operated around the coastline.

TYPE	REG/SER	CON. NO.	PI/NOTES	STATUS
□ Beech G18S	JA5505	BA-617		PV
□ Cessna 150J	JA3507	15070601	N60823, N1743C	PV
□ Robinson R-22HP Beta	JA7679	0205	N90813	PV

KURE MARITIME MUSEUM (JA73)

Address:	5-20 Takara-machi, Kure-shi, Hiroshima 737-0029.
Tel:	0823-25-3017
Fax:	0823-25-7400
Admission:	Tuesday-Sunday 0900-1800.
Location:	About 25 km south east of Hiroshima city.

This new collection acquired the Zero that was on show for many years at the now closed Kyoto-Arashima Museum. Also on show are many models, photographs and documents tracing the development of ships.

TYPE	REG/SER	CON. NO.	PI/NOTES	STATUS
□ Mitsubishi A6M7 Zero Sen Model 63	'210-118B'			PVX

KUTCHAN ARMY CAMP MONUMENT (JA74)

Address:	232-2 Takasago, Kutchan-cho, Abuta-gun, Hokkaido 044-0076.
Tel:	0136-22-1195
Admission:	By prior permission only.
Location:	About 2 km south of the town.

The town has an army camp with a helicopter landing facility. Preserved as a monument is an example of the Kawasaki-Vertol KV-107. The aircraft was damaged in the early 1970s and later withdrawn.

TYPE	REG/SER	CON. NO.	PI/NOTES	STATUS
□ Kawasaki-Vertol KV-107-II-4	51724	4046		RA

MAEGAWARA ARMY CAMP MONUMENT (JA75)

Address:	2728 Kourauchi-machi, Kurume-shi, Fukuoka pref. 839-0852.
Tel:	0942-43-5215
Admission:	By prior permission only.
Location:	In the town.

After World War I this long established camp housed many German prisoners captured in China. The site is now home to Army units and two helicopters have been preserved as monuments.

TYPE	REG/SER	CON. NO.	PI/NOTES	STATUS
□ Fuji-Bell 205 Iroquois (HU-1H)	41613	13		RA
□ Kawasaki-Hughes 369M (OH-6D)	31123			RA

MAKOMANAI ARMY CAMP MONUMENT (JA76)

Address:	17 Makomanai, Minami-ku, Sapporo-shi, Hokkaido pref 005-0008.
Admission:	By prior permission only.
Location:	In the southern part of the city.

This large Army camp in the southern part of Sapporo now has one aircraft preserved as a monument. A Sabre which was in the collection disappeared over the winter of 2004/2005. Also two Kawasaki-Vertol KV-107s have gone. One was in the grounds of the camp and the other was in a local park.

TYPE	REG/SER	CON. NO.	PI/NOTES	STATUS
□ Fuji-Bell 205 Iroquois (HU-1H)	41658	58		RA

MATSUMOTO ARMY CAMP MEMORIAL (JA77)

Address:	1-1 Takamiya-nishi, Matsumoto-shi, Nagano pref. 390-8508.
Tel:	0263-26-2766
Admission:	By prior permission only.
Location:	In the south western part of the town.

The prototype Vertol 107 made its maiden flight in April 1958 and was the first turbine powered helicopter produced by the company. A Japanese built example is preserved as a monument.

TYPE	REG/SER	CON. NO.	PI/NOTES	STATUS
☐ Kawasaki-Vertol KV-107-II-4	51739	4072		RA

MATSUSHIMA AIR BASE COLLECTION (JA78)

Address:	Yamoto, Higashi-Matsushima-shi, Miyagi pref. 981-0503.
Tel:	0225-82-2111
Admission:	By prior permission only.
Location:	About 20 km north east of Sendai city off Route 45.

Based at this field is the 4th. Kokudan (Air Wing) operating Mitsubishi F-2s and Kawasaki T-4s. The Blue Impulse aerobatic team was established at Hamamatsu in 1960 and flew F-86F Sabres until February 1981. More than five hundred performances were given with the Sabre including one at the opening of the 1964 Olympic Games in Tokyo and another at 'Expo 70'. In July 1981 the team was reformed with up to eight T-2s.

TYPE	REG/SER	CON. NO.	PI/NOTES	STATUS
☐ Lockheed 580 (T-33A)	51-5626		(USAF)	RA
☐ Lockheed 683-07-14 Starfighter (F-104J)	36-8535	683B-3035		RA
☐ Mitsubishi T-2(K)	29-5176	135		RA
☐ Mitsubishi T-2(Z)	59-5109	09		RA
☐ North American NA-173 Sabre (F-86D)	84-8134	173-130	51-5986	RA
☐ North American NA-182 Texan (T-6G)	52-0080		(USAF)	RA
☐ North American NA-238 Sabre (F-86F)	82-7789	238-19	56-2791	RA
☐ Sikorsky S-55B (H-19C)	81-4706	M55-002		RA

MEIHOH GOLF GARDEN MONUMENT (JA79)

Address:	370 Kokura, Maizuru-shi, Kyoto pref. 625-0020.
Tel:	0773-62-1884
Admission:	On permanent view.
Location:	About 2.5 km north east of Higashi-Maizuru station.

There has been a major naval base in the town, which is the closest to North Korea, since the 1920s. A Beech 18 which served as an instrument trainer has been preserved at a nearby golf centre as a reminder of this heritage.

TYPE	REG/SER	CON. NO.	PI/NOTES	STATUS
☐ Beech C18S Expeditor (C-45F), (UC-45F) (JRB-4) (SNB-4)	6415	8647	44-87388, Bu66427	RA

METABARU ARMY BASE MONUMENT (JA80)

Address:	7 Tateno, Yoshinogari-cho, Kankazi-gun, Saga pref. 842-0032
Tel:	0952-52-2161
Admission:	By prior permission only.
Location:	About 20 km south of Hakata city.

The airfield houses helicopter units of the Japanese Army. Among the types flown are UH-1Hs, AH-1s and OH-6s. Two aircraft have been preserved as monuments and are located near to the main gate.

TYPE	REG/SER	CON. NO.	PI/NOTES	STATUS
☐ Hughes 269B (TH-55J)	61317	0217		RA
☐ Kawasaki-Hughes 369M (OH-6J)	31017			RA

The collection at Matsushima Air Force Base includes this Mitsubishi T-2. (Steve Comber)

This Mitsubishi F-1 is preserved at Misawa Air Force Base. (Steve Comber)

The prototype NAMC YS-11 is preserved in the Museum of Aeronautical Sciences at Tokyo's Narita Airport. (Gerry Manning)

MIHO AIR BASE COLLECTION (JA81)

Address: 2258 Koshinozu-cho,
Sakai-minato-shi,
Totori pref. 684-0053.
Tel: 0859-45-0211
Admission: By prior permission only.
Location: About 10 km north east of Matsue city.

Miho is used by a transport wing which also trains crews for the whole fleet. Currently in use are Kawasaki C-1s along with NAMC YS-11s. Forty eight Curtiss Commando aircraft were used from the mid-1950s and the last few, including the example on show, soldiered on until withdrawn in 1977. The collection has been placed just inside the main gate and types withdrawn from service over the last few years can be seen.

TYPE	REG/SER	CON. NO.	PI/NOTES	STATUS
☐ Curtiss-Wright CW-20B Commando (C-46A)	91-1139	30570	42-101115, (China), (Taiwan)	RA
☐ Fuji T-1B	35-5860			RA
☐ Fuji T-3	11-5543			RA
☐ Lockheed 580 (T-33A)	51-5647		(USAF)	RA
☐ Lockheed 683-07-14 Starfighter (F-104J)	46-8602	683B-3102		RA
☐ Mitsubishi F-1	20-8260	123?		RA
☐ North American NA-190 Sabre (F-86D)	04-8202	190-448	52-4045	RA
☐ Sikorsky S-62J	63-4776	M62013		RA

MISAWA AIR FORCE BASE COLLECTION (JA82)

Address: 432 FW/CC,
125-7 Ushiro-kubo,
Misawa-shi
Aomori pref. 033-8604.
Tel: 0176-53-4121
Admission: By prior permission only.
Location: About 20 km north west of Hachinohe city.

Units operating from this field include fighter units, a missile squadron, and airborne early warning group and a helicopter detachment. Among the small collection of preserved aircraft are a Mitsubishi F-1 and a Sabre. Two aircraft flown by the U.S.A.F. from their Japanese bases can also be seen.

TYPE	REG/SER	CON. NO.	PI/NOTES	STATUS
☐ General Dynamics 401 Fighting Falcon (F-16A)	78-0053	61-49		RA
☐ McDonnell M.98DJ Phantom II (F-4C)	64-0679	911		RA
☐ Mitsubishi F-1	80-8223	79		RA
☐ North American NA-227 Sabre (F-86F)	'55-7508'	227-110	55-3925, 62-7508	RAX

MISAWA AVIATION AND SCIENCE MUSEUM (JA83)

Address: Kitayama Chinnai 158,
Misawa,
Aomori Pref 033-022.
Tel: 0176-50-7777
Fax: 0176-50-7559
Location: Close to the north east side of Misawa Airport.

This impressive museum opened in 2003 and has areas devoted to many aspects of science with several 'hands-on' exhibits designed to test the visitor. Misawa has had a long association with aviation and on October 5th 1931 Clyde Pangbourne and Hugh Herndon took off from a field in their Bellanca Skyrocket 'Miss Veedol'. They ditched their undercarriage over the sea to increase range and endurance. Forty one hours and fifteen minutes later they made a belly landing at Wenatchee in Washington state and so completed the first non-stop crossing of the Pacific Ocean. A faithful replica of their aircraft, incorporating some original parts, was built in the U.S.A. The Gasuden Koken was a long-range research monoplane built in the mid-1930s. On May 13th 1938 the aircraft took off from Kisarazu Naval Air Base. The Koken flew twenty nine laps of a four sided route and established a closed-course record of eleven thousand six hundred and fifty one kilometres. After this the monoplane flew a few more times and is believed to have been burned along with other captured aircraft at Haneda. Einosuke Shirato was a well known commercial pilot in the 1920s and his company designed and built several types. A replica of one of his early aircraft can be seen. Sanji Narahara constructed four biplanes between 1910 and 1911. His No.2 achieved the altitude of over two hundred feet which was unusual for the time.

TYPE	REG/SER	CON. NO.	PI/NOTES	STATUS
☐ Bellanca CH-400 Skyrocket (R)	'NR796W'			PVX
☐ Fuji T-3	91-5516	016		PV
☐ Gasuden Koken (R)				PV
☐ General Dynamics 401 Fighting Falcon (F-16A)	78-0021	61-27		PV

TYPE	REG/SER	CON. NO.	PI/NOTES	STATUS
☐ Kawasaki-Hughes 369M (OH-6D)	31184			PV
☐ Lockheed 185 Orion (P3V-1) (P-3A) (UP-3A)	Bu150526	185-5052		PV
☐ Lockheed 580 (T-33A)	81-5344	1144		PV
☐ Lockheed 683-07-14 Starfighter (F-104J)	76-8699	683B-3199		PV
☐ Mitsubishi F-1	00-8247	110		PV
☐ Mitsubishi MU-2C (LR-1)	22009	809		PV
☐ Mitsubishi T-2(K)	29-5177	136		PV
☐ Mitsubishi T-2(Z)	59-5105	05		PV
☐ Narahara 2 (R)				PV
☐ Nihon Kokuki Seizo Kabushiki Kaisha (NAMC) YS-11A-227	JA8776	2157		PV
☐ Pitts S-1C Special	N122EZ	JW-1		PV
☐ Shiroto Asahi-go (R)				PV
☐ Westland-Sikorsky WS-51 Dragonfly 1A	JA7014	WA/H/91	G-ANAM	PV

MITSU KEIKI COLLECTION (JA84)

Address:	301 Shimogawai, Awaji-shi, Hyogo pref 656-1522.
Tel:	0799-85-1133
Fax:	0799-85-2602
Admission:	Aircraft on permanent view.
Location:	In the town which is about 20 km west of Sumato.

This company is setting up an exhibition of aircraft at its premises. Five types, three indigenous designs and two licence built models, have arrived. The Fuji T-1 was Japan's first post-war jet type and the majority produced were operated by the 13th Hiko Kyoikudan at Gifu from 1960. The unit moved to Ashiya two years later and now flies the Kawasaki T-4 from this airfield. The Vertol KV-107 was selected as the standard medium helicopter for all three services. Licence production commenced at Kawasaki's Gifu factory in the late 1960s. and over one hundred and fifty were built with several being sold to civilian operators.

TYPE	REG/SER	CON. NO.	PI/NOTES	STATUS
☐ Fuji T-1B	35-5862			PV
☐ Fuji-Bell 205 Iroquois (HU-1H)	41669	69		PV
☐ Kawasaki-Vertol KV-107-IIA-4	51816	4121		PV
☐ Mitsubishi F-1	70-8207	53		PV
☐ Mitsubishi MU-2C (LR-1)	22004	804		PV

MITSUBISHI AIRCRAFT FACTORY MUSEUM (JA85)

Address:	Mitsubishi Heavy Industries, Komaki-Minami Factory, Toyoyama-cho, Nishi kasugai-gun, Aichi pref. 480-0201.
Tel:	0568-28-1112
Admission:	By prior permission only.
Location:	About 15 km north of Nagoya city off Route 41.

The Mitsubishi company entered the aviation field in 1920 and over the next quarter of a century produced a wide range of civil and military aircraft. The firm returned to aircraft manufacture in the 1950s and has constructed both its own designs and licence built American types. The Komaki plant assembled three hundred F-86Fs between 1956 and 1961. The first three Japanese Starfighters were built and flown in California and then dismantled and shipped to the Mitsubishi factory. Seventeen kits followed before the first of one hundred and eighty built entirely in Japan came off the line. Both single and two seat versions were constructed. One hundred and twenty seven HSS-2s were built at Komaki between 1964 and the mid-1980s. Two of the classic World War II types produced by the company have been recovered and restored for the display. The Zero entered service in 1937 and over eleven thousand were completed. The example on show has been superbly rebuilt from a recovered wreck. In the latter stages of World War II the B-29 Superfortress was causing havoc as current fighters could not reach the altitude of the high flying bombers. In late 1943 one of two submarines taking details of the Messerschmitt Me 163 to Japan was sunk. As only incomplete data arrived Mitsubishi set about creating a similar machine. On its maiden flight in July 1945 the J8M1 crashed near Yokoku killing the test pilot Lieutenant Toyohiko Inuzaka. Before this several glider versions were built to test the flight characteristics of the design. Only seven powered examples were completed by the end of the conflict. The derelict fuselage of the Shusui spent a period on show at the Kakamigahara Aerospace Museum before returning to its manufacturers. New components have been constructed so that a completely restored aircraft can now be seen.

TYPE	REG/SER	CON. NO.	PI/NOTES	STATUS
☐ Lockheed 683-07-14 Starfighter (F-104J)	56-8672	683B-3172		RA
☐ Mitsubishi A6M5 Zero Sen Model 52		4708		RA
☐ Mitsubishi J8M1 Shusui				RA
☐ Mitsubishi T-2	19-5101	01		RA
☐ North American NA-231 Sabre (F-86F)	62-7702	231-2	55-5049	RA
☐ Sikorsky S-61 Sea King (HSS-2B)	8084	M61-093		RA

MIYAZAKI UNIVERSAL COLLEGE (JA86)

Address:	7439 Hirohara, Miyazaki-shi, Miyazaki pref. 880-0125.
Tel:	0985-39-2249
Admission:	By prior permission only.
Location:	In the city.

Several aircraft are on display at this college. They include a pair of Beech Mentors, one former Air Force and one ex-Navy machine. Also on show are three of the twenty eight Queen Airs used by the Navy as instrument trainers from the early 1960s. A few Enstrom Shark helicopters were imported into Japan in the late 1970s. The E33 Bonanza was used at several civilian flying schools in the country.

TYPE	REG/SER	CON. NO.	PI/NOTES	STATUS
☐ Beech E33 Bonanza				RA
☐ Beech A45 Mentor (T-34A)	9012	FM.26	51-0386	RA
☐ Beech A45 Mentor (T-34A)	71-0420	FM.60		PV
☐ Beech 65 Queen Air				RA
☐ Beech 65 Queen Air			Front fuselage only.	PV
☐ Beech 65 Queen Air	6716	LC-225		RA
☐ Enstrom 280C Shark	JA7637	1160		RA
☐ Kawasaki-Bell 47G-2 (H-13H)				RA
☐ Piper PA-28-140 Cherokee				RA

MODERN TRANSPORTATION MUSEUM (JA87)

Address:	11-103 Chome Namiyoke, Minato-ku Osaka 552-0001.
Tel:	06-581-5771
Admission:	Tuesday-Saturday 0930-1700.
Location:	Close to Benten-cho Station on the Osaka Loop Line.

This museum opened in January 1962 to commemorate the completion of the Osaka loop line. The main theme of the exhibition is the history and development of the Japanese railway system. There are many railway engines from the steam era up to modern diesels on show. Several passenger carriages and freight vehicles can also be seen. The development of the 'Bullet' train is portrayed in detail. Other forms of transport also feature in the displays. The Kawasaki KAL-1 was the first post-war indigenous design to fly when it made its maiden flight on July 21st 1953. Two prototypes were built for liaison duties with the Air Force but the type did not go into production. In addition to the three American built civil aircraft there are many models, engines and photographs tracing the development of air transport across the country.

TYPE	REG/SER	CON. NO.	PI/NOTES	STATUS
☐ Aero Commander 680F	JA5075	1001-40	N6137X	PV
☐ Cessna 172	JA3112	36039	N8239B, JA3112, N62120	PV
☐ Cessna 195				PV
☐ Kawasaki KAL-1	JA3074	1002		PV

MUSEUM OF AERONAUTICAL SCIENCES (JA88)

Address:	Iwayama, Shibayamamachi, Sanbu-gun, Chiba pref. 289-1608.
Tel:	0479-78-0557
Admission:	Tuesday-Sunday 1000-1700 (Closed Tuesday after a Monday public holiday)
Location:	Near to the terminal building of Narita Airport which is about 50 km east of Tokyo.

In 1978 the town of Chibaken Shibyama suggested that an exhibition building should be erected at the new Tokyo International Airport to be built at Narita. Construction of the museum started in February 1988 and it was opened to the public on August 1st 1989. The building has three circular exhibition halls and an outside park. There is also a library and research facility and above the central hall is an observation room to view the activity at Narita. In the foyer hangs a replica of the Farman HF-7, which in December 1910 was the first aircraft to fly in Japan. The aim of the exhibition is to present the history of aviation along with technological developments. In the aircraft construction section there is a cut-away Fuji FA-200, components, engines and a multi-vision TV display. A wind tunnel demonstrates the theory of flight and there are replica cockpits to show the instrumentation of a light aircraft and a helicopter. There is a section devoted to Japanese aviation where models of significant types can be seen. The operations of Narita Airport are explained with a large working model. The smaller aircraft are on show in the building and these include gliders, helicopters and homebuilt types. The outside park contains two successful transports, the YS-11 and the MU-2. The YS-11 made its maiden flight in August 1962 and entered airline service in March 1965. The Nihon company produced one hundred and eight two examples of the twin-engined turboprop transport. The YS-11 served with airlines around the world. The last airline service in Japan by the type took place in

September 2006. The prototype and the front fuselage of a production version are in the exhibition. Small numbers are still flying in other countries. The MU-2 first flew in in September 1963 and over the next twenty years over seven hundred and fifty were sold with the majority going to the U.S.A. Many corporate transports are still in use. The prototype Fuji FA-300 twin was developed in conjunction with Rockwell in the U.S.A. Only one was built in Japan and this made its maiden flight on November 13th 1975. Just over thirty were constructed in America before the joint venture was terminated. A range of popular civil types produced by the Cessna company can be seen along with two Beech designs. The Puma was used in the fire-fighting role in the Tokyo region.

TYPE	REG/SER	CON. NO.	PI/NOTES	STATUS
☐ Aero Commander 680E	JA5074	872-85	N9364R	PV
☐ Aeronca 7AC Champion	JA3686	7AC-1224	N82587	PV
☐ Beech E33 Bonanza	JA3440	CD-1196	N7617N	PV
☐ Beech 56TC Baron	JA5159	TG-77	N8004R	PV
☐ Cessna 150H	JA3420	15068602	N22901 – front fuselage only.	PV
☐ Cessna 172G	JA3316	17254890	N1395F	PV
☐ Cessna 175A Skylark	JA3136	56769	N8069T, N11B	PV
☐ Cessna 195	JA3007	7870	N1587D	PV
☐ Cessna 411A	JA5151	411A0280	N3280R	PV
☐ Cessna 421B	JA5238	421B0602	N1505G	PV
☐ Farman HF-7 (R)				PV
☐ Fuji FA-200-180 Aero Subaru	JA3528	101		PV
☐ Fuji FA-300/Model 700	JA5258	30001	JQ5001	PV
☐ Hughes 369HS	JA9298	102-0423S	N9120F	PV
☐ Kamov Ka-26D	JA7990	7303804		PV
☐ Kawasaki-Bell 47G-2	JA7310	214	Front fuselage only.	PV
☐ Keihikoki SS-2	JA2132	70-34		PV
☐ Mita 3-1 Kai	JA2100	68-15		PV
☐ Mitsubishi MU-2B	JA8628	005		PV
☐ Mong Sport	N911S	12175		PV
☐ Nihon Kokuki Seizo Kabushiki Kaisha (NAMC) YS-11	JA8611	1001/2001		PV
☐ Nihon Kokuki Seizo Kabushiki Kaisha (NAMC) YS-11-115	JA8711	2048	Front fuselage only.	PV
☐ Ninomiya Insect Flying Machine (R)				PV
☐ Robinson R-22 Beta	JA7758	0961		PV
☐ Sagami-1 [Estupian-Hovey WD-II Whing Ding]				PV
☐ Sikorsky S-62J	JA9156	M62-014		PV
☐ Sud SA.330F Puma	JA9512	1141		PV
☐ Wright Flyer (R)				PV

MUSEUM ONRAKUKAN (JA89)

Address:	1494 Kurogawa, Asakura-shi, Fukoka pref 838-0072.
Tel:	0946-29-0345
Email:	onrakukak@k-int-jp
Admission:	Wednesday-Sunday 1000-1700.
Location:	About 20 km south east of Hakata.

This collection which concentrates mainly on music has plans to construct a 'Peace Museum'. Items for this exhibition are being collected and many personal items, photographs and documents have been gathered. Four aircraft are currently on display to bring attention to this project. The Zero was for many years on show at the now closed Air and Space Museum at Nagoya Airport. This aircraft was recovered many years ago from a jungle crash site and was painstakingly rebuilt. The Mitsubishi MH-2000 helicopter first flew in July 1996. This type which could carry up to twelve people made its maiden flight in 1996. Two prototypes and four development aircraft were completed and a small number of production examples have been sold before production was terminated.

TYPE	REG/SER	CON. NO.	PI/NOTES	STATUS
☐ Beech A45 Mentor (T-34A)	71-0435	FM.75	Front fuselage only.	PV
☐ Fuji KM-2				PV
☐ Mitsubishi A6M3 Zero Sen Model 32	Y2-128			PV
☐ Mitsubishi MH-2000	JA003M			PV

NAHA AIR BASE COLLECTION (JA90)

Address:	Toyama, Haha-shi, Okinawa pref, 901-0194.
Tel:	098-857-1191
Admission:	By prior permission only.
Location:	In the southern part of the island.

This airfield on Okinawa serves as the civilian airport for the island as well as housing military units. The 83rd Air Group of the JASDF operates fighters and trainers along with a support flight for transport duties. In addition a search and rescue detachment resides at the field. A wing of the JMSDF flies P-3 Orions on reconnaissance duties.

TYPE	REG/SER	CON. NO.	PI/NOTES	STATUS
☐ Beech 65 Queen Air	06-3095	LC-335	6728 (Japan)	RA
☐ Lockheed 580 (T-33A)	81-5327	1127		RA
☐ Lockheed 683-07-14 Starfighter (F-104J)	76-8688	683B-3188		RA

NAKA NIPPON KOKU SENMON GAKKO COLLEGE (JA91)

Address:	1577-5 Hazama. Seki-Shi. Gifu Prefecture 501-3924.
Tel:	0575-24-2521
Admission:	Daily 0850-1650.
Location:	In the south western suburbs of Seki city which is about 40 km north of Nagoya.

The aircraft owned by this college are used mainly for instruction but they are also available for public viewing. In addition there are displays of engines, models, instruments and components.

TYPE	REG/SER	CON. NO.	PI/NOTES	STATUS
☐ Beech E33 Bonanza	JA3430	CD-1186	N7532N	PV
☐ Beech E33 Bonanza	JA3433	CD-1189	N7536N	PV
☐ Beech E33 Bonanza	JA3439	CD-1195	N7616N	PV
☐ Beech E33 Bonanza	JA3441	CD-1197	N7618N	PV
☐ Beech E33 Bonanza	JA3434	CD-1206	N7851R	PV
☐ Beech E33 Bonanza	JA3445	CD-1219	N2826B	PV
☐ Beech E33 Bonanza	JA3449	CD-1223	N2841B	PV
☐ Beech E33 Bonanza	JA3450	CD-1224	N2842B	PV
☐ Beech E33 Bonanza	JA3451	CD-1225	N2843B	PV
☐ Cessna 172K	JA3458	17257744	N78750, N1738C	PV
☐ Kawasaki-Bell 47G-2 (H-13H)		277		PV
☐ Kawasaki-Hughes 369HS	JA9065	6617		PV
☐ Kawasaki-Hughes 369HS	JA9075	6621		PV
☐ Kawasaki-Hughes 369HS	JA9099	6627		PV
☐ Kawasaki-Hughes 369HS	JA9204	6647		PV
☐ Kawasaki-Hughes 369HS	JA9209	6648		PV
☐ Lockheed 683-07-14 Starfighter (F-104J)	76-8710	683B-3210		PV

NAKA FURANO ARBORETUM MONUMENT (JA92)

Address:	Nishi1-Kita12, Nakafurano-cho, Sorachi-gun, Hokkaido 071-0795.
Admission:	Daily
Location:	About 3 km north of the of the town.

The Starfighter has been preserved as a monument at this arboretum which features a wide range of threes in a picturesque setting. The aircraft honours people who have served with the military forces.

TYPE	REG/SER	CON. NO.	PI/NOTES	STATUS
☐ Lockheed 683-07-14 Starfighter (F-104J)	36-8510	683B-3010		PV

NANREKU MISHO KOEN (JA93)

Address:	803 Hirajyo, Misho-cho, Minamiuwa-gun, Ehime pref. 798-4110.
Tel:	0895-72-3212
Admission:	By prior permission only.
Location:	About 100 km south of Matsuyama city.

The wreck of a Kawanishi N1K2-J Shiden Kai was discovered by divers in Jyohen Hisayoshi Bay on November 18th. 1978. The airframe was raised the following July and has now been rebuilt. A display honouring the pilots who died in World War II can also be seen in the complex in this municipal park. The Shiden Kai fighter was developed from the Kyofu floatplane and the Shiden land based fighter. First appearing in 1944 the N1K2-J was an outstanding aircraft but production was slowed down by the bombing of several factories.

TYPE	REG/SER	CON. NO.	PI/NOTES	STATUS
☐ Kawanishi N1K2-J Shiden Kai				PV

NATIONAL SCIENCE MUSEUM (JA94)

Address:	7-20 Ueno-Koen, Taito-ku, Tokyo 110-0007.
Tel:	03-822-0111
Admission:	Tuesday-Sunday 0900-1630.
Location:	In the city centre near the Keisei Ueno railway station.

Five buildings in Ueno Park in the centre of the city are used by this museum. Displays in the main one trace the evolution of life and this exhibition leads to the Natural History Hall. The Discovery Building houses many 'hands-on' displays where visitors can try their skills on a number of carefully designed pieces of apparatus. The Science and Technology Building covers both fields from early times up to the present. The Air and Space Building traces the history and science of flight using many modern techniques. There are a number of models, engines and photographs on view. One area displays examples of all the main Japanese rockets along with the first satellite produced in the country. The visitor can view the workings of a wind tunnel and try out a flight simulator reproducing the instrumentation of the YS-11 transport. The oldest surviving aircraft on show is the Maurice Farman. Several examples of the type were built by the Army in 1917/8 and the survivor was stored for many years in the rafters of a laboratory at Tohoku University. This biplane was restored after World War II and then spent a period on display at the Yasukuni Shrine before moving to this museum. The Alouette II, imported into Japan in 1961, was the first turbine powered civil helicopter used in the country. Apart from the Zero the aircraft are now in store whilst major development of the exhibition halls takes place.

TYPE	REG/SER	CON. NO.	PI/NOTES	STATUS
☐ Farman MF-6	266			RA
☐ Mitsubishi A6M2 Zero Sen Model 21	'53-122'			PVX
☐ Salmson 2A2			Front fuselage only – on loan to Kakamigahara A. Mus.	–
☐ Sikorsky S-58	JA7201	58945		RA
☐ Stork B Man Powered Aircraft				RA
☐ Sud-Est SE.3130 Alouette II	JA9002	1615		RA

NEMURO AIR BASE MONUMENT (JA95)

Address:	4-15 Koyo-cho, Nemuro-shi, Hokkaido 087-8555.
Tel:	0153-24-8004.
Admission:	By prior permission only.
Location:	On the outskirts of the town.

During World War II there was an important naval air base near the town and after the hostilities ended American units occupied the site. A Starfighter is preserved as a memorial.

TYPE	REG/SER	CON. NO.	PI/NOTES	STATUS
☐ Lockheed 683-07-14 Starfighter (F-104J)	36-8550	683B-3050		RA

NIHON KOKU GAKUEN COLLECTION (JA96)

Address:	455 Utsuya, Futabamachi, Kita-komagun, Yamanashi 407-0108.
Tel:	0551-28-3355
Admission:	By prior permission only.
Location:	In the city which is about 140 km west of Tokyo.

The Japan Aviation Academy has a range of military aircraft which are mainly used for training. Students are educated in all aspects of engine and airframe maintenance. The college has regular open days to display the collection. Also to be seen are models, engines and components illustration technical developments. The majority of the aircraft are former Army machines.

TYPE	REG/SER	CON. NO.	PI/NOTES	STATUS
☐ Cessna 305C Bird Dog (L-19E-1)	11209			RA
☐ Cessna 305C Bird Dog (L-19E-1)	11210			RA
☐ Fuji-Bell 204B-2 Iroquois (HU-1B)	41545	MH-46		RA
☐ Hughes 269B (TH-55J)	61313	0204		RA
☐ Hughes 269B (TH-55J)	61332	0332		RA
☐ Kawasaki-Bell 47G-2 (H-13H)	30104	113		RA
☐ Kawasaki-Bell 47G-2 (H-13H)	30117	146		RA
☐ Kawasaki-Bell 47G-2 (H-13H)	30136	168		RA
☐ Kawasaki-Hughes 369M (OH-6J)	31030	6331		RA
☐ Kawasaki-Hughes 369M (OH-6J)	31099	6403		RA
☐ Kawasaki-Hughes 369M (OH-6J)	31101	6405		RA

TYPE	REG/SER	CON. NO.	PI/NOTES	STATUS
☐ Kawasaki-Hughes 369M (OH-6J)	31106	6410		RA
☐ Kawasaki-Hughes 369M (OH-6J)	31108	6412		RA
☐ Kawasaki-Vertol KV-107-II-4	51702	4016		RA
☐ Lockheed 580 (T-33A)	61-5228	1028		RA
☐ North American NA-182 Texan (T-6G)	52-0041		(USAF)	RA
☐ North American NA-190 Sabre (F-86D)	04-8205	190-714	52-9989	RA
☐ Sikorsky S-55B (H-19C)	40026	M55-035		RA

NIHONBARA ARMY BASE MUSEUM (JA97)

Address: Takimoto,
Nagi-cho,
Katsuta-gun,
Okinawa pref. 708-1393
Tel: 0868-36-5151
Admission: By prior permission only.
Location: About 50 km north east of Okayama city.

The Japanese Army has set up a museum at the base. The history of the site and army flying are portrayed in the displays. Three helicopters are parked outside the building along with some vehicles.

TYPE	REG/SER	CON. NO.	PI/NOTES	STATUS
☐ Fuji-Bell 204B-2 Iroquois (HU-1B)				RA
☐ Kawasaki-Hughes 369M (OH-6J)				RA
☐ Kawasaki-Vertol KV-107-IIA-4	51801	4086		RA

NIIGATA SCIENCE MUSEUM (JA98)

Address: 2010-1b Hasugata Higashi Meike,
Niigata-shi,
Niigata 950-0941.
Tel: 025-283-3331
Admission: Daily 0930-1630 (Closed December 28th- January 3rd).
Location: In the city.

Opened in November 1981, the museum exhibitions highlight many aspects of science. There are comprehensive displays showing how scientific discoveries have affected nature and the lives of humans. Many modern techniques are used to portray the wide range of topics covered. There are several 'hands-on' exhibits for the visitor to try. The development of local transport is featured and the astronomical section contains a planetarium and the largest reflecting telescope for public use in Japan. The sole aircraft on show is a Mitsubishi MU-2. The aircraft is displayed outside the building with a Redstone rocket and a steam locomotive.

TYPE	REG/SER	CON. NO.	PI/NOTES	STATUS
☐ Mitsubishi MU-2A				PV

NISHI-NIHON AVIATION ASSOCIATION (JA99)

Address: 1088-45 Tokunaga,
Nishi-ku,
Fukuoka-shi,
Fukuoka pref. 819-0375.
Email: naawinds@aol.com
Admission: By prior permission only.
Location: At Aso airfield and a workshop in the city.

The West Japan Aviation Society mainly restores classic wooden gliders. The majority are rebuilt to airworthy condition and flown from the airfield located near Mount Aso. The Komadori primary was built in the 1940s and restored in 2000. The Yomadori secondary dates from 1959 and this was rebuilt in 1993. The SM206 was a twin fuselage transport glider originally flown in World War II. The group acquired a few components and is building a new example. The clubhouse and workshop in the city recreate a typical glider factory of the inter-war period. The Wright Flyer replica was built in the workshops and took to the air on December 17th 2004. This was exactly one hundred and one years to the day after the Wright brothers historic flights at Kittyhawk in North Carolina.

TYPE	REG/SER	CON. NO.	PI/NOTES	STATUS
☐ Hagiwara H-22A				RAC
☐ Hagiwara H-23C				RAA
☐ Komadori Primary Glider	JA0175			RA
☐ SM206	JA2006		JA0008	RAC
☐ Super Ogachi				RA
☐ Wright Flyer (R)				RA
☐ Yamadori Glider				RAC

NOHMIN KENSYU CENTER (JA100)

Address:	1-367 Toyotomi-Byohbuyama, Syariki-mura, Nishi-Tsugaru-gun, Aomori pref. 038-3302.
Tel:	0173-56-3163
Admission:	Daily 0900-1600.
Location:	About 35 km north west of Aomori city.

Basically a community centre, the building houses a small quantity of local history material. The development of the surrounding area is portrayed with many interesting personal items on view. Courses covering a variety of subjects, including agricultural training, are organised by the local education board. The single seat Starfighter is displayed in the park surrounding the complex along with a Nike missile. The Mitsubishi built aircraft is one of the two hundred and ten assembled at the Komaki factory and it served with front line squadrons for many years. The Nike missile was an important deterrent during the cold war period and the Americans built sites in Japan.

TYPE	REG/SER	CON. NO.	PI/NOTES	STATUS
☐ Lockheed 683-07-14 Starfighter (F-104J)	36-8530	683B-3030		PV

NYUTABARU AIR BASE COLLECTION (JA101)

Address:	Shintomi-cho, Koyu-gun, Miyazaki pref. 889-1492.
Tel:	0983-35-1121
Admission:	By prior permission only.
Location:	About 20 km north of Miyazaki city off Route 10.

Fighter squadrons have resided at this base for over thirty years. Currently McDonnell F-15 Eagles, McDonnell F-4 Phantoms and Kawasaki T-4s are operated along with a rescue detachment of helicopters and fixed wing types. The 202nd Hikotai was formed in 1972 and initially flew the Starfighter before in 1982 becoming the first unit to operate the Eagle. This unit was disbanded and replaced by the 23rd. T-33s were also used before the arrival of the T-4. The preserved aircraft are displayed in a park inside the base. The T-33 is a recent addition.

TYPE	REG/SER	CON. NO.	PI/NOTES	STATUS
☐ Lockheed 580 (T-33A)	91-5410	1210		RA
☐ Lockheed 683-07-14 Starfighter (F-104J)	36-8538	683B-3038	Front fuselage only	RA
☐ Lockheed 683-07-14 Starfighter (F-104J)	'36-8535'	683B-3156	46-8656	RAX
☐ Mitsubishi T-2	'69-5127'			RAX
☐ North American NA-182 Texan (T-6G)	'72-0169'	182-229	51-14542, 72-0178	RAX
☐ North American NA-190 Sabre (F-86D)	04-8187	190-416	52-4013	RA
☐ North American NA-256 Sabre (F-86F)	92-7916	256-36	57-6373	RA

OHKUBO ARMY CAMP MONUMENT (JA102)

Address:	Furogaido, Hirono-cho, Uji-shi, Kyoto pref. 611-031.
Tel:	0774-44-0011
Admission:	By prior permission only.
Location:	In the town.

This camp which houses a number of resident units has set up a display near the main gate. Three Fuji built Iroquois helicopters can be seen along with a number of military vehicles and weapons. These helicopters served with Army units around the country and were used for many tasks including troop transport.

TYPE	REG/SER	CON. NO.	PI/NOTES	STATUS
☐ Fuji-Bell 204B-2 Iroquois (HU-1B)	41542	MH-43		RA
☐ Fuji-Bell 205 Iroquois (HU-1H)	41631	31		RA
☐ Fuji-Bell 205 Iroquois (HU-1H)	41660	60		RA

OHTSU ARMY CAMP MONUMENT (JA103)

Address:	1-1-1 Saigawa, Ohtsu, Shiga pref. 520-002
Tel:	077-523-0034
Admission:	By prior permission only
Location:	About 10 km east of Kyoto city by Lake Biwa.

Two former Air Force jets and a helicopter have been preserved at this camp. The F-86D version of the Sabre served with four squadrons between 1958 and 1968. The Mitsubishi F-1 fighter first flew in 1977.

TYPE	REG/SER	CON. NO.	PI/NOTES	STATUS
□ Kawasaki-Bell 47G-2 (H-13H)	30141	1235		RA
□ Mitsubishi F-1	90-8232	95		RA
□ North American NA-190 Sabre (F-86D)	14-8222	190-828	52-10103	RA

OJI TECHNICAL HIGH SCHOOL DISPLAY (JA104)

Address:	3-6-1 Ojicho-honmachi, Kita Katsuragi-gun, Nara pref 636-0012.
Tel:	0745-72-4081
Admission:	By prior permission only.
Location:	In the town.

Two aircraft have been put on show at this school which trains many students for jobs in the aviation industry and careers in the services. The Fuji T-1 was the first post-war jet type designed in Japan. The prototype made its maiden flight in 1958 powered by a Bristol Siddeley Orpheus jet. The last ones were withdrawn in 2006.

TYPE	REG/SER	CON. NO.	PI/NOTES	STATUS
□ Fuji T-1B	35-5863			Ra
□ Kawasaki-Hughes 369M (OH-6D)	31133			RA

OLD CAR CENTRE KUDAN (JA105)

Address:	Yamadaoka Naraha-machi, Futaba-gun, Fukishima pref 979-0513
Tel:	0240-25-5760
Fax:	0240-25-5760
Admission:	Second and third Saturday and Sunday of each month and National Holidays 1000-1600.
Location:	About 3 km south of Kido station.

This car museum has many vehicles on show along with associated items. Well over one hundred classic cars are in the exhibition which also includes motor cycles. These are from manufacturers around the world and many rarities can be seen. There is a collection of motoring posters and instruments. The history of the Japanese car industry can be followed with many photographs and models. A collection of former military aircraft is displayed in the grounds and in the exhibition hall. These are types which have flown with all three Japanese services. The Kawasaki company has built many American types under licence. Its first Bell 47D made its maiden flight in 1952 and later versions soon left the production lines. The KH-4 version features a lengthened cabin which could accommodate four people, an increased load and a redesigned control system. The prototype made its maiden flight in August 1962 and over two hundred were completed.

TYPE	REG/SER	CON. NO.	PI/NOTES	STATUS
□ Beech A65 Queen Air	03-3093	LC-322	6722	PV
□ Cessna 305C Bird Dog (L-19E) (O-1E)	11214			PV
□ Fuji KM-2	6243	TM.13		PV
□ Hughes 269B (TH-55J)	61307	0145		PV
□ Kawasaki-Bell 47G-3B-KH4 (H-13KH)	30216	2097		PV
□ Kawasaki-Hughes 369M (OH-6J)	8761	6341		PV
□ Lockheed 580 (T-33A)	71-5305			PV
□ Lockheed 583-10-17 Starfighter (F-104DJ)	26-5001	583B-5401	16-5001	PV
□ Lockheed 583-10-17 Starfighter (F-104DJ)	26-5005	583B-5405	16-5005	PV
□ Lockheed 683-07-14 Starfighter (F-104J)	76-8705	683B-3205		PV
□ Mitsubishi T-2(Z)	59-5115	15	Front fuselage only.	PV
□ North American NA-182 Texan (T-6G)	'72-0022'		52-0022	PVX
□ North American NA-256 Sabre (F-86F)	12-7996	256-116	57-6453	PV

OMINATO NAVAL AIR STATION COLLECTION (JA106)

Address:	4-1 Ominato, Mutsu-shi, Aomori pref. 035-8511.
Tel:	0175-24-1111
Admission:	By prior permission only.
Location:	About 50 km north west of Aomori city.

The airfield was in use during World War II and was later occupied by American forces. They flew a variety of types from the site including fighters and transports. Currently the site is home to a unit operating the Sikorsky SH-60J on anti-submarine duties. Three aircraft are now displayed at the base. The Navy used the Beech T-34A and the developed KM-2 on training and communications duties. The Sikorsky HSS-2B was built under licence by Mitsubishi and has now been replaced by the SH-60J in the Air Sea Rescue role.

TYPE	REG/SER	CON. NO.	PI/NOTES	STATUS
☐ Beech A45 Mentor (T-34A)	9009	FM.1	51-0361	RA
☐ Fuji KM-2	6244	TM.14		RA
☐ Sikorsky S-61 Sea King (HSS-2B)	8167	M61-186		RA

OZUKI NAVAL AIR STATION COLLECTION (JA107)

Address:	1068-5 Matsuzoe, Oaza Matsuya, Shimonoseki-shi, Yamaguchi pref. 750-1121.
Tel:	0832-82-1180
Admission:	By prior permission only.
Location:	About 20 km north east of Shimonoseki city off Route 2.

Training squadrons have been based at this field for over thirty years. The 201st Kyoiku Kokutai was formed at Kanoya in September 1961 and moved to Ozuki in March 1965. The first type used was the Texan which served until 1966 when the Mentor arrived. The Fuji KM-2 took over in the late 1970s and is now gradually being replaced by the Fuji T-5 which is a turboprop development of the Beech Mentor. A search and rescue unit operating the Sikorsky UH-60J is also in residence. The design was built in Japan by Mitsubishi and is based on the Black Hawk. Examples of the three main training types have been preserved.

TYPE	REG/SER	CON. NO.	PI/NOTES	STATUS
☐ Beech A45 Mentor (T-34A)	9005	FM.73	71-0433	RA
☐ Fuji KM-2	6280	TM.50		RA
☐ Fuji KM-2	6292	TM.62		RA
☐ North American NA-88 Texan (AT-6D) (SNJ-5)	6164	88-16974	42-85193, Bu84963	RA

PEACE MUSEUM FOR KAMIKAZE PILOTS (JA108)

Address:	17881 Chiran-ko Kawabe-gun, Kagoshima pref. 897-0302.
Tel:	0993-83-2525
Fax:	0993-83-4859
Email:	heiwakaikai@town.chiran.kagoshima.jp
Admission:	Daily 0900-1700.
Location:	About 50 km south of Kagoshima city.

The museum was founded to honour the suicide pilots who flew missions in the latter stages of World War II. The Tachiarai Flight Training School was formed at Chiran in 1942 and trained volunteers for special missions. Chiran was the southernmost special attack base on mainland Japan and when the situation became serious in 1945 it was the principal site for Kamikaze operations. Over one thousand pilots lost their lives in the battle for Okinawa during this period. The Heiwa-Kannon Temple was built at Chiran in 1955 and a bronze statue of a Kamikaze pilot was unveiled in 1974. The following year a museum containing war relics was opened. More items were acquired and in the early 1990s a new complex surrounded by a pleasant park was constructed. The story of the missions is portrayed in vivid detail with many photographs, documents and memorabilia on show. Many final letters from the pilots can be seen. The aircraft collection has increased in recent years. The museum is a poignant reminder of the young lives sacrificed. A photograph shows clearly part of a floatplane in one of the halls. It is not clear if it is a complete aircraft or just major components. I have not been able to obtain any further information and any help would be appreciated.

TYPE	REG/SER	CON. NO.	PI/NOTES	STATUS
☐ Floatplane.				PV
☐ Kawasaki Ki-61-II Hien		5070		PV
☐ Nakajima Ki-43 Hayabusa (FSM)				PV
☐ Nakajima Ki-84-1-Ko		1446	62387, N3385G	PV

RUMOI ARMY CAMP MONUMENT (JA109)

Address:	1-6 Midorigaoka, Rumoi-shi, Hokkaido 077-8555.
Tel:	0164-42-2655
Admission:	By prior permission only.
Location:	In the southern part of the town.

The Bell UH-1H Iroquois is the larger version of the type and features a cabin which can take a dozen troops. Fuji built more than one hundred for the army and one is preserved as a monument.

TYPE	REG/SER	CON. NO.	PI/NOTES	STATUS
☐ Fuji-Bell 205 Iroquois (HU-1H)	41624	24		RA

SADO AIR BASE COLLECTION (JA110)

Address:	2-27 Kanai-shinpo, Sado-shi, Niigata pref. 952-1208.
Tel:	0259-63-4111
Admission:	By prior permission only.
Location:	About 3 km north east of Sado City.

The Air Force have a base at the airport on this picturesque island which is a popular tourist destination. There are no squadrons based at the camp but military aircraft regularly fly into the site. Two aircraft are preserved at the field and a Starfighter is located at a nearby sports park.

TYPE	REG/SER	CON. NO.	PI/NOTES	STATUS
☐ Lockheed 580 (T-33A)	51-5658			RA
☐ Lockheed 683-07-14 Starfighter (F-104J)	46-8573	683B-3073	In nearby sports park.	PV
☐ Mitsubishi F-1	00-8246	109		RA

SENDAI ARMY CAMP MUSEUM (JA111)

Address:	1-1 Minami-Mokkan, Miyagino-ku, Sendai-shi, Miyagi pref. 983-8580.
Tel:	022-231-1111
Admission:	By prior permission only.
Location:	About 3 km east of Sendai Station.

A small museum has been set up at this camp which is the North Eastern Army Headquarters. The history of military flying is portrayed with an exhibition of models, documents, photographs and uniforms. Two former Air Force types, a Texan and a Sabre, were preserved but now only one helicopter remains.

TYPE	REG/SER	CON. NO.	PI/NOTES	STATUS
☐ Kawasaki-Hughes 369M (OH-6D)	31156			PV

SHIBATA ARMY CAMP MONUMENT (JA112)

Address:	6-4-16 Ohtemachi, Shibata-shi, Niigata pref. 957-8530
Tel:	0254-22-3151
Admission:	By prior permission only.
Location:	About 20 km north east of Niigata city.

Helicopters regularly use the facilities at this camp. A Bell Iroquois, built under licence by Fuji Heavy Industries, has been preserved as a monument. Units of the JGSDF flew the type for many years. Also displayed around the grounds are several military vehicles, tanks and pieces of artillery.

TYPE	REG/SER	CON. NO.	PI/NOTES	STATUS
☐ Fuji-Bell 204B-2 Iroquois (HU-1B)	41539	MH-40		RA

SHIDAYAMA ARMY CAMP COLLECTION (JA113)

Address:	Hakata-cho, Izumi-chi, Osaka pref. 594-8502
Admission:	By prior permission only.
Location:	About 15 km south of Osaka city.

The preserved aircraft at this camp have changed with the departure of a former Air Force Texan and a Hughes OH-6J and the arrival of more ex-Army helicopters including a Kawasaki-Vertol KV-107. These are displayed around the grounds along with several military vehicles and some large guns.

TYPE	REG/SER	CON. NO.	PI/NOTES	STATUS
☐ Fuji-Bell 204B-2 Iroquois (HU-1B)	41682	MH-83		RA
☐ Fuji-Bell 205 Iroquois (HU-1H)	41682	82		RA
☐ Kawasaki-Hughes 369M (OH-6D)	31148			RA
☐ Kawasaki-Vertol KV-107-IIA-4	51807	4098		RA

SHIMOFUSA NAVAL AIR BASE COLLECTION (JA114)

Address: 1614-1 Fujigaya,
Kashiwa-shi,
Chiba pref. 277-8661.
Tel: 0471-91-2321
Admission: By prior permission only.
Location: About 25 km north east of Tokyo.

The resident group (Shimofusa Kyoiku Kokugu) specialises in multi-engine training. The five preserved aircraft are located in a park just inside the main gate. Thirty five Beech Expeditors were used as instrument trainers from 1957 until 1966 when they were replaced by the Queen Air which served in this role for almost two decades. The KV-107 reflects the role of the rescue group and the SH-60J is a recent addition to the display.

TYPE	REG/SER	CON. NO.	PI/NOTES	STATUS
☐ Beech C18S Expeditor (C-45F) (UC-45F) (JRB-4)	6428	7912	44-47504, Bu85116	RA
☐ Beech 65 Queen Air	6718	LC-229		RA
☐ Kawasaki-Vertol KV-107-IIA-3A	8607	4090		RA
☐ North American NA-88 Texan (AT-6D) (SNJ-5)	6175	88-17959	42-86178, Bu90751	RA
☐ Sikorsky S-70 Sea Hawk (SH-60J)	8206			RA

SHINMACHI ARMY CAMP MONUMENT (JA115)

Address: 1080 Shinmachi,
Takasaki-shi,
Gunma pref. 370-1394
Tel: 0274-42-1121
Admission: By prior permission only.
Location: In the northern part of the town.

Preserved as a monument at this army base is one of the eighteen Kawasaki-Vertol KV-107A-II-4 helicopters delivered to the service. The aircraft spent most of its active life at Kasumigaura. The large transport helicopter was a frequent visitor to many Army camps and was used to transport troops.

TYPE	REG/SER	CON. NO.	PI/NOTES	STATUS
☐ Kawasaki-Vertol KV-107-IIA-4	51814			RA

SHIZUHAMA AIR BASE COLLECTION (JA116)

Address: 1602 Kamikosugi,
Ohigawa-cho,
Shida-gun,
Shizuoka pref. 421-0201
Tel: 054-622-1234 ext 406
Admission: By prior permission only.
Location: About 10 km south of Fujieda city.

The base is one of six used by units of Flying Training Command. The Fuji T-3, a development of the Beech Mentor, is operated by the resident 11th Hiko Kyoikudan. Fifty of this type were delivered in the late 1970s. The 11th, formed at Hamamatsu in July 1954, was equipped with Beech Mentors and moved to Ozuki in March 1956. A transfer to its current home took place in May 1964 and the T-3 was introduced in 1978/9. The collection of trainers and fighters is located in a park near the main gate of the base. All of the types on show gave excellent service and were operated in numbers from most bases around the country.

TYPE	REG/SER	CON. NO.	PI/NOTES	STATUS
☐ Beech A45 Mentor (T-34A)				RA
☐ Beech A45 Mentor (T-34A)	61-0390	FM.30		RA
☐ Fuji T-3	91-5511	011		RA
☐ Lockheed 580 (T-33A)	51-5612		(USAF)	RA
☐ Lockheed 683-07-14 Starfighter (F-104J)	76-8696	683B-3196		RA
☐ North American NA-121 Texan (AT-6F)	52-0011		(USAAF)	RA
☐ North American NA-176 Sabre (F-86F)	62-7417	176-292	51-13361	RA
☐ North American NA-190 Sabre (F-86D)	04-8183	190-382	52-3979	RA

SODEURA PARK MONUMENT (JA117)

Address:	125-1 Tobihiramatsu, Iwata-shi, Shizuoka pref. 438-0216.
Admission:	Daily.
Location:	About 10 km east of Hamamatsu.

The Sabre served in large numbers with the JASDF from 1955 until 1982. An example has been put on show in the town park to serve as a memorial to Air Force personnel from the locality.

TYPE	REG/SER	CON. NO.	PI/NOTES	STATUS
☐ North American NA-231 Sabre (F-86F)	72-7749	231-49	55-5096	PV

TACHIARAI AVIATION MUSEUM (JA118)

Address:	417-3 Takada, Miwa-cho, Asakura-gun, Fukuoka pref. 838-0814.
Tel:	0946-23-1227
Admission:	Daily 0930-1700
Location:	About 30 km. south east of Fukuoka city.

In World War II there was a military airfield at Tachiarai and during World War II many personnel serving at the base lost their lives. In 1986 Muneshige Fuchigami set up a museum to honour these aviators. A display was set up in Tachiarai station and many photographs, documents, flags, uniforms, models and items of memorabilia were put on show. On September 10th 1996 a Nakajima Ki-27 was discovered in Hakata bay. The airframe was recovered and is now being restored with the aim of eventually flying it. The Ki-27 low wing fighter first flew at Ojima on October 15th 1936. Almost three thousand four hundred were produced by the parent company at Ota and by Mansu at Harbin. The Ki-27 first saw combat in May 1939 in the Mongolian border region against Russian forces The type was in service throughout World War II and in the last months of the conflict several were used on suicide missions against Allied shipping. A Japanese built T-33 can also be seen.

TYPE	REG/SER	CON. NO.	PI/NOTES	STATUS
☐ Lockheed 580 (T-33A)	71-5293	1093		PV
☐ Nakajima Ki-27				PV

TACHIKAWA ARMY AIR BASE COLLECTION (JA119)

Address:	5 Midori-Machi, Tachikawa-shi, Tokyo 190-8501.
Tel:	042-524-9321
Admission:	By prior permission only.
Location:	About 25 km west of Tokyo.

Flying units of the Army are based at this field on the outskirts of Tokyo. A collection of aircraft has been put on display. Most are types flown on a variety of duties including liaison and training An exception is the civilian Cessna 195 A small number of these classics arrived in the country in the early 1950s.

TYPE	REG/SER	CON. NO.	PI/NOTES	STATUS
☐ Cessna 195	JA3069	16092	N2107C, N11B	RA
☐ Cessna 305C Bird Dog (L-19E) (O-1E)	11364			RA
☐ Fuji-Bell 205 Iroquois (HU-1H)	41647	47		RA
☐ Kawasaki-Hughes 369M (OH-6D)	31154			RA
☐ Kawasaki-Hughes 369M (OH-6J)	31098	6402		RA
☐ Mitsubishi MU-2C (LR-1)	22003	803		RA

TAIWA ARMY CAMP MONUMENT (JA120)

Address:	Yoshioka-Nishihara, Taiwa-cho, Kurokawa-gun, Miyagi pref. 981-3684
Tel:	022-345-2191
Admission:	By prior permission only.
Location:	In the town.

A camp in this historic town houses army personnel. Helicopters regularly land within the boundaries of the installation and a Japanese built Hughes has been preserved as a memorial.

TYPE	REG/SER	CON. NO.	PI/NOTES	STATUS
☐ Kawasaki-Hughes 369M (OH-6D)	31136			RA

TAKAYAMA AVIATION PARK (JA121)

Address:	Higashi-wake, Ayakami-cho, Ayauta-gun, Kagawa pref. 761-2205.
Tel:	0878-78-2211
Admission:	Daily 0900-2200.
Location:	About 15 km south west of Takamatsu city off Route 32.

This aviation park has recently been established near the local Army airfield. The first military aircraft to arrive at the site was a Mitsubishi T-2B weapons trainer version. The Cessna 170B was sold to Japan in 1956 and flown for twenty one years. The Kawasaki-Bell 47 is an improved version developed by the Japanese company.

TYPE	REG/SER	CON. NO.	PI/NOTES	STATUS
☐ Cessna 170B	JA3106	26295	N2751C	PV
☐ Kawasaki-Bell 47G-3B-KH4	JA7465	2104		PV
☐ Mitsubishi T-2(K)	69-5126	26		PV

TAKEYAMA ARMY CAMP COLLECTION (JA122)

Address:	1-1 Misachihama, Yokosuka-shi, Kanagawa pref. 238-0317.
Tel:	0468-56-1291
Admission:	By prior permission only.
Location:	About 30 km south of Tokyo.

No active machines are normally based at this army heliport. Four aircraft are preserved in the adjacent camp. Nine Fuji built Mentors were transferred to the Army from the Air force in 1964 and were flown until 1978.

TYPE	REG/SER	CON. NO.	PI/NOTES	STATUS
☐ Beech A45 Mentor (T-34A)	60503	KD.16	41-0326	RA
☐ Fuji-Bell 204B-2 Iroquois (HU-1B)	41501	MH-02		RA
☐ Fuji-Bell 204B-2 Iroquois (HU-1B)	41555	MH-56		RA
☐ Kawasaki-Hughes 369M (OH-6J)	31064	6368		RA

TAKIGAHARA ARMY CAMP MONUMENT (JA123)

Address:	2092-2 Nakabata, Gotemba-shi, Shizuoka pref 412-8550.
Tel:	055089-0711
Admission:	By prior permission only.
Location:	In the town.

Gotemba, in the shadow of Mount Fuji, was established in 1955. The army camp has excellent training facilities in the nearby rugged countryside. Many units spent periods at the camp to carry out duties in the neighbouring hills. The Iroquois is preserved as a memorial along with some military vehicles.

TYPE	REG/SER	CON. NO.	PI/NOTES	STATUS
☐ Fuji-Bell 204B-2 Iroquois (HU-1B)	41580	MH-81		RA

TAKIKAWA SKY MUSEUM (JA124)

Address:	139-4 Nakajima-machi, Takikawa-shi, Hokkaido 073-0035.
Tel:	0125-24-3255
Admission:	April-November daily 0900-1700. December-March Tuesday-Sunday 0900-1600. Closed December 29th-January 4th.
Location:	About 90 km north east of Sapporo city off Route 12.

This glider field has designated its hangar complex as a museum. A collection of photographs and models tracing the development of gliding and the history of the site has been staged in the entrance area. Two gliders are preserved in the building. The Hagiwara H-23 two seater made its maiden flight in September 1956 and over forty were built with several remaining in use. The Kirigamine Hato K-14A primary has been produced in some numbers for clubs in Japan. The active sailplanes range from training types up to high performance machines from Germany and Poland. Rudolf Kaiser designed and built his Ka-1 in his parents house. This small sailplane was intended for his personal use and first flew in 1952. Erwin Köhler saw the potential of the design and produced a few kits for amateur constructors. Kaiser had joined Egon Scheibe at his Dachau factory and but he also carried out work for the Schleicher company who put into production several of his designs. The single seat Ka-6 Rhönsegler first flew in 1965 and has appeared in several versions. The club flies later Schleicher designs including the two-seat ASK-13 and the advanced ASK-21 which uses composite materials in its construction. Gliding has always been a popular sport in Poland and their designs have achieved success in many contests over the last seventy years. The types from there are in use. Edward Marganski designed the single seat Swift which first flew in 1991 and this was developed into the tandem seat Fox. Sailplane work has been carried out at many polytechnics in Europe and the one at Warsaw has produced a number of designs.including the PW-2 Gapa. This primary trainer first flew in 1985 and a small number are in use. The two Robins are used as tugs.

TYPE	REG/SER	CON. NO.	PI/NOTES	STATUS
☐ Glaser-Dirks DG.400M	JA2401	4-218	(D-KIDG)	PVA
☐ Glasflugel H205 Club Libelle	JA2186	136		PVA
☐ Grob G.102 Club Astir IIIb	JA102G	5635Cb	D-4166	PVA
☐ Grob G.102 Standard Astir III	JA2296	5540S		PVA
☐ Hagiwara H-23C-3	JA2055	69		PV
☐ Kirigamine Hato K-14A	JA0090	21		PV
☐ Marganski MDM-1 Fox	JA2544	P-16		PVA
☐ Politechnika Warszawska PW-2D Gapa	JA0194	U-03		PVA
☐ Robin DR.400/180R Remorqueur	JA40TW	1296	D-ENGS	PVA
☐ Robin DR.400/180R Remorqueur	JA4067	1902		PVA
☐ Rolladen-Schneider LS-4	JA2505	4421	D-3123	PVA
☐ Rolladen-Schneider LS-6-c	JA2530	6346		PVA
☐ Scheibe SF-28A Tandem Falke	JA2562	5721		PVA
☐ Schempp-Hirth Discus A	JA32BD	486		PVA
☐ Schempp-Hirth Janus CM	JA2419	32/247		PVA
☐ Schleicher Ka-6CR Rhönsegler	JA2512	6018	D-1775	PVA
☐ Schleicher Ka-6CR Rhönsegler	JA2331	6605	D-1027	PVA
☐ Schleicher ASK-13	JA2173	13488		PVA
☐ Schleicher ASK-13	JA2321	13634AB		PVA
☐ Schleicher ASK-21	JA2326	21217		PVA
☐ Schleicher ASW-19B	JA2348	19416		PVA
☐ Schleicher ASW-20CL	JA2337	20774		PVA
☐ Schleicher ASW-20L	JA2266	20144	D-3324	PVA
☐ Szybowcowy Zaklad Doswiadczalny S.Z.D.55-1	JA2514	551193050		PVA

TATEYAMA NAVAL AIR BASE COLLECTION (JA125)

Address:	Miyagi, Tateyama-shi, Chiba pref. 294-8501.
Tel:	0470-22-3191
Admission:	By prior permission only.
Location:	About 50 km south east of Tokyo.

Tateyama was the first Naval Air Station in post-war Japan when it opened on September 16th. 1953. Since then it has been a major helicopter base. The first type operated was the Bell 47 and over the years Westland-Sikorsky WS-55s, Sikorsky S-55s, S-58s, S-61s and S-70s have been used. Three helicopters and two fixed wing aircraft have been preserved in a park a short distance from the main gate. The S-61A has recently joined the display after a period in store. Another new arrival is the Sea Hawk.

TYPE	REG/SER	CON. NO.	PI/NOTES	STATUS
☐ Beech A65 Queen Air	6726	LC-333		RA
☐ Fuji KM-2	6259	TM.29		RA
☐ Sikorsky S-61 Sea King (HSS-2B)	8085	M61-094		RA
☐ Sikorsky S-61A	8185			RA
☐ Sikorsky S-70 Sea Hawk (SH-60J)	8221			RA

TOKOROZAWA AVIATION MUSEUM (JA126)

Address:	1-13 Namiki, Tokorozawa, Saitama pref. 359-0042.
Tel:	04-2996-2225
Admission:	Tuesday-Sunday 0930-1700.
Location:	About 40 km west of Tokyo.

Tokorozawa was chosen in 1907 as the site for the first airfield in Japan. The field opened on April 1st 1911 and four aircraft were in residence. Two were biplanes, a Henri Farman and a Wright, and two were monoplanes a Blériot and a Grade. The first flight was made four days later by the Farman piloted by Yoshitoshi Tokugawa. The aircraft was aloft for eighty seconds and covered eight hundred metres. This historic field saw many developments over the next few decades and many pilots trained at the site. The museum opened on April 3rd 1993 and the lobby area contains a replica of the first indigenous design, the Kaishiki biplane. The main building includes an IMAX theatre, a data centre, a workshop, a flight simulator and a control tower. The majority of the aircraft are exhibited in a hangar like structure and a range of military and civil types can be seen. A replica of a Nieuport 81E has been constructed and parts of an original example of this French biplane are in the collection. Forty 81Es were imported into Japan in 1919. The type was also built under licence at Tokorozawa by the Army before production was transferred to the Mitsubishi company in 1922. The Nakajima 91 parasol wing fighter appeared in the late 1920s and about four hundred were produced. The type was in service until the late 1930s. The remains of one were found and the aircraft is undergoing a slow restoration in the workshops. Replicas of a number of significant types are on show. The Fokker D VIII parasol wing fighter appeared in the latter stages of World War I and saw some use in combat. The only known survivor of the type is a fuselage in Italy. SPAD fighters served with distinction with several Allied forces in the conflict. Thirty five Sentinels were flown by the Army and the last were withdrawn in 1958. A rarity is the Kawasaki KAL-2, the sole example operated by the Army. In the workshop area is a Cessna 310 with several panels removed to show the construction of the airframe. This well planned museum has much to offer for both the enthusiast and the casual visitor. The Commando and the YS-11, which are parked nearby, are not owned by the museum but they are listed below as they will be seen by visitors to the site.

TYPE	REG/SER	CON. NO.	PI/NOTES	STATUS
☐ Beech A45 Mentor (T-34A)	60508	KD.36	51-0346 (JASDF)	PV
☐ Bell 47D-1 Sioux (H-13E)	30003	1004	H-3003	RA
☐ Cessna 170B	JA3052	25370	N3128B	PV
☐ Cessna T310P	JA5170	310P0205	N5905M	PV
☐ Curtiss-Wright CW-20B Commando (C-46A)	91-1143	293	43-47222, (China) – in park next to museum.	PV
☐ Fokker D VIII (FSM)	'4253/18'			RAX
☐ Fuji T-1B	25-5856			PV
☐ Fuji-Bell 204B-2 Iroquois (HU-1B)	41547	MH-48		PV
☐ Fuji-Bell 204B-2 Iroquois (HU-1B)	41560	MH-61		RA
☐ Hang Glider				PV
☐ Hughes 269B (TH-55J)	61328	0310		PV
☐ Kaishiki 1 (R)				PV
☐ Kawasaki KAL-2	20001	1022	40-1555	PV
☐ Kawasaki-Bell 47G-3B-KH4 (H-13KH)	30213	2094		RA
☐ Kawasaki-Hughes 369M (OH-6J)	31065	6369		PV
☐ Kawasaki-Vertol KV-107-II-4	51734	4063		RA
☐ Kirigamine Hato K-14	JA0148	043		PV
☐ Mil Mi-8PA	JA9549	26001	Possible identity.	PV
☐ Nakajima 91				PVC
☐ Nieuport 81E	J-TECH	512	Major components.	PVD
☐ Nieuport 81E (R)	'J-TECH'			PVX
☐ Nihon Kokuki Seizo Kabushiki Kaisha (NAMC) YS-11-213	JA8732	2101	Next to local railway station.	PV
☐ North American NA-173 Sabre (F-86D)	84-8102	173-477	51-8344	PV
☐ North American NA-182 Texan (T-6G)	52-0099		(USAF)	PV
☐ Piper J-3C-65 Cub	JA3925	6328	NC35361, N35361	PV
☐ Piper PA-18-135 Super Cub (L-21B)	12032	18-2773	53-3773	PV
☐ Sikorsky S-55B (H-19C)	40001	55690		PV
☐ Société Pour l'Aviation et ses Derives (SPAD) XIII (R)	'S4523'			RAX
☐ Stinson V-76 Sentinel (L-5G)	10412		45-35025	PV
☐ Vertol V.44A	50002	42.20		PV

TOKUSHIMA NAVAL AIR BASE COLLECTION (JA127)

Address:	Sumiyoshi, Matsushige-machi, Itano-gun, Tokushima pref. 771-0218.
Tel:	088-699-5111
Admission:	By prior permission only.
Location:	About 8 km south of Tokushima city.

This base is home to units flying the Beech King Air and the Sikorsky S-61AH. The Queen Air was operated from 1963 and the type was gradually replaced by the King Air from 1974. In 1958 two squadrons flying the Grumman Tracker were based at the field and were subsequently joined by a third in 1963.

TYPE	REG/SER	CON. NO.	PI/NOTES	STATUS
☐ Beech 65 Queen Air	6702	LC-146	Front fuselage only.	RA
☐ Beech TC90 King Air	6802	LJ-598	N1846W	RA
☐ Grumman G-89 Tracker (S2F-1) (S-2A)	4150	661	Bu144700	RA
☐ Sikorsky S-62J	8926	M62-022		RA

TOKYO METROPOLITAN COLLEGE OF INDUSTRIAL TECHNOLOGY – ARAKAWA CAMPUS COLLECTION (JA128)

Address:	8-17-1 Minami-Senju, Arakawa-ku, Tokyo 116-0003.
Tel:	03-3801-9898
Admission:	On request.
Location:	In the north eastern suburbs of the city

The college has trained aeronautical engineers for many years and over this period has acquired a number of interesting aircraft. In 1995 several of these were put on display in a brand new gallery along with engines, models and components. All the airframes have been restored to a high standard. The Chrislea Super Ace was developed from the Ace prototype of 1946. Twenty eight were built at Exeter between 1947 and 1952. Five of these were completed but never flown and the construction of four more was abandoned. The example on show was built in 1949 and sold to Japan three years later for use by the Honda company. The type featured unconventional flying controls comprising of a wheel mounted on a column protruding from the dashboard. The Auster Cirrus Autocar is one of five imported in 1952. The aircraft flew for nine years before crashing at Fujisawa in August 1961. It was then withdrawn from use and moved to the college. The prototype Autocar powered by a Gipsy Major engine flew in 1950 and featured wide rear cabin to accommodate the pilot and three passengers. The J/5G fitted with a Cirrus Major engine had more power and a better performance. The Sikorsky R-4 Hoverfly was the first helicopter type to be produced in quantity. The prototype made its maiden flight in January 1942 and one hundred and thirty one were built. The improved R-6 followed in 1943 and two hundred and twenty five of this model were constructed. The Yomiuri Y-1 was the first Japanese designed helicopter. Only one was built in the early 1950s. The Toyu company built the prototype of its TT-10 low wing tandem seat trainer in 1952. Powered by a 140 h.p. Lycoming engine only a few were completed. This company also constructed some Fletcher FD-25s under licence and two of these can be seen. The prototype of this rugged agricultural design was intended for use in New Zealand where over three hundred were eventually built in a number of variants. The Stolp SA.100 Starduster designed by Louis Stolp and George Adams made its maiden flight in November 1957. A company was soon set up to sell plans, components and materials for the biplane. The two seat SA.300 followed and this has proved to be a popular type with homebuilders. A number of other designs have been produced.

TYPE	REG/SER	CON. NO.	PI/NOTES	STATUS
☐ Auster J/5G Cirrus Autocar	JA3029	3054		PV
☐ Chrislea C.H.3 Super Ace Series 2	JA3062	112	G-AKVD, (VH-BRP)	PV
☐ Fletcher FD-25A	JA3050	531		PV
☐ Fletcher FD-25B	JA3092	2		PV
☐ Fuji-Bell 204B	JA9023	CH-12		PV
☐ Jiyu Koku Kenkyujyo JHX-1				PV
☐ Kawasaki-Bell 47G-2	JA7021	1012		PV
☐ North American NA-173 Sabre (F-86D)	84-8117	173-242	51-6098	PV
☐ Piper PA-22-135 Tri-Pacer	JA3036	22-776	N2397A	PV
☐ Sikorsky VS-316B Hoverfly II (R-6A)	43-45390		May be 43-45490	PV
☐ Stolp SA.300 Starduster Too				PV
☐ Toyo Koku TT-10	JA3026	531		PV
☐ Yomiuri Y-1	JA7009	1		PV

TOYOKAWA ARMY BASE MONUMENT (JA129)

Address:	Honohara, Toyokawa-shi, Aichi pref. 422-8602.
Tel:	0533-86-3151
Admission:	By prior permission only.
Location:	About 10 km north of Toyohashi city.

The Japanese Army operated many Bell Iroquois helicopters from a number of bases around the country and the helicopters were frequent visitors to most camps. One example is preserved here as a monument along with a collection of military vehicles, tanks, pieces of artillery and several memorials.

TYPE	REG/SER	CON. NO.	PI/NOTES	STATUS
☐ Fuji-Bell 204B-2 Iroquois (HU-1B)	41557	MH-58		RA

TSUIKI AIR BASE COLLECTION (JA130)

Address:	Chikujoh-machi, Chikujoh-gun, Fukuoka pref. 829-0151.
Tel:	0930-56-1121
Admission:	Daily 0800-1700 – with prior permission.
Location:	About 60 km east of Fukuoka City.

This Japanese built Starfighter is one of the preserved aircraft at Naha Air Force Base. (Gerry Manning)

This Toyo Kohu TT-10 is in the collection of Tokyo Metropolitan University. (Shinsuke Yamamoto)

This An-2 and Mil Mi-8 are preserved Army Museum in Vientiane. (via Tom Singfield)

The station opened in 1942 as an Imperial Navy base and towards the end of World War II housed Kamikaze units. The U.S.A.F. used the site as an emergency field until 1954 when they transferred it to the JASDF who flew T-33s in the training role for a decade. The 8th. Air Wing was formed in 1954 and first used F-86F Sabres. Phantoms were operated from 1971 until 1990. The two squadrons currently fly the F-15 Eagle, the Mitsubishi F-1 and F-2, the Mitsubishi T-2 and the Kawasaki T-4. A small history room is located in one of the buildings. The development of the base and its units is shown with many models, photographs, documents and uniforms.

TYPE	REG/SER	CON. NO.	PI/NOTES	STATUS
☐ Lockheed 580 (T-33A)	51-5627		(USAF)	RA
☐ Lockheed 683-07-14 Starfighter (F-104J)	36-8546	683B-3046		RA
☐ Mitsubishi F-1	80-8222	78		RA
☐ Mitsubishi F-1	90-8232	95		RA
☐ Mitsubishi F-1	00-8236	99		RA
☐ North American NA-173 Sabre (F-86D)	84-8115	173-230	51-6086	RA
☐ North American NA-256 Sabre (F-86F)	92-7922	256-42	57-6379 – front fuselage only	RA
☐ North American NA-256 Sabre (F-86F)	92-7938	256-58	57-6395	RA

UNITED STATES NAVAL AIR STATION ATSUGI COLLECTION (JA131)

Address:	Ayase-shi, Kanagawa pref. 252-1101.
Tel:	0467-78-8611
Admission:	By prior permission only.
Location:	About 35 km south east of Tokyo.

The base is home to units of both the United States and Japanese Navies. The airfield was in use during World War II and on August 30th 1945 General Douglas MacArthur arrived in his C-54 Skymaster in order to accept the Japanese surrender aboard the U.S.S. Missouri. The site was badly damaged and for five years was used as an American storage depot. A decision was made to rebuild the site as a Naval Air Station and after a great deal of work the base was commissioned on December 1st 1950. Five aircraft are preserved in the American part of the field. Both the Phantom and the Skyhawk have served with the based units in recent times. The Tomcat also flew from the base and this aircraft is a fairly new addition to the collection. The Sea King has been used on search and rescue missions from Atsugi. For many years the Texan on show in this area was believed to be Bu112165 but recently an aircraft bearing U.S. markings on the port side and Japanese on the starboard has appeared. Presumably this is a repaint of the original but this needs to be confirmed.

TYPE	REG/SER	CON. NO.	PI/NOTES	STATUS
☐ Douglas A-4E Skyhawk (A4D-5)	'Bu150122'	13244	Bu151074 – on loan from NMNA, FL, USA.	RAX
☐ Grumman G-303 Tomcat (F-14A)	Bu161141	368	On loan from NMNA, FL, USA.	RA
☐ McDonnell M.98EV Phantom II (F-4J) (F-4S)	Bu155807	3094	On loan from NMNA, FL, USA.	RA
☐ North American NA-121 Texan (AT-6F) (SNJ-6)	Bu112165	121-42998	44-82276 – on loan from NMNA, FL, USA – possible identity.	RAX
☐ Sikorsky S-61B Sea King (SH-3D) (SH-3H)	Bu152704	61367	On loan from NMNA, FL, USA.	RA

YAKUMO AIR BASE MONUMENT (JA132)

Address:	33 Midori-cho, Yakumo-cho, Futami-gun, Hokkaido 049-3118.
Tel:	0137-62-2262.
Admission:	By prior permission only.
Location:	Just south of the town.

The facility designated as a sub-base was officially opened in June 2007 when an air show took place. A Kawasaki built Lockheed T-33 has been preserved at the airfield as a monument.

TYPE	REG/SER	CON. NO.	PI/NOTES	STATUS
☐ Lockheed 580 (T-33A)	81-5351	1151		RA

YAO ARMY CAMP MONUMENT (JA133)

Address:	1-81 Kuhkoh, Yao-shi, Osaka pref. 581-0043.
Tel:	0729-49-5131
Admission:	By prior permission only.
Location:	In the southern part of the town.

The Army has a helicopter base at the airfield which is also home to private aircraft and general aviation companies. A Beech Mentor which was used on a variety of duties has been preserved as a monument. In 1964 the JGSDF acquired nine Fuji built T-34s transferred from the JASDF. These were operated by detachments at Utsunomiya and Iwakuni. Some military vehicles and tanks are also displayed.

TYPE	REG/SER	CON. NO.	PI/NOTES	STATUS
☐ Beech A45 Mentor (T-34A)	60509	KD.39	51-0349	RA

YASUKUNI JINJA YUSHUKAN (JA134)

Address:	1-1 Kudan-Kita 3 Chome, Chiyoda-ku, Tokyo 102-8246.
Tel:	03-261-8326
Email:	info@yasukuni.org.jp
Admission:	March-October daily 0900-1730; November-February daily 0900-1700. 0900-1700.
Location:	In the city.

This shrine honours the war dead of the country by exhibiting personal items and weapons. First set up in 1882 the building was enlarged after World War I to cover this conflict, the Japan-China and the Japan-Russia wars. The structure was severely damaged in an earthquake in 1923 and a temporary exhibition opened the following year. A new building was constructed and opened in 1931. This was enlarged in 1934. The exhibition re-opened in 1961 on one floor. In December 1985 work started on restoring the complex to its original state and this enlarged display was ready in July 1986. Fourteen exhibition rooms cover all the conflicts the country has been involved in since the civil war of 1877. A number of earlier items can also be seen. In the large hall is a Yokosuka D4Y-1 'Judy' carrier bomber which was found in a derelict state on Yap in the Caroline Islands. This historic aircraft has been restored to its original colours. The prototype D4Y made its maiden flight at Yokosuka in December 1940 and the type was soon put into production at the Aichi factory ant Nagoya. Eventually about two thousand were completed and this total includes the two hundred constructed at Hiro. The aircraft served with distinction in many battles and its last use was in a kamikaze attack off Okinawa in August 1945. The Ohka was conceived by Ensign Mitsuo Ohta as a rocket powered suicide aircraft. The type was to be carried aloft in the bomb bay of a modified Mitsubishi G4M 'Betty'. The Ohka would then glide towards its target before switching on any of the three small rocket motors mounted at the rear of the fuselage. Of wooden construction the un-powered prototype was built in a few weeks. After trials it was decided to fit jet engines to increase the range. In all over seven hundred and fifty were built in a number of versions. The Zero is one of those recovered by Nobuo Harada who rebuilt the classic fighter to its wartime configuration.

TYPE	REG/SER	CON. NO.	PI/NOTES	STATUS
☐ Mitsubishi A6M5 Zero Sen Model 52	'81-161'	4241		PVX
☐ Yokosuka D4Y1 Suisei	4-13	4316		PV
☐ Yokosuka MXY-7 Ohka 11 (FSM)				PV

YOKOTA UNITED STATES AIR FORCE BASE (JA135)

Address:	Fussa-shi, Tokyo 197-0001.
Tel:	0425-51-0700
Admission:	By prior permission only.
Location:	About 30 km west of Tokyo.

Two aircraft on United States Air Force Museum charge are displayed at this base. The Sabre served at the field in the 1950s when the site was used by fighter squadrons. In recent years helicopter units have been in residence. The classic jet was operated in the area for many years and fought with distinction in the Korean War. Many examples of the type were later supplied to the Japanese Air Force when the country was allowed to set up a service and operate military aircraft. The CT-39 was used in the communications and transport role.

TYPE	REG/SER	CON. NO.	PI/NOTES	STATUS
☐ North American NA-172 Sabre (F-86E)	51-2832	172-115		RA
☐ North American NA-265 Sabreliner (T-39A) (CT-39A)	61-0675	265-78	May no longer be here.	RA

YONAGO ARMY BASE COLLECTION (JA136)

Address:	2603 Ryomitsuyanagi, Yonago-shi, Tottori pref. 683-0853.
Tel:	0859-29-2161
Admission:	By prior permission only.
Location:	About 5 km south east of Miho Air Base.

A small airstrip is located at this army base but no aircraft are normally in residence. Helicopters are regular visitors to provide support to the resident units. Five rotary wing types have been preserved at the site. All are American designs produced under licence in Japan and they have given excellent service.

TYPE	REG/SER	CON. NO.	PI/NOTES	STATUS
☐ Fuji-Bell 204B-2 Iroquois (HU-1B)	41528	MH-29		RA
☐ Fuji-Bell 205 Iroquois (HU-1H)	41676			RA
☐ Kawasaki-Hughes 369M (OH-6D)	31149			RA
☐ Kawasaki-Hughes 369M (OH-6J)	31032	6333		RA
☐ Kawasaki-Vertol KV-107-II-4	51742	4075		RA

YUHKARI KOUTSU KOHEN (JA137)

Address:	Koganehara. Matsudo-shi. Chiba 270-0021.
Admission:	Daily 0800-1700.
Location:	About 20 km north east of Tokyo.

The park is designed to interest children in all forms of transport. Several cars and a steam locomotive can be seen and there are exhibitions tracing the development of road and rail services. The only aircraft is the Sikorsky S-62 helicopter. Operated by the Navy in the search and rescue role this aircraft was in service from 1965 until May 1981. It was moved to the park the following November. The name means Eucalyptus Transportation Park and there are many trees of this species planted around the site.

TYPE	REG/SER	CON. NO.	PI/NOTES	STATUS
☐ Sikorsky S-62J	8922	M62-010		PV

ZENTSUJI ARMY CAMP COLLECTION (JA138)

Address:	2-1-1 Minami-machi, Zentsuji-shi, Kagawa pref. 765-8502,
Tel:	0877-62-2311
Admission:	By prior permission only.
Location:	In the town.

The camp housed prisoners during World War II and is now home to a number of units. Three helicopters once flown by the army have been preserved along with an ex-Air Force Sabre.

TYPE	REG/SER	CON. NO.	PI/NOTES	STATUS
☐ Fuji-Bell 204B-2 Iroquois (HU-1B)	41522	MH-23		RA
☐ Kawasaki-Hughes 369M (OH-6J)	31110			RA
☐ Kawasaki-Vertol KV-107-II-4	51735	4064		RA
☐ North American NA-190 Sabre (F-86D)	04-8191	190-779	52-10014	RA

ZERO HANGAR VISITOR CENTER (JA139)

Address:	Marine Corps Air Station. Misumicho. Iwakuni-shi. Yamaguchi pref. 740-0025.
Tel:	0827-21-4161 ext. 6175.
Admission:	By prior permission only.
Location:	About 40 km south west of Hiroshima.

The base is home to both JMSDF and U.S. Marine units. In the American area is the sole hangar remaining from the World War II era. Over one hundred Zero fighters were normally in residence during this period along with many training types. The base was only attacked once during the conflict and the damage caused by strafing American aircraft can be seen on the front wall of the building. The Marine Corps moved in after peace was declared and have steadily improved the facilities over the years. For many years the hangar was unused but Colonel Donald McCarthy, the American Commanding Officer from 1983 to 1986, decided to set up a Visitor Center as a memorial to the efforts which have ensured that America and Japan are now at peace. A full size replica of a Zero built by Mitsubishi in 1984 for film use is on show along with many items tracing the history of World War II and the subsequent residence by U.S. forces. Photographs and models feature prominently in the display. The Center was dedicated on May 4th 1986. The Skyhawk is parked by the American gate to the base.

TYPE	REG/SER	CON. NO.	PI/NOTES	STATUS
☐ Douglas OA-4M Skyhawk (TA-4F)	Bu154638	13756	On loan from MCAGM, VA, USA.	RA
☐ Mitsubishi A6M5 Zero Sen Model 52 (R)				RA

JORDAN

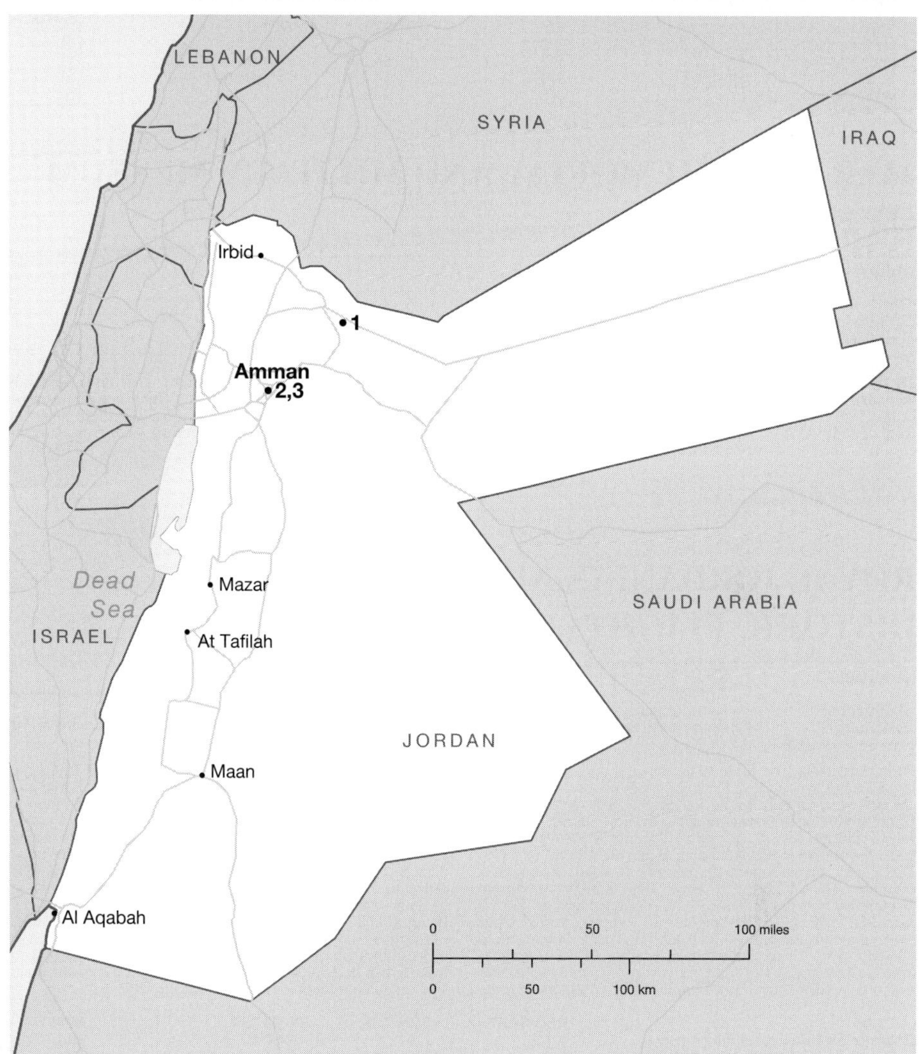

KING HUSSEIN AIR COLLEGE COLLECTION (JY1)

Address:	Mafraq.
Admission:	By prior permission only.
Location:	Just east of the town which is about 50 km north east of Amman.

The Arab Legion Air Force was established in 1948 two years after the country gained full independence. The initial equipment was one Dragon Rapide and this was soon joined by two Tiger Moths and four Proctors. The title Royal Jordanian Air Force was adopted in 1955 and since then the force has grown into an efficient unit operating modern combat types. The base at Mafraq was built by the Royal Air Force in the early 1950s before being handed over to Jordan. Formerly a fighter station the site is now home to the Air Force College which trains all pilots for the service. An original squadron building is being converted for display purposes. Documents, photograph and uniforms will be put on show. Several of the preserved aircraft are mounted near the main gate. The Hunter, delivered in 1971, is maintained in taxying condition.

TYPE	REG/SER	CON. NO.	PI/NOTES	STATUS
☐ Canadair CL-90 Starfighter (CF-104) [Lockheed 683-04-12]	104743	683A-1043	12743 (Canada), 104743 (Canada), 62-743 (Turkey)	RA
☐ Hawker P.1099 Hunter FGA.73B (P.1067 Hunter F.4)	842	HABL 003142	XF987, G-9-265	RA
☐ Lockheed 183-93-02 Starfighter (F-104A)	919	183-1079	56-0791	RA
☐ Northrop N-156B Freedom Fighter (F-5B)	232		(USAF)	RA
☐ Scottish Aviation Bulldog 125A	403	BH125A/301	G-BCAW, JY-ADZ	RA
☐ Scottish Aviation Bulldog 125A	419	BH125A/434	1141 (Jordan)	RA
☐ Westland Scout AH.1				RA

MARTYR'S MEMORIAL AND MILITARY MUSEUM (JY2)

Address:	Sarh al Shaheed Street, Amman.
Tel:	5664240
Admission:	Sunday-Friday 0900-1600.
Location:	In the centre of the city.

The Royal Jordanian acquired several ex-R.A.F. Hunters in the late 1950s and early 1960s. The majority were destroyed in the 1967 Six-Day War with Israel and replaced by gifts from Saudi Arabia and purchases from Britain. Later conflicts further depleted stocks. A number then arrived from Abu Dhabi and these were later passed on to Amman. When the decision was taken to put a Hunter on show at the Memorial Museum to the Unknown Soldier there were no examples of the famous fighter in Jordan so one was bought in England.

TYPE	REG/SER	CON. NO.	PI/NOTES	STATUS
☐ Hawker P.1067 Hunter F.4		HABL 003114	XF946, 7804M	PVX

ROYAL JORDANIAN AIR FORCE HISTORIC FLIGHT (JY3)

Address:	King Abdullah Air Base, Amman.
Admission:	By prior permission only.
Location:	In the north eastern suburbs of the city.

Formed in 1994, the flight made its first appearance at the International Air Tattoo at Fairford in the July of that year. The aircraft were initially based in the Jet Heritage hangars at Hurn Airport near Bournemouth. The first aircraft acquired was a former Swiss Air Force Vampire T.55 which was presented to the Royal Air Force Benevolent Fund in 1990. This classic jet is now in the colours of a No. 2 Squadron example. The Hunter T.7, once very familiar at British displays in its red scheme, now masquerades in No. 1 Squadron markings. The single seat Vampire arrived from Switzerland in June 1994 and has now been fitted with a standard nose. Three former Swiss single seat Hunters came from Switzerland in 1999 and one was subsequently sold. The Autocrat, modified to almost Beagle Husky configuration was acquired in England in 1995. The Northrop F-5 has been operated in several versions by the Jordanian Air Force and still equips front line squadrons. One is a problem as the Air Force states it is a two seater but the serial fits with a single seat version. Perhaps it was fitted with a two seat nose during its career. The Dove, once operated by the Royal Flight, came back to England to be modified to Riley 400 standard. The airframe was the fifth to be converted by McAlpine Aviation at Luton. After a spell in France it returned to Jordan and after being stored for a time it joined the collection. Two early Starfighters are preserved on the base and may be restored to airworthiness in due course. The airfield was established as a joint Britsh and Jordanian military field and for many years was the main international airport for the city.

TYPE	REG/SER	CON. NO.	PI/NOTES	STATUS
☐ Auster 5A/160 Autocrat (J/1 Autocrat)	A-410	2204	G-AIPW	RAA
☐ Canadair CL-90 Starfighter (CF-104) [Lockheed 683-04-12]	899	683A-1199	12899, 104899, 104899 (Turkey) – Jordanian Air Force state aircraft is a two seater – identity doubtful.	RA
☐ De Havilland D.H.100 Vampire FB.6	'109'	615	J-1106 (Switzerland), HB-RVO, G-BVPO	RAAX
☐ De Havilland D.H.104 Dove 7	JY-RJU	04540	121 (Jordan)	RAA
☐ De Havilland D.H.115 Vampire T.55	'209'	976	U-1216 (Switzerland), ZH563, G-BVLM	RAAX
☐ Hawker P.1099 Hunter F.58	'712'	41H/697394	J-4025 (Switzerland), G-BWKC	RAAX
☐ Hawker P.1099 Hunter F.58	'843'	41H/697442	J-4075 (Switzerland), G-BWKA	RAAX
☐ Hawker P.1101 Hunter T.7	'800'	41H/693749	N-307 (Netherlands), ET-274 (Denmark), G-9-432, G-BOOM	RAAX
☐ Lockheed 183-93-02 Starfighter (F-104A)	918	183-1059	56-0771	RA
☐ Lockheed 183-93-02 Starfighter (F-104A)	905	183-1063	56-0775, 4211 (Taiwan)	RA
☐ Northrop N-311 Tiger II (F-5E)				RAA
☐ Riley Dove 400 (De Havilland D.H. 104 Dove 5 (1))	JY-AEU	04288	TJ-ABG, TJ-ACC, D-102, G-ATGK, F-BORJ	RA
☐ Sud-Est SE.3160 Alouette III				RAA

KAZAKHSTAN

BAIKONUR SPACE MUSEUM (KA1)

Address: Baikonur.
Admission: By prior permission only.
Location: About 3 km north of the town.

Baikonur was the major launch site for Soviet rockets and since the break up of the Union the Russians have continued to use the facilities. A museum is located within the camp and the displays trace the history of the space programme. A number of rockets can be seen along with the houses used by Korolev and Gagarin. In the town are both replica and genuine launch vehicles plus a Lisunov Li-2.

TYPE	REG/SER	CON. NO.	PI/NOTES	STATUS
☐ Lisunov Li-2 [Douglas DC-3 modified]	'CCCP-26959'			PVX

CHILDREN'S PARK (KA2)

Address: Almaty.
Admission: Daily 0800-dusk.
Location: In the eastern part of the city.

Many activities for children take place in the park. There is a small military display which includes two aircraft and a number of vehicles along with a model railway track. The Yak-50 is preserved nearby.

TYPE	REG/SER	CON. NO.	PI/NOTES	STATUS
☐ Mikoyan-Gurevich MiG-21bis	08			PV
☐ Mil Mi-8	85			PV
☐ Yakovlev Yak-50	95		At Aero Club offices in the city.	PV

CITY PARK (KA3)

Address: Karaganda.
Admission: Daily 0800-dusk.
Location: In the centre of the city.

There is a small military display in the park and two aircraft can be seen. There is also an excellent narrow gauge railway which runs around the large site. There are many plants and trees to be seen.

TYPE	REG/SER	CON. NO.	PI/NOTES	STATUS
☐ Aero L-29 Delfin				PV
☐ Antonov An-2TP	UN-09661	1G 75-45	CCCP-09661	PV

PRIOZERSK MEMORIAL (KA4)

Address:	Ullitsa Lenina, Priozersk.
Admission:	On permanent view.
Location:	In the town.

The Balkhash Complex on the outskirts of the town housed a tracking station for nuclear missiles during the latter years of the Soviet Union. The MiG-21PFM is located in the town.

TYPE	REG/SER	CON. NO.	PI/NOTES	STATUS
☐ Mikoyan-Gurevich MiG-21PFM	43			PV

SEMEY MEMORIAL (KA5)

Address:	Semey.
Admission:	On permanent view.
Location:	In the town.

From 1949 until 1991 the area was used for nuclear weapon tests by the Soviet Union. Several sites for this work were located around the vast area. A then secret town was built about one hundred kilometres from the city which was then known as Semipalatinsk. The MiG-17 is mounted on a pylon in the town. This is a poignant reminder of the Soviet period as the tests have caused major health problems in the region.

TYPE	REG/SER	CON. NO.	PI/NOTES	STATUS
☐ Mikoyan-Gurevich MiG-17	01			PV

SHYMKENT AIR BASE MEMORIAL (KA6)

Address:	Shymkent Air Base, Shymkent.
Admission:	About 5 km north west of the town.
Location:	On permanent view

The town is home to a former Soviet Air Base which is now used by the Kazakhstan Air Force and serves as the civil airport for the town. The Su-7B is mounted on a pylon by the military gate.

TYPE	REG/SER	CON. NO.	PI/NOTES	STATUS
☐ Sukhoi Su-7B				PV

TALDYKORGAN AIR BASE MEMORIAL (KA7)

Address:	Taldykorgan Air Base, Taldykorgan.
Admission:	By prior permission only.
Location:	About 8 km north of the town.

There was a major Soviet Air Force Base close to the town and this is now used by the Kazakhstan Air Force. The Yak-28 is preserved on the site and is surrounded by plaques and weapons.

TYPE	REG/SER	CON. NO.	PI/NOTES	STATUS
☐ Yakovlev Yak-28R				RA

ZHEKAZGAN MEMORIAL (KA8)

Address:	Bulvar Seyfullina, Zhekagan.
Admission:	On permanent view
Location:	In the town.

By tradition cosmonauts returning safely from flights at the Baikoner Cosmodrome plant a tree alongside the boulevard. The MiG-17 has been preserved as part of this memorial. There are plaques giving the names of those who have made the trips into space and details of their flights are listed.

TYPE	REG/SER	CON. NO.	PI/NOTES	STATUS
☐ Mikoyan-Gurevich MiG-17	01			PV

KUWAIT

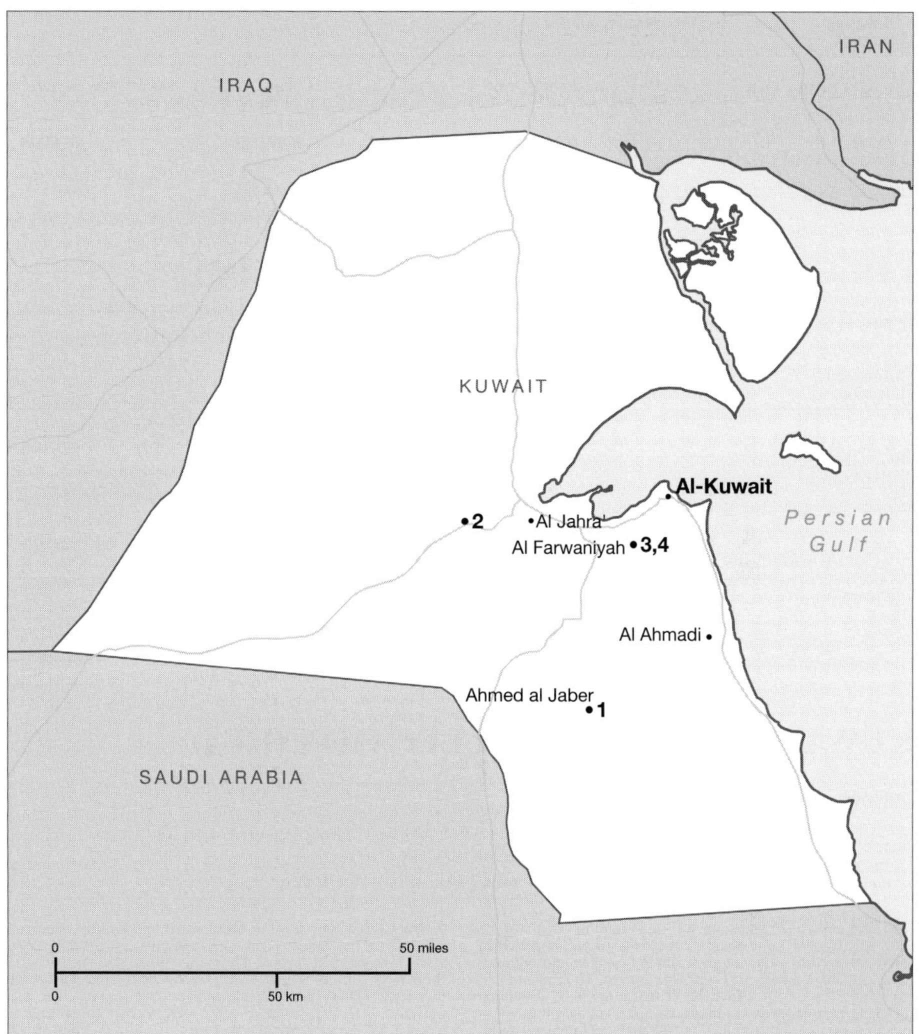

AHMED AL JABER AIR BASE COLLECTION (KU1)

Address:	Ahmed Al Jaber.
Admission:	By prior permission only.
Location:	About 60 km south west of Kuwait City.

The base is now home to squadrons flying F/A-18 Hornets. For many years there was a substantial American presence at the field but this has now been reduced. The three Lightnings are spectacularly mounted in formation close to the main gate and the Jet Provost is parked among the buildings.

TYPE	REG/SER	CON. NO.	PI/NOTES	STATUS
☐ English Electric P.26 Lightning F.53	53-415	95308	G-27-83	PV
☐ English Electric P.26 Lightning F.53	53-416	95309	G-27-84	PV
☐ English Electric P.26 Lightning F.53	53-417	95310	G-27-85	PV
☐ Hunting-Percival P.84 Jet Provost T.51				RA

ALI AL SALEM AIR BASE COLLECTION (KU2)

Address:	Ali Al Salem.
Admission:	By prior permission only.
Location:	About 40 km west of Kuwait City.

The field houses helicopter squadrons and training units. One of the Lightnings is displayed by the main gate and the other is inside the camp. A visitor reported that one of the stored Mirages was being prepared for display.

TYPE	REG/SER	CON. NO.	PI/NOTES	STATUS
☐ Dassault Mirage F.1CK				RA
☐ English Electric P.26 Lightning F.53	53-422	95315		RA
☐ English Electric P.26 Lightning F.53	53-423	95316	G-27-91 -.	RA

EDUCATIONAL SCIENCE MUSEUM (KU3)

Address:	Abdulla-al-Mubarah Street, Safat 13079.
Tel:	2421268
Admission:	Saturday-Thursday 0830-1200.
Location:	In the eastern part of the city.

Displays at this museum located in a modern building on the waterfront, trace modern developments with particular emphasis on the oil industry. Natural history is also featured with an excellent collection of stuffed animals and birds. The exhibition makes use of computer based techniques. There is an excellent planetarium along with an IMAX theatre. Four aircraft are on display. The Dakota is painted as one which was delivered to Gulf Aviation in 1960, The company flew DC-3s in the region for many years.

TYPE	REG/SER	CON. NO.	PI/NOTES	STATUS
☐ Auster J/5L Aiglet Trainer	K-AAAI	3134	G-ANXY, K-AAAI, 9K-AAI	PV
☐ Douglas DC-3A-467 Skytrain (C-47B) (Dakota IV)	'G-AMZZ'	14361/25806	43-48545, KJ867, G-AGKE, VR-AAB, TJ-ABN, JY-ABN, VR-AAB, G-AGKE, (5B-CAZ), (N27AA)	PVX
☐ English Electric P.26 Lightning F.53	53-418	95311	G-27-86, G-AXEE	PV
☐ Hunting-Percival P.84 Jet Provost T.51	103	2/24	Also reported as 102.	PV

KUWAIT AIR FORCE COLLECTION (KU4)

Address:	P.O. Box 1170, Safat, 13012 Kuwait.
Tel:	4848300
Admission:	By prior permission only.
Location:	The International Airport is about 15 km south of Kuwait City.

Kuwait gained its independence from Britain in 1961 and the state was almost immediately claimed by Iraq. The British forces ensured that the takeover did not happen and within a short time the Kuwaiti Air Force was formed. The first combat aircraft used were six armed Jet Provosts flown by seconded R.A.F. aircrew. Eleven Hunters soon followed and the two in the collection are from a batch of four Belgian built examples. These were purchased by Hawker-Siddeley Aviation and converted in England. In 1968 fourteen Lightnings arrived. Twelve were single seaters and the other pair two seat trainer versions. In the early 1970s a batch of Strikemasters was purchased and these were later followed by Mirages and Skyhawks. Prior to the 1991 Gulf War plans had been put forward for a museum but these were temporarily shelved. Aircraft for the display are now hangared at the military base at the International Airport. Thirty single seat and six two seat Skyhawks, similar to the A-4M version, arrived in Kuwait in the mid-1970s. Three of these have been saved for the museum. In 1953 an aero club was formed operating a number of Austers bought in England. One of the Aiglet Trainers is now in the hangar. One hundred and three examples of the type were produced at Rearsby and all bar one were powered by Gipsy Major engines. The exception was fitted with a Cirrus Major and was flown in many races. Two Westland Whirlwinds were operated in Kuwait and one with no markings was seen in the hangar.

TYPE	REG/SER	CON. NO.	PI/NOTES	STATUS
☐ Auster J/5F Aiglet Trainer	K-AAAE	3120	G-ANNW, K-AAAE, 9K-AAE	RA
☐ Dassault Mirage F.1C	4	4	In French markings.	RA
☐ Dassault Mirage F.1CK	715			RA
☐ Douglas A-4KU Skyhawk	805	14552	Bu160184	RA
☐ Douglas TA-4KU Skyhawk	881	14578	Bu160210	RA
☐ Douglas TA-4KU Skyhawk	882	14579	Bu160211	RA
☐ English Electric P.26 Lightning F.53	53-412	95292	G-27-80	PV
☐ English Electric P.26 Lightning F.53	53-421	95314	G-27-89	RA
☐ English Electric P.27 Lightning T.55	55-411	B1/95029	G-27-79	RA
☐ Hawker P.1099 Hunter FGA.57 (F.6)	213	8785	IF-41 (Belgium), G-9-80	PV
☐ Hawker P.1099 Hunter FGA.57 (F.6)	214	8968	IF-69 (Belgium), G-9-129	RA

TYPE	REG/SER	CON. NO.	PI/NOTES	STATUS
☐ Hunting-Percival P.84 Jet Provost T.51	101	10/23		RA
☐ Hunting-Percival P.84 Jet Provost T.51	105			RA
☐ Hunting-Percival P.84 Jet Provost T.51	104	3/24		RA
☐ Westland-Sikorsky WS-55 Whirlwind Series 1			Probably either c/n WA/318 G-APXA, 9K-BHA or c/n WA/319 G-APXB, 9K-BHB.	RA

KYRGYZSTAN

AVIATION MUSEUM (KYR1)

Address:	Bishkek
Admission:	Currently closed.
Location:	In the city.

I found a photograph of the MiG-21 mounted outside a large building. The caption stated that it was at a currently closed aviation museum. Further details would be most welcome.

TYPE	REG/SER	CON. NO.	PI/NOTES	STATUS
☐ Ilyushin Il-28			In town.	PV
☐ Mikoyan-Gurevich MiG-21F	01			PV

KANT MEMORIAL (KYR2)

Address:	Kant.
Admission:	On permanent view.
Location:	In the town.

Russian Air Force aircraft regularly use this base which was constructed by the Soviet union. A MiG-21 has been mounted in the town to serve as a memorial to those who have flown from the field.

TYPE	REG/SER	CON. NO.	PI/NOTES	STATUS
☐ Mikoyan-Gurevich MiG-21UM	01			PV

TOKMOK MEMORIALS (KYR3)

Address:	Tokmok.
Admission:	On permanent view.
Location:	In the south eastern part of the town.

There are two memorials in the town. A MiG-23 is pole mounted at one site along with a rocket and a plinth. Nearby is an Ilyushin Il-28. Both are presumed to be dedicated to local military heroes.

TYPE	REG/SER	CON. NO.	PI/NOTES	STATUS
☐ Ilyushin Il-28				PV
☐ Mikoyan-Gurevich MiG-23S	25			PV

LAOS

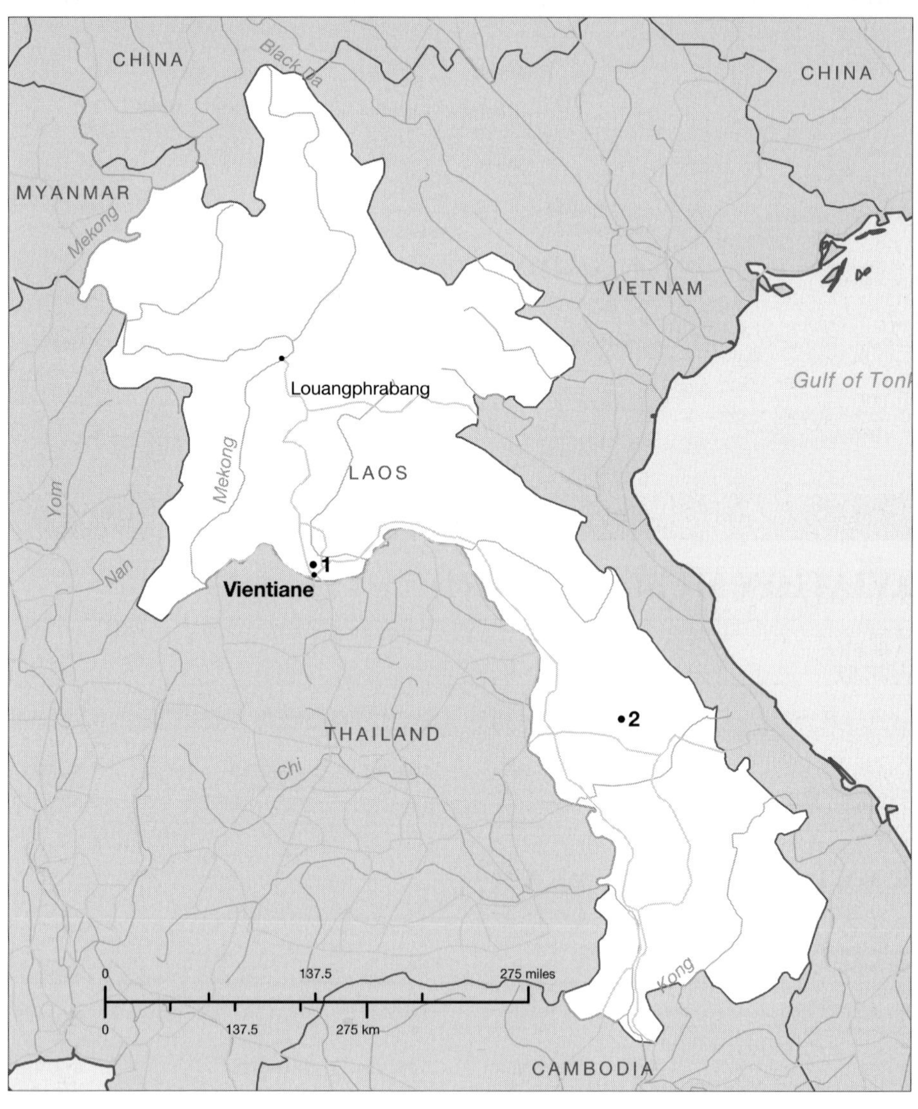

LAO PEOPLE'S ARMY MUSEUM (LAO1)

Address:	Phonekheng Road, Vientiane.
Admission:	Monday-Friday 0800-1100 1300-1600.
Location:	In the north eastern part of the city.

This new museum was opened by President Khamtay Siphandone in December 2005. The ground floor of the impressive building houses military vehicles from the conflicts with both the French and the U.S.A. On the first floor are photographs of these campaigns along with artefacts, documents, and weapons. The early history of the country is portrayed. Also in this section is a drone used for aerial photography. The two aircraft are displayed outside. The inscription on the An-2 reads 'The Lao Front for National Construction'. The remains of the former American aircraft were on show in the old exhibition and are believed to be in store. A visitor was told that several airframes are in the collection and these will join the display in the near future.

TYPE	REG/SER	CON. NO.	PI/NOTES	STATUS
☐ Antonov An-2	074			PV
☐ Bell 204 Iroquois (UH-1C)	66-15094	1822		RAD
☐ Cessna R172E Mescalero (T-41B)	67-15163	R1720164		RAD
☐ Mil Mi-8	RDPL-34043			PV
☐ North American NA-174 Trojan (T-28A) (T-28D)	51-7746	174-599	Rear fuselage only.	RAD

SAVANNAKHET PROVINCIAL MUSEUM (LAO2)

Address:	Ban Thanel, Muang Khant Khanthabri, Khoueng Savannakhet.
Tel:	041-213927
Admission:	Monday-Friday 0800-1130 1300-1600. (If still open)
Location:	In the town.

This local history museum is located in a former French Mansion. Outside in the grounds is a collection of military vehicles, weapons and the damaged Trojan. The building is in a poor state of repair and many items have been moved into safe storage. The site may be sold to a developer who has plans to construct a hotel.

TYPE	REG/SER	CON. NO.	PI/NOTES	STATUS
☐ North American NA-174 Trojan (T-28A) (T-28D)				PV

LEBANON

LEBANESE AIR FORCE MUSEUM (LEB1)

Address:	Rayak Air Base.
Admission:	By prior permission only.
Location:	Just west of the town which is itself about 50 km east of Beirut.

The Lebanese Air Force was formed in 1949 six years after the country was established. The Royal Air Force sent a team of advisors and two Percival Prentices arrived in the country. Other training aircraft were acquired and in 1953 orders were placed for both single and two seat Vampires. The first Hawker Hunters, six ex-RAF aircraft, were delivered in late 1958 and these were joined by four former Belgian machines in 1965. Six single seaters and three two seaters arrived in the mid-1970s. A small batch of Fouga Magisters was acquired and at least two were German built. Six Scottish Aviation Bulldogs were purchased for training duties. In recent years helicopters have played a significant role in the country. Despite the unstable situation a display has been assembled at Rayak. This airfield was built by the Germans and their Allies during World War I. The site was used by the French Air Force until 1949 when they left the area. After a long period of disuse it was taken over by the Lebanese Air Force. There are several other aircraft in store on the base and hopefully the collection will expand in the future.

TYPE	REG/SER	CON. NO.	PI/NOTES	STATUS
☐ De Havilland D.H.115 Vampire T.55	L-154	15484		RA
☐ Fouga CM.170R Magister	L-602	505	505 (France), L-442, L-402	RA
☐ Hawker P.1099 Hunter F.6	'L-271'	S4/U/3338	XF461, L-171 – possible identity.	RAX
☐ Scottish Aviation Bulldog 126	L-142	BH126/365	G-BCTM	RA
☐ Scottish Aviation Bulldog 126	L-144	BH126/367	G-BCTO	RA
☐ Scottish Aviation Bulldog 126	L-145	BH126/368	G-BCTP	RA
☐ Sud-Est SE.3130 Alouette II	L-302	1598	L-202	RA
☐ Sud SA.316B Alouette III	L-329	1980	L-229	RA
☐ Sud SA.342L Gazelle	L-801	1824		RA

MALAYSIA

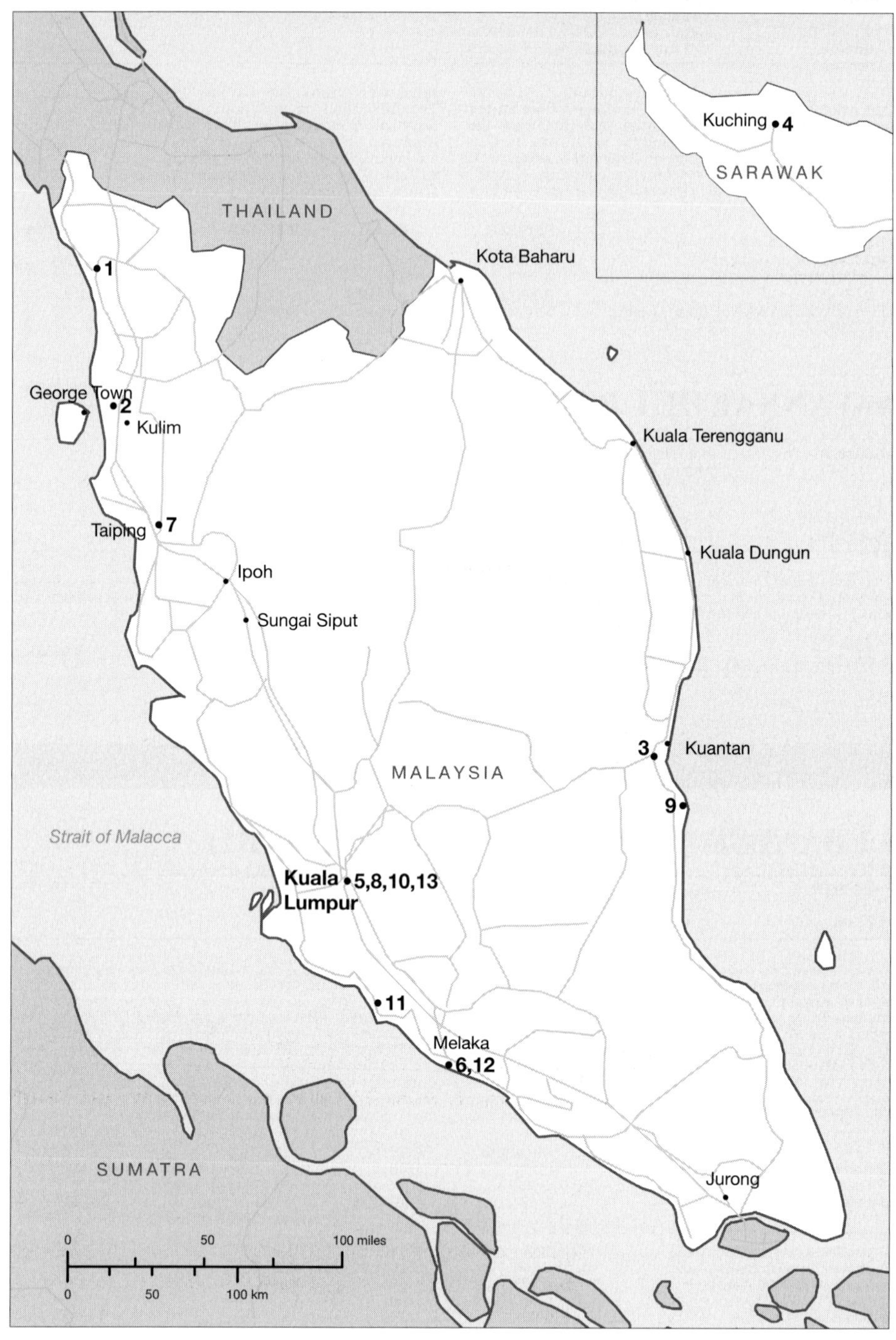
Kuching
4
SARAWAK
THAILAND
Kota Baharu
1
George Town
2
Kulim
Kuala Terengganu
Taiping
7
Kuala Dungun
Ipoh
Sungai Siput
3
Kuantan
MALAYSIA
9
Strait of Malacca
Kuala Lumpur
5,8,10,13
11
Melaka
6,12
SUMATRA
Jurong
0
50
100 miles
0
50
100 km

ALOR SETAR BASE COLLECTION (MALA1)

Address:	Flying Training Academy, 2nd Air Base, Alor Setar 05150.
Admission:	By prior permission only.
Location:	On the western outskirts of the town.

Alor Setar saw brief use by Blenheims of No. 62 Squadron of the Royal Air Force in 1941 before the Japanese invaded the country. Currently the base is home to the Flying Training Academy of the Royal Malaysian Air Force as well as the Air Force Technical College. Several aircraft once used by the school are on show and others have been added to the display. Fifteen Bulldogs were ordered to replace the Provosts which had given excellent service for many years. Prior to this Tiger Moths and Harvards had been operated. The Bell 47 was used for many years by the Helicopter Training School at Keluang. Currently in use for pilot instruction are Pilatus PC.7s and Datwyler MD-3s.

TYPE	REG/SER	CON. NO.	PI/NOTES	STATUS
☐ Bell 47G-5A Sioux	'M26-00'	25153 (?)	M26-05 (?)	RAX
☐ Canadair CL-41G-5 Tebuan	M22-03	2197	FM1126	RA
☐ Commonwealth CA-27 Sabre 32 [North American F-86F]	'FM1900'	CA27-???		RAX
☐ De Havilland D.H.125-400B	M24-02	25209	FM1201, FM1802	RA
☐ De Havilland D.H.C.1 Chipmunk T.10	FM1022	C1/0226	WD287, FM1022, 9M-ANI, 9V-BAE, VH-BBK – if identity correct.	RA
☐ Douglas A-4PTM Skyhawk (A4D-2N) (A-4C)				RA
☐ Douglas TA-4TPM Skyhawk (A4D-2N) (A-4C)	M32-06	12349	Bu145103	RA
☐ Northrop N-311 Tiger II (F-5E)	M29-04	R.1118	74-1448, FM2206	RA
☐ Percival P.56 Provost T.51 (T.1)	FM1031	P.56/029	WV446, G-23-1	RA
☐ Percival P.56 Provost T.51 (T.1)	FM1032	P.56/092	WV550-G-23-2	RA
☐ Scottish Aviation Bulldog 102	FM1221	BH102/116		RA
☐ Scottish Aviation Bulldog 102	FM1231	BH102/160		RA

BUTTERWORTH AIR BASE COLLECTION (MALA2)

Address:	6th Air Base, Jln Talok, Butterworth 12990.
Admission:	By prior permission only.
Location:	About 5 km north of the town.

Butterworth opened for Royal Air Force use in October 1941 and was soon occupied by the Japanese. The R.A.F. moved back in during January 1946 and in the late 1940s and early 1950s missions were flown against local guerrillas. The base was handed over to the Royal Australian Air Force in July 1958 who were in residence for thirty years. They still have detachments based at the field and aircraft spend short periods at Butterworth. At the current time fighter units of the Malaysian Air Force use the site along with a helicopter squadron. Four aircraft are preserved at the field. Two are Australian built Sabres which have served with both air forces.

TYPE	REG/SER	CON. NO.	PI/NOTES	STATUS
☐ Commonwealth CA-27 Sabre 32 [North American F-86F]	'FM1905'	CA27-???	FM1901	RAX
☐ Commonwealth CA-27 Sabre 32 [North American F-86F]	FM1903	CA27-103	A94-363, FM1363 – may still be here.	RA
☐ Commonwealth CA-29 Mirage IIIO (A) [Dassault Mirage III]	A3-59	CA29-59		RA
☐ Douglas A-4PTM Skyhawk (A4D-2N) (A-4C)	M32-34			RA

KUANTAN AIR BASE COLLECTION (MALA3)

Address:	4th Air Base, Jln Gambang Batu, Kuantan 26150.
Admission:	By prior permission only.
Location:	About 10 km south west of the town.

The airfield was occupied by the Royal Air Force in the 1930s and taken over by the Japanese when they invaded Malaya in 1941. The site is now home to squadrons of the Royal Malaysian Air Force operating the British Aerospace Hawk and the Mikoyan-Gurevich MiG-29. The first examples of the Russian fighter arrived in Malaysia in the mid-1990s. Two types which formerly flew from the field have been preserved.

TYPE	REG/SER	CON. NO.	PI/NOTES	STATUS
☐ British Aerospace Hawk 208	M40-30	448/MS010	(ZH787)	RA
☐ Canadair CL-41G-5 Tebuan	M22-06	2201	FM1131	RA
☐ Douglas A-4PTM Skyhawk (A4D-2N) (A-4C)	M32-22			RA
☐ Douglas A-4PTM Skyhawk (A4D-2N) (A-4C)	M32-33			RA

KUCHING AIR BASE MONUMENT (MALA4)

Address:	5th Air Base, Kuching 93350.
Admission:	By prior permission only.
Location:	Just south of the town.

The airfield was used by squadrons of the Royal Air Force before Malaysia became an independent country. Helicopters and transport aircraft are currently in residence. A Caribou is preserved near the military ramp on the south side of the field. A large civil terminal has been constructed on the other side of the runway.

TYPE	REG/SER	CON. NO.	PI/NOTES	STATUS
☐ De Havilland D.H.C.4A Caribou	M21-03	247	FM1102, FM1403	RA

MUZIUM ANGKATAN TENTERA (MALA5)

Address:	Jalan Padang Tembak, Kuala Lumpur 50634.
Tel:	03-2692-0133
Fax:	03-2693-9608
Admission:	Saturday-Thursday 1000-1800.
Location:	In the north eastern suburbs of the city

The Royal Malaysian Armed Forces Museum was established in 1985 in the grounds of the Defence Ministry. On show are exhibits tracing the history of the country from early days. The visitor can see a display of paintings and heraldic objects in addition to the military items. Wars, which have been fought in the area, feature prominently as do the does the development of military forces in the country. A large outside area is home to a range of vehicles and guns. The only aircraft is one of the twenty Canadair Tebuans delivered in 1967. The type is derived from the Tutor and featured a strengthened undercarriage and underwing attachment points.

TYPE	REG/SER	CON. NO.	PI/NOTES	STATUS
☐ Canadair CL-41G-5 Tebuan	M22-05	2201	FM1130	PV

MUZIUM PENGANGKUTAN MELAKA (MALA6)

Address:	Kompleks Istana, Jalan Kota, Melaka 75000.
Tel:	06-282-6526
Fax:	06-282-6745
Admission:	Aircraft on permanent view.
Location:	In the centre of the town.

Located in a city which existed in the third century, this transport park is next to the museum which traces the history and culture of the area. The main building is a replica of the old Sultanate Palace. Situated opposite is the Proclamation of Independence Memorial where the displays portray the history of Malaysia from the early days up to the declaration of independence at Padang Pahlawan on August 31st 1957. Exhibited in the grounds of the complex is one of the fifteen Twin Pioneers ordered by Malaysia in the late 1950s. This aircraft was displayed for a period at the Air Force Museum in Kuala Lumpur before moving to its new home. Also to be seen are railway engines, carriages and motor vehicles.

TYPE	REG/SER	CON. NO.	PI/NOTES	STATUS
☐ Scottish Aviation Twin Pioneer 3	FM1064	583		PV

MUZIUM PERAK (MALA7)

Address:	Jalan Taming Sari, Taiping 34000.
Tel:	0605-807-2057
Fax:	0605-806-3043 Info@jma.gov.my
Admission:	Daily 0900-1700.
Location:	In the centre of the town.

The museum is the oldest in the country and was built by the British in 1883. Housed in the impressive building are displays tracing the local history and culture. The camouflaged Sabre is parked outside.

TYPE	REG/SER	CON. NO.	PI/NOTES	STATUS
☐ Commonwealth CA-27 Sabre 32 [North American F-86F]	'FM1917'	CA27-104	A94-364, FM1364, FM1904	PVX

MUZIUM POLIS DIRAJA MALAYSIA (MALA8)

Address:	5 Jalan Perdana, Kuala Lumpur 50480.
Tel:	03-2272-5689
Admission:	Tuesday-Sunday 1000-1800.
Location:	In the city near the National Mosque.

This museum traces the history of police work in the country from the setting up of the force by the British. On show are many photographs, documents and uniforms. Vehicles and equipment can also be seen. Aircraft and helicopters now play an important role in the service and a Cessna flown for many years can be seen.

TYPE	REG/SER	CON. NO.	PI/NOTES	STATUS
☐ Cessna U206G Stationair	9M-PSC	U20605247		PV

MUZIUM SULTAN ABU BAKAR (MALA9)

Address:	Jalan Sultan Ahmed, Pekan 40000.
Tel:	09-422-1371
Fax:	09-422-1572
Admission:	Tuesday- Sunday0900-1700. Closed Monday 1215-1445.
Location:	In the town which is on the east coast about 50 km from Kuantan.

Opened in 1976, the museum traces the local cultural and ethnological history in its varied displays. The building was used by the British Resident from the 1880s and during World War II it served as the regional Japanese Army Headquarters. On show outside is an Australian built Sabre. Malaysia was given ten former R.A.A.F. machines in 1969 and six more plus two for training arrived two years later. A former Malaysian Navy Wasp helicopter is parked nearby.

TYPE	REG/SER	CON. NO.	PI/NOTES	STATUS
☐ Commonwealth CA-27 Sabre 32 [North American F-86F]	FM1905	CA27-103	A94-363, FM1363	PV
☐ Westland Wasp HAS.1	M499-01	F9667	XV632	PV

MUZIUM SULTAN ALAM SHAH (MALA10)

Address:	Persiaran Perdagangan, Shah Alam 40000.
Tel:	03-559-0050
Admission:	Daily 0900-1800 (Closed Friday 1215-1415)
Location:	Close to the State Mosque in the city.

Displays at this museum trace the history and culture of the Sultanate of Selangor. Natural history and the arts are also featured. The only aircraft on show is a former Royal Air Force Provost supplied to Malaysia in the 1960s. The British design was used for pilot training at the Air Force Academy at Alor Setar.

TYPE	REG/SER	CON. NO.	PI/NOTES	STATUS
☐ Percival P.56 Provost T.51 (T.1)	FM1045	P.56/371	XF874 – possible c/n and p.i.	PV

MUZIUM TENTERA DARAT (MALA11)

Address:	Batu 4, Ken Si Rusa, Port Dickson 71050.
Tel:	06-647-2166
Admission:	Wednesday-Sunday 1000-1700.
Location:	In the town.

The museum, which traces the history of the Malaysian Army, opened in October 1995. The military history of the region is portrayed from the early days up to modern times. There are displays of uniforms, photographs, weapons and communications equipment. Several military vehicles including tanks, lorries and a motor cycle are on view. A steam train is parked in the grounds. Three aircraft are on show. The Air Force operated a fleet of Skyhawks and these were withdrawn in the mid-1990s. Eighteen Caribous were flown on transport duties from their base at Kuching. Ten Air Force Alouettes were transferred to the Army in the mid-1990s.

TYPE	REG/SER	CON. NO.	PI/NOTES	STATUS
☐ De Havilland D.H.C.4A Caribou				PV
☐ Douglas A-4PTM Skyhawk (A4D-2N) (A-4C)				PV
☐ Sud-Est SE.3160 Alouette III				PV

MUZIUM TENTERA LAUT DIRAJA (MALA12)

Address:	Bandar Hilar, Melaka 75000.
Tel:	06-283-0296
Admission:	Tuesday-Thursday Saturday-Sunday 0900-1800; Friday 0900-1200 1500-1800.
Location:	In the western part of the town.

The Royal Malaysian Navy initially set up a museum at Lumut but the collection was moved to Melaka several years ago. The National Maritime Museum is located nearby. A small number of Westland Wasp helicopters were flown from ships and the shore base at Lumut. One has been preserved at the museum. Also on show are a patrol boat, weapons, uniforms, photographs and documents tracing the history of the service.

TYPE	REG/SER	CON. NO.	PI/NOTES	STATUS
☐ Westland Wasp HAS.1	M499-07	F9596	XT426	PV

MUZIUM TENTERA UDARA DIRAJA MALAYSIA (MALA13)

Address:	Jalan Lampangan Terbang Lama, Kuala Lumpur 50460.
Tel:	03-2141-1133
Fax:	03-2414-4134
Email:	nazriaziz@hotmail.com
Admission:	Monday-Friday 0800-1600; Saturday 0800-1700; Sunday 1000-1700.
Location:	At Sungai Besi Airfield which is about 6 km south of the city centre.

The airfield at Sungai Besi was the civil field for the city until the early 1940s when Royal Air Force units moved in. The site was captured by the Japanese and then reclaimed by the R.A.F. at the end of World War II. The R.A.F. finally left on October 25th 1960 and handed over the base to the now independent country of Malaya. The Royal Federation Air Force was formed at Sungai Besi on June 2nd 1958 with fourteen personnel and one Twin Pioneer. The title Royal Malaysian Air Force was adopted in September 1963 when the federation was established. Over the last forty years a variety of aircraft have been used. Archive material was collected on an informal basis and this led to the setting up of the museum which opened on June 1st 1985. Housed in a former R.A.F. hangar along with associated buildings the displays trace the history of the airfield and military flying in the country. The first Twin Pioneer used was moved from the National Museum in the mid-1990s. Delivered in 1958 it was used on V.I.P. duties until 1967. British aircraft feature prominently in the display. Along one wall of the hangar is a series of murals depicting types used by the service.

TYPE	REG/SER	CON. NO.	PI/NOTES	STATUS
☐ Bell 47G-2	M26-08	1959		PV
☐ Bell 47G-5A Sioux	M26-01	25147		RA
☐ Bell 47G-5A Sioux	M26-03	25151		RA
☐ Canadair CL-41G-5 Tebuan	'FM2201'	2194	FM1123, M22-01	PVX
☐ Canadair CL-41G-5 Tebuan	'FM1125'	2200	FM1129, M22-04	PVX
☐ Cessna 310F	FM1041	310F0129	N5829X, FM1041, 9M-ANL	PV
☐ Commonwealth CA-27 Sabre 32 [North American F-86F]	FM1902	CA27-102	A94-362, FM1362	PV
☐ Commonwealth CA-27 Sabre 32 [North American F-86F]	FM1907	CA27-107	A94-367, FM1367	PV
☐ De Havilland D.H.82A Tiger Moth	'T7245'	85592	DE638, G-ANEJ	PVX
☐ De Havilland D.H.104 Dove 8	FM1051	04521		PV
☐ De Havilland D.H.C.1 Chipmunk T.20	'FM1022'	C1/0606	F9-62/97 (Thailand)	PVX
☐ De Havilland D.H.C.4A Caribou	M21-04	248	FM1102, FM1404	PV
☐ Douglas A-4PTM Skyhawk (A4D-2N) (A-4C)	M32-30	12324	Bu145078	PV
☐ Douglas A-4PTM Skyhawk (AD4-2N) (A-4C)	M32-29			PV
☐ Grumman G-231 Albatross (CSR-110)	M35-01	G-451	9303 (Canada), N9427, 573 (Chile), N8497H	PV
☐ Noorduyn Harvard IIB [North American NA-77 (AT-16)]	FT383	14A-1423	43-13124 – possible identity.	PV
☐ Percival P.56 Provost T.51 (T.1)	FM1036	P.56/020	G-AMZM	RA
☐ Percival P.56 Provost T.51 (T.1)	FM1035	P.56/040	XE506, G-23-5	PV
☐ Percival P.56 Provost T.51 (T.1)	FM1037	P.56/278	XF547	PV
☐ Rakan Musa RMX-4			Fuselage only.	PV
☐ Rand-Robinson KR-2	9M-KPA			PV
☐ Riley Heron 2D/A2 (De Havilland D.H.114 Heron 2D)	'FM1054'	14144	FM1061	PVX
☐ Rotorway Executive				PV
☐ Rotorway Scorpion	9M-ARY			PV
☐ Scottish Aviation Bulldog 102	M25-08	BH102/150	FM1229	PV
☐ Scottish Aviation Bulldog 102	M25-10	BH102/160	See Alor Setar.	PVD
☐ Scottish Aviation Pioneer 2	FM1016	154		PV
☐ Scottish Aviation Twin Pioneer 1	FM1001	529	G-APJT	PV
☐ Sud-Est SE.3160 Alouette III	FM1316	1303	FM1087	PV
☐ Westland Wasp HAS.1	M499-04	F9666	XT784	PV

The spectacular Kuala Lumpur skyline can seen behind this de Havilland Caribou which is at the Royal Malaysian Air Force Museum at Sungai Besi. (Lloyd Robinson)

This armed Provost is on show in the Defence Services Museum in Yangon. (Peter R.Arnold)

A general view of the aircraft park at the Armed Forces Museum in Oman. (Martin Cassidy)

This Strikemaster is on show at the Armed Forces Museum in Oman. (Martin Cassidy)

MONGOLIA

CHOIR AIR BASE MONUMENT (MON1)

Address:	Choir.
Admission:	On peramnent view.
Location:	About 15 km north of the town.

The base was constructed by the Soviet Union, when there was tension with China, and used until 1992. The site is now derelict and a large statue of a Soviet Warrior remains along with a pole mounted MiG-21.

TYPE	REG/SER	CON. NO.	PI/NOTES	STATUS
☐ Mikoyan-Gurevich MiG-21				PV

MILITARY AIRCRAFT MUSEUM (MON2)

Address:	Choybalsan Air Force Base.
Admission:	By prior permission only.
Location:	About 5 km north east of the town.

Aviation started in Mongolia with the arrival of a Junkers F 13 in 1925. A military air service was established soon after and at the current time due to the collapse of the Soviet Union and huge debts little flying takes place. A collection of aircraft is being assembled at the base and the aim is to set up a museum.

TYPE	REG/SER	CON. NO.	PI/NOTES	STATUS
☐ Mikoyan-Gurevich MiG-15	25			RA
☐ Mikoyan-Gurevich MiG-15UTI				RA
☐ Mikoyan-Gurevich MiG-21PFM	137			RA
☐ Mil Mi-4	1100			RA
☐ Mil Mi-24V				RA
☐ Yakovlev Yak-18U	TAA13			RA

MONGOLIAN MILITARY MUSEUM (MON3)

Address:	Lkhagvasuren Gudamzh, Ulaanbaatar.
Tel:	454492
Admission:	Summer 1000-1800; Winter 0900-1700.
Location:	About 2 km east of the city centre.

This excellent museum opened in 1996 and has a wide range of exhibits from pre-historic to modern times. The exploits of the warriors who roamed the steppes and raided into Europe are highlighted. Since the 1920s the main source of military equipment has been the Soviet Union. Inside the building are large scale models of four Polikarpov types, the R-1, R-5, I-16 and U-2 plus a Yakovlev Yak-9. In the outside park are armoured vehicles, tanks and guns. Two complete aircraft, which should join the collection, are currently at the airport.

TYPE	REG/SER	CON. NO.	PI/NOTES	STATUS
☐ Antonov An-14A	MONGOL0905	600905	At airport.	PV
☐ Ilyushin Il-2			Fuselage section only.	PVD
☐ Ilyushin Il-14M	MONGOL104		At airport.	PV
☐ Mil Mi-4				PV
☐ Mil Mi-4	1100		By 109 Squadron HQ.	RA
☐ Mil Mi-24V	00406			PV

MYANMAR

DEFENCE SERVICES MUSEUM (MY1)

Address:	Shwedagan Pagoda Street, Yangon.
Admission:	Saturday-Thursday 1000-1600.
Location:	In the northern suburbs of the city.

On April 1st 1937 Burma became a separate territory from British India. The country gained its independence in January 1948. For the next seven years Burma was beset by a series of rebellions. In the early years of independence Britain provided support to the Air Force and supplied a number of aircraft. The country changed its name to Myanmar in 1989. The Union of Burma Air Force came into being in 1953 and the initial equipment included Spitfires, Mosquitos, Oxfords and Tiger Moths. In the mid-1950s forty armed Percival Provosts were ordered and these served until the late 1960s when a batch of Lockheed AT-33s arrived. The first jet type to serve with the Air Force was the Vampire T.55. Four were delivered in September 1954 and the remaining quartet arrived the following March. This impressive museum opened in early 1996 and traces the history of the armed forces of the country. On show are photographs, documents, components, engines, flags and trophies. Over half the aircraft in the exhibition are of British origin. A Seafire and a Spitfire are parked next to each other. The Seafire was delivered in 1952 and the Spitfire arrived from Czechoslovakia three years later. The rear fuselage of another Spitfire has been used in a diorama representing the crash of a Sea Fury in Thailand on February 4th 1961. Three Sea Furies were sent to intercept an aircraft dropping supplies to insurgent forces. In the ensuing battle Pilot Officer Noel Peters was shot down and killed. Eighteen single seat and three two seat versions of the Sea Fury were delivered in 1958. Ten British built Chipmunks were supplied in the early 1950s. Three Slingsby gliders can be seen suspended from the roof. Types recently in service include the Otter, one of nine used, and one of the dozen SIAI-Marchetti SF.260s delivered in the late 1970s. Myanmar was the last country to operate the Kaman Huskie and one is on show. A recent addition is the Polish designed W-3 helicopter.

TYPE	REG/SER	CON. NO.	PI/NOTES	STATUS
☐ Beagle D5/180 Husky	UB2112			PV
☐ De Havilland D.H.82A Tiger Moth	UB156			PV
☐ De Havilland D.H.115 Vampire T.55	UB503	15478		PV
☐ De Havilland D.H.C.1 Chipmunk T.10	UB154	C1/0419	UBC10, T-154	PV
☐ De Havilland D.H.C.3 Otter	UB653	277	4653	PV
☐ Douglas DC-3A-467 Skytrain (C-47B)	'UB736'		(USAAF), RI-007 (Indonesia)	PV
☐ Hawker Sea Fury FB.11	UB471		WH585, G-9-21 – now reported as UB458.	PV
☐ Kaman K-600-3 Huskie (H-43B) (HH-43B)	UB6166		(USAF)	PV
☐ Kawasaki-Bell 47G-2	UB6082	136	UB682	PV
☐ Kawasaki-Vertol KV-107-II-4	UB6009		Possibly Vertol V-44A	PV
☐ Lockheed 580 (T-33A) (AT-33A)	T-3530		(USAF), UB530	PV
☐ Mil Mi-2	6410			PV
☐ Mil Mi-2	6412			PV
☐ Panstwowe Zaklady Lotnicze (PZL) W-3 Sokol	6508	310405		PV
☐ Percival P.56 Provost T.53	UB211	P.56/309		PV
☐ SIAI-Marchetti SF.260MB	UB2010	234/21-010		PV
☐ Slingsby T.45 Swallow	UB0014	1564		PV
☐ Slingsby T.49 Capstan	UB0006	1534		PV
☐ Slingsby T.51 Dart	UB0001	1528		PV
☐ Sud-Est SE.3160 Alouette III	UB6108	1180		PV
☐ Supermarine 361 Spitfire LF.IXe	'UB466'		(RAF) 2026 (Israeli), UB431 – rear fuselage only – Sea Fury serial.	PVX
☐ Supermarine 361 Spitfire LF.IXe	UB421	CBAF-IX-550	TE5??, 2024 (Israel)	PV
☐ Supermarine 377 Seafire F.XV	UB409	CO.9621	PR376, G-15-220	PV
☐ Supermarine 377 Seafire F.XV	'UB415'	WASE1 4106	SR462, G-15-225, UB414	RA

MINGALADON AIR BASE COLLECTION (MY2)

Address:	Mingaladon Air Base, Yangon.
Admission:	By prior permission only
Location:	In the eastern suburbs of the city.

The airfield is the main international airport for the city. One of the T-33s is parked by the gate to the military The C-47 is preserved close to the ramp and the other T-33 resides among the buildings.

TYPE	REG/SER	CON. NO.	PI/NOTES	STATUS
☐ Douglas DC-3A-467 Skytrain (C-47B)				RA
☐ Lockheed 580 (T-33A)				RA
☐ Lockheed 580 (T-33A)	3514			RA

NORTH KOREA

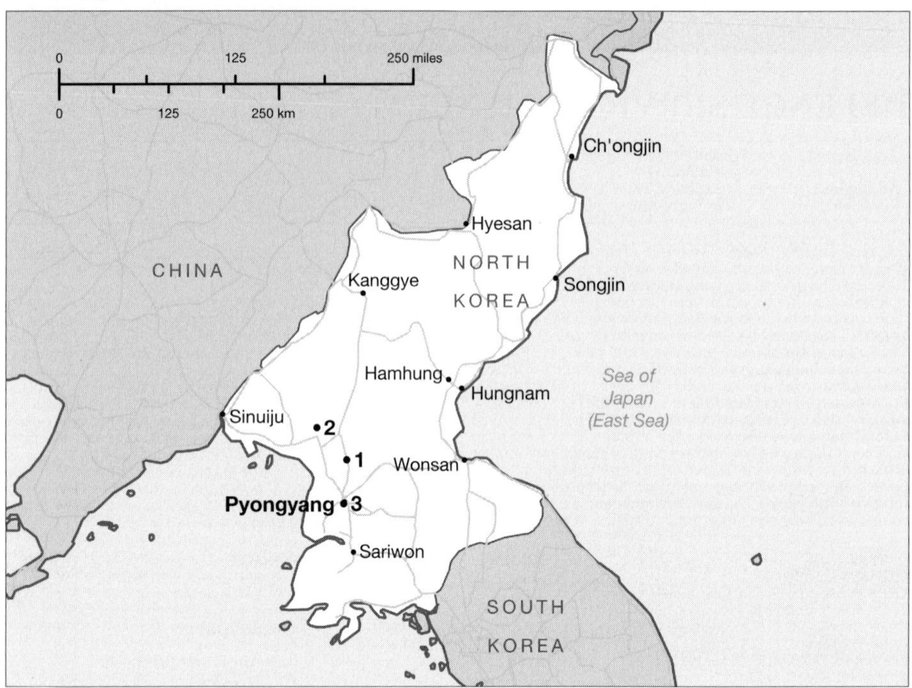

SUNCHON AIR BASE MONUMENT (NK1)

Address:	Sunchon.
Admission:	By prior permission only.
Location:	About 3 km west of the town.

The North Korean Air Force has operated a variety of Soviet and Chinese designed types. Sukhoi Su-25s were flown from Sunchon. The Yak-18 is preserved by the Officer's Mess.

TYPE	REG/SER	CON. NO.	PI/NOTES	STATUS
☐ Yakovlev Yak-18				RA

TAECHON COLLECTION (NK2)

Address:	Taechon.
Admission:	By prior permission only.
Location:	South east of the town.

Three aircraft appear to be preserved near the town. The Li-2 is perched on a ridge overlooking a valley and the two MiG's are in a compound nearby. Further information would be most welcome.

TYPE	REG/SER	CON. NO.	PI/NOTES	STATUS
☐ Lisunov Li-2 [Douglas DC-3 modified]				RA
☐ Mikoyan-Gurevich MiG-17				RA
☐ Mikoyan-Gurevich MiG-21				RA

VICTORIOUS FATHERLAND LIBERATION WAR MUSEUM (NK3)

Address:	Pyongyang.
Admission:	By prior permission only for foreigners.
Location:	In the city centre near the river.

The Korean Peninsula was a unified country for many centuries. The rulers adopted an isolationist policy and few foreigners visited the area. In 1910 Japan forcibly took over the state and it remained in their control until 1945. During this time military airfields were constructed and occupied by the Imperial Japanese forces. At the end of World War II the country was divided with the Soviet Union occupying the land to the north of the 38th Parallel and the United States the area to the south. In June 1950 forces from the north crossed the boundary and invaded the south. A bitter three-year war followed with the major powers backing their respective sides. After the 1953 armistice North Korea became virtually isolated from the west. Tourists are not normally allowed to visit the country. This vast museum traces the military history of the state since it came into being on September 9th 1948. There are also some exhibits from earlier periods with many weapons and items of military clothing to be seen. On view are a number of types flown by the service. The Yakovlev Yak-9, which equipped the first fighter regiment in the country, was used by the communist forces at the start of the Korean War. This fighter derived from the Yak-7 first flew in 1942 and was soon put into production. And the last examples left the factory in 1948. MiG-15s made their first combat appearance in this conflict and three are displayed. This famous fighter was unknown in the west until seen by American pilots. Over fifty Yak-18s were used for basic flying training by the North Korean forces and they were in service for many years. One hall exhibits the wreckage of U.S. aircraft shot down and a Bell 47 which strayed over the border.

TYPE	REG/SER	CON. NO.	PI/NOTES	STATUS
☐ Bell 47D-1 Sioux (H-13E) (OH-13E)				PV
☐ Bell 205 Iroquois (UH-1D)				PVD
☐ Douglas AD-4N Skyraider				PVD
☐ Grumman G-79 Panther (F9F-2)			(USN)	PVD
☐ Lavochkin La-9				PV
☐ Mikoyan-Gurevich MiG-15bis	009			PV
☐ Mikoyan-Gurevich MiG-15bis	1032			PV
☐ Mikoyan-Gurevich MiG-15bis	25		In North Korean markings.	PV
☐ North American NA-190 Sabre (F-86D)	52-10031	190-756		PVD
☐ Vought F4U-4 Corsair				PVD
☐ Yakovlev Yak-9P				PV
☐ Yakovlev Yak-18	03			PV

OMAN

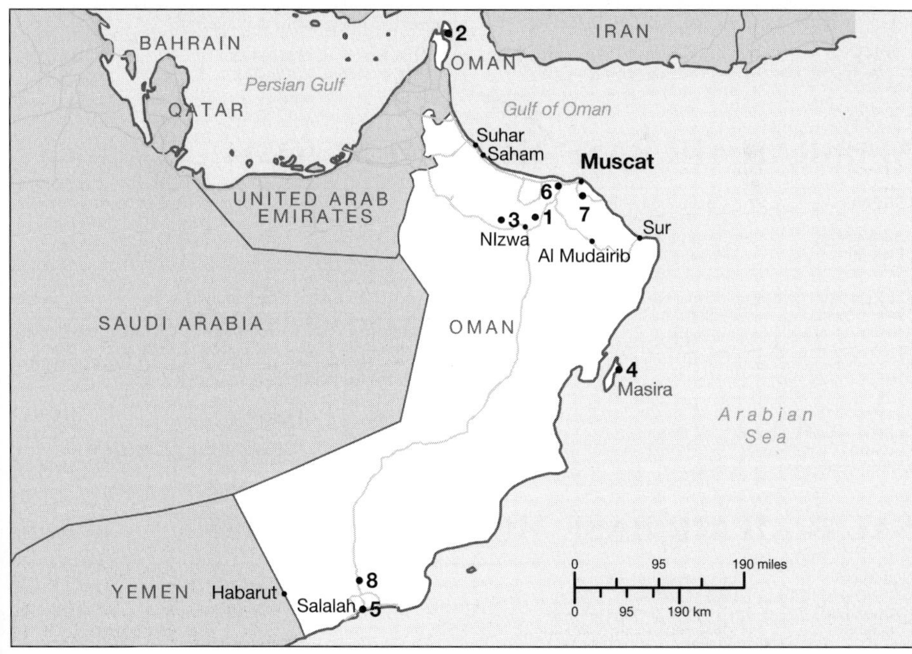

GHALLAH AIR BASE MONUMENT (OM1)

Address:	Commanding Officer, RAFO Ghallah.
Admission:	By prior permission only.
Location:	Just south of the town.

Three aircraft are preserved at this military base. The two Hunters are parked on the main parade ground with the Strikemaster nearby. Both Hawker aircraft were refurbished in England before going to Jordan.

TYPE	REG/SER	CON. NO.	PI/NOTES	STATUS
☐ British Aircraft Corporation 167 Strikemaster 82A	420	EEP/JP/3258	G-27-222	RA
☐ Hawker P.1099 Hunter F.73 (F.6) (FGA.9)	825		XG255, 825 (Jordan)	RA
☐ Hawker P.1099 Hunter F.73A (P.1067 Hunter F.4)	844	HABL 003104	XF936, G-9-255, 844 (Jordan)	RA

KHASAB AIR BASE MONUMENT (OM2)

Address:	Commanding Officer RAFO Khasab.
Admission:	By prior permission only.
Location:	Just west of the town.

Khasab is currently home to a squadron operating Agusta-Bell 205 helicopters. A Dutch built Hunter has been preserved as a monument at the field which also handles civil flights.

TYPE	REG/SER	CON. NO.	PI/NOTES	STATUS
☐ Hawker P.1101 Hunter T.67 (P.1099 Hunter F.6)	803	8930	N-257 (Netherlands), G-9-266, 219 (Kuwait)	RA

LANSAB AIR BASE MONUMENT (OM3)

Address:	Commanding Officer, RAFO Lansab
Admission:	By prior permission only.
Location:	About 20 km south west of Muscat.

The Air Force ordered twenty five Strikemasters and they served at both Masirah and Salalah. They type was withdrawn from service in January 2000. One has been preserved as a monument at this base.

TYPE	REG/SER	CON. NO.	PI/NOTES	STATUS
☐ British Aircraft Corporation 167 Strikemaster 82A	418	EEP/JP/3256	G-27-220	RA

MASIRAH AIR BASE MONUMENT (OM4)

Address:	Commanding Officer, RAFO Masirah.
Admission:	By prior permission only
Location:	Just north east of Dhuwwah.

The Royal Air Force set up a flying boat facility here in the early 1930s. Masirah was used by Imperial Airways on their services to India. An airfield was constructed in 1943 and R.A.F. bomber squadrons arrived. At the end of World War II the airfield saw use by many airlines including B.O.A.C., Skyways, Lancashire Aircraft Corporation, Ethiopian Airlines and Indian Overseas Airlines. The facilities were improved in the early 1960s and the Royal Air Force kept a presence with detachments of fighters and bombers. Masirah was the last R.A.F base in the Gulf and this closed in March 1977. The airfield is now home to squadrons operating the British Aerospace Hawk, Pilatus PC.9s and the Pakistani built Super Mushshak.

TYPE	REG/SER	CON. NO.	PI/NOTES	STATUS
☐ British Aircraft Corporation 167 Strikemaster 82A	414	EEP/JP/3252	G-27-216	RA
☐ Hawker P.1101 Hunter T.67 (P.1099 Hunter F.6)	804	41H/679905	XE530, G-9-267, 220 (Kuwait)	RA

SALALAH AIR BASE MONUMENT (OM5)

Address:	Commanding Officer RAFO Salalah.
Admission:	By prior permission only.
Location:	Just north of the town.

Salalah is a former Royal Air Force base which was turned over to the Omani forces in the 1970s. Helicopter and transport units are now in residence. Two aircraft have been preserved as monuments.

TYPE	REG/SER	CON. NO.	PI/NOTES	STATUS
☐ British Aircraft Corporation 167 Strikemaster 82A	417	EEP/JP/3255	G-27-219	RA
☐ Hawker P.1099 Hunter F.73A (P.1067 Hunter F.4)	847	HABL 003123	XF968, G-9-264, 847 (Jordan)	RA

SEEB AIR BASE MONUMENT (OM6)

Address:	Commanding Officer, RAFO Seeb.
Admission:	By prior permission only.
Location:	About 20 km west of Muscat.

Seeb is a former Royal Air Force base which is now home to helicopter and transport units. A former R.A.F. Hunter which arrived in Oman via Jordan is preserved by the main gate as a monument.

TYPE	REG/SER	CON. NO.	PI/NOTES	STATUS
☐ Hawker P.1099 Hunter F.73A (F.6)	831	41H/688062	XJ645, G-9-274, 831 (Jordan)	RA

SULTANATE OF OMAN ARMED FORCES MUSEUM (OM7)

Address:	Office of Chief of Administration and Logistics, P.O. Box 113, Muscat, Sultanate of Oman.
Tel:	612645
Admission:	Sunday, Monday, Wednesday,Thursday 0830-1300; Thursday 1600-1800.
Location:	Off Bait Al Falaj Road 9 in the city.

Housed in one of the oldest buildings in Muscat, this museum traces the history of the military forces in the country. In the 1840s the site was used as the summer home for the local rulers. From World War I until 1978 it was the Headquarters of the Omani army. The idea of a museum was put forward in the 1980s when the gathering of material started. The display opened in the early 1990s and an impressive collection of military hardware, uniforms, documents and photographs can be seen. Several military vehicles, tanks and large guns are on show. The Sultan of Oman's Air Force was formed in 1959 with mainly British personnel. The first combat types were acquired in the late 1960s and most aircraft have been of British origin. Six aircraft are on show at the museum. The Beaver and Provost were purchased in the United Kingdom in the late 1980s and have been painted in false colours to represent machines which served in the area. The Fokker built Hunter was later used by Jordan before arriving in Oman. Twenty seven Agusta-Bell 205A's were delivered in the 1970s and the composite airframe displayed carries the serial of the first of this batch. The BAC Strikemaster flew as a front line type for many years and the last were withdrawn from use in early 2000.

TYPE	REG/SER	CON. NO.	PI/NOTES	STATUS
☐ Agusta-Bell 205A	'701'		Composite	PVX
☐ British Aircraft Corporation 167 Strikemaster 82A	'023'	EEP/JP/3886	G-27-252,423	PVX
☐ De Havilland D.H.C.2 Beaver AL.1	'213'	1489	XP824	PVX
☐ Hawker P.1099 Hunter FGA.73B (F.6)	841	8964	N-279 (Dutch), G-9-287, 541 (Jordan)	PV
☐ Percival P.56 Provost T.1	'XF868'	P.56/057	WV494, 7922M, G-BGSB	PVX
☐ Short SC.7-3M-400 Skyvan	904	SH.1877	G-14-49	PV

THUMRAIT AIR BASE MONUMENT (OM8)

Address:	Commanding Officer RAFO Thumrait.
Admission:	By prior permission only.
Location:	Just north of the town.

In recent years this important airfield has been used by both Royal Air Force and United States Air Force aircraft. For several years the Omani Air Force operated Hunters from the site but these were replaced by the Jaguar in the late 1970s and the type is still in residence. A Hunter and a Strikemaster are preserved as monuments in a landscaped area next to the road from the main gate to the hangars. In addition to the Jaguar units a squadron flying the General Dynamics F-16 is now based at Thumrait.

TYPE	REG/SER	CON. NO.	PI/NOTES	STATUS
☐ British Aircraft Corporation 167 Strikemaster 82	403	EEP/JP/405	G-27-104	RA
☐ Hawker P.1099 Hunter F.73 (F.6) (F.60)	'450'	S4U 3327	XF450, G9-211, 603 (Saudi Arabia), 723	RAX

PAKISTAN

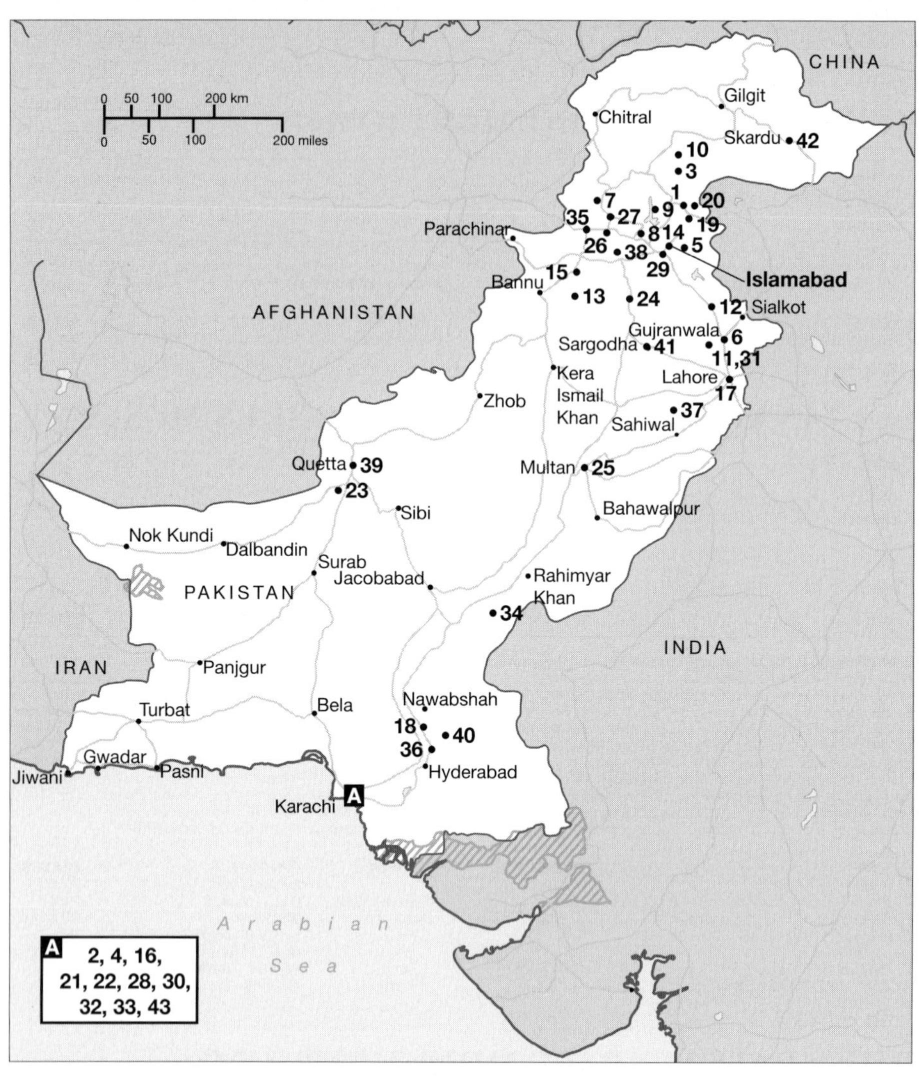

ABBOTTABAD PUBLIC SCHOOL AND COLLEGE MEMORIAL (PAK1)

Address:	Abbottabad 25000.
Admission:	By prior permission only.
Location:	In the north eastern part of the town.

This school was set up by Pakistani Railways in 1959 but after two years they relinquished control. Many former pupils have served with the military and the F-6 is preserved as a memorial to them.

TYPE	REG/SER	CON. NO.	PI/NOTES	STATUS
☐ Shenyang F-6 [Mikoyan-Gurevich MiG-19SF]	7628			

BAQAI CADET COLLEGE MEMORIAL (PAK2)

Address:	Gadap Road, Off Super Highway, Karachi 74600.
Tel:	021-441-0258
Fax:	021-441-0321
Email:	bcc@baqai.edu.pk
Admission:	By prior permission only.
Location:	In the north eastern suburbs of the city.

The Baqai Foundation is a charitable organisation which has set up a number of hospitals and dental schools. They also run the Cadet College which has a Shenyang F-6 as a memorial to former students.

TYPE	REG/SER	CON. NO.	PI/NOTES	STATUS
☐ Shenyang F-6 [Mikoyan-Gurevich MiG-19SF]	5548			RA

BATRASI SCOUT CADET COLLEGE MEMORIAL (PAK3)

Address:	Mansehra Post Office 21330.
Tel:	0987-550284
Fax:	0987-550281
Email:	info@pscc.edu.pk
Admission:	By prior permission only.
Location:	In the town.

The Scout Association purchased the land in 1960 with the aim of constructing a residential school. However, it was not until 1996 that the college opened. An F-6 is preserved in the grounds.

TYPE	REG/SER	CON. NO.	PI/NOTES	STATUS
☐ Shenyang F-6 [Mikoyan-Gurevich MiG-19SF]	9622			RA

CENTRAL ORDNANCE DEPOT MEMORIAL (PAK4)

Address:	New Town, Karachi 74800.
Admission:	By prior permission only.
Location:	In the northern part of the city.

The depot stores and maintains weapons for all branches of the services. One aircraft, a Shenyang F-6, and a number of vehicles serve as a memorial to personnel who have lost their lives.

TYPE	REG/SER	CON. NO.	PI/NOTES	STATUS
☐ Shenyang F-6 [Mikoyan-Gurevich MiG-19SF]	1505			RA

CHAKLALA AIR FORCE BASE COLLECTION (PAK5)

Address:	Chaklala Cantonment, Chaklala, Rawalpindi 46200.
Admission:	By prior permission only.
Location:	About 5 km east of the city.

The Headquarters of the Air Force was for many years located at this important base not far from the capital, Islamabad. Now the command has moved into buildings in the city. Transport and communications squadrons are currently in residence. Amongst the types operated are the Lockheed C-130 Hercules, Harbin Y-12s, Cessna 172s and MFI-17s. The collection of preserved aircraft parked around the site includes the sole Beech Twin Bonanza flown by the force. The Shenyang F-6 was a front line fiighter for many years.

TYPE	REG/SER	CON. NO.	PI/NOTES	STATUS
☐ Beech G50 Twin Bonanza	GH-112	GH-112		RA
☐ Canadair CL-13B Sabre 6 [North American F-86E]	1733	1733	(Germany)	RA
☐ Lockheed 580 (T-33A)	'53-9195'	580-7261	52-5195	RAX
☐ Shenyang F-6 [Mikoyan-Gurevich MiG-19S]	1825			RA

CHAWINDA WAR MEMORIAL (PAK6)

Address:	Chawinda 51310.
Admission:	On permanent view
Location:	In the centre of the town.

The memorial honours all service men who have lost their lives in conflicts since Pakistan gained its independence. On show is one of the batch of Canadian built Sabres supplied via Germany.

TYPE	REG/SER	CON. NO.	PI/NOTES	STATUS
☐ Canadair CL-13B Sabre 6 [North American F-86E]	1655	1655	BB+???, JB+248	PV

DIR MUSEUM (PAK7)

Address:	University of Malakand, Chakdara, Dir 18000.
Tel:	0936-761446
Admission:	Daily 1000-1700.
Location:	In the town.

The exhibits at this museum mainly consist of archaeological items found in the area. A series of digs was carried out in the late 1960s. The Chinese built MiG is displayed in the university grounds.

TYPE	REG/SER	CON. NO.	PI/NOTES	STATUS
☐ Shenyang F-6 [Mikoyan-Gurevich MiG-19S]	8912			PV

GHULAM ISHAQ KHAN INSTITUTE MEMORIAL (PAK8)

Address:	Topi 23640.
Tel:	0938-271858
Fax:	0938-271877
Admission:	By prior permission only.
Location:	In the eastern part of the town.

The institute offer courses in many fields of engineering, science and technology. In January 2008 a Cessna T-37C crashed in the grounds killing the pilot and a local resident. The Chengdu F-6 has been preserved as a memorial and plaques and flags commemorate the recent losses of life.

TYPE	REG/SER	CON. NO.	PI/NOTES	STATUS
☐ Shenyang F-6 [Mikoyan-Gurevich MiG-19SF]	4126			RA

HASAN ABDAL CADET COLLEGE MEMORIAL (PAK9)

Address:	Hasan Abdal 43730.
Tel:	057-252-0200
Email:	info@ccha.edu.pk
Admission:	By prior permission ony.
Location:	In the western part of the town.

The college was set up in 1954 and was the first in the country to train students for service in the military forces. There are a number of memorials around the grounds including a tank and the F-6.

TYPE	REG/SER	CON. NO.	PI/NOTES	STATUS
☐ Shenyang F-6 [Mikoyan-Gurevich MiG-19SF]	5551			RA

HAZARA UNIVERSITY MEMORIAL (PAK10)

Address:	Mansehra 21300.
Tel:	0997-53072
Admission:	By prior permission only.
Location:	About 14 km north of the town.

This university was set up in the 1990s and now offer courses in a wide range of subjects. A Shenyang F-6 has been put on display to remind students of the strong military heritage in Pakistan.

TYPE	REG/SER	CON. NO.	PI/NOTES	STATUS
☐ Shenyang F-6 [Mikoyan-Gurevich MiG-19SF]	8919			RA

INTER SERVICES SELECTION BOARD – GUJRANWALA MEMORIAL (PAK11)

Address:	Gujranwala Cantonnment, Gujranwala 52250.
Tel:	055-386-6036
Admission:	By prior permission only.
Location:	In the western part of the town.

The board has offices in a number of locations around the country. Candidates undergo tests and sit exams at these centres. The Sabre is parked by the building to serve as a reminder of the traditions of the services.

TYPE	REG/SER	CON. NO.	PI/NOTES	STATUS
☐ North American NA-227 Sabre (F-86F)	55-3854	227-39		RA

JHELUM CANTONMENT MEMORIAL (PAK12)

Address:	GT Road, Jhelum 49600.
Admission:	By prior permission only.
Location:	In the southern part of the town.

The camp was built by the British in the mid-nineteenth century. A number of battles were fought in the area and in 1857 thirty five British soldiers were killed. The F-6 serves as a memorial to all local conflicts.

TYPE	REG/SER	CON. NO.	PI/NOTES	STATUS
☐ Shenyang F-6 [Mikoyan-Gurevich MiG-19SF]	1910			RA

KALABAGH AIR FORCE BASE MEMORIAL (PAK13)

Address:	Kalabagh 42200.
Admission:	By prior permission only.
Location:	Just north of the town.

The Air Force has a base at the field which also serves as the civil airport for the region. The Canadian built Sabre is preserved as a monument to those who have served over the years at Kalabargh over the years.

TYPE	REG/SER	CON. NO.	PI/NOTES	STATUS
☐ Canadair CL-13B Sabre 6 [North American F-86E]	1790	1790	JB+125	RA

KAMRA – MINHAS AIR FORCE BASE COLLECTION (PAK14)

Address:	Kamra 43301.
Admission:	By prior permission only
Location:	About 10 km south east of Basia,

The field is named after Pilot Officer Rashid Minhas who gained the Nishan-E-Haider award for gallantry. On August 20th 1971 he was a student pilot preparing for a lesson. He was knocked out by his instructor who wished to defect to India in a Lockheed T-33. Minhas regained consciousness and struggled to gain control. He successfully achieved his aim and deliberately crashed the aircraft to prevent it crossing the border.

TYPE	REG/SER	CON. NO.	PI/NOTES	STATUS
☐ North American NA-176 Sabre (F-86F)	51-13315	176-246	51-13315, C.5-54 (Spain)	RA
☐ Pakistan Aeronautical Complex Mushshak [Svenska Aeroplan Aktiebolaget – Malmo Flygindustri (SAAB-MFI) 17 Supporter]				RA
☐ Shenyang F-6 [Mikoyan-Gurevich MiG-19S]	10606			RA

KOHAT AIR FORCE BASE COLLECTION (PAK15)

Address: Kohat 26000.
Admission: By prior permission only.
Location: In the south western suburbs of the town.

Kohat was built in 1922 as one of the stations serving the North West Frontier. Types operated included the B,E.2c, Bristol F.2Bs, D.H.9s and the Westland Wapiti. During World War II fighter squadrons with Hurricanes and Spitfires took up residence. The Pakistani Air Force took over in 1948 and for a time it was used for training purposes. The last operational squadron operating Hawker Fury monoplanes left during 1963. The base is now held in reserve and sees occasional use.

TYPE	REG/SER	CON. NO.	PI/NOTES	STATUS
☐ Canadair CL-13B Sabre 6 [North American F-86E]	1595	1595	BB+165, BB+365,JB+122	RA
☐ North American NA-227 Sabre (F-86F)	55-4018	227-203	55-4018, (Germany)	RA
☐ Shenyang F-6 [Mikoyan-Gurevich MiG-19S]	4109			RA
☐ Shenyang F-6 [Mikoyan-Gurevich MiG-19S]	9625			RA

KORANGI CREEK AIR FORCE BASE COLLECTION (PAK16)

Address: Karachi 75200.
Tel: 021-509-0246
Location: In the southern suburbs of the city.

The base, built by the Royal Air Force in 1923, also served as a logistics base for the aircraft repair depot at Drigh Road with many items arriving by sea or air. The R.A.F. remained at the site until 1949. A technical school was set up by the Pakistani Air Force and for many years engineering officers received their training at Korangi Creek. This unit was moved to the academy at Risalpur in 1986. Now the site is home to schools training senior N.C.O.'s and instructors.

TYPE	REG/SER	CON. NO.	PI/NOTES	STATUS
☐ Canadair CL-13B Sabre 6 [North American F-86E]	1810	1810	JB+368	RA
☐ North American NA-202 Sabre (F-86F)	53-1176	202-105		RA
☐ Shenyang F-6 [Mikoyan-Gurevich MiG-19S]	1419			RA
☐ Shenyang F-6 [Mikoyan-Gurevich MiG-19S]	1617			RA
☐ Shenyang F-6 [Mikoyan-Gurevich MiG-19S]	4107			RA

LAHORE AIR FORCE BASE MEMORIAL (PAK17)

Address: Lahore 54600.
Tel: 042-950-7961
Fax: 042-950-7965
Email: prolhrpaf@yahoo.com
Admission: By prior permission only.
Location: In the south eastern part of the city.

Before partition the airfield was used as a maintenance depot by the Indian Air Force. The Pakistan Air Force based transport aircraft at Lahore for a time but it is now the site of a college and a defence systems unit.

TYPE	REG/SER	CON. NO.	PI/NOTES	STATUS
☐ Canadair CL-13B Sabre 6 [North American F-86E]	1670	1670	JB+105 – at nearby Army Camp.	RA
☐ North American NA-176 Sabre (F-86F)	51-13407	176-338		RA

LARKANA CADET COLLEGE MEMORIAL (PAK18)

Address: P.O. Box 40, Larkana 77150.
Tel: 0741-480091
Fax: 0741-480460
Admission: By prior permission only.
Location: In the town.

The setting up of this college was first put forward in 1975 but due to the turbulent political situation it did not open until 1993. A Shenyang F-6 is on show in the grounds as a memorial to former students.

TYPE	REG/SER	CON. NO.	PI/NOTES	STATUS
☐ Shenyang F-6 [Mikoyan-Gurevich MiG-19SF]	5531			RA

The only Twin Bonanza used by the Pakistan Air Force is preserved at Chaklala Air Force Base. (Paul Harrison Photography).

This Canadair built Sabre is preserved at Kalabargh Air Force Base. (Paul Harrison Photography).

This Martin built Canberra is preserved at Masroor Air Force Base. (David Holman)

LAWRENCE COLLEGE MEMORIAL (PAK19)

Address:	Ghora Gali, Murree 47150.
Tel:	051-926-9056
Email:	info@lawrence.edu.pk
Admission:	By prior permission only.
Location:	In the northern part of the town.

The school was set up in the 1850s to provide education for the sons of British soldiers killed on duty. Many former pupils served with the British, Indian and Pakistani forces. The F-6 serves as a memorial to these.

TYPE	REG/SER	CON. NO.	PI/NOTES	STATUS
☐ Shenyang F-6 [Mikoyan-Gurevich MiG-19SF]	8923			RA

LOWER TOPA AIR FORCE BASE MEMORIAL (PAK20)

Address:	Murree Hills, Lower Topa 47150.
Admission:	By prior permission only.
Location:	In the north eastern part of the town.

In the 1930s the British established a military training facility at Lower Topa. This tradition carried on after independence and now the base carries out many administrative tasks and an Air Force school is nearby.

TYPE	REG/SER	CON. NO.	PI/NOTES	STATUS
☐ North American NA-191 Sabre (F-86F)	52-5031	191-727		RA

MALIR AIR FORCE BASE COLLECTION (PAK21)

Address:	Malir, Karachi 75070.
Admission:	By prior permission only
Location:	In the eastern suburbs of the city.

Malir was set up in 1948 as a signals and radar training station and has expanded greatly since. One task is to maintain units around the country in a state of residence. Several military schools are on the base including the main training establishment for artillery. A large town has grown up and the preserved aircraft are positioned at a number of locations around the vast site.

TYPE	REG/SER	CON. NO.	PI/NOTES	STATUS
☐ Canadair CL-13B Sabre 6 [North American F-86E]	1627	1627	BB+367, JA+113	RA
☐ Canadair CL-13B Sabre 6 [North American F-86E]	1693	1693	(Germany) – At School of Artillery.	RA
☐ Canadair CL-13B Sabre 6 [North American F-86E]	1722	1722	(Germany)	RA
☐ Canadair CL-13B Sabre 6 [North American F-86E]	1764	1764	BB+272	RA
☐ Shenyang F-6 [Mikoyan-Gurevich MiG-19S]	7839			RA

MASROOR-RAFFIQUI AIR FORCE BASE COLLECTION (PA22)

Address:	Karachi 75750.
Tel:	021-243-5800
Admission:	By prior permission only.
Location:	About 10 km west of the city.

The airfield was constructed in 1940/1 to serve as a temporary transit post and transport base for units of the United States Army Air Corps. In the years just after World War II this base, then called Mauripur, was home to R.A.F. squadrons. Units flying the Dakota were present from October 1945 until 1947 and Halifax transports and Tempests also spent a short time at the field. Just prior to partition Dakotas of No. 6 Squadron of the Indian Air Force were in residence. The R.A.F. maintained a presence until the 1955 as many transport flights staged through the field. When Pakistan was constituted in July 1947 a communications squadron using Austers, Harvards, a Viking, a Dakota and a pair of Doves was set up. In 1967 the station was renamed after the base commanding officer Masroor Hussain, killed when his B-57 Canberra suffered a bird strike. The collection of preserved aircraft is dispersed around the airfield and the camp. In 1951 the United States Air Force selected the Canberra as a night intruder bomber but the English Electric factories did not have the capacity for the order so the Martin company was selected to build the aircraft under licence. Just over four hundred variants of the type were built in the U.S.A. Twenty five B-57Bs were acquired by Pakistan in 1959.

TYPE	REG/SER	CON. NO.	PI/NOTES	STATUS
☐ Canadair CL-13B Sabre 6 [North American F-86E]	1629	1629	BB+369, JA+115 (?), JD+243	RA
☐ Canadair CL-13B Sabre 6 [North American F-86E]	1754	1754	BB+176, JB+234	RA
☐ Canadair CL-13B Sabre 6 [North American F-86E]	1769	1769	(Germany)	RA
☐ Canadair CL-13B Sabre 6 [North American F-86E]	1789	1789	(Germany)	RA
☐ Dassault Mirage IIIO(A) (IIIO(F))	503		(Australia).	RA
☐ Lockheed 183-93-02 Starfighter (F-104A)	56-0879	183-1167		RA
☐ Lockheed 580 (T-33A)	58-0451	580-1500		RA
☐ Lockheed 580 (T-33A)	53-5127	580-8466		RA
☐ Martin 272B Canberra (B-57B)	53-947	300	53-3947	RA
☐ Martin 272B Canberra (B-57B)	53-956	309	53-3956	RA
☐ Shenyang FT-5	71-0203			RA
☐ Shenyang FT-5			In Children's Park on base.	RA
☐ Shenyang J-6 [Mikoyan-Gurevich MiG-19SF]	3811			RA

MASTUNG CADET COLLEGE MEMORIAL (PAK23)

Address: HCD Road, Mastung.
Email: info@ccm.edu.pk
Admission: By prior permission only.
Location: About 5 km west of the town.

The idea of a military college was put forward in the late 1970s and the first sixty students were admitted in 1987. A withdrawn Shenyang F-6 is preserved as a memorial to former students who have lost their lives.

TYPE	REG/SER	CON. NO.	PI/NOTES	STATUS
☐ Shenyang F-6 [Mikoyan-Gurevich MiG-19SF]	1911			RA

MIANWALI AIR FORCE BASE MEMORIAL (PAK24)

Address: Mianwali 42200.
Admission: By prior permission only.
Location: In the southern suburbs of the town.

The World War II airfield at Mianwali was derelict for about twenty years. In the 1960s construction of a new fighter base began and was activated in 1971. Units were soon in conflict with Indian Air Force aircraft and also attacked ground targets.

TYPE	REG/SER	CON. NO.	PI/NOTES	STATUS
☐ Shenyang F-6 [Mikoyan-Gurevich MiG-19SF]	7712			RA

No. 2 CORPS HEADQUARTERS MONUMENT (PAK25)

Address: Multan 60700.
Admission: By prior permission only.
Location: In the town.

Multan is the headquarters of the Army unit which has responsibility for a number of armoured and infantry units. The Sabre is preserved at the complex along with military vehicles.

TYPE	REG/SER	CON. NO.	PI/NOTES	STATUS
☐ North American NA-202 Sabre (F-86F)	53-1216	202-145		RA

NOWSHERA GARRISON HEADQUARTERS MEMORIAL (PAK26)

Address: Nowshera 24100.
Admission: By prior permission only.
Location: In the centre of the town.

There has been an Army presence in the town since the British set up a cantonment. The Pakistan School of Artillery is located here and the F-6 is displayed by the Headquarters building.

TYPE	REG/SER	CON. NO.	PI/NOTES	STATUS
☐ Shenyang F-6 [Mikoyan-Gurevich MiG-19SF]	5356			RA

PAKISTAN AIR FORCE ACADEMY COLLECTION (PAK27)

Address: Risalpur 24080.
Admission: By prior permission only.
Location: In the north western suburbs of the city.

The Royal Air Force set up a base at Risalpur in the 1920s and patrols along the North West Frontier were carried out. The field was home to both training and fighter units during World War II. For a period before partition Royal Indian Air Force Spitfires were in residence. The Pakistan Air Force soon set up a flying training school and in the early 1980s a decision was made to set up the academy. New buildings were erected and units moved in from around the country. There are now four main units at the site. These are the College of Flying Training, the College of Aeronautical Engineering, the Flying Instructors School and the Parachute Training School. The collection of preserved aircraft represents types flown by graduates of the academy. The aircraft currently used for training are the Cessna T-37, the Mushshak and the K-8. The Mushshak is a locally assembled verson of the SAAB MFI-17 Supporter. The K-8 jet is a joint venture between Pakistan and China. The prototype flew in 1990 and several examples have been exported.

TYPE	REG/SER	CON. NO.	PI/NOTES	STATUS
☐ Lockheed 183-93-02 Starfighter (F-104A)	56-875	183-1163	56-0875	RA
☐ Lockheed 580 (T-33A) (RT-33A)	53-5533	580-8872		RA
☐ North American NA-168 Texan (T-6G)	T4246			RA
☐ North American NA-193 Sabre (F-86F)	52-5412	193-141		RA
☐ North American NA-202 Sabre (F-86F)	53-1163	202-92		RA
☐ Shenyang FT-5	0103			RA
☐ Shenyang F-6 [Mikoyan-Gurevich MiG-19S]	1918	1918		RA

PAKISTAN AIR FORCE MUSEUM (PAK28)

Address: Sharea-Faisal Air Force Base,
Faisal Road,
Karachi 74350.
Tel: 021-921-8326
Fax: 021-498-9278
Email: info@pafmuseum.com.pk
Admission: Daily 0900-2200.
Location: About 15 km east of the city.

Drigh Road, opened in the 1920s, was responsible for the assembly and overhaul of all R.A.F. aircraft based in India. In the inter-war period aircraft used on North West Frontier operations often visited the station. The only resident squadron was No. 31 which moved its Westland Wapitis to the field in 1931 after an earthquake damaged its base at Quetta. The first Indian Air Force squadron was established at the field in April 1933. During World War II the resident Maintenance Units overhauled vast numbers of aircraft for front line duties. The station was handed over to Pakistan in 1947 and renamed Faisal. The first P.A.F. Museum formed at Risalpur in 1961 and moved to Peshawar the following year. In addition a Fighter Gallery containing models was established at Sargodha in 1986. In the same year the Commander at Faisal put forward a plan to set up a museum at this historic site. Approval was given in 1994 and the aim was to open on August 14th 1997, the Golden Jubilee of the country. A hangar built in 1917, and in recent times used for storage, was chosen for the exhibition. Construction of an entrance and an outside display park soon started along with renovation of the building. The story of the Air Force over the last half century is portrayed in detail. On show are many models, uniforms, badges and documents. The conflicts with India in 1965 and 1971 are highlighted with details of the aerial battles fought. The star of the aircraft collection is the Vickers Viking which was the personal transport of the founder of the country, Mohammed Ali Jinnah. The airliner arrived in Pakistan in June 1948 and was flown for several years. The twin engined transport was carefully dismantled at Peshawar and moved over one thousand miles to the museum. The Auster and Tiger Moth had suffered in storage and both have been restored to display condition. A number of the aircraft are placed on plinths in the well designed landscaped outside park and these are illuminated by floodlights at night. The Gnat force-landed in Pakistan during one of the conflicts with India. A range of types used in recent years is on show in this impressive collection and as types are withdrawn they will join the exhibition. The Douglas Invader served with the French Air Force in Indo China in the early 1950s. After a spell in storage in the Philippines it was sold for civilian use. In 1965, under American ownership, the aircraft was impounded at Karachi Airport for illegal gun running. A period of Pakistani ownership followed before it was withdrawn in 1980. Two versions of the Mirage are in the collection. In 1990 Pakistan acquired fifty Australian aircraft and the hulk of one of these is in the museum storage yard. On show is a 5PA version which was specifically designed for Pakistani use. Six Kaman Huskie helicopters were ordered for use on base rescue work. The Tiger Moth was used widely in the sub-continent by the R.A.F. and after partition and independence many were passed on to the local military. The British Taylorcraft company produced versions of the high wing monoplane both for civil and military use. The Aiglet Trainer first flew in 1951 and was fully aerobatic. The Pakistan Air Force ordered fifteen which were delivered in the early 1950s. A few were later used by civilian aero clubs. The SAAB MF-17 Supporter is derived from the Bjorn Andreasson designed MFI-9 which was produced by Malmo Flygindustri. The larger MFI-15 trainer was exported to several countries. The MFI-17 was intended for ground attack use with hardened wing points. Over a hundred kits were supplied by the Swedish company and now around three hundred locally built examples have been delivered to the Pakistan Air Force and Army plus several exports. Two damaged Scheibe SF-25 Falkes await their turn in the restoration queue. A small number of these powered gliders were used for primary pilot training. Four former Afghan Air Force types have joined the exhibition. There are several airframes in store awaiting rebuilds for the display.

TYPE	REG/SER	CON. NO.	PI/NOTES	STATUS
☐ Aero Commander 680E	892-S	892-101	AP-ALL	PV
☐ Antonov An-12	380		In Afghan markings.	RA
☐ Antonov An-26	278	47313902	276 (Afghanistan)	PV
☐ Auster J/5F Aiglet Trainer	W4108	2728		PV
☐ Beech 95 Travel Air	TD57111			PV
☐ Canadair CL-13B Sabre 6 [North American F-86E]	1626	1626	BB+366, JA+112	PV
☐ Canadair CL-13B Sabre 6 [North American F-86E]	53-1632	1632	BB+373 – on main base.	RAD
☐ Canadair CL-13B Sabre 6 [North American F-86E]	1756	1756	JB+108, JB+244 – identity doubtful.	PV
☐ Canadair CL-13B Sabre 6 [North American F-86E]	1792	1792	(Germany)	PV
☐ Canadair CL-13B Sabre 6 [North American F-86E]	1794	1794	(Germany)	RAC
☐ Canadair CL-90 Starfighter (CF-104) [Lockheed 683-04-12]	8-862	683A-1162	12862 (Canada), 104862 (Canada) – in Turkish markings.	PV
☐ Cessna 180G	AP-AOU	51322	N4622U	PV
☐ Cessna 305A Bird Dog (L-19A) (O-1A)	76012			PV
☐ Commonwealth CA-29 Mirage IIIO(A) (IIIO(F)) [Dassault Mirage III]	A3-48	CA29-48	In Australian markings.	RAD
☐ Dassault Mirage 5PA	70-424			PV
☐ De Havilland D.H.82A Tiger Moth	D501			PV
☐ Douglas A-26B Invader	AP-AVV	27847	44-34568, 434568 (France), N202PP	RAC
☐ Folland Fo.141 Gnat F.1	IE1083	GT.013	In Indian markings.	PV
☐ Hovey Beta Bird	AP-BCU	1		PV
☐ Kaman K-600-3 Huskie (H-43B) (HH-43B)	4553	179	62-4553	RAD
☐ Kaman K-600-3 Huskie (H-43B) (HH-43B)	4556	182	62-4556	PV
☐ Kaman K-600-3 Huskie (H-43B) (HH-43B)				RAD
☐ Lockheed 183-93-02 Starfighter (F-104A)	56-798	183-1086		PV
☐ Lockheed 283-93-03 Starfighter (F-104B)	57-1309	283-5021		PV
☐ Lockheed 580 (T-33A)	53-259	580-8598	53-5259	PV
☐ Lockheed 580 (T-33A)	55-3113	580-9683		PV
☐ Lockheed 580 (T-33A)	T33-451	580-9895	55-4451	PV
☐ Lockheed 580 (T-33A)	56-601	580-9951	56-1601	PV
☐ Lockheed 580 (T-33A)	55-216			PV
☐ Lockheed 580 (T-33A) (RT-33A)	53-5090	580-8429		PV
☐ Martin 272B Canberra (B-57B)	957	310	53-3957, 53-11957	PV
☐ Martin 272C Canberra (B-57C)	53-3846	237		RAD
☐ Mikoyan-Gurevich MiG-21bis	957		In Afghan markings.	PV
☐ Mil Mi-24		3532463615084	In Afghan markings.	RAD
☐ North American NA-168 Texan (T-6G)	T4200			PV
☐ North American NA-227 Sabre (F-86F)	628		(USAF)	PV
☐ North American NA-227 Sabre (F-86F)	55-3850	227-35	On main base gate.	PV
☐ North American NA-227 Sabre (F-86F)	55-5005	227-238		PV
☐ Pakistan Aeronautical Complex Mushshak [Svenska Aeroplan Aktiebolaget – Malmo Flygindustri (SAAB-MFI) 17 Supporter]	90-5314			PV
☐ Pazmany PL-2				PV
☐ Quickie Aircraft Quickie 2 (Rutan 54)	85-001			PV
☐ Scheibe SF-25C Falke	44139	44139	D-KDDN, AP-AYN	RAD
☐ Scheibe SF-25C Falke	44140	44140	D-KDDO, AP-AYO	RAD
☐ Shenyang F-6 [Mikoyan-Gurevich MiG-19S]	624		At nearby naval base.	PV
☐ Shenyang F-6 [Mikoyan-Gurevich MiG-19S]	1083			PV
☐ Shenyang F-6 [Mikoyan-Gurevich MiG-19S]	4120			PV
☐ Shenyang F-6 [Mikoyan-Gurevich MiG-19S]	5519			PV
☐ Shenyang F-6 [Mikoyan-Gurevich MiG-19S]	7624			RAD
☐ Shenyang F-6 [Mikoyan-Gurevich MiG-19S]	10434			PV
☐ Shenyang F-6 [Mikoyan-Gurevich MiG-19S]	47-1003			PV
☐ Shenyang F-6 [Mikoyan-Gurevich MiG-19S]	47-1606			RAD
☐ Shenyang FT-5	71-5618			PV
☐ Shenyang FT-6 [Mikoyan-Gurevich MiG-19U]	10103			PV
☐ Sud-Est SE.3160 Alouette III	1477	1477		RAD
☐ Vickers 649 Viking 1B	J-750	261		PV

PAKISTAN ARMY MUSEUM (PAK29)

Address:	Iftikhar Khan Janjua Road, Rawalpindi 46000.
Tel:	051-5613-2608
Fax:	051-5613-4965
Email:	ctahir@hotmail.com
Admission:	Daily 1000-1600.
Location:	In the southern part of the city.

The first aircraft used by the force were Auster 5s and 6s donated by the British after the country gained independence. Soon Cessna Bird Dogs and Bell H-13s were acquired and a pilot training school was established. Flying units operating a variety of rotary and fixed wing types are stationed around the country. The museum traces the history of military activity in the area from the Moghul times and many early items can be seen. The period of British rule in the Indian sub-continent is also portrayed. The development of the Pakistan Army over the last sixty years is followed in detail. On show are photographs, uniforms, documents and an impressive collection of weapons. There is a collection of military vehicles, tanks and missiles on display. The fuselage of an unknown glider is at the museum. This is believed to be of Indian design and it is in a poor condition.

TYPE	REG/SER	CON. NO.	PI/NOTES	STATUS
☐ Bell 47G-3B Sioux (OH-13S)	140	3026	63-9140	PV
☐ Bell 47G-3B Sioux (OH-13S)	146	3032	63-9146	PV
☐ Cessna 305C Bird Dog (L-19E) (O-1E)	544			PV
☐ Glider			Fuselage only.	PVD

PAKISTAN INTERNATIONAL AIRLINES PLANETARIUM – KARACHI (PAK30)

Address:	University Road, Gulshan-i-Iqbal 15, Karachi 75300.
Tel:	021-474026
Admission:	Daily 0900-1800
Location:	Just north of the city centre.

In 1946 Orient Airways was set up in Karachi and after Pakistan gained its independence it was assimilated into the new national airline. The company has set up this planetarium in the city. Regular shows take place and there is a comprehensive exhibition tracing the history of the universe. Parked outside is a Boeing 720 which flew with the company from 1974 until 1986. After a period in store it was moved to the site. There are displays tracing the history and development of the airlines and models of types flown can be seen.

TYPE	REG/SER	CON. NO.	PI/NOTES	STATUS
☐ Boeing 720-047B	AP-AXM	18749	N93151	PV

PAKISTAN INTERNATIONAL AIRLINES PLANETARIUM – LAHORE (PAK31)

Address:	University Grounds, Lake Road, Lahore 54000.
Tel:	042-210810
Admission:	Daily 0900-1800.
Location:	In the north western suburbs of the city.

The second of the planetariums established by Pakistan International Airlines is also home to a Boeing 720. Like the one at Karachi it was originally delivered to Western Airlines in the U.S.A. in the mid-1960s. The 720 was designed as a smaller and faster version of the 707 series. The prototype made its maiden flight in November 1959 and over the next five years one hundred and fifty four were delivered. A small display traces the history of the airline and models, photographs, documents and uniforms can be seen.

TYPE	REG/SER	CON. NO.	PI/NOTES	STATUS
☐ Boeing 720-047B	AP-AXL	18818	N93152	PV

PAKISTAN MARITIME MUSEUM (PAK32)

Address:	Habib Ibrahim Rehmatullah Road, Karachi 74350.
Tel:	021-425-1687
Admission:	Thursday-Tuesday 1000-2200.
Location:	In the eastern suburbs of the city.

This museum is located in a naval park in the city. The grounds have been landscaped and a large lake has been constructed. Floating in the water are several boats including the submarine ‘Hangor’ which sunk the Indian Navy Blackwood class frigate ‘Khukri’ in the 1971 war. The ‘Hangor’ arrived at the museum in December 2007 and was dedicated in a ceremony attended by high ranking officers. Also here are a Minesweeper, a midget submarine and a traditional river boat which was constructed by workmen using only basic tools. A replica of a coastal lighthouse has been constructed and visitors can obtain a panoramic view of the site from the top of the tower. A replica of part of a submarine is parked on the shore and this can be entered to see a perspective of life under the sea. The indoor displays trace the maritime history of the region from early times. Many models, documents and photographs can be seen. There is a gallery devoted to maritime life and hanging from the ceiling is the skeleton of a whale washed ashore in the 1960s. On the shore are examples of weapons and maritime equipment. The only aircraft on show is the Atlantic which is one of the former French Navy machines acquired for spares use. The airframe has recently been restored and painted in full Pakistani colours. The Navy operates small numbers of the type on coastal patrols from its base at the nearby Faisal airfield.

TYPE	REG/SER	CON. NO.	PI/NOTES	STATUS
☐ Breguet 1150 Atlantic	53	53	53 (France)	PV
☐ Helicopter				RA

PAKISTAN STEEL CADET COLLEGE MEMORIAL (PAK33)

Address:	Bin Qasim, Karachi 74600.
Admission:	By prior permission only.
Location:	In the eastern part of the city.

The college was set up in the town which is the location of a major steel works. The establishment opened in 1981 and many students have served with the military forces. The F-6 is a memorial to those who have died.

TYPE	REG/SER	CON. NO.	PI/NOTES	STATUS
☐ Shenyang F-6 [Mikoyan-Gurevich MiG-19SF]	10503			

PANO AQIL CANTONMENT MEMORIAL (PAK34)

Address:	Pano Aqil.
Admission:	By prior permission only.
Location:	In the southern part of the town.

This vast area houses a number of military bases and training schools. At two different sites Shenyang F-6 fighters have been preserved as memorials to those who have lost their lives.

TYPE	REG/SER	CON. NO.	PI/NOTES	STATUS
☐ Shenyang F-6 [Mikoyan-Gurevich MiG-19SF]	10435			RA
☐ Shenyang F-6 [Mikoyan-Gurevich MiG-19SF]	10438			RA

PESHAWAR AIR FORCE BASE MEMORIAL (PAK35)

Address:	Peshawar 25000.
Admission:	By prior permission only.
Location:	The base is in the western part of the city.

The airfield was constructed for British use and R.A.F. Squadrons were in residence from 1922 up to the end of World War II. The Pakistani Air Force took over the field and initially Hawker Tempests were flown. These were soon replaced by the Fury. In addition Austers flew on army co-operation duties. At the current time the base is home to fighter and helicopter squadrons. Types in use include the Nanchang A-5 and the Shenyang FT-6. The station flight operates the locally assembled Mushshak. A Sabre serves as a memorial at the base and other aircraft are preserved at military sites and schools and colleges around the city.

TYPE	REG/SER	CON. NO.	PI/NOTES	STATUS
☐ North American NA-202 Sabre (F-86F)	53-1107	202-36	At AFHQ.	RA
☐ North American NA-202 Sabre (F-86F)	53-1109	202-38	At nearby University.	RA
☐ North American NA-227 Sabre (F-86F)	55-5001	227-234	Nearby in town.	PV
☐ North American NA-227 Sabre (F-86F)	55-5005	227-238		RA
☐ Shenyang F-6 [Mikoyan-Gurevich MiG-19SF]	10610		At nearby school.	RA
☐ Shenyang F-6 [Mikoyan-Gurevich MiG-19SF]	7710		At nearby University.	RA
☐ Shenyang F-6 [Mikoyan-Gurevich MiG-19SF]	7836		At 104 Air Defence Division HQ.	RA
☐ Shenyang F-6 [Mikoyan-Gurevich MiG-19SF]	9611		At nearby school.	RA

PETARO CADET COLLEGE MEMORIAL (PAK36)

Address:	Petaro 76120.
Tel:	022-202-2021
Admission:	By prior permission only.
Location:	About 5 km north east of the town.

The college was founded at Mirpurhas in 1957 and moved to its present purpose built site two years later. The F-6 is preserved in the grounds along with a number of military vehicles.

TYPE	REG/SER	CON. NO.	PI/NOTES	STATUS
☐ Shenyang F-6 [Mikoyan-Gurevich MiG-19SF]	9621			RA

RAFIQUI AIR FORCE BASE COLLECTION (PAK37)

Address: Shorkot 35010.
Admission: By prior permission only.
Location: Just south of Shorkot Road.

The airfield was constructed after the 1965 conflict with India and has always housed fighter squadrons. These currently in residence operate Dassault Mirages and Chengdu F-7s. The base is named after Squadron Leader Sarfraz Ahmed Rafiqui who lost his life on September 6th 1965. He was leading three Sabres in an attack on Halwara airfield in India when they were attacked by ten Hawker Hunters. He caused one to crash but his guns then jammed and he was shot down. For his exploits he was awarded Pakistan's highest military honours.

TYPE	REG/SER	CON. NO.	PI/NOTES	STATUS
☐ Lockheed 580 (T-33A)	58-0453	580-1502	At nearby Army Camp.	RA
☐ Mikoyan-Gurevich MiG-15UTI	71-0203			RA
☐ Mikoyan-Gurevich MiG-15UTI				RA

SAKESAR AIR FORCE BASE MEMORIAL (PAK38)

Address: Sakesar 41160.
Admission: By prior permission only.
Location: In the southern part of the town.

The base houses a radar unit and the Air Defence School which moved from Korangi Creek in 1975. The site has played a prominent role in border conflicts. The F-6 flew many patrols in this area and one has been preserved.

TYPE	REG/SER	CON. NO.	PI/NOTES	STATUS
☐ Shenyang F-6 [Mikoyan-Gurevich MiG-19SF]	9626			RA

SAMUNGLI AIR FORCE BASE COLLECTION (PAK39)

Address: Samungli Road,
Quetta 87600.
Tel: 081-885249
Admission: By prior permission only.
Location: About 10 km north west of the city.

The airfield was used by the Royal Air Force in World War II and also Indian squadrons were in residence. After partition the site was abandoned for a time but then camps for cadets took place. Samungli was improved and put on a Care and Maintenance status. Squadrons on detachment used the field. In 1978 the base was upgraded and fighter units operating Sabres moved in. The Shenyang F-6 arrived in 1965 and the last examples of the type were withdrawn at Samungli in 2002. The preserved aircraft are a reminder of the base history. The Canadian built former Luftwaffe Sabre can be seen in a park by a local lake. An unusual arrival occurred in May 1981 when a hijacked Afghan Air Force Mil Mi-8 landed at the base with defectors on board.

TYPE	REG/SER	CON. NO.	PI/NOTES	STATUS
☐ Canadair CL-13B Sabre 6 [North American F-86E]	1747	1747	(Germany) – at Hanna Lake in the city.	PV
☐ North American NA-202 Sabre (F-86F)	53-1192	202-121		RA
☐ Shenyang F-6 [Mikoyan-Gurevich MiG-19S]	7637			RA
☐ Shenyang F-6 [Mikoyan-Gurevich MiG-19S]	8925			RA

SANGHAR CADET COLLEGE MEMORIAL (PAK40)

Address: Via Tando Adam,
Jam Nawaz Ali 68050.
Email: info@ccsanghar.com
Admission: By prior permission only.
Location: About 10 km east of Tando Adam.

The college was set up in the early 1990s to train students for the forces. Since 2000 it has been controlled by the Pakistan Navy. The F-6 serves as a memorial to former students who have lost their lives.

TYPE	REG/SER	CON. NO.	PI/NOTES	STATUS
☐ Shenyang F-6 [Mikoyan-Gurevich MiG-19SF]	1608			RA

SARGODHA AIR FORCE BASE COLLECTION (PAK41)

Address:	Sargodha Air Force Base, Sargodha 40100.
Tel:	0451-724511
Admission:	By prior permission only.
Location:	In the southern suburbs of the city.

Sargodha was operational during World War II but the airfield then became disused. Royal Air Force fighter squadrons were normally in residence. A Pakistani Air Force care and maintenance unit moved in during 1951. Six years later a decision was taken to restore and upgrade the facilities. The first squadrons flying Sabres moved in during 1959. The Lockheed F-104 Starfighter arrived in 1961 and was the first Mach 2 fighter to serve with the PAF. Chinese Shenyang F-6s moved in soon after. During the 1965 war with India the base was to the forefront in operations along the joint border. The 1971 conflict also saw Sargodha squadrons once again taking part in air battles in the region. For a period Dassault Mirages were also flown by the resident units. Now the base is home to F-16s and a missile wing. Two of the preserved aircraft are displayed in the grounds of the nearby Pakistan Air Force College and the remainder are located on the field.

TYPE	REG/SER	CON. NO.	PI/NOTES	STATUS
☐ Canadair CL-13B Sabre 6 [North American F-86E]	1809	1809	JB+117 – At PAF College.	RA
☐ Lockheed 183-92-02 Starfighter (F-104A)	56-874	183-1162	56-0874	RA
☐ North American NA-176 Sabre (F-86F)	51-13226	176-157	At PAF College.	RA
☐ North American NA-176 Sabre (F-86F)	513447	176-378	51-13447	RA
☐ North American NA-202 Sabre (F-86F)	53-1182	202-111		RA
☐ Shenyang F-6 [Mikoyan-Gurevich MiG-19S]	1504			RA
☐ Shenyang F-6 [Mikoyan-Gurevich MiG-19S]	1613			RA
☐ Shenyang F-6 [Mikoyan-Gurevich MiG-19S]	1612			RA
☐ Shenyang F-6 [Mikoyan-Gurevich MiG-19S]	1819			RA

SKARDU CADET COLLEGE MEMORIAL (PAK42)

Address:	Skardu 15201
Tel:	05831-58431
Email:	skardovian@yahoo.com
Admission:	By prior permission only.
Location:	In the town.

This military college was the first to be set up in this northern area of the country. The first students were admitted in 2001 and already many have gone on to join the military forces. A Shenyang F-6 is parked in the grounds to remind the current scholars of the traditions of the Air Force.

TYPE	REG/SER	CON. NO.	PI/NOTES	STATUS
☐ Shenyang F-6 [Mikoyan-Gurevich MiG-19SF]	4117			RA

SOUTHERN AIR COMMAND HEADQUARTERS MEMORIAL (PAK43)

Address:	National Stadium Road, Karachi 76550.
Tel:	021-951-2113
Email:	prohqsac@gmail.com
Admission:	By prior permission only.
Location:	In the north western part of the city.

The Southern Air Command is responsible for a number of air bases in the region. Two of these house front line fighter units. The F-6 is preserved as a memorial in the grounds of the buildings.

TYPE	REG/SER	CON. NO.	PI/NOTES	STATUS
☐ Shenyang F-6 [Mikoyan-Gurevich MiG-19SF]	1624			RA

PHILIPPINES

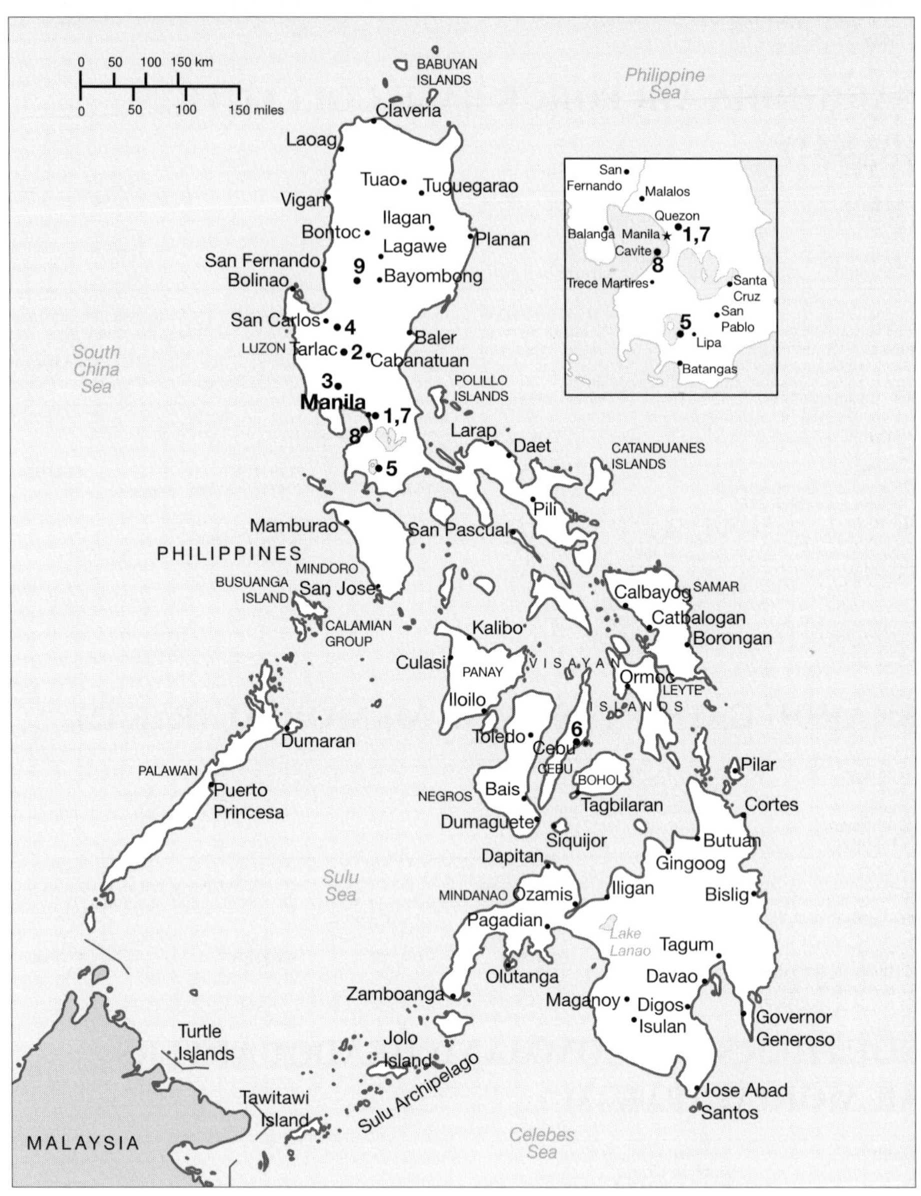

ARMED FORCES HEADQUARTERS DISPLAY (PH1)

Address:	Camp Aguinaldo, Quezon City, Manila 1110.
Admission:	By prior permission only.
Location:	In the southern part of Quezon city.

A display has been set up in the grounds of the complex which houses the headquarters buildings. Two aircraft and a number of military vehicles and pieces of artillery are preserved on the site.

TYPE	REG/SER	CON. NO.	PI/NOTES	STATUS
☐ Bell 205 Iroquois (UH-1H)	15931	12503	70-15931	RA
☐ North American NA-173 Sabre (F-86D)	'69411'		(USAF)	RAX

ARMED FORCES MUSEUM OF THE PHILIPPINES (PH2)

Address:	Camp Aquino, McArthur Highway, Tarlac 2300.
Admission:	Daily 0900-1700.
Location:	In the town.

The museum traces the development of military forces in the country. Wars and internal conflicts are highlighted in the displays with many photographs, documents and uniforms to be seen. In 1896 Tarlac became the first area to rise against the Spanish occupiers and the story of this event can be followed. The first Philippine Republic had its seat of government in the town. The period when the Americans governed the islands features prominently. There are several tanks, large weapons and military vehicles on show in the grounds.

TYPE	REG/SER	CON. NO.	PI/NOTES	STATUS
☐ Lockheed 580 (T-33A)	29585	580-7735	52-9585	PV

BASA AIR FORCE BASE COLLECTION (PH3)

Address:	5th Fighter Wing, Basa Air Force Base, Florida Blanca 2007.
Admission:	By prior permission only.
Location:	About 110 km north of Manila near Pampanga.

This important fighter field was built by the Americans in the latter stages of World War II and was named Florida-Blanca Air Base. The Philippine Air Force took up residence in August 1947. The following year the base was renamed after Lieutenant Cesar Basa, the first pilot in the country to be killed in aerial combat. The collection of preserved aircraft, located in a park near the main gate, shows types which have operated from the field in the past. The Mustang was one of the first types to serve with the newly formed Air Force after World War II and examples of classic fighter remained operational until 1960. Sabre units were based at the field for many years and the last of the twenty five Crusaders operated were withdrawn in 1988. The site was badly damaged in the 1991 Mount Pinatubo eruption. The aircraft currently in use by the resident squadron is the AS.211. The design by SIAI-Marchetti in Italy was taken over and produced by the Aermacchi company.

TYPE	REG/SER	CON. NO.	PI/NOTES	STATUS
☐ Beech A45 Mentor (T-34A)	'535'	FM.95	095	PVX
☐ Lockheed 580 (T-33A)	53636	580-8975	53-5636	PV
☐ Lockheed 580 (T-33A) (RT-33A)	35457	580-8796	53-5457	RA
☐ North American NA-173 Sabre (F-86D)	18436	173-569	51-8436	RA
☐ North American NA-176 Sabre (F-86F)	113468	176-399	51-13468, C.5-154 (Spain)	PV
☐ North American NA-191 Sabre (F-86F)	25158	191-854	52-5158	RA
☐ Northrop N-156A Freedom Fighter (F-5A)	'69103'			PVX
☐ Northrop N-156A Freedom Fighter (F-5A)	10499	N.6160	64-10499	RA
☐ Vought F-8H Crusader (F8U-2N) (F-8D)	47060		Bu147060	PV

CLARK AIR FORCE BASE COLLECTION (PH4)

Address:	A. Bonifacio Avenue, Clark International Airport, Pampanga 2010. Admission Unknown.
Location:	About 6 km north west of the city.

The United States set up Fort Stolsenburg in 1903 and opened a flying school on the site nine years later. In 1919 the base was named Clark Field. In early 1942 the site was captured by Japanese forces and used by them until it was recaptured in January 1945 after a bitter battle lasting three months. Clark Air Force Base was again a major American airfield. On June 10th 1991 the nearby Mount Pinatubo erupted and the site was soon covered with a layer of ash. The cost of refurbishment was considered not to be a viable project and the site was turned over to the Philippine government. The airfield is now used for civilian flights. A group of enthusiasts is planning to set museum tracing the history of Clark and has acquired a small collection of aircraft. Memorabilia, photographs and documents have been collected along with models and uniforms.

TYPE	REG/SER	CON. NO.	PI/NOTES	STATUS
☐ Bell 205 Iroquois (UH-1D) (UH-1H)	66860	5343	66-0860	RA
☐ Bell 205 Iroquois (UH-1H)	109	11115	68-16456 – front fuselage only.	RA
☐ Bell 205 Iroquois (UH-1H)	15355	11643	69-15355	RA
☐ Bell 205 Iroquois (UH-1H)	'09171'	645		PVX
☐ Lockheed 580 (T-33A)	52257	580-7323	52-9257	PV
☐ North American NA-174 Trojan (T-28A) (AT-28D)	'645'		'171'	PVX
☐ Northrop N-156A Freedom Fighter (F-5A)	10507	N.6168	64-10507	PV
☐ Northrop N-156B Freedom Fighter (F-5B)	40780	N.8138	74-0780	RA
☐ Vought F-8H Crusader (F8U-2N) (F-8D)	48661		Bu148661	PV

FERNANDO AIR FORCE BASE COLLECTION (PH5)

Address: 100th Training Wing,
Fernando Air Force Base,
Lipa City 4218.
Admission: By prior permission only.
Location: About 80 km south of Manila.

Lipa Army Air Base was constructed in 1942 by the Japanese using captured Americans and local residents as forced labour. In May 1948 the field was named after Lieutenant Colonel Basilio Fernando who was killed in January 1946 in the U.S.A. whilst training on a B-25 Mitchell. The SF-260WP was once the personal aircraft of the then Base Vice-Commander Colonel Yap and carries the sign 'Cougar 99' on the front fuselage.

TYPE	REG/SER	CON. NO.	PI/NOTES	STATUS
☐ Philippines Air Force Marko	XT-001		Fuselage only.	RA
☐ North American NA-174 Trojan (T-28A) (AT-28D)	660	174-353	51-7500	RA
☐ SIAI-Marchetti SF.260MP	122			RA
☐ SIAI-Marchetti SF.260WP	635	15-35	I-FILF	RA

MACTAN AIR FORCE BASE MONUMENT (PH6)

Address: 2nd Tactical Operations Wing,
Cebu 6015.
Admission: By prior permission only.
Location: In the south eastern part of the city.

Two aircraft are preserved at the base which houses a unit flying the OV-10 Bronco on ground attack duties. The Provider and Sabre served with the Air Force for many years and both types were often seen at the base.

TYPE	REG/SER	CON. NO.	PI/NOTES	STATUS
☐ Fairchild 473 Provider (205) (C-123B) (C-123K)	54264	20073	54-0624	RA
☐ North American NA-191 Sabre (F-86F)	524835	191-531	52-4835	RA

MUSEO PAMBATA (PH7)

Address: Roxas Boulevard,
Manila 1000.
Tel: 02-523-1797
Email: info@museopambata.org
Admission: Tuesday-Sunday 0800-1700.
Location: In the centre of the city near the American Embassy.

The displays at this museum are designed to stimulate children's interest in many aspects of culture, science and technology. The rooms inside all have specific themes. The Iroquois on show is painted in false rescue colours.

TYPE	REG/SER	CON. NO.	PI/NOTES	STATUS
☐ Bell 205 Iroquois (UH-1H)	66-16328	8522		PV

PHILIPPINE AIR FORCE MUSEUM (PH8)

Address: c/o Air Force Heaquarters,
Villamor Air Base,
Manila 1309.
Tel: 02-854-6729
Email: pafmuseum2003@yahoo.com
Admission: Daily 0800-2000.
Location: About 15 km south of the city at the airport.

An aviation branch of the Philippine Constabulary was formed in May 1935 and flew a few Curtiss JN-4s and Stearman 73s and 76s. These biplanes were mainly used in seeking bandit hideouts. The force evolved into the Army Air Corps with American assistance. Japan invaded the Philippines during World War II and many of the aircraft were destroyed in the first raid. An independent republic was established in 1946 and the Philippine Air Force came into being on July 1st 1947 with the renaming of the Army Air Corps. This museum was set up in May 1974 and the displays traced the history of military flying in the country. On July 1st 2007 the collection moved to a new purpose built complex. The date was the sixtieth anniversary of the formation of the service. On show in the galleries are uniforms, weapons and memorabilia. Three aircraft (the PT-13, the P-51 and the Super Pinto) are in the exhibition hall. The remainder are parked in the well laid out grounds. The Albatross, which joined the display in the mid-1990s, is believed to be the oldest example of the type left. The Mitsubishi built Sikorsky S-62A and the YS-11 were formerly used by the Presidential Flight.

TYPE	REG/SER	CON. NO.	PI/NOTES	STATUS
☐ Beech A45 Mentor (T-34A)	59-7106	FM.106		PV
☐ Bell 204 Iroquois (UH-1B)	22570			PV
☐ Boeing-Stearman E75 Kayder (PT-13D)	551	75-7551	42-17488	PV
☐ Cessna R172F Mescalero (T-41D)	88958	R1720316	68-8958, 88958 (South Vietnam)	PV
☐ Douglas DC-3A-467 Skytrain (C-47B) (VC-47D)	48301	14117/25562	43-48301, 48301 (South Korea), RP-C83	PV
☐ Grumman G-64 Albatross (SA-16A) (HU-16A)	48607	G-26	48-0607	PV
☐ Lockheed 580 (T-33A)	29806	580-8066	52-9806	PV
☐ Nihon Kokuki Seizo Kabushiki Kaisha (NAMC) YS-11A-253	RP-77	2179	JA8785	PV
☐ North American NA-122 Mustang (P-51D)	3733	122-41167	44-74627, 73373 – probable i/d.	PV
☐ North American NA-188 Texan (T-6G)	150162	188-25 (?)	51-15162 (?)	PV
☐ North American NA-191 Sabre (F-86F)	52-4468	191-164		PV
☐ North American NA-226 Trojan (T-28C) (AT-28D)	40533	226-110	Bu140533	PV
☐ Northrop N-156A Freedom Fighter (F-5A)	13326	N.6095	64-13326	PV
☐ SIAI-Marchetti SF.260WP	639	15-39	I-FILL	PV
☐ Sikorsky S-58 Seahorse (HUS-1) (UH-34D)	15131	581769	Bu153131	PV
☐ Sikorsky S-62J	62018	M62-018		PV
☐ Temco T-160 Super Pinto	44234			PV
☐ Vought F-8H Crusader (F8U-2N) (F-8D)	47056		Bu147056	PV

PHILIPPINE MILITARY ACADEMY DISPLAY (PH9)

Address:	Fort del Pilar, Baguio City.
Tel:	074-447-2634
Admission:	By prior permission only.
Location:	On the outskirts of the city.

The Academia Militar was set up in October 1898 but was only in existence until the following January. In 1905 a police college opened in Manila and this moved to Baguio City three years later. The site closed in 1941 with the Japanese occupation. The academy reopened in 1947 and now trains officers for all the services.

TYPE	REG/SER	CON. NO.	PI/NOTES	STATUS
☐ Bell 205 Iroquois (UH-1H)	22954	13938	77-22954	RA
☐ SIAI-Marchetti SF.260MP	617	15-17		RA
☐ Vought F-8H Crusader (F8U-2N) (F-8D)	'48696'		Bu148686	RAX

QATAR

DOHA MILITARY BASE COLLECTION (QA1)

Address:	Al Udaid Air Base, Qatar
Admission:	By prior permission only.
Location:	In the eastern suburbs of the city.

The Qatar Air Force was formed in 1974 and the first jets supplied were four Hunters. These were all former Dutch Air Force aircraft refurbished in England. Since then the types used have mainly been of British or French origin. The first Mirage version to enter service was the F.1DDA and this was followed by the F.1EDA. Most of these were later sold to Spain. The force has later variants of the Mirage in use and also operates a small number of helicopters. Three aircraft, all in false markings, are preserved around the base.

TYPE	REG/SER	CON. NO.	PI/NOTES	STATUS
☐ Dassault Mirage F.1EDA	'QA83'			RAX
☐ Hawker P.1101 Hunter T.79 (T.7)	'QA04'	41H/695338	N-316 (Netherlands), G-9-191, QA-13	RAX
☐ Westland-Sikorsky WS-55 Whirlwind Series 3	'QA03'	WA.612	QA01	RAX

The Philippine Air Force operated several Vought Crusaders and one has been preserved at the Clark Air Force Base. (Phil Yeadon)

Above: This Bell Iroquois can be seen at the Museo Pambata in Manila. (Phil Yeadon)

Left: This Yak-38 is preserved as at memorial at Artem. (Gleb Osokin)

RUSSIA IN ASIA

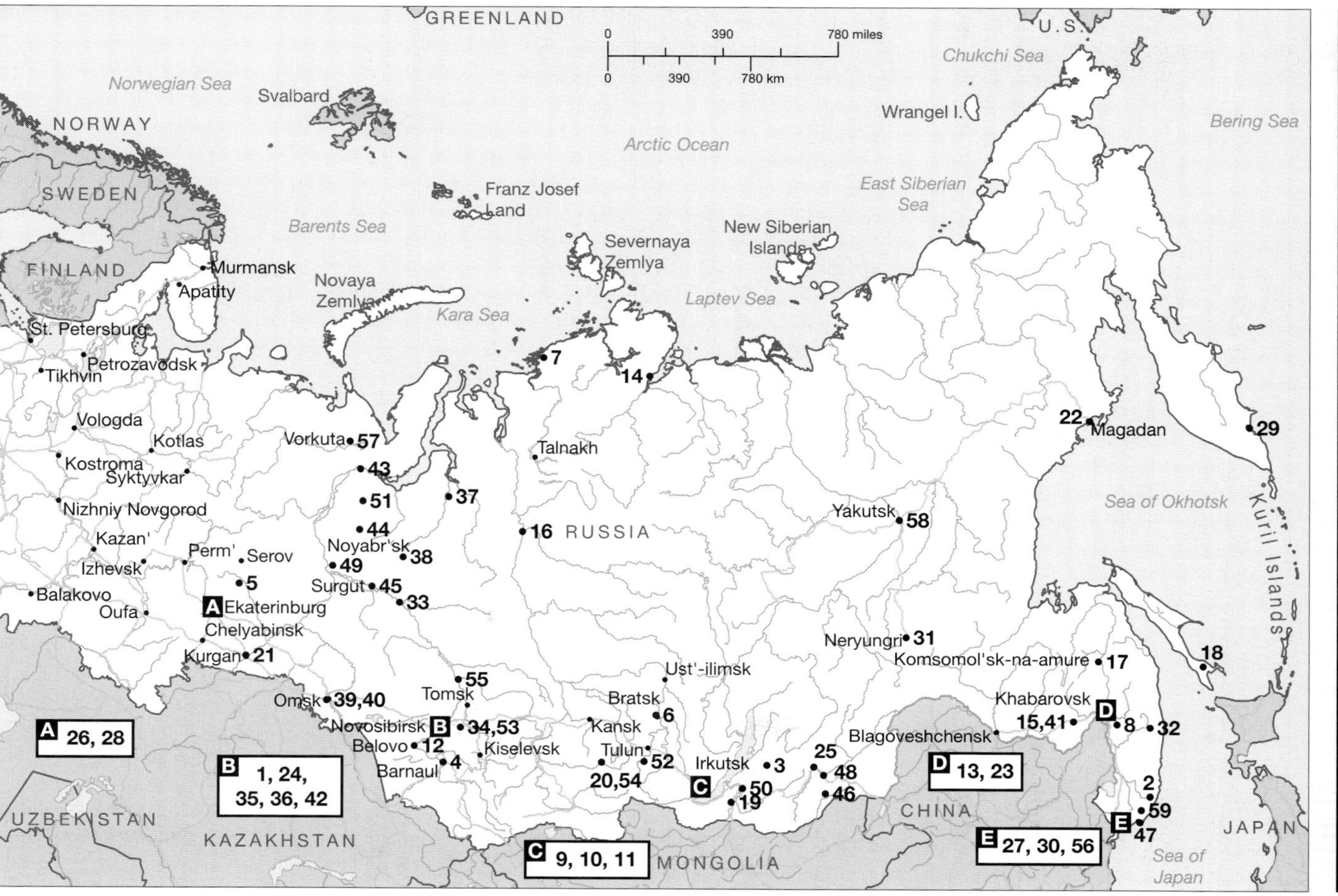

ANTI AIRCRAFT DEFENCE FORCE MUSEUM (RUS1)

Address: Tolmachevo Air Base, Ob
Admission: By prior permission only.
Location: Just west of the town.

A photograph shows a pylon mounted MiG-17F outside this museum. Also on show are missiles and some military vehicles. The base used to house a MiG-31 unit but this is believed to have been disbanded so the museum may not exist. Further details of the collection would be most welcome.

TYPE	REG/SER	CON. NO.	PI/NOTES	STATUS
☐ Mikoyan-Gurevich MiG-17F	04			RA

ARTEM MEMORIAL (RUS2)

Address: 692756 Artem.
Admission: On permanent view.
Location: In the south western suburbs of the town.

More than one hundred Yakovlev Yak-38 V/STOL are known to have been built for use on aircraft carriers. One has been placed in a park as a memorial to naval aviators from the region. The aircraft is mounted on a plinth which contains plaques giving names and details. Statues surround the site.

TYPE	REG/SER	CON. NO.	PI/NOTES	STATUS
☐ Yakovlev Yak-38	87			PV

BADA AIR BASE MEMORIAL (RUS3)

Address: Bada Air Base, Bada.
Admission: On permanent view.
Location: About 3 km north east of the town.

The airfield is home to squadrons flying the Sukhoi Su-24 fighter. The base occupied by MiG-21s for some years and a version of this well used fighter has recently been erected as a memorial. This aircraft honours the flight and ground crews who have lost their lives whilst serving the Soviet Union and Russia.

TYPE	REG/SER	CON. NO.	PI/NOTES	STATUS
☐ Mikoyan-Gurevich MiG-21bis	44			PV

BARNAUL COLLECTION (RUS4)

Address: 656000 Barnaul.
Admission: On permanent view.
Location: At a number of locations in the town.

There are several aircraft on display around this town. The Delfin is pole-mounted near a military school which closed some years ago. The L-39C is on the site of a former naval base which now serves as an industrial estate. The Yak-52 is mounted outside the local ROSTO offices. The type is used for primary training by the organisation and was also used by its predecessor DOSAAF. A Tu-104 in Aeroflot colours, which spent many years displayed in a local park, was recently scrapped due to extensive corrosion.

TYPE	REG/SER	CON. NO.	PI/NOTES	STATUS
☐ Aero L-29 Delfin	84		Near former military school.	PV
☐ Aero L-39C Albatros	11			PV
☐ Yakovlev Yak-28P	01	146001042	Near former military school.	PV
☐ Yakovlev Yak-52	15		At ROSTO offices.	PV

BEREZOVO MEMORIAL (RUS5)

Address: Berezovo.
Admission: On permanent view
Location: At the airport which is just east of the town.

The airfield opened in the 1930s and services to local towns took place. Helicopters now play an important part in transporting people and equipment to the outlying oil sites. The Mil Mi-1 honours this work.

TYPE	REG/SER	CON. NO.	PI/NOTES	STATUS
☐ Mil Mi-1	CCCP-40214			PV

BRATSK MEMORIAL (RUS6)

Address:	665370 Bratsk.
Admission:	On permanent view.
Location:	In the town.

The local military airfield housed units operating the MiG-25U and the MiG-31 up to 2002. For several years MiG-17s flew from the field. An example of this fighter has been erected in the town to honour those who lost their lives flying from Bratsk. The field is now the civil airport for the town.

TYPE	REG/SER	CON. NO.	PI/NOTES	STATUS
☐ Mikoyan-Gurevich MiG-17F				PV

DIKSON MEMORIAL (RUS7)

Address:	Dikson.
Admission:	On permanent view.
Location:	Near the airport which is to the west of the town.

The town, named after a Swedish explorer, is the most northerly port in Russia. During winter it is in complete darkness for a month. Dikson is one of the most isolated settlements in the world. The airfield saw military use in the past by Tupolev Tu-4 bombers on flights in the Polar region. An example of the Li-2 serves as a memorial.

TYPE	REG/SER	CON. NO.	PI/NOTES	STATUS
☐ Lisunov Li-2T [Douglas DC-3 modified]	RA-04219			PV

GAROVKA AIR BASE MEMORIAL (RUS8)

Address:	Garovka.
Admission:	By prior permission only.
Location:	About 5 km south of the town.

This military airfield now houses helicopter units operating Mil Mi-8s and Mil Mi-26s. The green-painted Lisunov Li-2 serves as a memorial to those who have lost their lives flying from the field.

TYPE	REG/SER	CON. NO.	PI/NOTES	STATUS
☐ Lisunov Li-2 [Douglas DC-3 modified]			At Garovka.	RA

IRKUT CORPORATION MUSEUM (RUS9)

Address:	3 Novatorov Street, 664020 Irkutsk.
Tel:	03952-322909
Fax:	03952-322945
Email:	market@irkut.ru
Admission:	By prior permission only.
Location:	In the north west suburbs of the town.

The factory was set up in 1932 and since then has manufactured over six and a half thousand aircraft. Designs from the Antonov, Ilyushin, Mikoyan, Petlyakov, Tupolev and Yakovlev bureaux have been built at the site. In recent years Beriev Be-200s, MiG-23s, MiG-17s, Sukhoi Su-27UBs and Su-30s have left the lines. A small museum tracing the history of the factory has been set up. The Irkut Corporation came into being in the 1990s and the first design from its light aircraft section was the A-002 autogyro. The prototype made its maiden flight in the spring of 2002 and small numbers have been manufactured.

TYPE	REG/SER	CON. NO.	PI/NOTES	STATUS
☐ Irkut A-002	'A-002'			RAX
☐ Mikoyan-Gurevich MiG-27UB	07			RA
☐ Yakovlev Yak-112	RA-00112			RA
☐ Yakovlev Yak-28PP	45			RA
☐ Yakovlev Yak-28PP	75		At Shiryamovo Factory.	PV

IRKUTSK HIGHER MILITARY TECHNICAL SCHOOL COLLECTION (RUS10)

Address:	664036 Irkutsk.
Tel:	03952-271536
Admission:	By prior permission only.
Location:	In the south eastern suburbs of the town.

Many such colleges were set up in the days of the Soviet Union to train engineers and fitters. Nearly all had a collection of instructional airframes and engines for the students to work on. Displays of photographs and models portray the history of aviation and military development in the country. A type of interest is the Ilyushin Il-76MDPP fitted with electronic jamming equipment. This variant of the versatile transport was not put into production. Several versions of the supersonic Tupolev Tu-22 bomber are in the collection. The prototype first flew in 1958 and the type entered production in the early 1960s. Reconnaissance models were produced and others were converted for engine and systems test-bed work. Three MiG fighters are in the collection.

TYPE	REG/SER	CON. NO.	PI/NOTES	STATUS
□ Aero L-39C Albatros	72			RA
□ Aero L-39C Albatros	318			RA
□ Antonov An-2R	CCCP-05767	1G 154-07		RA
□ Antonov An-24T	60			RA
□ Ilyushin Il-76	602	033402031	CCCP-86602	RA
□ Ilyushin Il-76M	CCCP-86834	0003422655		RA
□ Ilyushn Il-76MDPP	CCCP-86889	0013434009		RA
□ Mikoyan-Gurevich MiG-15				RA
□ Mikoyan-Gurevich MiG-23	27			RA
□ Mikoyan-Gurevich MiG-29	59			RA
□ Mil Mi-6	86	4681901		RA
□ Mil Mi-8				RA
□ Mil Mi-8	08			RA
□ Mil Mi-8	42			RA
□ Mil Mi-8	65			RA
□ Mil Mi-8	63	9775237 (?)		RA
□ Mil Mi-24	64			RA
□ Sukhoi Su-17	04			RA
□ Sukhoi Su-24	57			RA
□ Sukhoi Su-27	03			RA
□ Tupolev Tu-22	42			RA
□ Tupolev Tu-22M0	41			RA
□ Tupolev Tu-22M1	37	2426024		RA
□ Tupolev Tu-22M2	40			RA
□ Tupolev Tu-22M3	51			RA

IRKUTSK MILITARY COLLEGE COLLECTION (RUS11)

Address:	Sovetskaya Street 176, 664036 Irkutsk.
Admission:	By prior permission only.
Location:	In the south easter part of the town.

Students at this college are trained in a variety of duties. Two aircraft are preserved in the grounds to show the contribution of the Air Force to military life. The Mi-4 helicopter can be seen in a local park.

TYPE	REG/SER	CON. NO.	PI/NOTES	STATUS
□ Mikoyan-Gurevich MiG-23M	02			RA
□ Mikoyan-Gurevich MiG-29	75			RA
□ Mil Mi-4	26		In nearby park.	PV

KAMEN-ON-OB MEMORIAL (RUS12)

Address:	Kamen-on-Ob.
Admission:	On permanent view.
Location:	In the town.

This historic town, founded in the seventeenth century, has supplied many people to the military. A MiG-21PFM fighter has recently been dedicated as a town memorial to honour their contributions.

TYPE	REG/SER	CON. NO.	PI/NOTES	STATUS
□ Mikoyan-Gurevich MiG-21PFM	100			PV

KHABAROVSK MEMORIALS (RUS13)

Address: Khabarovsk
Admission: On permanent view.
Location: Around the town.

Three aircraft are preserved around the town which has both civil and military airfields. The Mil Mi-1 helicopter is painted in Vostok airlines colours and is mounted on a plinth at the airport. The Polish built Antonov An-2 can be seen near the main railway station. This classic biplane served in large numbers in the harsh conditions.

TYPE	REG/SER	CON. NO.	PI/NOTES	STATUS
☐ Antonov An-2TP	CCCP-02461	1G 119-04	Near railway station.	PV
☐ Mil Mi-1A	RA-00137		CCCP-00137 – at Airport.	PV
☐ Sukhoi Su-7B	01		At military town.	Ra

KHATANGA AIRPORT MEMORIAL (RUS14)

Address: Khatanga Airport,
663260 Khatanga.
Admission: On permanent view.
Location: Just south of the village.

This remote airport was home to military aircraft in the 1970s and now serves as the starting point for many polar excursion flights. The Kazan built Mil Mi-8 is parked near the terminal building.

TYPE	REG/SER	CON. NO.	PI/NOTES	STATUS
☐ Mil Mi-8T	RA-22295	7112	CCCP-22295	PV

KHURBA AIR BASE MEMORIAL (RUS15)

Address: Khurba Air Base,
Khurba.
Admission: By prior permission only.
Location: Just east of the town.

Units operating the Sukhoi Su-24 are stationed at this base which also houses a detachment of helicopters. A MiG-17 has been preserved as a memorial to those who lost their lives flying from the field.

TYPE	REG/SER	CON. NO.	PI/NOTES	STATUS
☐ Mikoyan-Gurevich MiG-17	01			RA

KOGALYM TOWN COLLECTION (RUS16)

Address: 628486 Kogalym.
Admission: On permanent view.
Location: At a number of locations.

Three aircraft are displayed around the town. The Tupolev Tu-154 was withdrawn from use in the late 1990s and is used as an internet cafe. The MiG-25 and Mil-2 serve as memorials.

TYPE	REG/SER	CON. NO.	PI/NOTES	STATUS
☐ Mikoyan-Gurevich MiG-25PU	45			PV
☐ Mil Mi-2				PV
☐ Tupolev Tu-154B-1	RA-85261	78A261	CCCP-85261	PV

KOMSOMOLSK AIRCRAFT FACTORY MUSEUM (RUS17)

Address: 1 Sovetskaya Street
681018 Komsomolsk-na-Amure.
Tel: 42172-63609
Fax: 42172-63451
Email: knaapo@kmscom.ru
Admission: By prior permission only.
Location: About 20 km south west of the town.

Opened in 1931 for the production of the Tupolev ANT-7 (R-6), this factory later built several Ilyushin designs. In the 1950s the plant was one of six designated to construct the MiG-17. The first example left the line in 1956. Since the early 1940s most Sukhoi designs have been produced at the site. The museum traces the history of the factory with many models, documents, components and photographs on show. Several aircraft built at the site are on show and a second MiG-17 is mounted at the gate to this giant facility. The Tupolev ANT-7 first flew in 1929 and this twin engined monoplane was used by the military and civil airlines.

TYPE	REG/SER	CON. NO.	PI/NOTES	STATUS
☐ Ilyushin Il-2m3				RA
☐ Ilyushin Il-4 (DB-3EF)		3051		RA
☐ Lisunov Li-2 [Douglas DC-3 modified]				RA
☐ Mikoyan-Gurevich MiG-17				RA
☐ Mikoyan-Gurevich MiG-17	81	3613	At factory gate.	RA
☐ Mikoyan-Gurevich MiG-21bis				RA
☐ Mikoyan-Gurevich MiG-23MLD	30			RA
☐ Sukhoi Su-17	24			RA
☐ Sukhoi Su-27				RA
☐ Tupolev ANT-7 (R-6)				RA

KOREAN AIR LINES FLIGHT 007 MEMORIAL (RUS18)

Address:	Yuzhno-Sakhalinsk.
Admission:	On permanent view.
Location:	In the town.

On September 1st 1983 a Korean Air Lines Boeing 747 was shot down by a Sukhoi Su-15 off the coast of Sakhalin Island. The Soviet authorities claimed the airliner had violated their airspace. All the two hundred and sixty nine passengers and crew were lost. Large portions of wreckage were later recovered. A memorial to this event has been erected on the shore near the crash site. The centrepiece of the display is a Sukhoi Su-15TM.

TYPE	REG/SER	CON. NO.	PI/NOTES	STATUS
☐ Sukhoi Su-15TM	40			PV

KOTELNIKOVO MEMORIAL (RUS19)

Address:	Kotelnikovo.
Admission:	On permanent view.
Location:	In the town.

The settlement started as a village to house workers building and maintaining the local railways. The former DOSAAF Delfin honours those who have lost their lives in flying accidents.

TYPE	REG/SER	CON. NO.	PI/NOTES	STATUS
☐ Aero L-29 Delfin				PV

KRASNOYARSK CIVIL AVIATION TECHNICAL SCHOOL (RUS20)

Address:	Gladnow Street 6, 660013 Krasnoyarsk.
Tel:	03912-364586
Admission:	By prior permission only.
Location:	Aircraft at Yemelyanovo Airport which is about 40 km north west of the city.

In the Soviet era the national airline 'Aeroflot' set up training establishments in many cities. This school keeps its collection of types operated in recent years at the main airport for the town.

TYPE	REG/SER	CON. NO.	PI/NOTES	STATUS
☐ Antonov An-2P	RA-70365	1G 138-59	CCCP-70365	RA
☐ Antonov An-26	RA-26554	3202	CCCP-26554	RA
☐ Ilyushin Il-62M	RA-86453	1622323	CCCP-86453	RA
☐ Let L-410UVP	RA-67148	800414	CCCP-67148	RA
☐ Mil Mi-2	RA-20995	529730046	CCCP-20995	RA
☐ Mil Mi-8	CCCP-24472	98628762		RA
☐ Tupolev Tu-154B	RA-85165	76A165	CCCP-85165	RA
☐ Tupolev Tu-154B-2	RA-85418	80A418	CCCP-85418	RA
☐ Yakovlev Yak-40	RA-87386	9411732	CCCP-87386	RA

Right: This Yakovlev Yak-28P is preserved outside a former military school in Barnaul. (Gleb Osokin)

Below: The locally designed A-002 autogyro is preserved at the Irkut Corporation Museum. (Aidan Curley)

The entrance to the Irkutsk Military College is guarded by this MiG-29. (Aidan Curley)

KURGANSK AVIATION MUSEUM (RUS21)

Address:	Kurgan Airport, 640000 Kurgan.
Tel:	03522-478387
Admission:	Daily 1000-1700.
Location:	In the north eastern part of the city.

This excellent museum opened a few years ago and has collected a large number of items. The informative indoor exhibition traces the history of aviation with specific reference to local events. On show are many original documents, newspaper cuttings, models, components, engines, photographs and uniforms. There are several displays devoted to record breaking pilots and their flights. The aircraft collection includes many types which have seen service in Russia in recent years. The front fuselage on the Antonov An-2 is open to visitors whilst the complete example outside is painted in Polar colours. Aeroflot used large numbers of the biplane in the development of outlying regions of the country. Ranges of both Mikoyan-Gurevich and Sukhoi combat types can be compared. The Sukhoi Su-7 made its maiden flight in prototype form in the spring of 1956. Several versions appeared over the years and many were exported. The interior of the Ilyushin Il-14 is fitted out as a training aircraft for parachutists. The equipment they used is displayed along the side of the fuselage.

TYPE	REG/SER	CON. NO.	PI/NOTES	STATUS
☐ Antonov An-2			Front fuselage only.	PV
☐ Antonov An-2	RA-62458	1G 41-27	CCCP-62458	PV
☐ Antonov An-24B	CCCP-46296	77303808		PV
☐ Ilyushin Il-14T	10	14700194		PV
☐ Mikoyan-Gurevich MiG-17	05	04210609		PV
☐ Mikoyan-Gurevich MiG-19P	04	22110032		PV
☐ Mikoyan-Gurevich MiG-21PF	01	76212207		PV
☐ Mikoyan-Gurevich MiG-23UB	11	0102		PV
☐ Mil Mi-2	27			PV
☐ Sukhoi Su-7B	69	1608		PV
☐ Sukhoi Su-17UM3	19	63411		PV
☐ Sukhoi Su-24	02			PV
☐ Sukhoi Su-25	08	25508101026		PV
☐ Sukhoi Su-27	01	36911009709		PV
☐ Yakovlev Yak-40	UK-87848	9331730	CCCP-87848	PV

MAGADAN MILITARY AIRCRAFT MEMORIAL (RUS22)

Address:	Prospekt Lenina, Magadan 42400.
Admission:	On permanent view.
Location:	In the north eastern part of the city.

The memorial honours military aviation in this strategically important region. Two versions, a single-seat and a two-seat, of the Sukhoi Su-15 can be see. This combat jet first flew in prototype form in May 1962. Production was allocated to the Novosibirsk factory but none were made until the completion of the Yak-28 run.

TYPE	REG/SER	CON. NO.	PI/NOTES	STATUS
☐ Mikoyan-Gurevich MiG-21bis	31	150YAH15		PV
☐ Mil Mi-2	34	545210057 (?)		PV
☐ Sukhoi Su-15TM	11			PV
☐ Sukhoi Su-15UT	91			PV

MILITARY MUSEUM OF THE FAR EAST REGION (RUS23)

Address:	Shevchenko 20, 68000 Khabarovsk.
Tel:	04212-326350
Admission:	Tuesday-Sunday 1000-1700
Location:	In the western part of the city centre.

The military history of the region is portrayed in this interesting museum. The landing of British troops at Vladivostok is shown in a photographic display. Also on display are many documents, weapons and uniforms. There is a collection of tanks in the yard outside the building and a number of missiles can also be seen. The sole aircraft is a MiG-17F and there are components from crash sites in the indoor exhibition.

TYPE	REG/SER	CON. NO.	PI/NOTES	STATUS
☐ Mikoyan-Gurevich MiG-17F	11			PV

MILITARY TECHNICAL MUSEUM (RUS24)

Address:	Novosibirsk.
Admission:	Unknown
Location:	In the town.

Whilst researching I came across a photograph of a Yak-9 mounted outside a building. Also there were several tanks, military vehicles and pieces of artillery to be seen. Further details would be most welcome.

TYPE	REG/SER	CON. NO.	PI/NOTES	STATUS
☐ Mil Mi-2			At nearby school.	PV
☐ Yakovlev Yak-9				PV

MINISTRY OF DEFENCE MUSEUM (RUS25)

Address:	Ul. Leninska 86, 672010 Chita.
Admission:	Tuesday-Friday 1100-1300 1400-1800; Saturday-Sunday 1400-1700.
Location:	In the centre of the city.

This museum, close to the border between Russia and China, has special exhibitions devoted to the conflicts between the two countries. Many photographs, documents, models and uniforms are on show.

TYPE	REG/SER	CON. NO.	PI/NOTES	STATUS
☐ Mikoyan-Gurevich MiG-15				PV
☐ Mil Mi-2				PV
☐ Yakovlev Yak-3				PV

MUSEUM OF ARMAMENT AND MILITARY EQUIPMENT (RUS26)

Address:	620000 Ekaterineburg.
Admission:	Unknown
Location:	In the city.

This museum has a large outside display. There are several tanks and armoured personnel carriers on view in the outside park. Also to be seen are missiles, missile launchers and airfield radar equipment.

TYPE	REG/SER	CON. NO.	PI/NOTES	STATUS
☐ Mikoyan-Gurevich MiG-25PD	46			PV
☐ Mikoyan-Gurevich MiG-27K	34			PV
☐ Sukhoi Su-17M3	97			PV
☐ Sukhoi Su-24	35			PV

MUSEUM OF FIGHTING GLORY OF THE PACIFIC BOUNDARY DISTRICT (RUS27)

Address:	17 Semyerovska Street, 690091 Vladivostok.
Tel:	218074
Admission:	Tuesday-Saturday 0900-1700.
Location:	In the city.

The exhibitions cover art and culture as well as the work of Border Guard Units. There are many paintings and sculptures to be seen as well as documents, uniforms, maps and photographs.

TYPE	REG/SER	CON. NO.	PI/NOTES	STATUS
☐ Kamov Ka-25PL				PV

MUSEUM OF MILITARY TECHNOLOGY (RUS28)

Address:	620000 Ekaterineburg.
Admission:	By prior permission only.
Location:	In the centre of the city.

An officer's school is located in this important military town. The museum is housed in this complex and traces the development of weapons and transport. Many military vehicles, tanks and guns can be seen. The four complete aircraft all served in large numbers with the Soviet Air Force. The BI-1 was the first rocket powered fighter in the world. Only seven were built and the first prototype made its maiden flight in May 1942. Engine problems hindered the development programme and production of the type was cancelled. The remains of a Lockheed U-2, reputed to be Gary Powers aircraft, have been reported here. The wreckage in the Central Museum of the Armed Forces in Moscow is also claimed to be from this aircraft. Two combat jets and a helicopter are also on show.

TYPE	REG/SER	CON. NO.	PI/NOTES	STATUS
☐ Bereznyak-Isayey BI-1 (FSM)				PV
☐ Lockheed U-2C (U-2A)	56-6693 (?)	360	Parts only – see Central Museum of the Armed Forces.	PVD
☐ Mikoyan-Gurevich MiG-21F-13	67			PV
☐ Mil Mi-8T	15			PV
☐ Sukhoi Su-7B	12			PV

MUSEUM OF REGIONAL STUDIES (RUS29)

Address: 684010 Kamchatka.
Admission: Aircraft on permanent view.
Location: At Yelizovo Airport which is just east of the village.

This organisation is responsible for a number of museums in the area. The displays trace many aspects of the history and culture of the region. The aircraft is preserved among buildings close to the terminal building at Yelizovo Airport. The classic type served on Aeroflot routes in the area for many years.

TYPE	REG/SER	CON. NO.	PI/NOTES	STATUS
☐ Lisunov Li-2 [Douglas DC-3 modified]	CCCP-84699			PV

MUSEUM OF THE PACIFIC FLEET AIR FORCE (RUS30)

Address: Vladivostok
Admission: By prior permission only.
Location: Near the city.

For many years there have been rumours of a museum tracing the history of military aviation in the region. A Lisunov Li-2 has recently been reported but there are believed to be other aircraft in the collection. A building in the city once housed an exhibition tracing the history of the naval part of the fleet but this is now closed.

TYPE	REG/SER	CON. NO.	PI/NOTES	STATUS
☐ Lisunov Li-2F [Douglas DC-3 modified]				RA

NERUNGRI AIRPORT MEMORIAL (RUS31)

Address: Nerungri Airport,
Nerungri.
Admission: On permanent view.
Location: About 5 km north of Chulman.

This airport was served by Aeroflot for many years and is now used by many independent airlines. An example of the Yak-40, painted in Aeroflot colours, has been put on show to remember this era.

TYPE	REG/SER	CON. NO.	PI/NOTES	STATUS
☐ Yakovlev Yak-40	RA-87639	9142019	CCCP-87639	PV

NIKOLAYEVSK AVIATION MUSEUM (RUS32)

Address: Nikolayevsk Airport,
682430 Nikolayevsk-na Amure.
Tel: 042135-23402
Location: About 10 km west of the town.

Before the break up of the Soviet Union this town was an important link on the Far Eastern Division routes of Aeroflot. Local enthusiasts have collected aircraft and memorabilia for this museum. A display has been set up in one of the original airport buildings. Models, photographs and documents trace the development of civil aviation in the region. Several engines, components and airport vehicles have also been acquired. The Mil Mi-8 was used for passenger and survey work in the area for over two decades. Many Antonov An-2s, Ilyushin Il-14s and Mil Mi-2s were operated from the airport. Other types are being sought to enhance the exhibition.

TYPE	REG/SER	CON. NO.	PI/NOTES	STATUS
□ Antonov An-2				PV
□ Ilyushin Il-14				PV
□ Mikoyan-Gurevich MiG-15				PV
□ Mil Mi-1T	CCCP-10106			RAC
□ Mil Mi-2	CCCP-20970	549643026		PV
□ Mil Mi-8P	CCCP-22182	2103		PV

NIZHNEVARTOVSK AVIATION MUSEUM (RUS33)

Address:	Nizhnevartovsk Airport. 628460 Nizhnevartovsk.
Tel:	0346-649-2401
Admission:	Aircraft on permanent view.
Location:	About 5 km south of the town.

The approach road to the airport has four large models of jet airliners mounted on pylons by a fence. Outside the terminal is a spectacular monument and inside is a collection of memorabilia photographs and models tracing the history of flying in the region. The facilities at the field have been improved as it is in an important region for gas production. The five aircraft are mounted on plinths in the attractive landscaped gardens which surround the buildings. All are painted in the standard Aeroflot colours of blue and white. Helicopters have played an important role in the development of facilities in the region. Mikhail Mil was born in Irkutsk and grew up in Siberia. He worked for other designers before setting up his own bureau. Their first product was the Mi-1, the first Soviet helicopter, which made its maiden flight in September 1948. The giant Mi-6 was the largest helicopter in the world when it took to the air in September 1957. Around eight hundred were completed and the type has proved to be invaluable serving the gas fields around the town

TYPE	REG/SER	CON. NO.	PI/NOTES	STATUS
□ Antonov An-2P	RA-70705	1G 130-07	CCCP-70705	PV
□ Mil Mi-1	RA-68117			PV
□ Mil Mi-2	RA-15686			PV
□ Mil Mi-4A	RA-36574	17157		PV
□ Mil Mi-6A	RA-21075	0717		PV

NOVOKUZNETSK AIRPORT MEMORIAL (RUS34)

Address:	Spichenkovo Airport, Novokuznetsk.
Admission:	On permanent view.
Location:	About 16 km west of the town.

This important industrial town is also near to many ski resorts. The airport has been modernised and is now capable of handing medium sized airliners. The Mil-2 has been preserved to show the importance of aviation in the region. The helicopter was first flown by Aeroflot and later by Aero Kuznetsk.

TYPE	REG/SER	CON. NO.	PI/NOTES	STATUS
□ Mil Mi-2	RA-23570	525607038	CCCP-23570	PV

NOVOSIBIRSK AVIATION PRODUCTION ASSOCIATION MUSEUM (RUS35)

Address:	15 Polzunova Street, 630051 Novosibirsk.
Tel:	03832-798095
Email:	aircraft@napa.sib.ru
Admission:	By prior permission only.
Location:	At Elitsovka which is about 8 km north of the city.

The factory was established in 1931 and has now produced almost thirty thousand aircraft. The first type to be constructed in large numbers was the Polikarpov I-16 fighter. This stubby low wing monoplane was first flown by Valery Chkalov on the last day of 1933. Many versions of the type later appeared. Over the last three quarters of a century Lavochkin Lagg-3s, Yakovlev Yak-7s, Yak-9s, Yak-28s, MiG-15s, MiG-17s, MiG-19s, Sukhoi Su-9s, Su-11s and Su-15s, Su-24s, Su-34s and Antonov An-38's have come off the lines. The museum traces the history of the plant with many models, photographs and documents on show. A collection of types constructed at Novosibirsk has been gathered for this interesting museum.

TYPE	REG/SER	CON. NO.	PI/NOTES	STATUS
☐ Mikoyan-Gurevich MiG-17	01			RA
☐ Polikarpov I-16	153			RA
☐ Sukhoi Su-9	03			RA
☐ Sukhoi Su-15TM	04			RA
☐ Sukhoi Su-24	09			RA
☐ Yakovlev Yak-9				RA
☐ Yakovlev Yak-28P	02			RA

NOVOSIBIRSK MILITARY AVIATION MUSEUM (RUS36)

Address: Novosibirsk Air Force Headquarters, 630000 Novosibirsk.
Tel: 03832-399332
Admission: By prior permission only.
Location: In the southern part of the town.

A museum has been set up in the military town which contains the local Air Force Headquarters. There are several military airfields in the region operating a variety of types. Five aircraft are known to be in the collection but there may well be others. The earliest is an example of the Lisunov Li-2 derived from the famous Douglas DC-3. The Li-2 served in the transport role in the Soviet Union for many years and over four thousand eight hundred were built. Admission to this collection is normally reserved for military personnel.

TYPE	REG/SER	CON. NO.	PI/NOTES	STATUS
☐ Aero L-39C Albatros	55			RA
☐ Lisunov Li-2 [Douglas DC-3 modified]				RA
☐ Mikoyan-Gurevich MiG-23MLD	09			RA
☐ Mikoyan-Gurevich MiG-29	54			RA
☐ Sukhoi Su-17M4	17			RA

NOVY URENGOJ MEMORIAL (RUS37)

Address: Novy Urengoj.
Admission: On permanent view.
Location: In the town.

This remote town is surrounded by vast gas and oil fields. Helicopters have played an increasing role in the development of these industries. A green Mil Mi-8 has been preserved in the town as a memorial.

TYPE	REG/SER	CON. NO.	PI/NOTES	STATUS
☐ Mil Mi-8				PV

NOYABRSK MEMORIAL (RUS38)

Address: 626726 Noyabrsk.
Admission: On permanent view.
Location: At the airport which is about 5 km west of the town.

In 1975 a Mil Mi-8 landed in the region in the search for oil. A new town soon sprung up and workers moved in. An airport was constructed and flights brought in necessary supplies. A Mil Mi-8 has been preserved at the field to show the part the type played in developing this remote region of Siberia.

TYPE	REG/SER	CON. NO.	PI/NOTES	STATUS
☐ Mil Mi-8	RA-22851	98315254	CCCP-22581	PV

OMSK AVIATION TECHNICAL SCHOOL (RUS39)

Address: Tsentralny Airport, Omsk 644143.
Admission: By prior permission only.
Location: About 5 km south west of the city.

The school was set up by Aeroflot to train airframe and engine fitters for its vast fleet. The work has carried on and a collection of instructional airframes resides in an area of the airport. The types are typical of those used by the former national airline. An example of the first Soviet jet airliner, the Tu-104, is the most interesting. This aircraft was delivered from the Kazan factory in 1959 and transferred to the West Siberia division in 1973.

TYPE	REG/SER	CON. NO.	PI/NOTES	STATUS
☐ Antonov An-2P	RA-07344	1G 149-48	CCCP-07344	RA
☐ Antonov An-2R	RA-40732	1G 172-04	CCCP-40732	RA
☐ Antonov An-24	CCCP-46730	37300501		RA
☐ Antonov An-24				RA
☐ Antonov An-26	RA-26612	4904	CCCP-26612	RA
☐ Ilyushin Il-76	CCCP-76502	063407206		RA
☐ Let L-410UVP	RA-67165	790201	CCCP-67165	RA
☐ Mil Mi-8				RA
☐ Mil Mi-8				RA
☐ Tupolev Tu-104B	CCCP-42417	920404		RA
☐ Tupolev Tu-154	CCCP-85015	71A015		RA
☐ Tupolev Tu-154A	RA-85081	74A081	CCCP-85081	RA
☐ Tupolev Tu-154B-1 (TU-154A)	RA-85064	74A064	CCCP-85064	RA
☐ Yakovlev Yak-40				RA

OMSK CIVIL AVIATION PLANT MUSEUM (RUS40)

Address:	112 Surovtseva Street, 644015 Omsk.
Tel:	03812-553040
Fax:	03812-553040
Email:	nfo@ozga.com
Admission:	By prior permission only.
Location:	In the eastern part of the town.

The factory was set up in 1945 to overhaul Polikarpov Po-2 biplanes and their engines. Work was later carried out on Yakovlev Yak-12s and Mil Mi-4s. The plant was privatised in the 1990s and since then large numbers of Mil types have passed through the workshops. A museum has been set up and on show are photographs, models and documents tracing the history of the factory. The Mil-8, in company colours, is parked by the main gate.

TYPE	REG/SER	CON. NO.	PI/NOTES	STATUS
☐ Mil Mi-8	RA-22277	6956	CCCP-22277	RA

PEREYASLOVKA AIR BASE MEMORIAL (RUS41)

Address:	Verino.
Admission:	By prior permission only.
Location:	Just west of the village which is about 40 km south of Khabarovsk.

The base has been home to combat types for many years and until recently Sukhoi Su-24s were in residence. Reports suggest this unit may have been disbanded. A MiG-21 has been preserved as a memorial.

TYPE	REG/SER	CON. NO.	PI/NOTES	STATUS
☐ Mikoyan-Gurevich MiG-21	33			RA

POKRYSHKIN MEMORIAL MUSEUM (RUS42)

Address:	Vocational School 2, 630108 Novosibirksk.
Tel:	03832-418-544
Admission:	By prior permission only.
Location:	In the centre of the town.

This museum, dedicated to the famous fighter pilot A.I. Pokryshkin who was three times decorated 'Hero of the Soviet Union', has been set up in the school. On display in the halls are many photographs, models, documents and personal items tracing his life. In 1941 Pokryshkin scored his first victory in the Odessa region whilst flying a MiG-3. He rose to the rank of Air Marshal and was the second highest scoring Soviet ace in World War II with fifty-five enemy aircraft shot down. After the end of hostilities he remained in the Air Force and was passed over for promotion during the Stalin era as he had a preference for non-Soviet types. He was one of the first to fly the jet powered MiG-9. Over half of almost five thousand Bell Airacobras delivered to the Soviet Union were ferried via Alaska. The remains of a crashed example were found several years ago near Yakutia and brought to Novosibirsk. The pilot had got lost on the flight and force landed in the Tundra. His remains were found nearby. This aircraft was restored by a team of volunteers and is believed to be in store. An expansion of the exhibition is in the planning stages and will hopefully house the Airacobra. Also in the town is a restored MiG-3 painted in the colours of one flown by Pokryshkin. A wreck was recovered in the area and rebuilt under the direction of the Russian Air Force Museum at Monino near Moscow. The plans for exhibiting this fighter have not been finalised and it remains in store in the Novosibirsk region.

TYPE	REG/SER	CON. NO.	PI/NOTES	STATUS
☐ Bell 26C Airacobra (P-39N)				RA

SALEKHARD AIRPORT DISPLAY (RUS43)

Address:	22 Aviatsionnaya Street, 629004 Salekhard.
Tel:	034922-74261
Fax:	034922-43012
Admission:	Aircraft on permanent view.
Location:	About 7 km north of the town.

Aviation came to the region in 1935 when a Tupolev ANT-9 fitted with skis landed on the frozen River Ob. A landing strip was developed in the latter stages of World War II and after the end of the conflict squadrons of the Soviet Air Force were in residence. Gas and oil has been found in the locality and the facilities have been steadily developed. Services to many cities are operated and the field is one of the standby diversions for aircraft on Trans-Polar flights between Europe and North America. An impressive display of restored airliners has been mounted on plinths beside the road to the terminal building. The oldest is the Lisunov Li-2 built at the Khimki factory near Moscow in the 1940s. The airliner was registered to Aeroflot in 1959 and transferred to their central region in 1972. Withdrawn the following year it was first noted on display in 2000. It is painted in an Aeroflot polar colour scheme with a red tail and wing tips. Four Mil helicopters are on show with the Mi-1 and Mi-6 in the markings of Yamal Airlines. The company was established at Salekhard in 1997 and operates a fleet on airliners and helicopters to many cities across Russia. The Antonov An-26 and Yakovlev Yak-40 were regular visitors in the Aeroflot era and both are exhibited in the standard white and blue colours. The An-26 was originally developed as a military transport with a better performance than the An-24.

TYPE	REG/SER	CON. NO.	PI/NOTES	STATUS
☐ Antonov An-2	CCCP-79854			PV
☐ Antonov An-26B	CCCP-26608	4805		PV
☐ Lisunov Li-2 [Douglas DC-3 modified]	CCCP-73956	18435804	CCCP-65720	PV
☐ Mil Mi-1	RA-10001			PV
☐ Mil Mi-4	RA-28029			PV
☐ Mil Mi-6A	RA-21050	0660	CCCP-21050	PV
☐ Mil Mi-8	RA-25778	4478		PV
☐ Yakovlev Yak-40	RA-87262	9321826	CCCP-87262	PV

SOVETSKY MEMORIAL (RUS44)

Address:	Tyumenskaya Airport, 625000 Sovetska.
Admission:	On permanent view
Location:	About 4 km south of the town.

The region was developed in the 1960s and 1970s following the discovery of oil. A new town along with an airport was constructed and this now serves flights from several cities. The Antonov An-2 was very suitable for the harsh conditions and an example of the biplane has been preserved at the airport. This memorial is dedicated to the pilots and construction workers who have lost their lives in opening up the area.

TYPE	REG/SER	CON. NO.	PI/NOTES	STATUS
☐ Antonov An-2	RA-01208		CCCP-01208	PV

SURGUT AIRPORT MEMORIAL (RUS45)

Address:	Surgut Airport, 628422 Surgut.
Admission:	On permanent view.
Location:	About 10 km north of the town.

The town is one of the oldest in Siberia and dates from around 1590. Oil and gas were discovered in the 1960s and rapid expansion took place. Around a dozen airlines now fly from the airport. Among them is Utair who have a major base at Surgut. Helicopters are used in the region and plinth mounted is an example of the large Mi-6.

TYPE	REG/SER	CON. NO.	PI/NOTES	STATUS
☐ Mil Mi-6A	RA-21046	0656	CCCP-21046	PV

TAKSIMO STATION MUSEUM AND SURVEY MEMORIAL (RUS46)

Address:	BAM Station, 670031Taksimo.
Admission:	On permanent view.
Location:	In the centre of the town.

The BAM railway was built in the early 1970s to serve as an alternative to the Trans-Siberian Railway. The idea had been first put forward in the 1930s. A small museum has been set up at the local railway station which is at the end of the electrified section of the route. Mounted on a plinth outside the station is a Tupolev ANT-4 which crashed in Lake Barencharoe on one of the original aerial surveys. After forty years under water the aircraft was recovered in the 1970s and restored by a volunteer group from the railway builders. The aircraft mounted on floats rests in a dramatic pose at the top of a plinth. Around sixty floatplanes were completed and after their military days were over many flew with Aeroflot. With the Air Force they were used mainly as torpedo bombers.

TYPE	REG/SER	CON. NO.	PI/NOTES	STATUS
☐ Tupolev ANT-4 (TB-1P)	CCCP-K11			PV

TUMEN MEMORIAL (RUS47)

Address:	ROSTO, Tumen.
Admission:	On permanent view.
Location:	In the town.

When the Soviet Union split up the Russian Defence, Sport and Technical Organisation was formed. This took over from DOSAAF (Voluntary Society of Assistance to the Army Air Force and Navy.

TYPE	REG/SER	CON. NO.	PI/NOTES	STATUS
☐ Aero L-29 Delfin	60			PV

TUNGUR MEMORIAL (RUS48)

Address:	Tungur, Altay.
Admission:	On permanent view.
Location:	In the town.

The region is popular with tourists and has seen increasing use of helicopters in recent years. An example of the Mil Mi-2, which has been produced in vast numbers, has been mounted as a memorial.

TYPE	REG/SER	CON. NO.	PI/NOTES	STATUS
☐ Mil Mi-2				PV

UGORSK MEMORIAL (RUS49)

Address:	Ugorsk.
Admission:	On permanent view.
Location:	In the town.

The area is yet another which has developed with the discovery of oil and gas. There are no airfields close to the town but a Yak-28 has been dedicated as a memorial to local aviators who have been killed.

TYPE	REG/SER	CON. NO.	PI/NOTES	STATUS
☐ Yakovlev Yak-28	54			PV

ULAN-UDE AVIATION PLANT MUSEUM (RUS50)

Address:	1 Khorinskaya Street, Ulan-Ude 670009.
Tel:	03012-257-475
Email:	uuaz@uuaz.ru
Admission:	By prior permission only.
Location:	About 9 km east of the town.

The factory opened in 1939 and the first task carried out was the repair of Polikarpov I-16s and Tupolev SB-2s. Soon the manufacture of Polikarpov Po-2 fuselages was started. Since these early days types built included Lavochkin La-5s, La-7s, La-9s, MiG-15UTIs, Yak-25s, An-24s and MiG-27Ms. The first helicopters Ka-15s, Ka-18s and Ka-25s left the lines in the late 1950s and now the Mi-8T and Mi-171 are produced. Co-operation with the Sukhoi OKB started in the early 1980s and versions of the Su-25 and Su-39 are built in the large factory. There is a museum in the plant tracing the history of the site.

TYPE	REG/SER	CON. NO.	PI/NOTES	STATUS
☐ Mikoyan-Gurevich MiG-15				RA

URAY AIRPORT MEMORIAL (RUS51)

Address:	Uray Airport, 628285 Uray.
Admission:	On permanent view.
Location:	About 4 km south east of the town.

The town was set up in the 1960s to coincide with the gas and oil boom. The Mi-4 painted in a red and blue scheme has been mounted at the airport as a memorial to helicopter crews who have been killed in the area.

TYPE	REG/SER	CON. NO.	PI/NOTES	STATUS
☐ Mil Mi-4A	CCCP-14308	16174		PV

VICTORY PARK – ANGARSK (RUS52)

Address:	665000 Angarsk.
Admission:	On permanent view.
Location:	In the south western part of the town.

The city was set up in the 1960s and is now a centre for the nuclear industry. The park was built to commemorate the victory of the Soviet Union in the Great Patriotic War (World War II). The only aircraft on show is an example of the MiG-23BN. This attack version of the fighter first flew in 1970. It was built in large numbers and exported to many countries in Europe, Africa and Asia as well as to Cuba.

TYPE	REG/SER	CON. NO.	PI/NOTES	STATUS
☐ Mikoyan-Gurevich MiG-23BN	31			PV

VICTORY PARK – KEMEROVO (RUS53)

Address:	650010 Kemerovo.
Admission:	On permanent view.
Location:	In the centre of the town.

This large park contains many memorials including one dedicated to the 'Home Front Workers'. Many citizens of the Soviet Union worked in factories, on the railways and transports systems as well as and carrying out general maintenance duties in the community. There is also a missile and a tank to be seen along with the Delfin.

TYPE	REG/SER	CON. NO.	PI/NOTES	STATUS
☐ Aero L-29 Delfin	76			PV

VICTORY PARK – KRASNOYARSK (RUS54)

Address:	660000 Krasnoyarsk.
Admission:	On permanent view.
Location:	In the city.

This park contains a large memorial dedicated to the success in World War II. During the conflict Krasnoyarsk was home to an important military airfield. This site has now been absorbed into the city and is covered by large apartment blocks. Two other aircraft are preserved in the vicinity. These are a MiG-21F-13 and a Yak-52.

TYPE	REG/SER	CON. NO.	PI/NOTES	STATUS
☐ Mikoyan-Gurevich MiG-17	01			PV
☐ Mikoyan-Gurevich MiG-21F-13			04 – nearby.	PV
☐ Yakovlev Yak-52	18		Nearby.	PV

VICTORY PARK – MARIINSK (RUS55)

Address:	652160 Mariinsk.
Admission:	On permanent view.
Location:	In the town.

On show in this park are memorials dedicated to local people who lost their lives in the Great Patriotic War. A recent arrival is the Yakovlev Yak-52 trainer – a type which did not fly until 1979.

TYPE	REG/SER	CON. NO.	PI/NOTES	STATUS
☐ Yakovlev Yak-52				PV

Above: This Sukhoi Su-15TM serves as a memorial to those who lost their lives when Korean Air Lines Flight 007 was shot down in September 1983. (Gleb Osokin)

Right: A collection of preserved aircraft can be seen at Nizhnevartovsk Airport. An Antonov An-2 is shown here. (Gleb Osokin)

Two of the gate guards at Dhahran Air Force Base are this Lockheed T-33 and North American F-86F Sabre. (Paul Jackson)

VLADIVOSTOK MEMORIALS (RUS56)

Address:	690090 Vladivostok.
Admission:	On permanent view
Location:	At a number of sites around the city.

Four aircraft are known to be preserved as memorials around the city. The Yakovlev Yak-40 is at the main airport which is about forty kilometres north of the centre. The aircraft was delivered to the Far Eastern Division of Aeroflot in 1973 and acquired by Vladivostok Air in 1993. The airliner was recently withdrawn from use and put on show during 2007. There are many military bases in the region and the MiG-15UTI is dedicated to those who have flown from these. This aircraft is mounted on a plinth in a local park. The pylon mounted MiG-23MLD is honours all who have served in the guards regiments. These elite troops served with distinction in the Great Patriotic War and are still a force in the current Russian Army. Helicopters were flown by Aeroflot in the area and the Mil Mi-2, preserved in the town, was later used by Vladivostok Air.

TYPE	REG/SER	CON. NO.	PI/NOTES	STATUS
☐ Mikoyan-Gurevich MiG-15UTI	01	812923		PV
☐ Mikoyan-Gurevich MiG-23MLD	02			PV
☐ Mil Mi-2	RA-23310	529141045	CCCP-23310	PV
☐ Yakovlev Yak-40	RA-87325	9330430	CCCP-87325 – at airport.	PV

VORKUTA AIRPORT MEMORIAL (RUS57)

Address:	Vorkuta Airport, 720000 Vorkuta.
Admission:	On permanent view.
Location:	About 3 km west of the town.

The city has its origins in the forced labour camps set up in the Stalin era. During the cold war period strategic bombers were based in the area. The airport now handles passenger flights and on the opposite, south, side of the runway is a small military area. The Mil-4 painted in a red and blue Aeroflot scheme resides on a plinth by the terminal. The Ilyushin Il-14 is preserved close to the military ramp.

TYPE	REG/SER	CON. NO.	PI/NOTES	STATUS
☐ Ilyushin Il-14	20			PV
☐ Mil Mi-4	CCCP-66857			PV

YAKUTSK MEMORIALS (RUS58)

Address:	Yakutsk
Admission:	On permanent view.
Location:	In the town.

Two memorials are located in the town. The Bell Airacobra, which is believed to be a genuine aircraft, is dedicated to the pilots who flew the type in Russian skies in the Great Patriotic War. Over half the P-39s produced were delivered to the Soviet Union. Some were delivered by sea but the majority were flown via Alaska and landed in Siberia before moving on to operational bases. Quite a few crashed on this arduous ferry flight over the hostile terrain which existed both sides of the Bering Strait. The airfield at Yaktusk saw many landings by the type. The flights were carried out by members of the 7th ferrying group. The Airacobra was a popular fighter and many of the country's highest scoring aces claimed many kills on the type. The Mil Mi-I is located at Magan Aiport which is a short distance north west of the city. The helicopter was used in the region for many years and was mounted as a memorial some time ago. This honours pilots who have lost their lives. The airfield is used for general aviation and is home to a considerable number of fixed wing aircraft and helicopters.

TYPE	REG/SER	CON. NO.	PI/NOTES	STATUS
☐ Bell 26C Airacobra (P-39Q)	42-20613			PV
☐ Mil Mi-1M	RA-13315	401024	CCCP-13315	PV

ZOLOTAYA DOLINA MEMORIAL (RUS59)

Address:	Zolotaya Dolina.
Admission:	On permaqnent view.
Location:	In the town.

The Sukhoi Su-15TM is spectacularly mounted as a memorial to local aviators who died in military service. The TM version of the fighter appeared in the late 1970s. Based on the Su-15T it was fitted with improved engines and control systems. Production of the type started in 1970 and continued for at least five years.

TYPE	REG/SER	CON. NO.	PI/NOTES	STATUS
☐ Sukhoi Su-15TM	31			PV

SAUDI ARABIA

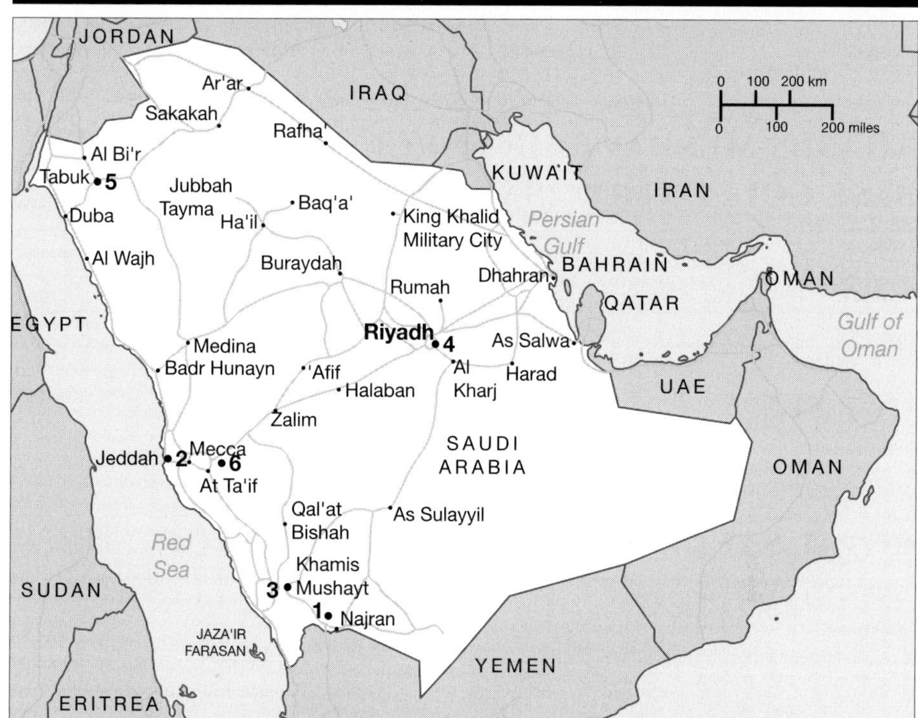

DHAHRAN AIR FORCE BASE COLLECTION (SAU1)

Address:	King Abdul-Al-Aziz Air Base, Dhahran.
Tel:	03-891-1313
Admission:	By prior permission only.
Location:	Near the city which is on the east coast of the country.

This important base is home to squadrons operating the F-15 Eagle, and Tornado. The airfield opened in 1923 and a small number of surplus de Havilland D.H.9s were delivered. The preserved aircraft are spread around the site. A collection of memorabilia tracing the history of the airfield is located in a room on the base.

TYPE	REG/SER	CON. NO.	PI/NOTES	STATUS
☐ British Aircraft Corporation 167 Strikemaster 80A	1135	366	G-27-312, G-BFOO	RA
☐ English Electric P.1B Lightning F.1		95013	XG313, G-27-115	RA
☐ English Electric P.27 Lightning T.54 (T.4)	54-607	B1/95077	XM989, 54-650	RA
☐ Hawker P.1099 Hunter F.60 (F.6)	60-604	41H/688090	XJ715, G-9-213	RA
☐ Kawasaki-Vertol KV-107-II-5	05			RA
☐ Lockheed 580 (T-33A)	1503		(USAF)	RA
☐ Lockheed 580 (T-33A)			(USAF)	RA
☐ North American NA-191 Sabre (F-86F)	709	191-926	52-5230, 558	RA
☐ North American NA-191 Sabre (F-86F)			(USAF)	RA
☐ North American NA-191 Sabre (F-86F)			(USAF)	RA
☐ Panavia PA200 Tornado IDS	765	3250	ZE126	RA

JEDDAH AVIATION MUSEUM (SAU2)

Address:	Old Airport, Jeddah.
Admission:	Not yet open.
Location:	In the northern part of the city.

Plans were approved in the spring of 2006 to establish a museum on the site of the old airport. The displays would trace the history of aviation in the region with models, photographs and documents. The original control tower was demolished several years ago and a long term aim is to build a replica of this. The Beech 18 is mounted on a pylon close to the proposed site and will probably be incorporated in the display.

TYPE	REG/SER	CON. NO.	PI/NOTES	STATUS
☐ Beech D18S (TC-45G)		AF-81	51-11524, N9535Z	PV

KHAMIS MUSHAYT AIR FORCE BASE COLLECTION (SAU3)

Address:	King Khalid Air Force Base, Khamis Mushayt.
Admission:	By prior permission only.
Location:	About 10 km east of the town

Fighter squadrons are located at this important base. One of the Lightnings is positioned by the main gate and the other two aircraft are located in a small heritage park in the main camp.

TYPE	REG/SER	CON. NO.	PI/NOTES	STATUS
☐ English Electric P.26 Lightning F.53	224	95293	G-27-57, G-AWOO, 53-687, 1306	RA
☐ English Electric P.26 Lightning F.53	'224'			RAX
☐ North American NA-193 Sabre (F-86F)	714	193-250	52-5521	RA

ROYAL SAUDI AIR FORCE MUSEUM (SAU4)

Address:	Saqr Al-Jazeerah, Riyadh.
Admission:	Tuesday-Sunday 0800-1200 1600-1800.
Location:	In the northern part of the city near exit 10 of the Ring Road.

In World War I Arab forces, supported by the British, assisted the local rulers in regaining their lands. Detachments of the Royal Air Force were based in the area. Conflicts continued until the mid-1920s when the Hejaz forces were defeated and the country became unified. Six D.H.9s captured from the Hejaz were taken over. Four Westland Wapitis were acquired in 1931. The first Saudi military pilots were trained in Italy in 1935/6 and returned with three Caproni Ca.100s and a trio of Caproni Ca.101s. This impressive museum opened in late 1999. The first exhibition hall was completed in nine months and a second followed. These are linked by a glass tower and hangar which houses the DC-3 presented to King Abdul Aziz by President Roosevelt in 1947. The oldest genuine aircraft is a Caproni Ca.100 obtained from the Caproni Museum in Italy A rarity is the Temco Buckaroo developed from the classic Globe Swift. Only sixteen of the type were built with ten going to Saudi Arabia. Informative displays tracing the history of the service can be seen in the hall.

TYPE	REG/SER	CON. NO.	PI/NOTES	STATUS
☐ Agusta-Bell 206A Jet Ranger	1220			PV
☐ Agusta-Bell 212	1437	3667		PV
☐ Beech C18S Expeditor (C-45F) (UC-45F)	'55226'			RA
☐ Beech A45 Mentor (T-34A)	619	G-783	55-226	PV
☐ British Aircraft Corporation 167 Strikemaster 90	911	11		PV
☐ British Aircraft Corporation 167 Strikemaster 90	1110	22	G-27-17, 910	RA
☐ British Aircraft Corporation 167 Strikemaster 90	1124	355		PV
☐ British Aircraft Corporation 167 Strikemaster 90	1127	358	G-27-293, 358	PV
☐ Caproni Ca.100 Caprocino	I-BIZZ	3488	MM56271	PV
☐ Cessna 172	N8846B	36546		RA
☐ Cessna 310	131			PV
☐ De Havilland D.H.9A (FSM)				PV
☐ De Havilland D.H.100 Vampire FB.52	504			RA
☐ De Havilland D.H.100 Vampire FB.52	541			PV
☐ De Havilland D.H.C.1 Chipmunk T.20	600	C1/1003	G-5-15	PV
☐ Douglas A-26B Invader	612	18826	43-22679	PV
☐ Douglas DC-3A-467 Skytrain (C-47B)	'HZ-SA-R-1'	15902/32650	44-76318, SA-R-1, HZ-AAX, SA-R-1	PVX
☐ Douglas DC-4 Skymaster	450			PV
☐ English Electric P.25 Lightning F.52 (F.2)	610	95123	XN770, 52-656, 52-610	PV
☐ English Electric P.27 Lightning T.54 (T.4)	54-608	B1/95080	XM992, 54-651	RA
☐ English Electric P.27 Lightning T.55	230	B1/95030	G-27-25, 219	PV
☐ Hawker P.1099 Hunter F.6	'60-602'		XJ634	PVX
☐ Hawker P.1099 Hunter F.6 (FSM)	'60-604'			PVX
☐ Lockheed 382C-39D Hercules (C-130H)	460	382C-4567		PVC
☐ Lockheed 580 (T-33A)	1510			PV
☐ McDonnell M.199-1C Eagle (F-15C)	1315		80-0098	PV
☐ North American NA-84 Texan (AT-6B)	'91-713'	84-7640	41-17262	PVX
☐ North American NA-88 Texan (AT-6D)	206			PV

☐ North American NA-159 Trojan (T-28A)	713	159-225	49-1713	PV
☐ North American NA-191 Sabre (F-86F)	5518			PV
☐ Northrop N-311 Tiger II (F-5E)	1504	R.1162	74-1504, 923	PV
☐ Panavia PA200 Tornado ADV	2915	3359	ZE910, 3453	PV
☐ Temco TE.1B Buckaroo (T-35A)	'34-470'		53-4474	PV
☐ Westland Wapiti IIA (FSM)				PV

TABUK AIR BASE COLLECTION (SAU5)

Address:	King Faisal Air Base, Tabuk.
Admission:	By prior permission only.
Location:	Just south east of the town.

Combat units are resident at this base which also serves as the civil airport for the region. The unidentified DC-3 and one of the Lightnings are mounted on poles at different locations outside the site.

TYPE	REG/SER	CON. NO.	PI/NOTES	STATUS
☐ Douglas DC-3A-456 Skytrain (C-47A)				PV
☐ English Electric P.26 Lightning F.53	219	95305	G-27-6?, 53-698	RA
☐ English Electric P.26 Lightning F.53	227	95306	G-27-6?, 1310	PV

TAIF AIR FORCE BASE COLLECTION (SAU6)

Address:	King Fahd Air Base, Taif.
Admission:	By prior permission only.
Location:	About 10 km north east of Al Hawiyah.

Housed at this field are squadrons flying the F-15 Eagle, the F-5 Tiger and helicopters. Several aircraft have been preserved around the base. The preserved Lightning crashed in January 1980 and has been rebuilt.

TYPE	REG/SER	CON. NO.	PI/NOTES	STATUS
☐ Douglas A-26B Invader	64371	27950	44-34671, 301	RA
☐ English Electric P.26 Lightning F.53	1303	95289	G-27-54, 53-684, 208	RA
☐ Lockheed 580 (T-33A)	1905		(USAF)	RA
☐ McDonnell M.199-1C Eagle (F-15C)	511	808	80-0105	RA
☐ North American NA-191 Sabre (F-86F)	2515		(USAF)	RA
☐ Northrop N-311 Tiger II (F-5E)	1002			RA

SINGAPORE

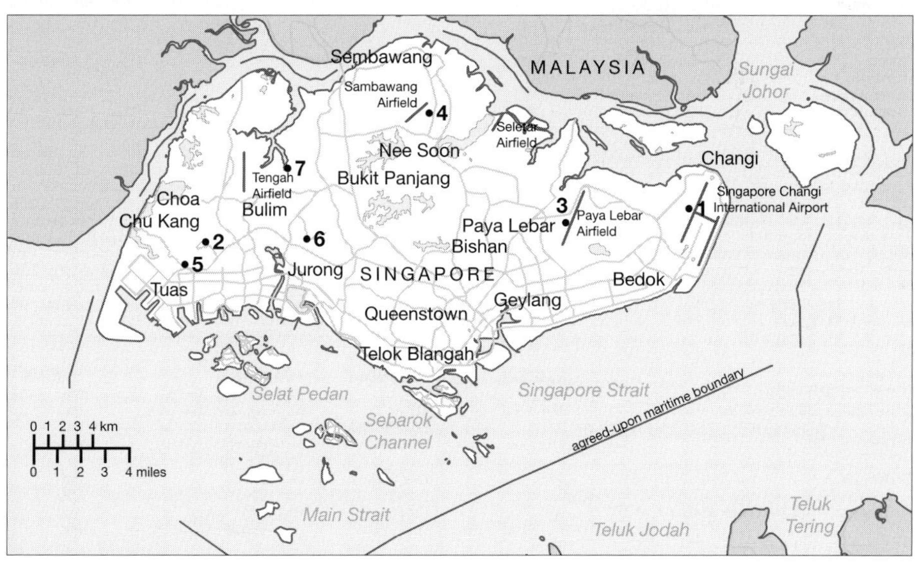

CHANGI AIRPORT MEMORIAL (SI1)

Address:	P.O. Box 1, Changi, Singapore 918141.
Tel:	6542-1122
Admission:	By prior permission only.
Location:	In the eastern part of the island.

Changi was a former Royal Air Force Base that was handed over to the Republic of Singapore Air Force. In the mid-1970s a decision was made to develop the site as the main International Airport for the country. The military steadily moved out and at the turn of the century the Air Force Museum moved to Paya Lebar.

TYPE	REG/SER	CON. NO.	PI/NOTES	STATUS
☐ Grumman G-111 Albatross (G-64) (SA-16A) (SA-16B) (HU-16B)		G-228	51-7178, PK-OAH	RA

NANYANG TECHNOLOGICAL UNIVERSITY – HALL OF FAME AVIATION GALLERY (SI2)

Address:	Nanchang Avenue, Singapore 639798
Tel:	065-6791-1744
Fax:	065-6791-1604
Admission:	By prior permission only.
Location:	In the south western part of the city.

The university runs a number of courses on aviation related topics. A display has been set up to educate the students in the history of flying in the region. Two aircraft are on show along with displays of photographs, models, components and documents. Both types served with the local Air Force.

TYPE	REG/SER	CON. NO.	PI/NOTES	STATUS
☐ Bell 205 Iroquois (UH-1H)	257			RA
☐ Douglas A-4SU Skyhawk (A4D-2N) (A-4C)	924	12721	Bu148528	RA

REPUBLIC OF SINGAPORE AIR FORCE MUSEUM (SI3)

Address:	400 Airport Road, Payar Lebar Airbase 534234.
Tel:	065-6461-8507
Fax:	065-6461-8505
Email:	afmuseum@startnet.gov.sg
Admission:	Tuesday-Sunday 0830-1700.
Location:	In the eastern part of the island.

Singapore left the Federation of Malaysia in August 1965 and established an Air Force in 1968. Initially Cessna 172s were used for training. The service has expanded over the last three decades and now has several squadrons equipped with combat jets. A museum was set up at Changi in September 1988 and the exhibition opened in July 1991. A British Army camp was built at Changi in the late 1920s and during the Japanese occupation an airfield was constructed. The Royal Air Force decided to use the field as a transport base and the station opened in April 1946 and remained in use until 1971. The Republic of Singapore Air Force took over the site soon after. The collection moved to a new purpose built complex at Paya Lebar in 2000. The official opening took place in March 2001.The history of military flying from the early days of the Malayan Volunteer Air Force is portrayed. Almost fifty Hunters and sixteen Strikemasters have been used. The Cessna 172 was once painted with a false serial. Twenty SIAI-Marchetti SF.260MS trainers were delivered along with six of the SF.260WS version. They were operated by 150 Squadron at Seletar. Also outside are two Bloodhound missiles and their handling and control systems. There are galleries depicting the history of the service with models, photographs, documents, badges, trophies and uniforms.

TYPE	REG/SER	CON. NO.	PI/NOTES	STATUS
☐ Bell 204 Iroquois (HU-1B) (UH-1B)	258	251	60-3605	PV
☐ Bell 204 Iroquois (UH-1B)	264	917	63-8692, 264, N483SA	PV
☐ British Aircraft Corporation 167 Strikemaster 84	301	EEP/JP/1921	G-27-130	PV
☐ Cessna 172K	110	17258110	N79464, N1619, 110, 9V-BEU, '107'	PV
☐ Douglas A-4S Skyhawk (A4D-2) (A-4B)	607	12259	Bu145013	PV
☐ Douglas TA-4S Skyhawk (A4D-2) (A-4B) (TA-4B)	651	12293	Bu145047 – front fuselage only.	PV
☐ Douglas TA-4SU Skyhawk (A4D-2N) (A-4C)	900	12476	Bu147742 – also reported as c/n 12506.	PV
☐ Eurocopter AS.550U-2	210			PV

TYPE	REG/SER	CON. NO.	PI/NOTES	STATUS
☐ Hawker P.1099 Hunter FGA.74 (F.6)	510	41H/680082	XG296, G-9-303 – on base gate.	PV
☐ Hawker P.1099 Hunter FGA.74A (F.6)	501	41H/680061	XG260, G-9-300	PV
☐ Hawker P.1099 Hunter FR.74B (F.6)	527	S4U 3334	XF458, G-9-364	PV
☐ Lockheed 580 (T-33A)	364	580-6288	51-6956, 16596 (French), F-BJDT	PV
☐ SIAI-Marchetti SF.260MS	123	13-04	I-SIND ?	PV
☐ Sud-Est SE.3160 Alouette III	'200'	1271	1271	PVX

SEMBAWANG AIR BASE MEMORIAL (SI4)

Address: Sembawang
Singapore 757752.
Admission: By prior permission only.
Location: Just south of the town.

This former Fleet Air Arm airfield is now home to all helicopter squadrons of the Republic of Singapore Air Force. Two examples of the ubiquitous Iroquois are preserved at the site.

TYPE	REG/SER	CON. NO.	PI/NOTES	STATUS
☐ Bell 204 Iroquois (UH-1B)	254	657	62-4597 – possible identity.	RA
☐ Bell 205 Iroquois (UH-1H)	238		(USAF)	RA

SINGAPORE DISCOVERY CENTRE (SI5)

Address: 510 Upper Jurong Road,
Singapore 628925.
Tel: 065-0792-6188
Fax: 065-0792-1255
Email: info@sdc.com.sg
Admission: Tuesday- Sunday 0900-1800.
Location: In the western part of the island.

Exhibits at this innovative centre are designed to show the latest developments in industry and the natural world. There are many 'hands-on' displays to test and inform visitors. Three aircraft are now on show. In 1972 forty former U.S. Navy A-4B Skyhawks were purchased and upgraded, eight in America and the remainder in Singapore. Since then further modifications have been carried out. Almost forty examples of the Iroquois have been operated by the Air Force and many are still in use. A classic Hunter is also on view.

TYPE	REG/SER	CON. NO.	PI/NOTES	STATUS
☐ Bell 204 Iroquois (UH-1B)	268	736	63-8514	PV
☐ Douglas A-4S Skyhawk (A4D-2) (A-4B)	600	11912	Bu142850	PV
☐ Douglas TA-4S Skyhawk (A4D-2) (A-4B) (TA-4B)	690	12225	Bu144979 – at nearby military camp.	PV
☐ Hawker P.1099 Hunter FGA.74 (F.6) (FGA.9)	505	41H/680085	XJ632, G-9-302	PV

SINGAPORE SCIENCE CENTRE (SI6)

Address: 15 Science Centre Road,
Off Jurong Town Hall Road,
Singapore 609081.
Tel: 065-6425-2500
Fax: 065-6565-9533
Email: enquiry@science.edu.sg
Admission: Tuesday-Sunday 1000-1800.
Location: In the western part of the island

The developments in many fields of science are traced in the imaginative displays at this museum. The visitor can wander through a large representation of the human body and view the functions of the organs. One gallery is devoted to the history of flight and space exploration. An Airspeed Consul should soon be back on show in the colours of the first operated by Malayan Airways. The company became Malaysian Airlines in 1963 and three years later Malaysian-Singapore Airlines. Soon after Singapore left the Malaysian Federation in 1965 the airline split and Singapore Airlines came into being. The aircraft on show was acquired from the Royal Air Force Museum in England and flown to Singapore in a Boeing 747. The Consul was restored by engineering staff at Changi Airport in time for the fortieth anniversary of the company. The wooden airframe had absorbed moisture during its period of storage in England and a great deal of work had to be carried out on the structure. The two Cheetah engines were obtained on long term loan from New Zealand. After a spell exhibited at the training centre of the company the Consul moved to this centre in the winter of 1997/8. The airframe deteriorated during its time on show and is now with a company in New Zealand for a complete rebuild.

TYPE	REG/SER	CON. NO.	PI/NOTES	STATUS
☐ Airspeed AS.65 Consul (AS.10 Oxford I)	'VR-SCD'	5136	R6029, G-AJLR – original c/n 759.	PV
☐ Bell 47G-2	VH-JCN	2556	CF-MUZ, C-FMUZ	PV
☐ Flightship Ground Effects Airfish 3				PV

TENGAH AIR BASE MEMORIAL (SI7)

Address:	Tengah, Singapore 699806.
Admission:	By prior permission only.
Location:	North west of the town.

Royal Air Force Tengah opened in 1939 and from 1942 until 1945 was used by the Imperial Japanese Air Force. Now it is the main base for fighter squadrons of the R.S.A.F. The Skyhawk is preserved by the main gate.

TYPE	REG/SER	CON. NO.	PI/NOTES	STATUS
☐ Douglas A-4S Skyhawk (A4D-2) (A-4B)	'628'		(USN), 657	RAX

SOUTH KOREA

AIR PARK (SKO1)

Address:	Shingdaebang-dong, Dongkak-gi, Seoul 156-071.
Tel:	02-2181-1120
Admission:	Open 24 hours.
Location:	In Boramae Park which is about 6 km south west of the city centre.

The site was home to the Air Force Academy from 1958 until December 1985. A large tower commemorating this is located in the park. The area was developed as a recreational park with many facilities for visitors. There are sports halls and tennis courts as well as a zoo. Two aircraft were placed on show a few years ago and this led to the idea of a museum. The new collection opened in November 2007 and more airframes are expected.

TYPE	REG/SER	CON. NO.	PI/NOTES	STATUS
☐ Bell 204 Iroquois (UH-1B)	38734	959	63-8734	PV
☐ Cessna 318C Tweety Bird (T-37C)	31687	42030	73-1687	PV
☐ Cessna 337M Super Skymaster (O-2A)	10834	337M0199	68-10834	PV
☐ Fairchild 473 Provider (205) (C-123B) (C-123K)	40622	20071	54-0622	PV
☐ Lockheed 580 (T-33A)	70606	580-1335	57-0606 – identity doubtful.	PV
☐ McDonnell M.98EN Phantom II (F-4D)	40948	1345	64-0948	PV
☐ North American NA-193 Sabre (F-86F)	525483	193-212	52-5483	PV
☐ Northrop N-156B Freedom Fighter (F-5B)	42117		74-2117	PV

BUSAN ARMY CAMP COLLECTION (SKO2)

Address:	Busan.
Admission:	By prior permission only.
Location:	In the northern part of the town.

Three aircraft are preserved at this camp which is jointly occupied by South Korean and United States forces. The types have been operated in considerable numbers by the services in both countries.

TYPE	REG/SER	CON. NO.	PI/NOTES	STATUS
☐ Cessna 305A Bird Dog (O-1A) (L-19A)				RA
☐ Cessna 318C Tweety Bird (T-37C)				RA
☐ North American NA-191 Sabre (F-86F)				RA

CAMP HUMPHREYS ARMY BASE COLLECTION (SKO3)

Address:	USAG Humphreys, Pyeontack, Gyeonggi-do.
Tel:	031-619-8598
Email:	area3pao@korea.army.mil
Admission:	By prior permission only.
Location:	About 10 km east of Anjung-ni.

The airfield was originally constructed by the Japanese in 1919 and used by the Imperial Air Force until 1945.The Americans took over the site in 1950 and modernised the facilities. The camp was a major base during the Korean War. The site was renamed in 1962 after CWO Benjamin Humphreys who was killed in a helicopter crash near the field. The base is one of the largest American Army bases in Asia and houses many support units and a prison.

TYPE	REG/SER	CON. NO.	PI/NOTES	STATUS
☐ Bell 205 Iroquois (UH-1H)	69-15482	11790		RAD
☐ Bell 209 Huey Cobra (AH-1G) (AH-1F)	71-21051	21122		RA
☐ Grumman G-134 Mohawk (OV-1D)	'69-17001'	28D	69-17017	RAX
☐ Hughes 369M Cayuse (HO-6) (OH-6A)	65-12934	0019		RA

CHANGWON MUSEUM ON NORTH KOREA (SKO4)

Address:	485 Yonge-Dong, Changwon-si, Gyeongsangnam-do.
Tel:	0551-282-2332/3
Admission:	Summer daily 1000-1700; winter daily 1000-1600.
Location:	In the centre of the city.

This museum is dedicated to the war with North Korea which took place between June 1950 and July 1953. The story of the conflict is portrayed in detail with many vivid reminders of the harsh conditions encountered. Amongst the items on show are tanks, guns and a mini submarine as well as many photographs, documents and maps tracing the history of the war and highlighting the battles fought. Uniforms and personal items can also be seen. The aircraft are parked outside and can be viewed when the museum is closed. The types have all seen service in the country with both American and Korean units and flew in the conflict. Helicopters played an increasing role in the conflict and were used for observation and medical evacuation duties.

TYPE	REG/SER	CON. NO.	PI/NOTES	STATUS
☐ Cessna 305A Bird Dog (L-19A) (O-1A)				PV
☐ De Havilland D.H.C.2 Beaver (L-20A) (U-6A)				PV
☐ Hiller UH12C Raven (H-23G) (OH-23G)				PV
☐ North American NA-174 Trojan (T-28A)	17588	174-441	51-7588	PV

CHEONJU AIR BASE MEMORIAL (SKO5)

Address: Cheongju
Admission: By prior permission only.
Location: About 5 km north of the town.

The base opened in 1978 and has now been developed as an international airport. Fighter and rescue squadrons of the Korean Air Force are based at the field. Two helicopters have been preserved as memorials. The Bell 212 is essentially a conversion of the 205 fitted with two engines to give the helicopter more power. The first flew in April 1969 and has been exported to many countries around the world.

TYPE	REG/SER	CON. NO.	PI/NOTES	STATUS
☐ Bell 204 Iroquois (UH-1B)	060		(USAF)	RA
☐ Bell 212	30505	30505		RA

CHEORUISAMGAK WAR MEMORIAL HALL (SKO6)

Address: Goseokjeong,
Dongsun-cup,
Cheorwon-gun,
Gangwon-do.
Tel: 033-450-5558
Admission: Daily 0900-1600.
Location: About 7 km west of Sincheorwon.

The site was the scene of a bitter battle in the early 1950s. The area is known as the 'Iron Triangle' was just north of the 38th Parallel and now lies in North Korea. The informative displays in the hall trace the story of the war and the battle. Outside is the display of aircraft, vehicles and weapons. All of the types on show played a significant part in the War and served with both the South Korean and United States Air Forces. Nearby is the Iron Triangle Observatory where the visitor can observe the site of the conflict. Tours of the 'Demilitarized Zone' start from the hall and include visits to some of the infiltration tunnels dug by the forces of the north. This 'buffer zone' has separated the two countries for over half a century and is observed by both sides.

TYPE	REG/SER	CON. NO.	PI/NOTES	STATUS
☐ Cessna 305D Bird Dog (305A) (L-19A) (O-1A) (O-1G)	12-295	22609	51-12295	PV
☐ North American NA-174 Trojan (T-28A)	17-643	171-496	51-7643	PV
☐ North American NA-191 Sabre (F-86F)	'14-751'	191-447	52-4751,24-751	PVX
☐ North American NA-191 Sabre (F-86F)	25-075	191-771	52-5075	PV

CHILDREN'S HALL (SKO7)

Address: 626 Hwanggeum-dong,
Suseong-gu,
Daegu.
Tel: 053-763-5693
Admission: Daily 1000-1700.
Location: In the southern part of the city near the National Museum.

This innovative museum has displays to arouse a variety of interests. The topics covered include many aspects of astronomy, science, natural history and technology. Regular demonstrations of many topics take place and there are also many 'hands-on' displays.In the area behind the building are railway locomotives and carriages, motor vehicles and the two aircraft which served in South Korea.

TYPE	REG/SER	CON. NO.	PI/NOTES	STATUS
☐ North American NA-191 Sabre (F-86F)	24706	191-401	52-4706	PV
☐ Sikorsky S-55D Chickasaw (H-19B) (UH-19B)	'73946'			PVX

CHUNCHEON WAR MEMORIAL HALL (SKO8)

Address:	239-1 Samchongdong, Chucheon-si, Gangwan-do.
Tel:	0361-54-3726
Admission:	Daily 0900-1700.
Location:	About 1km west of the town

During the Korean War many battles were fought in the rugged countryside around this town. Displays in the hall commemorate the conflict and many photographs, uniforms, dioramas and weapons can be seen. Three aircraft, representing types flown in action, have been acquired. The Bird Dog won the competition for an observation and liaison aircraft and the first production examples were delivered to the U.S. Army in 1950.

TYPE	REG/SER	CON. NO.	PI/NOTES	STATUS
☐ Cessna 305A Bird Dog (L-19A) (O-1A)	13018		(USAF)	PV
☐ Hiller UH12C Raven (H-23G) (OH-23G)				RA
☐ North American NA-191 Sabre (F-86F) (RF-86F)	24-863	191-559	52-4863	PV

DABUDONG WAR MEMORIAL HALL (SKO9)

Address:	Dabudong-ri, Gasan-myeon, Chigok-gun, Gyeonsngbuk-do.
Tel:	054-973-6313
Admission:	Daily 0900-1700
Location:	Beside Dabu I.C.

This impressive building in the form of a tank was constructed to commemorate the victory over North Korean forces in the 1950 battle. The story of the engagement is portrayed in detail and there is a large archive containing military records. A collection of military vehicles can be seen along with the two aircraft.

TYPE	REG/SER	CON. NO.	PI/NOTES	STATUS
☐ Cessna 318C Tweety Bird (T-37C)	80930	41220	66-0930, 0930 (Brazil)	PV
☐ North American NA-176 Sabre (F-86F)	13193	176-124	51-13193	PV

DAEGU AIR FORCE BASE COLLECTION (SKO10)

Address:	Cumsa-dong, Daegu-si.
Tel:	053-476-0250
Admission:	By prior permission only.
Location:	About 3 km north east of the town.

Daegu has been used by both South Korean and American units for many years. The collection of preserved aircraft represents types which have previously flown from the field.

TYPE	REG/SER	CON. NO.	PI/NOTES	STATUS
☐ Cessna 305A Bird Dog (L-19A) (O-1A)	944		(USAF)	RA
☐ Cessna 318C Tweety Bird (T-37C)				RA
☐ Cessna 318C Tweety Bird (T-37C)	60902	41065	T37C-0902 (Brazil)	PV
☐ Douglas DC-4 Skymaster (C-54D)	72562	10667	42-72562	RA
☐ Lockheed 580 (T-33A)	35134	580-8473	53-5134	RA
☐ McDonnell M.98EN Phantom II (F-4D)	40931	1236	64-0931	RA
☐ McDonnell M.98HO Phantom II (F-4E)	80453	3600	68-0453	RA
☐ North American NA-176 Sabre (F-86F)	13207	176-138	51-13207	RA
☐ North American NA-176 Sabre (F-86F)	13396	176-327	51-13396	RA
☐ North American NA-176 Sabre (F-86F)	13508	176-439	51-13508	RA
☐ Northrop N-156A Freedom Fighter (F-5A)	'38453'			RAX
☐ Pazmany PL-2				RA

DAEJEON DISPLAY (SKO11)

Address:	Munghwa-dong, Jung-gu, Daejeon.
Admission:	On permanent view.
Location:	In the centre of the city.

The old Korean Air Force base is now the site of the new city of Daejeon and contains the civic centre. The airfield became surrounded by housing and industry so a decision to was made to close it. Three ex-military aircraft have been preserved in a park to serve as a reminder of the previous use of the site.

TYPE	REG/SER	CON. NO.	PI/NOTES	STATUS
□ Cessna 305A Bird Dog (L-19A) (O-1A)	12308			PV
□ Lockheed 580 (T-33A)	35271	580-8610	53-5271	PV
□ North American NA-176 Sabre (F-86F)	13180	176-111	51-13180, C.5-20 (Spain)	PV

DAEJEON NATIONAL CEMETERY (SKO12)

Address:	Yuseong-gu, Daejeon-si.
Tel:	042-820-7011
Admission:	March-October daily 0600-1800; November-February 0700-1800.
Location:	About 15 km west of the city.

This vast site opened in the early 1980s and many dignitaries are buried in its grounds. Several impressive monuments can be seen. A collection of aircraft and military vehicles has been assembled. The types on show have all served in the country with both the Korean and American forces. They are displayed to honour the contribution the military forces have made in the history of the country. The only naval aircraft is the Tracker. The South Korean Navy used the type on coastal patrols from a number of airfields.

TYPE	REG/SER	CON. NO.	PI/NOTES	STATUS
□ Cessna 185B Skywagon (U-17A)	0001		(USAF)	PV
□ Cessna 305A Bird Dog (L-19A) (O-1A)	90538		(USAF)	PV
□ De Havilland D.H.C.2 Beaver (L-20A) (U-6A)	58600		(USAF)	PV
□ Grumman G-121 Tracker (S-2E)	149267	111C	Bu149267	PV
□ Hiller UH12C Raven (H-23G) (OH-23G)				PV
□ Lockheed 580 (T-33A)	61585	580-9321	56-1585	PV
□ North American NA-174 Trojan (T-28A)	17639	174-492	51-7639	PV
□ North American NA-191 Sabre (F-86F)	52-4451	191-47		PV

GANGNEUNG UNIFICATION PARK (SKO13)

Address:	Aninjin-ri, Gangdong-myeon, Gangneung-si.
Admission:	Daily 1000-1800.
Location:	On Route 7 about 8 km from Gangneung.

On September 18th 1996 a North Korean submarine ran aground on the coast on an infiltration mission. The crew and the commandos aboard tried to make it back to the north via the 'Demilitarized Zone' but most were shot and others committed suicide. An exhibition highlighting the division of the country and the bitter war fought in the early 1950s opened in 2001. A pavilion tracing the history of the war has been erected and many interesting items are on show. The destroyer 'Jeongbuk' (formerly USS Everitt F. Larsen) can also be seen. The Skymaster, used by President Park between 1969 and 1973, is mounted on a ledge overlooking the sea. The aircraft was withdrawn from use and stored at Osan Air Force Base before being moved to the park. Around the extensive grounds are many memorials dedicated to those who lost their lives

TYPE	REG/SER	CON. NO.	PI/NOTES	STATUS
□ Douglas DC-4 Skymaster (C-54D)	17201	22151	43-17201	PV

GENERAL YOO CHI-GON MEMORIAL (SKO14)

Address:	288-2 Yang-ri, Yuga-myeon, Dalseong-gun, Daegu.
Tel:	053-615-7575
Admission:	Daily 0900-1800.
Location:	Near the Mount Biseul National Forest.

The memorial honours the General who was a well-known fighter pilot in the Republic of Korea Air Force. The story of is military career is told with a number of plaques on view. Two aircraft have been put on show at this isolated picturesque mountain site. The Sabre was formerly displayed outside the Hankuk Fibre Glass factory at Miryang and moved to its new home in 2004. Cessna T-37s served in the training role.

TYPE	REG/SER	CON. NO.	PI/NOTES	STATUS
□ Cessna 318C Tweety Bird (T-37C)	31686	42029	70-1686	PV
□ North American NA-193 Sabre (F-86F)	25450	193-179	52-5450	PV

Two aircraft a Cessna T-37C and a North American F-86F can be seen at the General Yoo-chi Gon Memorial near Daegu. (Shinsuke Yamamoto)

Above: The students at the Korean Aerospace University have designed a number of light aircraft including this low wing single seater. (John Mounce)

Right: This colourful Cessna T-37 is displayed outside Sacheon Air Base. (Shinsuke Yamamoto).

GIMHAE AIR FORCE BASE COLLECTION (SKO15)

Address:	Gangseo-gu, Busan-si.
Admission:	By prior permission only,
Location:	About 10 km north west of Busan.

The site is home to Gimhae International Airport and a transport base of the air force. Currently in use with the military are Lockheed C-130s and CASA-IPTN CN-235s along with helicopters. In addition major maintenance work is carried out. The collection of preserved aircraft is displayed around the site.

TYPE	REG/SER	CON. NO.	PI/NOTES	STATUS
☐ Curtiss-Wright CW-20B-2 Commando (C-46D)	O-77592	32988	44-77592	RA
☐ Curtiss-Wright CW-20B-2 Commando (C-46D)	77674	33070	44-77674	RA
☐ Douglas DC-4 Skymaster (C-54E)	'49124'	27340	44-9114, 49114	RAX
☐ Fairchild 473 Provider (205) (C-123B) (C-123J)	54510	20171	55-4510, 54510 (SNVAF)	RA
☐ Fairchild 473 Provider (205) (C-123B) (C-123J)	55-523	20184	55-4523	RA
☐ Fairchild 473 Provider (205) (C-123B) (C-123K)	54-511	20172	55-4511	RA
☐ Fairchild 473 Provider (205) (C-123B) (C-123K)	54561	20222	55-4561	RA

GWANGJU AIR BASE MEMORIAL (SKO16)

Address:	Gwangju.
Admission:	By prior permission only.
Location:	In the south western part of the town.

The Korean Air Force bases fighter squadrons at the field which also serves as the civil airport for the town. There is also an American presence at the site. Two aircraft are preserved as memorials.

TYPE	REG/SER	CON. NO.	PI/NOTES	STATUS
☐ Lockheed 580 (T-33A)	70671	580-1300	57-0671- possible identity.	RA
☐ North American NA-191 Sabre (F-86F)	'0829'	191-525	52-4829 – possible identity.	RA

GYERYONG DAE DISPLAY (SKO17)

Address:	Gyeryong Dae.
Admission:	By prior permission.
Location:	In the town.

The city is home to the Korea Tri-Services Headquarters and several military schools. Three aircraft have been reported as being preserved at one of these locations but the exact one is not known.

TYPE	REG/SER	CON. NO.	PI/NOTES	STATUS
☐ McDonnell M.98HO Phantom II (F-4E)	80353	3412	68-0353	RA
☐ North American NA-190 Sabre (F-86D)	52990	190-715	52-9990 – possible identity.	RA
☐ North American NA-193 Sabre (F-86F)	25494	193-233	52-5494 – possible identity.	RA

HISTORIC PARK OF GEOJE PRISONER OF WAR CAMP (SKO18)

Address:	San 90-8, Gohyeon-ri, Sinhyeon-eup, Geoje-si, Gyeongsangnam-do.
Tel:	055-639-8125.
Admission:	Daily 0900-1800.
Location:	In the centre of the island.

A site on the island was used to house North Korean prisoners during the 1950-53 war. A museum showing the history of the camp has been set up with many dioramas depicting the harsh conditions. A reconstruction of some of the buildings can be seen along with ruins of some of the originals. Normally the site housed around four thousand inmates but about one hundred and seventy thousand passed through its gates. Two aircraft are currently on show but the T-37 which was exhibited for a few years was not seen recently.

TYPE	REG/SER	CON. NO.	PI/NOTES	STATUS
☐ Bell 204 Iroquois (UH-1B)	14096	1220	64-14096	PV
☐ North American NA-174 Trojan (T-28A)	17854	174-707	51-7854	PV

HODAM AIR AND SPACE CENTER (SKO19)

Address:	Sachang-ri, Muan-gun, Jeollanam-do.
Tel:	0636-453-1977
Admission:	Tuesday-Sunday 1000-1700.
Location:	Close to Muan railway station.

This private collection was set up by General Ockin Muan in 1997. The exhibition hall was opened on April 22nd 1998. The building holds a display of a large number of photographs which trace the development of aircraft from the early days and show the exploration of the moon and Mars. Components and engines can also be seen. The founder's personal military records are on show along with items of memorabilia including precious stones. The aircraft are parked outside the hall and include two Soviet designs which defected from North Korea. Types flown in the conflict by American and South Korean forces feature prominently.

TYPE	REG/SER	CON. NO.	PI/NOTES	STATUS
☐ Bell 205 Iroquois (UH-1H)	16891	9085	66-16891	PV
☐ Cessna 305D Bird Dog (305A) (L-19A) (O-1A) (O-1G)	239		(USAF), 529	PV
☐ Fairchild 205 Provider (C-123B)	54-0687	20136	54-0687, 5687, '54-0684'	PV
☐ Lockheed 580 (T-33A)	61706	580-1056	56-1706	PV
☐ McDonnell M.98EN Phantom II (F-4D)	50589	1494	65-0589	PV
☐ Mikoyan-Gurevich MiG-15	239			PV
☐ Nanchang Y-5 [Antonov An-2]	18132			PV
☐ North American NA-124 Mustang (P-51D)	'030'		(USAAF)	PVX
☐ North American NA-174 Trojan (T-28A)	17826	174-679	51-7826	PV
☐ North American NA-182 Texan (T-6G)	202			PV
☐ North American NA-191 Sabre (F-86F)	25115	191-811	52-5115	PV
☐ Northrop N-156A Freedom Fighter (F-5A)	69-146	N.6250	66-9146	PV

IMJINGAK WAR MUSEUM (SKO20)

Address:	1325-1 Majung-ri, Musan-eup, Gyeonggi-do.
Tel:	0348-52-2565
Admission:	Daily 0900-1800.
Location:	About 30km north west of Seoul.

Several major battles, including the famous last stand of the Gloucester Regiment in April 1951, took place in this area. The museum traces the history of these conflicts with many impressive displays. The use of aircraft for observation had been a success in World War II and this role continued in the Korean War. The Bird Dog proved to be most efficient in this task. In the early stages of the conflict it became apparent that the U.S. Army needed a rugged light transport with STOL capabilities and the Beaver was chosen. The Sabre was the front line fighter during the war and engaged in many major battles with the communist MiG-15s.

TYPE	REG/SER	CON. NO.	PI/NOTES	STATUS
☐ Cessna 305A Bird Dog (L-19A) (O-1A)	12248	22562	51-12248	PV
☐ De Havilland D.H.C.2 Beaver (L-20A) (U-6A)	16772	209	51-16772	PV
☐ North American NA-191 Sabre (F-86F) (RF-86F)	'51845'	191-206	52-4510 – possible identity.	PVX

INHA UNIVERSITY JUNGSEOK AVIATION TECHNICAL HIGH SCHOOL DISPLAY (SKO21)

Address:	253 Yonghyun-dong, Nam-gu, Incheon 402-751.
Tel:	032-860-7030.
Admission:	DC-3 on permanent view.
Location:	In the southern suburbs of the city.

The DC-3 served in Alaska at the end of World War II and was then sold to Alaska Airlines. The airliner was sold to Korean National arriving in the country in the late 1950s. After over thirty six thousand flying hours it was withdrawn in 1971 and donated to the university. Now it is displayed in the campus with a display board tracing its history and that of the airline. Several aircraft, including the Boeing 727, are at the Inha Technical College and four more at the Jungseok School. All three institutions are next to each other on the large campus.

TYPE	REG/SER	CON. NO.	PI/NOTES	STATUS
☐ Aero Commander 560				RA
☐ Beech C18S Expeditor (SNB-2)	HL-2012	7242	Bu29611, (Japan)	RAD
☐ Bell 47G				RA

TYPE	REG/SER	CON. NO.	PI/NOTES	STATUS
☐ Boeing 727-281	HL7348	20435	JA8328, HL7348, MT-1054, JU-1054 – identity doubtful.	PV
☐ Cessan 318C Tweety Bird (T-37C)				PV
☐ Cessna 305A Bird Dog (L-19A) (O-1A)	HL-1037	22982	51-12527	PV
☐ Cessna 337A Super Skymaster	HL-2005	33700283	N6283F	PV
☐ Douglas DC-3A-456 Skytrain (C-47A)	HL2002	20203	43-15737, NC91005 – may not be this aircraft.	PV
☐ Hughes 500				PV

JEONGSEOK AVIATION PAVILION (SKO22)

Address: Gasi-ri,
Pyoseon-myeon,
Seogwipo-si,
Jeju Island.
Tel: 064-784-5322
Admission: Daily 1000-1700.
Location: Next to Jeongseok Airport.

This modern structure houses displays tracing the history of aviation and airlines. A replica cockpit of an Airbus is on show along with many models and components. Hanging in the foyer is a locally built light aircraft of unusual design. Outside is an example of the Korean designed Chang Kong 91 low wing aircraft. At one time it was thought that only one was built but a recent visit found another in the Korea Aerospace University Museum and as that one is c/n A2 perhaps two were completed. Korean Air has a collection of preserved aircraft on the airfield and these can be viewed on a number of occasions in the year.

TYPE	REG/SER	CON. NO.	PI/NOTES	STATUS
☐ Korean Institute of Aeronautical Technology Chang-Kong 91				PV
☐ Light Aircraft				PV

KAI AEROSPACE MUSEUM (SKO23)

Address: 802 Yucheon-ri,
Sanam-myeon,
Sacheon-si,
Gyeongsangnam-do.
Tel: 055-851-6545
Admission: Daily 0900-1700.
Location: About 2 km west of the town.

The company has been involved in the manufacture of aircraft under licence and in developing and producing its own designs for many years. The museum opened in August 1992 with several aircraft from the closed Korean War Museum in Seoul on show. Two exhibition halls were built along with an outside display area. The Freedom Hall highlights the Korean War and a prized exhibit is a Russian built ZIS limousine. The car was used by the President Kim Il-Jong of North Korea and was captured by South Korean troops in October 1950. The vehicle was taken to America and in the early 1980s it was found in New Jersey. The historic machine was purchased, returned to Korea in 1982, and restored. On show here are dioramas and weapons. The Aerospace Hall covers the development of flight and the history of the company is traced. Outside are several significant types. The first Mustang wing of the Republic of Korea Air Force was formed in 1950 and the unit was soon engaged in combat. The Sabre served with distinction in the Korean War and was the backbone of Korean Air Force fighter squadrons for many years. The B-29 Superfortress was used in the latter stages of World War II and also served in Korea. Very few examples of the giant Globemaster have been preserved. Over five hundred were delivered to the United States Air Force. Modern jets have been added and more types are expected. There is also a small collection of preserved aircraft at the airbase.

TYPE	REG/SER	CON. NO.	PI/NOTES	STATUS
☐ Bell 204 Iroquois (UH-1B)	14003	1127	64-14003	PV
☐ Boeing 345 Superfortress (B-29)	45-21739	13633		PV
☐ Cessna 305A Bird Dog (L-19A) (O-1A)	'09-995'	23416	53-7995	PVX
☐ Cessna 318C Tweety Bird (T-37C)	21361	42019	72-1361	PV
☐ Douglas 1317 Globemaster II (C-124C)	52-943	43852		PV
☐ Douglas A-26A Invader (A-26B) (TB-26B) (B-26K)	'84-651'	27398	44-34119, 64-17651 – (On-Mark B-26K)	PVX
☐ Douglas DC-3A-456 Skytrain (C-47A) (VC-47A) (EC-47Q)	O-93704	13645	43-93704	PV
☐ Douglas DC-4 Skymaster (C-54G)	O-50582	36035	45-0582	PV
☐ Fairchild 473 Provider (205) (C-123B) (C-123K)	54654	20225	55-4654, 54654 (SNVAF)	PV
☐ General Dynamics 401 Fighting Falcon (F-16C) (FSM)	'92-000'			PVX
☐ Grumman G-99 Cougar (F9F-8) (F-9J)	Bu141152	399C		PV
☐ Korean Aerospace Industries KT-50 (FSM)				PV
☐ Lockheed 580 (T-33A)	61656	580-1006	56-1656	PV
☐ McDonnell M.98HO Phantom II (F-4E)	80-355	3416	68-0355	PV
☐ North American NA-173 Sabre (F-86D)	424	173-557	51-8424	PV
☐ North American NA-174 Trojan (T-28A)	17625	174-478	51-7625	PV

☐ North American NA-191 Sabre (F-86F)	24-865	191-561	52-4865	PV
☐ North American NA-195 Texan (T-6G) (LT-6G)	51-17354	195-1		PV
☐ Northrop N-156A Freedom Fighter (F-5A)	10552	N.6213	65-10552	PV
☐ Sikorsky S-55D Chickasaw (H-19D) (UH-19D)	64283	5511??	56-4283	PV
☐ Vought F4U-4 Corsair	Bu81415	8140	Bu81415, N5219V	PV
☐ Wright Flyer (R)				PV

KOREA AEROSPACE UNIVERSITY AEROSPACE MUSEUM (SKO24)

Address:	200-1 Hwajeon-dong, Deogyang-gu, Goyang-city, Gyeonggi-do 412-791.
Tel:	02-300-0466
Admission:	Tuesday-Sunday 1000-1700.
Location:	About 10 km north west of Seoul city centre.

The origins of the university date back to 1952 when an aviation college was established. Now the institution offers courses in a wide range of subjects. The museum opened on June 15th 2004 and has several interesting exhibits. Two former military jets can be seen along with a range of light aircraft. The X-4 and X-5 are two designs by students and the Velocity is an American canard four seater built using composite materials.

TYPE	REG/SER	CON. NO.	PI/NOTES	STATUS
☐ Aeronca 7BCM Champion (L-16A)	HL1001			PV
☐ Cessna 318C Tweety Bird (T-37C)	31694	42037	73-1694	PV
☐ Fuji FA-200-180 Aero Subaru	HL1041	215		PV
☐ Hankuk Aviation University X-4				PV
☐ Hankuk Aviation University X-5				PV
☐ Korean Institute of Aeronautical Technology Chang-Kong 91	HL1078	A2		PV
☐ Mooney M.20J	HL1066	24-3225		PV
☐ Northrop N-156B Freedom Fighter (F-5B)	63-8449	N.8012		PV
☐ Velocity Aircraft Velocity				PV

KOREA AIR FORCE ACADEMY MUSEUM (SKO25)

Address:	Namil Myeon, Cheongju-si 361-763, Chungcheongbuk-do.
Tel:	043-290-6332
Email:	info@afa.ac.kr
Admission:	Monday-Friday 0900-1600.
Location:	About 8 km south of Cheongju city and 2 km north east of Seongmu Air Force Base.

A collection of aircraft has been assembled in the grounds of this institution which trains officers for the Air Force. Examples of types used in recent years can be seen. The airfield at the site houses training units and a detachment of helicopters. Among the airframes to be seen are three flown by defectors from North Korea and China. The Academy was founded in 1949 and had a number of homes before moving to its current location in 1985. A building on the campus houses an exhibition tracing the development of the institution and of the history of flight. On show are many photographs, documents, models and components. The airframes include three defectors from the north. The Pazmany PL-1 first flew in the early 1960s and was developed into the PL-2. The two types proved popular with home builders. The PL-2 has been constructed in several Asian counties and served with Air Forces in Indonesia, South Korea, Sri Lanka and Taiwan. René Fournier flew his first motor-glider in 1960. Over the next few years he developed the design and the RF-5 was put into production in Germany and over two hundred were produced. The academy operated a small number for basic flying training. The Curtiss Commando was widely used in Asia both during and after World War II. Many were allocated to local air forces in the 1950s and 1960s. This classic transport can be compared with other cargo types.

TYPE	REG/SER	CON. NO.	PI/NOTES	STATUS
☐ Aero Commander 680 (L-26C) (U-9C)	59-630		(USAF)	PV
☐ Bell 204 Iroquois (UH-1B)	40905	1063	64-13939	PV
☐ Cessna 305A Bird Dog (L-19A) (O-1A)	63810			PV
☐ Cessna 305D Bird Dog (305A) (L-19A) (O-1A) (O-1G)	12523	22978	51-12523	PV
☐ Cessna 318C Tweety Bird (T-37C)	21360	42018	72-1360	PV
☐ Cessna 318E Dragonfly (A-37B)	'40905'	43174	68-10823, 68-823	PVX
☐ Cessna R172E Mescalero (T-41B)	15061	R1720062	67-15061	PV
☐ Chengdu J-7 I [Mikoyan-Gurevich MiG-21F-13]	045		3961 (?)	PV
☐ Curtiss-Wright CW-20B-2 Commando (C-46D)	78053	33449	44-78053	RA
☐ Douglas DC-4 Skymaster (C-54D)	'O-40905'	10799	42-72694	PVX
☐ Fairchild 473 Provider (205) (C-123B) (C-123K)	40662	20111	54-0662, (VNAF)	RA
☐ Harbin H-5 [Ilyushin Il-28]	038			PV
☐ Lockheed 580 (T-33A)	'73665'		(USAF), 023	PVX

TYPE	REG/SER	CON. NO.	PI/NOTES	STATUS
☐ McDonnell M.98HO Phantom II (F-4E)	68-0310	3330		RA
☐ North American NA-122 Mustang (P-51D)	'053'		(USAF), 168	PVX
☐ North American NA-174 Trojan (T-28A)	51-7813	174-676	51-7813, '901'	PVX
☐ North American NA-182 Texan (T-6G) (LT-6G)	106			RA
☐ North American NA-191 Sabre (F-86F)	64-928	191-624	52-4928 (?)	PV
☐ North American NA-201 Sabre (F-86D)	'62935'		(USAF)	PVX
☐ North American NA-238 Sabre (F-86F)	64-651	191-347	52-4651	RA
☐ North American NA-238 Sabre (F-86F)	62-837	238-65	56-2837	RA
☐ Northrop N-156A Freedom Fighter (F-5A)	10-529	N.6190	65-10529, (SNVAF)	PV
☐ Northrop N-156B Freedom Fighter (F-5B)	89-095	N.8073	68-9095	PV
☐ Pazmany PL-2	HL-1072			PV
☐ Piper J-3C-65 Cub (L-4J)	029			PV
☐ Shenyang J-6 [Mikoyan-Gurevich MiG-19SF]	053			PV
☐ Sikorsky S-55D Chickasaw (H-19D) (UH-19D)	'86203'		(USAF), 86230	PVX
☐ Stinson V-76 Sentinel (L-5G)	481014			PV

KOREA AIR FORCE TECHNICAL HIGH SCHOOL COLLECTION (SKO26)

Address:	306-3 Soksa-ri, Geumsan-myeon, Jinju-si, Gyeongsangnam-do.
Tel:	055-750-5231
Admission:	By prior permission only.
Location:	In the eastern suburbs of the city.

A collection of aircraft has been assembled at this school which trains students in many aspects of aviation. A display has been set up by the main gate and there are several other airframes inside the campus. Some of these are used for instructional duties. Three widely used trainers are in the collection.

TYPE	REG/SER	CON. NO.	PI/NOTES	STATUS
☐ Bell 204 Iroquois (UH-1B)	14054	1178	64-14054	RA
☐ Cessna 318C Tweety Bird (T-37C)	80919	41193		RA
☐ Cessna 318C Tweety Bird (T-37C)	80928	41218		RA
☐ Cessna 305A Bird Dog (L-19A) (O-1A)	12767			RA
☐ Douglas DC-4 Skymaster (C-54D)	O-72694	10799	42-72694	RA
☐ Fairchild 473 Provider (205) (C-123B) (C-123K)	54-0678	20127	54-0678, (South Vietnam)	RA
☐ Fournier RF-5	1602			RA
☐ Fournier RF-5	HL-1608			RA
☐ Lockheed 580 (T-33A)	35280	580-8619	53-5280	RA
☐ North American NA-77 Texan (AT-6A)	53867			RA
☐ North American NA-173 Sabre (F-86D)	'10235'		(USAF)	RAX
☐ North American NA-174 Trojan (T-28A)	17816	174-669	51-7816	RA
☐ North American NA-174 Trojan (T-28A)	17821	174-674	51-7821	RA
☐ North American NA-191 Sabre (F-86F)	52-4490	191-186		RA
☐ North American NA-191 Sabre (F-86F)	'52855'	191-551	52-4855, 24855	RAX
☐ North American NA-191 Sabre (F-86F)	52-4880	191-576		RA
☐ Shenyang F-6C [Mikoyan-Gurevich MiG-19SF]	283		In North Korean markings.	RA

KOREA AVIATION POLYTECHNIC COLLEGE COLLECTION (SKO27)

Address:	438 Igeum-dong, Sacheon-si, Gyeongsagnam-do 666-706.
Tel:	055-830-3400
Fax:	055-830-3114
Admission:	By prior permission only.
Location:	About 10 km south of the airfield off Route 3.

Five former military aircraft are preserved by the main gate at the college which trains students in many aspects of airframe and engine maintenance. There may be other instructional airframes in the buildings. Several Douglas Skymasters flown by the Korean Air Force have been preserved. The T-33 was in service for many years and was eventually replaced by the Cessna T-37 at the Tactical Training Wing at nearby Sachon.

TYPE	REG/SER	CON. NO.	PI/NOTES	STATUS
☐ Cessna 318B Tweety Bird (T-37C)	60881	41012	64-14753 – possible identity.	RA
☐ Douglas DC-4 Skymaster (C-54D)	O-72571	10676	42-72571	RA
☐ Lockheed 580 (T-33A)	61638	580-9988	56-1638	RA
☐ North American NA-176 Sabre (F-86F)	13199	176-130	51-13199	RA
☐ North American NA-193 Sabre (F-86F)	52-5483	193-212	52-5483, 25483	RA

KOREA MILITARY ACADEMY COLLECTION (SKO28)

Address:	51-1 Gongnung 2-do, Nowon-gu, Seoul 139-242.
Tel:	02-976-242
Admission:	By prior permission only – regular tours take place.
Location:	In the north eastern suburbs of the city.

The academy was set up in the 1950s and now trains officers in many aspects of military life. A display has been set up in the grounds and this includes the two aircraft as well as military vehicles. On the daily tours visitors are shown around some of the buildings and the grounds where a marching display can be seen.

TYPE	REG/SER	CON. NO.	PI/NOTES	STATUS
☐ Cessna 305A Bird Dog (L-19A) (O-1A)	11679			RAX
☐ Hiller UH12C Raven (H-23G) (OH-23G)				RA

KOREA NATIONAL DEFENSE UNIVERSITY AEROSPACE MUSEUM (SKO29)

Address:	205 Susaek-dong, Eunpyang-gu, Seoul 122-875.
Tel:	02-300-2313
Fax:	02-309-6230
Email:	kndu212@kndu.ac.kr
Admission:	By prior permission only.
Location:	In the city.

This university offers many courses on military matters as well as general aeronautical subjects. An aerospace museum has been reported as being here and the only known aircraft is the Cessna T-37C.

TYPE	REG/SER	CON. NO.	PI/NOTES	STATUS
☐ Cessna 318C Tweety Bird (T-37C)	31694	42037	73-1694	PV

KOREA NAVAL ACADEMY MUSEUM (SKO30)

Address:	Jinhasi, Gyungnam 645-797, Gyeongsangnam-do.
Tel:	055-549-1182
Fax:	055-542-0033
Email:	navymuseum@hanmir.com
Admission:	Monday-Friday 0900-1630; Saturday 0900-1130.
Location:	About 30 km west of Busan.

The academy opened in January 1946 and among the artefacts preserved was the personal collection of Admiral Yi Soon-shin, one of the nation's most famous sailors. The museum opened in 1976 with three exhibition rooms. One is devoted to the Admiral, one to the Korean Navy and one to the Academy. On show were weapons, documents, photographs and models. Floating nearby is replica of the Admiral's 'Turtle' ship. Two of the aircraft are preserved at the Naval College which trains officers for the service. The Bird Dog is one of the few OE-2 versions which were fitted with Cessna 180 wings and armament racks.

TYPE	REG/SER	CON. NO.	PI/NOTES	STATUS
☐ Cessna 321 Bird Dog (OE-2) (O-1C)	148251		Bu148251 – at nearby Naval College	RA
☐ Grumman G-121 Tracker (S2F-3S) (S-2E)	9257	101C	Bu149257	PV
☐ Grumman G-121 Tracker (S2F-3S) (S-2E)	149851	126C	Bu149851 – at nearby Naval College.	RA

KOREAN AIR COLLECTION (SKO31)

Address:	Jeongseok Airport, Jeju Island.
Admission:	By prior permission only.
Location:	Just south of Ha Dong.

The airline, which was founded in 1962, has preserved three aircraft at the airport which is also home to their flight academy. The Jeongseok Aviation Pavilion is close to the field and on occasions arrange tours to view the airliners. The Constellation was originally delivered to the United States Air Force in December 1948 and was in use until 1956. After fourteen years in store it was sold as a sprayer and served in the U.S.A. and Canada. It was donated to Korean Air in 2005 and flown to Gimhae for repainting in the airline's colours: the company operated a single example of the type in the late 1950s and early 1960s. The Boeing 747 was delivered to Korea in May 1973 and flew on international routes for around thirty years. The early Airbus was originally intended for Iberia but instead was delivered to Asia in 1975 and has recently been withdrawn. The airline trains many pilots at the remote site on the island off the south coast of the country.

TYPE	REG/SER	CON. NO.	PI/NOTES	STATUS
☐ Airbus Industrie A300B4-2C	HL7219	016	F-WLGB	RA
☐ Boeing 747-2B5B	HL7463	20770	N1798B,HL7410,N747BA	RA
☐ Lockheed 749A-79-36 Constellation (C-121A) (VC-121A) (C-121A)	'HL-102'	749A-2601	48-0609, N9464, C-GXKO, N494TW	RAX

MEMORIAL HALL FOR INCHEON OPERATION (SKO32)

Address:	514 Okyon-dong, Yeonsu-gu, Inchon-si.
Admission:	April-September Tuesday-Sunday 1000-1700 October-March Tuesday-Sunday 1000-1630.
Location:	About 4 km south of Dong-Incheong station.

This massive complex, which opened on September 15th 1984, commemorates the operation which led to the successful defence of South Korea from Commumist forces. General MacArthur led the assault on September 15th 1950 and a statue of him has been erected. Inside there is an exhibition tracing the story of the landing and of the Korean War. On show are many photographs and maps along with uniforms documents and items of memorabilia. There is also a cultural and educational centre along with a cinema.

TYPE	REG/SER	CON. NO.	PI/NOTES	STATUS
☐ Cessna 305A Bird Dog (L-19A) (O-1A)	14576	21354 (?)	51-4576	PV
☐ North American NA-227 Sabre (F-86F)	'55-007'	227-240	55-5007	PVX

MOKPO NAVAL AIR STATION MEMORIAL (SKO33)

Address:	Mokpo.
Admission:	By prior permission only.
Location:	In the southern part of the town.

The town has a long naval tradition and the port has been in existence for many years. The airfield handles civil flights and is also home to naval helicopters. A Tracker has been preserved as a memorial. The Korean Navy flew the twin engined type from Mokpo on coastal patrols and search missions for many years.

TYPE	REG/SER	CON. NO.	PI/NOTES	STATUS
☐ Grumman G-89 Tracker (S2F-1) (S2F-2U) (US-2C)	133376	N48	Bu133376	RA

NAKTONGGANG VICTORY MEMORIAL MUSEUM (SKO34)

Address:	San 227-1, Daemyung 9 Dong, Nangu, Daegu City
Tel:	053-621-9880/9881.
Admission:	Daily 1000-1700.
Location:	About 6 km south of Tongdaegu station.

Many battles were fought along the river in August 1950 during the defence of the Busan perimeter. Displays at this museum trace these conflicts and many photographs, uniforms, vehicles and weapons can be seen. The two aircraft are types which flew in the conflict with many Bird Dogs operating on observation and liaison duties. The Sabre was the major front line fighter with the Korean Air Force for many years.

TYPE	REG/SER	CON. NO.	PI/NOTES	STATUS
☐ Cessna 305D Bird Dog (305A) (L-19A) (O-1A) (O-1G)	14601		51-4601	PV
☐ North American NA-173 Sabre (F-86D)	18456	173-589	51-8456	PV

NATIONAL CEMETERY (SKO35)

Address:	San 44-7, Dongjak-dong, Dongjak-gu. Seoul.
Tel:	02-814-5451
Admission:	May-October daily 0800-1800; November-April daily 0800-1700.
Location:	In the southern suburbs of the city near Donjak metro station.

The cemetery was established in 1956 on the orders of President Syngman Rhee. He decreed that people who had lost their lives in the Korean Indepence War, the Korean War and the Vietnam War could be buried at the site. Three aircraft are displayed to honour the pilots who have lost their lives in military service. The Texan was used for training and in ground support duties. The Tracker represents the contribution of the Navy.

TYPE	REG/SER	CON. NO.	PI/NOTES	STATUS
☐ Grumman G-121 Tracker (S2F-3S) (S-2E)	9258	102C	Bu149258	PV
☐ North American NA-173 Sabre (F-86D)	'52-445'	173-578	51-8445, 10-445 – possible identity.	PVX
☐ North American NA-88 Texan (AT-6D)	202	88-15983	42-84202 – possible identity.	PV

NATIONAL SCIENCE MUSEUM (SKO36)

Address:	32-2 Gusong-du, Yusung-gu, Daejeon.
Admission:	March-October 0900-1730; November-February 0930-1630.
Location:	In the city.

The museum moved from Seoul in 1990 to a large purpose built complex which has innovative displays on all aspects of science and technology. A Sabre is the only aircraft on show.

TYPE	REG/SER	CON. NO.	PI/NOTES	STATUS
☐ North American NA-176 Sabre (F-86F)	13203	176-134	51-13203	PV

OSAN AIR FORCE BASE (SKO37)

Address:	USO Osan, AMC Terminal, APO AP 96278-2098.
Tel:	0333-661-3491.
Admission:	By prior permission only.
Location:	About 40 km south of Seoul.

The Battle of Bayonet Hill took place at the site in February 1951. The Americans decided to construct a new airfield and work commenced the following year and combat units have been here for more than half a century.

TYPE	REG/SER	CON. NO.	PI/NOTES	STATUS
☐ Fairchild-Republic A-10A Thunderbolt II	76-0515	A10-62		RA
☐ McDonnell M.98HO Phantom II (F-4E)	'69-0291'	3831 (?)		RAX
☐ North American NA-193 Sabre (F-86F)	'12910'	193-269	52-4573	RAX

PEACE AND FREEDOM PROTECTION MUSEUM (SKO38)

Address:	San 38-1, Sangbongam-dong, Dongducheon-si, Gyeonggi-do.
Admission:	Tuesday-Sunday 1000-1600.
Location:	About 2 km south east of Soyosan railway station.

The displays trace the history of the Korean War and the effects the conflict has had on the inhabitants of the area. The importance of a peaceful life and ensuring that people live a free society is highlighted.

TYPE	REG/SER	CON. NO.	PI/NOTES	STATUS
☐ Cessna 305A Bird Dog (L-19A) (O-1A)	12-319		51-12319	PV
☐ Fairchild 473 Provider (205) (C-123B) (C-123J)	64392	20276	56-4392	PV
☐ Lockheed 580 (T-33A)	70726	580-1375 (?)	57-0726 is c/n 580-1453	PV

POHANG AIR BASE COLLECTION (SKO39)

Address:	Pohang.
Admission:	By prior permission only.
Location:	In the south eastern part of the town.

The field handles civil flights but the Korean Navy has one of its main bases at the site. A patrol unit operating Lockheed Orions is in residence along with helicopter squadrons. Three aircraft are preserved in the camp.

TYPE	REG/SER	CON. NO.	PI/NOTES	STATUS
☐ Cessna 305A Bird Dog (L-19A) (O-1A)				RA
☐ De Havilland D.H.C.2 Beaver (L-20A) (U-6A)				RA
☐ Grumman G-121 Tracker (S-2E)				RA

SACHEON AIR FORCE BASE COLLECTION (SKO40)

Address:	Sacheon-si, Gyeongsangnam-do.
Admission:	By prior permission only.
Location:	Just north of the town.

The airfield is now home to a training wing operating the indigenous KT-1. The turbo-prop trainer claims to be the first type in its class to be designed by computer. The prototype made its maiden flight in 2001 and exports have been made to a number of countries in Asia and also to Turkey. The preserved aircraft include types formerly in use. Korean Aerospace Industries have a factory and their museum on the site.

TYPE	REG/SER	CON. NO.	PI/NOTES	STATUS
☐ Cessna 305A Bird Dog (L-19A) (O-1A)	12698			RA
☐ Cessna 318B Tweety Bird (T-37B)	60885	41021	67-14758 – possible identity – preserved by road to Jinju.	PV
☐ Cessna 318C Tweety Bird (T-37C)	60896	41048	T37C-0896 (Brazil)	RA
☐ Cessna 318C Tweety Bird (T-37C)	0933	41223	T37C-0933 (Brazil)	RA
☐ Lockheed 580 (T-33A)	18722	580-6506	51-8722	RA
☐ North American NA-88 Texan (AT-6D)	48527		(USAAF)	RA
☐ North American NA-174 Trojan (T-28A)	17646	171-499	51-7646	RA
☐ North American NA-191 Sabre (F-86F)	'14587'		(USAF)	RAX

SAPGYOHO MARINE PARK (SKO41)

Address:	187-3 Unjeong-ri, Danjin-gu, Chungcheongnam-do.
Tel:	041-362-3321
Admission:	Daily 0900-1800.
Location:	In the eastern part of the city.

Two ships, a destroyer and a large tank landing craft are moored at the quay. Visitors can tour both these vessels. On shore is an exhibition building highlighting the development of military ships with many models, photographs and drawings on view. The Tracker is parked outside the main hall.

TYPE	REG/SER	CON. NO.	PI/NOTES	STATUS
☐ Grumman G-89 Tracker (S2F-1) (S2F-2U) (US-2C)	Bu133385	N56		PV

SEOSAN AIR BASE COLLECTION (SKO42)

Address:	Seosan.
Admission:	By prior permission only.
Location:	About 10 km west of Hemi.

The base was constructed for use by Korean F-16 Fighting Falcons. A collection of preserved aircraft has been assembled along the road from the main gate to the administrative area. They represent types which have served with the Korean Air Force over the last half-century.

TYPE	REG/SER	CON. NO.	PI/NOTES	STATUS
☐ Cessna 318E Dragonfly (A-37B)	14817	43042	67-14817	RA
☐ Lockheed 580 (T-33A)	41593	580-9329	54-1593	RA
☐ North American NA-174 Trojan (T-28A)			(USAF)	RA
☐ North American NA-193 Sabre (F-86F)	25292	193-21	52-5292	RA
☐ Northrop N-156A Freedom Fighter (F-5A)	10532	N.6193	65-10532, 10532 (South Korea), 10532 (Vietnam)	RA

SEOUL AIR FORCE BASE COLLECTION (SKO43)

Address:	Seognam City, Seoul.
Admission:	By prior permission only.
Location:	In the southern eastern suburbs of the city.

The airfield was in use during the Korean War and many American units flew from the site. Air Force fighter, transport and special operation squadrons used the base. The U.S. Navy also was in residence for a period. At the current time the United States Army maintain a facility with helicopters and fixed wing types. The Korean Air Force has transport squadrons flying from the airfield. The preserved aircraft are dispersed around the site and there are also a number of decoy aircraft which may be saved for future display. The Liftmaster served with both the United States Navy and Air Force before delivery to Korea in the early 1970s.

TYPE	REG/SER	CON. NO.	PI/NOTES	STATUS
☐ Bell 212	30507	30507		RA
☐ Cessna 318C Tweety Bird (T-37C)	80920	41195		RA
☐ Douglas DC-6A Liftmaster (R6D-1) (C-118A)	17661	43723	Bu131620, 51-17661	
☐ Fairchild 473 Provider (205) (C-123B) (C-123K)	64394	20278	56-4394	RA
☐ North American NA-190 Sabre (F-86D)	24287	190-690	52-4287	RA
☐ North American NA-190 Sabre (F-86D)	'24094'			RAX
☐ North American NA-193 Sabre (F-86F)	50326	193-235	52-5326 -possible identity.	RA
☐ Northrop N-156A Freedom Fighter (F-5A)	69131	N6235	66-9131, 69131 (South Vietnam)	RA

SEOUL NATIONAL SCIENCE MUSEUM (SKO44)

Address:	2 Waryong-dong, Jeongu-gu, Seoul 110-360.
Tel:	02-3668-2200
Admission:	Daily 0930-1730.
Location:	In the city next to Cjanggyeonggung,

The National Science Museum opened in 1945 but its facilities were completely destroyed in the Korean War. A new complex was constructed and this opened in 1960. A decision was made to move the exhibition to a purpose built structure at Daejeon. The buildings were then taken over by the current occupants. The trace the development of all aspects of science. There is an excellent collection of fossils and ores to be seen. Many classes are held to instruct visitors in the history and modern developments in many fields. The museum includes a theatre showing a wide range of scientific films and a large concert hall.

TYPE	REG/SER	CON. NO.	PI/NOTES	STATUS
☐ North American NA-173 Sabre (F-86D)	'55-352'			PVX

SOKCHO ARMY AIR BASE MEMORIAL (SKO45)

Address:	Sokcho.
Admission:	By prior permission only.
Location:	North west of the town.

The Korean Army has a number of bases around the country and operates a variety of fixed and rotary wing types. An example of the successful Bird Dog has been preserved as a memorial.

TYPE	REG/SER	CON. NO.	PI/NOTES	STATUS
☐ Cessna 305 A Bird Dog (L-19A) (O-1A)				RA

SUWON AIR FORCE BASE COLLECTION (SKO46)

Address:	Suwon, X-do
Admission:	By prior permission only.
Location:	In the southern suburbs of the town.

The airfield was used by American squadrons in the Korean War. Now the site is home to Korean Air Force units flying F-4s and F-5s. The collection of preserved aircraft includes one which flew into the airfield when its pilot defected from the North. A display park has been set up just inside the main gate. The United State Air Force based many Sabres in the country during the Korean War. At the end of the conflict many units remained a for a period. A decision to equip the Korean Air Force with the F-86 was taken and over the next few years both F-86D and F-86F models were flown. The last examples of the type were not withdrawn until the late 1980s.The first Phantoms for Korea were ordered in 1968 and two years later F-4Ds safely guided a MiG-15 flown by a defector on to South Korean soil. The Northrop F-5 has also flown with front line squadrons for many years The Shenyang F-6 also flew in from the North and landed at a military airfield.

TYPE	REG/SER	CON. NO.	PI/NOTES	STATUS
☐ Lockheed 580 (T-33A)	41554	580-9185	54-1554	RA
☐ McDonnell M.98EN Phantom II (F-4D)	80330	3668	68-0330	RA
☐ North American NA-190 Sabre (F-86D)	'51928'			RAX
☐ North American NA-191 Sabre (F-86F)	50625	191-321	52-4625 – possible identity.	RA
☐ North American NA-191 Sabre (F-86F)	50870	191-566	52-4870 – possible identity.	RA
☐ North American NA-191 Sabre (F-86F)	52096	191-992	52-5096 -possible identity.	RA
☐ Northrop N-156A Freedom Fighter (F-5A)	'63408'		(USAF)	RAX
☐ Shenyang F-6 [Mikoyan-Gurevich MiG-19SF]	529		In North Korean markings.	RA

UNIFICATION OBSERVATORY (SKO47)

Address:	Hyeonnae-Myeon, Goseon-gun, Gangwan-do.
Admission:	Daily 0900-1700 (Closes at 1550 in winter)
Location:	About 80 km north of Gangchung city.

The building opened to the public in September 1992. Located in a picturesque site on Mount Odusan at the junction of the Hangkan River from the south and the Imjingak River from the north the exhibitions trace the history of the country and the prospects for unification. A high tower with an observation gallery offers views across the 'Demilitarized Zone', the mountains in the north and to Seoul in the south.

TYPE	REG/SER	CON. NO.	PI/NOTES	STATUS
☐ Lockheed 580 (T-33A)	61629	580-9979	56-1629	PV
☐ North American NA-124 Mustang (P-51D)	669	124-44525	44-84669, 201 (South Korea), '51-8424'	PV

WAEGWAN WAR MEMORIAL (SKO48)

Address:	Seokjeok-myeon, Chilgok-gun, Gyeonsngbuk-do.
Tel:	054-975-9155
Fax:	054-975-9155
Admission:	Daily 0900-1700.
Location:	In the town.

The museum opened on July 1st 1978 and commemorates the fierce battles which were fought along the Nakdong River. The archives contain comprehensive records of the conflict. Outside is a display of weapons along with flags of nations who fought in the area.

TYPE	REG/SER	CON. NO.	PI/NOTES	STATUS
☐ Cessna 305A Bird Dog (L-19A) (O-1A)	529			PV

WAR MEMORIAL MUSEUM (SKO49)

Address:	8 Yongsangdong 1-ka, Yongsan-ku, Seoul 140-021
Tel:	02-709-3114
Fax:	02-709-3127.
Admission:	March-October Tuesday-Sunday 0930-1800; November-February Tuesday-Sunday 0930-1700.
Location:	In the southern part of the city centre.

This impressive museum opened on June 14th 1994 on a large site in Seoul. The massive building has exhibition rooms each devoted to a period in the military history of the country. Outside is a memorial plaza with a lake and an area where the larger aircraft and a vast number of military vehicles, tanks and weapons are located The Military History Room traces early times when Koreans fought off invaders. Original equipment and replicas show how combat developed over this period. In the Korean Defense Industries Room the visitor can see examples of locally made products. The Korean War features prominently in the exhibition and there are a number of life size dioramas showing the hardships experienced by residents in the combat zones. One side of the building is occupied by the Large Equipment Room where a number of aircraft are suspended from the ceiling. South Korea came into existence on August 15th 1948 and a small Air Force was set up the following year. Among the aircraft used were a few L-5 Sentinels and one is now on show. When North Korea invaded the South to start the Korean War America supplied many aircraft to the new force and also established bases in the country. Types used by the South Korean Air Force since its formation have been collected. One of the first transport aircraft used was the Commando and a small number soldiered on until the late 1960s. The C-119 was donated by Taiwan as all the Korean examples had been scrapped. A number of North Korean aircraft which have force landed in the South can also be seen. The Antonov An-2 was flown by two defecting Civilian Aviation Administration of China pilots on September 16th 1961. Several Shenyang F-6s have been reported as landing at South Korean bases during the 1980s. A Combat Experience Room has also been constructed and this makes use of the latest techniques to give visitors the idea of aspects of war.

Right: The only aircraft at the Waegwon War Memorial is this Cessna Bird Dog. (Shinsuke Yamamoto)

The display at the AIDC factory at Shalu includes this Northrop F-5E. (Clarence Fu)

The only XC-2 built is preserved at the AIDC factory at Taichung. (Aidan Curley)

TYPE	REG/SER	CON. NO.	PI/NOTES	STATUS
☐ Bell 47G-2 Sioux (H-13H) (OH-13H)				PV
☐ Bell 204 Iroquois (UH-1B)	12542	693	62-12542	PV
☐ Bell 209 Huey Cobra (AH-1J)	29066	29066		PV
☐ Boeing 464-201-7 Stratofortress (B-52D)	'501512'	17221	55-0105	PVX
☐ Cessna 305A Bird Dog (L-19A) (O-1A)	'112537'	22972 (?)	51-12517, 112517	PVX
☐ Cessna 305D Bird Dog (305A) (L-19A) (O-1A) (O-1G)	16-954	22826	51-16954	PV
☐ Cessna 318C Tweety Bird (T-37C)	21366	42024	72-1366	PV
☐ Curtiss-Wright CW-20B-2 Commando (C-46D)	'10541'	23364	44-78541, 8541	PVX
☐ Daewoo KTX-1 Yeo Meung	02			PV
☐ De Havilland D.H.C.2 Beaver (L-20A) (U-6A)	116837	386	51-16837	PV
☐ Douglas DC-4 Skymaster (C-54D)	42-72740	10845		PV
☐ Fairchild 110 Flying Boxcar (C-119F) (C-119G)	3199	10739	51-7996 – in Taiwanese markings.	PVX
☐ Fairchild 473 Provider (205) (C-123B) (C-123J)	'10389'	20273	56-4389, 64389	PVX
☐ Grumman G-89 Tracker (S2F-1) (S-2A)	6595	504	Bu136595	PV
☐ Hiller UH12C Raven (H-23G) (OH-23G)	15205	1714	64-15205	PV
☐ Homebuilt				PV
☐ Lockheed 580 (T-33A)	35129	580-8468	53-5129	PV
☐ McDonnell M.98DJ Phantom II (F-4C)	40766	1063	64-0766	PV
☐ Mikoyan-Gurevich MiG-15UTI	128		In North Korean markings.	PV
☐ Nanchang Y-5 [Antonov An-2]	3131		In Chinese markings.	PV
☐ North American NA-121 Texan (AT-6F)	82536	121-43258	44-82536	PV
☐ North American NA-122 Mustang (P-51D)	205	122-39953	44-73494	PV
☐ North American NA-173 Sabre (F-86D)	18502	173-635	51-8502	PV
☐ North American NA-174 Trojan (T-28A)	18730	174-683	51-7830, 35129	PV
☐ North American NA-191 Sabre (F-86F)	24308	191-4	52-4308	PV
☐ Northrop N-156A Freedom Fighter (F-5A)	89-046	N.6412	68-9046	PV
☐ Shenyang F-6C [Mikoyan-Gurevich MiG-19SF]	6-6207		In North Korean markings.	PV
☐ Sikorsky S-51 Dragonfly (H-5H)	49-2007			PV
☐ Sikorsky S-55D Chickasaw (H-19B) (UH-19B)	34425		53-4425	PV
☐ Stinson V-76 Sentinel (L-5G)	59203			PV
☐ Sud SA.319B Alouette III	770301	2278		PV
☐ Yakovlev Yak-18				PV

WAR MEMORIAL MUSEUM BUSAN (SKO50)

Address:	Choeup-dong, Busanjin-gu, Busan-si.
Admission:	Daily 0900-1700.
Location:	About 2 km north of Seomyeon, Busan City.

The displays at this museum highlight the conflicts which took place in the local area. Many fierce battles were fought and nearby is a large United Nations Cemetery. The city was largely untouched but the surrounding areas suffered. Three aircraft are currently on show. All three types made valuable contributions to the American effort to stop the invasion from the north. Outside is an impressive collection of tanks, military vehicles and large guns. Inside are collections of photographs, maps documents tracing the story of the war. Many personal items can be seen and there are a few captured weapons on show.

TYPE	REG/SER	CON. NO.	PI/NOTES	STATUS
☐ Cessna 305D Bird Dog (305A) (L-19A) (O-1A) (O-1G)				PV
☐ Hiller UH12C Raven (H-23G) (OH-23G)	15181	1690	64-15181	PV
☐ North American NA-191 Sabre (F-86F)	637	191-333	52-4637	PV

WONJU AIR FORCE BASE COLLECTION (SKO51)

Address:	Wonju-si, Gangwon-do.
Admission:	By prior permission only.
Location:	About 5 km north of the city.

This long established base is currently home to fighter units operating F-4 Phantoms and F-5 Freedom Fighters along with Cessna A-37 Dragonfly used in the attack role. The preserved aircraft are located around the site. The airfield was operational during the Korean War and many bloody battles took place in the area. The base is home to the 'Black Eagles' aerobatic team which was formed in the late 1960s and flew Northrop F-5 Freedom Fighters. After twenty seven years the Cessna T-37 was introduced and one of the preserved examples is painted in their colours. The aircraft carry out their routine at many shows in the region.

TYPE	REG/SER	CON. NO.	PI/NOTES	STATUS
☐ Cessna 318B Tweety Bird (T-37B)				RA
☐ Cessna 318C Tweety Bird (T-37C)	73-696	42039	73-1696	RA
☐ Lockheed 580 (T-33A)	41552	580-9183	54-1552	RA
☐ North American NA-193 Sabre (F-86F)		193-169	52-5440 – possible identity.	RA
☐ Northrop N-156A Freedom Fighter (F-5A)	79-801			RA

YECHEON AIR BASE MEMORIAL (SKO52)

Address:	Yuncheon.
Admission:	By prior permission only.
Location:	About 15 km west of the town.

The base is currently home to fighter squadrons along with units flying training aircraft. A Sabre has been mounted on a pole just inside the main gate. This serves as a memorial to those who have served at the field.

TYPE	REG/SER	CON. NO.	PI/NOTES	STATUS
☐ North American NA-191 Sabre (F-86F)				RA

SRI LANKA

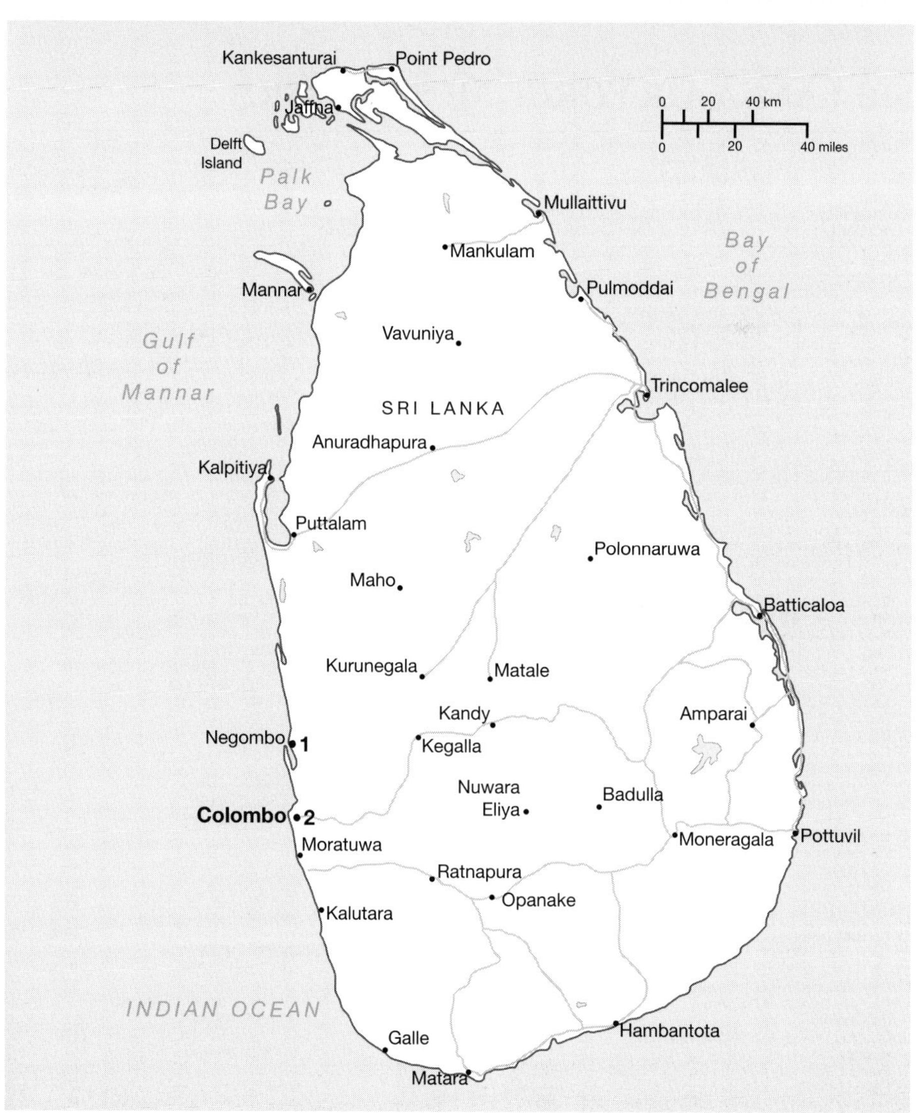

KATUNAYAKE-NEGOMBO BASE COLLECTION (SR1)

Address: Negombo.
Admission: By prior permission only.
Location: On the west coast about 40 km north of Colombo.

This base is home to the front line squadrons of the Air Force. The site was originally chosen as the location of the Air Force Museum but the growth of the airfield resulted in a move to Ratamalana. Four preserved aircraft are at the base. Only three complete Boulton Paul Balliols are known to survive.

TYPE	REG/SER	CON. NO.	PI/NOTES	STATUS
☐ Bell 47G-2 Sioux (H-13H) (OH-13H)	CH577	2060	57-1822	RA
☐ Boulton Paul P.108 Balliol T.2	CA310	BPA.10C	WG224, G-APCN	RA
☐ Hunting-Percival P.84 Jet Provost T.51	CJ707	1/5		RA
☐ Mikoyan-Gurevich MiG-17	'CH706'		CF906	RAX

SRI LANKA AIR FORCE MUSEUM (SR2)

Address: Ratmalana Air Force Base,
Colombo.
Tel: 0941-2441044
Email: coap&su@airforce.lk
Admission: By prior permission only.
Location: On the southern outskirts of the city east of Galle Road.

This former British colony established the Royal Ceylon Air Force in 1950 two years after gaining its independence. Among the first aircraft acquired were twelve Chipmunks and nine Balliols. Five Vampire T.55s were also ordered but they were returned to England without being unpacked from their crates due to a change in Government policy. The first transport type, a Dove, arrived in 1955 and since then small numbers of Herons and Dakotas have been used. Four Herons were acquired in the late 1950s and two were converted to the Riley variant by the Air Force Engineering Wing in 1981. A Soviet mission visited the country in 1971 and this resulted in the supply of one MiG-15UTI, five MiG-17Fs and two Kamov Ka-26s. The idea of a museum was put forward in 1978 and the former R.A.F. Katunayake was chosen for the collection. Airfield expansion necessitated a move and a site at China Bay on the east coast was proposed but terrorist activity in this region caused the plans to be abandoned. In the mid-1980s construction of the exhibition buildings at Ratmalana commenced and the display opened in June 1988. Four hangars are in use and the largest houses the airworthy machines. Almost all the types flown by the service since its formation have been preserved. Five Tiger Moths were operated in the early 1950s and the example in the collection was acquired from the Ratmalana Flying Training School in 1982 and rebuilt. This classic biplane flew again on September 19th 1988. The PL-2 was the first aircraft manufactured by the Sri Lankan Air Force. Construction commenced in 1977 and the maiden flight took place on April 11th 1980. The Dragonfly was the first helicopter used by the force. The history of the service is portrayed in the informative displays with many photographs, documents, uniforms and personal effects on show. In Hangar 3 there is an exhibition of vehicles which includes transport and breakdown lorries, fire engines and airfield equipment. A compound within the museum area contains a number of wrecked aircraft.

TYPE	REG/SER	CON. NO.	PI/NOTES	STATUS
☐ Antonov An-32B	CR865	3510	Front fuselage only.	PVD
☐ Avro 748 Series 2/222	CR831	1587	G-ATEJ, CF-MAL, TG-MAL, C-GCZY, 4R-ACR	PV
☐ Avro 748 Series 2A/272	CR830	1691	A2-ZFT, ZS-SBW, G-GGOB, ZS-SBW, G-GGOB	PV
☐ Beech E18S	CS450	BA-433	4R-AAU	PVA
☐ Bell 47G-2 Sioux (H-13H) (OH-13H)	CH580	2382	58-5369	PV
☐ Boulton Paul P.108 Balliol T.2	CA302		WG227	PV
☐ Centenary Micrilight	CX-02			PV
☐ Cessna 337F Super Skymaster	CC656			PVA
☐ Cessna 337F Super Skymaster	CC651	33701461	72-1461	PV
☐ De Havilland D.H.82A Tiger Moth	CX123	83645	T7179, G-AKEE, VP-CAW, CY-AAW	PVA
☐ De Havilland D.H.104 Dove 5	CS401	04463		PV
☐ De Havilland D.H.104 Dove 5	CS405	04501		PV
☐ De Havilland D.H.104 Dove 5	CS406	04502		PV
☐ De Havilland D.H.114 Heron 2D	CR801	14135		PV
☐ De Havilland D.H.C.1 Chipmunk T.20	CT102	C1/0155	(WB706)	PVA
☐ De Havilland D.H.C.1 Chipmunk T.20	CT103	C1/0156	(WB709)	PVA
☐ De Havilland D.H.C.1 Chipmunk T.20	CT107	C1/0664		PVA
☐ De Havilland D.H.C.1 Chipmunk T.20	CT109	C1/0701	CT109, 4R-AAV	PVD
☐ De Havilland D.H.C.1 Chipmunk T.20	CT110	C1/0851	CT-110, 4R-AAW	PVA
☐ De Havilland D.H.C.1 Chipmunk T.20	CT111	C1/0856		PV
☐ Douglas DC-3A-467 Skytrain (C-47B) (Dakota IV)	CR821	14019/25464	43-48203, KG787, VP-CAS, CY-ACG, 4R-ACG	PV
☐ Douglas DC-3A-467 Skytrain (C-47B) (Dakota IV)	CR822	16808/33556	44-77224, KP254, G-AMJY, 4R-ACI	PV
☐ Fabrica Militar de Aviones IA.58A Pucará	CA605	101		PV
☐ Hiller UH12B	4R-AAO	561	CY-AAO	PV
☐ Hunting-Percival P.84 Jet Provost T.51	CJ711	4/6		PV

☐ Hunting-Percival P.84 Jet Provost T.51	CJ704	8/2		PV
☐ Kamov Ka-26	CH525	7001410	CH557	PV
☐ Mikoyan-Gurevich MiG-15UTI	CF901			PV
☐ Mikoyan-Gurevich MiG-17	CF904			PV
☐ Mikoyan-Gurevich MiG-17	CF905			PVD
☐ Mil Mi-24V	CH615	3532421622231		PV
☐ Pazmany PL-2	CX122			PV
☐ Riley Heron 2D/A2 (De Havilland D.H.114 Heron 2D)	CR804	14139		PV
☐ Scottish Aviation Pioneer 1	CC602	148		PV
☐ SIAI-Marchetti SF.260TP	CT124			PV
☐ SIAI-Marchetti SF.260W	CT161			PV
☐ SIAI-Marchetti SF.260W	CT162			PV
☐ SIAI-Marchetti SF.260W	CT164			PVD
☐ SIAI-Marchetti SF.260W	CT167			PV
☐ SIAI-Marchetti SF.260W	CT168			PV
☐ SIAI-Marchetti SF.260W	CT169			PVD
☐ SIAI-Marchetti SF.260W	CT171			PV
☐ Sud SA.365C Dauphin	CH531	5005		PVA
☐ Sud SA.365C Dauphin	CH532	5006	F-WXFL	PV
☐ Sud SA.365C Dauphin	CH533	5007		PVA
☐ Westland-Sikorsky WS-51 Dragonfly 1A	CH501	WA/H/137		PV

SYRIA

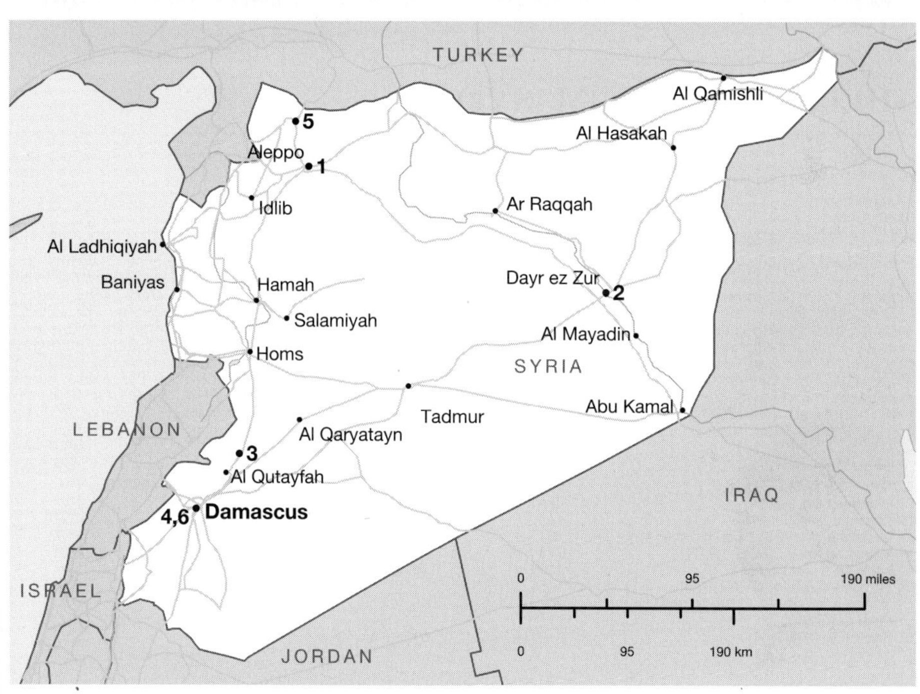

ALEPPO AIR BASE MONUMENT (SY1)

Address:	Alepo.
Admission:	By prior permission only.
Location:	In the south eastern part of the city.

The base is home to helicopter units and also serves as a major maintenance base. The Ilyushin Il-28 is preserved near to the main gate and the MiG-21 is at an Army barracks west of the field.

TYPE	REG/SER	CON. NO.	PI/NOTES	STATUS
☐ Ilyushin Il-28				RA
☐ Mikoyan-Gurevich MiG-21			At nearby barracks.	RA

DAYR EZ ZUR AIR BASE MONUMENT (SY2)

Address:	Dayr ez Zur.
Admission:	On permanent view.
Location:	About 5 km south east of the town.

The field has housed fighter units for many years and currently is home to squadrons flying the MiG-21. The preserved MiG-17 is mounted in the middle of a roundabout by the main gate to the field.

TYPE	REG/SER	CON. NO.	PI/NOTES	STATUS
☐ Mikoyan-Gurevich MiG-17				PV

DUMAYR AIR BASE MONUMENT (SY3)

Address:	Dumayr.
Admission:	By prior permission only.
Location:	About 5 km south east of the town.

This important fighter base has squadrons flying MiG-21s, MiG-23s and MiG-25s along with Sukhoi Su-22s. A preserved example of the MiG-21 is by the man gate and serves as a monument.

TYPE	REG/SER	CON. NO.	PI/NOTES	STATUS
☐ Mikoyan-Gurevich MiG-21				RA

MILITARY MUSEUM (SY4)

Address:	Sultan Salim Mosque, Bayrouth Avenue, Damascus.
Admission:	Wednesday-Monday 0800-1400.
Location:	In the city Centre near the National Museum.

Syria gained its independence in the latter stages of World War II and the Air Force initially used bases left by the departing French. Aircraft were supplied by the U.K., U.S.A., and France. In 1948 combat experience was gained when Syria invaded Israel. The conflict ended in January 1949 and orders were placed for new types. The first jets, Meteors and Vampires arrived in the early 1950s along with a number of Spitfires. In 1955 Syria entered into an agreement with the Soviet Union and for many years almost all the combat aircraft, trainers, transports and helicopters came from this source. Six MiG-15UTIs and sixty MiG-17s were flown along with twenty five single seat MiG-15s. The museum was set up in the 1980s and the displays trace the military history of the country. The Texan was first operated in the 1950s. The MiG-21 and Su-22 are fairly recent additions to the exhibition. The Campbell Cricket is one of a batch supplied to Kuwait in 1970 for 'fish-spotting' duties. The wrecks of two Israeli fighters, shot down in the many border conflicts, have been put on show. There is a display of tanks, weapons and military vehicles along with many uniforms, badges and flags.

TYPE	REG/SER	CON. NO.	PI/NOTES	STATUS
☐ Aero L-29 Delfin	105	094105	Also reported as c/n 460815	PV
☐ Campbell Cricket	G-AXVL	CA/328		PV
☐ Dassault Mirage IIIBJ	123		In Israeli markings.	PVD
☐ McDonnell M.98HO Phantom II (F-4E)	161		In Israeli markings.	PVD
☐ Mikoyan-Gurevich MiG-15UTI	273			PV
☐ Mikoyan-Gurevich MiG-17F	1196	367290		PV
☐ Mikoyan-Gurevich MiG-21PFM	1864			PV
☐ North American NA-88 Texan (AT-6D)	44		(USAAF)	PV
☐ Piper J-3C-65 Cub	31			PV
☐ Sukhoi Su-7BM	813	8101 (?)		PV

MINAKH AIR BASE MONUMENT (SY5)

Address:	Minakh.
Admission:	By prior permission only.
Location:	About 20 km south of A'zaz.

Training and helicopter squadrons reside at the field. The Delfin served here for many years and two have been preserved. One is located by the main gate, along with the MiG-21, and the other is on the field.

TYPE	REG/SER	CON. NO.	PI/NOTES	STATUS
☐ Aero L-29 Delfin				RA
☐ Aero L-29 Delfin				RA
☐ Mikoyan-Gurevich MiG-21PF				RA

WAR MEMORIAL MUSEUM (SY6)

Address:	Damascus.
Admission:	Wednesday-Monday 0800-1400.
Location:	In the north eastern part of the city

This new exhibition commemorating the October 1973 against Israel opened in the late 1990s. The story of the conflict is portrayed in detail. A panoramic cinema shows films of the conflict. Two types which were used at the time have been put on show. The wreck of the Phantom is on show along with the remains of a few others. There is an excellent display of military vehicles, tanks and items of artillery to be seen in the outside park.

TYPE	REG/SER	CON. NO.	PI/NOTES	STATUS
☐ McDonnell M.98HO Phantom II (F-4E)		3602	68-0454, (Israel)	PVD
☐ Mikoyan-Gurevich MiG-21MF	676			PV
☐ Mil Mi-8T	1278			PV

TAIWAN

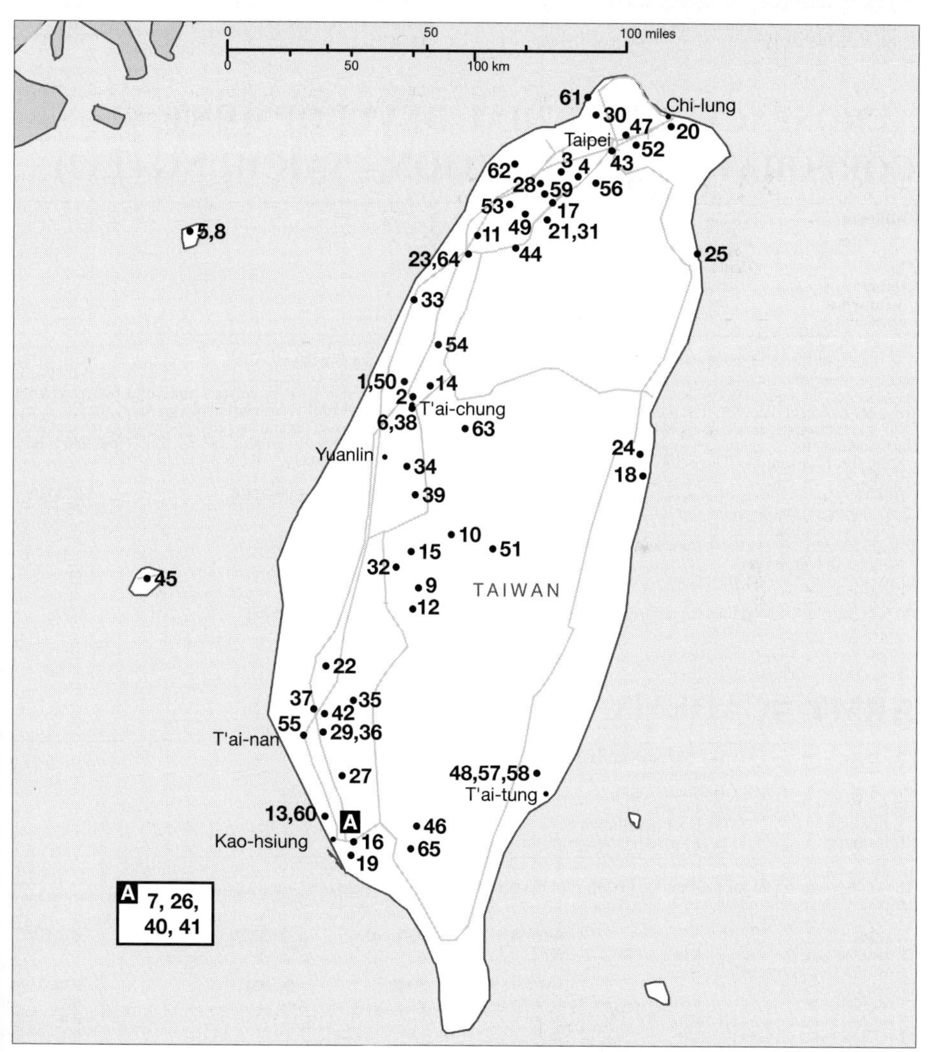

AEROSPACE INDUSTRIAL DEVELOPMENT CORPORATION COLLECTION – SHALU (TA1)

Address: 38-3 Chungchin Road,
Shalu,
Taichung County 433.
Tel: 04-2624-4053
Email: Hsingchinlin@aidc.com.tw
Admission: By prior permission only.
Location: North of Taichung City by the south eastern part of Ching Chuan Kang Air Force Base.

This factory has placed three aircraft on display. The Air Force operated four Boeing 727s on VIP duties from Sungshan. The XA-3, which is at the nearby training centre, is a single seat version of the AT-3 trainer. Only two examples of this type were completed and it did not enter production.

TYPE	REG/SER	CON. NO.	PI/NOTES	STATUS
☐ Aero Industry Development Center (AIDC) XA-3	0902		71-7002 – at nearby Hsiangyuan Training Centre.	RA
☐ Boeing 727-109	2722	19520	B-1820	RA
☐ Northrop N-156A Freedom Fighter (F-5A)	1272	N.6468	69-7102	RA
☐ Northrop N-156B Freedom Fighter (F-5B)	1280	N.6481	69-7115	RA
☐ Northrop N-311 Tiger II	5308	VG.1035	81-0015	RA

AEROSPACE INDUSTRIAL DEVELOPMENT CORPORATION COLLECTION – TAICHUNG (TA2)

Address: 111-12 Lane 68
Fushing North Road
Taichung City.
Tel: 04-2707-0001
Email: aidc@ms.aidc.com.tw
Admission: By prior permission only.
Location: In the northern part of the city.

The Bureau of Aircraft Industry was formed in 1948 at Nanjing on the Chinese mainland and moved to Taiwan two years later. Its successor, the Aero Industry Development Center, came into existence on March 1st 1969. The present name was adopted in 1995 and the organisation will eventually be privatised. One of the first programmes undertaken by AIDC was the manufacture of fifty five Pazmany PL-1Bs. In the early 1980s it re-engined and upgraded fifty North American T-28s as the T-CH-1. The AT-3 trainer was an original design and the type first flew in September 1980. Two prototypes and sixty two production examples were built. A twin turboprop transport, the XC-2, was developed in the 1970s and the prototype made its maiden flight in February 1979. Examples of the four types have been preserved at the factory.

TYPE	REG/SER	CON. NO.	PI/NOTES	STATUS
☐ Aero Industry Development Center (AIDC) Chieshou [Pazmany PL-1B]	5823			PV
☐ Aero Industry Development Center (AIDC) T-CH-1 Chung Hsing	0701		63-3001	PV
☐ Aero Industry Development Center (AIDC) XAT-3	0802		69-6002	PV
☐ Aero Industry Development Center (AIDC) XC-2			68-5001	PV

ARMY ACADEMY COLLECTION (TA3)

Address: 113 Chungshan East Road, Section 4,
Chungli City,
Taoyuan County.
Tel: 03-436-0927
Admission: By prior permission only.
Location: In the eastern suburbs of the city.

The college was set up for the training of non-commissioned officers. Courses in a number of subjects are available to the students. The collection of preserved aircraft includes one former police helicopter.

TYPE	REG/SER	CON. NO.	PI/NOTES	STATUS
☐ Aero Industry Development Center (AIDC) A-CH-1 Chung Hsing (T-CH-1)	0747		70-3047	RA
☐ Bell 205 Iroquois (UH-1H)	404	18104	65-2104	RA
☐ Hughes 269C	AP-011			Ra
☐ Hughes 269C Osage (TH-55A)	2106			RA
☐ Hughes 269C Osage (TH-55A)	2121			RA

ARMY CHEMICAL SCHOOL COLLECTION (TA4)

Address:	ChiehShou Road, Section 2, Pate City, Taoyuan County.
Admission:	By prior permission only.
Location:	In the city.

The school trains personnel in combating chemical warfare and research into weapons. Three aircraft have been preserved in the grounds along with a number of vehicles and pieces of artillery.

TYPE	REG/SER	CON. NO.	PI/NOTES	STATUS
☐ Cessna 305D Bird Dog (305A) (L-19A) (O-1A) (O-1G)	9306		54-5336	RA
☐ De Havilland D.H.C.2 Beaver (L-20A) (U-6A)	8017	1137	56-0399	RA
☐ Hughes 269C Osage (TH-55A)	2122			RA

AUGUST 23RD BOMBARDMENT MEMORIAL HALL (TA5)

Address:	Chiang Kai-Shek Memorial Forest, Kinhu, Kinmen.
Tel:	082-330599
Admission:	Daily 0830-1730.
Location:	In the centre of Kinmen Island next to Tai Lake.

This museum was opened in 1988 to commemorate the thirtieth anniversary of the campaign in the Taiwan Strait crisis. The story of this conflict is portrayed in detail. At this time the Sabre was a front line fighter.

TYPE	REG/SER	CON. NO.	PI/NOTES	STATUS
☐ North American NA-172 Sabre (F-86F)	6192	172-240	51-12949	PV

AUGUST 23RD CAMPAIGN MEMORIAL PARK (TA6)

Address:	Chongde 9 Road and Chiangpiang East 3 Street, Taichung City.
Admission:	On permanent view.
Location:	In the town.

The park honours the 1958 artillery bombardment which helped in the defence of Taiwan. In addition to the aircraft there are examples of military vehicles and weapons on show. The Starfighter is from the batch of aircraft which were used to train Luftwaffe pilots at Luke Air Force Base in Arizona.

TYPE	REG/SER	CON. NO.	PI/NOTES	STATUS
☐ Lockheed 583-10-20 Starfighter (TF-104G)	4193	583D-5770	63-8454, (27+66), 38464	PV
☐ Northrop N-311 Tiger II (F-5E)	5283	VG.1010	80-0304	PV

CHENCHING LAKE RECREATIONAL PARK MEMORIAL (TA7)

Address:	Niaosung, Kaohsiung County.
Admission:	During daylight hours.
Location:	On the outskirts of the town.

This park is home to many recreational pursuits. The Sabre is parked outside the Youth Activity Center and serves as a reminder of those who have served with the military forces. Taiwan received more than three hundred Sabres between 1954 and the end of 1958. Additional examples arrived later and the fighter served with squadrons around the island. F-86D models joined the Air Force in 1959 and served at Hsinchu.

TYPE	REG/SER	CON. NO.	PI/NOTES	STATUS
☐ North American NA-191 Sabre (F-86F)	6134	191-324	52-4628	PV

CHIANG CHINGKUO MEMORIAL HALL (TA8)

Address:	Chungshan Memorial Forest, Kinning Hsiang, Kinmen County.
Tel:	082-313197
Admission:	On permanent view.
Location:	In the centre of Kinmen Island.

Kinmen Island has seen a number of conflicts with the mainland. To remind visitors of the military importance of the area four aircraft have been put on show and a display has been set up in the hall.

TYPE	REG/SER	CON. NO.	PI/NOTES	STATUS
☐ Fairchild 110 Flying Boxcar (C-119F)	3192	123	51-8120	PV
☐ Hughes 269C Osage (TH-55A)	2117			PV
☐ Lockheed 583-10-20 Starfighter (TF-104G)	4186	583D-5762	63-8458, (27+60), 38458	PV
☐ Northrop N-156B Freedom Fighter (F-5B)	1113	N.8131	73-1612	PV

CHIAYI AIR FORCE BASE COLLECTION (TA9)

Address:	1 Rongdian Road, Shueishang, Chiayi City.
Tel:	05-236-0505
Admission:	By prior permission only.
Location:	Southwest of the city.

This base has housed fighter units of the Air Force for many years and currently is home to the first F-16 Fighting Falcons operated by the service. One F-16A and one F-16B arrived at the field on April 14th 1997 and the type replaced the Northrop F-5. Four fighters which served at the field are preserved along with a T-33 which was used for pilot training. The Albatross was based at Chiayi where the Search and Rescue Squadron has its headquarters. Currently Sikorsky S-70 helicopters are used in this role.

TYPE	REG/SER	CON. NO.	PI/NOTES	STATUS
☐ Grumman G-111 Albatross (G-64) (SA-16A) (SA-16B) (HU-16B)	1012	G-8	48-0595, 11012	RA
☐ Lockheed 580 (T-33A)	'3074'	580-1359	57-0530, 67-0634, 3075	RAX
☐ North American NA-192 Super Sabre (F-100A)	'0101'	192-65	53-1570, 0235	RAX
☐ North American NA-243 Super Sabre (F-100F)	0005	243-263	56-3987	RA
☐ Northrop N-311 Tiger II (F-5E)	5241	V.1141	76-1636	RA
☐ Republic F-84G Thunderjet	'F-84132'		'11158'	RAX

CHICHI MILITARY PARK (TA10)

Address:	Chichi, Nantou County.
Tel:	049-276-2546 (Railway Museum)
Admission:	On permanent view.
Location:	In the town close to the railway station.

The area was badly damaged in an earthquake in 1999 and a major reconstruction programme started. The railway line and station were rebuilt and attractions to encourage tourists were planned. A museum was set up in the station and a military display was located nearby. Also to be seen are tanks, military vehicles and weapons. Over fifty C-119s were flown by the Taiwanese Air Force and was the last to operate the transport.

TYPE	REG/SER	CON. NO.	PI/NOTES	STATUS
☐ Fairchild 110 Flying Boxcar (C-119G)	3184	11003	52-5844	PV
☐ Lockheed 683-04-10 Starfighter (RF-104G)	4303	683-4056	62-12252	PV

CHINA INSTITUTE OF TECHNOLOGY – HSIN CHU CAMPUS (TA11)

Address:	200 Chunghua Street, Henshang Hsiang, Hsinchu County 312.
Tel:	03-593-5707
Fax:	03-593-6297
Admission:	By prior permission only.
Location:	Close to the village.

The Institute was established in the late 1960s as a junior college and has now changed its role to offer courses in many areas. The aeronautical engineering department is located at the Hsin Chu campus. In common with many academic institutions the aircraft serve both as instructional airframes and display pieces. Four recently withdrawn military types contrast with the five civilian machines. The Boeing 727 was used as an executive transport for high-ranking military personnel. Engines, airframe components, systems and models can be found in the workshops. A small display tracing the history of aviation can also be found.

TYPE	REG/SER	CON. NO.	PI/NOTES	STATUS
☐ Boeing 727-109C	2723	20111		RA
☐ Britten-Norman BN-2A-26 Islander	B-11110	575	G-BEIY	RA
☐ Britten-Norman BN-2A-26 Islander	B-11123	2032	G-BNAE	RA
☐ Britten-Norman BN-2A-27 Islander	B-11126	2193	G-BLNS	RA
☐ Cessna 150F	N6799F	15063399		RA
☐ Fairchild 110 Flying Boxcar (C-119F)	3158	10710	51-7971	RA
☐ Lockheed 583-10-20 Starfighter (TF-104G)	4195	583F-5933	(KF+233), 66-13622, (28+03), 13622	RA
☐ Northrop N-311 Tiger II (F-5E)	5145	V.1045	75-0318	RA
☐ Piper PA-28-140 Cherokee	N56857	28-7425052		RA

CHINCHE COMMUNITY PARK MEMORIAL (TA12)

Address: Chinche Village,
Shuishan,
Chiayi County.
Admission: On permanent view.
Location: In the village.

This community park hosts many events for local people. Displayed as a memorial to residents who have joined the services is a Northrop F-5E which served with 5 TFW at Hualien for many years.

TYPE	REG/SER	CON. NO.	PI/NOTES	STATUS
☐ Northrop N-311 Tiger II (F-5E)	5251	VE.1003	77-0334	PV

CHINESE AIR FORCE MUSEUM (TA13)

Address: P.O. Box 90277,
Air Force Academy,
Kangshan,
Kaohsiung County.
Email: afm@cc.cafa.edu.tw
Admission: Sunday 0900-1630.
Location: About 10 km north west of Kaohsiung City.

Military flying began in China in 1910 when a Russian pilot demonstrated a Blériot monoplane in Beijing. During the next few years aircraft were purchased from France and Britain. The turbulent political climate led to the formation of a number of air arms maintained by local warlords and elected rulers. Stability was not restored for many years and aircraft arrived in the country from the U.S.A., Italy and Germany. The Republic of China was formed by Sun Yat-sen in 1912 and the country was unified under the leadership of Chiang Kai-shek in 1928. The Communists led by Mao Tse-tung set up their power base in the north west of the country after the Long March in 1934/5. In 1950 the Nationalists withdrew to Taiwan. The Taiwanese Air Force Academy was set up at Kangshan in 1949 as the Chiang Kai-shek forces gradually left the mainland. All aircrew officers undertake an academic programme as well as flying training or courses leading to ground based duties. In September 1983 a decision was made to set up a museum at the academy. Work on the building and outside air park started in May 1986 and was soon completed. The indoor displays trace the history of military flying from the early days and feature many models, dioramas, photographs, uniforms, engines and components. The majority of types used by the force since the mid-1950s have been preserved. The C-46 on show was exchanged with South Korea for a C-119 and the P-51 arrived from the Philippines with a serviceable F-5A going the other way. The Kaydet was used for training at the Academy for many years. The DC-6B was originally delivered to Panagra in 1952 and spent a decade flying on their routes before moving to Taiwan. The Boeing 720 was used as a presidential aircraft before retiring to the museum. Also on show are a number of machines which have been flown to Taiwan by defectors from mainland China. The Harbin H-5 crash-landed in November 1965 and one of the crew was killed. The Shenyang J-5 landed on the island on November 14th 1983 with Wang Xuecheng of the 18th Regiment of the 6th Naval Division at the controls. The two J-6s were both from the 145th Regiment of the 49th Division, one arrived in November 1987 and the other in September 1989. The J-6Z which defected on July 7th 1977 was the first reconnaissance version of the MiG-19 seen in the west.

TYPE	REG/SER	CON. NO.	PI/NOTES	STATUS
☐ Aero Industry Development Center (AIDC) A-CH-1 Chung Hsing (T-CH-1)	0742		69-3042	PV
☐ Aero Industry Development Center (AIDC) Chieshou [Pazmany PL-1B]	5842			PV
☐ Beech C18S Kansan (AT-11)				PV
☐ Beech D18S	AT-11005	A-488		PV
☐ Boeing 720-051B	18351	18351	N721US	PV
☐ Boeing-Stearman A75N1 Kaydet (PT-17)	054			PV
☐ Cessna 305D Bird Dog (305A) (L-19A) (O-1A) (O-1G)	9301	22446	51-12132	PV

TYPE	REG/SER	CON. NO.	PI/NOTES	STATUS
□ Cessna 310A Blue Canoe (L-27A) (U-3A)	3601	38014	57-5859	PV
□ Curtiss-Wright CW-20B Commando (C-46A)	'C-46045'		(USAAF), (South Korean)	PVX
□ Douglas DC-3A-467 Skytrain (C-47B)	7219	14622/26067	43-48806, 48806 (China)	PV
□ Douglas DC-6B-1225A	C-43536	43536	N6536C	PV
□ Fairchild 110 Flying Boxcar (C-119F)	3190	109	51-8106	PV
□ Fairchild 473 Provider (205) (C-123B) (C-123K)	603	20189	55-4528	PV
□ Grumman G-89 Tracker (S2F-1) (S-2A)	2102	22	Bu133051, 102	PV
□ Grumman G-111 Albatross (G-64) (SA-16A) (SA-16B) (HU-16B)	1023	G-34	49-076, 11023	PV
□ Grumman G-121 Tracker (S-2E)	2128	246C	Bu152359	PV
□ Harbin H-5 [Ilyushin Il-28]	0195			PV
□ Lockheed 183-93-02 Starfighter (F-104A)	4241	183-1111	56-0823	PV
□ Lockheed 483-04-06 Starfighter (F-104D)	4166	483-5038	57-1326	PV
□ Lockheed 580 (T-33A)	3025	580-8178	52-9872, T-33025	PV
□ Lockheed 683-10-19 Starfighter (F-104G)	4413	683D-6044	62-12345, R-345 (Denmark)	PV
□ Lockheed 683-10-19 Starfighter (F-104G)	4344	683D-6115	64-17770	PV
□ McDonnell M.36Y Voodoo (RF-101A)	5658	58	54-1506	PV
□ Mikoyan-Gurevich MiG-15bis	1765			PV
□ Mikoyan-Gurevich MiG-21MF	2318	742318	In Hungarian markings.	PV
□ Noorduyn Harvard IIB [North American NA-77 (AT-16)]	214			PV
□ North American NA-122 Mustang (P-51D)	'053'		(USAAF) (Philippines)	PVX
□ North American NA-174 Trojan (T-28A)	2823	174-202	51-3664, T-2823	PV
□ North American NA-191 Sabre (F-86F)	'6408'		(USAF), F-86049	PVX
□ North American NA-192 Super Sabre (F-100A)	0211	192-56	53-1561	PV
□ North American NA-243 Super Sabre (F-100F)	0001	243-244	56-3968	PV
□ Northrop N-156A Freedom Fighter (F-5A)	1270	N.6464	69-7098, 1270 (Taiwan), 97098 (Morocco)	PV
□ Northrop N-156B Freedom Fighter (F-5B)	1104	N.8045	66-9237	PV
□ Northrop N-156T Talon (T-38A) (AT-38A)	'3842'	N.5170	61-0804, '0001'	PVX
□ Republic F-84G Thunderjet	'130'		'51-16657'	PVX
□ Shenyang J-5 [Mikoyan-Gurevich MiG-17F]	83065			PV
□ Shenyang J-6 [Mikoyan-Gurevich MiG-19SF]	40208			PV
□ Shenyang J-6 [Mikoyan-Gurevich MiG-19SF]	40307			PV
□ Shenyang JJ-6 [Mikoyan-Gurevich MiG-19U]	3171			PV

CHING CHUAN KANG AIR FORCE BASE COLLECTION (TA14)

Address:	600 Section 4, Chungching Road, Taichung City, Tiichung County.
Tel:	04-2562-3411
Admission:	By prior permission only.
Location:	North of Taichung City.

Built by the Americans in the 1950s, this large base is home to the 3rd Tactical Fighter Wing flying the indigenous Ching-Kuo. Seventy examples serve with the three resident squadrons. Starfighters were operated from the field for many years and the last were withdrawn in the late summer of 1995. Two variants of the type have been preserved along with a T-33 used for general duties and training.

TYPE	REG/SER	CON. NO.	PI/NOTES	STATUS
□ Lockheed 580 (T-33A)	3325	580-1109	56-1759	RA
□ Lockheed 583-10-20 Starfighter (TF-104G)	4147	583C-5506	61-3030	RA
□ Lockheed 683-04-10 Starfighter (RF-104G)	4301	683C-4054	62-12250	RA
□ North American NA-193 Sabre (F-86F)	6071	193-171	52-5442	RA
□ Northrop N-311 Tiger II (F-5E)	5102	V.1002	74-0959	RA
□ Northrop N-311 Tiger II (F-5E)	5304	VG.1031	81-0011	RA

CHUCHI PARK MEMORIAL (TA15)

Address:	Chuchi, Chiayi County.
Admission:	On permanent view.
Location:	In the northern part of the town.

The Taiwanese Air Force flew almost three hundred and fifty examples of the F-5E. The first one entered service in 1975. One has been preserved as a memorial in the local park.

TYPE	REG/SER	CON. NO.	PI/NOTES	STATUS
□ Northrop N-311 Tiger II (F-5E)	5229	V.1129	76-1624	PV

Above: The Haipuchihwanfu Temple Military History Park displays this Hughes TH-55. (Clarence Fu)

The Chinese Air Force Museum at Kangshan is home to this Curtiss Commando. (Aidan Curley)

Taiwan was the last country to fly the Fairchild C-119 and this example is preserved at Pingtung Air Force Base. (Aidan Curley)

CHUNG CHENG ARMED FORCES PREPARATORY SCHOOL MEMORIAL (TA16)

Address:	1 Kaihsuan Road, Fengshan City, Kaohsiung County.
Tel:	07-741-4188
Admission:	By prior permission only.
Location:	South of the city.

The school was established in 1976 and a junior department was added fifteen years later. The majority of the pupils go on to join the military. Two fighters are preserved in the grounds.

TYPE	REG/SER	CON. NO.	PI/NOTES	STATUS
☐ Lockheed 183-93-02 Starfighter (F-104A)	4258	183-1164	56-0876	RA
☐ North American NA-192 Super Sabre (F-100A)	0105	192-35	53-1540	RA

CHUNG CHENG INSTITUTE OF SCIENCE AND TECHNOLOGY COLLECTION (TA17)

Address:	190 Sanyu 1st Street, Dashi-jen Taoyuan County 335.
Tel:	03-380-0960
Fax:	03-380-1519
Email:	aero@ccit.edu.tw
Admission:	By prior permission only.
Location:	About 10 km south of Taoyuan City.

The aircraft here serve both as display machines and as instructional airframes. One of the one hundred and eighteen F-100A Super Sabres supplied to Taiwan is in the collection. The single seat Pazmany PL-4 first appeared in the U.S.A. in 1972 and sets of plans and kits were made available to amateur constructors. The type features a fully enclosed cockpit and folding wings. The PL-4 won the 'Outstanding New Design' award at the 1972 EAA Convention at Oshkosh. Another American homebuilt type is the Rotorway Scorpion helicopter. This design was developed from the Schramm Javelin which first flew in 1965. The type was offered in kit form. The improved Scorpion Too had a larger fuselage and a higher powered engine.

TYPE	REG/SER	CON. NO.	PI/NOTES	STATUS
☐ Aero Industry Development Center (AIDC) A-CH-1 Chung Hsing (T-CH-1)	0741	1470	69-3041	RA
☐ Bell 47G-2 Sioux (H-13H) (OH-13H)	313	2551	59-4968	RA
☐ De Havilland D.H.C.2 Beaver (L-20A) (U-6A)	8023	1081	56-0375	RA
☐ Lockheed 683-07-14 Starfighter (F-104J)	'4547'	683B-3047	36-8547	RAX
☐ North American NA-192 Super Sabre (F-100A)	0302	192-76	53-1581	RA
☐ Pazmany PL-4	6435	3564	64-3501	RA
☐ Rotorway Scorpion Too	7538	3875	75-3801	RA

CHUNGHUA VOCATIONAL HIGH SCHOOL (TA18)

Address:	101 Chihsing 4th Street, Chian, Hualien County.
Tel:	03-853-8565
Fax:	03-853-7126
Admission:	By prior permission only.
Location:	South of Hualien City.

The five aircraft are also used in the training of engineers as well as being displayed. The workshops also contain airframe parts, engines and instruments. The Hughes 269 made its maiden flight in October 1956 and the United States Army took a small batch for evaluation. Five years later an order for a dual control version the TH-55A was placed. The Osage was to be the standard basic training helicopter. Large numbers were produced for both the civil and military markets with many exported. The Schweizer company purchased the design rights in 1986.

TYPE	REG/SER	CON. NO.	PI/NOTES	STATUS
☐ Hughes 269C Osage (TH-55A)	2109			RA
☐ Lockheed 683-10-19 Starfighter (F-104G)	4367	683-2025	KF+101, BG+120,63-13242, (20+20), 63-13242	RA
☐ North American NA-191 Sabre (F-86F)	6237		Rear fuselage only.	RA
☐ Northrop N-156B Freedom Fighter (F-5B)	1116	N.8134	74-0776	RA
☐ Northrop N-311 Tiger II (F-5E)	5123	V.1023	74-0980	RA

CHUNGSHAN INDUSTRIAL AND COMMERCIAL SCHOOL DISPLAY (TA19)

Address:	79 Chengchi Road, Taliao, Koahsiung County.
Tel:	07-781-5311
Admission:	By prior permission only.
Location:	In the town.

The school is the largest of its kind in southern Taiwan and trains students in a variety of skills needed in modern commerce and industry. The Northrop Tiger II is preserved in the grounds.In the buildings are engines, components and instruments used to train engine and airframe fitters.

TYPE	REG/SER	CON. NO.	PI/NOTES	STATUS
☐ Northrop N-311 Tiger II (F-5E)	5149	V.1049	75-0322	RA

CONSCRIPTION PARK (TA20)

Address:	1 Yi 1st Road, Jhaongjhang District, Keelung City 202.
Admission:	On permanent view.
Tel:	02-2420-1122
Location:	In the eastern part of the city.

The town has set up a display of weapons in the picturesque park. Military vehicles, tanks and missiles can be seen. One of the highlights of the exhibition is an Armstrong Steel Breechloader gun dating from the mid-nineteenth century. This British design was fitted to many ships around the world. The city is a major port so this is an appropriate place for it to reside. The only aircraft at the present time is the two seater Starfighter.

TYPE	REG/SER	CON. NO.	PI/NOTES	STATUS
☐ Lockheed 583-10-20 Starfighter (TF-104G)	4196	583D-5936	(KF+236), 66-13625, (28+06), 13625	PV

FAN SHU VOCATIONAL SCHOOL COLLECTION (TA21)

Address:	50 Chungyuan Road, Section 1, Lungtang, Taoyuan County.
Tel:	03-479-6345
Admission:	By prior permission only.
Location:	In the northern part of the town.

The school offers a variety of courses leading to qualifications in many trades. Collaboration with industry has led to research projects being carried out. Airframe and engine fitters are trained at the school which currently has three aircraft. The Cessna Bird Dog served with the Taiwanese Army for many years and was ideal for flying into unprepared airstrips in the remote areas of the island. The Northrop Tiger was developed from the Freedom Fighter and deliveries to many countries were made under the MAP scheme.

TYPE	REG/SER	CON. NO.	PI/NOTES	STATUS
☐ Cessna 305D Bird Dog (305A) (L-19A) (O-1A) (O-1G)	9313			RA
☐ Cessna 305D Bird Dog (305A) (L-19A) (O-1A) (O-1G)	9316			RA
☐ Northrop N-311 Tiger II (F-5E)	5215	V.1115	76-0845	RA

HAIPUCHIHWANFU TEMPLE MILITARY HISTORY PARK (TA22)

Address:	Matou, Tainan County.
Admission:	In the town.
Location:	By prior permission only.

The temple has preserved two aircraft as memorials to local servicemen. Northrop F-5Es served in large numbers with the Taiwanese Air Force and Hughes TH-55s were also used by the Army.

TYPE	REG/SER	CON. NO.	PI/NOTES	STATUS
☐ Hughes 269C Osage (TH-55A)	2101			RA
☐ Northrop N-311 Tiger II (F-5E)	5121	V.1021	74-0978	RA

HSIN CHU AIR FORCE BASE COLLECTION (TA23)

Address:	1 Jiyang Road, Hsinchu City, Hsinchu County.
Tel:	03-533-4111
Admission:	By prior permission only.
Location:	In the western suburbs of the city.

On May 5th 1997 the first five Mirage 2000-5s arrived at this base after shipment from France. A collection of types which served at the field has been preserved. The first F-86F Sabres were delivered to Taiwan in November 1954 and saw combat use in the isolated conflicts with aircraft of the People's Liberation Army Air Force.

TYPE	REG/SER	CON. NO.	PI/NOTES	STATUS
☐ Aero Industry Development Center (AIDC) A-CH-1 Chung Hsing (T-CH-1)				RA
☐ Grumman G-121 Tracker (S-2E)	2125			RA
☐ Lockheed 183-93-02 Starfighter (F-104A)	4255	183-1153	56-0865	RA
☐ Lockheed 580 (T-33A)	'3333'	580-1103	56-1753, 3323	PVX
☐ Lockheed 583-10-20 Starfighter (TF-104G)	4171	583D-5744	61-3073, (27+42), 13073	RA
☐ Lockheed 683-04-10 Starfighter (RF-104G)	4398	683-8204	KG+304, BB+251, 67-14890, (24+50), 14890 – in nearby park.	PV
☐ Lockheed 683-10-19 Starfighter (F-104G)	4393	683-8071	KG+171, 65-12753, (23+72), 12753	RA
☐ North American NA-191 Sabre (F-86F)	6273	191-130	52-4434	RA
☐ North American NA-192 Super Sabre (F-100A)	'0225'	192-150	53-1655, 0141'	PVX

HUALIEN AIR FORCE BASE COLLECTION (TA24)

Address:	179 Jiashing Village, Hsincheng, Hualien County.
Tel:	03822-3158
Admission:	By prior permission only.
Location:	In the northern suburbs of the city.

The airfield has been home to a tactical fighter wing for many years. Versions of the F-5 have been flown for almost forty years. The General Dynamics F-16 arrived in 1999 and now equips several squadrons. Small numbers of the Voodoo were used by Taiwan. A civil terminal was opened in 1962.

TYPE	REG/SER	CON. NO.	PI/NOTES	STATUS
☐ Aero Industry Development Center (AIDC) T-CH-1B Chung Hsing	0752		70-3052	RA
☐ Lockheed 683-10-19 Starfighter (F-104G)	4375	683-2038	KF+114, DA+242,BG+129, 63-13254, (20+31), 63-13254	RA
☐ McDonnell M.36Y Voodoo (RF-101A)	5654	45	54-1499	RA
☐ North American NA-227 Sabre (F-86F)	'053'		(USAF), 55020'	RAX
☐ Northrop N-156B Freedom Fighter (F-5B)	'1101'	N.8049	67-21272, 1106	RAX
☐ Northrop N-311 Tiger II (F-5E)	5185	V.1085	75-0358	RA

ILAN COUNTY MILITARY SHRINE (TA25)

Address:	Number 9 Road, Suao, Ilan County.
Tel:	03-936-4567
Admission:	On permanent view.
Location:	Near the new Suao Railway Station.

The shrine has been set up to honour those who have lost their lives in serving their country. The area is home to a number of military bases. A former Luftwaffe Starfighter has been put on show.

TYPE	REG/SER	CON. NO.	PI/NOTES	STATUS
☐ Lockheed 683-10-19 Starfighter (F-104G)	4381	683-2093	KF+168, DC+244, BG+111, 63-13265, (20+80), 63-13265	PV

KAOHSIUNG COUNTY MILITARY SHRINE (TA26)

Address:	Gonyang Road, Niaosung, Kaohsiung County.
Admission:	On permanent view.
Location:	At the junction of Gonyang Road with Chongcheng Road.

Over seven hundred people are honoured at this site located on the slopes of the picturesque Chingsan mountain. A two seat Starfighter obtained from the Luftwaffe in the mid-1980s can be seen. Twenty seven were obtained from this source to supplement the fourteen delivered earlier.

TYPE	REG/SER	CON. NO.	PI/NOTES	STATUS
☐ Lockheed 583-10-20 Starfighter (TF-104G)	4182	583D-5758	63-8454, (27+56), 38454	PV

KAOYUAN UNIVERSITY DISPLAY (TA27)

Address:	1821 Chungshan Road, Luchu, Koahsiung County.
Tel:	07-607-7777
Admission:	By prior permission only.
Location:	In the town.

This large university is well known for its research into many aspects of technology. The Aeronautical Engineering Department has two airframes and a display of components, engines and instruments in its workshops. The aircraft are used for instructional purposes as well as being on display at open days.

TYPE	REG/SER	CON. NO.	PI/NOTES	STATUS
☐ Cessna 152	N95751	15285965		RA
☐ Lockheed 683-04-10 Starfighter (RF-104G)	4378	683-2076	63-13260	RA

KUANYIN MILITARY HISTORY PARK (TA28)

Address:	Kuangshin Village, Kuanyin, Taoyuan County.
Admission:	On permanent view.
Location:	In the town.

The park is being developed to honour the contribution military forces have made to the country. On show are vehicles, weapons and a former Taiwan Air Force Hughes Osage helicopter.

TYPE	REG/SER	CON. NO.	PI/NOTES	STATUS
☐ Hughes 269C Osage (TH-55A)	2122			RA

KWEIJEN ARMY AIR BASE COLLECTION (TA29)

Address:	188 Nanding Road, Kweijen, Tainan County.
Tel:	06-330-4340
Admission:	By prior permission only.
Location:	About 7 km south east of Tainan City.

A variety of fixed wing aircraft and helicopters have been flown by Army units over the years. Five types are preserved at this important base. The O-1G version of the Bird Dog was a conversion of the earlier O-1A model originally used by the U.S.A.F. for Forward Air Control duties in Vietnam. The Bell 47 was the first helicopter flown by the Taiwanese military and a small number remained in use until the mid-1980s. The Pazmany PL-1 was designed in America for homebuilders and the prototype first flew in 1962. Fifty eight of the improved PL-1B were built in Taiwan to serve as primary trainers for the Air Force.

TYPE	REG/SER	CON. NO.	PI/NOTES	STATUS
☐ Aero Industry Development Center (AIDC) Chieshou [Pazmany PL-1B]	'2001'		63-1049, 5839	RAX
☐ Bell 47G-2 Sioux (H-13H) (OH-13H)		2409	59-4916	RA
☐ Cessna 305D Bird Dog (305A) (L-19A) (O-1A) (O-1G)	9307	22413	51-12099	RA
☐ De Havilland D.H.C.2 Beaver (L-20A) (U-6A)	8025	756	53-7940	RA
☐ Hughes 369M Cayuse (HO-6) (OH-6A)	908	1170	69-17210	RA

LINKUO RESORT COLLECTION (TA30)

Address:	13-1 Shafu Village, Linkuo, Taipei County.
Tel:	02-2606-2712
Admission:	On permanent view.
Location:	To the north of the town.

Two aircraft have recently been put on show at this picturesque holiday resort to add to the attractions offered to the visitor. Also displayed in the park are a number of vehicles and machinery.

TYPE	REG/SER	CON. NO.	PI/NOTES	STATUS
☐ Cessna 172D	JA3182	50027	N2427U	PV
☐ Piper PA-28-140 Cherokee				PV

LUNGTANG MILITARY PARK (TA31)

Address:	Chunghsing Road, Lung Tang, Taoyuan County.
Admission:	Daily 0900-1800.
Location:	Near the junction of Chunghsing Road and Beilong Road near the Public Stadium.

This park displays a number of tanks and military vehicles in addition to the three aircraft. Two aircraft are not strictly part of the exhibition but can be seen at the gate of a local Army Camp.

TYPE	REG/SER	CON. NO.	PI/NOTES	STATUS
☐ Cessna 305D Bird Dog (305A) (L-19A) (O-1A) (O-1G)	'54-0412'		(USAAF), 9302 – at Army Base.	RAX
☐ De Havilland D.H.C.2 Beaver (L-20A) (U-6A)	'56-1103'	280	51-16805, 8021 – at Army Base.	RAX
☐ Hughes 269C Osage (TH-55A)	2110			PV
☐ Northrop N-311 Tiger II (F-5E)	5230	V.1130	76-1625	PV

MEISNAN PARK MEMORIAL (TA32)

Address:	Meishan, Chiayi County.
Admission:	On permanent view.
Location:	In the town.

A Northrop F-5E has been put on display in this park as a memorial to local people who have served with the Taiwanese Air Force. The supersonic jet fighter was in service for many years.

TYPE	REG/SER	CON. NO.	PI/NOTES	STATUS
☐ Northrop N-311 Tiger II (F-5E)	5182	V.1082	75-0355	PV

MILITARY AIRCRAFT PARK (TA33)

Address:	Datong Road, Hsihu, Changhua County.
Admission:	On permanent view.
Location:	In the town.

This display has been set up in the home town of the former Commander-in-Chief of the Chinese Air Force, General Chen Chaomin. He later became the Deputy Defense Minister and was responsible for important negotiations which led to the acquisition of modern combat aircraft. The park was specially built to honour his achievements. Three jet fighters can be seen and all the types served in large numbers in the country. The display is dominated by the C-119. Taiwan was the last country to fly the freighter on military duties and the final examples were withdrawn in December 1998. The R-CH-1 can be seen at a nearby Temple.

TYPE	REG/SER	CON. NO.	PI/NOTES	STATUS
☐ Aero Industry Development Center (AIDC) R-CH-1 Chung Hsing (T-CH-1)	0749		70-3049 – At nearby Temple.	PV
☐ Fairchild 110 Flying Boxcar (C-119F)	3160	10724	51-7985	PV
☐ Lockheed 683-04-10 Starfighter (RF-104G-1)	4400	683-8230	KG+330, EB+106, (YA+???), 67-22517, (24+80), 22517	PV
☐ North American NA-261 Super Sabre (F-100F)	'0011/31566'	261-6	58-6980, 0009	PVX
☐ Northrop N-311 Tiger II (F-5E)	5140	V.1040	74-0997	PV

This Supermarine Walrus was rebuilt in the workshops of the RAAF Museum at Point Cook. [AUS108] (Douglas Rough)

This classic biplane is operated by Tiger Moth World at Torquay in Victoria. [AUS111] (Gerry Manning)

Several gliders, including this Slingsby Gull, can be seen in the RAAFA Museum on the outskirts of Perth. [AUS119] (Lloyd Robinson)

A view of the main hangar at MOTAT. A Short Solent is parked behind the Avro Lancaster. [NZ15] (MOTAT)

Above: This Beaver is part of the New Zealand Warbirds fleet and has been painted in the colours of one flown in the Antarctic.[NZ18]

Left: This Avro 626 can be seen in Air Force World at Wigram. [NZ31] (Brian Nicholls)

Right: The Croydon Aviation Heritage Trust hangar at Mandeville is home to a number of de Havilland types including this Fox Moth. [NZ36] (Brian Nicholls)

Above: This Polikarpov I-153 was rebuilt in Russia for the Alpine Fighter Collection at Wanaka. [NZ42] (Brian Nicholls)

Right: This Albatros B II replica is on show at the impressive Omaka Aviation Heritage Centre. [NZ44] (Dave McDonald)

Left: This Sikorsky S-55 can be seen at the Museo de Los Ninos in San José. The helicopter has recently been restored. [COS2] (Diego Alvardo)

Below: This rare Vought Kingfisher is at the Museo de la Revolucion in Havana. [CU6] (Nigel Ponsford)

There is a collection of preserved aircraft at the military base of San Antonio de los Banos. This MiG-21bis is mounted near the gate. [CU7] (Nigel Hitchman)

The museum at Playa Giron which highlights the 'Bay of Pigs' conflict displays this Hawker Fury. [CU8] (Nigel Ponsford)

The Museo del Aire near Havana exhibits this MiG-23UB. [CU9] (Nigel Hitchman)

The old Terminal at Ilopango houses the Museo Nacional de Aviacion where this restored Bellanca 14-13-3 can be seen. [EL2] (Paul Seymour)

This rare North American NA-16 is at the Museo del Aire at Toncontin Air Base. [HO2] (Paul Seymour)

This Vought Corsair is in the museum at Toncontin Air Base. [HO2] (Eduardo Cardenas)

This Republic F-105 Thunderchief is on show at the Planetarium and Science Centre in Guadalajara. [MEX1] (Iván Nesbit)

This formation of training aircraft is by the main gate of the Military Aviation School at Zapopan. The trio contains a Stearman Kaydet, a North American Texan and a Pilatus PC.7. [MEX5] (Tim Spearman)

Among the aircraft on show at the Mexican Air Force Museum in Guadalajara is this Vampire F.3. [MEX26] (Iván Nesbit)

This Bell 47 is in the grounds of the Technical Museum in Mexico City. [MEX28]

Left: A number of aircraft are preserved at Córdoba. The collection includes an example of the indigenous Pucara. [ARG2] (Santiago Rivas)

Below: Several Meteor F.4s are preserved in Argentina. This example is at Estancia Santa Romana. [ARG10] (Santiago Rivas)

The Argentine Navy Museum at Bahia Blanca is home to this Luscombe Silvaire. [ARG50] (Douglas Rough)

Two Avro Lincolns have survived in Argentina. This example is at Villa Reynolds Air Force Base. [ARG53] (Santiago Rivas)

The aircraft industry in Argentina has produced a number of successful designs and this Guarani II is on show at Móron. [ARG57] (Santiago Rivas)

The Pulqui was designed by Kurt Tank and the sole prototype is in the National Aeronautical Museum at Móron. [ARG57] (Santiago Rivas)

Above: This Latécoère 25-3R was restored at Quilmes and is painted in Aeropostale colours. [ARG57] (Mike Nelson)

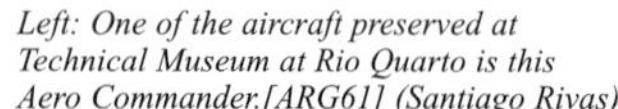

Left: One of the aircraft preserved at Technical Museum at Rio Quarto is this Aero Commander.[ARG61] (Santiago Rivas)

One of the gate Guards at La Paz is this North American T-6. [BO3] (Gerry Manning)

This Meteor F.8 is preserved at the Brazilian Air Force Academy at Pirassununga. [BR1] (AFA)

This Aerotec Uirapuru is preserved at Natal Air Force Base. [BR4] (Chris Lofting)

The Air Base at Recife is home to this B-17 Fortress. [BR5] (Chris Lofting)

Left: This Waco CSO is on show at the Museu Aeroespacial. [BR33] (John Mounce)

One of two R.W.D. 13s known to survive can be seen in the Museum Asas de Um Sonho at Sao Carlos. [BR34] (Renato Spillimbergo)

Parked outside the VARIG Museum at Porto Alegre is this early DC-3. [BR43] (VARIG)

The Chilean Army has a collection of preserved aircraft at its Rancagua base. Shown here is a CASA 212. [CH5] (Álvaro Romero)

Above: The Chilean Naval Base at Vina del Mar has a collection of preserved aircraft including this Embraer EMB.111AN. [CH6] (Álvaro Romero)

Right: The Chilean National Aeronautical Museum has just restored this de Havilland D.H.60 Gipsy Moth. [CH8] (Álvaro Romero)

This rare Junkers W 34 can be seen in the museum at Bogota. [COL6] (Mike Nelson)

Above: This Meteor FR.9 is preserved at the Ecuador Air Force Museum near Quito. [EC9] (Eduardo Cardenas)

Left: There is a collection of preserved aircraft inside the gate at Nu Guazu Air Base near Ascunion. Among the aircraft is this Brazilian designed Neiva Universal. [PAR2] (Gerry Manning)

This Faucett-Stinson F.19 is preserved at Lima. [PE1] (Tim Spearman)

This Cessna A-37 is preserved at the Air Force Base at Piura. [PE2] (Eduardo Cardenas)

The only known surviving Douglas DB-8A-3P is preserved with the National Aeronautical Museum at Las Palmas near Lima. [PE13] (Gerry Manning)

Above: This Castaibert VI was badly damaged in the fire at the Montevideo Museum. The aircraft has now been restored for display. [UR4] (Wilman Fuentes)

Left: This Morane-Saulnier MS.147 can be seen in the Venezuelan Air Force Museum in Maracay. [VE8] (Mike Nelson)

This Flamingo G-2-W was used by Jimmy Angel when he discovered the highest waterfall in the world. The restored aircraft is on show at the airport at Ciudad Bolivar in Venezuela. [VE9] (Gerry Manning)

MILITARY HISTORY PARK (TA34)

Address:	Sport Park, Erhlun, Yunlin County.
Admission:	On permanent view.
Location:	In the town.

The park has been set up to honour local people who have served in the forces of Taiwan. On show are vehicles and weapons and a recently withdrawn Northrop F-5E Tiger. The type entered service in 1975 and well over two hundred served in the country. The F-5E still flies with a number of units.

TYPE	REG/SER	CON. NO.	PI/NOTES	STATUS
☐ Northrop N-311 Tiger II (F-5E)	5138	V.1038	74-0995	PV

NANHUA WATER RESERVOIR (TA35)

Address:	154 Beiliao Village, Nanhua, Tainan County.
Tel:	06-577-2896
Admission:	On permanent view.
Location:	North east of the town.

The reservoir, started in 1986 and completed in 1993, is an important tourist site set in picturesque countryside. There are many walks in along the banks of the lake and in the surrounding woodland.

TYPE	REG/SER	CON. NO.	PI/NOTES	STATUS
☐ Fairchild 110 Flying Boxcar (C-119F)	3202	10706	51-8016	PV
☐ Lockheed 683-07-14 Starfighter (F-104J)	'4526'	683B-3026	36-8526 (Japan) – in false Taiwanese markings.	PVX
☐ Northrop N-311 Tiger II (F-5E)	5128	V.1028	74-0985	PV

NATIONAL CHENGKUNG UNIVERSITY KWEIJEN COLLECTION (TA36)

Address:	Kweijen, Tainan County 701.
Tel:	06-239-2811
Email:	Em50000@email.ncku.edu.tw
Admission:	By prior permission only.
Location:	About 14 km south east of Tainan City.

Three aircraft are located at the Institute of Aeronautics and Astronautics at this university where a wide range of courses can be followed. The Air Force operated over one hundred Super Sabres.

TYPE	REG/SER	CON. NO.	PI/NOTES	STATUS
☐ Aero Industry Development Center (AIDC) Chieshou [Pazmany PL-1B]	5802			RA
☐ Lockheed 683-07-14 Starfighter (F-104J)	4514	683B-3116	46-8616 (Japan)	RA
☐ North American NA-192 Super Sabre (F-100A)	'0233'	192-105	53-1610, 0113	RAX

NATIONAL CHENGKUNG UNIVERSITY TAINAN DISPLAY (TA37)

Address:	1 Tasueh Road, Tainan City.
Tel:	07-741-4188
Admission:	By prior permission only.
Location:	In the north eastern part of the town.

The university offers many courses. The Department of Aeronautical Engineering has a small display in the foyer of its building. The centrepiece is the former Police Hughes helicopter.

TYPE	REG/SER	CON. NO.	PI/NOTES	STATUS
☐ Hughes 269C	AP-014			RA

NATIONAL CHUNGHSING UNIVERSITY MEMORIAL (TA38)

Address:	250 Kuokuang Road, Taichung City.
Tel:	04-2287-3181
Admission:	By prior permission only
Location:	In the city.

The university offers a wide range of courses and many students are in attendance. Two former Air Force aircraft are preserved in the grounds to serve as a reminder of the military tradition of Taiwan.

TYPE	REG/SER	CON. NO.	PI/NOTES	STATUS
☐ Aero Industry Development Center (AIDC) Chieshou [Pazmany PL-1B]	5804			RA
☐ North American NA-192 Super Sabre (F-100A)	0234	192-137	53-1642	RA

NATIONAL FORMOSA UNIVERSITY (TA39)

Address:	64 Wehua Road, Huwei, Yunlin County 632.
Tel:	05-631-5000
Fax:	05-631-5999
Admission:	By prior permission only.
Location:	In the town.

Five airframes are on show at this institution which also uses them for instructional purposes. The Sabreliner was registered to a private owner in Oklahoma before it was sold to the University.

TYPE	REG/SER	CON. NO.	PI/NOTES	STATUS
☐ Cessna 152	N714YF	15284895		RA
☐ Kawasaki-Bell 47G-3B-KH4	B-12107	1009		RA
☐ Lockheed 580 (T-33A)	3056	580-1013	56-1663 – front fuselage only.	RA
☐ Lockheed 580 (T-33A)	3321	580-1071	56-1721	RA
☐ North American NA-276 Sabreliner (T-39A) (CT-39A)	N1929P	276-48	62-4495	RA

NATIONAL SCIENCE AND TECHNOLOGY MUSEUM (TA40)

Address:	720 Chiu-Ju 1st. Road, Kaohsiung 807.
Tel:	07-380-0089
Fax:	07-387-8748
Email:	ublic@mail.ntsm.gov.tw
Admission:	Tuesday-Sunday 0900-1700.
Location:	In the city.

This museum traces the development of many aspects of science and technology with particular reference to Taiwan. The museum runs courses in a variety of subjects and special exhibitions are regularly staged. The only aircraft on show is the Mitsubishi built Starfighter painted in false markings.

TYPE	REG/SER	CON. NO.	PI/NOTES	STATUS
☐ Lockheed 683-07-14 Starfighter (F-104J)	'4303'	683B-3096	46-8596, 4522 – in false Taiwanese markings.	PVX

NATIONAL SUN YAT-SEN UNIVERSITY MEMORIAL (TA41)

Address:	70 Lienhai Road, Kaohsiung City.
Tel:	07-525-2000
Admission:	By prior permission only.
Location:	In the southern part of the city.

The university is named after Sun Yat-sen who many consider to be the founder of modern China. The Starfighter, built by the Mitsubishi company, is preserved in the grounds of the campus.

TYPE	REG/SER	CON. NO.	PI/NOTES	STATUS
☐ Lockheed 683-07-14 Starfighter (F-104J)	4515	683-3118	46-8618 (Japan)	RA

NATIONAL TAINAN INDUSTRIAL VOCATIONAL HIGH SCHOOL COLLECTION (TA42)

Address: 193 Chungshan South Road,
Yungkan,
Tainan County.
Tel: 06-2322131
Admission: By prior permission only.
Location: In the town.

The school was founded in 1942 when the country was occupied by the Japanese. Students were offered courses in civil engineering and woodwork. The initial name was the Tainan Technical College but over the years many titles have been adopted. The four airframes are used for both instructional and display purposes.

TYPE	REG/SER	CON. NO.	PI/NOTES	STATUS
☐ Aero Industry Development Center (AIDC) Chieshou [Pazmany PL-1B]	5840			RA
☐ North American NA-176 Sabre (F-86F)	6306	176-274	51-13343	RA
☐ North American NA-176 Sabre (F-86F)	6299	176-295	51-13364	RA
☐ North American NA-192 Super Sabre (F-100A)	0215	192-72	53-1577	RA

NATIONAL TAIWAN UNIVERSITY MEMORIAL (TA43)

Address: 1 Roosevelt Road,
Taipei.
Admission: By prior permission only.
Location: In the city.

Many former students of the university have served with the Air Force. One of the Super Sabres operated by front line squadrons for a long period has been preserved in the grounds as a monument.

TYPE	REG/SER	CON. NO.	PI/NOTES	STATUS
☐ North American NA-192 Super Sabre (F-100A)	0218	192-84	53-1589	RA

PAKUA MOUNTAIN PARK (TA44)

Address: 139 County Road,
Pakua Mountain,
Changhua County.
Admission: On permanent view.
Location: Behind the Buddha landmark.

The park is one of the main sightseeing locations in the city. There are many designated walks around the picturesque site. The aircraft have recently been added as a further attraction.

TYPE	REG/SER	CON. NO.	PI/NOTES	STATUS
☐ Fairchild 110 Flying Boxcar (C-119G)	3183	10965	51-8000	PVX
☐ Lockheed 683-10-19 Starfighter (F-104G)	4417	683-6094	63-13645, R-645 (Denmark)	PV
☐ Northrop N-311 Tiger II (F-5E)	5125	V.1025	74-0982	PV

PENGHU COUNTY MILITARY CEMETERY (TA45)

Address: 1-2 Linto Village,
Huhsi
Penghu County.
Tel: 06-927-2415
Admission: Daily.
Location: In the centre of the village.

The cemetery is the resting place for local military personnel who have lost their lives in both peace and war. The F-5B is a two seat operational training version and about twenty were used in Taiwan.

TYPE	REG/SER	CON. NO.	PI/NOTES	STATUS
☐ Northrop N-156B Freedom Fighter (F-5B)	1112	N.8130	73-1611	PV

PINGTUNG AIR FORCE BASE COLLECTION (TA46)

Address:	333 Shengli Road, Pingtung City, Pingtung County.
Tel:	08-765-6111
Admission:	By prior permission only.
Location:	In the western suburbs of the town.

There are two military airfields at Pingtung. They have been home to transport units for many years. When the Chinese Nationalists moved to Taiwan they took with them some C-47s supplied under the World War II Lend-Lease scheme. Others were acquired and the type served until the 1980s.

TYPE	REG/SER	CON. NO.	PI/NOTES	STATUS
☐ Douglas DC-3A-456 Skytrain (C-47A)	7273	20260	43-15794, 15794	RA
☐ Fairchild 110 Flying Boxcar (C-119G)	3120	10964	51-8070	RA
☐ Lockheed 580 (T-33A)	3322	580-1072	56-1722 – in nearby park.	PV

PRIVATE COLLECTION – HSIAOPING (TA47)

Address:	Hsiaoping, Taipei County.
Admission:	By prior permission only.
Location:	In the village.

A collector of militaria has acquired one of the North American Super Sabres which served with the Air Force for many years. The aircraft was formerly based at Hsinchu.

TYPE	REG/SER	CON. NO.	PI/NOTES	STATUS
☐ North American NA-192 Super Sabre (F-100A)	0212	192-	53-1563	RA

PRIVATE COLLECTION – TAITUNG (TA48)

Address:	Taitung City, Taitung County.
Admission:	By prior permission only.
Location:	In the city.

A collector of transport items has acquired the fuselage of a Dornier Do 228. The aircraft was based at Taitung with Formosa Airlines and flew on regional services. No other information is availabe.

TYPE	REG/SER	CON. NO.	PI/NOTES	STATUS
☐ Dornier Do 228-201	B-12238	8111	D-CAAC – fuselage only.	RA

SHIN SHING INDUSTRIAL AND BUSINESS VOCATIONAL SCHOOL COLLECTION (TA49)

Address:	Second Campus, Yongfong Road, Bade City, Taoyuan County.
Tel:	03-379-6996
Admission:	By prior permission only.
Location:	Near Taoyuan Hospital

The aircraft here include three airframes still registered in the USA. Several Bird Dogs served with both the Air Force and the Army for a number of years. The O-1G is a conversion of the basic airframe for the United States Air Force who flew the type in Vietnam in the Forward Air Controller role. The O-1G also served with the U.S. Marines. The workshops also contain engines and airframe components.

TYPE	REG/SER	CON. NO.	PI/NOTES	STATUS
☐ Beech 200 Super King Air	N30AH	BB-529		RA
☐ Cessna 150F	N8264S	15061864		RA
☐ Cessna 150F	N6959F	15063559		RA
☐ Cessna 305D Bird Dog (305A) (L-19A) (O-1A) (O-1G)A	9312			R
☐ Lockheed 683-10-19 Starfighter (F-104G)	4424	683-6099	64-17754	RA

SHALU PARK MEMORIAL (TA50)

Address:	Shalu, Taichung County.
Admission:	On permanent view,
Location:	In the town near the Library.

The town has put on show an American built Starfighter which was delivered to Taiwan after being flown by Luftwaffe pilots in Arizona. The aircraft honours local airmen.

TYPE	REG/SER	CON. NO.	PI/NOTES	STATUS
☐ Lockheed 683-10-19 Starfighter (F-104G) (RF-104G)	4371	683-2033	63-13249	PV

SHUILI MEMORIAL PARK (TA51)

Address:	Shuili, Nantou County.
Admission:	On permanent view,
Location:	In the town.

Two jet fighters are displayed in the park to honour those who have served with the military forces. The Starfighter is one of five Mitsubishi built two seaters delivered to Taiwan.

TYPE	REG/SER	CON. NO.	PI/NOTES	STATUS
☐ Lockheed 583-10-17 Starfighter (F-104DJ)	4595	583B-5417	36-5017 (Japan)	PV
☐ Northrop N-311 Tiger II (F-5E)	5220	V.1120	76-0490	PV

SUNGSHAN AIR FORCE BASE MEMORIAL (TA52)

Address:	Taipei County.
Admission:	By prior permission only.
Location:	In the north eastern suburbs of the city.

The Air Force bases transport aircraft at the field which also serves as the downtown civil airport for the city. One of the fleet of C-47s operated for many years has been preserved as a memorial and is parked behind the hangars.

TYPE	REG/SER	CON. NO.	PI/NOTES	STATUS
☐ Douglas DC-3A-456 Skytrain (C-47A)	15924	20390	43-15924, 15924 (Taiwan), 7231 (Taiwan)	RA

TA SHING SENIOR HIGH SCHOOL MEMORIAL (TA53)

Address:	142 Yungshan Road Taoyuan, Taoyuan County,
Tel:	03-386-2330
Admission:	By prior permission only.
Location:	In the city.

Two former military aircraft have been put on show at this school. The pair serve as memorials to former students who have served with the military forces of Taiwan. The Osage was flown by both Air Force and Army units and the police used serveral examples of the civil version of the helicopter.

TYPE	REG/SER	CON. NO.	PI/NOTES	STATUS
☐ Hughes 269C Osage (TH-55A)	2112			RA
☐ Lockheed 683-10-19 Starfighter (F-104G)	4412	683-6041	62-12342	RA

TAICHUNG MILITARY MARTYR'S SHRINE (TA54)

Address:	87 Chengkung Road, Tachia, Taichung County.
Admission:	Daily
Location:	In the town.

Construction of a military memorial park started in 1958. The site houses a cemetery and a memorial building. There is also a landscaped park with many varieties of trees. Two examples of the Starfighter can be seen. One is a single seater and the other a dual control trainer. Taiwan flew the controversial fighter from many bases around the country. A tank is also on show in the park along with monuments, plaques and flags.

TYPE	REG/SER	CON. NO.	PI/NOTES	STATUS
☐ Lockheed 583-10-20 Starfighter (TF-104G)	4178	583D-5753	61-3082	PV
☐ Lockheed 683-10-19 Starfighter (F-104G)	4416	683-2033	KF+109, DA+237, BG+127, 62-12349, (20+26), 13249	PV

TAINAN AIR FORCE BASE COLLECTION (TA55)

Address:	1000 Section 2, Datong Road, Tainan City, Tainan County.
Tel:	06-268-4815
Admission:	By prior permission only
Location:	About 40km north of Kaohsiung.

A small display has been set up at this fighter base where the indigenous F-CK-1 Chung Kuo is flown by the 1st. Tactical Fighter Wing. The prototype of the single seat version made its maiden flight in May 1989 and the two seater variant followed in 1990. The type entered service in 1994 and one hundred and thirty were produced. Parked near the main gate are some of the preserved aircraft and a Matador missile. The T-33 was flown by most fighter units for training and communications work. The Northrop F-5 flew from the field before the arrival of the F-CK-1 and one has been preserved to remind airmen of this time. Taiwan was the largest Sabre operator apart from the United States. Over three hundred were supplied between 1954 and 1958 and at least another hundred, including some F-86Ds, arrived later. This classic fighter was in service in the country for many years.

TYPE	REG/SER	CON. NO.	PI/NOTES	STATUS
☐ Aero Industry Development Center (AIDC) T-CH-1 Chung Hsing	0711		65-3011	RA
☐ Cessna 305D Bird Dog (305A) (L-19A) (O-1A) (O-1G)	9304	21606	51-4721, '51-5133'	RA
☐ Lockheed 580 (T-33A)	T-33343	580-1498	57-0769	RA
☐ North American NA-176 Sabre (F-86F)	6047	176-325	51-13394	RA
☐ Northrop N-311 Tiger II (F-5E)	5157	V.1057	75-0330	RA

TAIPEI COUNTY MILITARY SHRINE (TA56)

Address:	25 Chungyi Street, Shulin City, Taipei County.
Tel:	02-2689-4924
Admission:	On permanent view.
Location:	In the city.

Several counties in Taiwan have set up shrines to honour local military personnel. This site includes a cemetery and landscaped park. There is an area where the names of those who perished can be seen. The two seat Starfighter was used by the Luftwaffe to train pilots in the better weather conditions of Arizona.

TYPE	REG/SER	CON. NO.	PI/NOTES	STATUS
☐ Lockheed 583-10-20 Starfighter (TF-104G)	4192	583D-5771	63-8465, (27+67), 38465	PV

TAITUNG AIR FORCE BASE COLLECTION (TA57)

Address:	3 Section3, Zhihang Road, Taitung City, Taitung County.
Tel:	089-223911
Admission:	By prior permission only.
Location:	In the north eastern part of the town.

The base has been home to a tactical fighter wing for many years and currently operates the F-5E and F-5F versions of the Tiger II. Previously the F-5A and F-5B Freedom Fighters were in use. A civilian terminal was built in the 1970s and this has been developed to cope with modern airliners. Between 1973 and 1986 AIDC built three hundred and eight F-5Es and F-5Fs under licence from Northrop. The type entered service in 1975 and served at many bases. The indigenous Ching Kuo started to replace it in the late 1990s.

TYPE	REG/SER	CON. NO.	PI/NOTES	STATUS
☐ Northrop N-156A Freedom Fighter (F-5A)	1281	N.6482	69-7116	RA
☐ Northrop N-156B Freedom Fighter (F-5B)	1105	N.8047	66-9239	RA
☐ Northrop N-311 Tiger II (F-5E)	5223	V.1123	76-1618	RA

TAITUNG COUNTY MILITARY SHRINE (TA58)

Address:	Taian Village, Beinan, Taitung County.
Admission:	Daily 0900-1700.
Location:	About 5 km north west of the city.

One of the former Luftwaffe Starfighters used in Arizona has been placed on display at the site. A cemetery is the resting place of the local military personnel who have lost their lives in the service of their country. The complex consists of an impressive gate leading into a courtyard where there is a temple.

TYPE	REG/SER	CON. NO.	PI/NOTES	STATUS
☐ Lockheed 583-10-20 Starfighter (TF-104G)	4179	583D-5754	61-3083, (27+52), 13083	PV

TAIWAN TAOYUAN INTERNATIONAL AIRPORT MUSEUM (TA59)

Address:	P.O. Box 9, Taoyuan International Airport, Taoyuan County 337.
Tel:	03-398-2179
Fax:	03-398-2667
Email:	tgp25014@cksairport.gov.tw
Admission:	Tuesday-Sunday 0900-1650.
Location:	About 25 miles south west of Taipei.

This museum opened on October 31st 1981 on the birthday of Chiang Kai-shek, who was President of the country from its formation in 1950 until his death a quarter of a century later. A two storey triangular building with an outside aircraft park was built. The Boeing company designed and constructed the complex for the Civil Aviation Commission. The museum was the first in Asia to trace in detail the development of aviation in the region. Formerly known as the Chung Cheng Aviation Museum, the collection has recently changed its name. There are five major themes highlighted in the innovative displays. These are Civil Aviation, Flight Technology, the Chinese Air Force, the History of Flight and Space Flight. All areas contain the latest audio-visual techniques, photographs, models and dioramas. Hanging in the entrance hall is a replica of the Wright Flyer to symbolise the start of powered flight. The range of aircraft exhibited is wide and covers most forms of aviation. Jet fighters used by the Air Force can be seen along with training types. An example of the classic Sabre can be compared with the developed F-100. Both types were produced in large numbers and served with many air forces including Taiwan. The local aviation industry is represented in the display with several aircraft and models on show, Several Grumman Albatross amphibians were in use up to the mid-1980s to provide search and rescue cover around the island before being replaced by helicopters. The C-47 served with Far East Air Transport and is painted in the colours of one used by the Civil Aeronautics Administration who used the type on calibration duties. This aircraft flew with airlines in Australia and Papua New Guinea when its military days were over. Two versions of the North American Trojan can be seen. AIDC in Taiwan modified fifty airframes. These were fitted with a turboprop engine and designated the T-CH-1. Sud Aviation in France converted one hundred and sixty four for close support duties in Algeria. A more powerful motor was fitted along with armour protection for the pilot and underwing bomb pylons. The Cessna R182 set a world record in 1984 for a 3500lb single engined aircraft. Light civil aircraft, a hang glider and microlights have also been put on display with many engines and components. There is a display of models of airliners in the colours of many of the airlines who operate in the region. The complex history of the local Air Force is portrayed with many models, uniforms, badges and photographs. The only aircraft on show in this area is the licence built Pazmany PL-1B which trained many pilots. Visitors to the museum can observe the workings of the international airport from a tower and a display tracing its history can be seen. The site opened in 1979 as Chiang Kai-Shek International Airport until its recent change of name. Airlines from around the world fly into the site.

TYPE	REG/SER	CON. NO.	PI/NOTES	STATUS
☐ Aero Industry Development Center (AIDC) Chieshou [Pazmany PL-1B]	5836			PV
☐ Aero Industry Development Center (AIDC) T-CH-1 Chung Hsing	0702		63-3002	PV
☐ Bell 47G-2 Sioux (H-13H) (OH-13H)	1108			PV
☐ Cessna 150L Commuter	N18107	15073790		PV
☐ Cessna R182 Skylane RG	N756FY	R18201068		PV

TYPE	REG/SER	CON. NO.	PI/NOTES	STATUS
☐ Douglas DC-3A-456 Skytrain (C-47A)	'B-126'	13612	42-93674, VH-ANY, VH-AVK, VH-MMM, B-259	PVX
☐ Grumman G-111 Albatross (G-64) (SA-16A) (SA-16B) (HU-16B)	1024	G-47	49-089, 11024	PV
☐ Grumman G-89 Tracker (S2F-1) (S-2A)	2001		(USN) – front fuselage only.	PV
☐ Grumman G-89 Tracker (S2F-1) (S-2A)	2103	28	Bu133057	PV
☐ Hang Glider				PV
☐ Lockheed 183-93-02 Starfighter (F-104A)	4254	183-1134	56-0846	PV
☐ Lockheed 580 (T-33A)	3338	580-1261	57-0532, T-33338	PV
☐ Lockheed 580 (T-33A)	3082	580-1366	57-0637 – front fuselage only.	PV
☐ Lungshiang LS-4				RA
☐ McDonnell M.36Y Voodoo (RF-101A)	5660	56	54-1505	PV
☐ North American NA-172 Sabre (F-86F)	6098	172-177	51-2894, F86098	PVX
☐ North American NA-192 Super Sabre (F-100A)	0207	192-45	53-1550	PV
☐ Northrop N-156A Freedom Fighter (F-5A)	1224	N.6287	66-9183	PV
☐ Sud Fennec [North American NA-174 Trojan (T-28A)]	2833	174-202	51-3664, 93 (France), N14107	PV
☐ Vector 600				PV
☐ Wright Flyer (R)				PV

TAIWANESE AIR FORCE TECHNICAL SCHOOL COLLECTION (TA60)

Address:	P.O. Box 90395, Kangshan, Kaohsiung County.
Admission:	By prior permission only.
Location:	In the town.

Several aircraft are displayed around the site of this school which trains mechanics in many trades. They remind students of the traditions of the service. The first of ninety two Northrop F-5As were delivered in the mid-1960s. In 1973 forty-eight were reclaimed by the U.S.A. and transferred to the South Vietnamese Air Force. This type can be compared with the later F-5E Tiger which was a redesigned and improved version of the F-5A with modern systems and a greater weapons capacity. The airframes are also used for instruction. The workshops contain many engines, components and instruments and there is a small display tracing the history of the school and the Air Force. Photographs and models can also be seen.

TYPE	REG/SER	CON. NO.	PI/NOTES	STATUS
☐ Aero Industry Development Center (AIDC) R-CH-1 Chung Hsing (T-CH-1)	0720		67-3020	RA
☐ Lockheed 583-10-20 Starfighter (TF-104G)	4177	583D-5751	61-3080, (27+49), 13080	RA
☐ Northrop N-156A Freedom Fighter (F-5A)	1235	N.6305	66-9201, 69201 (South Vietnam)	PV
☐ Northrop N-156A Freedom Fighter (F-5A)	1276	N.6477	69-7111	RA
☐ Northrop N-311 Tiger II (F-5E)	5171	V.1071	75-0344	PV
☐ Northrop N-311 Tiger II (F-5E)	5221	V.1121	76-1616	PV

TAMKANG UNIVERSITY – TAMSUI CAMPUS COLLECTION (TA61)

Address:	151 Inchuan Road, Tamsui, 25137 Taipei County.
Tel:	02-2621-5656
Fax:	02-2622-3204
Email:	aca_aff@mail.thu.edu.tw
Admission:	On permanent view.
Location:	About 20 km north west of Taipei City.

The university has four sites in the area. An interesting collection of aircraft can be seen at the aeronautical section of this university. Some of the airframes are also used for instruction. A small number of reworked Beech 18s were supplied to the Air Force in the early 1950s. The example in the collection was originally built as an AT-11. The Super Sabre served with one of the fighter wings in the 1950s and the F-100 had a long an distinguished military career. Apart from the United States Taiwan was one of the largest users of the supersonic fighter. The Beech D18 was flown on local services by Far East Air Transport.

TYPE	REG/SER	CON. NO.	PI/NOTES	STATUS
☐ Aero Industry Development Center (AIDC) Chieshou [Pazmany PL-1B]	5845			PV
☐ Beech D18S	B-205	A-493	AT-11010	PV
☐ Cessna U206A Super Skywagon	B-11101	U2060634	N4934F	PV
☐ North American NA-192 Super Sabre (F-100A)	0214	192-66	53-1571	PV

TAOYUAN NAVAL AIR STATION MEMORIAL (TA62)

Address:	Taoyuan County.
Admission:	By prior permission only.
Location:	North west of Taoyuan City.

The airfield was used by the Air Force for many years and housed fighter and trainer units. The site was transferred to the Navy on November 1st 2006 to become home to two squadrons flying the Grumman S-2T Tracker. The service had flown the piston engine version of the aircraft for many years and thirty two were fitted with the new power units. The prototype of the Tracker made its maiden flight in December 1952 and over the next over one thousand twelve hundred were built in America and Canada and served in many countries. The type is now popular on fire fighting duties in the U.S.A. The Hughes helicopter was formerly preserved at Hualien.

TYPE	REG/SER	CON. NO.	PI/NOTES	STATUS
☐ Hughes 500MD/ASW	6906	990430D		RA

TZUMING HIGH SCHOOL MEMORIAL (TA63)

Address:	388 Kuante Road, Taiping, Taichung County.
Admission:	By prior permission only.
Location:	In the town.

Many former pupils of this school have served with all branches of the military in Taiwan. A Northrop Tiger II has been preserved as a memorial to all who enlisted and lost their lives in the service of their country.

TYPE	REG/SER	CON. NO.	PI/NOTES	STATUS
☐ Northrop N-311 Tiger II (F-5E)	5109	V.1009	74-0966	RA

YUNGKANG PARK (TA64)

Address:	Lane 377, Tungta Road, Section 3, Hsinchu City.
Admission:	On permanent view.
Location:	In the city.

For many years there has been an important fighter base near the city. Lockheed Starfighters were operated by the resident squadrons and one has been put on show in the park as a reminder. This is a reconnaissance version fitted with cameras in the forward fuselage. In service several were modified to standard F-104G configuration. The aircraft on show was built by the Fokker ccmpany in the Netherlands.

TYPE	REG/SER	CON. NO.	PI/NOTES	STATUS
☐ Lockheed 683-04-10 Starfighter (RF-104G)	4398	683B-8204	67-14890	PV

YUNG TA INSTITUTE OF TECHNOLOGY AND COMMERCE DISPLAY (TA65)

Address:	316 Chungshan Road, Linluo, Pingtung County.
Tel:	08-723-3733
Admission:	By prior permission only.
Location:	In the northern part of the town.

The institute offers courses in a variety of subjects and many former students have served in the armed forces. The Tiger is displayed in the grounds and the former Police Hughes helicopter resides in a workshop.

TYPE	REG/SER	CON. NO.	PI/NOTES	STATUS
☐ Hughes 269C	AP-012			RA
☐ Northrop N-311 Tiger II (F-5E)	5137	V.1037	74-0994	RA

THAILAND

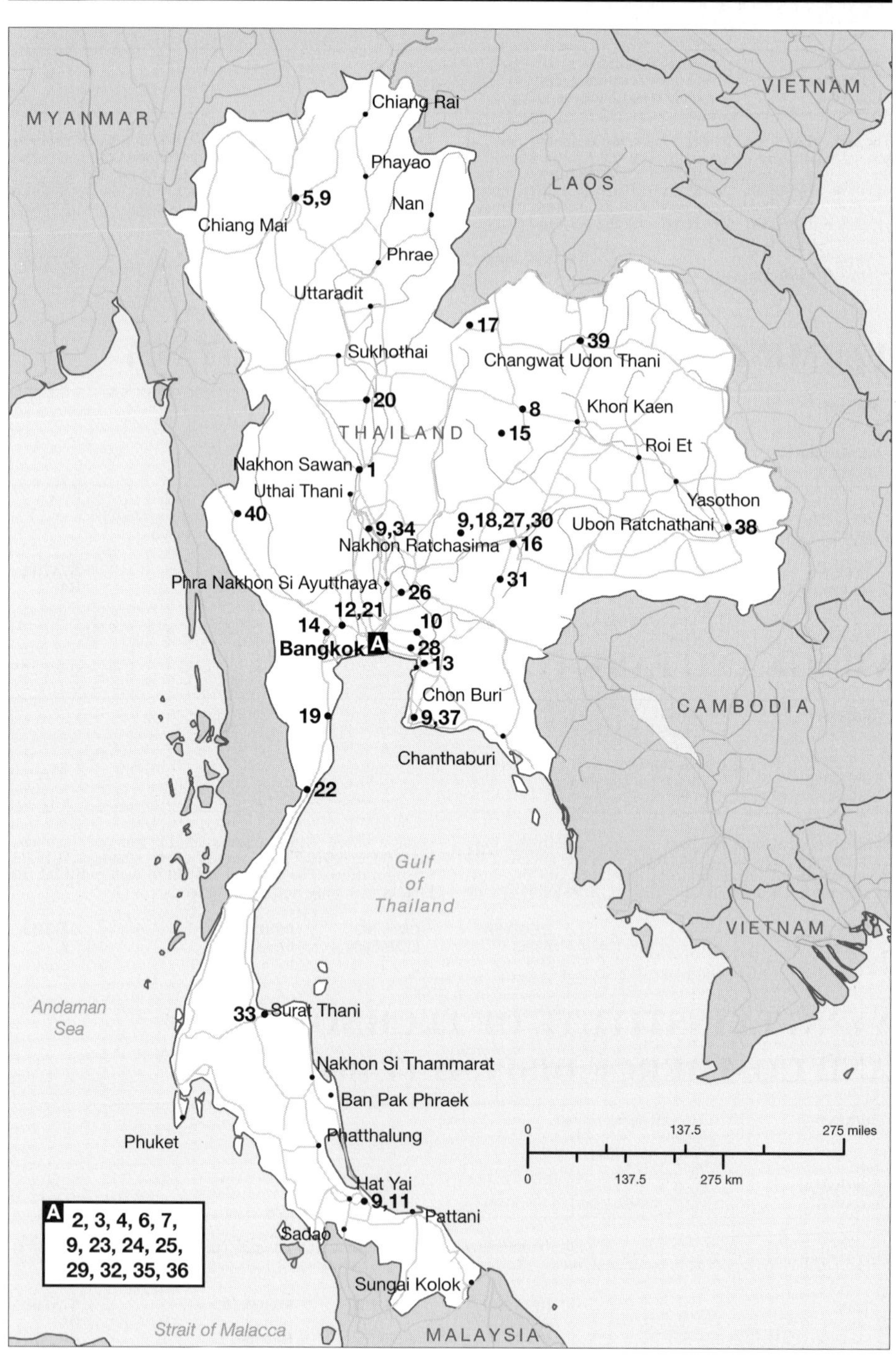
MYANMAR
VIETNAM
LAOS
THAILAND
CAMBODIA
VIETNAM
MALAYSIA
Chiang Rai
Phayao
5,9
Chiang Mai
Nan
Phrae
Uttaradit
17
39
Changwat Udon Thani
Sukhothai
20
8
Khon Kaen
15
Roi Et
Nakhon Sawan
1
Uthai Thani
Yasothon
40
9,34
9,18,27,30
Ubon Ratchathani
38
Nakhon Ratchasima
16
31
Phra Nakhon Si Ayutthaya
26
12,21
14
10
Bangkok
A
28
13
Chon Buri
19
9,37
Chanthaburi
22
Gulf of Thailand
Andaman Sea
33
Surat Thani
Nakhon Si Thammarat
Ban Pak Phraek
Phuket
Phatthalung
Hat Yai
9,11
Pattani
Sadao
Sungai Kolok
Strait of Malacca
0
137.5
275 miles
0
137.5
275 km
A
2, 3, 4, 6, 7,
9, 23, 24, 25,
29, 32, 35, 36

AGRICULTURAL SERVICE MUSEUM (TH1)

Address:	Nakhon Sawan Airfield, Amphoe Muang, Nakhon Sawan 60000.
Tel:	056-255030 (airfield)
Admission:	Daily.
Location:	About 5 km south east of the town.

The Government Agricultural Service operates a fleet of fixed wing aircraft and helicopters on a variety of duties around the country. Nakhon Sawan is one of the major bases and a display has been set up tracing the history and work of the service.

TYPE	REG/SER	CON. NO.	PI/NOTES	STATUS
☐ Cessna 180J Skywagon 180	210	18052362	N4254D	PV
☐ Cessna 310Q	811	310Q0651	N7868Q	PV
☐ Cessna U206G Stationair	1112	U20604615	N9965M	PV
☐ Fletcher FU-24A-954	605	287	ZK-FTT	PV
☐ North American NA-360 Bronco (OV-10C)	J5-31/16	360-15	Bu159418 – at University in town.	RA

ARMY CAMP MONUMENT (TH2)

Address:	Viphavadi-Rangsit Highway, Bangkok.
Admission:	By prior permission only.
Location:	In the northern part of the city.

The Thai Army has used many helicopters in recent years from its bases around the country. An example of the Iroquois, now in poor condition, is preserved at this large camp.

TYPE	REG/SER	CON. NO.	PI/NOTES	STATUS
☐ Bell 204 Iroquois (UH-1C)				RA

BANG KHAEN ARMY BASE COLLECTION (TH3)

Address:	Thanon Phanon Yothin, Bangkok 10220.
Admission:	By prior permission only.
Location:	In the north eastern suburbs of the city.

Army helicopters reside at this base in the suburbs of Bangkok. A small number of Bell 47s flew with the service on observation and training duties. One of the few Sikorsky S-62s operated is also preserved.

TYPE	REG/SER	CON. NO.	PI/NOTES	STATUS
☐ Bell 47G-3B Sioux (OH-13S)	5345			RA
☐ Bell 47G-3B Sioux (OH-13S)	5405	3273	64-15405	RA
☐ Cessna 305A Bird Dog (L-19A) (O-1A)	1358	21032	50-1358, 11031 (Japan)	RA
☐ Sikorsky S-62J	2004	M62-004		RA

BANGKOK NATIONAL SCIENCE CENTRE FOR EDUCATION (TH4)

Address:	Thanon Sukhumvit 928, Bangkok 10110.
Tel:	02-392-5960
Email:	nsce@sci-educ.nfe.go.th
Admission:	Tuesday-Sunday 0930-1630.
Location:	Near the Ekkami Bus Station.

Formerly known as the Bangkok Science Museum the new name reflects the change in emphasis of the aims of the centre. Courses and training camps are among the many activities which take place for students. There is a planetarium on the site. The four aircraft are parked in the grounds of the building.

TYPE	REG/SER	CON. NO.	PI/NOTES	STATUS
☐ Douglas DC-3A-456 Skytrain (C-47A) (Dakota III)	9414	9414	42-23552, FD868, G-AGHN, VH-BZB, HS-TDF	PV
☐ Lake LA-4-250 Buccaneer	HS-TCR	250	N1007L or may be HS-TCS c/n 251 N1008L	PV
☐ North American NA-191 Sabre (F-86F)	4482	191-178	52-4482, Kh17-21/04	PV
☐ Piper PA-23-250 Aztec	HS-TCZ	27-397	N4887P	PV

CHIANG MAI AIR FORCE BASE COLLECTION (TH5)

Address:	Wing 41, Chiang Mai Air Force Base Chiang Mai 50170.
Tel:	053-202617
Admission:	By prior permission only.
Location:	On the south western outskirts of the town.

The resident wing operates OV-1 Broncos in the counter insurgency role. Over the years Texans, Trojans and Dragonflies have been used in this important task over the jungles in the north of the country. The Provider and Sabre are preserved by the Headquarters Building and the Trojan is parked by the north gate to the field. The airfield is one of the main bases for the Foundation for the Preservation and Development of Thai Aviation (Tango Squadron) and many of their large fleet of aircraft are based here.

TYPE	REG/SER	CON. NO.	PI/NOTES	STATUS
☐ Fairchild 205 Provider (C-123B)	'4113'	20225	55-4570, L4k-13/18	RAX
☐ North American NA-174 Trojan (T-28A) (AT-28D)	JF13-97/13	174-116	51-3578	RA
☐ North American NA-191 Sabre (F-86F)	051232	191-728	52-5032, Kh17-53/06	RA

CIVIL AVIATION TRAINING SCHOOL DISPLAY (TH6)

Address:	Thanon Phanon Yothin 1032/555, Bangkok 10900.
Tel:	02-272-5741
Fax:	02-272-4210
Admission:	By prior permission only.
Location:	At Chatuchak in the northern suburbs of the city.

The school trains students in all aspects of airframe, engine and avionics maintenance. Four aircraft have been put on display in the grounds of the college. In addition there are a number of instructional types in the building. Engines, instruments, airframe components and systems can also be found in the well equipped workshops. The New Zealand built T6/24 was developed from the successful Australian Victa Airtourer The Caravelle was formerly flown by Thai Airways on their routes in the region.

TYPE	REG/SER	CON. NO.	PI/NOTES	STATUS
☐ Aero Engine Services T6/24 Airtourer	HS-TCO		Possible identity.	RA
☐ Aero Engine Services T6/24 Airtourer	HS-TCL	B-563	ZK-DDK – possibly c/n B-??? HS-TCN.	RA
☐ Cessna 180	201	30574	N11B	RA
☐ Fairchild-Hiller FH-1100	1505	59		RA
☐ Hiller UH12E	HS-TZE	2312		RA
☐ Hughes 269A		62-0090		RA
☐ Kawasaki-Bell 47G-3B-KH4	1104	2088		RA
☐ North American NA-182 Texan (T-6G)			114?30	RA
☐ Piper PA-23-250 Aztec	HS-TCY	27-381		RA
☐ Piper PA-23-250D Aztec	HS-TCR	27-4372		RA
☐ Sud-Est SE.210 Caravelle III (I)	HS-TGI	25	SE-DAC- front fuselage only.	RA

DON MUANG AIR FORCE BASE COLLECTION (TH7)

Address:	Don Muang Air Force Base, Bangkok 10210.
Admission:	On permanent view
Location:	About 15 km north east of the city centre.

This large military base, which opened in 1914, is situated on the opposite side of the runaway from the former Bangkok International Airport. Housed at the site are the Air Force Headquarters and Academy along with a Transport Wing operating a variety of types. The Air Force Museum and a detachment of 'Tango Squadron' are also in residence. Well over sixty C-47s were operated by the service and many flew with the local unit for years. Forty F-86Fs were delivered in 1961 and they served with two squadrons until replaced by the Northrop F-5 in 1966. The preserved aircraft can be found at a number of locations around the vast site.

TYPE	REG/SER	CON. NO.	PI/NOTES	STATUS
☐ Bell 205 Iroquois (UH-1H)	'455'	8622	66-16428, 16428 (South Vietnam)	RAX
☐ Cessna 150M	60406		VH-JFZ (?)	RA
☐ Cessna 318E Dragonfly (A-37B)	J6-12/15	43345	71-0807	RA
☐ Douglas DC-3A-456 Skytrain (C-47A)	293789	13740	42-93789, L2-34/13	RA

TYPE	REG/SER	CON. NO.	PI/NOTES	STATUS
☐ Douglas DC-3A-456 Skytrain (C-47A)	100536	18999	42-100536, L2-6/90 – rear fuselage only.	RA
☐ Fairchild 473 Provider (205) (C-123B) (C-123K)	'55-569'	20209	55-4548, 50548 (South Vietnam), L4k-6/16	RAX
☐ North American NA-159 Trojan (T-28A) (AT-28D)	JF13-85/11	159-113	49-1601	RA
☐ North American NA-174 Trojan (T-28A) (AT-28D)	13740	174-278	51-3740, JF13-98/13	RA
☐ North American NA-176 Sabre (F-86F)	Kh17-42/06	176-151	51-13220, C.5-48 (Spain) – front fuselage only.	PV
☐ Sud-Est SE.210 Caravelle III	XU-JTB	53	F-WJTA, F-BJTA	RA

FORT PHORKHUNPAMUENG MONUMENT (TH8)

Address: Phetchabun 67000.
Admission: By prior permission only.
Location: On the outskirts of the town.

The First Cavalry Aviation Division of the Royal Thai Army is based at the fort. Based at the site are helicopters and fixed wing aircraft. A Cessna Bird Dog is preserved by the Officers' Mess.

TYPE	REG/SER	CON. NO.	PI/NOTES	STATUS
☐ Cessna 305A Bird Dog (L-19A) (O-1A)	7459	22198	51-7459	RA

FOUNDATION FOR THE PRESERVATION AND DEVELOPMENT OF THAI AIRCRAFT (TH9)

Address: P.O. Box 620610,
Thanon Phaholyothin 171,
Don Muang Air Force Base,
Bangkok 10210.
Tel: 0662-534-5013
Fax: 0662-531-3767
Email: webmaster@tangosquadron.org
Admission: By prior permission only.
Location: Location Codes: 1 Chiang Mai Air Force Base; 2 Don Muang Air Force Base; 3 U-Tapao Navy Base; 4 Lopburi Army Aviation Center; 5 Takhli Air Force Base; 6 Hat Yai Air Force Base. For exact locations refer to airfields.

In January 1991 a number of pilots and ground staff from No. 41 Wing based at Chiang Mai set up a group with the main aim of preserving historic aircraft in flying order. The name Royal Thai Air Classics Association was adopted but the nickname 'Tango Squadron' was soon used. This honoured Group Captain Veerayuth Didysarin who was known as 'Tang' throughout the Air Force. The name was changed to the Association for the Preservation and Development of Thai Aircraft and was registered as a foundation in January 1992. King Bhumibol became a Patron on April 29th 1993. The first project undertaken was the rebuild of a T-28 Trojan which had been displayed outside a radio station at Chian Rai since 1984. The aircraft was moved to the local airport and after two months work was flown to Chiang Mai by Group Captain Didysarin. Hangars at Chiang Mai, Lopburi and Don Muang now house the fleet and there are workshops at all three sites. A Spitfire was rescued from a long period on a pylon and will be rebuilt to flying condition. A second was in the hangars but this has moved on to the Crown Prince's Palace in the city. About thirty examples of this famous fighter were bought in the late 1940s. The wreckage of a 'Flying Tigers' Tomahawk was found in the jungle near Chiang Mai in 1992, fifty years after it crashed attacking the base which was then occupied by the Japanese. This unit, officially known as the American Volunteer Group, operated against the Japanese from bases in China. Between December 1941 and July 1942 the three squadrons downed two hundred and eighty six enemy aircraft for the loss of twelve of their own. The Travel Air 2000 was the first civil aircraft in the country when it was imported in 1932 by Corporal Leun Pongsopone who had been granted a flying scholarship at St. Louis in the U.S.A. After a long period in the Army Aviation Museum at Lop Buri this classic biplane is now in airworthy condition. The Travel Air Company was formed in 1925 by Walter Beech and Clyde Cessna and over six hundred 2000s were produced. In the early 1950s a batch of Tiger Moths was acquired for both military and civilian use. The example in the collection spent a long period in Malaysia before being purchased. In 1940 Thailand ordered six P-64s from North American Aviation. The U.S. Government requisitioned the batch to prevent them falling into Japanese hands. The two Sentinels have recently arrived from the U.S.A. and both were restored in the Don Muang workshops. Several were used on observation and liaison duties in the 1950s. Twenty four New Zealand built CT-4As and six CT-4Bs were bought by the Air Force as basic trainers. The Grumman Bearcat has recently been restored to flying condition and is resplendent in period Thai colours. The North American P-50 replica was converted from a standard Texan. Thailand ordered six of the type in the late 1930s to replace the obsolete Curtiss and Vought biplane fighters. However, due to the political situation in Southeast Asia the United States Government revoked the export licence and the aircraft served as fighter trainers at Luke Field in Arizona. Aircraft from 'Tango Squadron' are used on environmental projects including rainmaking and forest patrol. Members are searching for types that have been used by Thai forces and hopefully some of these will be found and added to the fleet. The organisation has made rapid progress in a short time and the number of active aircraft is steadily increasing.

TYPE	REG/SER	CON. NO.	PI/NOTES	STATUS
☐ Aero Commander 690A	81491	11340	N81491, HS-TFA	RA.2
☐ Aero Engine Services CT/4A Airtrainer	2009	CT4-002		RA.5
☐ Beech 65-A80 Queen Air	06892	LD-199		RA.2
☐ Beech 95-55 Baron				RA.5
☐ Beech E90 King Air	'00-923'	LW-26		RA.2

Type	Reg./Serial	C/n	PI/Notes	Status
☐ Bell 47G-3B Sioux (OH-13S)	15877	3926	67-15877	RAA.4
☐ Canadian Car & Foundry Harvard 4 [North American NA-186]	N1264	CCF4-20	20229, CF-UVN – mocked up as Kate 'AI-315'	RAAX.1
☐ Cessna 172M	HS-PAA	17263629		RAA.2
☐ Cessna 305A Bird Dog (L-19A) (O-1A)	1620	21322	50-1620, 11036 (Japan)	RA.2
☐ Cessna 305A Bird Dog (L-19A) (O-1A)	7415	22154	51-7415	RA.1
☐ Cessna 305A Bird Dog (L-19A) (O-1A)	T2-15/13	22856	51-16971	RAA.2
☐ Cessna 305A Bird Dog (L-19A) (O-1A)	51-12472	22914	May be 56-2472.	RA.1
☐ Cessna 305A Bird Dog (L-19A) (O-1A)	T2-26/15	22980	51-12525, 12525 (Philippines)	RAA.2
☐ Cessna 305A Bird Dog (L-19A) (O-1A)	T2-23/15	23238	51-12781	RAA.2
☐ Cessna 305A Bird Dog (L-19A) (O-1A)	HS-XTZ		(USAF), T2-19/14	RAA.1
☐ Cessna 305A Bird Dog (L-19A) (O-1A)	T2-30/15		(USAF), 2643 – possible identity.	RAA.1
☐ Cessna 305C Bird Dog (L-19E) (O-1E)	HS-OOJ	305M0073	61-3020, 3020, T2-40/16	RA.1
☐ Cessna 318E Dragonfly (A-37B)		43137	68-10786, 10786 (South Vietnam)	RA.5
☐ Cessna 318E Dragonfly (A-37B)	J6-19/28	43169	68-10818	RA.2
☐ Cessna 318E Dragonfly (A-37B)	J6-7/15	43340	71-0802, 10802 (South Vietnam)	RA.2
☐ Cessna 318E Dragonfly (A-37B)	J6-9/15	43341	71-0803, 10803 (South Vietnam)	RA.1
☐ Cessna 318E Dragonfly (A-37B)	J6-15/15	43348	71-0810	RA.5
☐ Cessna R172E Mescalero (T-41B)	5008	R1720009	67-15008	RA.1
☐ Cessna R172E Mescalero (T-41B)	5039	R1720040	67-15039	RA.1
☐ Champion 7GCAA	HS-FPD	258-73	N732JD	RAA.2
☐ Curtiss H81-A2 Tomahawk IIB	P8115	15452		RAD.1
☐ De Havilland D.H.82A Tiger Moth	21	84695	T6269, G-AMOU, VR-RBZ, 9M-ALJ, N200D	RAA.1
☐ De Havilland D.H.82A Tiger Moth	N973JS	86156	EM973, G-ANNU, ZK-BFB	RAA.1
☐ De Havilland D.H.C.1 Chipmunk T.20	F9-35/95	C1/0411		RAA.1
☐ De Havilland D.H.C.1 Chipmunk T.20	F9-64/97	C1/0619		RAA.2
☐ De Havilland D.H.C.1 Chipmunk T.20	F9-65/97	C1/0626		RAA.2
☐ De Havilland D.H.C.1 Chipmunk T.20	F9-66/97	C1/0634		RAA.2
☐ De Havilland D.H.C.1 Chipmunk T.20				RAC.2
☐ Douglas DC-3A-456 Skytrain (C-47A) (Dakota III)	L2-12/96	12248	42-108840, A65-36, VH-EBF, HS-TDI, 212248	RA.1
☐ Grumman G-58 Bearcat (F8F-1) (F8F-1B)	Bu122120	D.804		RAA.3
☐ Grumman-American AA-1C Lynx	HS-ATT	AA1C-0120		RAD.2
☐ Helio H-295 Super Courier (U-10D)		1247	66-14345	RA.1
☐ Henderson Little Bear	N996TB	TB0002		RAA.1
☐ Hughes 269C Osage (TH-55A)			Pod only.	RAD.5
☐ Hughes 269C Osage (TH-55A)	6735	0842	67-16375	RAA.4
☐ Hughes 269C Osage (TH-55A)		1181033	67-16926 – pod only.	RAD.5
☐ Hughes 269C Osage (TH-55A)		580868	67-16761 – pod only.	RAD.5
☐ Kawasaki-Bell 47G-3B-KH4 (H-13KH)		2201	Pod only.	RAD.5
☐ Lockheed 580 (T-33A)	BF11-40/31	580-1267	57-0538	RA.2
☐ Lockheed 580 (T-33A)	BF11-42/21	580-1353	57-0686	RA.6
☐ Lockheed 580 (T-33A)	BF11-43/31	580-1517	58-0648	RA.6
☐ Lockheed 580 (T-33A)	BF11-44/31	580-1523	58-0474	RA.6
☐ Lockheed 580 (T-33A)	BF11-45/31	580-1574	58-0525	RA.6
☐ Lockheed 580 (T-33A)	BF11-28/25	580-7222	51-9168, 19168 (France), F-GBEP	RA.6
☐ Lockheed 580 (T-33A)	BF11-34/26	580-7582	51-17522, 117522 (France), F-GBEU	RA.1
☐ Lockheed 580 (T-33A)	BF11-38/26	580-7689	51-17544, 117544 (France), F-GBEZ	RA.6
☐ Lockheed 580 (T-33A)	BF11-35/26	580-8298	53-4959, 34959 (France), F-GBES	RA.6
☐ Lockheed 580 (T-33A)	BF11-31/25	580-8621	53-5282, 35282 (France), F-GBEQ	RA
☐ Maule MX-7-235 Super Rocket	108	10108C		RAD.5
☐ North American NA-50 (P-64) (R)	NX30CE	88-12956	Converted from NA-88 Texan (SNJ-4) Bu27560	RAA.2
☐ North American NA-121 Texan (AT-6F)	115/94		Probably a composite.	RAC.1
☐ North American NA-174 Trojan (T-28A) (AT-28D)	JF13-96/13	174-72	51-3534	RAA.2
☐ North American NA-174 Trojan (T-28A) (AT-28D)	JF13-56/08	174-86	51-3548	RAA.1
☐ North American NA-176 Sabre (F-86F)	13-345	176-276	51-13345 – in Korean markings.	RAC.2
☐ North American NA-182 Texan (T-6G)	F8-148/00	182-317	51-14630, 114630	RAA.1
☐ North American NA-182 Texan (T-6G)		182-344	51-14657	RA.1
☐ North American NA-182 Texan (T-6G)	F8-210/00	182-349	51-14662, 114662	RAA.2
☐ North American NA-191 Sabre (F-86F)	24-463	191-159	52-4463 – in Korean markings.	RA.2
☐ North American NA-191 Sabre (F-86F)	4335	191-743	52-5047	RA.5
☐ North American NA-200 Trojan (T-28B) (AT-28D)	JF13-104/15	200-244	Bu138173	RAA.1
☐ North American NA-200 Trojan (T-28B) (AT-28D)	JF13-109/15	200-34	Bu137671	RAA.1
☐ North American NA-200 Trojan (T-28B) (AT-28D)	JF13-114/15	200-47	Bu137685	RAA.1
☐ North American NA-200 Trojan (T-28B) (AT-28D)	JF13-120/18	200-74	Bu137711	RAA.1
☐ North American NA-200 Trojan (T-28B) (AT-28D)			Front fuselage only.	RA.1
☐ North American NA-201 Sabre (F-86D) (F-86L)	Kh17k-6/06	201-287	53-0843	RA.5
☐ North American NA-342 Bronco (OV-10C)	BJ5-01/2513	342-1	Bu158396	RA.1
☐ North American NA-342 Bronco (OV-10C)	BJ5-5-05/2514	342-5	Bu158400	RA.1
☐ North American NA-342 Bronco (OV-10C)	BJ5.5-09/2514	342-9	Bu158404	RA.1
☐ Pilatus PC.6/B2-H2 Turbo Porter	1315	782		RAD.5
☐ Piper J-3C-65 Cub	NC88293	15911	NC88293, N88293	RAA.1
☐ Piper J-3C-90 Cub (J-3C-65)	HS-XTY/2222	7173	NC38665, N38665	RAA.1
☐ Piper PA-22-108 Colt	N4831Z	22-8405	Fuselage frame only.	RAD.1
☐ Piper PA-22-135 Tri-Pacer	N3480A	22-1751	Fuselage only.	RAD.2
☐ Piper PA-22-135 Tri-Pacer			Fuselage frame only.	RAD.2

TYPE	REG/SER	CON. NO.	PI/NOTES	STATUS
☐ Piper PA-22-135 Tri-Pacer			Fuselage frame only.	RAD.2
☐ Piper PA-22-150 Tri-Pacer	N4316A	22-3668	Fuselage only.	RAD.2
☐ Piper PA-22-150 Tri-Pacer	N5991D	22-4641	Fuselage only.	RAD.1
☐ Piper PA-22-160 Tri-Pacer	N9417D	22-6391	Fuselage only.	RAD.2
☐ Piper PA-22-160 Tri-Pacer	N9439D	22-6413	Fuselage only.	RAD.2
☐ Piper PA-22-150 Tri-Pacer			Fuselage frame only.	RAD.2
☐ Rhein Flugzeugbau Fantrainer 600	F18k-1/27	002		RAD.5
☐ Royal Thai Air Force RTAF-4 Chantra	F17-4/17	005		RAD.5
☐ Royal Thai Air Force RTAF-4 Chantra	F17-7/17	008		RA.2
☐ SIAI-Marchetti SF.260MT	F15-12/20	14.13/288		RAD.5
☐ Stinson V-76 Sentinel (L-5E)	'T-07'		42-98148, N9795F – on data plate but may be 44-18100.	RAAX.1
☐ Stinson V-76 Sentinel (L-5G)	N45AK	76-4618	45-35034, N49454	RAA.1
☐ Supermarine 390 Spitfire PR.XIX	Kh14-27/97		PS836	RAC.2
☐ Travel Air 2000			Contains original fuselage.	RA.2
☐ Travel Air 2000	HS-IAM		Contains many new parts.	RAA.2
☐ Travel Air 4000	HS-PSP	948	NC8846, N99X	RAC.2
☐ Unknown Biplane				RA.2

GOLDEN JUBILEE MUSEUM OF AGRICULTURE (TH10)

Address:	Kaset Heliport, Khlong Luang 12120.,
Tel:	02-529-2212
Admission:	Tuesday-Sunday 0930-1530.
Location:	About 20 km east of Bangkok.

The displays at this museum trace the development of agriculture in the country. On show are implements and tractors along with pieces of machinery. There are many photographs, documents and maps in the informative exhibition. Aircraft have placed an important part in recent years and two types can be seen.

TYPE	REG/SER	CON. NO.	PI/NOTES	STATUS
☐ Britten-Norman BN-2 Islander	501	26	G-AWID	PV
☐ Hughes 369	1013	970200D		PV

HAT YAI AIR FORCE BASE COLLECTION (TH11)

Address:	Hat Yai Air Force Base, Hat Yai 90110.
Admission:	By prior permision only.
Location:	About 10 km south west of the town.

No operational units are currently based at this airfield. The resident No. 56 Wing flying T-33s disbanded several years ago. Two aircraft are preserved and several other T-33s are stored for use by Tango Squadron.

TYPE	REG/SER	CON. NO.	PI/NOTES	STATUS
☐ Lockheed 580 (T-33A)	BF11-37/26	580-6536	51-8752, 18752 (France), F-GBEY	RA
☐ Lockheed 580 (T-33A) (RT-33A)	BTF11-8/13	580-8612	53-5273	RA

JESADA TECHNICAL MUSEUM (TH12)

Address:	100 Moo2, Ngewrui, Nakhon Chaisi, Nakhon Pathom 73120.
Tel:	034-339-408
Admission:	Daily 1000-1800
Location:	About 20 km west of Bangkok. Location codes: 1 Main site at Nakhon Chaisi; 2 Nakhon Ratchasima Airport; 3 Satellite site at Nakhon Chaisi;

This private collection was set up in the mid-1990s by businessman Jesada Dejsukulrit. Over four hundred cars are at the site along with aircraft, ships and railway items. There are also bicycles, motor cycles and commercial vehicles in the exhibition. There are plans to move the museum to another location but at the present time the aircraft are dispersed round the area. Two large jet airliners, both of which were flown in Thailand, will be on show in 2008. The Tri-Star was barged to the museum. The Alouettes are former Luftwaffe machines.

TYPE	REG/SER	CON. NO.	PI/NOTES	STATUS
☐ Boeing 747-246B	HS-UTB	20529	JA8113, N554SW, TF-ABQ, N910BW	PV.2

TYPE	REG/SER	CON. NO.	PI/NOTES	STATUS
☐ Douglas DC-3A-456 Skytrain (C-47A)	N2270M	10239	42-24377, NC36412, LR-AAO, OD-AAO, G-AODD, UB-715, N2270M	PV.1
☐ Fairchild 473 Provider (205) (C-123B) (C-123K)	576	20025	54-0576, L4k-1/16	PV.3
☐ Fairchild 473 Provider (205) (C-123B) (C-123K)	L4k-20/19	20237	55-4576	PV.3
☐ Lockheed L-1011 Tri-Star	XU-700	193A-1055	N327EA, VR-HOK, N155MC, HS-LTB – due in 2008.	PV.1
☐ Piper PA-38-112 Tomahawk	HS-TCU	38-79A0317	N2441D	PV.1
☐ Sikorsky S-58 Seahorse (HUS-1) (UH-34D)			Major components.	PVD.1
☐ Sikorsky S-58 Seahorse (HUS-1) (UH-34D)		581793	Bu153699, 3699 (Laos)	PV.1
☐ Sud-Est SE.3130 Alouette II	75+16	1274	PG+131, PC+131, PC+201	PV.1
☐ Sud-Est SE.3130 Alouette II	75+19	1277	PC+134, PG+203	PV.1

JOMTIEN WATERPARK (TH13)

Address: Thapphraya Road,
Jomtien.
Admission: Not yet complete.
Location: About 2 km east of Highway 3 near Km 154 north of Ba Na Chom Thian.

This attraction is still under construction and four aircraft have arrived. A number of rides have been built and there is also an amusement park. Three of the airframes have been acquired from Laos.

TYPE	REG/SER	CON. NO.	PI/NOTES	STATUS
☐ Antonov An-24RV		67310610	RDPL-34006	PV
☐ Antonov An-24RV		67310708	RDPL-34010 – possible identity.	PV
☐ Fairchild 473 Provider (205) (C-123B) (C-123K)	565	20226	55-4565, L4k-11/18	PV
☐ Mil Mi-8T		23508	RDPL-34044 – possible identity.	PV

KAMPHAENG SAEN AIR FORCE BASE COLLECTION (TH14)

Address: Flying Training School,
Kamphaeng Saen Air Force Base,
Kamphaeng Saen 73140.
Admission: By prior permission only.
Location: About 50 km west of Bangkok.

The main flying training school for the Air Force is located at this base. Three types formerly flown from the field have been preserved. Eighteen Canadian built Chipmunks were purchased and these were followed by forty eight constructed in England. The type served at the school for many years.

TYPE	REG/SER	CON. NO.	PI/NOTES	STATUS
☐ Cessna 318C Tweety Bird (T-37C)	'19-04'		(USAF)	RAX
☐ De Havilland D.H.C.1 Chipmunk 1B-2-S2	F9-06/93	96-134		RA
☐ Fairchild 205 Provider (C-123B)	BL4-19/15	20154	54-0705 – at nearby Commando Training Centre.	PVX
☐ Lockheed 580 (T-33A)	'1127'	580-8142	52-9836, F.11-15/10	PVX

KHAO KHO WAR MEMORIAL PARK (TH15)

Address: 33 Mu 11,
Bang Nam,
Phetchuaban 67110
Tel: 01226-0565
Admission: Daily 0900-1700.
Location: About 40 km north west of Phetchuaban.

Set up in the Khao Kao National Park the memorial honours government troops who lost their lives in fierce battles with communist insurgents. A display in a small building traces the conflict. Photographs, documents, uniforms and many personal items are displayed. Three aircraft are displayed along with military equipment.

TYPE	REG/SER	CON. NO.	PI/NOTES	STATUS
☐ Bell 205 Iroquois (UH-1H)	6377			PV
☐ Bell 47G-3B-1 Sioux (TH-13T)		3559	66-8059 – possible identity.	PV
☐ Cessna 305A Bird Dog (L-19A) (O-1A)	3121			PV
☐ Northrop N-156A Freedom Fighter (F-5A)	69161	N.6265	66-9161 – rear fuselage only.	PV

KOROAT AIR FORCE BASE COLLECTION (TH16)

Address:	1 Wing, Korat Air Force Base, Nakhon Ratchasima.
Admission:	By prior permission only.
Location:	In the south western suburbs of the town.

This important fighter base houses units operating the General Dynamics F-16. Up to 2004, Aero L-39AZ Albatros trainers were in residence. Three aircraft have been preserved at the airfield.

TYPE	REG/SER	CON. NO.	PI/NOTES	STATUS
☐ Cessna 318B Tweety Bird (318A) (T-37A) (T-37B)	'RR.17-23'	40090	56-3518, BF.12-17/23	RAX
☐ Lockheed 580 (T-33A)	BF.11-26/13	580-9727	53-6106	RA
☐ North American NA-191 Sabre (F-86F)	Kh.17-2/04	191-637	52-4941	RA

LOEI WAR MEMORIAL PARK (TH17)

Address:	Loei Airport, Loei 42000.
Admission:	On permanent view.
Location:	On Highway 201 next to Loei Airport which is about 6 km south of the town.

A small memorial park has been set up near the airport to honour local people who have lost their lives. The Trojan was used by the Americans in the Vietnam War and proved its worth in counter insurgency duties. Several were flown in Thailand in this role. The Wren 460 is a STOL conversion of a Cessna airframe.

TYPE	REG/SER	CON. NO.	PI/NOTES	STATUS
☐ North American NA-159 Trojan (T-28A) (AT-28D)		159-199	49-1687, JF13-79/11	PV
☐ Wren 460 [Cessna 182G Skylane]		55190/4	N3790U, HS-PCA, 5190	PV

LOP BURI AIR FORCE BASE COLLECTION (TH18)

Address:	2 Wing, Lop Buri Air Force Base, Lop Buri 15160.
Admission:	By prior permission only.
Location:	About 15 km north of the town.

The airfield is home to the Army Aviation Centre as well as Air Force units. Currently in use are Bell UH-1H Iroquois and Bell 422 helicopters. The Sikorsky S-58T was withdrawn from use in 2003. This type is a conversion of the basic airframe and is fitted with a turboprop engine. Sikorsky produced kits and the work was carried out by California Helicopter International. A collection of preserved aircraft is located in the Air Force area. A line of withdrawn DC-3s is parked on the ramp and other types are located around the camp. The Bronco was flown on counter insurgency and border patrol duties against drug traffickers.

TYPE	REG/SER	CON. NO.	PI/NOTES	STATUS
☐ Bell 205 Iroquois (UH-1H)	'20311'	13311	72-21612, 2202 (Thai Navy)	RAX
☐ Douglas DC-3A-456 Skytrain (C-47A) (AC-47A)	L2-52/19	20025	43-15559, 559 (Air America) – possible identity.	RA
☐ Douglas DC-3A-456 Skytrain (C-47A) (Dakota III)	L2-35/14	12498	42-108865, KG463, VP906 (India), H-706 (Pakistan), G-ANLJ, F-OAQE, F-KHAA, 42-108865 (Cambodia),	RA
☐ Douglas DC-3A-467 Skytrain (C-47B)	L2-19/00	14692/26137	43-48876, 348876 (France)	RA
☐ Douglas DC-3A-467 Skytrain (C-47B) (VC-47D) (RC-47))	L2-24/01	15361/26806	43-49545, 349545 (France), 43-49545, 349545 (South Vietnam)	RA
☐ North American NA-176 Sabre (F-86F)	Kh17-44/06	176-165	51-13234	RA
☐ North American NA-200 Trojan (T-28B) (AT-28D)	'58853/35885'	200-373	Bu138302, 38302, JF13-105/14	PV
☐ North American NA-342 Bronco (OV-10C)	J5-6/14	342-6	Bu158401	RA
☐ Sikorsky S-58T (Sikorsky S-58 Seahorse (HUS-1) (UH-34D))	H4k-61/19	581480	Bu149378	RA
☐ Sikorsky S-58T (Sikorsky S-58 Seahorse (HUS-1) (UH-34D))	H4k-17/06	581642	63-8251	RA

NARESUAN CAMP COLLECTION (TH19)

Address:	Hua Hin 77110.
Admission:	By prior permission only.
Location:	About 10 km south of the town

The site is named after the sixteenth century King Naresuan the Great and is home to military and police units. The airfield is used for the training of paratroopers. The two SD.360 fuselages are used for preliminary jump training. The type was used on internal services for several years.

TYPE	REG/SER	CON. NO.	PI/NOTES	STATUS
☐ De Havilland D.H.C.4A Caribou	12271	271		PV
☐ Short SD.330-200	HS-TSB	SH.3086	G-14-3086	RA
☐ Short SD.360	HS-SKN	SH.3680	G-14-3680, G-BMEO, HS-TSE – fuselage only.	RA
☐ Short SD.360	HS-SKO	SH.3681	G-14-3681, G-BMEP, HS-TSF – fuselage only.	RA

PHITSANULOK AIR FORCE BASE COLLECTION (TH20)

Address:	46 Wing, Phitsanulok Air Force Base, Phitsanulok 65000.
Admission:	By prior permission only.
Location:	In the southern suburbs of the town.

The base currently houses transport units. Also on the site is an army aviation camp operating a variety of fixed wing types and helicopters. During the Vietnam War United States Air Force squadrons flew from the airfield. Currently in use are Nomads and C-47TPs. In the late 1940s in England the basic C-47 airframe was modified to take turboprop engines. Twenty years later one was converted in the U.S.A. Basler at Oshkosh in Wisconsin has now produced over fifty BT-67s and most have been acquired by Air Forces in Africa, Asia and Latin America. The Nomad first flew in Australia in 1971 and one hundred and sixty were produced.

TYPE	REG/SER	CON. NO.	PI/NOTES	STATUS
☐ Douglas DC-3A-456 Skytrain (C-47A) (VC-47A)	152	16776/33484	44-77152, (Cambodia), L2-44/18	RA
☐ Government Aircraft Factory N.22B Nomad	L.9-6/25	N22B-138	VH-UVJ	RA
☐ North American NA-200 Trojan (T-28B) (AT-28D)	802	200-165	Bu137802, JF13-112/15	RA

POLICE CADET ACADEMY MONUMENT (TH21)

Address:	Nakhon Prathom, Sampran 73110.
Tel:	03431-2009
Admission:	By prior permission only.
Location:	About 20 km west of Bangkok.

The academy was set up to provide training for entrants to the service. Students have the opportunity to follow many academy courses. Aircraft and helicopters are used widely on police work. A Caribou is preserved in the grounds as a reminder of this work. Three examples of the type were used by the police.

TYPE	REG/SER	CON. NO.	PI/NOTES	STATUS
☐ De Havilland D.H.C.4A Caribou	12257	257		RA

PRACHUAP KIRI KHAN AIR FORCE BASE COLLECTION (TH22)

Address:	53 Wing, Prachuap Kiri Khan Air Force Base, Prachuap Kiri Khan 77000.
Admission:	By prior permission only.
Location:	In the southern suburbs of the town.

In the early 1970s the United States Air Force initiated a programme for an armed light aircraft for use in South East Asia. The Fairchild AU-23A, a version of the Pilatus Porter, was selected. Thirty-six were produced and thirty-three were delivered to Thailand. The wing uses the type on border surveillance and counter insurgency work. A collection of types which have been used on similar duties can be seen at the base.

TYPE	REG/SER	CON. NO.	PI/NOTES	STATUS
☐ Cessna 305A Bird Dog (L-19A) (O-1A)	1539			RA
☐ Helio H-295 Super Courier (U-10D)	'53144'			RAX
☐ North American NA-88 Texan (AT-6D)	'53'			RAX
☐ North American NA-159 Trojan (T-28A) (AT-28D)	91538	159-50	49-1538, JF13-90/13	RA
☐ North American NA-360 Bronco (OV-10C)	BJ.5-20/16	360-4	Bu159137	RA

Above: The Thai Agricultural Service has set up a museum at Nakhon Sawan and this Fletcher FU-24 is among the exhibits. (Steve Darke)

Right: Tango Squadron at Chaiang Mai maintains this North American AT-28D in flying condition. (John Mounce)

The Air Base at Ta Khli has this F-84G Thunderjet in its collection. (Steve Darke)

ROYAL THAI AIR FORCE ACADEMY COLLECTION (TH23)

Address:	Thanon Phaholayothin 171/1, Bangkok 10210.
Tel:	02-534-3624
Admission:	By prior permission only.
Location:	About 15 km north east of the city on Route 1.

The academy took its first students in 1953 and now offers courses in engineering and science subjects as well as military training. A collection of aircraft and weapons are preserved in the grounds. Thailand obtained its first Sabres in 1960 and the initial batch replaced the Grumman Bearcats flown by No. 13 Squadron at Don Muang. The F-86 was in service until 1972. In 1964 twenty former U.S. Air National Guard F-86Ls arrived in the country.

TYPE	REG/SER	CON. NO.	PI/NOTES	STATUS
☐ North American NA-191 Sabre (F-86F)	5022	191-718	52-5022, Kh17-7/04	RA
☐ North American NA-200 Trojan (T-28B) (AT-28D)	JF.13-113/15	200-228	Bu138157	RA
☐ North American NA-200 Trojan (T-28B) (AT-28D)	JF.13-115/15	200-355	Bu138284	RA
☐ North American NA-201 Sabre (F-86D) (F-86L)	30892	201-336	53-0892, Kh17k-11/06	RA

ROYAL THAI AIR FORCE MUSEUM (TH24)

Address:	Thanon Phaholayothin 171/1, Don Muang Air Force Base, Bangkok 10210.
Tel:	02-534-1853
Admission:	Monday-Friday 0800-1600; Saturday-Sunday 0830-1600.
Location:	About 15 miles north east of the city on Route 1.

This museum was set up in 1952 and officially opened on March 27th 1959. The collection grew rapidly and in 1968 the museum moved to a new complex which was ready on January 24th 1969. The history of military aviation, which started in Thailand in 1911, is portrayed in detail. On show are many photographs and documents along with a superb collection of models showing every type flown. Uniforms, unit badges, engines and components can also be seen. In 1911 three Army officers were sent to France for pilot training. Four Nieuport monoplanes and three Breguet biplanes returned with the group. A replica of a Nieuport 2N was built and displayed outside the museum for many years. Sadly this machine suffered in the damp climate and was eventually scrapped. The first military airfield was located at what is now the Royal Bangkok Sports Club. In 1914 the operation moved to Don Muang and the Air Force has used the site ever since. In 1917 war was declared on the Central Powers and an expedition was sent to Europe to fight on the Allied side. In 1941 a border dispute broke out with the French Vichy Government who controlled Indo-China. In December of that year Japan invaded the country and the Air Force was engaged in combat. Over the years Thailand has purchased aircraft from many countries. In addition the military workshops at Don Muang and Bang Sue produced licence built aircraft while developing indigenous designs. Many types enjoyed a very long service life. For example the last Avro 504 was not withdrawn until 1945 and the Boeing 100E flew until 1949. The first aircraft to be built under licence, in 1915, was a Breguet 14 using local materials and an imported engine. In the 1980s a deal with Jean Salis resulted in a replica Breguet 14 arriving at the museum with a Bearcat moving to France. In the late 1920s the workshops produced the Boripatra bomber and the Prjatipok fighter. Three accurate replicas of the Boripatra biplane were produced in the early 1990's. Two are on show at the museum and the third is now parked outside the RTAF Officers Club in the city. The highlight of the collection is the range of inter war biplanes. The Boeing 100E was flown against the Bristol Bulldog and the Heinkel HD 43 and although it won the competition only two evaluation aircraft were supplied. The choice for the standard fighter fell on the Vought V.93. Twelve were delivered from America and about seventy were constructed at Bang Sue. The sole survivor of the type is a licence built example. The first biplane Corsair flew at Anacosta in Maryland in 1926. The design set world altitude, speed and endurance records the following year. The type was developed over the next seven years and well over six hundred were produced. The Thai Air Force flew the Corsair from 1934 until 1949. The Hawk was one of the outstanding fighter aircraft of this period. Twelve Hawk IIs were supplied by Curtiss and twenty four Hawk IIIs were built locally. From the same period are two low wing monoplanes, the Curtiss Hawk 75 and the Tachikawa Ki-36. The latter was supplied during the Japanese occupation of the country. Many types used in the post World War II period have been preserved. The Navy received a small number of Helldivers in the mid-1950s. This type was used for four years and only a few have survived around the world. The Prince has recently been restored after spending many years dismantled outside the buildings. The aircraft was delivered to Thailand in 1952 and was used on survey duties around the country. Three products from the local Air Force Workshops are the RTAF-2, which resembles a single finned Beech Bonanza, the RTAF-4 and the RTAF-5. Fourteen British constructed Chipmunk T.20s were rebuilt with a larger rudder, a wider cockpit with a new canopy, a Continental IO-360 engine and called the RTAF-4 Chandra. The RTAF-5 has the same configuration as the North American Bronco but is much smaller. As types are withdrawn from service examples are joining the display and more airframes are expected in the near future. This excellent museum traces the complex history of an Air Force which has operated a wide range of types.

TYPE	REG/SER	CON. NO.	PI/NOTES	STATUS
☐ Beech C18S Expeditor (C-45F) (UC-45F)	'L1-5/90'	8411	44-87152, L1-6/90	PVX
☐ Beech 35 Bonanza		D-1483	NC3997N, (Thai Navy), HS-SFE, HS-TBE	PV
☐ Bell 47G-2 Sioux (H-13H) (OH-13H)	H7-9/15	1894	56-2182	PV
☐ Bell 206B-3 Jet Ranger	H8-1/38	4362		PV
☐ Bell 212 Iroquois (UH-1N)	H6k-1/19	31692		PV
☐ Boeing 100E		1488		PV

☐ Breguet 14P (R)		1	F-AZBH	PVX
☐ Cessna 305A Bird Dog (L-19A) (O-1A)	T2-27/15	23059	51-12604	PV
☐ Cessna 305C Bird Dog (L-19E) (O-1E)	T2-29/15	23629	56-2507	PV
☐ Cessna 318C Tweety Bird (T-37C)	BF.12-09/13	42001	69-7068	PV
☐ Cessna 318E Dragonfly (A-37B)	J6-13/15	43346	71-0808, 10808 (South Vietnam)	PV
☐ Curtiss 68B Hawk III				PV
☐ Curtiss H-75N Hawk		12763		PV
☐ Curtiss 84G Helldiver (SB2C-5)	4	366	Bu83410, J3-4/94	PV
☐ De Havilland D.H.82A Tiger Moth	21/94	82794 (?)	R4877 (?), G-AMGB (?)	PV
☐ De Havilland D.H.C.1 Chipmunk 1B-2-S2	F9-5/93	95-133		PV
☐ De Havilland D.H.C.1 Chipmunk T.20	F9-24/95	C1/0382		PVA
☐ Douglas DC-3A-456 Skytrain (C-47A)	L2-39/15	19010	42-100547	PV
☐ Douglas A-1H Skyraider (AD-6)	14/072		Composite – containing parts of c/n 9701 Bu134472, 133472 (South Vietnam)	PV
☐ Fairchild 24J				PV
☐ Fairchild 205 Provider (C-123B)	L4-6/07	20004	54-0555	PV
☐ Fairey Firefly FR.1	SF11	F7402	MB410, B.J/4-11	PV
☐ Grumman G-44A Widgeon		1449	NC86623	PV
☐ Grumman G-58 Bearcat (F8F-1)	Kh15-178/98	D.205	Bu94956	PV
☐ Helio H-395 Super Courier (U-10B)	63-8103	576	Fin from c/n 1234 66-14332	PV
☐ Hiller UH12B	4/96	597		PV
☐ Hoffman H-36 Dimona	R1-5/27	3526		PV
☐ Kaman K-600-3 Huskie (H-43B) (HH-43B)	'H5-4/05'	115	60-0291, H5-2/05	PVX
☐ Kawasaki-Bell 47G-3B-KH4 (H-13KH)		2040		PV
☐ Lockheed 580 (T-33A)	BF11-23/13	580-9405	53-5929	PV
☐ Lockheed 580 (T-33A) (RT-33A)	BTF11-5/10	580-9215	53-5814	PV
☐ Man Powered Aircraft			Japanese design.	PV
☐ Nakajima Ki-27				PVD
☐ National Aeronautical Workshops Boripatra (R)				PVX
☐ National Aeronautical Workshops Boripatra (R)				PVX
☐ Nihon Kogata K-14				PV
☐ Nihon Kogata K-15				PV
☐ North American NA-121 Texan (AT-6F)	'RR007/92'	121-42518	44-81796, F8-99/941	PVX
☐ North American NA-182 Texan (T-6G)		182-353	51-14666	PVX
☐ North American NA-191 Sabre (F-86F)	Kh17-10/04	191-756	52-5060	PV
☐ North American NA-200 Trojan (T-28B) (AT-28D)	O-37661	200-24	Bu137661	PV
☐ North American NA-201 Sabre (F-86D) (F-86L)	Kh17k-5/06	201-125	53-0681	PV
☐ North American NA-342 Bronco (OV-10C)	J5-10/14	342-10	Bu158405	PV
☐ Northrop N-156A Freedom Fighter (F-5A)	Kh18-13/37	N.6008	63-8371	PV
☐ Northrop N-156A Freedom Fighter (RF-5A)	TKh18-3/13	RF.1038	69-7158	PV
☐ Pazmany PL-2	PL-2			PV
☐ PDQ Aircraft PDQ-2			Probable type.	PV
☐ Percival P.50 Prince 3A	'T1-1/96'	P.50/41	G-AMNT, T1-1/98	PVX
☐ Piper J-3C-65 Cub (L-4J)		13513	45-4773, S3-4/90	PV
☐ Republic F-84G Thunderjet	'878'		51-10582	PVX
☐ Rhein Flugzeugbau Fantrainer 400	BF18-01/27	003	D-EIWK	PV
☐ Rhein Flugzeugbau Fantrainer 600	BF18k-15/32	004		PV
☐ Royal Thai Air Force RTAF-2			BTho-2/1	PV
☐ Royal Thai Air Force RTAF-4 Chantra	03		F17-3/17	PV
☐ Royal Thai Air Force RTAF-5			BTho-5/1	PV
☐ SIAI-Marchetti SF.260MT	RR.08-17	14-08	I-THAI, F15-08/17	PV
☐ Sikorsky S-55B	H3-3/97	55757		PV
☐ Sikorsky S-58 Seahorse (HUS-1) (UH-34D)	150556	581683	Bu150556	PV
☐ Sikorsky S-58T (S-58)	H4k-64/30	581117	581117 (France), N1170U, 911 (Kaset)	PV
☐ Sikorsky VS-372 Dragonfly (YR-5A)	H1k-1/96		43-46607	PV
☐ Stinson V-76 Sentinel (L-5B)		76-3272	44-16985, KJ464, S4-10/90	PV
☐ Supermarine 379 Spitfire FR.XIVe		6S.662808	SM914, G-15-111, Kh14-1/93	PV
☐ Swearingen SA.226AT Merlin IVA	TL6-1/22	AT-071	N5650M – due soon.	–
☐ Tachikawa Ki-55				PV
☐ Vought V-93S Corsair		14682		PV
☐ Westland-Sikorsky WS-51 Dragonfly 1A	H1-4/96	WA/H/120	G-AMJW, G-17-2,	PV

ROYAL THAI AIR FORCE WORKSHOPS MONUMENT (TH25)

Address:	Thanon Rama V, Bangkok.
Admission:	By prior permission only.
Location:	In the northern part of the city.

The workshops were set up in the 1920s and have produced a number of original designs for the service. A replica of the Boripatra is preserved outside the Officer's Club.

TYPE	REG/SER	CON. NO.	PI/NOTES	STATUS
☐ National Aeronautical Workshops Boripatra (R)				RA

ROYAL THAI ARMED FORCES ACADEMIES PREPARATORY SCHOOL COLLECTION (TH26)

Address:	Nakhon Nayan 26110
Tel:	037-306025
Email:	afaps@live.com
Admission:	By prior permission only.
Location:	In the town.

The school was established in Bangkok in 1958 and a few years ago moved to a new complex in Nakhon Nayan. Students normally spend two years taking a number of courses before moving on to the service academies. The aircraft are displayed in the grounds along with tanks, military vehicles and weapons.

TYPE	REG/SER	CON. NO.	PI/NOTES	STATUS
☐ Bell 205 Iroquois (UH-1H)			At nearby school.	RA
☐ Cessna 318E Dragonfly (A-37B)	'1803'	43209	69-6364, J6-20/28	RAX
☐ Fairchild 205 Provider (C-123B)	55-569	20230	55-4569, 54569 (South Vietnam), L4k-7/16	RA
☐ North American NA-200 Trojan (T-28B)				RA
☐ North American NA-201 Sabre (F-86D) (F-86L)	'30676'	201-70	53-0626, Kh17k-3/06	RAX
☐ Northrop N-156A Freedom Fighter (F-5A)	69160	N.6264	69-6190, Kh18-2/10	RA
☐ Northrop N-311 Tiger II (F-5E)	91695	TU.1009	79-1695, Kh18Kh-26/24	RA

ROYAL THAI ARMY AVIATION MUSEUM (TH27)

Address:	Army Aviation Centre, Lopburi 15160.
Tel:	036-486415
Admission:	By prior permission only.
Location:	About 15 km north of the town.

The Thai Army has a large aviation section and has established a museum at its headquarters. Memorabilia, photographs and documents have been collected and there are plans to convert a building for display purposes. Examples of types flown by the service are preserved and located by the main gate, close to the education centre and on the airfield. The Piper Cub was one of the first types used and an immaculate example is in the museum workshop building. Large numbers of Bird Dogs were flown and the rugged Beaver was ideally suited to operating in the jungle terrain. In 1982 a major operation was staged against opium producers and smugglers in the north of the country and helicopters played a significant part in these raids.

TYPE	REG/SER	CON. NO.	PI/NOTES	STATUS
☐ Aero Commander 500	'2540/FR9'	1267-90	N78392, 78392	RAX
☐ Bell 47G-2 Sioux (H-13H) (OH-13H)	4948	2531 (?)	59-4948 (?)	RA
☐ Bell 47G-3B Sioux (OH-13S)	15425	3293	64-15425	RA
☐ Cessna 305A Bird Dog (L-19A) (O-1A)	1601	21295	50-1601, 11091 (Japan)	RA
☐ Cessna 305A Bird Dog (L-19A) (O-1A)	4951	21843	51-4953	RA
☐ Cessna 305A Bird Dog (L-19A) (O-1A)	7353	22087	51-7353	RA
☐ Cessna 305C Bird Dog (L-19E) (O-1E)	2517	23639	56-2517	RA
☐ De Havilland D.H.C.2 Beaver (L-20A) (U-6A)	15462			RA
☐ De Havilland D.H.C.2 Beaver (L-20A) (U-6A)	16151	547	52-6151	RA
☐ De Havilland D.H.C.2 Beaver (L-20A) (U-6A)	'16257'	555	52-6157, 26157	RAX
☐ Douglas DC-3A-467 Skytrain (C-47B) (AC-47D) (EC-47D)	HS-DOA	15066/26511	43-49250, 49250 (Thailand), L2r-1/07	RA
☐ Hughes 269C Osage (TH-55A)	5404	1270748	67-15404	RA
☐ Kawasaki-Bell 47G-3B-KH4 (H-13KH)		2039		RA
☐ Piper J-3C-65 Cub (L-4J)	1348			RA
☐ Vertol V.114 Chinook (CH-47A)	413148	B.120	64-13148	RA

ROYAL THAI NAVY MUSEUM (TH28)

Address:	126 Sukhumvit Road, Samut Prakan 10270.
Admission:	Monday-Friday 0900-1600.
Location:	In the south eastern suburbs of the city.

The country has a long maritime tradition and the first navy was established in the nineteenth century. The museum is located close to the Royal Thai Naval Academy. The Navy operates a fleet of fixed wing aircraft and helicopters from U-Tapao. Parked outside is one of the two Albatross amphibians flow by the force between 1958 and 1981. Inside, displays trace the maritime history of the nation and the navy with many models of ships, documents, uniforms and photographs on show.

TYPE	REG/SER	CON. NO.	PI/NOTES	STATUS
☐ Grumman G-111 Albatross (G-64) (SA-16A) (SA-16B) (HU-16B)	7235	G-321	51-7235	PV

ROYAL THAI POLICE MUSEUM (TH29)

Address:	Thanon Rham Inthra, Bangkok 10700.
Admission:	On permanent view.
Location:	About 15 km north east of the city centre.

The Thai police have, in recent years, used fixed and rotary wing aircraft to patrol the borders of the country on anti-drug operations. A museum has been set up in the headquarters of the border service. The history of the force is portrayed in the displays in the building. On show are many photographs, uniforms, models, documents and personal items. The Dakota is mounted over the gate to the complex and the remainder of the aircraft are parked just inside the main entrance. The Beagle Husky was delivered in 1967 to the King of Thailand.

TYPE	REG/SER	CON. NO.	PI/NOTES	STATUS
☐ Aero Engine Services T6/24 Airtourer	1909	B-577	ZK-DHH	PV
☐ Beagle D5/180 Husky	1409	3687		PV
☐ Cessna 310F	702	310F0117	N5817X	PV
☐ Dornier Do 28D-7 Skyservant	1815	4015	N6770	PV
☐ Douglas DC-3A-467 Skytrain (C-47B)	'219789'	15332/26777	43-49516, 349516 (Vietnam), 349516 (Cambodia), L2-43/18	PVX
☐ Hiller UH12E	'1009'	2314	1006	PVX
☐ Kawasaki-Bell 47G-3B-KH4 (H-13KH)	3?-1119	2198	47-1119	PV
☐ Sikorsky S-55A	600	55940		PV
☐ Sikorsky S-62A	801	62020	N9F	PV

ROYAL THAI SPECIAL FORCES MUSEUM (TH30)

Address:	Army Aviation Centre, Lop Buri 15160.
Admission:	By prior permission only.
Location:	About 15 km north of the town.

The work of the force is highlighted in this museum. Units have been active in many local conflicts over the years. The work training combat units from Laos and Cambodia is featured. The conflicts with communist guerillas are also portrayed. On show is a collection of weapons and equipment used on their secret missions.

TYPE	REG/SER	CON. NO.	PI/NOTES	STATUS
☐ Bell 205 Iroquois (UH-1H)	2538			RA
☐ Cessna 305A Bird Dog (L-19A) (O-1A)	6941			RA

SARABURI AERO PARK (TH31)

Address:	Amphur Kaeng Khoi, Saraburi 18140.
Admission:	On permanent view.
Location:	About 10 km south east of the town.

The airfield is being developed by the Foundation for the Preservation and Development of Thai Aircraft (Tango Squadron). The site will eventually include a museum, outdoor display area and workshops as well as a V.I.P. resort and spa. The organisation has moved its store of thirty-four Bird Dogs to Saraburi. They have been joined by seven ex-Air Force examples so over forty are lined up in an impressive display along the entrance road.

TYPE	REG/SER	CON. NO.	PI/NOTES	STATUS
☐ Cessna 305A Bird Dog (L-19A) (O-1A)	1490	21164	50-1490	PV
☐ Cessna 305A Bird Dog (L-19A) (O-1A)	1539/T2-18/14	21213	50-1539	PV
☐ Cessna 305A Bird Dog (L-19A) (O-1A)	1554	21232	50-1554	PV
☐ Cessna 305A Bird Dog (L-19A) (O-1A)	1562	21243	50-1562 – wings from c/n 22129 51-7390, 7390	PV
☐ Cessna 305A Bird Dog (L-19A) (O-1A)	1574	21259	50-1574, 11024 (Japan)	PV
☐ Cessna 305A Bird Dog (L-19A) (O-1A)	1590	21280	50-1590 – wings from c/n 22386 51-12072, 2072	PV
☐ Cessna 305A Bird Dog (L-19A) (O-1A)	1603	21298	50-1603	PV
☐ Cessna 305A Bird Dog (L-19A) (O-1A)	1634	21326	50-1634	PV
☐ Cessna 305A Bird Dog (L-19A) (O-1A)	4581	21371	51-4581	PV
☐ Cessna 305A Bird Dog (L-19A) (O-1A)	4672	21557	51-4672	PV
☐ Cessna 305A Bird Dog (L-19A) (O-1A)	4717	21602	51-4717 – wings from c/n 21322 50-1620, 11036 (Japan), 1620.	PV
☐ Cessna 305A Bird Dog (L-19A) (O-1A)	4807	21692	51-4807	PV
☐ Cessna 305A Bird Dog (L-19A) (O-1A)	4834	21719	51-4834 – wings from 2807	PV
☐ Cessna 305A Bird Dog (L-19A) (O-1A)	4867/T2-41/16	21752	51-4867	PV
☐ Cessna 305A Bird Dog (L-19A) (O-1A)	4952	21844	51-4952	PV
☐ Cessna 305A Bird Dog (L-19A) (O-1A)	5008	21908	51-5008	PV
☐ Cessna 305A Bird Dog (L-19A) (O-1A)	5026	21930	51-5206	PV

☐ Cessna 305A Bird Dog (L-19A) (O-1A)	5077	21982	51-5077	PV
☐ Cessna 305A Bird Dog (L-19A) (O-1A)	7295	22029	51-7295	PV
☐ Cessna 305A Bird Dog (L-19A) (O-1A)	7390	22129	51-7390 – wings from c/n 21243 50-1562, 1562	PV
☐ Cessna 305A Bird Dog (L-19A) (O-1A)	T2-52/20	22334	51-12020	PV
☐ Cessna 305A Bird Dog (L-19A) (O-1A)	2037	22351	51-12037	PV
☐ Cessna 305A Bird Dog (L-19A) (O-1A)	2072	22386	51-12072 – wings from c/n 22117 51-7383, 7383	PV
☐ Cessna 305A Bird Dog (L-19A) (O-1A)	2086	22400	51-12086	PV
☐ Cessna 305A Bird Dog (L-19A) (O-1A)	2190	22504	51-12190	PV
☐ Cessna 305A Bird Dog (L-19A) (O-1A)	2293	22607	51-12293	PV
☐ Cessna 305A Bird Dog (L-19A) (O-1A)	2422/T2-8/10	22855	51-12422	PV
☐ Cessna 305A Bird Dog (L-19A) (O-1A)	2666/T2-24/14	23121	51-12666	PV
☐ Cessna 305A Bird Dog (L-19A) (O-1A)	2792	23249	51-12792, (South Vietnam)	PV
☐ Cessna 305A Bird Dog (L-19A) (O-1A)	2908	23365	51-12908	PV
☐ Cessna 305A Bird Dog (L-19A) (O-1A)	2647	23371	51-12647	PV
☐ Cessna 305A Bird Dog (L-19A) (O-1A)	2661	23385	51-12661	PV
☐ Cessna 305A Bird Dog (L-19A) (O-1A)	7969	23390	53-7969 – wings from 2547.	PV
☐ Cessna 305A Bird Dog (L-19A) (O-1A)	7972	23393	53-7972	PV
☐ Cessna 305C Bird Dog (L-19E) (O-1E)	2549	23671	56-2549 – wings from c/n 22209 51-7470, 7470	PV
☐ Cessna 305C Bird Dog (L-19E) (O-1E)	2557	23679	56-2557 – wings from c/n 21331 51-4564, 4564	PV
☐ Cessna 305C Bird Dog (L-19E) (O-1E)	2561	23683	56-2561	PV
☐ Cessna 305C Bird Dog (L-19E) (O-1E)	2562	23684	56-2562 – wings from c/n 23782 56-2660, 2660	PV
☐ Cessna 305C Bird Dog (L-19E) (O-1E)	2593	23715	56-2593	PV
☐ Cessna 305C Bird Dog (L-19E) (O-1E)	T2-39/16	23777	56-2655	PV
☐ Cessna 305C Bird Dog (L-19E) (O-1E)	T2-38/16	305M0058	61-3007	PV
☐ Cessna 411	0421	4110421	Fuselage only.	PV
☐ Enstrom F-28F	1714	736		PV
☐ Fairchild-Hiller Heliporter (AU-23A) [Pilatus PC-6/C-H2 Turbo Porter]	JH22-16/19	2075	74-2075	RAD
☐ Hiller UH12E	HS-TZB	2004	1002	PV
☐ Hiller UH12E	304	2140	N9761C	PV
☐ Kawasaki-Bell 47G-3B-KH4 (H-13KH)		2143		PV
☐ North American NA-191 Sabre (F-86F)	5085	191-781	52-5085	PV
☐ North American NA-88 Texan (AT-6D)	RR.220/5		(USAAF)	PV
☐ Supermarine 379 Spitfire FR.XIV	Kh14-5/93		RM873, G-15-115 – front fuselage only.	PV

SUKHOTAI PALACE COLLECTION (TH32)

Address:	Bangkok 10210.
Admission:	By prior permission only.
Location:	In the north western suburbs of the city.

A collection of former military aircraft is being assembled in the grounds of this royal palace. The Spitfire arrived in Thailand in 1954 but was only used for exhibition and instructional purposes. The airframe was painted in a Thai Air Force scheme when it underwent restoration in the mid-1990s.

TYPE	REG/SER	CON. NO.	PI/NOTES	STATUS
☐ Avro 748 Series 208	L5-2/16	1715	HS-TAF	RA
☐ Bell 212	H6k-2/19	31693	Possible identity.	RA
☐ Cessna 318B Tweety Bird (T-37B)	'F12-21/23'	40625	60-0137, F12-03/04	RAX
☐ Douglas DC-3A-467 Skytrain (C-47B)	L2-8/90	16101/32849	44-76517, KN422, 476517 (Thailand), 517 (Thailand)	RA
☐ General Dynamics 401 Fighting Falcon (F-16A)				RA
☐ Lockheed 580 (T-33A)	F11-24/13	580-9552	53-6020	RA
☐ Northrop N-156A Freedom Fighter (F-5A)	'80773'		Possibly a composite.	RA
☐ Northrop N-311 Tiger II (F-5E)				RA
☐ SIAI-Marchetti SF.260MT	F15-14/21		Possible identity.	RA
☐ Supermarine 390 Spitfire PR.XIX			PM630	RA

SURAT THANI AIR BASE MONUMENT (TH33)

Address:	7th. Wing, Surat Thani 84000.
Admission:	By prior permission only.
Location:	About 20 km west of the town.

The field also serves as the civil airport for the region. The Air Force has a fighter base at the site and currently operates Northrop Tiger IIs. An earlier F-5A Freedom Fighter has been preserved.

TYPE	REG/SER	CON. NO.	PI/NOTES	STATUS
☐ Northrop N-156A Freedom Fighter (F-5A)	Kh18-7/11	N.6340	67-21257	RA

TA KHLI AIR FORCE BASE COLLECTION (TH34)

Address:	4th Wing, Ta Khli Air Force Base, Ta Khli 60140.
Admission:	By prior permission only.
Location:	About 5 km west of the town on Route 1.

This important base has been used by fighter units for many years and a transport wing was also in residence for some time. For many years a Grumman Bearcat was mounted by one of the gates but this classic naval fighter was taken down and sold. Its place has now been taken by a Sabre and a Dragonfly.

TYPE	REG/SER	CON. NO.	PI/NOTES	STATUS
☐ Cessna 318E Dragonfly (A-37B)	'J6-12/15/4309'			RAX
☐ Cessna 318E Dragonfly (A-37B)			(USAF), J.6-18/25 – possible identity.	PV
☐ Cessna 318E Dragonfly (A-37B)	J.6-5/15	43338	71-0800	RA
☐ North American NA-191 Sabre (F-86F)	'Kh.17-8/04'	191-775	52-5079, Kh.17-38/04	PVX
☐ Republic F-84G Thunderjet	'Kh.17-5/04'		(USAF), 631174	RAX

THAI NATIONAL MEMORIAL (TH35)

Address:	Thanon Phaholayothin, Bangkok 10700.
Admission:	On permanent view.
Location:	About 3 km north of the RTAF Museum.

Two aircraft are displayed by the Memorial with the Provider parked across the road. the Army used the Bell 47 for many years in a number of roles. Eighty-eight Trojans were acquired and some are still in use.

TYPE	REG/SER	CON. NO.	PI/NOTES	STATUS
☐ Bell 47G-3B Sioux (OH-13S)	9182	3068	63-9182 – probable identity.	PV
☐ Fairchild 205 Provider (C-123B)	552	20001	54-0552, L4-7/07	RA
☐ North American NA-174 Trojan (T-28A) (AT-28D)	JF13-119/18	174-190	51-3652, Bu153652	PV

THAILAND RAILWAY HALL OF FAME (TH36)

Address:	Kamphaeng Phet 33, Bangkok.
Tel:	02-373-9976
Admission:	Saturday-Sunday 0500-1630.
Location:	About 10 km northeast of the city centre.

There are many engines, carriages and other interesting items of rolling stock in this collection. The history and development of railways in the country is portrayed in detail. Trams are also featured and on show is one of the earliest electric ones used in Bangkok. The wreckage of the Nakajima B5N2 was found near Kanchanaburi. The museum believes it to be one used by a Japanese General whilst surveying the construction of the so called 'Death Railway'. Parts of the fuselage and wings have been found along with an engine.

TYPE	REG/SER	CON. NO.	PI/NOTES	STATUS
☐ Nakajima B5N2				PVD

U-TAPAO NAVAL BASE COLLECTION (TH37)

Address:	U-Tapao 20180.
Admission:	By prior permission only.
Location:	About 10 km east of Sattahip.

The Thai Navy started an aviation wing in the early 1950s. The unit was equipped with ten Fairey Firefly fighters (one of which is in the Air Force Museum) and two Firefly trainers. Since then it has operated Air Sea rescue flights in the region and carried out liaison duties. In 1995 a small batch of Vought A-7 Corsairs arrived and the following year a number of former Spanish AV-8 Harriers were purchased. U-Tapao is the main shore base of the service and a variety of types operate from this important airfield.

TYPE	REG/SER	CON. NO.	PI/NOTES	STATUS
☐ Cessna 185D Skywagon (U-17A)	1309		71-1455, 11455 (South Vietnam)	RA
☐ Cessna 185D Skywagon (U-17A)	8643		66-14423, 4423	RA
☐ Cessna 305A Bird Dog (L-19A) (O-1A)	1304	21374	51-4582	RA
☐ Cessna 305A Bird Dog (L-19A) (O-1A)	7475	22214 (?)	51-7475	RA

TYPE	REG/SER	CON. NO.	PI/NOTES	STATUS
☐ Douglas DC-3A-467 Skytrain (C-47B)	43-49213	15029/26474		RA
☐ Grumman G-111 Albatross (G-64) (SA-16A) (SA-16B) (HU-16B)	1265	G-264	51-7199, Bu151265,	RA
☐ Grumman G-89 Tracker (S2F-1) (S-2A)	1102	325	Bu136416, 101	RA
☐ Grumman G-89 Tracker (S2F-1) (S-2A)	1103	339	Bu136430	RA

UBON RATCHATHANI AIR FORCE BASE COLLECTION (TH38)

Address:	21 Wing, Ubon Ratchathani Air Force Base, Ubon Ratchathani 34000.
Admission:	By prior permission only.
Location:	In the northern suburbs of the town.

This base is home to a wing operating a mixture of F-5E and F-5F Tiger IIs. The collection of preserved aircraft represents types which have flown from this airfield. The Provider was derelict for a time but has been restored.

TYPE	REG/SER	CON. NO.	PI/NOTES	STATUS
☐ Cessna 318E Dragonfly (A-37B)	'21123'	43342	71-0804	RAX
☐ Cessna 318E Dragonfly (A-37B)	'21124'	43347	71-0809	RAX
☐ Fairchild 205 Provider (C-123B)	575/L4-17/14	20024	54-0575	RA
☐ North American NA-174 Trojan (T-28A) (AT-28D)	732/JF13-118/18	174-270	51-3732	RA

UDON THANI AIR FORCE BASE (TH39)

Address:	23 Wing, Udon Thani Air Force Base, Udon Thani 41000.
Admission:	By prior permission only.
Location:	In the south western suburbs of the town.

Thailand acquired twenty operation Alpha Jets from the Luftwaffe in 2000 with another few arriving for spares use. All fly from Udon Thani. The collection of preserved aircraft includes two withdrawn Freedom Fighters.

TYPE	REG/SER	CON. NO.	PI/NOTES	STATUS
☐ North American NA-174 Trojan (T-28A) (AT-28D)	JF.13-116/18	174-18	51-3480	PV
☐ Northrop N-156B Freedom Fighter (F-5B)	Kh18k-6/30/23105	N.8121	73-1602	RA
☐ Northrop N-156B Freedom Fighter (F-5B)	Kh18k-7/30/23106	N.8122	73-1603	PV

VIETNAM VETERANS MUSEUM (TH40)

Address:	Camp Surasri, Tambon Latya, Ampheo Muang Kanchanaburi 71000.
Admission:	Daily 1099-1700.
Location:	–

The camp houses flying units of the Royal Thai Army and they are responsible for patrolling portions of the Thailand/ Myanmar border. Thai Forces served in the Vietnam War and many American units were stationed in the country. The museum has been set up to honour those who fought for Thailand. The history of the war is portrayed in detail. On show are many photographs depicting the harsh conditions encountered. Also to be seen are weapons, documents and uniforms along with vehicles. The collection of aircraft represents types flown in the conflict. Some of the Bird Dogs have been preserved in the main camp. The ubiquitous C-47 flew with the South Vietnamese Air Force in the early 1970s and is believed to have then gone to Cambodia.

TYPE	REG/SER	CON. NO.	PI/NOTES	STATUS
☐ Bell 205 Iroquois (UH-1H)	6246	12551	70-16246	PV
☐ Cessna 305A Bird Dog (L-19A) (O-1A)	2696		51-12696 or maybe O-1E c/n 23878 56-2696 – on camp.	RA
☐ Cessna 305A Bird Dog (L-19A) (O-1A)	2996		On camp.	RA
☐ Cessna 305A Bird Dog (L-19A) (O-1A)	1510	21184	50-1510	RA
☐ Cessna 305A Bird Dog (L-19A) (O-1A)	'1984'/2581	21641	51-4756	PV
☐ Cessna 305A Bird Dog (L-19A) (O-1A)	2130	22444	51-12130 – on camp.	RA
☐ Cessna 305C Bird Dog (L-19C) (O-1C)	2608	23730	56-2608 – on camp.	RA
☐ Cessna 305C Bird Dog (L-19E) (O-1E)	4231	23892	56-4231 – on camp.	RA
☐ Douglas DC-3A-467 Skytrain (C-47B)	010/L2-46/18	14826/26271	43-49010, 349010 (South Vietnam), (Cambodia?)	PV
☐ Fairchild 473 Provider (205) (C-123B) (C-123K)	L4Kh-17/18	20162	54-0713	PV

TURKEY

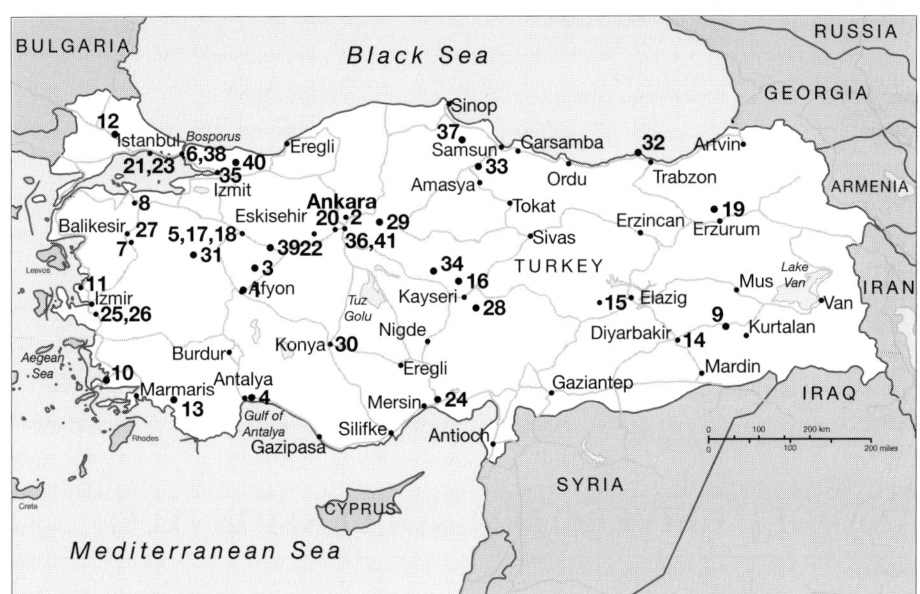

AFYON HAVA ÜSSÜ ANITI (TU1)

Address: Afyon 03040.
Admission: By prior permission only.
Location: About 5 km south east of the town.

This long established airfield is now a reserve base under the control of the 1st Tactical Air Force. The field also serves as the civil airport for the region. A Starfighter is preserved as a memorial.

TYPE	REG/SER	CON. NO.	PI/NOTES	STATUS
☐ Lockheed 583-10-20 Starfighter (TF-104G)	5722	583D-5722	61-3051, KF+221, DA+051, 27+21	RA

AKINCI HAVA ÜSSÜ KOLLEKSION (TU2)

Address: 4 Ana Jet Üssü Komutanligu, Akinci 06770.
Admission: By prior permission only.
Location: About 10 km north west of Ankara

Formerly known as Mürted this airfield is home to a fighter wing flying F-16s and the factory of Turkish Aircraft Industries. A collection of types used by the unit in the past has been assembled. Turkey acquired more than eighty Canadair Sabre 2s and 4s and these initially equipped a wing containing three squadrons. An aerobatic team called 'The White Swans' flew the type in the early 1960's. The Convair F-102 entered Turkish service in 1969 and these delta wing fighters served with squadrons for just over ten years.

TYPE	REG/SER	CON. NO.	PI/NOTES	STATUS
☐ Beech C18S Kansan (AT-11)	'46-840'	3377	42-36997, 6840	RAX
☐ Canadair CL-13 Sabre 2 [North American F-86E]	19103	3	19103 (Canada)	RA
☐ Convair 8-10 Delta Dagger (F-102A)	53392		55-3392	RA
☐ Lockheed 580 (T-33A)	35062	580-8401	53-5062	RA
☐ Lockheed 580 (T-33A)	35792	580-9131	53-5792	RA
☐ Lockheed 580 (T-33A)	53106	580-9676	55-3106, 53106 (France)	RA
☐ Lockheed 683-10-19 Starfighter (F-104G)	'260'			RAX
☐ Lockheed 683-10-19 Starfighter (F-104G)	7051	683-7051	KE+351, DC+109, DB+259, 21+82	RA

AKHISAR HAVA ÜSSÜ ANITI (TU3)

Address: Akhisar 45880.
Admission: By prior permission only.
Location: About 5 km south of the town.

The airfield serves as the civil airport for the area and also the Air Force maintains a reserve base. Two aircraft are preserved at the field with the Starfighter near the military gate and the T-33 in the camp.

TYPE	REG/SER	CON. NO.	PI/NOTES	STATUS
☐ Lockheed 580 (T-33A)	14153	580-5447	51-4153, 14153 (France)	RA
☐ Lockheed 683-10-19 Starfighter (F-104G)	7164	683-7164	KE+464, VA+140, 22+82	RA

ANTALYA HAVA ÜSSÜ ANITI (TU4)

Address: Antalya 07100.
Admission: By prior permission only.
Location: About 5 km east of the town.

The Air Force have a base on the field which is primarily the civil airport for the town. A former Spanish Air Force Starfighter has been mounted on a pole close to the approach road to the camp.

TYPE	REG/SER	CON. NO.	PI/NOTES	STATUS
☐ Lockheed 683-10-19 Starfighter (F-104G)	63-12718	683-6070	63-12718, C.8-4 (Spain)	RA

ANADOLU UNIVERSITESI KOLLEKSION (TU5)

Address: Yunuse Kampusu,
Eskisehir 26470.
Tel: 0222-335-0580
Fax: 0222-335-3616
Email: gensek@anadolu.edu.tr
Admission: By prior permission only.
Location: In the northern suburbs of the town.

The Turkish Police has its own helicopter service and since 1993 pilots have been trained at Anadolu. A small number of helicopters are detached at major towns throughout the country. The university has a campus at this civil airport and has a collection of preserved aircraft. The Viscount is also used for instructional duties. Turkish Airlines ordered five examples in the late 1950s and flew them until the early 1970s when the three survivors were transferred to the Air Force. The example on show was built at Hurn in late 1958. The Grumman Tracker which was flown by the Turkish Navy from its Topel base is located by the main gate. The two Mentors are currently stored in one of the hangars and at least one will be put on display in the near future.

TYPE	REG/SER	CON. NO.	PI/NOTES	STATUS
☐ Beech A45 Mentor (T-34A)	OK-02	CCF34-5	24202 (Canada), 54-5202	RA
☐ Beech A45 Mentor (T-34A)	OK-08	CCF34-11	24208 (Canada), 54-5208	RA
☐ Grumman G-121 Tracker (S-2E)	TCB-679	212C	Bu151679	RA
☐ Lockheed 683-10-19 Starfighter (F-104G)	64-8298	683-8298	KG+398, DB+118, DC+128, 25+23	RA
☐ Lockheed 683-10-19 Starfighter (F-104G)	12733	683D-6085	63-12733, C.8-15 (Spain) – at Maslak Campus in the town.	RA
☐ Vickers 794D Viscount	431	431	TC-SES	RA

ASKERI MÜZESI (TU6)

Address: Spor ve Sergi Sarayi Carsisi Harbiye,
Beyoglu,
Istanbul 80230.
Tel: 0212-232-1698
Fax: 0212-233-2720
Admission: Tuesday-Sunday 1000-1700.
Location: In the north western part of the city centre.

The country's military history is portrayed in this museum. The Ottoman period is highlighted with an excellent display of campaign tents, weapons, uniforms and flags. Outside is a gun mounted on a railway wagon and a collection of mortars. There are sections on both World War I and World War II showing the involvement of Turkish forces in these conflicts. The development of the Air Force since its formation is traced with many photographs on view. Three aircraft are displayed in the grounds. The Turkish Air Force obtained over four hundred and fifty Starfighters from other countries and the last were withdrawn in the mid-1990s. The Sioux was the first helicopter flown by the Turkish Army so it is appropriate for one to be on show. The Cessna Skywagon was also flown by the Army and over one hundred were operated around the country.

TYPE	REG/SER	CON. NO.	PI/NOTES	STATUS
☐ Bell 47G-3B Sioux (OH-13S)	10397	3959	69-16381	PV
☐ Canadair CL-90 Starfighter (CF-104) [Lockheed 683-04-12]	62-733	683A-1033	12733 (Canada), 104733 (Canada)	PV
☐ Cessna 185B Skywagon (U-17A)	13254	1850855	13254, TC-CDJ	PV

BALIKESIR HAVA ÜSSÜ KOLLEKSION (TU7)

Address: 9 Ana Jet Üssü Komutanligi,
Balikesir 10030.
Admission: By prior permission only.
Location: In the south eastern suburbs of the town.

This important base, which has been used by fighters for many years, is currently home to two squadrons of F-16s and a detachment of Bell UH-1H Iroquois helicopters. In the late 1950s a number of Beech Kansans were delivered and used mainly as navigational trainers. The type remained in use until 1983 and the majority of the survivors were preserved. In the early 1950s about three hundred F-84G Thunderjets were supplied and became the first jet operated by the Turkish Air Force. The Thunderjet served with the resident wing and was replaced by the Thunderstreak. Later F-104 Starfighters and F-5 Freedom Fighters flew from the base. Examples of these types have been preserved and show the range of fighters operated over the years.

TYPE	REG/SER	CON. NO.	PI/NOTES	STATUS
☐ Beech C18S Kansan (AT-11)	6865	4975	42-37678	RA
☐ Canadair CL-30 Silver Star 3 (CT-133) [Lockheed 580 (T-33AN)]	21536	T33-536	21536 (Canada)	RA
☐ Lockheed 683-04-10 Starfighter (RF-104G)	64-6622	683-6622	KC+133, EB+102, 21+01	RA
☐ Lockheed 683-10-19 Starfighter (F-104G)	61-2045	683-2045	KF+121, (DA+249), DA+243, 20+38	RA
☐ Lockheed 683-10-19 Starfighter (F-104G)	63-8090	683-8090	D-8090 (Netherlands), 63-8090	RA
☐ Lockheed 683-10-19 Starfighter (F-104G)	64-9145	683-9145	KH+160, DF+122, 26+11	RA
☐ Northrop N-156A Freedom Fighter (F-5A)	10531	N.6192	65-10531, 1216 (Taiwan), 10531 (Vietnam)	RA
☐ Northrop N-156A Freedom Fighter (F-5A)	'07121'	N.6487	69-7121, 97121 (Taiwan)	RAX
☐ Republic F-84F Thunderstreak	37214		53-7214, DB+369	RA
☐ Republic F-84G Thunderjet	'9-966'		51-10966, 10966	RA

BANDIRMA HAVA ÜSSÜ KOLLEKSION (TU8)

Address: 6 Ana Jet Üssü Komutanligi,
Bandirma 10220.
Admission: By prior permission only.
Location: Just south of the town.

Preserved near the gate to the base is a collection of types which have operated from the field in recent years. The Thunderstreak was flown in large numbers for many years. Almost three hundred Starfighters, including some of the Italian built F-104S version, were acquired with the majority arriving from European Air Forces. The Northrop F-5 entered service in 1965 and several are still in use and the in the collection came from Taiwan.

TYPE	REG/SER	CON. NO.	PI/NOTES	STATUS
☐ Beech C18S Kansan (AT-11)	6833	3297	42-36917	RA
☐ Lockheed 580 (T-33A)	54432	580-9876	55-4432, 54432 (France)	RA
☐ Lockheed 683-04-10 Starfighter (RF-104G)	63-8164	683-8164	KG+264, EA+122, 24+22	RA
☐ Lockheed 683-10-19 Starfighter (F-104G)	64-7186	683-7186	KE+486, VB+229, 23+03	RA
☐ Lockheed 683-10-19 Starfighter (F-104G)	22336	683D-6035	62-12336	RA
☐ Northrop N-156A Freedom Fighter (F-5A)	21158	N.6347	67-21158, 1252 (Taiwan)	RA
☐ Republic F-84F Thunderstreak	37040		53-7040, DD+234, DB+370, DB+243	RA
☐ Republic F-84G Thunderjet	111001		51-11001	RA

BATMAN HAVA ÜSSÜ ANITI (TU9)

Address: Batman 72040.
Admission: By prior permission only.
Location: Just north of the town.

This reserve airfield which is under the control of the 2nd Tactical Air Force came to prominence in the 1991 Gulf War when it was used by United States Air Force units.

TYPE	REG/SER	CON. NO.	PI/NOTES	STATUS
☐ Lockheed 580 (T-33A)	41608	580-9344		RA
☐ Lockheed 683-10-19 Starfighter (F-104G)	8321	683-8321	KG+421, DB+238, DA+129, 25+37	RA

BODRUM HAVA ÜSSÜ ANITI (TU10)

Address:	Bodrum- Milas 48200.
Admission:	By prior permission only.
Location:	About 35 km north east of the town.

The airport handles many flights into this historic tourist area. The Air Force maintains a base on one side of the field although there are no resident squadrons. The Starfighter is mounted as a memorial in this area.

TYPE	REG/SER	CON. NO.	PI/NOTES	STATUS
☐ Lockheed 683-10-19 Starfighter (F-104G)	'4-852'			RAX

ÇIGLI AIR HAVA ÜSSÜ KOLLEKSION (TU11)

Address:	2 Ana Jet Üssü Komutanligi,, Cigli.
Admission:	By prior permission only
Location:	About 15 km north west of Izmir.

Advanced pilot training is carried out by the resident squadrons of the wing. At the current time Cessna T-37s and Northrop T-38s are flown from the field. A number of preserved aircraft are located around the site. The Mentor has now been moved to the nearby reserve airfield of Kalkiç. Aircraft regularly carry out training flights at this site. Turkish Air Force Dakotas were a familiar sight at all airfields from the late 1940s. More than one hundred were delivered and gave excellent service. The last were retired in 1998 and a few of the survivors have been preserved. The classic T-33 was used to train many Turkish pilots. Almost one hundred and fifty Lockheed built aircraft were joined by about fifty Canadair examples. The type was first used in 1951 and the last were withdrawn in early 1997. The Iroquois is flown by many Army units around the country.

TYPE	REG/SER	CON. NO.	PI/NOTES	STATUS
☐ Beech A45 Mentor (T-34A)	OK-01	CCF34-4	24201 (Canada), 54-5201 – At nearby Kalkiç.	RA
☐ Bell 205 Iroquois (UH-1H)	69-15645	11933		RA
☐ Canadair CL-30 Silver Star 3 (CT-133) [Lockheed 580 (T-33AN)]	'21058'	T33-066	21066	RAX
☐ Canadair CL-30 Silver Star 3 (CT-133) [Lockheed 580 (T-33AN)]	'21121'	T33-436	21436	RAX
☐ Douglas DC-3A-456 Skytrain (C-47A)	6033	12950	42-93078, 42-6033 (Turkey), ETI-033, E-033	RA
☐ Lockheed 580 (T-33A)	17519	580-7579	51-17519	RA

ÇORLU HAVA ÜSSÜ ANITI (TU12)

Address:	Corlu 59860.
Admission:	By prior permission only.
Location:	About 10 km east of the town.

The airfield is currently held in reserve but plans have been put forward for a major upgrade so that it can handle the latest combat types. Construction of the new airfield is scheduled for the not too distant future. Two aircraft are preserved as memorials by the current gate but these will probably be moved during the work.

TYPE	REG/SER	CON. NO.	PI/NOTES	STATUS
☐ Lockheed 580 (T-33A)	14192	580-5486	51-4192, 14192 (France)	RA
☐ Lockheed 583-10-20 Starfighter (TF-104G)	59415	583C-5529	65-9415, CE.8-3	RA

DALAMAN HAVA ÜSSÜ KOLLEKSION (TU13)

Address:	Dalaman 48770
Admission:	By prior permission only.
Location:	About 5 km south of the town.

The Air Force maintains a base at the field which is now the international airport for the region. The three preserved aircraft represent types formerly flown from the site. The Air Force operated over four hundred Starfighters and the type was in front line service from 1963 until 1995. The aircraft were obtained from many countries including Germany, the Netherlands, Spain, Belgium Italy and Canada.

TYPE	REG/SER	CON. NO.	PI/NOTES	STATUS
☐ Lockheed 580 (T-33A)				RA
☐ Lockheed 683-10-19 Starfighter (F-104G)	63-8060	683-8060	D-8060 (Netherlands)	RA
☐ Northrop N-156A Freedom Fighter (F-5A)	69224	N.7047	66-9224, 224 (Norway)	RA

DIYARBAKIR HAVA ÜSSÜ KOLLEKSION (TU14)

Address:	8 Ana Jet Üssü Komutanligi, Diyarbakir 21200
Admission:	By prior permission only.
Location:	In the south western suburbs of the town.

Situated close to the borders with Iraq and Syria this important base houses two squadrons of F-16s and a detachment of UH-1 helicopters. The site is one of three under the control of the 2nd Tactical Air Force. Fighters have been in residence for many years and the preserved aircraft represent types previously flown from the field and those which have visited from other squadrons. Forty-four former Canadian Air Force Starfighters were delivered to Turkey from Sollingen in Germany in 1985/6 and these served until the mid-1990s. The country also flew large numbers of both Lockheed and European built examples of the F-104. Several examples of the type are stored on the airfield and some of these may be allocated for preservation.

TYPE	REG/SER	CON. NO.	PI/NOTES	STATUS
□ Beech C18S Kansan (AT-11)	6923	4026	42-37433	RA
□ Canadair CL-90 Starfighter (CF-104) [Lockheed 683-04-12]	63-808	683A-1108	12808 (Canada), 104808 (Canada)	RA
□ Canadair CL-90 Starfighter (CF-104) [Lockheed 683-04-12]	63-891	683A-1191	12891 (Canada), 104891 (Canada)	RA
□ Lockheed 580 (T-33A)	35791	580-9130	53-5791	RA
□ Lockheed 683-04-10 Starfighter (RF-104G)	8128	683-8128	KG+228, EA+116, 23+99	RA
□ Lockheed 683-10-19 Starfighter (F-104G)	2066	683-2066	20+57	RA
□ Lockheed 683-10-19 Starfighter (F-104G)	7108	683-7108	KE+408, (VA+126), 22+30	RA
□ North American NA-224 Super Sabre (F-100D)	52763	224-30	55-2763	RA
□ Northrop N-156A Freedom Fighter (RF-5A)	97152	RF.1032	69-7152	RA
□ Republic F-84F Thunderstreak	37007		53-7007, DC+369	RA
□ Republic F-84G Thunderjet	111218		51-11218	RA

ERHAC HAVA ÜSSÜ KOLLEKSION (TU15)

Address:	7 Ana Jet Üssü Komutanligi, Erhac 44300.
Admission:	By prior permission.
Location:	About 20 km north west of Malatya.

The resident wing operates the F-4E Phantom and also serves as the Operation Conversion Unit for the type. Several aircraft have now been upgraded to F-4E-2020 standard. Some were modified by Israeli Aircraft Industries at Lod and the others in the Turkish Air Force maintenance facility at Eskisehir. In addition there is also a detachment of Iroquois helicopters on the field. Until recently RF-4Es were also flown but these have now moved to Eskisehir. For a long period the squadrons flew versions of the North American Super Sabre. The first D model arrived in late 1958 and this variant was in service until 1989. In common with most Turkish bases there is a collection of preserved aircraft representing types previously operated. There are a number of Starfighters in use as instructional airframes and one will eventually be put on show.

TYPE	REG/SER	CON. NO.	PI/NOTES	STATUS
□ Beech C18S Kansan (AT-11)	6904	3538	42-37158	RA
□ Lockheed 580 (T-33A)	53092	580-9633	55-3092, 53092 (France)	RA
□ North American NA-224 Super Sabre (F-100D)	52782	224-49	55-2782, G-782 (Denmark)	RA
□ Republic F-84F Thunderstreak	28808		52-8808, 28808 (France)	RA

ERKILET HAVA ÜSSÜ KOLLEKSION (TU16)

Address:	Hava Lojistik Komutanligi, Erkilet 38080.
Admission:	By prior permission only.
Location:	About 5 km north of Kayseri.

The base is home to the headquarters of the Air Logistics Command. The resident unit the 12th Wing moved in during 1971 and currently operates Transall C-160Ds, Lockheed C-130 Hercules and licence built CASA-IPTN CN.235s. In addition a number of helicopters are based at the field. The collection of preserved aircraft is displayed around the base and in addition several stored C-47s also survive. The Polish designed Dromader was designed for agricultural work and first flew in 1976. More than seven hundred were produced and a number were operated in Turkey. One of the six former United States Air National Guard C-130B Hercules delivered in the early 1990s has been put on show. These aircraft replaced C-47s and several have been modified for ELINT missions.

TYPE	REG/SER	CON. NO.	PI/NOTES	STATUS
□ Douglas DC-3A-456 Skytrain (C-47A)	6076	12771	42-92917, 42-6076 (Turkey), CBK-76, ETI-76, 2-076, E-076 (Turkey)	RA
□ Douglas DC-3A-456 Skytrain (C-47A)	6039	13436	42-93516, 42-6039 (Turkey), ETI-39, H-039	RA

☐ Grumman G-121 Tracker (S-2E)	151663	196C	Bu151663	RA
☐ Lockheed 282-1B Hercules (C-130B)				RA
☐ Lockheed 580 (T-33A)	53093	580-9634	55-3093, 53093 (France)	RA
☐ Panstwowe Zaklady Lotnicze (PZL) M-18 Dromader				RA
☐ Piper PA-18-95 Super Cub (L-18C)				RA

ESKIŞEHIR HAVA ÜSSÜ KOLLEKSION (TU17)

Address: 1 Ana Jet Üssü Komuntanligi, Eskisehir 26100.
Admission: By prior permission only.
Location: About 5 km north east of the town.

The base is home to a fighter wing which in recent years has seen several types, including the F-100 Super Sabre, F-5 Freedom Fighter, F-4 Phantom and F-16 Fighting Falcon, in use. Turkey became a member of NATO in 1952 and this led to modern American equipment being supplied. Many airfields were upgraded and in addition several new bases were constructed. The first of three hundred Thunderjets were delivered and later the Thunderstreak and Thunderflash arrived. Examples of these three types have been saved. Almost eighty new Phantoms were delivered in the mid-1970s and these were followed a few years later by just over one hundred ex-U.S.A.F. machines. Eight newly built RF-4Es were delivered from the United States in 1978 and in the mid-1990s forty-seven former Luftwaffe examples were delivered by air to Turkey.

TYPE	REG/SER	CON. NO.	PI/NOTES	STATUS
☐ Beech C18S Kansan (AT-11)	6933	4581	42-37585	RA
☐ Canadair CL-13 Sabre 2 [North American F-86E]				RA
☐ Canadair CL-13 Sabre 2 [North American F-86E]	142	42	19142 (Canada)	RA
☐ Canadair CL-30 Silver Star 3 (CT-133) [Lockheed 580 (T-33AN)]	21410	T33-410	21410 (Canada)	RA
☐ Canadair CL-90 Starfighter (CF-104) [Lockheed 683-04-12]	62-751	683A-1051	12751 (Canada), 104751 (Canada)	RA
☐ Lockheed 580 (T-33A) (RT-33A)	41548	580-9179	54-1548, 41548 (France)	RA
☐ McDonnell M.98LG Phantom II (RF-4E)	69-7478	4081	69-7478, 35+31	RA
☐ North American NA-224 Super Sabre (F-100D)	52775	224-42	55-2775, G-775 (Denmark)	RA
☐ North American NA-243 Super Sabre (F-100F)	63946	243-222	56-3946	RA
☐ Northrop N-156A Freedom Fighter (F-5A)	10570	N.7018	65-10570, 570 (Norway)	RA
☐ Republic F-84F Thunderstreak	27123		52-7123	RA
☐ Republic F-84F Thunderstreak	27142		52-7142, P-110 (Netherlands)	RA
☐ Republic RF-84F Thunderflash	27234		52-7234, 27234 (France)	RA
☐ Republic F-84G Thunderjet	110987		51-10987, 110987 (France)	RA

ESKIŞEHIR HAVACILIK PARKI VE TEYYARE MÜZESI (TU18)

Address: Yeni Baglar Mahallesi, Bulgar Caddesi, Eskisehir 26100.
Tel: 0222-320-5291
Admission: Daily 0800-2000 (closes at 2200 in summer)
Location: Opposite The Yunus Emre campus of Anadolu University.

This museum was set up in the town to portray the history of Turkish aviation with particular reference to the local air base. The display opened in the late 1990s and in addition to the aircraft many photographs, documents, uniforms, equipment and components are on show. A range of aircraft from all branches of services can be seen. The Navy operated a fleet of Trackers from Topel from 1971 to 1993. Fifteen were later converted by Turkish Aerospace Industries into turbo-prop powered water bombers. The Alouette was flown by both the Army and the Police before joining the collection. All the combat types on show have been used by the wing at Eskiseher. The two civilian registered Super Cubs were used by the THK organisation after their military service. The museum has made rapid progress since its opening and more aircraft are expected.

TYPE	REG/SER	CON. NO.	PI/NOTES	STATUS
☐ Akarkali	A-2			PV
☐ Canadair CL-30 Silver Star 3 (CT-133) [Lockheed 580 (T-33AN)]	21321	T33-321	21321 (Canada)	PV
☐ Douglas DC-3A-456 Skytrain (C-47A)	'052'	18973	42-100510, 42-6032 (Turkey), CBK-32, ETI-32, 12-032 – fuselage only	PVX
☐ Grumman G-121 Tracker (S2F-3S) (S-2E)	TCB-849	124C	Bu149849	PV
☐ Lockheed 580 (T-33A)	16772	580-6104	51-6772, 16772 (France)	PV
☐ Lockheed 580 (T-33A)	29919	580-7890	52-9919	PV
☐ Lockheed 683-10-19 Starfighter (F-104G)	65-6667	683-6667	D-6667 (Netherlands)	PV
☐ Lockheed 683-10-19 Starfighter (F-104G)	65-7190	683-7190	KE+490, VB+233, 23+07	PV
☐ McDonnell M.98LG Phantom II (RF-4E)	69-7465	4043	69-7465, 35+18	PV
☐ North American NA-214 Super Sabre (F-100C)	31732	214-24	53-1732	PV

TYPE	REG/SER	CON. NO.	PI/NOTES	STATUS
☐ Northrop N-156A Freedom Fighter (F-5A)	13346	N.6115	64-13346 – front fuselage only.	PV
☐ Northrop N-156A Freedom Fighter (F-5A)	69212	N.7035	66-9212, 212 (Norway)	PV
☐ Piper PA-18-95 Super Cub (L-18C)	TC-YSB			PV
☐ Piper PA-18-95 Super Cub (L-18C)	TC-AUA	18-464	50-1808, 10325	PV
☐ Republic RF-84F Thunderflash	28733		52-8733, 28733 (France)	PV
☐ Sud-Est SE.3130 Alouette II	E-2077	2077	77+45	PV

ERZURUM HAVA ÜSSÜ ANITI (TU19)

Address: Erzurum 25080.
Admission: By prior permission only.
Location: About 10 km north west of the town.

The airport has one of the longest runways in the country and is capable of handing the largest airliners. The Air Force maintains a presence at the field and has a pole mounted Starfighter as a monument.

TYPE	REG/SER	CON. NO.	PI/NOTES	STATUS
☐ Lockheed 683-10-19 Starfighter (F-104G)	9135	683-9135	KH+156, DF+118, 26+07	RA

GUVERCINLIK MÜZESI (TU20)

Address: Kara Ordusu Havaciligi,
Guverncinlik 06640.
Admission: By prior permission only.
Location: About 10 km west of Ankara.

The airfield is the headquarters of army aviation in the country and is home to combat, training, observation and transport squadrons. The aviation branch of the service was established in 1948 at the Artillery School at Polati. The first types used were Piper Cubs and these were followed by Super Cubs, Bird Dogs and Dornier Do 27s. A number of Dornier Skyservants were bought in the 1960s and nineteen ex-Luftwaffe examples arrived in 1996. Helicopters, in the form of the Agusta-Bell 204, arrived in 1966. The museum has been set up to trace the history of the service and many photographs, documents and uniforms can be seen.

TYPE	REG/SER	CON. NO.	PI/NOTES	STATUS
☐ Agusta-Bell 204B				RA
☐ Agusta-Bell 204B	10456	3176		RA
☐ Agusta-Bell 204B	11032	3179		RA
☐ Agusta-Bell 212ASW	TCB-39	5195		RA
☐ Bell 209 Huey Cobra (AH-1G) (AH-1S)	'901'			RAX
☐ Bell 209 Huey Cobra (AH-1G) (TAH-1P)	'66-15531'	20395	67-15731 – possible identity.	RAX
☐ Bell 47G-3B Sioux (OH-13S)	10395	3946	67-15897	RA
☐ Bell 47G-3B-1 Sioux (TH-13T)	10437	3478	65-8045	RA
☐ Bellanca 7GCBC Citabria	10101	1076-79		RA
☐ Bellanca 7GCBC Citabria	10108	1083-79		RA
☐ Bellanca 7GCBC Citabria	10126	1110-79		RA
☐ Cessna 305C Bird Dog (L-19E) (O-1E)	10160			RA
☐ Cessna A185F Skywagon 185 (U-17B)		01636		RA
☐ Dornier Do 28D-1 Skyservant	10016	4081	D-9572, 58+06	RA
☐ Piper PA-18-135 Super Cub (L-21B)	'10101'	18-2589	52-6289, TC-EBY	RAX

HAVA HARP OKULU KOLLEKSION (TU21)

Address: Sahil Yolu,
Yesilkoy 34150.
Email: webmaster@hho.edu.tr
Admission: By prior permission only.
Location: Close to the south eastern corner of Ataturk Airport.

The Turkish Air Force Academy is located close to the airport which serves Istanbul. Displayed in the attractive grounds overlooking the sea are a number of aircraft. These have been put on show to remind personnel of the history and traditions of the service. Two are by the main gate, another pair can be seen on the parade ground and a couple of the Starfighters are located close to the athletic complex across the road.

TYPE	REG/SER	CON. NO.	PI/NOTES	STATUS
☐ Lockheed 583-10-20 Starfighter (TF-104G)	62-5711	583D-5711	61-3040, DA+040, BB+110, 27+10	RA
☐ Lockheed 683-10-19 Starfighter (F-104G)	64-8277	683-8277	KG+377, 25+13	RA
☐ Lockheed 683-10-19 Starfighter (F-104G)	64-8299	683-8299	KG+399, DB+119, 25+24	RA
☐ Lockheed 683-10-19 Starfighter (F-104G)	64-9078	683-9078	FX-38 (Belgium), 64-9078	RA
☐ Lockheed 683-10-19 Starfighter (F-104G)	64-9083	683-9083	FX-40 (Belgium), 64-9083	RA
☐ North American NA-217 Super Sabre (F-100C)	42059	217-320	54-2059	RA
☐ Republic F-84F Thunderstreak	28816		52-8816, 28816 (France)	RA

HAVA KUVVETIERI MÜZESI KOMUTANLIĞI (TU22)

Address:	Hava Lojistik Komutanligi, Etimesgut 06790. Ankara.
Tel:	0312-244-8550
Fax:	0312-245-0757
Admission:	Daily 0900-1630.
Location:	About 20 km west of Ankara.

The airfield is home to a transport wing and VIP aircraft for government use are in residence. This new museum opened in the late 1990s to complement the Air Force Museum at Istanbul. It was felt that the capital of the country should have a major collection of military aircraft. Airframes have been moved from bases around the country to give a representative range of types used in recent years. A replica of the P.Z.L.24 has been built and more are planned to show types operated in the past. The Hungarian Air Force donated a MiG-21. The displays are being developed and will trace the history of aviation and the Air Force in the country.

TYPE	REG/SER	CON. NO.	PI/NOTES	STATUS
☐ Beech C18S Kansan (AT-11)	'3-880'	3225	42-36845, 6830	PVX
☐ Beech A45 Mentor (T-34A)	TC-CCA	CCF34-9	24206 (Canada), 54-5206	PV
☐ Beech A45 Mentor (T-34A)	TC-CCH	CCF34-19	24216 (Canada), 54-5216	PV
☐ Bell 205 Iroquois (UH-1H)	69-16720	12008		PV
☐ Canadair CL-13 Sabre 2 [North American F-86E]	19190	90	19190 (Canada)	PV
☐ Canadair CL-90 Starfighter (CF-104) [Lockheed 683-04-12]	62-711	683A-1011	12711 (Canada), 104711 (Canada)	PV
☐ Canadair CL-90 Starfighter (CF-104) [Lockheed 683-04-12]	62-770	683A-1070	12770 (Canada), 104770 (Canada)	PV
☐ Canadair CL-90 Starfighter (CF-104) [Lockheed 683-04-12]	62-810	683A-1110	12810 (Canada), 104810 (Canada) – at nearby barracks.	PV
☐ Cessna R172F Mescalero (T-41D)	01410	R1720512	72-1410	PV
☐ Convair 8-12 Delta Dagger (TF-102A)	62368		56-2368	RA
☐ Douglas DC-3A-456 Skytrain (C-47A)	073	19529	43-15063, 43-6073	PV
☐ Lockheed 580 (T-33A)	14284	580-5579	51-4284, 14284 (France)	PV
☐ Lockheed 580 (T-33A)	54432	580-9876	55-4432 – front fuselage only.	PV
☐ Lockheed 583-04-15 Starfighter (CF-104D)	62-642	583A-5312	12642 (Canada), 104642 (Canada)	PV
☐ Lockheed 683-04-10 Starfighter (RF-104G)	8205	683-8205	KG+305, EB+108, 24+57	PV
☐ Lockheed 683-10-19 Starfighter (F-104S)	6859	683-6859	At nearby barracks.	RA
☐ McDonnell M.98LG Phantom II (RF-4E)	69-7490	4108	69-7490, 35+43	PV
☐ McDonnell M.98LG Phantom II (RF-4E)	69-7503	4133	69-7503, 35+56	PV
☐ Mikoyan-Gurevich MiG-21MF	9308	969308	In Hungarian markings.	PV
☐ North American NA-217 Super Sabre (F-100C)	41877	217-138	54-1877	PV
☐ North American NA-217 Super Sabre (F-100C)	41766	217-27	54-1766	PV
☐ Northrop N-156A Freedom Fighter (F-5A)	14465	N.6319	67-14465 – front fuselage only.	PV
☐ Northrop N-156A Freedom Fighter (F-5A)	10575	N.7023	65-10575, 575 (Norway)	PV
☐ Northrop N-156A Freedom Fighter (RF-5A)	21208	N.6395	67-21208	RA
☐ Panstwowe Zaklady Lotnicze (PZL) P.24G (FSM)	'2017'			PVX
☐ Republic F-84F Thunderstreak	7186		53-7186, DB+323	PV
☐ Republic RF-84F Thunderflash	11924		51-1924, P-24 (Netherlands)	PV
☐ Republic F-84G Thunderjet	'62-3011'		52-3011, 23011	PVX
☐ Shenyang F-6C [Mikoyan-Gurevich MiG-19SF]	4123		In Pakistani markings	PV
☐ SIAI-Marchetti SF.260D	2-815	815		PV
☐ Supermarine 361 Spitfire LF.IXe (FSM)	'329'			PVX
☐ Transall C-160D	69-039	D39	50+31	PV
☐ Wytwornia Sprzetu Komunikacyjnego (WSK) Lim-5 [MiG-17F]	159	1C 18-26	In Bulgarian markings.	PVX

HAVACILIK MÜZESI (TU23)

Address:	Yesilkoy Istanbul 39149
Tel:	0212-662-8552
Fax:	0212-663-1560
Admission:	Tuesday-Sunday 0900-1130 1300-1630
Location:	At Yesilyurt in the suburbs of Istanbul- on the southern edge of Ataturk Airport.

Foreign pilots flew British, French and German types on behalf of Turkish forces in the 1912/3 Balkan War. During World War I the Flying Corps was manned by mainly German personnel. The Turkish Republic was founded in 1923 and the Turk Hava Kumuru (Turkish Air League) was formed two years later. Its aims were to arouse public interest in aviation and to raise money for the purchase of aircraft. Aircraft factories were set up and an Air Force came into being. In the late 1920s and through the 1930s a variety of American, British, French, German and Polish types were operated along with a few indigenous machines. During World War II Turkey maintained a neutral position. At the end of the conflict Britain and the United States supplied large numbers of surplus aircraft. A decision to set up an air museum was made in April 1966 and a hangar at Cumaovasi near Izmir was obtained. Aircraft and memorabilia were collected and the display officially opened in 1971. The location was not on tourist routes and the exhibition closed seven years later. The museum moved to its current site in 1982 and was dedicated on October 16th 1985. Yesilkoy was an airfield during World War I and from this time there were plans for a museum but most of the material collected was destroyed. Halls are devoted to Turkish Aviation, Commanders of the Turkish Air Force and World Aviation. A hangar houses engines, components and about ten aircraft. The oldest is a Russian Grigorovich M.5 flying boat dating from 1914. The biplane was forced dawn near Gorele after a flight across the Black Sea. Two more rarities are the Curtiss-Wright Falcon and the P.Z.L. 24. Fifty Falcons were ordered in 1937 and used for training and ground attack duties. The high wing P.Z.L. 24 fighter first flew in 1933 and was improved over the next few years. Forty were ordered from Poland along with parts to construct a further twenty. The first Turkish assembled P.24 flew in May 1937 and production of later versions took place at the factory at Kayseri.

TYPE	REG/SER	CON. NO.	PI/NOTES	STATUS
☐ Altin Kanatlar (R)				PV
☐ Beech A45 Mentor (T-34A)	TC-CCH	CCF34-19	24216 (Canada), 54-5216, OK-16	PV
☐ Beech A45 Mentor (T-34A)	2-220	CCF34-24	24220 (Canada), TC-IHK	PV
☐ Beech C18S Kansan (AT-11)	6930	4561	42-37565	PV
☐ Bell 205 Iroquois (UH-1H)	69-15724	12012		PV
☐ Bellanca 7GCBC Citabria	10104	1079-79		PV
☐ Bellanca 7GCBC Citabria	TC-TQM	1101 79	10123	PV
☐ Canadair CL-13 Sabre 2 [North American F-86E]	19207	107		PV
☐ Canadair CL-13 Sabre 2 [North American F-86E]	19268	168		PV
☐ Canadair CL-226 Freedom Fighter (NF-5A) [Northrop N-156A]	3022	3022	K-3022 (Netherlands)	PV
☐ Canadair CL-226 Freedom Fighter (NF-5A) [Northrop N-156A]	3070	3070	K-3070 (Netherlands)	PV
☐ Cessna 185D Skywagon (U-17A)	11357	185-0846	64-17933, 11061, TC-CDF	PV
☐ Cessna 318C Tweety Bird (T-37C)	39835	40807	63-9835	PV
☐ Convair 8-10 Delta Dagger (F-102A)	53386		55-3386	PV
☐ Curtiss-Wright CW-22B Falcon	TC-TK15		2615(?)	PV
☐ De Havilland D.H.89A Dragon Rapide (D.H.89B Dominie I)	'TC-ERK'		Possibly c/n 6687 HG702, TC-HAD or c/n 6688 HG703, TC-DER.	PVX
☐ Dornier Do 27B-1	10293	261	PH+109, PC+110, (55+96), D-9521, D-EGTY	RA
☐ Dornier Do 27H-2	10294	2114	D-ECPI	RA
☐ Dornier Do 27H-2	10293	2142	D-EFCI	RA
☐ Dornier Do 28B-1	10012	3079	D-IBON	PV
☐ Dornier Do 28B-1	10013	3083	D-IBOT	PV
☐ Dornier Do 28D-2 Skyservant	10020	4021	N6772, D-IBBA, 10348	PV
☐ Dornier Do 28D-2 Skyservant	10022	4106	58+31	PV
☐ Douglas DC-3A-456 Skytrain (C-47A)	YSL-52	13877	43-30726, 43-6052 (Turkey),	PV
☐ Douglas DC-3A-467 Skytrain (C-47B)	H-008	15011/26456	43-49195, 43-6008 (Turkey)	PV
☐ Douglas DC-4 Skymaster (C-54D)	10683	10788	42-72683	PV
☐ Grigorovich M.5				PV
☐ Grumman G-121 Tracker (S2F-3S) (S-2E)	149877	152C	Bu149877	PV
☐ Lockheed 580 (T-33A)	35744	580-9083	53-5744	PV
☐ Lockheed 580 (T-33A) (RT-33A)	1543	580-9174	54-1543, 41543 (France)	PV
☐ Lockheed 583-10-20 Starfighter (TF-104G)	63-5725	583D-5725	61-3054, DA+054, TA+160, 27+24	PV
☐ Lockheed 683-10-19 Starfighter (F-104G)	12619	683C-4019	61-2619 – tail from c/n 683-8233 KG+333, EB+231, 24+83.	PV
☐ Lockheed 683-10-19 Starfighter (F-104G)	22344	683D-6043	62-12344	PV
☐ Lockheed 683-10-19 Starfighter (F-104G)	'0002'		Front fuselage only.	PVX
☐ Lockheed 683-10-19 Starfighter (F-104S)	74-6868	683-6868		PV
☐ Makona Ve Kimya Endustri Kumuru (MKEK) 4 Ugur	44	5144/1957	TC-KUJ, 'TC-KUS'	PVX
☐ McDonnell M.98HO Phantom II (F-4E)	67-0360	3234		PV
☐ Miles M.14A Magister	60	60/1946	TC-KAY	RA
☐ Miles M.14A Magister	TC-KAH	77/1948	TC-THK77 – possibly ex 3577	PV
☐ North American NA-182 Texan (T-6G)	7504	182-266	51-14579	PV
☐ North American NA-217 Super Sabre (F-100C)	54-2089	217-350	54-2089 (USA)	PV
☐ North American NA-223 Super Sabre (F-100D)	54-2245	223-125	54-2245 (USA)	PV
☐ North American NA-243 Super Sabre (F-100F)	56-3788	243-64	56-3788 (USA)	PV
☐ Northrop N-156A Freedom Fighter (F-5A)	'14460'	N.6320	66-14466	PVX
☐ Northrop N-156A Freedom Fighter (RF-5A)	97147	RF.1027	69-7147	PV
☐ Panstwowe Zaklady Lotnicze (PZL) 104 Wilga 35	TC-ECL	140545	SP-WAA	PV
☐ Panstwowe Zaklady Lotnicze (PZL) P.24G	'2415'		2015	PVX
☐ Piper PA-18-95 Super Cub (L-18C)				RA
☐ Piper PA-18-95 Super Cub (L-18C)	10306		(USAF)	PV
☐ Republic P-47D Thunderbolt	'DE-21'		44-33712, 7121 (?), TC-21	PVX
☐ Republic F-84F Thunderstreak	28941		52-8941	PV
☐ Republic RF-84F Thunderflash	11901		51-1901	PV
☐ Republic RF-84F Thunderflash	11917		51-1917	PV
☐ Republic F-84G Thunderjet	110572		51-10572	PV
☐ Republic F-84G Thunderjet	111057		51-11057, MM51-11057	RA
☐ Republic F-84G Thunderjet	19953		51-9953	PV
☐ Robinson R-22 Beta	10370	2061		PV
☐ Sadik AK-2000X				PV
☐ Scheibe Bergfalke IV	5824	5824	TC-PDJ	PV
☐ Siebelwerke ATG (SIAT) 223K-1 Flamingo	TC-EAF	026	D-EABU, 023 (Egypt)	PV
☐ Sikorsky S-55D Chickasaw (H-19B) (UH-19B)	52-7577	55714	52-7577 (USA)	PV
☐ Sud-Est SE.210 Caravelle 10B1R	TC-ABA	253	HB-ICN	PV
☐ Transall C-160D	69-022	D22	50+14	PV
☐ Turk Havi Kuvvetleri Mavi Isik-G				PV
☐ Vickers 794D Viscount	430	430	TC-SEL, 430, 'TC-SEV'	PV

INCIRLIK HAVA ÜSSÜ ANITI (TU24)

Address:	10 Ana Jet Üssü Komutanligi, Incirlik 01350.
Admission:	By prior permission only.
Location:	About 12 km east of Adana.

This important base is shared by the Turkish Air Force and the United States Air Force. There has been an American presence here for many years. Two aircraft are preserved as monuments at the Turkish part of the field.

TYPE	REG/SER	CON. NO.	PI/NOTES	STATUS
☐ Lockheed 683-10-19 Starfighter (F-104G)				RA
☐ Northrop N-156A Freedom Fighter (F-5A)	10567	N.7015	65-10567, 567 (Norway)	RA

IZELMAN PARK (TU25)

Address:	Izmir 35300.
Admission:	On permanent view.
Location:	In the south western suburbs of the town.

Two aircraft are displayed on poles in this park along with other items of military equipment. A former Luftwaffe Starfighter can be seen in the grounds of a nearby school.

TYPE	REG/SER	CON. NO.	PI/NOTES	STATUS
☐ Lockheed 580 (T-33A)	4952	580-9912	55-4952, M-41 (Netherlands)	PV
☐ Lockheed 683-10-19 Starfighter (F-104G)	12316	683-6015	62-12316 – with tail from Canadair CL-90 Starfighter c/n 683A-1033 12733 (Canada), 104733 (Canada), 63-733	PV
☐ Lockheed 683-10-19 Starfighter (F-104G)	65-8347	683-8347	KG+447, DB+253, DC+129, 25+52 – at a nearby school.	RA

IZMIR HAVA EGITIM KOMUTANLIGI KOLLEKSION (TU26)

Address:	Gaziemir, Izmir 35300.
Admission:	By prior permission only.
Location:	About 5 km south of Izmir.

This airfield houses a large school where technicians are trained for the Air Force. There are several instructional airframes and a collection of preserved types. Some aircraft serve in both roles. The base is responsible for the types displayed at Adnan Menderes International Airport which is nearby.

TYPE	REG/SER	CON. NO.	PI/NOTES	STATUS
☐ Douglas DC-3A-456 Skytrain (C-47A)	6062	20112	43-15646, 43-6062 (Turkey), TK-62, E-062	RA
☐ Lockheed 683-04-10 Starfighter (RF-104G)	12633	683C-4033	61-2633, 633 (Norway)	RA
☐ Lockheed 683-10-19 Starfighter (F-104G)	12620	683C-4020	61-2620 – at Int. Airport.	RA
☐ North American NA-223 Super Sabre (F-100D)	42172	223-52	54-2172	RA
☐ Northrop N-156A Freedom Fighter (F-5A)	21193	N.6380	67-21193	RA
☐ Northrop N-156A Freedom Fighter (F-5A)	14897	N.7060	67-14897, 897 (Norway)	PV
☐ Northrop N-156A Freedom Fighter (RF-5A)	97156	RF.1036	69-7156 – at Int. Airport.	PV
☐ Republic F-84F Thunderstreak	7196		53-7196, DB+349	RA

KAMAL ATATURK PARK (TU27)

Address:	Balikesir 10030.
Admission:	On permanent view.
Location:	In the centre of the town.

This large public park in the centre of the town is named after the founder of modern Turkey. The displays have been set up to show the development of the country and its armed forces. In addition to the two combat types there are monuments, a number of military vehicles and items of artillery.

TYPE	REG/SER	CON. NO.	PI/NOTES	STATUS
☐ Lockheed 683-10-19 Starfighter (F-104G)	64-7122	683-7122	KE+422, DD+114, 22+44	PV
☐ Republic F-84G Thunderjet	110011		51-10011	PV

Above: The Rahmi M. Koç Müzesi has this B-24 Liberator wreckage under restoration. (Steve Darke)

Right: The museum at Eskisehir has on show this Northrop F-5A (MDeniz Ayvaz)

This P.Z.L. P.24G is displayed at the Turkish Air Force Museum (John Mounce)

KAYSERI ANITI (TU28)

Address: Kayseri 38080.
Admission: On permanent view.
Location: In the south eastern suburbs of the town

One C-47 has been preserved as a memorial at this civilian airfield which is home to a several light aircraft. Another example of the type is located a short distance away in a field near some buildings. A number of these classic transports have been stored at nearby Erkilet so presumably they have come from this source.

TYPE	REG/SER	CON. NO.	PI/NOTES	STATUS
☐ Douglas DC-3A-456 Skytrain (C-47A)	H-025	19531	43-15065, 43-6025 (Turkey), YSL-25 (Turkey) – possible identity.	RA
☐ Douglas DC-3A-456 Skytrain (C-47A)				RA

KIRIKKALE ÜNIVERTESI ANITI (TU29)

Address: Km 7 Ankara, Kirikkale 71450.
Tel: 0318-357-3694
Email: info@kku.edu.tr
Admission: By prior permission only.
Location: About 7 km west of the town.

Many former students of this university have gone on to serve with the military. The Air Force has supplied a Starfighter to serve as a memorial to those who have lost their lives serving their country.

TYPE	REG/SER	CON. NO.	PI/NOTES	STATUS
☐ Lockheed 683-10-19 Starfighter (F-104G)	5945	683-5945	KF+245, KE+103, KE+203, DA+365, 28+15	RA

KONYA HAVA ÜSSÜ KOLLEKSION (TU30)

Address: 3 Ana Jet Üssü Komutanligi, Konya 42240.
Admission: By prior permission only.
Location: About 10 km north of the town.

In 1958 Turkey acquired the first of more than three hundred Super Sabres and the type remained in service for over a quarter of a century. This fighter was used extensively in the support of the 1974 occupation of Northern Cyprus. Konya was the main base for F-100 units and an example of each variant operated has been preserved along with examples of other fighters formerly flown by the Air Force. The base is currently home to units flying the F-4 Phantom, F-5 Freedom Fighter and the F-16 along with a detachment of helicopters. The Phantom first entered Turkish service 1974 and over two hundred have since been acquired. This total includes fifty four aircraft upgraded by Israeli Aerospace Industries. These will remain in service for many years. In 2000 a civil terminal was constructed and this now handles flights from several cities in Turkey.

TYPE	REG/SER	CON. NO.	PI/NOTES	STATUS
☐ Lockheed 580 (T-33A)	29922	580-7893	52-9922, M-27 (Netherlands)	RA
☐ McDonnell M.98HO Phantom II (F-4E)	68-0313	3335	68-0313 (USA)	RA
☐ North American NA-217 Super Sabre (F-100C)	42013	217-274	54-2013	RA
☐ North American NA-224 Super Sabre (F-100D)	52910	224-177	55-2910	RA
☐ North American NA-243 Super Sabre (F-100F)	63921	243-197	56-3921	RA
☐ Northrop N-156A Freedom Fighter (F-5A)	13344	N.6113	64-13344	RA
☐ Republic F-84F Thunderstreak	'3-131'		52-7131, P-104 (Netherlands)	RAX
☐ Republic F-84G Thunderjet	'3-133'		51-10133	RA

KUTAHYA HAVA ÜSSÜ KOLLEKSION (TU31)

Address: Hava Er EgitimTugayi, Kutahya 43020.
Admission: By prior permission only.
Location: About 3 km east of the town.

Two Starfighters are preserved at the main gate to this reserve airfield. The first units moved into the field in the 1930s and the site was used by both bomber and fighter squadrons from the end of World War II up to 1950. The remaining aircraft are located at the cadet training school just south of the base. The majority of these are mounted on poles in front of the main college. The Turkish Army used forty Citabrias on training and liaison duties for over twenty years. A hangar and other buildings are used by the local cultural museum. The history and development of the area is portrayed in the displays and many interesting items can be seen.

TYPE	REG/SER	CON. NO.	PI/NOTES	STATUS
☐ Bellanca 7GCBC Citabria	10105	1080-79		RA
☐ Canadair CL-90 Starfighter (CF-104) [Lockheed 683-04-12]	62-841	683A-1141	12841 (Canada), 104841 (Canada)	RA
☐ Douglas DC-3A-456 Skytrain (C-47A)				RA
☐ Lockheed 580 (T-33A)	35742	580-9081	53-5742	RA
☐ Lockheed 583-10-20 Starfighter (TF-104G)	63-5721	583D-5721	61-3050, DA+050, EA+371, 27+29	RA
☐ Lockheed 683-10-19 Starfighter (F-104G)				RA
☐ North American NA-222 Super Sabre (F-100C)	52724	222-16	55-2724	RA
☐ Northrop N-156A Freedom Fighter (F-5A)	21156	N.7054	67-21156	RA
☐ Republic F-84F Thunderstreak				RA

MERSIN ATINI (TU32)

Address: Mersin 33030.
Admission: On permanent view.
Location: On the coast road in the town.

A former Luftwaffe Starfighter has been mounted in this coastal town as a memorial to local airmen. The aircraft was based at Balikesir, Akinci and Diyarbakir during its operational service with the Air Force.

TYPE	REG/SER	CON. NO.	PI/NOTES	STATUS
☐ Lockheed 683-10-19 Starfighter (F-104G)	7005	683-7005	KE+305, DA+107, DR+107, DB+101, 21+37	PV

MERZIFON HAVA ÜSSÜ KOLLEKSION (TU33)

Address: 3 Ana Jet Üssü Komutanligi, Merzifon 05300
Admission: By prior permission only.
Location: About 5 km south east of the town.

The airfield has been a front line fighter base for over sixty years. The type currently in use is the F-16 Fighting Falcon which entered Turkish service in 1987. Almost two hundred were delivered. In the past licence built P.Z.L. P-24s, Hurricanes, Spitfires, Sabres and F-5 Freedom Fighters have flown from the site along with communications and training aircraft. Turkey operated more than one hundred and fifty Hurricanes and over two hundred Spitfires during World War II and the years after and several of these served at Merzifon. The preserved aircraft, all of which have been restored, are parked in an area near the headquarters building.

TYPE	REG/SER	CON. NO.	PI/NOTES	STATUS
☐ Beech C18S Kansan (AT-11)	6815	957	41-9531	RA
☐ Canadair CL-13 Sabre 2 [North American F-86E]	19419	319	19419 (Canada)	RA
☐ Lockheed 580 (T-33A)	51-4512	580-5807	51-4512, M-2 (Netherlands)	RA
☐ Lockheed 683-10-19 Starfighter (F-104G)	62-7017	683-7017	KE+317, DA+108, DF+241, 21+49	RA
☐ Northrop N-156A Freedom Fighter (RF-5A)	89103	RFG.1003	68-9103, 103 (Norway)	RA

MUCUR ATINI (TU34)

Address: Mucur 40550.
Admission: On permanent view.
Location: In the town.

The Turkish Air Force flew about two hundred T-33s between 1951 and 1997. The type served at most air bases in the country. One has been preserved as a monument in this town. This honours the many local people who have served with all the military services in both peace and war.

TYPE	REG/SER	CON. NO.	PI/NOTES	STATUS
☐ Lockheed 580 (T-33A)				PV

MÜZE DENIZ (TU35)

Address: Golcük, Izmit 41670.
Tel: 0262-414-6601 ext 1651.
Admission: Wednesday-Sunday 0900-1200 1430-1730 by appointment.
Location: In the northern part of the town which is about 20 km south west of Izmit.

In 1914 the first naval pilot flew a Nieuport floatplane but it was three years before a decision was made to establish a Turkish Naval Aviation Force. This service lasted only eight years and was reformed in 1971/2 when eight former Dutch Navy Trackers were delivered for observing shipping passing through the Dardanelles. Almost thirty of the S-2E variant were acquired between 1972 and 1987. This museum is located inside the vast Golcuk base. The indoor displays trace the history of the Navy and its airborne element. On show are many photographs, documents, uniforms and badges. There is an excellent collection of model ships to be seen. The Tracker is parked outside along with a number of ships, midget submarines and guns. The Navy currently flies a variety of helicopters along with a few fixed wing types including CN.235s for maritime patrol duties.

TYPE	REG/SER	CON. NO.	PI/NOTES	STATUS
☐ Grumman G-89 Tracker (S2F-1) (S-2A)	TCB-154	715	Bu147644, 154 (Dutch)	PV

ORTA DOĞU TEKNIK ÜNIVERSITESI (TU36)

Address:	06531 Ankara.
Tel:	0312-210-2000
Fax:	0312- 210-1105
Email:	halkilis@metu.edu.tr
Admission:	By prior permission only.
Location:	In the south western suburbs of the city.

This large institution was founded in the mid-1950s and has many departments. The Aerospace Faculty has a display of aircraft in the grounds surrounding its buildings. These airframes are also used for instruction. Inside are many components and engines used for training. The Cessna Skywagon is one of the batch of over eighty delivered to the Army from 1979. Several of the survivors transferred to the Turkish Air League (THK) in the late 1990s. The Dornier Skyservant is one of a pair used on ELINT duties. These were the last examples of the type in military use in Turkey. The Citabria one used by the Army has been painted with a false registration to symbolise the Air League which also operated the type.

TYPE	REG/SER	CON. NO.	PI/NOTES	STATUS
☐ Bellanca 7GCBC Citabria	'TC-THK'			RA
☐ Cessna 185D Skywagon (U-17A)	TC-CDL	1850860	64-17944, 11164	RA
☐ Dornier Do 28D-2 Skyservant	10070	4132		RA
☐ Douglas DC-3A-456 Skytrain (C-47A)				
☐ Lockheed 580 (T-33A)	14116	580-5410	51-4116, 14116 (France)	RA
☐ Lockheed 683-04-10 Starfighter (RF-104G)	63-8105	683-8105	D-8105 (Netherlands)	RA

OSMANCIK ANITI (TU37)

Address:	Osmancik 19500.
Admission:	On permanent view.
Location:	In the town.

A former Chief of Staff of the Turkish Air Force was born in this town. As a monument to his achievements in reaching such a high position an unidentified Starfighter has been preserved.

TYPE	REG/SER	CON. NO.	PI/NOTES	STATUS
☐ Lockheed 683-10-19 Starfighter (F-104G)	'4-955'			PVX

RAHMI M. KOÇ MÜZESI (TU38)

Address:	Hashcoy Caddesi 27, Sutluce, Istanbul 34445.
Tel:	0212-256-7153
Email:	rmkmuseum@kok.com.tr
Admission:	Tuesday-Friday 1000-1700: Saturday-Sunday 1000-1900.
Location:	In the northern part of the city.

The industrial development of the country is the main theme of the museum located in historic buildings on the shore of the Golden Horn. There are sections devoted to all forms of transport, engineering and communications. The aviation display has grown steadily in recent years. The Liberator cockpit section was raised from the sea in 1995. The bomber was built in San Diego and after a ferry flight across the Atlantic it was allocated to the 98th Bomber Group then based near Cairo. On August 1st 1943 it was part of a force raiding the Astro Romano refinery at Ploesti. On its approach to the target it was hit by a shell which exploded in the nose section causing a fatality and serious damage. The bombs were released manually and the B-24 set off for home. Engine problems led to a decision to divert to Cyprus but this was not to be and in a planned landing on the Turkish coast it hit the water. There are long term plans to recover more of the airframe which is still in a reasonable condition and a fuselage section and inner wings are now in the workshops. Theyare probably not from the same aircraft. This aircraft was named 'Hadley's Harem' and the story of its flight and recovery is portrayed. The Pitts Special was built in England by two Shuttleworth Collection engineers, Wally Berry and Bert Etheridge.

TYPE	REG/SER	CON. NO.	PI/NOTES	STATUS
☐ Beech A45 Mentor (T-34A)	TC-CCD/OK-12	CCF34-15	24212 (Canada), 54-5212	RA
☐ Bell 209 Huey Cobra (AH-1G) (AH-1S)	10655	20887	70-15943	PV
☐ Bellanca 7GCBC Citabria	10133	1117-79		PV
☐ Canadair CL-226 Freedom Fighter (NF-5A) [Northrop N-156A]	'70-00341'	3041	K-3041 (Netherlands), 70-3041 (Turkey) – front fuselage only.	PVX
☐ Consolidated 32 Liberator (B-24D)	41-24311	1106	Front fuselage only.	PV
☐ De Havilland D.H.100 Vampire FB.6	'WL505'	676	J-1167 (Switzerland), G-MKVI	RAX
☐ Dornier Do 28D-2 Skyservant	10041			PV
☐ Douglas DC-3A-456 Skytrain (C-47A)	TC-ALI	12830	42-92970, NC57779, N5108, N51080, N622NU, N62DN	PV
☐ Lockheed 683-10-19 Starfighter (F-104S)	75-6895	683-6895		PV
☐ Pitts S-1C Special	G-AXNZ	EB.1		PV

SIVRIHISAR HAVA ÜSSÜ ANITI (TU39)

Address: Sivrihisar.
Admission: By prior permission only.
Location: About 12 km west of the town

This reserve base has been used occasionally over the last quarter of a century by detachments of the United States Air Force. Two fighter aircraft are preserved as memorials to those who served at the field. Both types served in considerable numbers in Turkey and flew from bases around the country.

TYPE	REG/SER	CON. NO.	PI/NOTES	STATUS
☐ Lockheed 683-10-19 Starfighter (F-104G)				RA
☐ North American NA-217 Super Sabre (F-100C)	41903	217-164	54-1903	RA

TOPEL DENIZ ÜSSÜ ANITI (TU40)

Address: Kosekoy 41080.
Admission: By prior permission only.
Location: About 10 km east of the town.

The airfield is the main base of the aviation arm of the Turkish Navy. Two Grumman Trackers have been preserved as monuments. The S-2A version entered service in 1991 and this and the improved S-2E flew for over twenty years. The airfield was originally used by former Royal Air Force Bristol Beaufighters in 1948-9. The base was then known as Kocaeli. A decision to upgrade the facilities in order for it to become the new Naval Air Base was made in the early 1970s. The field was named after Gengiz Topel, a pilot killed in action over Cyprus in the 1974 conflict.

TYPE	REG/SER	CON. NO.	PI/NOTES	STATUS
☐ Grumman G-121 Tracker (S-2E)	149263	107C	Bu149263	RA
☐ Grumman G-89 Tracker (S2F-1) (S-2A)	148285	724	Bu148285, 163 (Netherlands)	RA

TURK HAVA KURUMU MÜZESI (TU41)

Address: Hippodrom Caddesi 2,
Ankara 06410.
Tel: 0312-311-3013
Email: thk@thk.org.tr
Admission: Daily 1000-1600.
Location: In the centre of the city.

The Turkish Air League was formed on February 16th 1925 with the aim of creating interest in aviation with particular emphasis on encouraging young people to take up flying. The headquarters was set up in Ankara and almost five hundred branches were established around the country. Money was raised for the purchase of aircraft for the armed forces and flying, gliding and parachute clubs were formed. In 1942 they set up at factory at Etimesgut where eighty Miles Magisters were built. In addition original designs were constructed. A museum has been established at the headquarters to trace the history of the league. The collection opened on May 19th 2002. On show are many documents, photographs and models. Three replica aircraft are on show. Just over twenty THK-4 gliders were built in the late 1940s and several were in use until the mid-1960s. The MKEK company took over the THK factory in 1952 and sixty Ugurs were supplied to the Air Force. The Robinson R-22 helicopter made its maiden flight in California in 1975. This two seater has proved to be extremely and well over four thousand have been built at Torrance. The League ordered several for basic rotary wing training at sites around the country and the Army also operated ten at its main base at Guvercinlik.

TYPE	REG/SER	CON. NO.	PI/NOTES	STATUS
☐ Makona Ve Kimya Endustri Kurumu (MKEK) 4 Ugur (FSM)				PV
☐ Panstwowe Zaklady Lotnicze (PZL) P.24G (FSM)				PV
☐ Robinson R-22 Beta	TC-TBM	2064		PV
☐ Turk Hava Kurumu THK-4 (R)				PV

UNITED ARAB EMIRATES

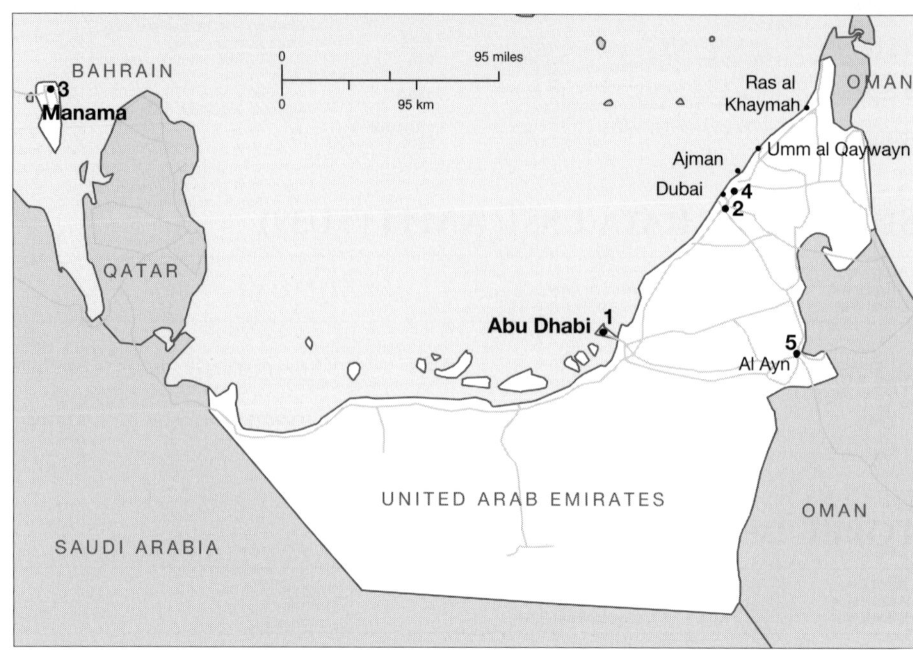

ABU DHABI MEN'S COLLEGE COLLECTION (UAE1)

Address:	P.O. Box 25026, Abu Dhabi.
Tel:	02-681-4600
Email:	enquiries@hct.ac.ae
Admission:	By prior permission only.
Location:	In the southern part of the city.

The college, which is part of the Abu Dhabi Higher College of Technology, uses four airframes for instructional purposes. These aircraft are on display at the regular open days

TYPE	REG/SER	CON. NO.	PI/NOTES	STATUS
☐ Aermacchi MB.326KH	204	6572/313		RA
☐ Bell 206B Jet Ranger	167	8688		
☐ Lockheed 1329 JetStar 6	S9-NAE	1329-5085	N9241R, N586, N5861, S9-NAE, VR-CCY	RA
☐ Piper PA-28-160 Cherokee				RA

AL MINHAD AIR BASE MONUMENT (UAE2)

Address:	Al Minhad, Dubai.
Admission:	Aircraft on permanent view.
Location:	About 30 km south of Dubai.

The base is home to all units of the Central Air Command of the U.A.E. Air Force. Hawks and helicopters are in residence. An example of the Hawk has been mounted in the centre of a roundabout near to the base main gate.

TYPE	REG/SER	CON. NO.	PI/NOTES	STATUS
☐ British Aerospace Hawk 63				PV

AL-MAHATTA MUSEUM (UAE3)

Address:	P.O. Box 138, Bahrain
Tel:	0973-338080
Email:	gfpr@batelco.com.bh
Admission:	Unknown.
Location:	In the western suburbs of the city.

Former Royal Air Force pilot Freddie Bosworth established Gulf Air in Bahrain in 1949. His first aircraft was an Avro Anson which was used for pleasure flying. A second Anson, a D.H.86 and an Auster were acquired and local services were flown. Bosworth was killed in England in 1951 in a test flight in a de Havilland Dove but the company continued to expand. Now it is a major international airline with a large fleet of jets flying around the world. To celebrate the fiftieth anniversary of the company an Anson was leased from Air Atlantique and painted in the colours of the first aircraft. This aroused such interest that another Anson, then under restoration in England, was bought. This was the first aircraft for the museum housed in a building on the site of the former Royal Air Force Sharjah which closed in 1971. The display opened to the public in March 2000.

TYPE	REG/SER	CON. NO.	PI/NOTES	STATUS
□ Avro 652A Anson C.19	'G-AKVW'		TX183, G-BMSF	PVX
□ De Havilland D.H.104 Dove 6	'G-AJPR'	04469	I-TONY, G-ARDE	PVX
□ De Havilland D.H.106 Comet C.2R (C.2)	G-AMXA	06023	G-AMXA, XK655 – front fuselage.	PV
□ De Havilland D.H.114 Heron 2 (Sea Heron C.20)	'G-ANFE'	14072	VR-NAQ, G-ARKU, XR443, G-ODLG, VH-NJP	PVX
□ Douglas DC-3A-456 Skytrain (C-47A) (Dakota III)	'G-AMZZ'	12254	42-92452, FZ669, 12943 (Canada), C-GCXE, N688EA	PVX

DUBAI MEN'S COLLEGE COLLECTION (UAE4)

Address:	P.O. Box 15825, Dubai.
Tel:	04-326-0333
Fax:	04-326-0303
Admission:	By prior permission only.
Location:	About 5 km south east of the city.

This college train engineers in many aspects of airframe and engine maintenance. A fleet of instructional airframes is housed on the campus and these are displayed at open days. The aircraft have been acquired from a number of sources. The Bell 47 helicopter served with the police in Malta after its Luftwaffe days were over. Students and staff built an aircraft as an exercise in both design and methods of construction. The Jet Provost was sold to a private owner in England when its Royal Air Force days were over. The Short Skyvan made its maiden flight in 1963 and examples were delivered to civilian operators and air forces around the world.

TYPE	REG/SER	CON. NO.	PI/NOTES	STATUS
□ Aermacchi MB.326KD	207	6614/337		RA
□ Agusta-Bell 47G-2	'A6-BEL'	262	AS+062, LA+106, AS+377, 74+20, 9H-AAG	RAX
□ Beech J50 Twin Bonanza	'A6-HCT'	JH-160		RAX
□ Bölkow BO 105C	786	S-363	P-786	RA
□ Zenith CH701				RA
□ Hunting-Percival P.84 Jet Provost T.3A (T.3)	'DMC-1'	PAC/W/10149	XN470, G-BXBJ	RAX
□ Piper PA-23-250 Aztec C	'DMC-2'	27-2757	N5643Y, G-ATHJ, A6-ZAZ	RAX
□ Short SC.7 Skyvan 3-100	320	SH.1981	G-14-1981, G-BMHH, AGAW121 (Abu Dhabi), 332	RA

KHALIFA BIN ZAYED AIR COLLEGE MONUMENT (UAE5)

Address:	Al Ain, Abu Dhabi.
Admission:	By prior permission only.
Location:	About 5 km north west of the town.

The college is responsible for pilot instruction for the United Arab Emirates Air Force. Academic courses and professional training for officers are also in the curriculum. The Grob G.115 is used for basic flying training and then the students pass on to the Pilatus PC.7. Advanced skills are learned on the Hawk. In addition helicopters pilots are also trained. An Aermacchi MB.326 has been preserved to remind students of the traditions of the force. The Air Force flew the Italian designed jet until the late 1990s.

TYPE	REG/SER	CON. NO.	PI/NOTES	STATUS
□ Aermacchi MB.326KD				RA

UZBEKISTAN

FERGANA AIR BASE MONUMENT (UZ1)

Address:	Fergana.
Admission:	By prior permission only.
Location:	In the south western suburbs of the town.

The Air Force bases transport aircraft at this former Soviet airfield. An Antonov An-12 which was delivered in 1980 and later transferred to Uzbekistan is preserved in the area of the Officers Club.

TYPE	REG/SER	CON. NO.	PI/NOTES	STATUS
☐ Antonov An-12BP	CCCP-12165	3341701		RA

LABOUR GLORY MUSEUM OF THE TASHKENT AIRCRAFT PRODUCTION CORPORATION (UZ2)

Address:	Plant 18, 61 Elbek Street, 100016 Tashkent.
Tel:	0371-296-2792
Email:	oms@tapo.ccc.uz
Admission:	Monday-Friday 0800-1700.
Location:	In the eastern suburbs of the city.

This museum, which traces the development of the factory, was set up in 1973. The indoor displays show the aircraft produced and manufacturing techniques. The four aircraft are mounted on special pedestals in the grounds of the complex. The Li-2 was put on show in 1975 to commemorate the thirtieth anniversary of the victory over fascism. Many of the eight hundred plus Ilyushin Il-14s were built at the factory before the Il-62 was produced.

TYPE	REG/SER	CON. NO.	PI/NOTES	STATUS
☐ Antonov An-12BP				PV
☐ Antonov An-8		8340101 (?)		PV
☐ Ilyushin Il-14	CCCP-27212	8344004		PV
☐ Lisunov Li-2 [Douglas DC-3 modified]				PV

MUSEUM OF DEFENCE MINISTRY (UZ3)

Address:	100 Akad Abdullaer Street, 100000 Tashkent.
Tel:	0371-133-0330
Admission:	By prior permission only.
Location:	In the centre of the city.

The displays trace the military history of the area from early days. The period when the region was part of the Soviet Union is featured. Two aircraft are on show along with weapons and vehicles.

TYPE	REG/SER	CON. NO.	PI/NOTES	STATUS
☐ Mikoyan-Gurevich MiG-17	'17'			RAX
☐ Mikoyan-Gurevich MiG-21	'21'			RAX

VIETNAM

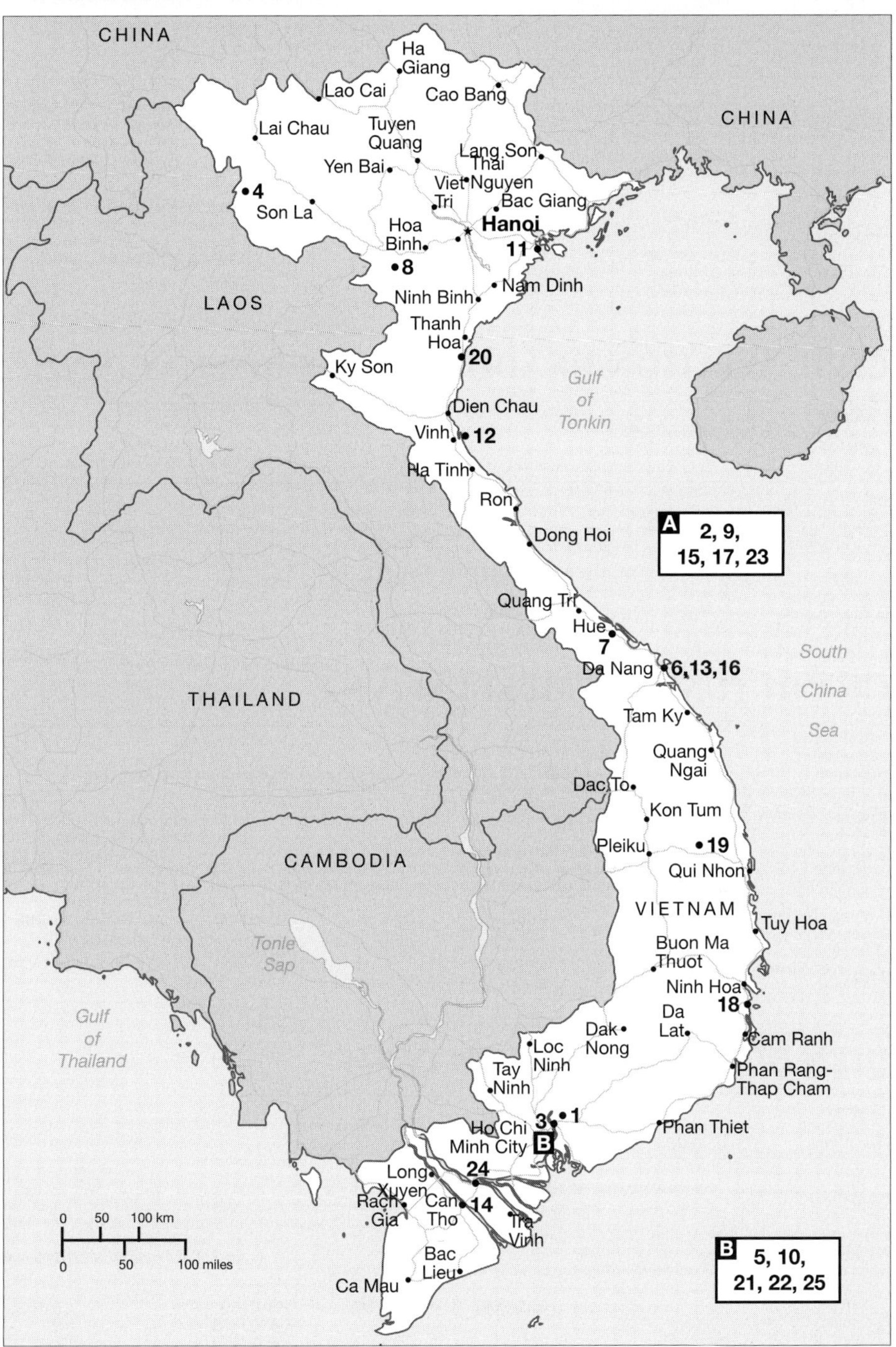
CHINA
Ha Giang
Lao Cai
Cao Bang
CHINA
Lai Chau
Tuyen Quang
Lang Son
Yen Bai
Thai Nguyen
Viet Tri
4
Son La
Bac Giang
Hanoi
Hoa Binh
11
8
Nam Dinh
Ninh Binh
LAOS
Thanh Hoa
20
Ky Son
Gulf of Tonkin
Dien Chau
Vinh
12
Ha Tinh
Ron
Dong Hoi
A 2, 9, 15, 17, 23
Quang Tri
Hue
7
Da Nang
6,13,16
South China Sea
THAILAND
Tam Ky
Quang Ngai
Dac To
Kon Tum
Pleiku
19
CAMBODIA
Qui Nhon
VIETNAM
Tuy Hoa
Tonle Sap
Buon Ma Thuot
Ninh Hoa
18
Da Lat
Dak Nong
Gulf of Thailand
Loc Ninh
Cam Ranh
Tay Ninh
Phan Rang-Thap Cham
3
1
Phan Thiet
Ho Chi Minh City
B
Long Xuyen
24
Rach Gia
Can Tho
14
Tra Vinh
0 50 100 km
0 50 100 miles
Bac Lieu
Ca Mau
B 5, 10, 21, 22, 25

BIEN HOA MILITARY MUSEUM (VN1)

Address:	Bien Hoa Air Base, Bien Hoa.
Admission:	Daily 0900-1700.
Location:	In the northern suburbs of the town south of the airfield.

A small museum has been established close to this famous air base. The display in one of the buildings traces the history of the airfield and the units which have flown from the site. The base was taken over by the South Vietnamese Air Force in 1955 and American units moved in during the early 1960s. The Bearcat has been on show for many years and is believed to be still here. The South Vietnmaese markings can be seen appearing on the Iroquois which has suffered in the harsh climate. The Chinook is parked some distance away.

TYPE	REG/SER	CON. NO.	PI/NOTES	STATUS
☐ Bell 205 Iroquois (UH-1H)	15780	12390	70-15780	PV
☐ Bell 205 Iroquois (UH-1H)	831	12441	70-15831	PV
☐ Grumman G-58 Bearcat (F8F-1B)	G1510	D.854	Bu121510, 121510 (France)	PV
☐ Mikoyan-Gurevich MiG-21PFM	6144			PV
☐ Vertol V.114 Chinook (CH-47B)	025/TN-42			PV

CIVIL AVIATION HEADQUARTERS DISPLAY (VN2)

Address:	119 Nguyen Son Street, Hanoi 10000.
Admission:	Dawn to Dusk.
Location:	In the north eastern suburbs of the city.

The CAA have put two aircraft on show at their headquarters. General Nguyen Son was a leading figure in Ho Chi Minh's forces during the battles with the French. This important road in the city has been named after him. The Ilyushin Il-14 is painted in the colours of one operated by Vietnam Airlines.

TYPE	REG/SER	CON. NO.	PI/NOTES	STATUS
☐ Antonov An-2	670			PV
☐ Ilyushin Il-14	'VN-C482'			PVX

CU CHI TUNNELS MUSEUM (VN3)

Address:	Chu Chi
Admission:	Daily 0900-1700.
Location:	About 30 km north of Ho Chi Minh City at the corner of the road from Cu Chi to Bien Hoa.

This vast complex of tunnels was dug by the Viet Minh in 1948 during their struggle against the French. During the Vietnam War the site was enlarged by the Viet Cong to more than two hundred and fifty kilometres of passages and used in the 1968 Tet offensive. The museum contains many weapons and a large photographic display. The visitor can see a video display tracing the history of the tunnels and fire an AK-47 Gun. Demonstrations of trip wire have been rigged up. The aircraft are at a number of locations in the area.

TYPE	REG/SER	CON. NO.	PI/NOTES	STATUS
☐ Bell 205 Iroquois (UH-1H)	15728	10658	68-15728	PV
☐ Bell 205 Iroquois (UH-1H)	126	10785	68-16126	PV
☐ Mikoyan-Gurevich MiG-17	935			PV
☐ Mikoyan-Gurevich MiG-21PF	6173			PV

DIEN BIEN PHU MUSEUM (VN4)

Address:	Dien Bien Phu.
Admission:	Daily 0800-1100 1300-1700.
Location:	In the town.

In 1954 a bitter battle took place in the area between the French forces and Vietnamese fighting for their independence. The victory of the local troops effectively ended colonial rule of the country. The museum was set up in 1984 and the displays trace the story of the conflict. There is a video to be seen and on show are uniforms weapons, photographs and documents along with a vivid diorama. Outside is a collection of artillery pieces plus wreckage from aircraft shot down in 1954 and in the later Vietnam War. Two types have been identified but there are many others. Significant battle sites in the area have been preserved and can be visited.

TYPE	REG/SER	CON. NO.	PI/NOTES	STATUS
☐ Douglas DC-3A-456 Skytrain (C-47A)			Crash remains.	PVD
☐ Republic F-105D Thunderchief	60-0411	D-99	Crash remains.	PVD

The Al-Mahatta Museum in Bahrain has several airliners exhibited in Gulf Air colours. A de Havilland Dove is pictured here. (M. Hayter via Rod Simpson)

The Air Force Museum in Hanoi exhibits this Kamov Ka-25bsh (Dave Lednicer)

Two Douglas Skraiders are on show at the Vietnam Military History Museum in Hanoi. One is pictured here. (Dave Lednicer)

Many Bell Iroquois were flown in Vietnam and this UH-1H is at the Vietnam Military History Museum in Hanoi. (Dave Lednicer)

HO CHI MINH CITY MUSEUM (VN5)

Address: 65 Ly Tu Trong, Ho Chi Minh City.
Tel: 08-829-9743
Admission: Daily 0800-1600.
Location: In the centre of the city.

Exhibits at this museum, located in the former Gia Long Palace, trace the story of the Communist Revolution in the region which eventually led to the current unified country. The palace was constructed in 1886 as the official residence of the Governor of Cochinchina. In 1962 President Diem of South Vietnam took up residence after the Presidential Palace was destroyed. He spent his last hours in office in the tunnels under the building before fleeing to Cholon. The displays start with the struggle against the French and many photographs from this period can be seen. The upstairs area is devoted to the war with America and contains many fascinating objects. There are mortars made from bicycle parts, a motor bike in which documents were smuggled in inner tubes and a false floored boat used to get guns into the city. A large model of the Chu Chi tunnels can be seen along with a photo gallery tracing Ho Chi Minh's campaign and the fall of the city. Three former American and South Vietnamese aircraft are on show along with a display of weapons and military vehicles. The development of the city from early times is also portrayed in the display.

TYPE	REG/SER	CON. NO.	PI/NOTES	STATUS
☐ Bell 205 Iroquois (UH-1H)	541	10440	68-15510	PV
☐ Cessna 318E Dragonfly (A-37B)	3724	43092	68-7945	PV
☐ Northrop N-156A Freedom Fighter (F-5A)	10271	N.6541	71-0271	PV

HO CHI MINH MUSEUM (VN6)

Address: 10 Nguyen Van Troi, Da Nang.
Admission: Tuesday-Sunday 0730-1100 1330-1630.
Location: In the southern suburbs of the city.

A small museum in the town traces the local military history. Uniforms, medals and trophies are among the many exhibits. The campaigns of Ho Chi Minh and the development of the local air base are highlighted in the displays. The early era is portrayed in detail. Three former South Vietnamese Air Force aircraft can be seen. Several military vehicles, tanks and weapons are also on show in the grounds.

TYPE	REG/SER	CON. NO.	PI/NOTES	STATUS
☐ Bell 205 Iroquois (UH-1H)	780	11418	69-15130	PV
☐ Cessna 185C Skywagon (U-17A)	042			PV
☐ Cessna 318E Dragonfly (A-37B)	68-10793	43144		PV

HUE MILITARY MUSEUM (VN7)

Address: 6 Le Loi Street, Hue.
Tel: 054-822152
Admission: Tuesday-Sunday 0700-1130 1330-1630
Location: In the town.

Many fierce battles were fought in the area and the displays at the museum trace these. There are many uniforms and weapons in the exhibition. The history of the locality is also portrayed in the displays. The wrecked Iroquois is on show in the grounds along with a number of military vehicles, tanks and heavy artillery.

TYPE	REG/SER	CON. NO.	PI/NOTES	STATUS
☐ Bell 204 Iroquois (UH-1C) (UH-1M)	643			PVD

KHE SANH COMBAT BASE MUSEUM (VN8)

Address: Khe Sanh.
Admission: Daily 0900-1100 1300-1700.
Location: Just north of the town.

An American base was set up at Khe Sanh in the early 1960s. An airstrip was opened in 1962 and units of the United States Marine Corps took up residence. Between January 21st and April 8th 1968 the defending forces were besieged by large numbers of Communist troops. Many bitter encounters took place before the base was abandoned in July 1968. The site was reoccupied in the 1970s. The area is now overgrown but the airstrip can still be seen in the jungle. The museum displays trace the history of the battle and the military presence in the area. On show are many photographs, documents, weapons and uniforms. The three helicopters, one wrecked, are displayed in the grounds along with guns, military vehicles and tanks.

TYPE	REG/SER	CON. NO.	PI/NOTES	STATUS
☐ Bell 205 Iroquois (UH-1H)	'20115'			PVDX
☐ Bell 205 Iroquois (UH-1H)	69-15883	12171		PV
☐ Vertol V.114 Chinook (CH-47A)	65-8025	B.197		PV

LENIN PARK DISPLAY (VN9)

Address:	Le Duan, Hanoi.
Admission:	Dawn to dusk.
Location:	South of the city centre.

This large picturesque park in the centre of the city, a swamp and a rubbish tip until the 1960s, has many attractions including a large lake, statues and an open-air theatre. Many walks were built and a variety of trees planted. In one corner of the site is an exhibition of military hardware. For many years the almost complete wreckage of a B-52 was laid out in the grass. The aircraft was downed in the eleven day bombing of Hanoi in December 1972. By the summer of 1997 the airframe was moved into a heap in the corner of the park and later scrapped. The MiG-17, which was on show in the 1980s, moved to Vinh.

TYPE	REG/SER	CON. NO.	PI/NOTES	STATUS
☐ Mikoyan-Gurevich MiG-21bis	5236	75076118		PV

MILITARY MUSEUM OF HO CHI MINH CITY (VN10)

Address:	2 Da Lo Le Duan, Ho Chi Minh City.
Admission:	Tuesday-Sunday 0800-1130 1330-1600.
Location:	In the eastern part of the city centre.

Established many years ago as the military museum for the region the displays were altered after the Vietnam War to highlight the campaign of Ho Chi Minh to set up a unified independent country. The history of the area is also told in detail. Ho Chi Minh's struggle against the French started in the 1940s and this led to partition of Vietnam. The war in the 1960s and 1970s features prominently. On show are an A-37 Dragonfly and an F-5 in what appears to be a former Iranian colour scheme. The latter aircraft fired on the city in the final days of the war in April 1975. A number of military vehicles can be seen including one of the T54 tanks which broke down the gates of the Presidential Palace on April 30th 1975. There is also a display of military vehicles and guns.

TYPE	REG/SER	CON. NO.	PI/NOTES	STATUS
☐ Cessna 318E Dragonfly (A-37B)	14821	43046	67-14821, 3710	PV
☐ McDonnell M.98HO Phantom II (F-4E)				PV
☐ Northrop N-156A Freedom Fighter (F-5A)	10272	N.6542	71-0272	PV

MUSEUM OF MILITARY ZONE 3 (VN11)

Address:	254 Le Duan Street, Hoan Kiem, Haiphong.
Tel:	031-876798
Admission:	Monday-Friday 1130-1500.
Location:	In the centre of the town near the railway station.

The town is the location of the headquarters of the third military district. A small display tracing the history of the region has been staged in rooms in the building and the MiG-17F is on show outside. The area saw battles in the struggle for independence against France in the 1940s and 1950s and again in the Vietnam War.

TYPE	REG/SER	CON. NO.	PI/NOTES	STATUS
☐ Grumman G-128 Intruder (A-6E)			Wing only.	PVD
☐ Mikoyan-Gurevich MiG-17F				PV

MUSEUM OF MILITARY ZONE 4 (VN12)

Address:	189 Le Duan, Vinh.
Tel:	038-855281
Admission:	Tuesday, Friday, Saturday 0700-1100 1400-1700.
Location:	About 3 km from the city centre.

The museum of the fourth military district displays a MiG-17F which served with No. 921 Regiment until the mid-1960s. This aircraft then spent a period on show in Lenin Park in Hanoi before moving to the museum. The area has had a military presence for over two hundred years and battles were fought against the French. Vinh suffered in the Vietnam War and large areas of the city were destroyed by aerial bombing raids.

TYPE	REG/SER	CON. NO.	PI/NOTES	STATUS
☐ Mikoyan-Gurevich MiG-17F	2010			PV

MUSEUM OF MILITARY ZONE 5 (VN13)

Address:	Da Nang.
Admission:	Unknown.
Location:	At the Air Force Base which is about 5 km south west of the city.

Da Nang was an important American base in the Vietnam War. The field was constructed by the French who used it until the mid-1950s. On February 1st 1965 the South Vietnamese Air Force made its first strike into the North from the airfield using Douglas Skyraiders. A small museum tracing the history of the airfield, its units and the personnel who served at the site has been set up in one of the buildings.

TYPE	REG/SER	CON. NO.	PI/NOTES	STATUS
☐ Bell 205 Iroquois (UH-1H)	390	11678	69-15390	PV
☐ Cessna 185B Skywagon (U-17A)				PV
☐ Cessna 318E Dragonfly (A-37B)	'0475'			PVX
☐ Mikoyan-Gurevich MiG-21PFM	6122			PV
☐ Northrop N-311 Tiger II (F-5E)	'7579'	R.1091	73-1638	PVX
☐ Shenyang J-5 [Mikoyan-Gurevich MiG-17F]	'2011'			PVX
☐ Shenyang J-6 [Mikoyan-Gurevich MiG-19SF]	'6058'			PVX

MUSEUM OF MILITARY ZONE 9 (VN14)

Address:	6 Hoa Binh, Can Tho.
Tel:	071-82217
Admission:	Tuesday,Thursday,Friday 0800-1100; 1400-1600; Sunday 0800-1100 1900-2100.
Location:	In the centre of the city.

Can Tho was the last major city in the south to be overrun by the North Vietnamese forces. This occurred on May 1st 1975, one day after the fall of Saigon. In the building are many photographs, weapons, uniforms, documents and dioramas portraying the conflict. One interesting exhibit is a homemade crossbow strung with knotted elastic bands. The aircraft are parked in the grounds along with a number of military vehicles, guns and tanks.

TYPE	REG/SER	CON. NO.	PI/NOTES	STATUS
☐ Bell 205 Iroquois (UH-1H)	521			PV
☐ Cessna 185B Skywagon (U-17A)			65-12723 quoted but incorrect for the type.	PV
☐ Cessna 318E Dragonfly (A-37B)	29	43175	68-10824	PV
☐ Mikoyan-Gurevich MiG-15				PV
☐ Mikoyan-Gurevich MiG-21PFM				PV

MUSEUM OF MILITARY ZONE THU DO / MUSEUM OF VICTORY OVER B-52s (VN15)

Address:	157 Pho Doi Can, Ba Dinh, Hanoi.
Tel:	04-823-7075
Admission:	Tuesday-Saturday 0800-1100 1300-1430.
Location:	

The museum was set up in November 1986 to trace military history of the region. The struggle against the French features prominently. The thousand year's cultural heritage of the city is portrayed. On show are many documents, photographs and items of memorabilia. In December 1972 United States Air Force B-52s bombed Hanoi night and day over a twelve day period. Several aircraft were downed and wreckage from some of these has been collected and put on show. In the large outside park are missiles and vehicles and items of artillery.

TYPE	REG/SER	CON. NO.	PI/NOTES	STATUS
☐ Boeing 464-253 Stratofortress (B-52G)			Wreckage from several aircraft shot down	PVD
☐ Mikoyan-Gurevich MiG-21F	5033			PV

MUSEUM OF QUANG NAM (VN16)

Address:	24 Le Duan, Da Nang.
Admission:	Tuesday-Sunday 0700-1100 1300-1500.
Location:	In the centre of the city.

Housed in a former colonial building the displays at this interesting museum are being renovated. The history of the town is portrayed in detail with models, costumes and documents on show. One section is devoted to the ethnic minorities which reside in the area. Local crafts can be seen and the highlight is a water driven harp.

TYPE	REG/SER	CON. NO.	PI/NOTES	STATUS
☐ Bell 205 Iroquois (UH-1H)	67-17555	9753		PV

MUSEUM OF THE AIR-DEFENCE AND AIR FORCE (VN17)

Address:	171 and 179 Troung Chinh, Thanoh Xuan, Hanoi.
Tel:	094-852-2658
Admission:	Daily 0800-1100 1330-1630.
Location:	In the southern suburbs of the city

The Air Force Museum opened on April 30th 1985 and is housed in a stark concrete building close to Bac Mai military airfield. The indoor displays trace the history of the Air Force with dioramas, models, photographs, weapons and components. In addition to the Vietnam War, the campaign against Pol Pot and the 1979 conflict with China are featured. The forward fuselage of a MiG-21F is in this area. Outside the main hall is a large display park dominated by Eastern bloc hardware. The giant Mil-6 helicopter flew into the site in April 1989. About ten were used by the Air Force. Nearby are a Mil-4, Mil-24 and a Kamov Ka-25. Amongst the MiG fighters is a Shenyang J-6 developed from the Mig-19 by the Chinese. Forty four were delivered to Vietnam in the late 1960s before relations between the two countries deteriorated. Two indigenous machines, the HL-1 and TL-1, are owned by the Hanoi Institute for Science and Technology who use them for instructional purposes. The nearby Air Defence Museum was set up in 1959 and the two organisations combined in 1999.

TYPE	REG/SER	CON. NO.	PI/NOTES	STATUS
☐ Aero L-29 Delfin	743	093643	702	PV
☐ Antonov An-2TD	02103	1G 188-29		PV
☐ Bell 204 Iroquois (HU-1A) (UH-1A)	027			PV
☐ Bell 205 Iroquois (UH-1H)	811	10008	67-17811	PV
☐ Bell 205 Iroquois (UH-1H)	68-15632	10562		PVD
☐ Bell 205 Iroquois (UH-1H)	10736	10666	68-15736	PVD
☐ Beriev Be-12			Due soon.	–
☐ Cessna 185B Skywagon (U-17A)	764			PV
☐ Cessna 318E Dragonfly (A-37B)	0475	43078	68-7931	PV
☐ Cessna 318E Dragonfly (A-37B)				PV
☐ Douglas A-1H Skyraider (AD-6)	'132'	10955	Bu139723	PVX
☐ Institute for Science and Technology HL-1	8402			RA
☐ Institute for Science and Technology TL-1	01			PV
☐ Kamov Ka-25BSh	7511			PV
☐ McDonnell M.98AM Phantom II (F-4B) (F-4N)	Bu153001	1440		PVD
☐ Mikoyan-Gurevich MiG-17F	2011			PV
☐ Mikoyan-Gurevich MiG-17F	2047			PV
☐ Mikoyan-Gurevich MiG-21MF			8008 (Poland)	PVX
☐ Mikoyan-Gurevich MiG-21MF	5151		Front fuselage only.	PV
☐ Mikoyan-Gurevich MiG-21MF	5121	10112		PV
☐ Mikoyan-Gurevich MiG-21PF	4326			PV
☐ Mikoyan-Gurevich MiG-21PFM	5020	8601		PV
☐ Mil Mi-4	1510		59510	PV
☐ Mil Mi-24A	7430	1200502		PV
☐ Mil Mi-6	7609	720856		PV
☐ Northrop N-156A Freedom Fighter (F-5A)	64-8434	N.6071	65-10547	PV
☐ Shenyang J-6 [Mikoyan-Gurevich MiG-19SF]	6058	^6-6436		PV
☐ Zlin Z-226 Trenér 6	101-A		OK-MFH	PV

NHA TRANG AIR FORCE BASE COLLECTION (VN18)

Address:	Nha Trang Air Base.
Admission:	Daily 0900-1500.
Location:	About 5 km south of the town.

This base is now the main pilot training school for the Air Force. The airfield was built by the French in 1949 and the first Vietnamese students started their training in 1951. Prior to this local trainees had been sent to France. During the 1960s combat units and American squadrons moved in. A collection of aircraft has been assembled to show students the traditions of the service. There is also a small museum on the base with photographs, memorabilia and uniforms on show. The Nanchang CJ-6A was used for basic training and the student then moved on to the L-29 Delfin or the MiG-15UTI. Operational conversion was carried out at wings around the country and the MiG-21U and MiG-21F-13 were used for this part of the pilot's career.

TYPE	REG/SER	CON. NO.	PI/NOTES	STATUS
☐ Aero L-29 Delfin	744	093644		PV
☐ Bell 205 Iroquois (UH-1H)	344			PV
☐ Cessna 185B Skywagon (U-17A)	767			PV
☐ Cessna 318E Dragonfly (A-37B)	70-1280	43295		PV
☐ Cessna R172F Mescalero (T-41D)	772	R1720408	69-7691	PV
☐ Mikoyan-Gurevich MiG-15UTI	263?			PV
☐ Mikoyan-Gurevich MiG-21F-13	4123			PV
☐ Mikoyan-Gurevich MiG-21U	4124			PV
☐ Nanchang CJ-6A				PV
☐ Shenyang J-5 [Mikoyan-Gurevich MiG-17F]				PV
☐ Shenyang J-5 [Mikoyan-Gurevich MiG-17F]				PV

PHU CAT MILITARY MUSEUM (VN19)

Address:	Phu Cat Air Force Base, Phu Cat.
Admission:	Unknown.
Location:	Just west of the village.

Three aircraft are on show at a museum at the air base which was built by the Americans in the mid-1960s. The field saw use by U.S.A.F. units during the conflict. Fighters and transports were flown from the field. The site was captured by forces of North Vietnam on March 31st 1975. Over one hundred MiG-21s were flown by the unified Air Force and were assisted by about sixty MiG-19s from both Soviet and Chinese production lines. The unified Air Force operated C-7 Caribou transports for a period and then fighter units moved in. The 920th Fighter Regiment flew MiG-21bis and MiG-21UMs and also a civil terminal was built.

TYPE	REG/SER	CON. NO.	PI/NOTES	STATUS
☐ Mikoyan-Gurevich MiG-21PFM	5041			PV
☐ Shenyang J-5 [Mikoyan-Gurevich MiG-17F]				PV
☐ Shenyang J-6 [Mikoyan-Gurevich MiG-19SF]	6066			PV

REGIMENTAL TRADITION MUSEUM (VN20)

Address:	Sao Vang, Tho Xuan.
Admission:	Unknown.
Location:	In the town.

This museum portrays the history of the local Army regiment. On show are uniforms, medals, photographs, documents, weapons and items of memorabilia. A number of military vehicles, tanks and artillery pieces are parked outside the building. During the Vietnam War the local airfield housed a number of units including the 927th Fighter Regiment operating MiG-21s. The two MiGs both carry false serials. The Dragonfly proved itself to be an outstanding attack aircraft in combat conditions and many were flown by the unified force.

TYPE	REG/SER	CON. NO.	PI/NOTES	STATUS
☐ Cessna 318E Dragonfly (A-37B)				PV
☐ Mikoyan-Gurevich MiG-17F	'1221'			PVX
☐ Mikoyan-Gurevich MiG-21PFM	'5126'			PVX

REUNIFICATION PALACE (VN21)

Address:	106 Nguyen Du, Ho Chi Minh City.
Tel:	08-829-0629
Admission:	Monday-Saturday 0730-1030 1300-1600, Sunday 0730-1600.
Location:	In the centre of the city.

The Norodom Palace was constructed on this site in 1871 to serve as the residence of the Governor-General of Indo-China. When the French departed in 1954 the President of South Vietnam, Ngo Dinh Diem, moved in. In February 1962 two South Vietnamese pilots attacked the building hoping to assassinate the President. They failed but the structure was severely damaged and then demolished. A new building, called the Independence Palace, was completed in 1966. On April 30th 1975 North Vietnamese tanks broke down the main gates thus effectively ending the existence of

South Vietnam as a separate state. Now known as the Reunification Palace, the building was modified for museum use. A display tracing the history of the country has been set up with items of military hardware among the exhibits. The tour includes visits to the conference rooms, the former presidential quarters, the war communications rooms and the basement tunnels. The two aircraft on show were used by the South Vietnamese Air Force in the early 1970s before being taken over by the new unified service.

TYPE	REG/SER	CON. NO.	PI/NOTES	STATUS
☐ Bell 205 Iroquois (UH-1H)	445	11733	69-15445	PV
☐ Northrop N-311 Tiger II (F-5E)	'01638'	R.1094	73-1368	PVX

TAN SON NHUT AIR FORCE MUSEUM (VN22)

Address:	San Bay, Tan Son Nhut.
Tel:	08-848-5383 (Airport)
Admission:	Daily 0800-1100 1300-1600.
Location:	In the northern suburbs of the city.

A museum has recently been set up near the civil terminal of the airport which serves Ho Chi Minh City. The airfield was built by the French to serve the capital of French Cochinchina. During World War II the field was home to transport squadrons of the Imperial Japanese Air Force. French units operating C-45 Expeditors and C-47 Skytrains were based at Tan Son Nhut up to the early 1950s. A military base was set up in 1953 and three years later the South Vietnamese Air Force moved its headquarters to the field. In the 1960s American units arrived and in the latter part of the decade it was reportedly the busiest airfield in the world. Vietnamese Air Force squadrons operating helicopters and transports are still in residence. The airfield is now surrounded by the ever expanding city and a new international airport has been built. Four of the aircraft in the collection, The A-37, the F5, the U-17 and the Mil-24 carry the same serials as examples in the Air Force Museum in Hanoi.

TYPE	REG/SER	CON. NO.	PI/NOTES	STATUS
☐ Bell 205 Iroquois (UH-1H)	0372	12350	70-15740	PV
☐ Cessna 318E Dragonfly (A-37B)	'0475'	43052	67-22486, 3720	PVX
☐ Cessna A185F Skywagon 185 (U-17B)	'764'		71-1042, '7621'	PVX
☐ Mikoyan-Gurevich MiG-21PFM	5326	8511		PV
☐ Mil Mi-8T	7812	9732601		PV
☐ Mil Mi-24A	'7430'			PVX
☐ Northrop N-156A Freedom Fighter (F-5A)	'7579'	N.6071	63-8434, 3532	PVX

VIETNAM MILITARY HISTORY MUSEUM (VN23)

Address:	28A Dien Bien Ph'u, Hanoi.
Tel:	04-733-6453
Fax:	04-733-4692
Email:	btqsvn@bt.vnn.vn
Admission:	Tuesday-Sunday 0800-1130 1300-1630.
Location:	In the centre of the city.

Formerly known as the People's Army Museum, this collection is located in a colonial French military building in the city. The informative indoor displays trace the history of the army from early days through the colonisation of Vietnam by the Chinese and French up to modern times. The exhibition starts from the period when the country was a kingdom and several early weapons and uniforms can be seen. The story of the underground army established during the 1930s up to independence in 1954 can be followed. The rooms display relics, models, memorabilia, photographs, uniforms and weapons. The turbulent history of the region is portrayed in the exhibition. The hall devoted to the battle of Dien Bien Phu is a highlight. Small parts from a B-52 shot down over the city are in one of the halls. Outside is a pedestal with a MiG-21PF at the top. This aircraft was flown by the 'ace' Via Ngoc Dinh during the Vietnam War. He is reported to have downed many American aircraft. The base of this pillar is surrounded by the wreckage of French, Chinese and American aircraft shot down in the various conflicts. Only the larger portions are listed. There are tanks from both the Soviet Union and America along with guns, missile launchers and armoured personnel carriers.

TYPE	REG/SER	CON. NO.	PI/NOTES	STATUS
☐ Bell 205 Iroquois (UH-1H)	67-17651	9849		PV
☐ Boeing 464-201-7 Stratofortress (B-52D)	56-0608	17291		PVD
☐ Cessna 310A Blue Canoe (L-27A) (U-3A)			Rear fuselage only.	PVD
☐ Cessna 318E Dragonfly (A-37B)	'43198'	43198	69-6353	PVX
☐ Douglas A-1E Skyraider (AD-5)	132436	9453	Bu134636	PV
☐ Douglas A-1H Skyraider (AD-6)	134636	9865	Bu134636	PV
☐ Douglas DC-3A-467 Skytrain (C-47B)			(USAAF)	PVD
☐ General Dynamics F-111A	67-0060	A1-105		PVD
☐ Grumman G-50 Hellcat (F6F-5)	239			PVD
☐ McDonnell M.98AM Phantom II (F4H-1) (F-4B)	Bu149448	165		PVD
☐ Mikoyan-Gurevich MiG-17F	'2047'			PV
☐ Mikoyan-Gurevich MiG-21MF	'5121'			PVX
☐ Mikoyan-Gurevich MiG-21PF	4324	2109		PV
☐ Republic F-105D Thunderchief	61-0061	D-256	Identity doubtful.	PVD
☐ Shenyang J-6 [Mikoyan-Gurevich MiG-19SF]	1018		Rear fuselage only.	PVD

VINH LONG MUSEUM (VN24)

Address:	Phan Boi Chau, Vinh Long.
Admission:	Closed at present.
Location:	In the northern part of the town near the river ferry.

The centre of the town is located on an island and by the waterfront is a museum which has been closed for some years. The displays once traced the history and culture of the region from the French colonial days up to the Vietnam War. In the gardens, which are still open, is a plastic covered structure housing tanks, military vehicles, large weapons and a flame thrower along with the collection of aircraft.

TYPE	REG/SER	CON. NO.	PI/NOTES	STATUS
☐ Bell 205 Iroquois (UH-1H)				PV
☐ Cessna 318E Dragonfly (A-37B)				PV
☐ Mikoyan-Gurevich MiG-21F-13				PV
☐ Northrop N-156A Freedom Fighter (F-5A)				PV

WAR REMNANTS MUSEUM (VN25)

Address:	28 Vo Vat Tan, Quang 3, Ho Chi Minh City.
Tel:	08-930-5587
Fax:	08-930-5153
Email:	arrmhcm@gmail.com
Admission:	Daily 0730-1145 1330-1730.
Location:	In the city centre.

This rather sombre exhibition traces a view of the period when there was a large American presence in the former South Vietnam. Once called the Museum of American War Crimes, vivid portrayals of the methods used against the Viet Cong forces can be seen. Many distressing photographs of the effects of napalm, defoliant spray and conventional weapons are on view. Mock-ups of the small 'tiger cages' from the notorious Con Son prison island have been reconstructed. From an earlier period is the guillotine used by the French at Ly Tu Trong prison. The name was changed to War Remnants Museum some years ago. Five aircraft used by the American and South Vietnamese forces are on show. The Dragonfly is surrounded by the arsenal of weapons it could carry. There is also a seven ton bomb which was dropped by parachute.

TYPE	REG/SER	CON. NO.	PI/NOTES	STATUS
☐ Bell 205 Iroquois (UH-1H)	15753	12041	69-15753 – boom from c/n 15125.	PV
☐ Cessna 318E Dragonfly (A-37B)	287	43300	70-1285, 287 (South Vietnam), '09',01285	PV
☐ Cessna A185F Skywagon 185 (U-17B)	1448	1851006	71-1448, 759	PV
☐ Douglas A-1H Skyraider (AD-6)	'39674'	10906	Bu139674	PVX
☐ Northrop N-156A Freedom Fighter (F-5A)	69170	N.6274	66-9170, (Iran), 172	PV

YEMEN

MILITARY MUSEUM (YE1)

Address:	Maydan-ai-Tahir, Sana'a.
Admission:	Saturday-Thursday 0900-1200 1600-2000.
Location:	In centre of the city.

Displays at this interesting museum trace the complex military history of the country from the Ottoman times up to the present day. There are ten halls in the building each tracing a particular period. Reconstructions of war pavilions used by the rulers in the middle ages have been built. On show are many weapons, uniforms and documents. One item of particular interest is a camel mounted cannon designed for forays into the harsh desert. There are several relics from the time when the British colony of Aden was located in the country. A number of vehicles, including a bullet ridden Cadillac, can be seen. The history of the modern day forces can be seen in the final hall. There is a section devoted to the Air Force The only aircraft exhibited is one of the twelve MiG-17Fs delivered to equip a fighter squadron soon after the country became a republic in 1962.

TYPE	REG/SER	CON. NO.	PI/NOTES	STATUS
☐ Mikoyan-Gurevich MiG-17F				PV

INDEX

All aircraft are listed alphabetically by manufacturer or designer (in the case of some gliders and homebuilt aircraft) followed by the type. Each country is denoted by a two/three letter code and each museum/collection a number e.g. IDA10 is tenth museum/collection in alphabetical order in India.

Country codes are as follows:-
AF Afghanistan; **BA** Bangladesh; **BRU** Brunei; **C** Cambodia; **CHI** China; **IDA** India; **IND** Indonesia; **IR** Iran; **IQ** Iraq: **IS** Israel; **JA** Japan; **JY** Jordan; **KA** Kazakhstan; **KU** Kuwait; **KYR** Kyrgyzstan; **LAO** Laos; **LEB** Lebanon; **MALA** Malaysia; **MON** Mongolia; **MY** Myanmar; **NK** North Korea; **OM** Oman; **PAK** Pakistan; **QA** Qatar; **RUS** Russia (Asian); **SAU** Saudi Arabia; **SI** Singapore: **SKO** South Korea; **SR** Sri Lanka; **SY** Syria; **TA** Taiwan; **TH** Thailand; **TU** Turkey; **UAE** United Arab Emirates; **UZ** Uzbekistan; **VN** Vietnam; **YE** Yemen.

The Krasnoyarsk Civil Aviation School collection includes this Antonov An-26. (Aidan Curley)

Taiwan operated many Super Sabres and this F-100F is in the Military Aircraft Park in Hsihu. (Aidan Curley)

AUSTRALASIA

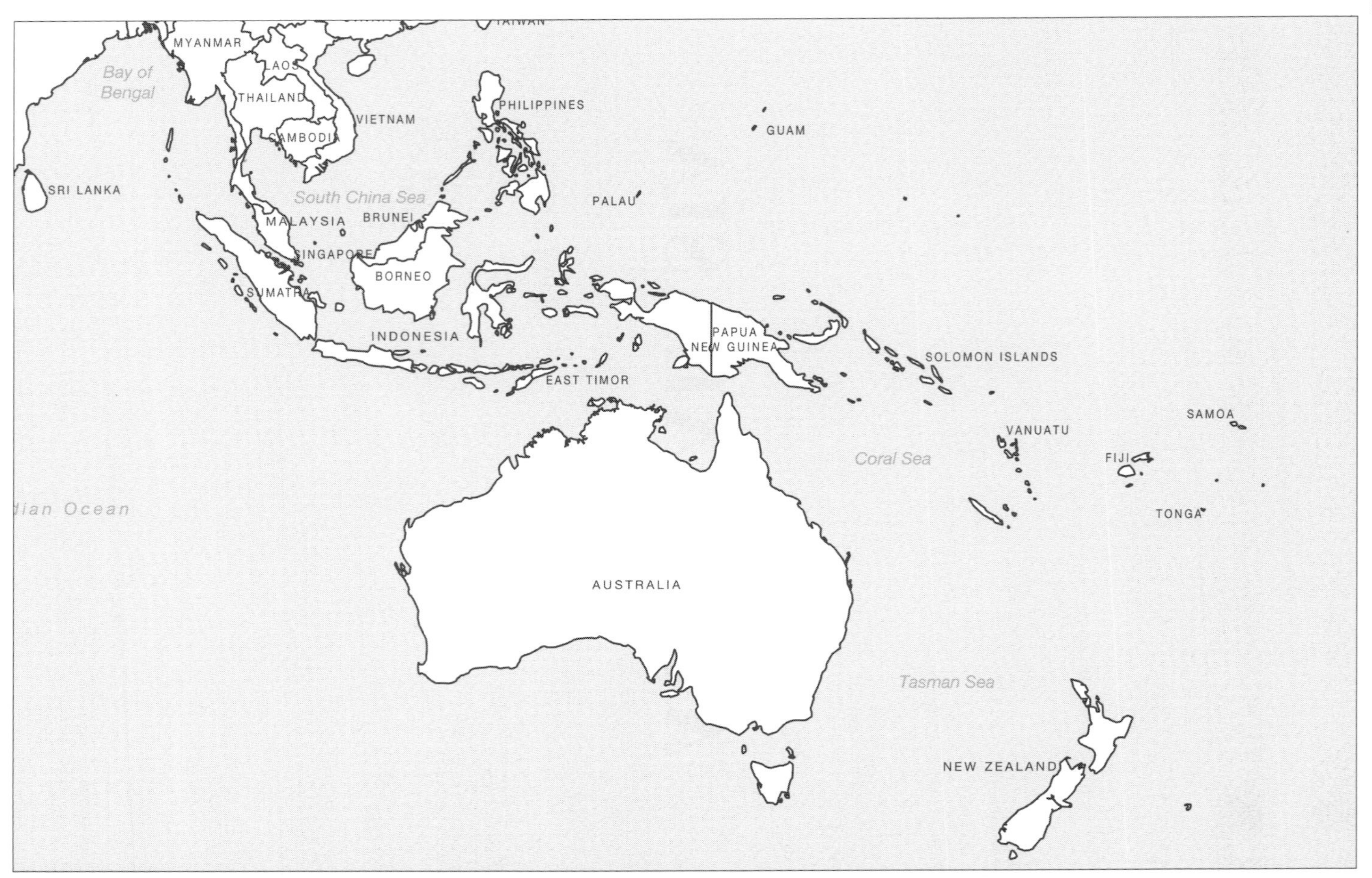
MYANMAR
Bay of Bengal
LAOS
THAILAND
VIETNAM
CAMBODIA
PHILIPPINES
GUAM
SRI LANKA
South China Sea
PALAU
MALAYSIA
BRUNEI
SINGAPORE
BORNEO
SUMATRA
INDONESIA
PAPUA NEW GUINEA
SOLOMON ISLANDS
EAST TIMOR
SAMOA
VANUATU
Coral Sea
FIJI
TONGA
AUSTRALIA
Tasman Sea
NEW ZEALAND

AUSTRALIA

AUSTRALIAN CAPITAL TERRITORY

AUSTRALIAN WAR MEMORIAL (AUS1)

Address:	Treloar Crescent, Campbell, Canberra, Australian Capital Territory 2612.
Tel:	02-6463-4211
Fax:	02-6243-4325
Email:	info@awm.gov.au
Admission:	Daily 1000-1700. Treloar Centre – by prior permission only.
Location:	At the north end of Anzac Parade about 3 km north east of Parliament House. The Treloar Centre is about 8 km north of the city centre.

The idea of a memorial honouring Australia's contribution to World War I was first put forward in 1917. Items were collected and exhibited in both Melbourne and Sydney in the 1920s and 1930s. Meanwhile, in 1908 a decision had been taken to construct a new capital for the country. A site at Canberra was chosen and work started in 1913 with the Federal Government moving there in 1927. A permanent home for the war memorial was agreed and the purpose built structure in Canberra opened on Armistice Day in 1941. As World War II was then in progress it was decided that this conflict should also be portrayed and now all wars in which Australian troops have served are featured. Sections covering the Korean War, the Malaysian operation and the Vietnam conflict are being developed. The stories of the battles are told using artefacts, medals, documents, photographs, armaments and vehicles. There are several small theatres where period films can be seen. Improvements to the aviation area have taken place over the years and the Bradbury Aircraft Hall opened on August 31st 2000. In 2008 a new area will house five First World War airframes. The Anzac Hall is dominated by the Lancaster which flew ninety missions during its service with 460 Squadron of the R.A.A.F. This famous bomber was recently restored and sections were removed for complete refurbishment. Also here are two German designs which were advanced for their time. The rocket powered Messerschmitt Me 163, developed from tailless gliders designed by Alexander Lippisch, first flew as a sailplane in 1941. Despite a number of problems with the Walter rocket the type entered production and first saw combat in the late summer of 1944. The first jet aircraft in the world, the Heinkel He 178, took to the air in November 1939 and Germany proceeded with the development of the engine. The Messerschmitt Me 262 became the first jet to be used operationally when it entered squadron service in the autumn of 1944. The new area will include the first aircraft to be acquired by the Memorial, the Albatros D Va. The aircraft was brought down intact in December by an R.E.8 and salvaged by 3 Squadron in 1917. The aircraft was restored in the 1960s by members of the Camden Museum of Aviation. The D.H.9 was flown from England to Australia in 1920 by Parer and McIntosh. The journey took over seven months and many setbacks occurred during the flight. The flight was the first by a single engined aircraft from England to Australia. This airframe was damaged during restoration in the 1980s when it was struck by a lorry. The display will trace the rapid development of aviation during this period. The Bradbury Hall also houses several significant aircraft, many with combat histories. For example the Spitfire on show shot down two Messerschmitt Bf 109s and the Kittyhawk served with 75 Squadron in Papua-New Guinea. A short distance from the city is the Treloar Warfare Technology Centre in Mitchell where a number of aircraft are stored and currently can only be viewed with special permission. The workshops are also located in this complex. The oldest machine in the collection is the Deperdussin, one of the first aircraft to be used at Point Cook. The Central Flying School was set up at the Victoria airfield in 1913 but it was not until the following year that pilot training commenced. Restored recently is the Wirraway in which Archer and Coulston of No. 4 Squadron shot down a Japanese Zero on December 26th 1942. Work has just finished on the Mosquito and this has involved the injection of chemicals to preserve most of the original woodwork. The Tachikawa Ki-54, which is awaiting restoration, was used by Lieutenant General Masuo Baba when he flew to Borneo on September 10th 1945 for the surrender ceremony. He was the commander of Japanese forces in the area and was executed in 1947 for his part in the war. Aircraft from the Korean War include a Meteor, which flew four hundred and eighty five missions, and a MiG-15. Also from this period is the Sea Fury which flew from both carriers and shore bases. Significant numbers from the Australian forces served in Vietnam and aircraft from this period are being acquired. The locally built Canberra also served in Malaya, The two Bell helicopters served in the conflict. Captain J Campbell won the D.F.C. whilst piloting the Bell 47 in February 1967. He landed several times in a minefield to rescue injured soldiers. Among the significant non-aviation items are boat used at Anzac Cove on Gallipoli in 1915 and a Japanese midget submarine which attacked shipping in Sydney Harbour in 1942. This excellent museum is continuing to improve its displays.

TYPE	REG/SER	CON. NO.	PI/NOTES	STATUS
☐ Albatros D Va	D.5390/17			PV.1
☐ Avro 504K	A3-4		H2174	PV.1
☐ Avro 652A Anson I	W2486		W2486, VH-BLG – front fuselage only – fitted with nose cone from R3581	PV.1
☐ Avro 683 Lancaster B.I	W4783		W4783, A66-2	PV.1
☐ Bell 47G-3B-1 Sioux	A1-404	3404		S.2
☐ Bell 204 Iroquois (UH-1B)	A2-1019	1019	63-13587	RA.2
☐ Commonwealth CA-5 Wirraway II [North American NA-33]	A20-103	103		PV.1
☐ Commonwealth CA-25 Winjeel	A85-441	CA25-41	Rear fuselage only.	RA.2
☐ Curtiss 87-A4 Warhawk (P-40E) (Kittyhawk IA)	A29-133	18605	41-36084, ET730, A29-133, (VH-NRW)	PV.1
☐ De Havilland D.H.9	G-EAQM		F1278	PV.1

TYPE	REG/SER	CON. NO.	PI/NOTES	STATUS
☐ De Havilland D.H.82A Tiger Moth	A17-704	DHA.836	(DX793), A17-704, VH-ABF	RA.2
☐ De Havilland D.H.98 Mosquito PR.41 (FB.40)	A52-319	DH.3236	(A52-210), A52-319, VH-WAD	PV.1
☐ Department of Aircraft Production Beaufort VIII [Bristol 152]	A9-557		Rear fuselage of Beaufort VIII A9-639 and parts from Beaufort VIII's A9-555 and A9-559.	RA.2
☐ Deperdussin Taxi Monoplane	CFS.5			PV.1
☐ Douglas DC-3A-467 Skytrain (C-47B) (Dakota IV)	A65-71	15686/27131	43-49870, A65-71/VHCIN	RA.2
☐ Fieseler Fi 103A-1		443313		PV.1
☐ Gloster Meteor F.8	A77-368		WA952 – front fuselage on display – remainder of airframe in store.	PV.1/ RA.2
☐ Government Aircraft Factory Canberra Mk.20 [English Electric EA.1]	A84-247	47		RA.2
☐ Hawker Sea Fury FB.11	'VX730'		VW232	PVX.1
☐ Henschel Hs 293A-1				RA.2
☐ Lockheed 414-08-10 Hudson IVA (A-28)	'VH-FXF'	414-6034	41-23175, A16-105, (VH-CMA), VH-BKY, VH-EWB, VH-EWS, VH-SMO, VH-AGP	RAX.2
☐ Messerschmitt Bf 109G-6/U-2	163824	163824	NF+FY, (G-SMIT)	PV.1
☐ Messerschmitt Me 163B-1a Komet	191907	191907	19107, AM222 (?)	PV.1
☐ Messerschmitt Me 262A-1	500200	500200	500200, VH519, AM81	PV.1
☐ Mikoyan-Gurevich MiG-15bis		2458	Front fuselage on display – remainder of airframe in store.	PV.1/ RA.2
☐ Mitsubishi A6M2 Zero Sen Model 21		5784		PV.1
☐ Nakajima Ki-43-II Hayabusha		5465	Parts including engine on show.	PV.1/ RA.2
☐ North American NA-111 Mustang (P-51D)	A68-648	111-36389	44-13106	PV.1
☐ North American NA-305 Bronco (OV-10A)	67-14639	305-46		S.2
☐ Pfalz D XII	2600/18	3150		PV.1
☐ Pilatus PC.6/B1-H2 Turbo-Porter	A14-690	690	HB-FEC	RA.2
☐ Republic P-47D Thunderbolt	42-75921		Major components recovered from crash site.	RA.2
☐ Royal Aircraft Factory S.E.5A	'C9539'		C1916, A2-4	PVX.1
☐ Supermarine 329 Spitfire F.IIa	P7973	CBAF-492		PV.1
☐ Tachikawa Ki-54c			Fuselage only	S

NATIONAL MUSEUM OF AUSTRALIA (AUS2)

Address:	Lawson Crescent, Acton, Canberra, Australian Capital Territory 2600.
Tel:	02-6208-5000
Fax:	02-6208-5099
Email:	information@nma.gov.au
Admission:	Daily 0900-1700.
Location:	In the western part of the city. Mitchell is about 8 km north of the city centre.

Set up in 1980 the museum collected a vast amount of material. For a few years a small visitor centre at Yarramundi exhibited a few items from the inventory. Plans for a permanent home were finalised in the mid-1990s. An international competition was launched for the design and the museum opened on March 11th 2000. The date coincided with the centenary of the Australian Federation Act. The innovative displays trace the land, nation and people of Australia with special emphasis on the social history of the country. The early period of the country from its first inhabitants is chronicled in detail. The discovery by a Dutch explorer in 1606 is featured. The British claimed the land in 1770 and set up the first penal colonies eighteen years later. Gold was discovered in the 1850s and the story of this is portrayed. The development of the country through two World Wars and the settlement of the outback is told in the displays. The transformation into modern cities can be seen. Three aircraft are in store in the Mitchell area of the city. The museum holds archive material from the famous Australian pilot and designer Edgar Percival. Born in Albury in 1898 he flew in World War I and then returned to Australia where he carried on a career in aviation. He went back to England and eventually set up his own company at Gravesend in Kent in 1934. A series of low wing monoplanes was produced and several of his designs were successful in races. In addition many long distance records were broken. Two of his types have been acquired. The Gull Six was delivered to Switzerland in January 1937 and remained there for forty years. Cliff Lovell brought the Gull to England in 1977 and restored it to the colours it carries today. The museum purchased the aircraft in 1986. The Proctor had a varied career in both England and Australia. Derived from the Gull, the type was built bin large numbers for communications work in World War II. After the end of the conflict many were sold on the civil market and the slightly larger Proctor V was produced. The Dove was acquired because of the contribution the type made on medical flights and airline work in the outback. The aircraft in the collection was delivered to Australia in 1960 for use by the Commonwealth Department of Health. For just over a year it was leased to Bay of Plenty Airways in New Zealand before returning to its intended duties.

TYPE	REG/SER	CON. NO.	PI/NOTES	STATUS
☐ De Havilland D.H.104 Dove 5	VH-DHK	04508	VH-DHK, ZK-BZP	RA
☐ Percival D.3 Gull Six	G-AERD	D.65	HB-OFU	RA
☐ Percival P.28B Proctor I	VH-FEP	K.279	P6245, G-AHTN, VH-BLC	RA

NEW SOUTH WALES

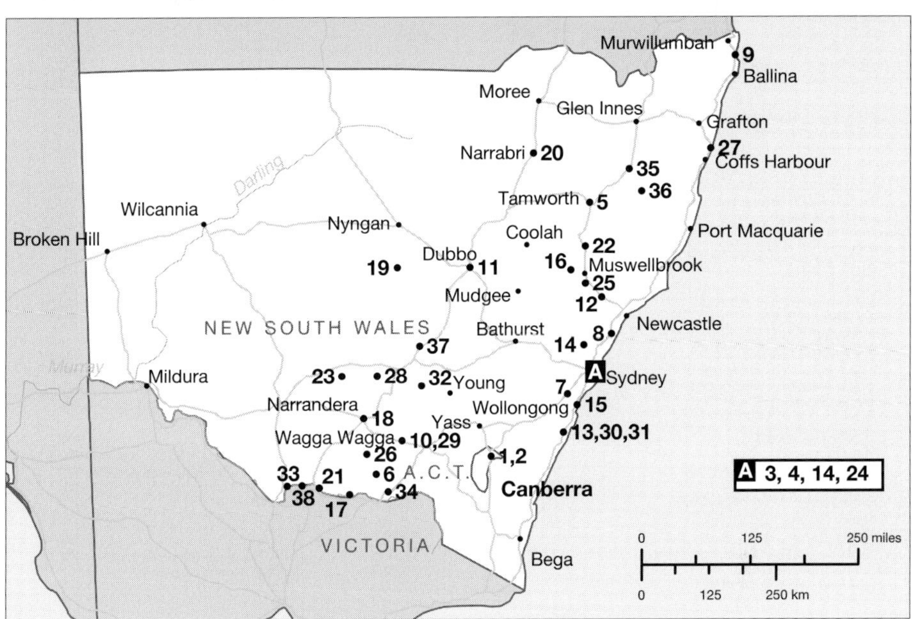

AUSTRALIAN AVIATION MUSEUM (AUS3)

Address:	Hangar 1995, Bankstown Airport, New South Wales 2200.
Tel:	02-9791—088
Fax:	02-9791-3197
Email:	aviationmuseum@bigpond.com
Admission:	Wednesday, Saturday-Sunday 1000-1600.
Location:	The airport is about 20 km south west of the city centre south of the Hume Highway – Route 54.

In the late 1980s Sir Charles Kingsford Smith's original hangar at Mascot faced demolition. A group of enthusiasts suggested relocating the building to Bankstown and this led to the idea of a museum. Ground was broken at the airport on February 15th 1994 and the hangar has now been re-erected on the site. An excellent collection portraying many aspects of aviation in the country has been gathered. On show are uniforms, models, components, photographs and documents. There are many unique aircraft on show. The Fawcett 120 was designed by Luigi Pellarini, who was associated with a number of Australian and New Zealand types. The prototype of this high wing four seater flew in the mid-1950s but after failing to gain an Army contract was put in store. The Clancy Skybaby parasol wing single seater appeared in 1931 and a few were later constructed by amateur builders. The Circle CW is the second version of an annular wing monoplane designed by Sydney resident, Ron Feast. The project started with a number of flying models and construction of the full size aircraft started in the late 1990s. After taxy trials at Bankstown the first flight took place at Camden in July 2001. Major modifications followed and the trials resumed in 2005. Harley Newman died in 1986 whilst flying his first gyrocopter. The one in the collection, his second, incorporated many improvements but it never flew. Several Dakotas were parked by the museum but these are due to move in the near future.

TYPE	REG/SER	CON. NO.	PI/NOTES	STATUS
☐ Avro 748 Series 2A/268	3C-QQP	1709	N15-709	PV
☐ Beech 35 Bonanza	VH-ANU	D-703	NC3256V, N3256V	RA
☐ Clancy Skybaby				PV
☐ Commonwealth CA-29 Mirage IIIO(A) (IIIO(F)) [Dassault Mirage III]	A3-44	CA29-44		PV
☐ Corby CJ-1 Starlet	28-493			PV
☐ De Havilland D.H.60 Moth (R)	'G-AUAE'		Fox Collection aircraft.	PVX
☐ De Havilland D.H.100 Vampire FB.31 (F.30)	A79-175	4059	A79-175, INST.32	RA
☐ De Havilland D.H.115 Vampire T.35				RA
☐ De Havilland D.H.115 Vampire T.35	A79-661	4183	A79-661, INST.49	RAC
☐ De Havilland D.H.125 Series 3B (1B)	VH-CAO	25015	VH-CAO, 9M-AYI	PV
☐ De Havilland D.H.A.3 Drover 3A (2)	VH-FBC	5019	VH-FDA, VH-UNK, VH-UMA, ZK-DDD – on loan from Powerhouse, NSW.	PV

TYPE	REG/SER	CON. NO.	PI/NOTES	STATUS
☐ Douglas DC-3A-467 Skytrain (C-47B) (Dakota IV)	VH-MMD	16553/33301	44-76969, A65-109/VHRGX, VH-MMD, P2-MMD P2-ANU	PV
☐ English Electric EA.1 Canberra T.4	A84-502	EEP71469	WT492 – on loan from HARS, NSW.	PV
☐ Fawcett 120	VH-BQC	1		PV
☐ Feast Circle CW	VH-RJI	R090		PV
☐ Fokker Dr I (R)				PV
☐ Glider Replica (Approx 1905 era)				PV
☐ Government Aircraft Factory N.22B Nomad	ZK-NDB	N22B-37	P2-IAC, VH-HHW – front fuselage only.	PV
☐ Government Aircraft Factory N.22B Nomad	VH-CPX	N22B-50		PV
☐ Government Aircraft Factory N.22B Nomad	VH-FAI	N22B-57	VH-FAI, CC-CBV	RAD
☐ Government Aircraft Factory N.22B Nomad	VH-FZP	N22B-58		PV
☐ Government Aircraft Factory N.22B Nomad	VH-SNX	N22B-103		RA
☐ Harley Neumann Gyrocopter				PV
☐ Lake LA-4-200 Buccaneer	VH-EJY	643	N1050L	PVD
☐ Luton L.A.4 Minor				PV
☐ Luton L.A.5 Major	VH-EVI	N18		PV
☐ Mayfly 3 Man Powered Aircraft				PV
☐ Piaggio P.166	VH-PNC	357	VH-PAP – part fuselage only.	RA
☐ Piaggio P.166	VH-GOB	400		PV
☐ Republic P-47D Thunderbolt				RAD
☐ Riley Heron 2D/A1 (De Havilland D.H.114 Heron 2D)	DQ-FDY	14108	G-5-15, CA+001, G-ASFI, CR-GAT, VH-CLW, T3-ATA	PV
☐ Royal Aircraft Factory S.E.5A (R)	'C9539'			RAX
☐ Scottish Aviation Twin Pioneer 3	9M-ARU	578	FM1061, 9M-ARU, (VH-EVC)	PV
☐ Scottish Aviation Twin Pioneer 3	9M-ASB	590	FM1070, 9M-ASB, (VH-EVD)	PV
☐ Sikorsky S-55B (HRS-2)	VH-ORA	55102	Bu129020, N8307 – on loan from FAA Museum.	PV
☐ Sydnetta Homebuilt				PV
☐ Taylor Glider (R)				PV
☐ Transavia PL-12-M300 Airtruk	VH-FXM	G577	VH-FXM, PK-EDD – composite.	RA
☐ Victa Airtourer 115				PV
☐ Volmer Jensen VJ-22 Sportsman	VH-AQO			PV
☐ Wheeler Skycraft Scout Mk.1	'95-10'			PVX
☐ Wheeler Tweety Hang Glider				PV
☐ Wytwornia Sprzetu Komunikacyjnego (WSK) SBLim-2 [MiG-15UTI]	'777'	712277	777 (Poland), (VH-LJP) in false Soviet markings.	PV

AUSTRALIAN NATIONAL MARITIME MUSEUM (AUS4)

Address:	2 Murray Street, Darling Harbour, Sydney, New South Wales 2000.
Tel:	02-9298-3777
Email:	info@anmm.gov.au
Admission:	Daily 0930-1700.
Location:	About 1 km west of the city centre.

This magnificent museum, located on Sydney's waterfront, opened in 1991. The seven indoor galleries trace the maritime history of the country with many boats, yachts and artefacts on view. Outside in the dock area are a number of vessels including the destroyer H.M.A.S. Vampire and a Russian 'Foxtrot' submarine.

TYPE	REG/SER	CON. NO.	PI/NOTES	STATUS
☐ Westland-Sikorsky WS-58 Wessex HAS.31B	N7-216	WA.216	WA216	PV

AVRO ANSON MUSEUM (AUS5)

Address:	Tamworth Airport, New South Wales 2340.
Tel:	02-6762-0605
Email:	tourism@tamworth.gov.au
Admission:	On permanent view.
Location:	About 6 km south west of the town south of the Oxley Highway – Route 34.

East West Airlines was formed at Tamworth in the late 1940s with a small fleet of Avro Ansons. The first aircraft to be operated by the airline was restored in Sydney and has now been placed in a purpose built museum close to the airport terminal. All Ansons were withdrawn from commercial service in 1962.

TYPE	REG/SER	CON. NO.	PI/NOTES	STATUS
☐ Avro 652A Anson I	VH-ASM		W2068	PV
☐ De Havilland D.H. 100 Vampire FB.31 (F.30)	A79-390	4053	At Hands of Fame Park in town.	PV

BUNN COLLECTION (AUS6)

Address:	Rmb.356, Albury, New South Wales 2644.
Tel:	02-6026-6128
Admission:	By prior permission only.
Location:	On a private strip 20 kms west of Albury off the Riverina Highway – Route 58.

Brothers Donald and Robert Bunn have collected many interesting aircraft at their private airstrip and workshop. In the hangar is the oldest airworthy aircraft in the country. The Moth VH-UAE was imported into Australia in November 1925 and was completely rebuilt in the late 1980s for a friend who keeps it at the field. Under rebuild is one of two Fox Moths known to have been built at Bankstown Airport near Sydney by the Australian de Havilland Company. Also in the workshop is Moth VH-UFV. First delivered to Australia in June 1927 this biplane was initially powered by a Cirrus engine. In 1939 it was fitted with a Gipsy I and two years later with a Gipsy Major. The Taylor Cub arrived in the country in 1937 and has been based on the farm for almost twenty years. There are a number of other Moths, Tiger Moths and a Moth Minor awaiting their turn in the restoration queue. Some of the aircraft reside on nearby airstrips and are not always here.

TYPE	REG/SER	CON. NO.	PI/NOTES	STATUS
☐ De Havilland D.H.60 Moth	VH-UAE	192	G-AUAE, VH-UAE, A7-88	RAA
☐ De Havilland D.H.60G Gipsy Moth	VH-UFV	1A	G-AUFV	RAC
☐ De Havilland D.H.60M Moth	VH-UMO	1379		RAC
☐ De Havilland D.H.82A Tiger Moth	VH-ARM	82800	R4883	RAA
☐ De Havilland D.H.82A Tiger Moth	VH-AUY	83153	T5410	RA
☐ De Havilland D.H.82A Tiger Moth	VH-ATN	DHA.100	A17-103	RAA
☐ De Havilland D.H.82A Tiger Moth	VH-BCN	DHA.876/T.267	A17-459	RAA
☐ De Havilland D.H.83 Fox Moth	VH-AAA	DHA.6	VH-AAA, (VH-BYA), VH-CAS, VH-GAS	RAC
☐ De Havilland D.H.94 Moth Minor	VH-AAM	94002		RAD
☐ De Havilland D.H.94 Moth Minor	VH-ACS	94047	G-AFOW – incorporates parts of c/n 94049 VH-ACO	RAA
☐ Piper J-5A Cub Cruiser				RA
☐ Piper PA-18-150 Super Cub	VH-FPI	18-7909021	N9721N	RA
☐ Taylor J-2 Cub	VH-UYT	958	VH-UYT, VH-PCM, VH-BPK	RAA

CAMDEN MUSEUM OF AVIATION (AUS7)

Address:	11 Stewart Street, Harrington Park, New South Wales 2567.
Tel:	02-9529-4169
Email:	info@camdenmuseumofaviation.com.au
Admission:	Currently closed but hoping to re-open in the near future.
Location:	In Narellan which is about 60 km south west of Sydney off Route 89.

Harold Thomas was an apprentice over seventy years ago with the original Australian National Airways operated by Sir Charles Kingsford Smith. He began collecting engines and in 1961 acquired his first complete aircraft. This led to the ides of setting up a museum. Premises were obtained at Camden Airport and the collection opened in 1963. Initially occupying half a hangar the number of aircraft grew steadily and eventually another complete hangar was in use. In 1979 a move was made to a site nearby at Narellan. A large hangar along with workshops, office and stores was constructed. Owned by Harold, his wife Verna and son Alan the collection also included several tanks and military vehicles. Sadly all three members of the family have died in recent years and the museum closed its doors. Now a group, which includes some of the younger members of the Thomas family, is working to reopen this interesting exhibition. Over sixty aero engines are in the hangar along with instruments, components, armaments and aircraft survival equipment. There are many models, photographs and items of memorabilia to enhance the display. A number of cockpit sections have also been collected. The never completed Gray Monoplane dating from 1929 incorporated several design features, including a split rudder, unknown at the time. Only a small number of Beaufighters have survived. Over three hundred and fifty Vultee Vengeance aircraft were operated by the R.A.A.F. The only remaining complete example of the type, the last Mark I built, is a prized exhibit. After its service days were over it was used as an instructional airframe at the Sydney Technical College. The Mosquito is undergoing a complete restoration which will take several more years. The Victa R-101 Gyroplane was first flown at Camden on May 3rd 1962 and development continued.

TYPE	REG/SER	CON. NO.	PI/NOTES	STATUS
☐ Avro 652A Anson I	R9883		R9883, VH-AVT, VH-AGA, "N5151'	PV
☐ Avro 694 Lincoln B.30A	A73-27		Cockpit section	PV
☐ Bell 47G-3B-1 Sioux	A1-410	3410		PV
☐ Bristol 171 Sycamore HC.51 (4)	XR592	13070	G-AMWI, 'XN635', XR592, VH-BAW	PV
☐ Commonwealth CA-16 Wirraway III [North American NA-33]	A20-685	1137		PV
☐ De Havilland D.H.60G Gipsy Moth	A7-75	1060	VH-ULT	PV
☐ De Havilland D.H.82A Tiger Moth	A17-680	82348	VH-ADH, A17-680, VH-ADH	PV
☐ De Havilland D.H.94 Moth Minor	VH-AGT	94075	A21-19	RA
☐ De Havilland D.H.98 Mosquito FB.VI	HR621			PVC
☐ De Havilland D.H.100 Vampire F.30	A79-14	4029	A79-14, INST.3 – fuselage only.	PV

TYPE	REG/SER	CON. NO.	PI/NOTES	STATUS
☐ De Havilland D.H.112 Sea Venom FAW.53	N4-897	12754	WZ897 – fuselage pod only	PV
☐ De Havilland D.H.112 Sea Venom FAW.53	WZ907	12764		PV
☐ De Havilland D.H.115 Sea Vampire T.22	XA101	15131	Cockpit section on show – remainder of aircraft in store.	PV
☐ De Havilland D.H.115 Vampire T.35	A79-642	4164		RA
☐ De Havilland D.H.115 Vampire T.35	A79-648	4170	Cockpit section.	PV
☐ Department of Aircraft Production Beaufighter 21 [Bristol 156]	A8-186			PV
☐ Department of Aircraft Production Beaufighter 21 [Bristol 156]	A8-386		Cockpit only	PV
☐ Department of Aircraft Production Beaufort IX [Bristol 152]	A9-703		Cockpit section	PV
☐ Fairey Firefly AS.5	VX388	F8420		PV
☐ Fairey Gannet AS.1	XA334	F9226		PV
☐ Falcon Glider			Fuselage frame only	PV
☐ Gere Sport				PV
☐ Gloster Meteor F.8	A77-868		WK674	PV
☐ Government Aircraft Factory Canberra Mk.20 [English Electric EA.1]	A84-209	9	Cockpit section only.	PV
☐ Gray Monoplane		1		PV
☐ Hawker Sea Fury FB.11	VW647			PV
☐ Percival P.44 Proctor 5	'NP336'	Ae.8	G-AGTB, VH-BCM, VH-SST, VH-BCM	PVX
☐ Victa R.101 Gyroplane	VH-MVB			PV
☐ Vultee V-72 Vengeance IA (A-31)	EZ999		41-31047, A27-99	PV

CATALINA FLYING MEMORIAL (AUS8)

Address:	CAN 103 492 440, Building 2, 35-41 Waterloo Road, Macquarie Park, New South Wales 2113.
Tel:	02-9870-7277
Fax:	02-9870-7299
Email:	info@catalinaflying.org.au
Admission:	By prior permission only.
Location:	At Rathmines on Lake Macquarie.

RAAF Rathmines on the shores of Lake Macquarie opened in 1939 and was responsible for the training of flying boat crews. During World War II it was the largest such base in the world. At the end of the conflict it housed an Officer Training Unit and finally closed in 1960. The site has been declared an historic monument. Members of the group are working to bring a Catalina back to the lake. A water bomber version was located in Portugal and this was prepared for the ferry flight. The departure was scheduled for November 2007 but an engine problem caused this to be postponed. Hopefully the aircraft will arrive in 2008 and there are plans for the aircraft to be restored to World War II configuration. A hangar will also be erected.

TYPE	REG/SER	CON. NO.	PI/NOTES	STATUS
☐ Consolidated 28-6A Catalina (PBY-6A)	VH-CAT	2029	Bu46665, N9555 C, CC-CNG, CC-CNP, EC-FXN, CC-CNP	RAA

CHALLINOR COLLECTION (AUS9)

Address:	Hangar 1, Murwillumbah Airfield, Murwillumbah. New South Wales 2484.
Tel:	02-6672-1592
Admission:	By prior permission only.
Location:	On the eastern outskirts of the town.

Brothers Nick and Greg Challinor bought their first aircraft, Tiger Moth VH-WTM, in the early 1970s and flew it round Australia. On this trip they found B.A. Eagle VH-UTI and after seven years restoration this flew again in 1979. A hangar was built at Murwillumbah airfield to house the two machines. Other local owners soon asked them to rebuild their aircraft. Over the years this work grew and a second hangar was erected. In the 1980s their late father Peter joined them and Mothcair Aviation Services was established. The high standard of work carried out is evident in the number of superbly restored types which have emerged from the workshop. The brothers have collected many interesting aircraft and the majority of these are awaiting rebuild. The Westland Widgeon was imported into Australia in 1929 and removed from the register in 1948 after crashing at Sugarloaf Point the previous year. The three Leopard Moths were all withdrawn in the 1950s.

TYPE	REG/SER	CON. NO.	PI/NOTES	STATUS
☐ Auster G AOP.4	VH-HPM	846	MT137, G-ANHM, VH-AZO, VH-ILS, VH-SNG	RA
☐ Cessna 180D	VH-TVB	51063	N8663X, A98-603	RAC

☐ De Havilland D.H.60X Moth	VH-UGN	411	G-AUGN	RA
☐ De Havilland D.H.82A Tiger Moth	VH-AZB	DHA.291	A17-272	RAC
☐ De Havilland D.H.82A Tiger Moth	VH-WTM	DHA.381	A17-346	RAA
☐ De Havilland D.H.82A Tiger Moth	VH-AGY	DHA.57	A17-60	RAA
☐ De Havilland D.H.83 Fox Moth	VH-UUS	4044	G-ACCS, VH-UUS, A41-3, VH-UUS, VH-CCH	RAC
☐ De Havilland D.H.85 Leopard Moth	VH-USK	7084		RA
☐ De Havilland D.H.85 Leopard Moth	VH-USM	7086		RA
☐ De Havilland D.H.85 Leopard Moth	VH-UVF	7126		RA
☐ Westland Widgeon III	VH-UKS	WA.1780		RA

CLYDE NORTH AERONAUTICAL PRESERVATION GROUP (AUS10)

Address: Wagga Wagga 2650.
Tel: 02-6971-2411
Admission: By prior permission only.
Location: At a number of locations in the eastern suburbs of Melbourne and Wagga Wagga,NSW

The group was formed in August 1989 with the aim of preserving items of aeronautical history. Most of the airframes were originally in the Melbourne area but have now moved to the Wagga Wagga area. Some aircraft were loaned out for a proposed museum but this never materialised and the group cannot trace their current location. Some restoration work is being carried out and there is a vast amount of archive material in store.

TYPE	REG/SER	CON. NO.	PI/NOTES	STATUS
☐ Avro 652A Anson I			Front fuselage only – missing.	–
☐ Avro 652A Anson I	MG972		Fuselage only.	RA
☐ Cessna 182B Skylane	VH-DSQ	52051	N2751G, VH-DSC – fuselage only.	RA
☐ Commonwealth CA-30 [Aermacchi MB.326H]	A7-068	CA30-68	Fuselage only – stored near Melbourne.	SD
☐ Commonwealth CA-30 [Aermacchi MB.326H]	A7-071	CA30-71	Fuselage only – missing.	–
☐ Consolidated 28-5A Catalina (PBY-5A)	Bu48368	1730	Front fuselage only – on loan to HARS, NSW.	–
☐ De Havilland D.H.115 Vampire T.35A (T.33)			Partial front fuselage.	RAD
☐ De Havilland D.H.115 Vampire T.35A (T.33)	A79-807	4087	Fuselage at Wagga Wagga – wings stored in Melbourne.	RA
☐ De Havilland D.H.82A Tiger Moth	A17-15	82569/15	Fuselage only – missing.	–
☐ Douglas DC-3-384 (C-69)	VH-ANN	3272	NC1947, 41-7687, VHCDB, VH-ANN, VH-GAH – front fuselage only.	RAD
☐ Douglas DC-3A-456 Skytrain (C-47A) (Dakota III)	A65-24	11974	42-92200 – front fuselage only.	RAD
☐ Douglas DC-4 Skymaster (C-54B)	VH-INX	18327	43-17127, N74628, ZS-BYO, G-ALEP – front fuselage – missing.	–
☐ Fairey Battle I			Front fuselage only.	RAD
☐ Fairey Battle I			Front fuselage only.	RAD
☐ Fairey Battle I			Front fuselage only – missing.	–
☐ Luton L.A.4 Minor			Missing.	–
☐ Rose Monoplane			Fuselage frame only – missing.	–

DUBBO MILITARY MUSEUM (AUS11)

Address: Newell Highway and Camp Road,
Dubbo,
New South Wales 2000.
Tel: 02-6884-5550
Fax: 02-6884-7324
Email: milmuse@lisp.com.au
Admission: Daily 0900-1600.
Location: About 10 km south of the town on Route 39.

This private collection was started forty years ago and is dedicated to all three services. On show in the main building is a B.S.A. motor cycle as used by dispatch riders, engines, radar equipment and armaments. Outside is a large area with many World War II vehicles. The Matilda tank fitted with an Australian designed flame thrower is believed to be the only one in the world still in working order. Landscaped dioramas have been constructed to show the vehicles in combat situations. Two aircraft are on show. The Neptune in the collection won the Fincastle Trophy in Canada in 1975. This aircraft was bought at R.A.A.F. Laverton in 1976 and has recently been sold but it is most likely to remain at the museum for some time.

TYPE	REG/SER	CON. NO.	PI/NOTES	STATUS
☐ Lockheed 726-45-17 Neptune MR.4 (P2V-7) (P2V-7S) (SP-2H)	A89-279	726-7279	Bu149079 – may be moving.	PV
☐ Westland-Sikorsky WS-58 Wessex HAS.31B	N7-219	WA.219	WA219 – fuselage only.	PVD

This Percival Gull is in store at the Museum of Australia in Canberra. (Nigel Hitchman)

Above: The Clancy Sky Baby first appeared in 1931. This later example can be seen in the Australian Aviation Museum at Bankstown. (Douglas Rough)

Left: Among the exhibits at Fighter World at Williamtown in New South Wales is this Australian built Mirage IIIO. (Gerry Manning)

FIGHTER WORLD (AUS12)

Address:	RAAF Base Williamtown, New South Wales 2314.
Tel:	02-4965-1810
Fax:	02-4965-1940
Email:	admin@fighterworld.com.au
Admission:	Daily 1000-1600.
Location:	Just north of the town which is about 15 km east of Raymond Terrace.

Williamtown is one of the front line bases in the country and currently houses units flying the Hornet. Over the years a number of withdrawn types were saved and placed on show as gate guardians. This led to the idea of a museum tracing the development of fighter aircraft. Funds were raised and a purpose built display hangar was opened in 1992. On show are models, photographs, engines, components and weapons. The technology involved in operating modem combat aircraft is highlighted along with the history of the base. An observation deck has been constructed so the visitor can observe the flying operations. Two hundred Mustangs were built in Australia serving from 1945 until 1959. Commonwealth built Sabres with squadrons for many years. Examples of single seat and two seat versions of both the Vampire and Mirage are on show. The Mirage served with squadrons at Williamtown until replaced by the Hornet. A scale replica of a Fokker Dr I hangs from the ceiling and arrivals from the Army Museum at Oakey in Queensland are two replica Spitfires and a replica Messerschmitt Bf 109. This trio of machines needed restoration before they could be placed on display.

TYPE	REG/SER	CON. NO.	PI/NOTES	STATUS
☐ Commonwealth CA-25 Winjeel	A85-428	CA25-28		PV
☐ Commonwealth CA-27 Sabre 32 [North American F-86F]	A94-951	CA27-51		PV
☐ Commonwealth CA-29 Mirage IIID [Dassault Mirage III]	A3-102	CA29-102		PV
☐ Commonwealth CA-29 Mirage IIIO(A) (IIIO(F)) [Dassault Mirage III]	A3-3	CA29-3		PV
☐ Commonwealth CA-29 Mirage IIIO(A) [Dassault Mirage III]	A3-97	CA29-97	Front fuselage only.	PV
☐ Commonwealth CA-30 [Aermacchi MB.326H]	A7-052	CA30-52		PV
☐ Commonwealth CA-30 [Aermacchi MB.326H]	A7-062	CA30-62		PV
☐ Commonwealth CA-30 [Aermacchi MB.326H]	A7-067	CA30-67	Front fuselage only.	PV
☐ De Havilland D.H.100 Vampire F.30	A79-1	4001	A79-1, INST.16	PV
☐ De Havilland D.H.115 Vampire T.35A (T.33)	A79-822	4102	A79-822, INST.39	PV
☐ De Havilland D.H.82A Tiger Moth	A17-347	DHA.382	A17-347, VH-AJG	PV
☐ Fokker Dr I (Scale R)	'425/17'			PVX
☐ Gloster Meteor F.8	'A77-385'		WK798, A77-875	PVX
☐ Government Aircraft Factory Jindivik 203B (IIIB)	N11-750			PV
☐ Hawker P.1099 Hunter FGA.74B (F.6)	546	S4U 3336	XF460 – in Singapore markings.	PV
☐ Messerschmitt Bf 109G (FSM)				PVX
☐ Mikoyan-Gurevich MiG-21UM	'U2146'	516905011	5011 (Poland), VH-XXI – in false Indian markings – on loan.	PVX
☐ Supermarine 361 Spitfire LF.IXe (FSM)	'NH457'			PVX
☐ Supermarine 361 Spitfire LF.XVIe (FSM)	'TE351'			PVX

FLEET AIR ARM MUSEUM (AUS13)

Address:	Box 7015, Naval Post Office, Nowra, New South Wales 2540.
Tel:	02-4424-1920
Fax:	02-4424-1999
Admission:	Daily 1000-1600.
Location:	About 8 km south west of the town.

The museum started in February 1974 in a hangar on the base. Seven years later the collection moved to its present site which then consisted of a number of World War II buildings and a large open area. The majority of the aircraft were exhibited outside and the need for a large hangar became obvious. A Heritage Trust was set up in August 1982 with the main aim of raising funds for the development of the museum. Late 1994 saw the opening of the magnificent building which now houses the majority of the collection. The museum became known as the Australian Museum of Flight and expanded its remit. Several Air Force and privately owned aircraft were placed on show. In September 2006 the museum reverted to its original aims and took up its present title. The collection is now managed by the Royal Australian Navy. The story of naval aviation in the country is portrayed in detail with a wide range of aircraft on show. The aviation branch of the Australian Navy was formally set up in 1948 but members of the service had been involved in flying duties since 1916. The mirror landing aid once used on the carrier H.M.A.S. Melbourne can be seen. Examples of many of the types used by the service since its formation are on show. Twenty eight Fairey Fireflies were operated from 1948 until 1966 and the type saw combat use in Korea. Four Dakotas were flown from 1948 to 1973 and the example on show is fitted with a modified nose which housed the radar used on the Sea Venom. Helicopters have played an increasing role in naval operations in recent years. Two Sycamores from a batch of thirteen flown between 1953 and 1964 can be seen along with several examples of the twenty seven Wessex used from 1962 to 1989. The Navy has also used the ubiquitous Iroquois. Three versions of the successful type can be seen in the collection. The Jindivik unmanned target aircraft was developed in Australia and made its first flight in the early 1950s. Over five hundred were produced and many were used at the ranges near Woomera and also at Llanbedr in Wales.

TYPE	REG/SER	CON. NO.	PI/NOTES	STATUS
☐ Bell 47G-3B-1 Sioux	A1-640	6640		PV
☐ Bell 204 Iroquois (UH-1B)	N9-882	882	63-12954	PV
☐ Bell 204 Iroquois (UH-1C)	N9-3102	3102	64-17622, N9-102 – on pole in town.	PV
☐ Bell 205 Iroquois (UH-1D) (UH-1H)	66-16290	5984		PV
☐ Bristol 171 Sycamore HC.51 (4)	XD653	13071	(G-AMWJ)	PV
☐ Bristol 171 Sycamore HR.50	XA220	13064		PV
☐ Commonwealth CA-16 Wirraway III [North American NA-33]	A20-651	1103	On loan from Museum of Victoria, VIC.	PV
☐ Commonwealth CA-25 Winjeel	A85-364	1527	On loan from RAAFM, VIC	PV
☐ Commonwealth CA-30 [Aermacchi MB.326H]	A7-077	CA30-77		PV
☐ De Havilland D.H.112 Sea Venom FAW.53		12777	WZ935, N4-935	PV
☐ De Havilland D.H.112 Sea Venom FAW.53	WZ937	12779		PV
☐ De Havilland D.H.115 Sea Vampire T.22	'XG766'	15645	XG770, N6-770	PVX
☐ Douglas A-4B Skyhawk (A4D-2)	'N13-154908'	11933	Bu142871	PVX
☐ Douglas DC-3A-456 Skytrain (C-47A) (Dakota III)	N2-43	12542	42-92711, A65-43/VHCUN, A65-43/VJORA	PV
☐ Fairey Firefly AS.6	WJ109	F8813		PV
☐ Fairey Gannet AS.1	XA434	F9304		PV
☐ Fairey Gannet T.5	XG888	F9417		RA
☐ Government Aircraft Factory Jindivik 203B (IIIB)	N11-605		A92-605	PV
☐ Government Aircraft Factory Jindivik 203B (IIIB)	N11-609		A92-609	PV
☐ Grumman G-121 Tracker (S-2E)	Bu151646	179C	Front fusealge only.	PV
☐ Grumman G-121 Tracker (S-2E)	N12-153582	338C	Bu153582	PV
☐ Grumman G-121 Tracker (S-2E)	N12-153600	344C	Bu153600	RAC
☐ Grumman G-121 Tracker (S-2E) (S-2G)	N12-153580	336C	Bu153580	PV
☐ Hargrove 1894 Glider (R)				PV
☐ Hargrove Glider (R)				PV
☐ Hawker P.1099 Hunter FGA.74B (P.1067 Hunter F.4)	'280'	41H/670805	WV331, 7783M, G-9-372, 543 (Singapore), VH-JGP	PVX
☐ Hawker Sea Fury FB.11	WG630			RA
☐ Skycraft Scout				PV
☐ Sopwith Pup (R)	'N5182'	TSP-1	VH-SOR	PVX
☐ Supermarine 309 Sea Otter I	JN200		JN200, VH-BQI – front fuselage only	PV
☐ Westland Scout AH.1	VH-NVY	F9490	WS101, N8-101	PV
☐ Westland-Sikorsky WS-58 Wessex HAS.31B	N7-221	WA.221	WA221	PV
☐ Wytwornia Sprzetu Komunikacyjnego (WSK) SBLim-2A (Lim-1) [MiG-15] [MiG-15UTI]	607	1A 06-007	607, VH-BPG	PVAX
☐ Wytwornia Sprzetu Komunikacyjnego (WSK) Lim-6bis [MiG-17F]	434	1J 04-34	434 (Poland), VH-ALG – on loan.	RA

FOX COLLECTION (AUS14)

Address:	24 Foxall Road, Kellyville, New South Wales 2155
Tel:	02-9625-2245
Admission:	By prior permission only.
Location:	Bankstown. Airport is about 20 km south west of Sydney. Wisemans Ferry is about 30 km north of Sydney.

Roy Fox is acquiring an interesting collection of classic aircraft. They are based either at Wisemans Ferry or in a private hangar at Bankstown. Two Comper Swifts are in the fleet. One is the sole survivor of the three Gipsy Major powered. This aircraft raced in England and the U.S.A. prior to World War II and recently spent many years in Western Australia. The Pobjoy engined examples last flew in the late 1960s. The Short Scion was initially Pobjoy powered but in 1946 Gipsy Minor engines were installed. The aircraft soon crashed and was rebuilt at Alice Springs. In the 1980s it was on show in the now closed Chewing Gum Field Aviation Museum in Queensland. Very few B.A. Eagles survive and the example in the collection was rebuilt by the Challinor brothers in the late 1970s before it went on show at Air World at Wangaratta. The Klemm spent its first five years in Switzerland before moving to Australia in 1942 after a spell in New Guinea. The Fox Moth was impressed for Air Force service in 1942 and then spent more the fifty years in store before it was restored.

TYPE	REG/SER	CON. NO.	PI/NOTES	STATUS
☐ British Aircraft Eagle 2	VH-UTI	109		RAA
☐ Comper C.L.A.7 Swift	VH-UVC	S.32/10	G-ACAG	RAC
☐ Comper C.L.A.7 Gipsy Swift	VH-ACG	GS32/2	G-ABWH, (NC27K), G-ABWH	RA
☐ De Havilland D.H.60 Moth (R)	'VH-UAE'		'G-AUAE' – at Australian Aviation Museum.	–
☐ De Havilland D.H.82A Tiger Moth	VH-CCD	DHA.823	(DX780), A17-673, VH-RNP	RAA
☐ De Havilland D.H.83 Fox Moth	VH-UVL	4015	G-ABXS, VH-UVL, A41-2	RAA
☐ De Havilland D.H.89A Dragon Rapide (D.H.89B Dominie I)	VH-UWB	6655	HG656, NZ527, ZK-ALB, VH-IAN, VH-UTV	RAA
☐ Klemm L 25d II	VH-UUR	796	HB-XAL	RAA
☐ Short S.16 Scion I	VH-UTV	S.793		RAC

HISTORICAL AIRCRAFT RESTORATION SOCIETY (AUS15)

Address:	P.O. Box 1071, Albion Park, New South Wales 2527.
Tel:	02-4257-4333
Fax:	02-4257-4388
Email:	info@hars.org.au
Admission:	By prior permission only.
Location:	At the airfield which is in the north eastern part of the town.

The society was formed in 1979 by a group of enthusiasts. They were concerned at the lack of interest in Australia's aviation history and the number of historic aircraft being allowed to decay. The first project undertaken was the restoration of a Harvard and work was also carried out on aircraft for other museums. A workshop in the Qantas area at Mascot Airport was obtained. Parts of a Bristol Beaufighter were restored for the U.S.A.F. Museum at Dayton in Ohio. In late 1996 the fuselage of a Puss Moth was completed for a private owner in Victoria. In 1989 work started on trying to find a Super Constellation which could be returned to airworthy condition. One was located at Tucson, Arizona in December 1991 and eventually purchased from the U.S.A.F. Museum. Restoration commenced the following year and the first flight took place on September 1994. On January 24th 1996 the Constellation took off from Tucson on its way across the Pacific and landed at Sydney on February 3rd. Resplendent in a red and white scheme similar to that once used by Qantas, the four engined classic is a regular performer at airshows. Members of the group own the three Neptunes and are associated with the operation of several other aircraft. In 2002 a move was made to Albion Park airfield where a new hangar and workshop complex were constructed. Administration and licensing offices along with archive and educational facilities were included. The Commonwealth factory produced the Wirraway which served as a trainer and general purpose aircraft from 1939 until 1959. The type was pressed into combat in World War II and flew missions in both Malaya and New Britain. Seven hundred and fifty five were built in seven different versions. The Australian de Havilland company designed the three engined Drover in the late 1940s but only twenty were built with a few serving with the Royal Flying Doctor Service. The Catalina which once served as a water bomber has been restored to represent one flown during and after World War II. The Huey Cobra gun ship served with American forces in the Vietnam conflict and a pair has been acquired for the collection. More types are sought.

TYPE	REG/SER	CON. NO.	PI/NOTES	STATUS
☐ Bell 209 Huey Cobra (AH-1S) (AH-1P)	76-22598	22032		RA
☐ Bell 209 Huey Cobra (AH-1S) (AH-1P)	76-22592	24026	76-22592, VH-SHC	RA
☐ Cessna 172F Mescalero (T-41A)	VH-ENY	17256336	67-14982, N4982R	RAA
☐ Cessna 172H	VH-MGY	17263144	N4394R	RA
☐ Cessna 180C	'A98-043'	50739	N9239T, VH-GKD, VH-WGD	RAAX
☐ Cessna 310B	VH-REK	35583	N5383A, VH-REK, P2-REK – at Bankstown, NSW.	RAA
☐ Commonwealth CA-3 Wirraway II [North American NA-33]	VH-JML	99	A20-99	RAA
☐ Commonwealth CA-16 Wirraway III [North American NA-33]	'A20-458'	1171	A20-719, VH-WRX	RAAX
☐ Commonwealth CA-25 Winjeel	VH-EAD	CA25-35	A85-435, VH-KHZ	RAA
☐ Commonwealth CA-27 Sabre 30 [North American F-86F]	A94-901	CA27-1		PV
☐ Consolidated 28-5A Catalina (PBY-5A)	Bu48368	1730	Front fuselage only – on loan from Clyde North APG, VIC.	RAC
☐ Consolidated 28-6A Catalina (PBY-6A)	'A24-362'	2043	Bu46679, N9562C, CC-CNF, CC-CCS, VH-PBZ	RAAX
☐ Convair 340-71 Samaritan (R4Y-1), (C-131F)	Bu141025	308		RA
☐ De Havilland D.H.82A Tiger Moth	VH-DHV	AW/TC/1	VH-AWH, VH-SNJ, VH-IVN	PV
☐ De Havilland D.H.115 Vampire T.35	VH-FJW	4159	A79-637	RA
☐ De Havilland D.H.115 Vampire T.35	A79-665	4187	A79-665, INST.49	RAC
☐ De Havilland D.H.A.3 Drover 2				RA
☐ De Havilland D.H.A.3 Drover 3	VH-DHM	5020	VH-AHZ, VQ-FAH, VP-PAE, VH-PAB	PVA
☐ Douglas DC-3A-467 Skytrain (C-47B) (Dakota IV)	VH-EAE	16348/33096	44-76764, A65-95/VHRFL, A65-95/VMHJV	RA
☐ Douglas DC-3A-467 Skytrain (C-47B) (Dakota IV)	VH-EAF	16358/33106	44-76774, A65-94/VHRFK, A65-94/VHJMN	RAA
☐ Douglas DC-4 Skymaster (C-54E)	VH-PAF	27352	44-9126, N9013V	RAA
☐ English Electric EA.1 Canberra T.4	A84-502	EEP71469	WT492 – on loan to Aus Av. Mus., NSW	–
☐ Fokker F.VIIa/3m (R)	VH-USU	SCA-28		RAA
☐ Grumman G-121 Tracker (S-2E) (S-2G)	N12-152812	281C	Bu152812	RA
☐ Lockheed 1049A-55-137 Super Constellation (1049A-55-86) (RC-121D) (EC-121H) (EC-121T)	N51006	1049A-4350	53-0535	RA
☐ Lockheed 1049F-55-96 Super Constellation (C-121C)	VH-EAG	1049F-4176	54-0157, N4115Q	RAA
☐ Lockheed 726-45-17 Neptune MR.4 (P2V-7) (P2V-7S) (SP-2H)	VH-LRR	726-7183	Bu147566, 147566 (France), N8187Z	RAA
☐ Lockheed 726-45-17 Neptune MR.4 (P2V-7) (P2V-7S) (SP-2H)	VH-NEP	726-7281	Bu149081, A89-281	RAC
☐ Lockheed 726-45-17 Neptune MR.4 (P2V-7) (P2V-7S) (SP-2H)	VH-IOY	726-7273	Bu149073, A89-273	RAA
☐ Nord N.1002 Pingouin II [Messerschmitt Bf 108B]	VH-OFS	285	285 (France), F-BGVD, OO-GVD, N108R	RAA
☐ Piaggio P.166	VH-MMP	365	G-APYP	RA
☐ Republic P-47D Thunderbolt				RAD

LUSKINTYRE AVIATION FLYING MUSEUM (AUS16)

Address:	Luskintyre Airfield, 252 Pywell Road, Luskintyre, New South Wales 2321.
Tel:	0418-628321
Email:	homepc@bravo.net.au
Admission:	When the airfield is open.
Location:	Just north east of the town.

The airfield was built in 1977 and is now home to an interesting collection of vintage aircraft. There is a restoration business on the site where others can be seen. Visitors can normally view the aircraft when anyone is present. Open days are often held and impromptu flying takes place. The predominant type is the Tiger Moth with both British and Australian built examples in residence. These range from bare fuselage frames up to superbly restored airworthy machines. One was built up from spares in Australia. One Tiger, VH-GVA, made a solo flight from England to Australia in the 1990s.The Stampe was obtained in England after it served with the Air Force and as a civil machine in France. Two Gipsy Moths are also present. One was built in England and survived a crash and subsequent fire in 1939 to be rebuilt. The Australian built example was completed in 1931 and crashed in 1933. Several months later it was fitted with a Gipsy Major engine and registered as a Moth Major. The aircraft will be rebuilt to its original configuration. Austers were popular in Australia in the 1950s and an example of the Aiglet can be seen. This type was derived from the J/1 Autocrat and was fitted with a Gipsy Major engine. The majority of the eighty six produced were exported. A late example of the classic Beech Bonanza can be seen along with an early Cessna 150 and a few homebuilt designs.

TYPE	REG/SER	CON. NO.	PI/NOTES	STATUS
☐ Auster J/1B Aiglet	VH-KBY	2697		RAA
☐ Beech V35 Bonanza	VH-DYX	D-8523		RAA
☐ Beech 65 Queen Air	VH-FDV	LC-203	N9506Q	RAA
☐ Cessna 150	VH-AWP	17353	N5853E, VH-RFQ	RAA
☐ Cessna 402	VH-BUD	0079	N3279Q	RAA
☐ Commonwealth CA-25 Winjeel	VH-NON	CA25-11	A85-411	RAA
☐ De Havilland D.H.60G Gipsy Moth	VH-ULU	878	G-AUHQ, VH-UHQ, VH-AAQ	RAA
☐ De Havilland D.H.60G Gipsy Moth (DH.60GIII Moth Major)	VH-URA	DHA.4		RA
☐ De Havilland D.H.82A Tiger Moth	VH-UYO	3623	VH-UYQ, A17-676, VH-CCE	RAA
☐ De Havilland D.H.82A Tiger Moth	VH-ZUP	82358	N9257, VH-AKN	RAA
☐ De Havilland D.H.82A Tiger Moth	VH-RAW	82372	N9271, NZ868, ZK-API	RA
☐ De Havilland D.H.82A Tiger Moth	VH-TSG	82562/DHA.8	A17-8, VH-RAW	RA
☐ De Havilland D.H.82A Tiger Moth	VH-LNW	82571/DHA.17	A17-17	RA
☐ De Havilland D.H.82A Tiger Moth	VH-LOW	82776	R4844, VH-BDF	RAA
☐ De Havilland D.H.82A Tiger Moth	VH-AMY	83116	R5257, VH-BLZ	RAA
☐ De Havilland D.H.82A Tiger Moth	VH-AQJ	DHA.22	A17-26	RAA
☐ De Havilland D.H.82A Tiger Moth	VH-MPF	DHA.26	A17-29, VH-ARP – fuselage frame only.	RA
☐ De Havilland D.H.82A Tiger Moth	VH-BGC	DHA.54	A17-57	RAA
☐ De Havilland D.H.82A Tiger Moth	VH-ROY	DHA.159	A17-158	RAA
☐ De Havilland D.H.82A Tiger Moth	VH-NEI	DHA.167	A17-166, VH-BFB, VH-DAN, VH-CKE – fuselage frame only.	RA
☐ De Havilland D.H.82A Tiger Moth	VH-DDA	DHA.169	A17-198, VH-AHL	RAA
☐ De Havilland D.H.82A Tiger Moth	VH-UYB	DHA.195	A17-194 – fuselage frame only – possible identity.	RA
☐ De Havilland D.H.82A Tiger Moth	A17-198	DHA.199	Possible identity.	RA
☐ De Havilland D.H.82A Tiger Moth	VH-JAU	DHA.205	A17-204, VH-BNW, VH-WFU	RAA
☐ De Havilland D.H.82A Tiger Moth	VH-BTX	DHA.226	A17-225, VH-ARA – fuselage frame only.	RA
☐ De Havilland D.H.82A Tiger Moth	VH-UTD	DHA.341	A17-322, VH-AYX	RA
☐ De Havilland D.H.82A Tiger Moth	VH-PVZ	DHA.439	A17-395, VH-BKD, VH-WFX, VH-PVA	RA
☐ De Havilland D.H.82A Tiger Moth	VH-MDV	DHA.470	PK-VVU, A17-626, VH-GWB	RAA
☐ De Havilland D.H.82A Tiger Moth	VH-PCG	DHA.793	DX736, A17-643, VH-BGH	RA
☐ De Havilland D.H.82A Tiger Moth	VH-WAP	DHA.826	DX783, A17-694,	RA
☐ De Havilland D.H.82A Tiger Moth	VH-AGN	DHA.832	DX789, A17-700	RAA
☐ De Havilland D.H.82A Tiger Moth	VH-BBC	DHA.842	(DX799), A17-710, VH-RSC	RAA
☐ De Havilland D.H.82A Tiger Moth	VH-KNX	DHA.922	A17-499, VH-RNX	RAA
☐ De Havilland D.H.82A Tiger Moth	VH-GVA	DHA.1014	A17-579, VH-GME	RAA
☐ De Havilland D.H.82A Tiger Moth	VH-BNX	DHA.1033	A17-598,	RA
☐ De Havilland D.H.82A Tiger Moth	VH-BNI	DHA.1048	A17-613	RAA
☐ De Havilland D.H.82A Tiger Moth	VH-LSK	DHA.1054	A17-619, VH-AZK	RAA
☐ De Havilland D.H.82A Tiger Moth	VH-ADW/'K2576'	DHA.1079	A17-748, VH-AZI, VH-CAD, VH-BSB	RAAX
☐ De Havilland D.H.82A Tiger Moth	VH-HCI	SA.87.5	Built from spares.	RA
☐ De Havilland D.H.C.1 Chipmunk T.10	VH-RSM	C1/0245	WB710, EI-AJB, VH-RSM, VH-WMT, VH-WMG	RAA
☐ Roloff RLU.1 Breezy	VH-AQE	N137		RAA
☐ SIAI-Marchetti SM.1019E	VH-JKW	1-062	MM57254	RA
☐ Stampe & Vertongen S.V.4B	VH-WEF	1040	1040 (France), F-BBGN, G-AVCO	RAA
☐ Vans RV-6A	VH-EML	V348		RAA

MULWALA & DISTRICT SERVICEMEN LEAGUE CLUB (AUS17)

Address:	Melbourne Street, Mulwala, New South Wales 2647.
Tel:	03-5744-2331
Fax:	03-5744-2430
Email:	reception@mulwalaservices.com.au
Admission:	On permanent view.
Location:	About 500 metres north of the bridge off the B400.

The aircraft was intended to be put on display at the Tocumwal Historic Aerodrome Museum but a lack of finance caused this plan to be shelved. The C-47 arrived at its new home on October 18th 2004 and has been assembled next to the main entrance to the club. Members intend to restore it to original condition.

TYPE	REG/SER	CON. NO.	PI/NOTES	STATUS
☐ Douglas DC-3A-467 Skytrain (C-47B) (Dakota IV)	A65-64	15195/26640	43-49379, A65-64/VHCUU, VH-JGL	PVC

NARRANDERA NO.8 ELEMENTARY FLYING TRAINING SCHOOL TIGER MOTH MEMORIAL (AUS18)

Address:	P.O. Box 89, Narrandera, New South Wales 2700.
Tel:	02-6959-1766
Admission:	Daily 0900-1700.
Location:	Just north of the town centre on the Newell Highway – Route 39.

The flying school was established at Narrandera in August 1940 and the first students arrived two months later. More than seven thousand personnel trained at the school before it closed in June 1945. This total included three thousand eight hundred and eighteen pilots. The idea of a memorial honouring the work of the school was put forward in 1981 and fund raising commenced the following year. The Tiger Moth was bought in 1982 and restored to its original all yellow colour scheme at the R.A.A.F. base at Wagga Wagga. The memorial was opened on October 2nd 1988 by Air Chief Marshal Sir Neville McNamara who trained at the school in 1942 and later returned as an instructor. Around the walls of the building is a comprehensive collection of photographs, documents and memorabilia tracing the history and work of the base and its personnel.

TYPE	REG/SER	CON. NO.	PI/NOTES	STATUS
☐ De Havilland D.H.82A Tiger Moth	A17-443	DHA.641		PV

NARROMINE AVIATION MUSEUM (AUS19)

Address:	P.O. Box 122, Narromine, New South Wales 2821.
Tel:	02-6889-7131
Email:	curator@narromineaviationmuseum.org.au
Admission:	Wednesday-Monday 1000-1700.
Location:	About 2 km north west of the town.

Aviation first came to the town in 1919 and a decade later the first regional aero club in Australia was formed. This organisation is still active at the airfield. During World War II a large pilot training base was set up and Tiger Moths were among the types used. Several buildings from this era are still in use and a diorama of the site can be seen in the exhibition hall. The museum was established in the 1990s to trace the history of aviation in the area and has many interesting items on show. Models, photographs, engines and components can be seen An aero club scrapbook from the 1930s is a prized exhibit. The aircraft are in the hangars and can be seen by arrangement. The Wright A was built to commemorate the centenary of flight and was completed in 2005. Gliding is a popular sport at Narromine and one vintage sailplane is under restoration. One Hawkridge Venture was built in England and the one in the collection was constructed by the Dubbo Gliding Club in 1950.

TYPE	REG/SER	CON. NO.	PI/NOTES	STATUS
☐ Commonwealth CA-27 Sabre 30 [North American F-86F]	A94-915	CA27-13		RA
☐ De Havilland D.H.82A Tiger Moth	VH-KBX	83183	T5458, VH-AIX	RAA
☐ Hawkridge Venture	VH-GDU			RAC
☐ Wright A (R)	VH-SOF	WBA.01		RAA

NYNGAN AND DISTRICT MUSEUM (AUS20)

Address:	Rawson Place, Nyngan, New South Wales 2825.
Tel:	02-6832-1052
Admission:	Monday-Friday 0900-1600.
Location:	In the town.

The displays at the museum, housed in the old railway station, trace the history and development of the community in peace and war. There are many items of memorabilia to be seen.

TYPE	REG/SER	CON. NO.	PI/NOTES	STATUS
☐ Bell 204 Iroquois (UH-1B)	A2-1022	1022	63-13590	PV

OAKLANDS LIONS CLUB DISPLAY (AUS21)

Address:	Oaklands, New South Wales 2646.
Admission:	By prior permission only.
Location:	In the town.

The Lions Club have a display in a series of derelict sheds. The only aviation item on show is the wooden fuselage of an aircraft built by the Williams family in the 1920s. Construction commenced in 1924 but the machine was never finished. The wings and engine were sold in the 1930s and lost.

TYPE	REG/SER	CON. NO.	PI/NOTES	STATUS
☐ Williams Aeroplane			Fuselage frame only.	PVD

PAY'S FLYING MUSEUM (AUS22)

Address:	Pay's Air Service, Scone Aerodrome, New South Wales 2337.
Tel:	02-6545-1166
Fax:	02-6545-2631
Email:	enquiries@paysairservice.com.au
Admission:	By prior permission only.
Location:	About 3 km west of the town which is about 150 km north west of Newcastle.

Col Pay operated and maintained a fleet of agricultural aircraft in both New South Wales and Queensland. Sadly he was killed testing an AT-802 in December 2007. The fate of this collection is still being decided. A Curtiss Kittyhawk was bought in 1985 and flown from 1989 until 1992 when it crashed at Wee Waa. The aircraft was rebuilt and sold to the U.S.A. in 1994. Another example of the type was then rebuilt.

TYPE	REG/SER	CON. NO.	PI/NOTES	STATUS
☐ Cessna 305A Bird Dog (L-19A) (O-1A)	VH-LQS	22559	51-12245, (South Vietnam)	RAA
☐ Cessna 318E Dragonfly (A-37B)	VH-CPD	43331	71-0793, 793 (Vietnam)	RAC
☐ Commonwealth CA-18 Mustang 21 [North American P-51D]	VH-AUB	1432	A68-107	RAA
☐ Curtiss 87-A4 Warhawk (P-40E) (Kittyhawk IA)	VH-KTY	19128	41-25109, ET433, NZ3094, (VH-KTH)	RAA
☐ De Havilland D.H.82A Tiger Moth	VH-PCL	3786	N6456, VH-BPW	RAA
☐ De Havilland D.H.C.1 Chipmunk 22 (T.10)	VH-AMV	C1/0174	WB722, G-AOSP, VH-BTL, VH-BWF	RAA
☐ North American NA-168 Texan (T-6G)	VH-HAJ	168-290	49-3186, N1751 built as NA-88 (AT-6C) c/n 88-11257 41-32862	RAA
☐ SIAI-Marchetti SM.1019E	VH-PAC	1-009	MM57202	RA
☐ SIAI-Marchetti SM.1019E	VH-PAI	1-025	MM57217	RA
☐ SIAI-Marchetti SM.1019E	VH-PAE	1-056	MM57248	RA

PIONEER PARK MUSEUM (AUS23)

Address:	Rememberance Avenue, Griffith, New South Wales 2680.
Tel:	02-6962-4196
Email:	darrell.Collins@griffith.nsw.gov.au
Admission:	Daily 0830-1700.
Location:	About 2 km north of the town centre.

Opened in 1971 the park displays more than fifteen original buildings moved to the site and a similar number of faithful period replicas. The result is a village showing life from the end of the last century up to the 1930s. There are also displays of machinery and engines many in working order. In the 1930s Lionel Gibbs assisted by his two brothers and a friend built a primary glider on their farm. The first trials took place in August 1936 and the machine flew on October 11th. On the eighth flight on October 25th the glider covered a distance of three quarters of a mile, reached a height of two hundred feet and was aloft for thirty seconds. Unfortunately the landing was misjudged and the fuselage badly damaged. The glider was repaired, made a few more flights and was then hung up in the shearing shed at the farm where it remained until donated to the park in the 1970s. Lionel Gibbs was killed when the Lancaster he was piloting was shot down over Holland in 1943.

TYPE	REG/SER	CON. NO.	PI/NOTES	STATUS
☐ Fairey Firefly TT.6 (AS.6)	'WB518'	F8656	WD828, VH-HMW – on display outside club in town centre.	PVX
☐ Gibbs Glider				RA

POWER HOUSE MUSEUM (MUSEUM OF APPLIED ARTS AND SCIENCES) (AUS24)

Address:	P.O. Box K346, Haymarket, Sydney, New South Wales 2000.
Tel:	02-9217-0111
Email:	info@phm.gov.au
Admission:	Daily 1000-1700.
Location:	In Harris Street, Ultimo which is about 2 km south west of the city centre.

In 1879 the Sydney Garden Palace Exhibition was staged and this led in the following year to the establishment of the Museum of Applied Arts and Sciences. In the early 1980s the collection moved into the superbly restored Powerhouse building which, for years, used to supply electricity for the trams of the city. In 1988 social history was added to the museum's brief. The exhibition is staged on a number of levels and subjects covered include transport, industry, the sciences, communications and information technology. The aviation exhibition includes a section on the pioneer experimenter Lawrence Hargrave. On show are some of his papers and models of his kites. The largest aircraft displayed is the Catalina 'Frigate Bird II' flown by P.G. Taylor on survey flights to South America in the early 1950s. The aircraft last flew in 1954 and was stored for twenty years. From 1974 to 1983 the flying boat was loaned to the Camden Aviation Museum before being restored by Hawker de Havilland and moved into the Powerhouse in 1987. The Cierva C.30A, first arrived in Australia in 1935, and was active until 1950. The Moth was in use from 1932 until it crashed at Barellan, NSW in 1943. Fortunately the airframe survived and was restored for the display. The Bell Jet Ranger was flown by Dick Smith on the first helicopter solo round the world flight in 1982/3. A number of unique Australian-built aircraft are in store. Among these is an example of the three seater open cockpit General Aircraft Genairco biplane. The fuselage was based on the de Havilland Moth and the wings on the Avro Avian. Arthur Butler flew a Comper Swift from England to Australia in the early 1930s. He designed and flew two similar and later set up the airline Butler Air Transport. The incomplete airframe of his second monoplane is awaiting restoration.

TYPE	REG/SER	CON. NO.	PI/NOTES	STATUS
☐ Bedson Resurgam 1			Incomplete.	RA
☐ Beech 65-B80 Queen Air	VH-AMB	LD-320	N7808L	PV
☐ Bell 206B-3 Jet Ranger	VH-DIK	3653		PV
☐ Blériot XI				PV
☐ Butler ABA-2 Bat	VH-ARG	1	Incomplete	RA
☐ Cameron R-77 Hot Air Balloon				RA
☐ Celio 4 Glider	VH-DSE	2970	Gondola only.	PV
☐ Celio Man Powered Helicopter				RA
☐ Cierva C.30A (Avro 671)	VH-USR	792		PV
☐ Clancy Skybaby	'N211SB'	6		PVX
☐ Cohen SK1-B Hang Glider				RA
☐ Consolidated 28-5 Catalina (PB2B-2)	VH-ASA	61154	Bu44248, (JX630), A24-385, (VH-AGB)	PV
☐ Cook Flying Machines Shadow BD	G-MTKS	066		RA
☐ Corby CJ-1 Starlet	VH-UWZ	N-56		RA
☐ De Havilland D.H.60X Moth	VH-UAU	614		PV
☐ De Havilland D.H.A.3 Drover 3A (2)	VH-FBC	5019	VH-FDA, VH-UNK, VH-UMA, ZK-DDD – on loan to AAM, NSW.	–
☐ Eagle XP-1				PV
☐ Enterprise Wings Foil 165 Hang Glider				RA
☐ General Aircraft Genairco	VH-UOG	16		RA
☐ Glidair GA-1 Twinplank	VH-GST			RA
☐ Kimberley Sky-rider				RA
☐ Moyes Boat Towed Hang Glider				RA
☐ Moyes Hang Glider				RA
☐ Stolaero Minimum Aircraft				RA
☐ Todhunter Man Powered Skycycle				RA
☐ Transavia PL-12 Airtruk	VH-TRN	601	Composite with parts from several airframes.	PV
☐ Wheeler Skycraft Scout Mk.1		001		PV

RAYMOND TERRACE MEMORIAL (AUS25)

Address:	Bettles Park, Raymond Terrace, New South Wales 2324.
Admission:	Aircraft on permanent view.
Location:	Just south of the town centre.

No. 76 Squadron is based at nearby RAAF Williamtown and currently flies British Aerospace Hawks. In the past it flew Sabres from the field and one painted in their colours is displayed in Raymond Terrace.

TYPE	REG/SER	CON. NO.	PI/NOTES	STATUS
☐ Commonwealth CA-27 Sabre 32 [North American F-86F]	A94-959	CA27-59		PV

RETURNED AND SERVICES LEAGUE MEMORIAL – COROWA (AUS26)

Address:	RSL Club, 30 Betterment Parade, Corowa, New South Wales 2646.
Tel:	02-6033-1022
Admission:	Aircraft on permanent view.
Location:	In the north eastern part of the town.

The Vampire is mounted outside the club as a memorial to those who have lost their lives. The aircraft was put on show several years ago and in the mid-1990s it was restored at Wagga Wagga and Corowa. A decision was made after World War II to produce the Vampire under licence to replace the R.A.A.F.'s Mustangs.

TYPE	REG/SER	CON. NO.	PI/NOTES	STATUS
☐ De Havilland D.H.100 Vampire F.30	A79-529	4022		PV

RETURNED AND SERVICES LEAGUE MEMORIAL – WOOLGOOGLA (AUS27)

Address:	RSL Club, Beach Street, Woolgoogla, New South Wales 2456.
Tel:	02-6654-1234
Admission:	Aircraft on permanent view.
Location:	Just east of the town centre.

The club has put on show an Iroquois which is dedicated to those lost in the Vietnam War. The helicopter is painted in the markings of one shot down on a rescue mission at Phouc Tuy on April 17th 1971. Australian forces served in large numbers in the conflict and the Iroquois was an important part of their contribution.

TYPE	REG/SER	CON. NO.	PI/NOTES	STATUS
☐ Bell 205 Iroquois (UH-1H)	'A2-767'	13330	72-21631	PVX

ROYAL AUSTRALIAN AIR FORCE URANQUITY MEMORIAL PARK (AUS28)

Address:	Olympic Highway, Uranquity, New South Wales 2652.
Admission:	On permanent view.
Location:	In the centre of the town.

The airfield was opened in 1941 as part of the Empire Air training Scheme. More than fifteen hundred pilots gained their wings over the next four years. The Memorial Park was opened on September 19th 1999 to commemorate the history of the field. An engine from Wirraway, a type used at Uranquity can be seen in the landscaped park. There are also a number of memorial boards with photographs tracing the short history of base. Types used at the field are featured along with the personnel who flew from the airfield.

This Fairey Firefly is on show at the Fleet Air Arm Museum at Nowra. (John Mounce)

The Mulwala and District Servicemens Club have preserved this Dakota. (Eric Munk)

The Sloane Biplane was built before World War I and it is now on show in the Yarrawonga/Mulwala Pioneer Museum. (Eric Munk)

ROYAL AUSTRALIAN AIR FORCE WAGGA WAGGA BASE MUSEUM (AUS29)

Address:	RAAF Wagga Wagga, Forest Hill, Wagga Wagga, New South Wales 2651.
Tel:	02-6937-4814
Admission:	Currently closed for refurbishment.
Location:	About 10 km east of the town on the Sturt Highway – Route 20.

The base is home to the main technical training school of the Air Force. Over the years many airframes have been used for instructional purposes and others have been preserved around the camp. The museum opened on June 24th 1995 in the former main guard room building. Interesting displays of photographs, medals, memorabilia uniforms and documents trace the history of the base. The development of technical training is also highlighted with a series of interesting exhibits. The majority of the preserved aircraft are lined up outside the museum.

TYPE	REG/SER	CON. NO.	PI/NOTES	STATUS
☐ Commonwealth CA-25 Winjeel	A85-403	CA25-03		PV
☐ Commonwealth CA-27 Sabre 30 [North American F-86F]	A94-909	CA27-9	Front fuselage only.	PV
☐ Commonwealth CA-27 Sabre 32 [North American F-86F]	A94-982	CA27-82		PV
☐ Commonwealth CA-29 Mirage IIIO(A) (IIIO(F)) [Dassault Mirage III]	A3-41	CA29-41	Composite with parts of CA29-8 A3-8.	PV
☐ Commonwealth CA-30 [Aermacchi MB.326H]				RA
☐ De Havilland D.H.115 Vampire T.35	A79-612	4134	A79-612, INST.26	PV
☐ De Havilland D.H.115 Vampire T.35	A79-623	4145	A79-623, INST.29 – fitted with booms of c/n 4084 A79-804, INST.32	PV
☐ Gloster Meteor F.8	A77-871		WK791	PV
☐ Gloster Meteor F.8	A77-874		WK909	RA
☐ Government Aircraft Factory Jindivik 303A	A92-511			RA
☐ Government Aircraft Factory Canberra Mk.20 [English Electric EA.1]	A84-226	26		RA
☐ Government Aircraft Factory Canberra Mk.20 [English Electric EA.1]	A84-235	35		PV

ROYAL AUSTRALIAN NAVY HISTORICAL FLIGHT (AUS30)

Address:	H.M.A.S Albatross, Nowra, New South Wales 2540.
Tel:	02-4421-1920
Admission:	By prior permission only.
Location:	About 8 km south west of the town.

Formed in 1985 with the aim of restoring as many types as possible to flying condition. Construction of a new facility for the flight next to the Fleet Air Arm Museum was completed by 2000. The official policy of the Navy is that for a type to join the flight there must be at least one other example preserved in the museum.

TYPE	REG/SER	CON. NO.	PI/NOTES	STATUS
☐ Bell 204 Iroquois (UH-1C)	VH-NVR	3101	64-17621, N9-101, N9-3101	RAA
☐ Bell 204 Iroquois (UH-1C)	VH-NVV	3104	65-12846, N9-104, N9-3104	RAA
☐ De Havilland D.H.112 Sea Venom FAW.53	WZ895	12752	WZ895, (VH-NVV)	RAC
☐ Douglas DC-3A-467 Skytrain (C-47B) (Dakota IV)	VH-NVD	16131/32879	44-76547, A65-86/VHRFC	RAA
☐ Douglas DC-3A-467 Skytrain (C-47B) (Dakota IV)	VH-NVZ	16135/32883	44-76551, A65-90/VHRFG, N2-90/VMSNK	RAA
☐ Fairey Firefly TT.6 (AS.6)	VH-NVU	F8654	WD826	RAC
☐ Grumman G-121 Tracker (S-2E) (S-2G)	VH-NVX	220C	Bu152333, N12-152333	RAA
☐ Hawker Sea Fury FB.11	VH-NVS	41H/613993	VW623	RAC
☐ Westland Scout AH.1	VH-NVW	F9525	XR603, 'N8-102'	RAC

SEA VENOM GROUP (AUS31)

Address:	c/o Fleet Air Arm Museum, Nowra, New South Wales 2540.
Admission:	By prior permission only.
Location:	In the Nowra area.

This group has been formed to restore the Sea Venom which until recently was stored in a derelict state at the Fleet Air Arm Museum at Nowra. The airframe will be moved to a workshop in the near future.

TYPE	REG/SER	CON. NO.	PI/NOTES	STATUS
☐ De Havilland D.H.112 Sea Venom FAW.53	WZ943	12785		RA

TEMORA AVIATION MUSEUM (AUS32)

Address:	I Menzies Street, Temora Airport, New South Wales 2606.
Tel:	02-6977-1088
Fax:	02-6977-1288
Email:	info@aviationmuseum.com.au
Admission:	Wednesday-Sunday 1000-1600.
Location:	In the north western suburbs of the town off Route 85.

No. 10 Elementrary Flying School was based at Temora in World War II. Many pilots underwent instruction at the site. The museum which is dedicated to the memory of the school opened in 2001. A superb collection of warbirds and classic jets has been acquired and regular air shows take place. The Spitfire VIII was allocated to the R.A.A.F. in 1945 and arrived too late for active duties. After four years in store it was sold to a technical college in Sydney and eventually ended up with Sid Marshall at Bankstown. After a spell on loan to the Camden Museum of Aviation it was acquired by Jack Davidson and sold to the late Col Pay in 1983. The Spitfire flew again on December 29th 1985 and has appeared at many shows in the region. The Vampire is the only Australian built example currently in flying condition. Both the Meteor and Canberra were flown as civil aircraft in England after their service days were over. The Commonwealth Boomerang fighter based on the Wirraway trainer was a stop-gap to fill the lack of combat aircraft in the RAAF. The prototype first flew in 1942 and one hundred and fifty were delivered. The type saw combat action against Japanese forces in Borneo and New Guinea.

TYPE	REG/SER	CON. NO.	PI/NOTES	STATUS
☐ Cessna 318E Dragonfly (A-37B)	VH-XVA	43130	68-10779, 779 (Vietnam)	PVA
☐ Cessna 318E Dragonfly (A-37B)	VH-DLO	43156	68-10805, 805 (Vietnam)	PVA
☐ Cessna 337M Super Skymaster (O-2A)	VH-OII	337M0113	67-21407, N5257G	PVA
☐ Commonwealth CA-13 Boomerang II	VH-MHR	945	A46-122	PVA
☐ Commonwealth CA-16 Wirraway III [North American NA-33]	VH-BFF	1105	A20-653 – composite.	PVA
☐ Commonwealth CA-27 Sabre 30 [North American F-86F]	A94-909	CA27-9	Composite.	RAC
☐ Commonwealth CA-27 Sabre 30 [North American F-86F]	A94-910	CA27-10		PV
☐ Commonwealth CA-27 Sabre 31 [North American F-86F]	A94-942	CA27-42		RA
☐ Commonwealth CA-27 Sabre 32 [North American F-86F]	A94-953	CA27-53		RA
☐ Commonwealth CA-27 Sabre 32 [North American F-86F]	A94-956	CA27-56		RA
☐ Commonwealth CA-27 Sabre 32 [North American F-86F]	VH-IPN	CA27-83	A94-983, FM1983, VH-PCM	RAC
☐ De Havilland D.H.82A Tiger Moth	VH-UVZ	3508	VH-UVZ, A17-691, VH-BBP, VH-PCD	PVA
☐ De Havilland D.H.115 Vampire T.35	VH-VAM	4139	A79-617, N11923	PVA
☐ English Electric EA.1 Canberra TT.18 (B.2)	'A84-234'		WJ680, G-BURM, VH-ZSQ	PVAX
☐ Gloster Meteor F.8	'A77-851'	G5/361641	VZ467, G-METE, VH-MBX, 'EE249'	PVAX
☐ Government Aircraft Factory Canberra Mk.20 [English Electric EA.1]	A84-223	23		PV
☐ Lockheed 414-08-10 Hudson IVA (A-28)	A16-112	414-6041	41-23182, BW363, A16-112, VH-BNJ, VH-EWA, (VH-AIU), VH-AGS, (VH-FXF), VH-KOY	RAA
☐ Ryan STM-2	VH-RSY	474	S-38 (Netherlands), A50-19, VH-AHE	PVA
☐ Supermarine 359 Spitfire HF.VIII	VH-HET/ 'A58-602'	6S.581740	MV239, A58-758	PVAX
☐ Supermarine 361 Spitfire LF.XVIe	VH-XVI	CBAF-10895	TB863, G-CDAN, ZK-XVI	PVA

TOCUMWAL HISTORIC AERODROME MUSEUM (AUS33)

Address:	P.O. Box 47, Tocumwal, New South Wales 2714.
Tel:	03-5874-2795
Admission:	Currently closed.
Location:	About 5 km east of the town.

The airfield was built in the early 1940s for use by the USAAF but it was taken over by the RAAF in 1942. A museum was set up in rooms around one of the hangars and a few light aircraft and sailplanes were acquired. These have gone and the exhibition is not open at the current time.

UIVER MEMORIAL (AUS34)

Address:	Borella Road, Albury Airport, New South Wales 2640.
Admission:	Aircraft in open storage.
Location:	In the eastern suburbs of the town.

In 1934 K.L.M. entered DC-2 named 'Uiver' was second in the speed section of the MacRobertson Air Race from Mildenhall in England to Melbourne. On its flight it force landed on the racecourse at Albury during bad weather at night. The aircraft was guided down by the lamps of cars. A memorial to this event was erected at the present day airport. A DC-2 was mounted on a plinth surrounded by a garden. The example at Albury was delivered to Eastern Air Lines in October 1934 and acquired by the R.A.A.F. in 1941. The aircraft was bought by the Albury Rotary Club in 1979 and restored for the display. The airliner was taken down a few years ago for restoration. The local council is now debating the future of the aircraft and may well decide to sell it and replace it with a monument. A trust fund was set up in 2006 to try and raise the necessary funds for a building but progress is slow.

TYPE	REG/SER	CON. NO.	PI/NOTES	STATUS
☐ Douglas DC-2-112	'PH-AJU'	1286	NC13736, A30-11	PVX

URALLA MILITARY MUSEUM (AUS35)

Address:	New England Highway, Uralla, New South Wales 2358
Tel:	02-6778-4600
Admission:	Daily 0900-1700.
Location:	In the centre of the town off Route 15.

This privately owned collection has on show many vehicles, uniforms, medals and documents dating from World War I to the present time. There are many personal items in the display halls. There is a Bofors machine gun from the Great War along with other weapons. The vehicles range include lorries and tanks.

TYPE	REG/SER	CON. NO.	PI/NOTES	STATUS
☐ Lockheed 414-08-10 Hudson IVA (A-28A)			Fuselage section	PVD
☐ Piaggio P.166	VH-FSA	360	D-IHAL	PV

WALCHA AND DISTRICT HISTORICAL SOCIETY MUSEUM (AUS36)

Address:	111 North Derby Street, Walcha, New South Wales 2354.
Tel:	02-6777-9119
Admission:	Saturday 1100-1600.
Location:	About 1 km north of the town centre and about 280 km north of Newcastle.

Nine buildings are on the site of this excellent local history museum. They include the original slab pioneer cottage erected on the first land grant in the region in the late 1850s. The Tiger Moth was donated to the society in 1965 by Aerial Agriculture and was the first aircraft to spread superphosphate in Australia. A hangar was specially built to house the aircraft where displays of photographs can also be seen.

TYPE	REG/SER	CON. NO.	PI/NOTES	STATUS
☐ De Havilland D.H.82A Tiger Moth	VH-PCB	DHA.41	A17-44, VH-ASQ	PV

WEST WYALONG HISTORICAL MUSEUM (AUS37)

Address:	16 Main Street, West Wyalong, New South Wales 2671.
Tel:	02-6972-2117
Admission:	By appointment only.
Location:	In the town centre.

The displays at this museum which is run by the Bland District Historical Society trace the history and development of the region. Gold was found in the area and the story of local mining is portrayed in detail. There are many items from the pioneering period on show. The DC-3 is preserved near the building.

TYPE	REG/SER	CON. NO.	PI/NOTES	STATUS
☐ Douglas DC-3A-456 Skytrain (C-47A)	N2-23	11973	42-92199, A65-23/VHCTB, A65-23/VJORB	PV

YARRAWONGA/MULWALA PIONEER MUSEUM (AUS38)

Address:	151 Melbourne Street, Mulwala, New South Wales 2647.
Tel:	03-5744-1402
Admission:	Wednesday-Sunday 1330-1700.
Location:	In the centre of the town.

This museum has an excellent collection of cars, farm machinery and domestic items tracing the development of the region. The aviation section outlines the history of flying in the area and four aircraft can be seen. The Sloane Biplane dates from 1911 and is substantially complete. The others date from the 1970s.

TYPE	REG/SER	CON. NO.	PI/NOTES	STATUS
☐ Estupian-Hovey WD-II Whing Ding				PV
☐ Hang Glider				PV
☐ Skycraft Scout		57		PV
☐ Sloane Biplane				PV

NORTHERN TERRITORY

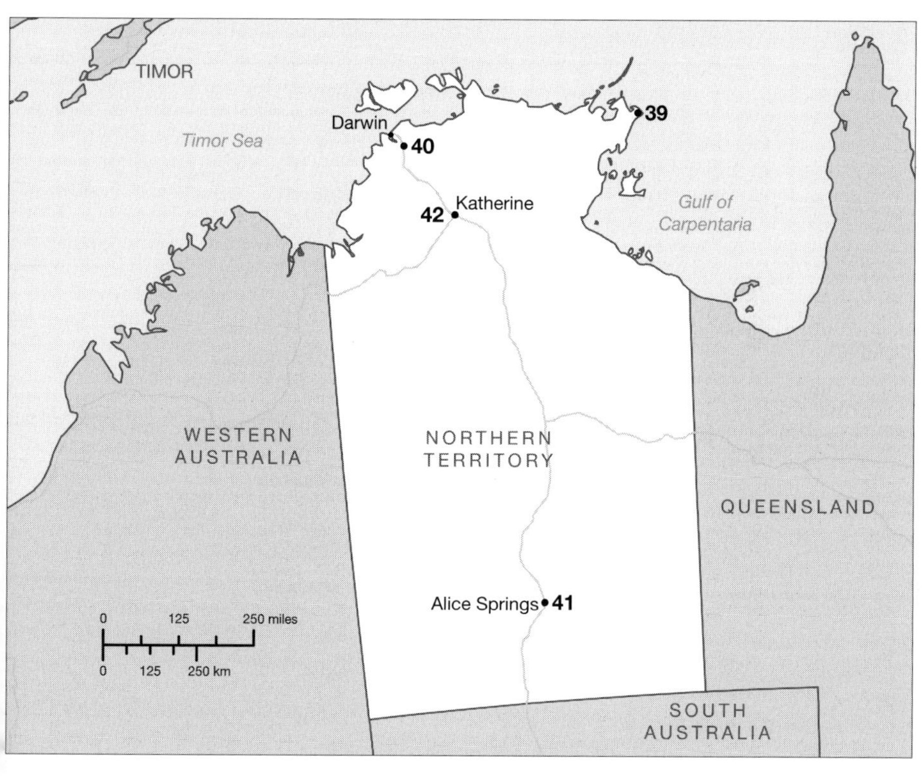

ARNHEM LAND HISTORICAL SOCIETY (AUS39)

Address:	P.O. Box 296, Nhulunby, Northern Territory 0881.
Tel:	041-1973-9002
Email:	govepest@bigpond.com
Admission:	On permanent view.
Location:	On the north eastern coast of Arnhem Land about 600 km east of Darwin.

Many aircraft wrecks exist is this remote part of Australia. In March 1945 a Beaufort crashed on the airstrip at Gove and useful components were removed. In 1980 the airframe was placed in a compound as a memorial to the crews who had flown from the field during World War II. The aircraft was taken to Brisbane and funds are being raised for its return. A Ventura joined the exhibition in 1989. The Beaufort had been flown by No. 13 Squadron from Gove between April and August 1945 in operations against Japanese shore bases and shipping in the New Guinea area. The Ventura was damaged by a fire which broke out during maintenance and was left behind when the unit moved on. No. 13 Squadron at Darwin took the aircraft as a restoration project but little work was done and again a fund has been launched to return it to Gove. The society is trying to preserve some of the World War II buildings, including the control tower, and set up a museum tracing the history of Gove airstrip.

TYPE	REG/SER	CON. NO.	PI/NOTES	STATUS
☐ Department of Aircraft Production Beaufort VIII [Bristol 152]	A9-501		Front fuselage only.	–
☐ Lockheed 237-27-01 Ventura (PV-1)	A59-61	237-5882	Bu34992 – in Darwin.	–

AUSTRALIAN AVIATION HERITAGE CENTRE (AUS40)

Address:	P.O. Box 37621, Winnellie, Northern Territory 0821.
Tel:	08-8947-2145
Fax:	08-8947-1000
Email:	ahsnt@bigpond.com
Admission:	Daily 0830-1700.
Location:	At 557 Stuart Highway (Route 1) near the airport which is about 10 km east of the town.

On December 10th 1919 the Vickers Vimy G-EAOU piloted by Ross and Keith Smith landed near Darwin on its flight from London to Sydney. This aircraft is now preserved in Adelaide. Over the next few years many aircraft on record breaking and pioneering flights made their first landing on Australian soil near Darwin. The area was also of strategic importance during World War II. The Aviation Historical Society of the Northern Territory was formed in 1976 with the aim of preserving relics salvaged after the destruction caused by Cyclone 'Tracy'. A museum opened in 1988 in a pre-World War II navy victualling yard. These buildings are now used as a storage and restoration area. B-52 bombers of the United States Air Force have been regular visitors to Darwin for many years and negotiations were started in the late 1980s to try to obtain an example for display. Success was achieved on March 27th 1990 when one landed on a flight from Guam. The aircraft was moved into the new hall constructed in fourteen weeks in 1989 – this structure is the largest single span building in the Northern Territory. The museum opened in 1990 as the Darwin Aviation Museum and took up its present title in September 1994. Further development of the site will include World War II hangars and airstrip revetments. A number of crash sites have been investigated and the results of these can be seen. The Zero was shot down during a raid on Darwin on February 19th 1942 and crashed at Snake Bay. The engine and a nacelle from a Dinah downed in July 1943 can be seen. An excellent collection of engines is also on display. These cover the early period of piston motors up to modern jets. The replica Spitfire was built in Queensland and honours the three hundred of the type which flew from Darwin from January 1943. The Wessex was one of six that assisted in the clean up operations following Cyclone 'Tracy' and Shell Australia is helping in the establishment of a display tracing the story of the disaster. The Dove was used on a route between Darwin and Dili in East Timor and the Commander was flown on coastal surveillance duties in the region. The Mitsubishi MU-2 is decorated with murals on the fuselage sides. This museum has made excellent progress in the last decade and although off the beaten track is well worth a visit. The history of aviation in the area is portrayed in the displays. There are sections devoted to the 1942 bombing of Darwin by Japanese aircraft and on the Australian contribution to the Vietnam War. The Huey Cobra was used by American forces in this bitter conflict. The Australian Air Force maintains a base at Darwin Airport where helicopters are now based. The history of this site is shown in the exhibition. To the south of the city is RAAF Tindall where F/A-18A Hornets are based. United States bombers were based at Darwin in World War II and the history of the 380th. Bomb Wing during their stay in Australia is portrayed. A comprehensive display of paintings and photographs is one of the highlights to be seen. Civil aircraft which have flown from the Darwin area are being collected to enhance the exhibition.

TYPE	REG/SER	CON. NO.	PI/NOTES	STATUS
☐ Aero Commander 500U	VH-EXD	1639-3	N6621V	PV
☐ Aero Jet Commander 1121	N159DP	1121-52	N701AP, N1121G, N696GW, N159YC, N159MP	PVD
☐ Auster J/5 Adventurer	VH-UED	3203		RA
☐ Beech 65-B80 Queen Air	VH-AMD	LD-504	TR-LUU	PVD
☐ Bell 209 Huey Cobra (AH-1G) (AH-1S)	71-21018	21089		PV
☐ Boeing 464-253 Stratofortress (B-52G)	59-2596	464359		PV
☐ Cessna 411	RP-C1077	4110171	(CF-UGG), PI-C1077	RA
☐ Commonwealth CA-1 Wirraway I [North American NA-33]			Centre section only.	PVD

TYPE	REG/SER	CON. NO.	PI/NOTES	STATUS
☐ Commonwealth CA-13 Boomerang II	A46-124	947	Centre section only.	PV
☐ Commonwealth CA-27 Sabre 30 [North American F-86F]	A94-914	CA27-14	Rear fuselage from c/n CA27-21 A94-921 – wings from a Mark 32	PV
☐ Commonwealth CA-29 Mirage IIID [Dassault Mirage III]	A3-105	CA29-105		PVD
☐ Commonwealth CA-29 Mirage IIIO(A) (IIIO(F)) [Dassault Mirage III]	A3-7	CA29-7	Fuselage only.	PV
☐ Commonwealth CA-29 Mirage IIIO(A) (IIIO(F)) [Dassault Mirage III]	A3-36	CA29-36		PV
☐ Consolidated 32 Liberator (B-24D)	42-40518	1595	Fuselage parts only.	PVD
☐ Consolidated 32 Liberator (B-24D)	42-41182	259	Forward fuselage only.	PVD
☐ Consolidated 32 Liberator (B-24L)	A72-88			PVD
☐ De Havilland D.H.82A Tiger Moth	'A17-4'	DHA.822/04	(DX779), A17-672, VH-BGT	PVX
☐ De Havilland D.H.104 Dove 1B	CR-TAG	04373	CR-AGT	PV
☐ De Havilland D.H.C.1 Chipmunk 22 (T.10)			Centre fuselage only.	RAD
☐ Douglas DC-3A-467 Skytrain (C-47B) (Dakota IV)	PK-RDB	16147/32895	44-76563, NZ3537, ZK-AOZ, 5W-FAA – rear fuselage and tail only.	PV
☐ Douglas DC-3A-467 Skytrain (C-47B) (Dakota IV)	A65-104/VHRFU	16547/33295	44-76963 – rear fuselage only.	PVD
☐ Gloster Meteor F.3	A77-1		EE427	PVD
☐ Hovey Delta Bird		10-0100		PV
☐ Lockheed 222-62-13 Lightning (F-4)	A55-3	222-5340	41-2122 – centre section only.	PVD
☐ Mitsubishi A6M2 Zero Sen Model 21	'BII-124'	5349		PVD
☐ Mitsubishi G4M3				RAD
☐ Mitsubishi Ki-46-II		2414	Minor components.	PVD
☐ Mitsubishi MU-2B-30	VH-NYM	037	N3565X, CF-CRL, C-FCRL, N37MU, ZK-WAL, VH-JWO	PV
☐ North American NA-87 Mitchell (B-25D)	41-30222	87-8387		PVC
☐ Piper J-2 Cub				RA
☐ Rutan 61 Long-Ez	VH-RAL	S33		PV
☐ Skycraft Scout				PV
☐ Supermarine 349 Spitfire F.Vc/Trop	A58-92		BS231 – major components only.	PVD
☐ Supermarine 359 Spitfire LF.VIIIc	A58-377		JG267 – major components only.	RAD
☐ Supermarine 359 Spitfire LF.VIIIc (FSM)	'A58-430'/ 'A58-606'			PVX
☐ Wasp Air Buggy				PV
☐ Westland-Sikorsky WS-58 Wessex HAS.31B	N7-202	WA.202	WA202	PV

CENTRAL AUSTRALIAN AVIATION MUSEUM (AUS41)

Address:	P.O. Box 2032, Alice Springs, Northern Territory 0871.
Tel:	08-8951-1120
Admission:	Monday-Friday 0900-1700; Saturday-Sunday 1000-1700.
Location:	In Memorial Avenue which is about 1 km west of the town centre.

A committee was formed in February 1977 with the aim of establishing a museum as a memorial to the pioneer aviators of Central Australia. In October 1976 a lease was obtained on the 1936 Connellan Airways hangar which was all that remained of the original Alice Springs Airport. The official opening took place on May 20th 1978. The first aircraft, the Drover, had arrived earlier that month. Only twenty examples of the three engined type were built and several served with the Royal Flying Doctor Service. In August 1978 members took part in the recovery of the Westland Widgeon 'Kookaburra' from the Tanami Desert. This aircraft had crashed on April 10th 1929 whilst searching for Sir Charles Kingsford Smith's Fokker F.VII 'Southern Cross'. The Widgeon force landed in the inhospitable desert and could not take off again. The crew of Keith Anderson and Bobby Hitchcock died beside their aircraft. The wreck is preserved in an adjacent building in an 'as found' as a memorial to the pair. The Wackett crashed in 1962 and has since been restored for display. The famous German sailplane designer Edmund Schneider emigrated to Australia after World War II and with his son Harry set up a company to produce more original types. The Kookaburra two seater first appeared in the early 1950s and was the backbone of club training for over a decade. Also on show are a number of engines, radios, photographs and memorabilia. The Rolls Royce Silver Ghost car used by E.J. Connellan to survey sites for landing strips is a prized exhibit.

TYPE	REG/SER	CON. NO.	PI/NOTES	STATUS
☐ Auster J/1B Aiglet	VH-ASQ	2747		PVA
☐ Beech D18S	VH-CLI	A-73	NC3010V, N3010V, ZK-BQE	PV
☐ Commonwealth CA-6 Wackett Trainer	VH-BEC	373	A3-139	PV
☐ De Havilland D.H.104 Dove 6	VH-DHH	04499		PV
☐ De Havilland D.H.A.3 Drover 3 (1) (1F) (2)	VH-FDC	5013		PV
☐ Douglas DC-3A-456 Skytrain (C-47A)	'VH-EWE'	13084	42-93199, A65-49/VHCIE, VH-BAK, VH-EAL, VH-EBH, VH-EBW, VH-BAA	PVX
☐ Percival P.30 Proctor II	'VH-ACM'	H.224	BV658, G-AHVG, VH-AVG	PVX
☐ Rotec Rally 2B				PV
☐ Schneider ES.52 Kookaburra 4	VH-GNM	66		PV
☐ Westland Widgeon III	G-AUKA	WA.1775		PVD

KATHERINE OUTBACK HISTORICAL MUSEUM (AUS42)

Address:	P.O. Box 93, Katherine, Northern Territory 0851.
Tel:	08-8972-3945
Fax:	08-8972-3946
Admission:	March-October Monday-Friday 1000-1600, Sunday 1400-1700; November-February Monday-Friday 1000-1300,Sunday 1400-1700
Location:	At old airport which is about 3 km east of the town and about 320 km south east of Darwin.

The Historical Society of Katherine has set up a museum in the buildings of the old airport for the town. The development of the region is highlighted in the informative displays. The Moth was built in 1930 and exported to Australia. In March 1934 it was purchased by Clyde Fenton, 'the first flying doctor' in the Northern Territory, who used it to visit his patients on the remote farms surrounding the town. The aircraft crashed a year later at Victoria River Downs Station. Rebuilt by the de Havilland company at Mascot Airport in Sydney the biplane flew with a number of owners until joining the museum in 1987.

TYPE	REG/SER	CON. NO.	PI/NOTES	STATUS
☐ De Havilland D.H.60M Moth	VH-UNI	1431	CH-252	PV

QUEENSLAND

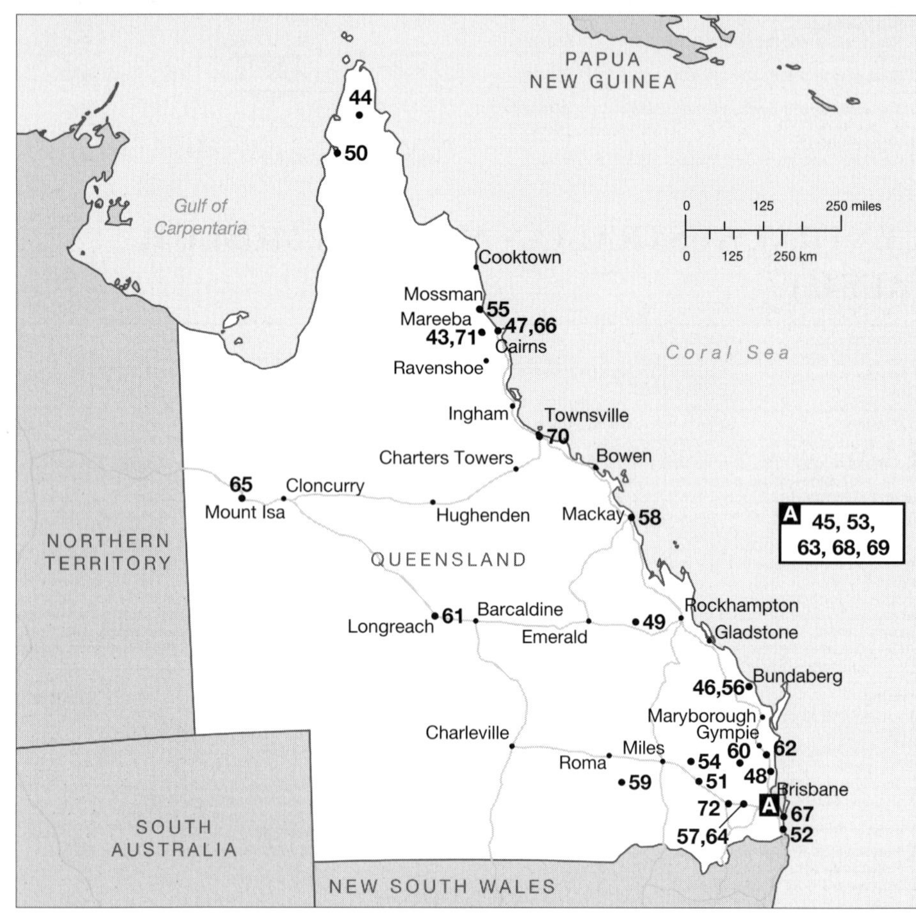

AVIATION AND MILITARY MUSEUM – THE BECK COLLECTION (AUS43)

Address:	P.O. Box 399, Kennedy Highway, Mareeba, Queensland 4880.
Tel:	07-4092-3979
Fax:	07-4092-6946
Email:	nbeck@ledanet.com.au
Admission:	Daily 1000-1600.
Location:	About 5 km south of the town on Route 1.

Sid Beck started the collection in 1972. Initially called the Townsville Aero Museum a site was obtained south west of the town. A large plastic 'igloo' was built and all items were stored under cover. The museum opened for a short time in the 1980s but it several years before a more suitable site was obtained. The exhibition at Mareeba on a regular basis in late 1995. In addition to the aircraft, military vehicles, aero engines and armaments are on show. The oldest aircraft in the collection is the P-39 which crashed at Weipa in the north of the state in 1942. The airframe was abandoned until recovered by a group from Cairns in 1972 and later in the year it joined the collection. The Stinson Sentinel was in civilian use in Hong Kong before coming to Australia. The Piaggio P.136 is the only one in the country. After use in Hong Kong and Macao it arrived in Australia in 1972 for use by Dolphinair. On the inaugural service from Townsville to Hinchinbrook Island it was damaged whilst landing at Cape Richards and sank. All on board were rescued but the aircraft was written off and acquired by the museum. The Wildcat mock-up was built for the set of the 1999 film the 'Thin Red Line'. Components from crash sites can be seen and these include some from a USAAF B-24D Liberator. The Commonwealth Wackett was the first original design by the company and is named after its designer Lawrence Wackett. The Sycamore on show is the last of the one hundred at seventy eight built at Filton and Weston-super-Mare. The helicopter made its maiden flight in December 1958 and was delivered to the Royal Australian Navy the following June.

TYPE	REG/SER	CON. NO.	PI/NOTES	STATUS
☐ Beech C23 Sundowner	VH-UXX	M-1784	N6784S	PV
☐ Bell 14A-1 Airacobra (P-39D)	41-6951	15-290		PVC
☐ Bristol 171 Sycamore HR.51	XN450	13505	G-18-178	PV
☐ Commonwealth CA-6 Wackett Trainer			Fuselage only.	PV
☐ De Havilland D.H.82A Tiger Moth	VH-BXF	DHA.152	A17-151, VH-AXF, VH-BXF, VH-BWF, VH-UEF – fuselage only.	PV
☐ De Havilland D.H.100 Vampire F.30	A79-89	4025	A79-89, INST.11	PV
☐ De Havilland D.H.112 Sea Venom FAW.53	N4-904	12761	WZ904	PV
☐ Douglas DC-3A-467 Skytrain (C-47B) (Dakota IV)	A65-73	15923/32671	44-76339, A65-73?CIP, A65-93/VMHJT	PV
☐ Fieseler Fi 103A-1 (FSM)				PV
☐ Government Aircraft Factory Canberra Mk.20 [English Electric EA.1]	A84-210	10		PV
☐ Grumman G-36 Wildcat (F4F-4) (FSM)	'84'			PVX
☐ Lockheed 726-45-17 Neptune MR.4 (P2V-7) (P2V-7S) (SP-2H)	A89-277	726-7277	Bu149077	PV
☐ Piaggio P.136L2	VH-BJP	243	VR-HFP, CR-TAM	PV
☐ Stinson V-76 Sentinel (L-5B)	VH-BEN	76-3312	44-17025, VR-HEO	PVC

BAMAGA AIRPORT MEMORIAL (AUS44)

Address:	Injinoo Airport, Bamaga, Queensland 4876.
Tel:	07-4055-9535
Fax:	07-4055-9918
Admission:	On permanent view.
Location:	About 10 km south east of the town.

The DC-3 was assembled by Fokker in Amsterdam and delivered to KLM in April 1937. The airliner was transferred to the Dutch East Indies and flew on KNILM routes before flying to Australia in March 1942 to escape from the advancing Japanese forces. The aircraft crashed at the airfield, then known to the Americans as Higgins Field, on May 5th 1945 and the wreck has been preserved as a memorial. The fuselage is by the roadside and along with a plaque. The Dutch company took out a licence to build the earlier DC-2 but only assembled airframes shipped from California. They held the sales agency for the DC-3 in Europe and over sixty were sold before the outbreak of World War II. The rusty front fuselage of a Beaufort can be found a short distance away in the bush. Injinoo is the most northerly airfield in the state and in 1943 was named Higgins Field after Flight Lieutenant Brian Higgins who was killed in action in May 1943.

TYPE	REG/SER	CON. NO.	PI/NOTES	STATUS
☐ Department of Aircraft Production Beaufort VA [Bristol 152]			Front fuselage only	PVD
☐ Douglas DC-3-194B (C-49H)		1941	PH-ALT, PK-ALT, 'VH-ALT', VHCXD, (44-83228)	PVD

BEAUFORT RESTORATION GROUP (AUS45)

Address:	490B Nudgee Road, Hendra, Queensland 4011.
Tel:	07-3268-7138
Email:	info@beaufortrestoration.com.au
Admission:	By prior permission only.
Location:	In the eastern suburbs of Brisbane.

The Bristol Beaufort first flew in England in October 1938 and was designed as a land based torpedo bomber. The Australian government chose the type for manufacture and set up production facilities. The main plants were at Mascot near Sydney and Fishermen's Bend close to Melbourne. Satellite factories made parts for the main lines. Between August 1941 and August 1944 seven hundred Beauforts were built in Australia. The type saw combat duties against the Japanese in a number of locations around the Pacific. The majority were scrapped after the end of the conflict but a few components survived on farms and in yards. The example owned by the group saw service at Pearce in Western Australia and Cape York in Queensland. Relegated to training duties at Tocumwal in New South Wales it was written off in January 1944. The aircraft was removed and stored for many years. In 1982 the fuselage and centre section were noted at the now closed museum at Mildura in Victoria. The parts were acquired and transported to the Brisbane area. Components from around the world have been acquired and the restoration to flying condition is proceeding. The aim is to have it in the air by 2011 – the ninetieth anniversary of the Royal Australian Air Force. This twin engined bomber will be an excellent addition to the number of airworthy warbirds now in Australian skies.

TYPE	REG/SER	CON. NO.	PI/NOTES	STATUS
☐ Department of Aircraft Production Beaufort VA [Bristol 152]	A9-152		Front fuselage only	RA
☐ Department of Aircraft Production Beaufort VIII [Bristol 152]	VH-KTW		A9-141 – composite	RAC

BUNDABERG AND DISTRICT HISTORICAL MUSEUM – HINKLER HOUSE MEMORIAL MUSEUM (AUS46)

Address:	Mount Perry Road, North Bundaberg, Queensland 4670.
Tel:	07-4152-0101
Fax:	07-4152-0004
Email:	e.cullen@interworx.com.au
Admission:	Daily 1000-1600.
Location:	About 4 km north of the town which is about 280 km north of Brisbane.

Exhibitions at this museum feature various aspects of life in the area. The history and development of the region is portrayed in a series of informative displays. In 1982 it came to the notice of a number of Bundaberg residents that Bert Hinkler's house in the Thornhill suburb of Southampton in England was under threat of demolition. The following year a group travelled to Thornhill and, after training, dismantled the house brick by brick before it was shipped to Queensland. The structure was rebuilt overlooking the school where Hinkler was educated and opened to the public on June 16th 1984. In 1914 Hinkler travelled to England and after a period working for the Sopwith company he joined the Royal Naval Air Service where he later trained as a pilot. He joined the Avro company at Hamble in 1919. During his time in England he designed and built one example of the Ibis powered by two 40 h.p. Salmson radials. The aircraft flew in 1930 and was later stored in a shed at the house in Thornhill. The airframe appeared in the Hampshire Aeroplane Hangar at Eastleigh Airport in the mid-1950s. The Ibis was needlessly scrapped at Lee-on-Solent in 1959. Members of the Bundaberg Museum committee and local model maker John Farmer constructed a replica of the Ibis for the museum between 1989 and 1991. A replica of his Avro Baby, which he flew in the early 1920s, is now in the exhibition hall.

TYPE	REG/SER	CON. NO.	PI/NOTES	STATUS
☐ Avro 534 Baby (R)	'G-EACQ'			PVX
☐ Hinkler Ibis (R)				PV

BUSH PILOTS AIRWAYS MEMORIAL (AUS47)

Address:	P.O. Box 594, Cairns Airport, Queensland 4870
Tel:	07-4052-3088
Fax:	07-4052-1943
Email:	enquiries@cairnsport.com.au
Admission:	Aircraft on permanent view.
Location:	About 5 km north of the town.

The Cairns Port Authority has preserved this DC-3 as a memorial. The aircraft was mounted on poles in the mid-1980s and initially painted in an Air Queensland colour scheme. Bush Pilots Airways was formed at Cairns in 1970 and operated DC-3's around the area. The company became Air Queensland in 1982. The aircraft is now in false Bush Pilots Airways colours.

TYPE	REG/SER	CON. NO.	PI/NOTES	STATUS
☐ Douglas DC-3A-456 Skytrain (C-47A) (Dakota III)	'VH-BPA'	12187	42-92392, FZ631, VH-EAN, VH-EBF, VH-EBU, VH-SBD, P2-SBD, P2-ANO, N5590C	PVX

CALBOOLTURE WARPLANE MUSEUM (AUS48)

Address:	Hangar 104, McNaught Road, Caboolture Airfield, Caboolture, Queensland 4510.
Tel:	07-5499-1144
Fax:	07-5499-0766
Email:	cawpm@qmail.com
Admission:	Daily 1000-1600.
Location:	About 3 km east of the town and east of the Bruce Highway- Route 1.

The suggestion for a warbird museum came from a group who were involved in winding up the Darling Downs Aviation Museum. After a great deal of discussion the display opened in June 1995 and has made rapid progress in a short time. An exhibition of engines, photographs and memorabilia has been staged. The aircraft are all the property of individual members of the museum. Owned by the Mustang Fighter Trust, the Commonwealth built example of the famous fighter was rebuilt in a hangar close to the museum. Two versions of the Wirraway can be seen. The aircraft are displayed in typical period markings. Jack MacDonald is restoring a rare Hawker Demon in a nearby workshop. This classic inter war biplane will go on show when the rebuild is complete.

TYPE	REG/SER	CON. NO.	PI/NOTES	STATUS
☐ Commonwealth CA-3 Wirraway II [North American NA-33]	'A20-176'	79	A20-81, VH-WWY	PVAX
☐ Commonwealth CA-16 Wirraway III [North American NA-33]	VH-MFW	1147	A20-695	PVA
☐ Commonwealth CA-18 Mustang 21 [North American P-51D]	VH-MFT/' A68-769'	1435	A68-110	PVA
☐ Commonwealth CA-25 Winjeel	'A85-445'	CA25-22	A85-422, VH-SOB	PVAX
☐ Hawker Demon I	A1-?			RAC
☐ Nieuport 17 (R)	VH-NIE	001		PVA
☐ Sopwith F.1 Camel (R)	A1-?			PV
☐ Wytwornia Sprzetu Komunikacyjnego (WSK) Lim-6bis (Lim-5M) [MiG-17F]	'402'	1F 01-02	102 (Poland)	PVX

CARNARVON GORGE WILDERNESS LODGE MEMORIAL (AUS49)

Address:	Via Rolleston, Queensland 4702.
Tel:	07-4984-4503
Fax:	07-4984-4500
Admission:	On permanent view.
Location:	About 50 km southwest of Rolleston.

The Lodge is set in a picturesque National Park. The C-47 which was flying from Brisbane crashed on November 9th 1943. The wreck has been preserved as a memorial to the crew.

TYPE	REG/SER	CON. NO.	PI/NOTES	STATUS
☐ Douglas DC-3A-456 Skytrain (C-47A)	42-23420	9282		PVD

COMALCO BICENTENNIAL MUSEUM PROJECT (AUS50)

Address:	Weipa, Queensland 4874.
Admission:	By prior permission only.
Location:	At a workshop in the town which is on the west coast of the Cape York Peninsula.

A report has been received that the remains of the Thunderbolt have been retrieved from a crash site. The plan is to rebuild the aircraft for a new museum in the town. Further details would be appreciated.

TYPE	REG/SER	CON. NO.	PI/NOTES	STATUS
☐ Republic P-47D Thunderbolt			Major components	RAC

FLYPAST MUSEUM OF AUSTRALIAN ARMY FLYING (AUS51)

Address: Headquarters,
Army Aviation Centre,
Oakey,
Queensland 4401.
Tel: 07-4691-7666
Email: AustArmyFlyingMuseum@defence.gov.au
Admission: Wednesday-Sunday 1000-1600.
Location: About 3 km north of the town which is about 30 km north west of Toowoomba.

The Australian Flying Corps was formed in 1912 as a branch of the Army. Pilots served with distinction during World War I and on March 20th 1917 Lieutenant F.H. MacNamara was awarded the Victoria Cross. Nine years later the Royal Australian Air Force was established and it was not until after World War II that the Army once again set up its own aviation section. The airfield at Oakey was built during World War II and was an important servicing and repair pair base for combat types from Pacific operations. The Army took over the site on July 1st 1968 and set up their aviation headquarters at the field. Plans to establish a museum were formulated in the late 1970s and four hangars were occupied. The story of army flying in the country is portrayed with many photographs, medals, uniforms, memorabilia and documents on view. In 1914 two Bristol Boxkites were among a batch of six aircraft brought back to Australia by two army officers who had been sent to England to train as instructors. The replica on show is one of three built by F.G. Miles at Ford in England for the film 'Those Magnificent Men in Their Flying Machines'. Fifty six Auster IIIs were flown by the military in Australia. The A.O.P.9 was donated by the British Army Flying Corps. The collection moved to a new facility in 2005.

TYPE	REG/SER	CON. NO.	PI/NOTES	STATUS
☐ Auster B.5 AOP.9	XP285	B5/10/171		PV
☐ Auster E AOP.3	A11-41	413	NK126, A11-41, VH-CYH	PVA
☐ Bell 47G-2 Sioux	A1-568	2568		RA
☐ Bell 47G-3B-1 Sioux	A1-406	3406		PV
☐ Bell 47G-3B-1 Sioux	VH-OKY	6672	A1-720	PVA
☐ Bell 205 Iroquois (UH-1D) (UH-1H)	A2-649	5649	66-1166	PV
☐ Bell 205 Iroquois (UH-1H)			Due soon.	RA
☐ Bristol Boxkite (R)		BM7280		PV
☐ Bristol 14 F.2B Fighter (R)	'C4623'	QA-32-1	VH-UDC – on loan.	PVAX
☐ Cessna 180D	A98-045	18051045	N8645X	PVA
☐ Cessna 305A Bird Dog (L-19A) (O-1A)	'12531'	21768	51-4883 – composite with parts from 51-7300.	PVAX
☐ Commonwealth CA-13 Boomerang II	A46-144	967	Incomplete.	PVC
☐ Commonwealth CA-19 Boomerang II	VH-BOM	1029	A46-206, N4234K	PV
☐ Commonwealth CA-25 Winjeel	A85-406	CA25-06		RAC
☐ Commonwealth CA-25 Winjeel	A85-432	CA25-32		PV
☐ Commonwealth CA-25 Winjeel	A85-449	CA25-49		RAC
☐ Department of Aircraft Production Beaufort V [Bristol 152]	A9-13		T9552 – on loan.	PVC
☐ Fokker Dr I (R)	'425/17'	1864DR	N864DR, VH-ALU	RA
☐ Fokker F.VIIa/3m (R)				SD
☐ Government Aircraft Factory N.2 Nomad	'A18-300'	N2-02	VH-SUR, A18-002, VH-SUR	PVX
☐ Government Aircraft Factory N.22A Nomad	A18-408	N22A-124		RA
☐ Government Aircraft Factory N.22M Nomad	A18-307	N22M-45		PV
☐ Hawker P.1101 Hunter T.75A (P.1067 Hunter F.4)	VH-RHO	HABL 003125	XF970, 528 (Singapore)	PV
☐ North American NA-174 Trojan (T-28A) (AT-28D)VA	VH-DUK	174-374	51-7521, 3403 (Laos)	P
☐ Pellerini Airjeep				RA
☐ Pilatus PC.6/B1-H2 Turbo-Porter	A14-652	652	HB-FDK, A14-652, VH-OWD	PVA
☐ Pilatus PC.6/B1-H2 Turbo-Porter	A14-704	730	HB-FFU, A14-730	RAC
☐ Southern Cross SC.1	VH-SCA	1	On loan from ANAM, VIC.	PV

GOLD COAST WAR MUSEUM (AUS52)

Address: 42 John Rogers Road,
Mudgeeraba,
Queensland 4213.
Tel: 07-5530-5222
Admission: Daily 0900-1800.
Location: Just west of the town.

The museum is part of a major tourist complex and offers a number of activities including paint-balling and skirmishing. A number of aircraft are located around the site. There is also a collection of artefacts in a building.

TYPE	REG/SER	CON. NO.	PI/NOTES	STATUS
☐ Bell 204 Iroquois (UH-1B)				PV
☐ Bell 204 Iroquois (UH-1B) (FSM)				PVX
☐ Bell 209 Huey Cobra (AH-1G) (FSM)				PVX
☐ Supermarine 349 Spitfire F.V (FSM)				PVX.

HART'S FLYING FIGHTER MUSEUM (AUS53)

Address:	400 Wirraway Avenue, Archerfield Airport, Brisbane, Queensland 4000.
Tel:	07-3272-9484
Admission:	Closed
Location:	In the southern suburbs of the city off Route 2.

This collection of flying warbirds included many interesting types. Several of the aircraft were seized by the police in 2006 and the museum was forced to close, A number of airframes have been put in store whilst their fate is decided. Several privately owned types were on display and the majority of these have moved to adjacent hangars, The aircraft listed below were with the museum when it closed but some have probably gone to other owners. The Fury is one of the batch obtained in Iraq by Ed Jurist and David Tallichet in the late 1970s. The aircraft were taken to the U.S.A. where many were restored and subsequently sold to owners around the world. The example on show has been restored to represent one flown by the Royal Australian Navy. The collection included many types which were used to train military pilots.

TYPE	REG/SER	CON. NO.	PI/NOTES	STATUS
☐ Aero L-39C Albatros	VH-SIC	433134	09 (Lithuania), LA-0554	RAA
☐ Beech D17S (UC-43)	VH-BBL	6763	44-67755, FT501, Bu32901, (NC172), LN-HAH, VH-MLC	RAC
☐ Bellanca 8KCAB Decathlon	VH-DEC	454-78		RAA
☐ Boeing-Stearman A75N1 Kaydet (PT-17)	N54774	75-2330	41-8771	RAC
☐ De Havilland D.H.82A Tiger Moth	VH-WEM	DHA.1081	A17-750, VH-AQH, VH-RVJ	RAA
☐ De Havilland D.H.C.1 Chipmunk 22 (T.10)	VH-SHX	C1/0847	WP981	RAA
☐ Fairchild 24W46	NC77648	W46-348	NC77648, N77648	RAC
☐ Grumman G-40 Avenger (TBM-3) (TBM-3E)	VH-TBM	4015	Bu91110, N6827C, ZK-TBM, 'NZ2518'	RAAX
☐ Hawker Fury FB.10	'WJ232'	41H/643827	326 (Iraq), N43SF, ZK-SFR, VH-SHF	RAAX
☐ Mudry CAP.232	VH-SHI	004		RAA
☐ North American NA-88 Texan (AT-6D) (SNJ-5)	VH-USN	88-17552	42-85771, Bu90624, N3620F, N13AA	RAA
☐ North American NA-159 Trojan (T-28A) (T-28D)	VH-AVC	159-31	49-1519, N8698H, 3408 (Laos)	RAA
☐ North American NA-174 Trojan (T-28A) (T-28D)	'Bu138364'	174-260	51-3722, 13722 (Philippines), 13722 (Thailand), VH-TRO	RAAX
☐ North American NA-200 Trojan (T-28B)	VH-SHT	200-330	Bu138259, N86AW	RAA
☐ Ryan STM-2	VH-AGW	465	S-29 (Dutch), A50-22	RAA
☐ Wytwornia Sprzetu Komunikacyjnego (WSK) SBLim-2M (Lim-1) [MiG-15] [MiG-15UTI]	'400'	1A 07-050	050	RAX
☐ Wytwornia Sprzetu Komunikacyjnego (WSK) Lim-5 [MiG-17F]	1619	1C 16-19		RA
☐ Yakovlev Yak-3M	VH-YZK	0470102	ZK-YAK	RAA
☐ Yakovlev Yak-9				RAC
☐ Yakovlev Yak-50	VH-YAX	832504	02 (DOSAAF)	RAA
☐ Yakovlev Yak-50	VH-YAY	852904		RAA

HEAVY BOMBARDMENT FIELD No.1 MEMORIAL (AUS54)

Address:	Alex Campbell Park, Brymaroo, Queensland 4403.
Admission:	Aircraft on permanent view.
Location:	In the town.

During World War II a large bomber airfield was constructed close to the town. RAAF and USAAF B-24 Liberators were in residence. The Canberra was mounted as a memorial to all who served at the field. The aircraft was dedicated by Group Captain Arthur Barnes DFC on February 28th 1987. Australian built Canberras entered service in the mid-1950s and were based at Amberley for almost thirty years. The bombers were also resident at Butterworth in Malaysia for a period and flew combat missions in Vietnam.

TYPE	REG/SER	CON. NO.	PI/NOTES	STATUS
☐ Government Aircraft Factory Canberra Mk.21 [English Electric EA.1]	A84-219	19		PV

HERITAGE RAINFOREST CENTRE (AUS55)

Address:	P.O. Box 339, Kuranda, Queensland 4872.
Tel:	07-4093-9311
Email:	info@kuranda.org
Admission:	Daily 1000-1600.
Location:	At the corner of Therwine Street and Kennedy Highway in the northern part of the town.

Displays at the centre highlight the environmental nature of a rainforest. Visitors can also tour the area and see the varied wildlife. The Dakota was used by the U.S.A.A.F. in Australia from 1942 to 1944 and was then sold to Ansett. The aircraft was withdrawn in 1976 and is now shown 'crashed' in dense undergrowth.

TYPE	REG/SER	CON. NO.	PI/NOTES	STATUS
☐ Douglas DC-3A-360 Skytrain (C-47)	'6903077'	6051	41-38668, VHCHF, VH-AEO, VH-DAS	PVDX

HINKLER GLIDER MUSEUM (AUS56)

Address:	P.O. Box 942, Bundaberg, Queensland 4670.
Tel:	07-4152-2333
Email:	info@bundabergregion.org
Admission:	Daily 0900-1700 except Public Holidays when open 1000-1500.
Location:	At the corner of Musgrave and Bourbong Streets in the town.

Bert Hinkler was born in Bundaberg in 1892 and stared experimenting with gliders when he was seventeen. In 1973 parts of the wing of his first machine were found under his North Bundaberg home. A replica of this machine, which flew at Mon Repos Beach in 1912, was constructed. The museum was set up at the tourist centre to display the replica. On show are the pieces of the original glider wing and a model of the Avian in which he flew from England to Australia in 1928. The Maule is a type used on flights over the Great Barrier Reef.

TYPE	REG/SER	CON. NO.	PI/NOTES	STATUS
☐ Hinkler Glider			Original wing parts.	PVD
☐ Hinkler Glider (R)				PV
☐ Maule MX-7 Super Rocket (R)				PV

IPSWICH AMBERLEY AVIATION MUSEUM (AUS57)

Address:	RAAF Amberley, Queensland 4306.
Admission:	Not yet open.
Location:	At RAAF Amberley which is about 10 km west of Ipswich.

Plans have been put forward to open a museum close to the Air Force base. A number of aircraft are currently preserved around the airfield and these are potential exhibits. Two aircraft have been acquired but progress is very slow. Hopefully an announcement on the plans will be made soon. The Caribou was damaged in a forced landing in Tasmania and after repairs was flown to Amberley where it is now stored. The Dakota served with four air forces and after many years in store at Bangkok it was flown to Australia.

TYPE	REG/SER	CON. NO.	PI/NOTES	STATUS
☐ De Havilland D.H.C.4A Caribou	A4-235	235		RA
☐ Douglas DC-3A-456 Skytrain (C-47A) (Dakota III)	N2271C	13864/25309	43-48048, KG765, C-406 (Pakistan), G-ANZE, UBT-714 (Burma)	RA

MACKAY TIGER MOTH MUSEUM (AUS58)

Address:	Casey Avenue, MacKay, Queensland 4740.
Tel:	04-2716-5796
Admission:	When the airfield is open.
Location:	At the airfield which is just south of the town.

The two Tiger Moths are used on joy riding flights in the area. A collection of memorabilia and photographs tracing the history of the type has been assembled. One of the fleet is British built and was acquired from New Zealand. The other was constructed at Bankstown near Sydney and is possibly a composite. The classic biplane is very popular in Australia and many are still active with clubs and private owners.

TYPE	REG/SER	CON. NO.	PI/NOTES	STATUS
☐ De Havilland D.H.82A Tiger Moth	VH-IVN	86128	EM945, G-AMPM, ZK-BBF	PVA
☐ De Havilland D.H.82A Tiger Moth	VH-AYW	DHA.400	A17-365 also quoted as c/n 281 A17-262 – possibly rebuilt using parts from c/n 281.	PVA

MEANDARRA ANZAC MEMORIAL MUSEUM (AUS59)

Address:	Meandarra Queensland 4422.
Admission:	Unknown.
Location:	In the town.

Local resident Rod Keys collected military items for more than thirty years. The local council purchased around twenty vehicles, guns, and a searchlight. Funds are being raised to construct a museum to commemorate ANZAC forces which have fought in major wars. The Canberra is parked outside.

TYPE	REG/SER	CON. NO.	PI/NOTES	STATUS
☐ Government Aircraft Factory Canberra Mk.21 (Mk.20) [English Electric EA.1]	A84-204	4	At Meandarra.	PV

O'REILLY GUEST HOUSE MUSEUM (AUS60)

Address:	Lamington National Park Road, Via Canungra, Queensland 4275.
Tel:	07-5544-0644
Fax:	07-5544-0638
Email:	reservations@oreillys.com.au
Admission:	When the guesthouse is open.
Location:	About 20 km south west of Nerang.

The Stinson came down in February 1937 in the Lamington National Park whilst on a flight from Brisbane to Sydney. Three of the seven on board survived but one was lost when he fell down a waterfall trying to get help. The remaining people trekked through the dense forest to reach safety. The library at the guest house contains some small parts of the original aircraft along with photographs and newspaper reports. A memorial to those lost in the crash has been erected in the grounds and a replica of the aircraft can be seen.

TYPE	REG/SER	CON. NO.	PI/NOTES	STATUS
☐ Stinson A (FSM)	'VH-UHH'			PVX

QANTAS FOUNDERS' OUTBACK MUSEUM (AUS61)

Address:	P.O. Box 737, Longreach Queensland 4730.
Tel:	07-4658-3737
Fax:	07-4658-0707
Email:	enquiries@qfm.com.au
Admission:	Daily 0900-1700
Location:	At the airport which is just east of the town on Route 66/71.

In 1920 Queensland and Northern Territory Air Service (Qantas) was formed at Winton and the following year it moved its headquarters to Longreach. Scheduled services were inaugurated in 1922 using the first hardened surface runway in the country. In 1930 the airline moved its offices to Brisbane and later to Sydney. The original hangar at Longreach has been converted into the first stage of the museum, which opened in June 1996. On show is a replica Avro 504K, the first type used by Qantas, a reconstruction of the office of Hudson Fysh who was one of the four founders of the company and a display of artefacts, memorabilia and photographs. The second stage which opened in 2002 shows the development of Qantas into a major international airline The outside park contains the larger aircraft. The first Boeing 707 used by the company was acquired in England and restored for the flight to its permanent home. Visitors can tour this and the 747.

TYPE	REG/SER	CON. NO.	PI/NOTES	STATUS
☐ Avro 504K (R)				PV
☐ Boeing 707-138B (707-138)	VH-XBA	17696	N31239, VH-EBA, CF-PWV, C-FPWV, (N112TA), N138TA, HZ123, '17696', HZ-123, N220AM, N138MJ, HZ-123	RA
☐ Boeing 747-238B	VH-EBQ	22145	VH-EBQ, DQ-FJI	PV

TYPE	REG/SER	CON. NO.	PI/NOTES	STATUS
☐ De Havilland D.H.61 Giant Moth (FSM)	'VH-UJB'			PVX
☐ Douglas DC-3A-456 Skytrain (C-47A)	VH-EAP	12873	42-93009, A64-44/VHCIA, VH-EAP, VH-EBY, VH-SBG, P2-SBG, P2-ANP, (N5590A), VH-BPL	PV

QUEENSLAND AIR MUSEUM (AUS62)

Address:	P.O. Box 2315, Brisbane, Queensland 4001.
Tel:	07-5492-5930
Fax:	07-5492-5930
Email:	qam@powerup.com.au
Admission:	Daily1000-1600.
Location:	At Caloundra Airfield which is about 3 km west of the town.

Formed in 1974, the museum initially occupied three temporary sites in the Brisbane area. In June 1986 the Caloundra City Council invited the museum to move its collection to the airport where a modem hangar was erected. The museum was officially opened by Mrs Ly Bennett, the wife of Air Vice Marshal Don 'Pathfinder' Bennett. The collection has grown steadily over the last ten years and a large outside area behind the hangar is also in use. Queensland has a rich aeronautical heritage and the story of flying in the state is portrayed in the interesting displays. On show are models, documents, uniforms, photographs and components. The collection includes several airliners which were used on services in the region. The Dove is painted in the colours of Mandated Airlines who operated it in Papua New Guinea. The Australian designed Nomad was flown by Sunstate Airlines and Barrier Reef Airways. Two aircraft in false colours are the Aztec painted as one flown in Papua New Guinea by TAA Sunbird Services and the Piaggio P.166 in the colours of Queensland Airlines. General Douglas MacArthur used the Dakota on at least one occasion during World War II; this aircraft is one of the oldest of the type surviving. Both the Drovers in the collection were flown by the Queensland Section of the Royal Flying Doctor Service. The Meteor F.8, the Hunter and the Sea Vixen were all obtained from the Sentosa Island display in Singapore. The Meteor has been restored to represent an aircraft of No. 77 Squadron R.A.A.F. as a tribute to those who served in Korea. In the hangar is the only Meteor TT.20 in Australia. This aircraft was operated on weapons trials at Woomera in South Australia before being donated to the museum in 1975. Geoffrey Winkner designed and built aircraft in both England and Australia. A replica of his 1931 Cabin Sport has been put on show. A rarity is one of the few Chrislea Super Aces built in England. The large Hangar 2 was finished in July 2004 and now the majority of the collection are under cover and protected from the sea air.

TYPE	REG/SER	CON. NO.	PI/NOTES	STATUS
☐ Avro 652A Anson I	MG226		Forward fuselage only.	RAC
☐ Avro 652A Anson I	VH-BIF		AX305	PV
☐ Beagle B.206 Series 2	VH-UNL	B.047	G-ATZR	PV
☐ Beech 95-C55 Baron	VH-ATB	TE-437	N6221V	PV
☐ Beech C18S Expeditor (SNB-2)	VH-CLG	4213	Bu39194, VH-BJJ	RAD
☐ Beech P35 Bonanza	VH-AWC	D-7227		RAD
☐ Bell 47G-3B-1 Sioux	A1-738	7418		RA
☐ Birdman Promotions TL-1A Grasshopper				PV
☐ Bristol 4 Scout D (R)	'5321'		'8976', 'CFS.4'	PVX
☐ Cessna 402A	VH-NQC	4020072	N4572Q, VH-ELP, P2-ELP	RA
☐ Chrislea C.H.3 Super Ace Series.2	VH-BRO	132		RAC
☐ Commonwealth CA-18 Mustang 22 [North American P-51D] (FSM)	'A68-201'			PVX
☐ Commonwealth CA-25 Winjeel	A85-410	CA25-10		PV
☐ Commonwealth CA-27 Sabre 31 [North American F-86F]	'A94-955'	CA27-35	A94-935	PVX
☐ Commonwealth CA-28 Ceres C	VH-CEU	CA28-19	VH-WOT – front fuselage only – see ANAM, VIC.	PV
☐ De Havilland D.H.71 Tiger Moth (R)			Fuselage shell only.	PV
☐ De Havilland D.H.82A Tiger Moth	VH-BKS	83118	R5259, VH-AHS, VH-BHK	PV
☐ De Havilland D.H.100 Vampire F.30	A79-476	4018	A79-876	RA
☐ De Havilland D.H.104 Dove 1B (1)	'VH-MAL'	04120	VP-KEJ, VH-MAL, VH-AWE, VH-GVE, VH-DSM, (VH-BCM), VH-DSM	PVX
☐ De Havilland D.H.110 Sea Vixen FAW.2 (FAW.1)	XJ490	110017		PV
☐ De Havilland D.H.110 Sea Vixen FAW.2 (FAW.1)	XJ607	110074	XJ607, 8171M – front fuselage only.	PV
☐ De Havilland D.H.112 Sea Venom FAW.53	WZ898	12755	Booms from WZ910.	PV
☐ De Havilland D.H.115 Vampire T.35A (T.33)	A79-828	4113		PV
☐ De Havilland D.H.A.3 Drover 3 (1) (2)	VH-FDR	5006	VH-DRB	PV
☐ De Havilland D.H.A.3 Drover 3 (1) (2)	VH-FDS	5007	VH-DRC	PV
☐ De Havilland D.H.C.1 Chipmunk T.10	VH-RVV	C1/0484	WG410	RA
☐ De Havilland D.H.C.4A Caribou	A4-173	173		PVD
☐ Douglas DC-3-194B (C-49H)	VH-ANR	1944	PH-ALW, PK-ALW, 11944 (USAAF), VHCXE, VHCXL, 42-83229	PV
☐ Fairey Gannet AS.1	XA331	F9223		PV
☐ Gloster Meteor TT.8 (F.8)	'A77-721'		WA880, SAFTECH-2	PVX
☐ Gloster Meteor TT.20 (NF.11)	WD647	5299		PV
☐ Government Aircraft Factory Canberra Mk.20 [English Electric EA.1]	A84-225	25		PV
☐ Government Aircraft Factory Jindivik 31A	WRE601/A92-529		Composite.	PV

☐ Government Aircraft Factory N.22B Nomad	VH-BFH	N22B-35	VH-BFH, OY-ATU, VH-BFH, ZK-SAL	PV
☐ Grumman G-89 Tracker (S2F-1) (S-2A)	Bu133160	131		PV
☐ Hawker P.1099 Hunter FGA.74B (F.6)	533	41H/679972	XE614	
☐ Hawker P.1101 Hunter T.7 (P.1067 Hunter F.4)	XF311	HABL 003072	XF311, A2566, SAFTECH-11	PV
☐ Hiller UH12E	VH-FFT	5116	Parts only – boom on ZK-HCQ.	RA
☐ Hiller UH12E-3 (UH12E-4)	ZK-HCQ	2030	VP-YXR, N5350V, G-ATDW – composite with parts from VH-FFE and c/n 5116 VH-FFT.	RA
☐ Lake LA-4-200 Buccaneer	VH-EJX	596	N65665	PV
☐ Lockheed 237-27-01 Ventura (PV-1)	A59-96	237-6371	Bu49555 – fuselage only.	PV
☐ McLeod K & S 102.5 Cavalier			Unfinished.	PV
☐ Nord N.262A-36 (N.262A-32)	VH-HIX	42	F-WOFD, F-BPNY, N26228, N29811	PV
☐ Percival D.3 Gull Six	VH-UTP	D.30	G-ACHA – original rear fuselage and centre section.	PVD
☐ Piaggio P.166A	'VH-PQA'	370	VH-BHK	PVX
☐ Piper PA-23-250 Aztec C	'VH-TGP'	27-2007	N5007Y, VH-MBX	PVX
☐ Piper PA-25-235 Pawnee	ZK-CEL	25-2747		RA
☐ Riley Heron 2D/A1 (De Havilland D.H.114 Heron 2D)	VH-KAM	14123	EC-AOF, G-ASVC, VQ-FAF, DQ-FAF	PV
☐ Robinson R-22 Beta	VH-LOT	0698	Composite with c/n 1901 VH-SBQ.	PV
☐ Sport Flight Engineering Sky Pup				PV
☐ Supermarine 300 Spitfire F.I (FSM)	'K9789'			PVX
☐ Supermarine 349 Spitfire F.Vc	LZ844		LZ844, A58-213, 'R6915 – on loan.	PV
☐ Swearingen SA.226TC Merlin	VH-BPV	TC-270	N5467M, VH-BPV, ZK-SWC	PV
☐ Vickers 756D Viscount	VH-TVJ	148	Front fuselage only.	PV
☐ Victa Airtourer 100	VH-CFE	18	VH-CFE, VH-CPE	PV
☐ Westland-Sikorsky WS-58 Wessex HAS.31A	N7-217	WA.217	WA217	PV
☐ Wicko Cabin Sports (R)	'VH-UPW'			PVX

QUEENSLAND MUSEUM (AUS63)

Address:	P.O. Box 3300, South Brisbane, Queensland 4101.
Tel:	07-9840-7555
Email:	inquirycentre@qm.qld.gov.au
Admission:	Daily 1000-1600.
Location:	On the south bank of the Brisbane River in the city centre.

The museum opened in the early years of the twentieth century and was housed in a building in Fortitude Valley until the early 1990s. A move was made to a site in the Queensland Cultural Centre which was opened by the Queen. The displays reflect the historical and cultural life of the state. The aviation collection contains a number of significant machines. The oldest is the Avro Baby in which Bert Hinkler flew non-stop to Turin on May 31st 1920 in nine and a half hours. He came second in the Baby in the Aerial Derby at Herndon two months later. The aircraft was shipped to Australia and on April 11th 1921 he flew non-stop the eight hundred miles from Sydney to his home town of Bundaberg, landing in the main street and taxying up to his garden gate. After a series of owners the Baby was presented to the museum. Hanging above it is the Avian prototype which Hinkler flew from England to Australia in 1928. Close by is the wreckage of the Avian flown by Sir Charles Kingsford Smith when he attempted to set an Australia–England record in 1931. W.N. Lancaster then used the Avian on an attack on the London–Cape Town record in 1933. The aircraft was lost and the wreck discovered in the Sahara Desert in March 1962. After a short period on display in London the remains were taken to Australia. The Beech Duke was flown by Denys Dalton when he set a round the world record for piston engined aircraft between July 20th. and 25th 1975. The Resurgam ultralight competed in the 1982 London–Paris race.

TYPE	REG/SER	CON. NO.	PI/NOTES	STATUS
☐ Avro 534 Baby	G-EACQ	534/1	K-131, G-EACQ, G-AUCQ, VH-UCQ	PV
☐ Avro 581E Avian (581) (581A)	G-EBOV	5116		PV
☐ Avro 616 Avian V	G-ABLK	523	G-ABLK, VH-UQG	PVD
☐ Bedson Resurgam 1				PV
☐ Beech 60 Duke	VH-TKE	P-6	N7010D, N2469K	PV
☐ Mignet HM-14 Pou-du-Ciel				PV

ROYAL AUSTRALIAN AIR FORCE AMBERLEY BASE COLLECTION (AUS64)

Address:	RAAF Amberley, Queensland 4306.
Tel:	07-5461-2401
Admission:	By prior permission only.
Location:	About 10 km west of Ipswich.

General Dynamics F-111 squadrons are in residence at this important base. Guarding the gate is an Australian built Canberra and three other examples of the type are parked on the vast field – one has been allocated to the National Museum in Papua New Guinea. Preserved on the base are a Mirage and a Sabre – these airframes are also used for training. For several years a workshop carried out rebuilds for the RAAF Museum at Point Cook The Douglas Havoc and Consolidated Catalina now on show were restored at Amberley.

TYPE	REG/SER	CON. NO.	PI/NOTES	STATUS
☐ Cessna 180A	A98-351	18050351	N5051E	RA
☐ Commonwealth CA-27 Sabre 32 [North American F-86F]	A94-962	CA27-62		RA
☐ Commonwealth CA-29 Mirage IIIO(A) [Dassault Mirage III]	A3-55	CA29-55		RA
☐ English Electric EA.1 Canberra Mk.21 (B.2)	A84-125	EEP71051	WD983	RA
☐ Government Aircraft Factory Canberra Mk.20 [English Electric EA.1]	A84-242	42		RA
☐ Government Aircraft Factory Canberra Mk.21 (Mk.20) [English Electric EA.1]	A84-201	1		PV
☐ Government Aircraft Factory Canberra Mk.21 (Mk.20) [English Electric EA.1]	A84-203	3	Allocated to Papua New Guinea.	RA

ROYAL FLYING DOCTOR SERVICE OF AUSTRALIA MEMORIAL – MOUNT ISA (AUS65)

Address:	11 Barkly Highway, Mount Isa, Queensland 4825.
Tel:	07-4743-2800
Fax:	07-4743-0521
Email:	rfds_mtisa@rfdsqld.com.au
Admission:	Aircraft on permanent view.
Location:	Just north east of the town.

The base at Mount Isa opened in 1964 after a move from Cloncurry. Over the years the based aircraft have carried out many missions and saved several lives. Mounted outside in the car park is an example of the Drover. The RFDS used six examples from the early 1950s. Only twenty Drovers were built and most were later fitted with American engines as they were underpowered. The example on show crashed in 1952 and was rebuilt.

TYPE	REG/SER	CON. NO.	PI/NOTES	STATUS
☐ De Havilland D.H.A.3 Drover 2	VH-DRD	5010	Composite with c/n 5017 VH-AZN	PV

ROYAL FLYING DOCTOR SERVICE OF AUSTRALIA VISITORS CENTRE – CAIRNS (AUS66)

Address:	1 Junction Street, Edge Hill, Cairns Queensland.
Tel:	07-4053-5687
Fax:	07-4032-1776
Email:	cnsvisitorcentre@rfdsqld.com.au
Admission:	Daily 0900-1700.
Location:	In northern suburbs of the town.

The service has bases around Queensland. Displays in the visitor centre show the history and development of the vital work carried out in the remote areas of the country. There are photographs of aircraft used along with uniforms and equipment. On show is a Beech Queen Air once used by the RFDS.

TYPE	REG/SER	CON. NO.	PI/NOTES	STATUS
☐ Beech 65-B80 Queen Air	VH-FDS	LD-509	(YV-119CP), N24083, VH-FDS, VH-LKE	PV

SEARLE COLLECTION (AUS67)

Address:	P.O. Box 399, Kallangar, Queensland 4503.
Admission:	By prior permission only.
Location:	At Coolangatta Airfield and at a private strip near Beaudesert.

Warbird collector Steve Searle is assembling an interesting collection of aircraft and plans to set up a museum. The rare Douglas Havoc was owned by collector Paul Mantz in the early 1950s and after that had a series of corporate and private owners. In 1989 it was presented to the National Air and Space Museum in Washington D.C. However a court decided the aircraft should be returned to the late owner's estate and the Havoc ended up with the Lone Star Flight Museum at Galveston in Texas. The aircraft was dismantled and shipped to Australia. When restored it will be painted in Australian World War II colours as eighty seven served in the country and the Pacific Theatre in World War II. The Hudson was bought in the U.S.A. in the spring of 2008. Almost two hundred and fifty examples of the type served with the Royal Australian Air Force and only a handful now survive. The plans are to restore the Hudson to represent one of this batch. One of the Sentinels flew in civilian ownership in India before being brought to Australia by well known restorer Malcolm Long.

TYPE	REG/SER	CON. NO.	PI/NOTES	STATUS
☐ Douglas A-20J Havoc	N3WF	21356	43-21709, NC67932, N67932, N22M	RA
☐ Grumman G-40 Avenger (TBM-3) (TBM-3E)	VH-MML	3919	Bu53857, N7017C, C-GFPM	RAA
☐ Grumman G-40 Avenger (TBM-3) (TBM-3S) (Avenger AS.3)	VH-VTB	3399	Bu53337,53337 (Canada) CF-IMI, N337GA	RAA
☐ Lockheed 414-56-03 Hudson IIIA (A-29A)				RAA
☐ Piaggio FWP.149D	VH-FWS	190	KB+150, AS+029, BF+427, 91+67, D-ENJF, N482FW	RAA
☐ Stinson V-76 Sentinel (L-5B)	VH-CCO	76-2178	44-16890,VT-CCO	RAA
☐ Stinson V-76 Sentinel (L-5E) (OY-1)	VH-NOY		44-?????,Bu03995	RAA

SHIPTON COLLECTION (AUS68)

Address:	P.O. Box72, Kippa-Ring, Queensland 4021
Admission:	By prior permission only.
Location:	At a priavte strip in the area.

This private collection includes a number of interesting aircraft. The Gipsy Moth was delivered to Australia in 1929 and was flown in Victoria. The biplane was impressed in 1940 and after its military days were over was dismantled. A rebuild incorporating parts from other aircraft took place in the 1980s. Two recent imports from the U.S.A. are the Fleet 2 and the cabin Waco YKS-6. Both types are uncommon in Australian skies. Several classsic Cessnas are maintained in flying condition. The two seat 120 appeared in 1946 and over two thousand were completed. The five seat 190 made its maiden flight in December 1945 and was developed into the 195.

TYPE	REG/SER	CON. NO.	PI/NOTES	STATUS
☐ Cessna 120	VH-NNW	13579	NC4121N, N4121N	RAA
☐ Cessna 172M	VH-IQM	17261997	N12408, N1760C	RAA
☐ Cessna 172M	VH-DXE	17262248	N12775	RAA
☐ Cessna 172M	VH-WXX	17267673	N1403U	RAA
☐ Cessna 172N	VH-RPL	17269292	N737BN	RAA
☐ Cessna 175	VH-UMA	56194		RAA
☐ Cessna 195B	VH-BVD	7519	N9327A	RAA
☐ De Havilland D.H.60M Moth	VH-ULP	1406	VH-ULP, A7-78 – composite	RAA
☐ Fleet 2				RAA
☐ North American NA-88 Texan (AT-6C) (Harvard IIA)	VH-TEX	88-9263	41-33157, EX184, NZ1006	RAA
☐ Waco YKS-6				RAA

SIR CHARLES KINGSFORD SMITH MEMORIAL (AUS69)

Address:	Eagle Farm Airport, Brisbane, Queensland 4007.
Tel:	07-3305-9233 (Airport Visitor Centre)
Admission:	On permanent view.
Location:	About 15 km north east of the city centre

In 1926 Charles Kingsford Smith purchased a Fokker F.VII/3m which had crashed on G.H. Wilkins' Arctic expedition. The aircraft was rebuilt by Boeing at Seattle. After five attempts on the world non-refuelled endurance record, backing was obtained for a trans-Pacific flight. The Fokker named 'Southern Cross' left Oakland on May 31st 1928 and landed at Brisbane on June 11th. Later the first flight across the Tasman Sea to New Zealand was made. A flight to England was completed in 1929 and the aircraft then crossed the Atlantic from Baldonnel in Ireland to Newfoundland ending its journey in New York. The Fokker returned to Australia by ship and was there modified to a sixteen seat airliner for use by Kingsford Smith's Australian National Airways. The Australian Government bought the historic aircraft in 1933 and it was later put on show at Eagle Farm Airport.

TYPE	REG/SER	CON. NO.	PI/NOTES	STATUS
☐ Fokker F.VIIa/3m	VH-USU	4954	1985 (US), G-AUSU	PV

TOWNSVILLE ANNEX OF THE ROYAL AUSTRALIAN AIR FORCE MUSEUM (AUS70)

Address:	Inngham Road, R.A.A.F. Townsville, Garbutt, Queensland 4814.
Tel:	07-4752-1712
Email:	info@raafmuseum.com
Admission:	Sunday 1000-1600. Closed Mid-December – early January.
Location:	On the south side of the airport which is the western suburbs of the town off Route A1.

In October 1941 No. 24 Squadron moved into Garbutt Airfield and during World War II the base became an major centre for operations in the Southwest Pacific. At the end of the conflict the site was used as a transit camp for returning personnel and prisoners of war. After the war No. 10 Squadron equipped with the Avro Lincoln moved in and the unit subsequently operated the Neptune from 1962 to 1977. In 1980 a collection of memorabilia was gathered to celebrate the fortieth anniversary of the base. This led to the idea of a museum and in 1983 a small building was refurbished by volunteers. The collection moved to its present site in 1991. The history of the base and its units is told in the informative displays. The Mustang is painted in the colours of an aircraft used by No. 3 Squadron in Italy in 1944. One of the Neptunes is stored on the base and the other serves as the gate guardian to the field.

TYPE	REG/SER	CON. NO.	PI/NOTES	STATUS
☐ Bell 205 Iroquois (UH-1H)	A2-382	9382	67-17184	PV
☐ Commonwealth CA-18 Mustang 23 [North American P-51D]	'KH797'	1462	A68-137, VH-PPV	PVX
☐ De Havilland D.H.115 Vampire T.35	A79-656	4178		RA
☐ De Havilland D.H.115 Vampire T.35A (T.33)	A79-804	4084		RA
☐ Lockheed 726-45-17 Neptune MR.4 (P2V-7) (P2V-7S) (SP-2H)	A89-272	726-7272	Bu149072	PV
☐ Lockheed 726-45-17 Neptune MR.4 (P2V-7) (P2V-7S) (SP-2H)	A89-280	726-7280	Bu149080	RA

WARBIRDS ADVENTURES MUSEUM (AUS71)

Address:	Mareeba Airport, Atherton Table, Queensland 4880.
Tel:	07-4092-7391
Email:	flights@warbirdsadventures.com
Admission:	Wednesday-Sunday 1000-1600.
Location:	About 3 km south of the town.

This collection is operated by the North Queensland Warbirds Association. A display has been set up in rooms around the hangar where components, uniforms, photographs and memorabilia can be seen. The active aircraft are regular performers at shows around the region. Under restoration in the adjacent workshop is a Curtiss P-40 which is being built up from components from several wrecked aircraft. The Chipmunk is one of three conversions made by the Sasin company for use in agricultural work.

TYPE	REG/SER	CON. NO.	PI/NOTES	STATUS
☐ Commonwealth CA-25 Winjeel	VH-XXE	CA25-53	A85-453	PVA
☐ Commonwealth CA-25 Winjeel	VH-XXD	CA25-55	A85-455	PVA
☐ Curtiss 87V Warhawk (P-40N)	VH-MIK		42-104977 – composite.	PVC
☐ Douglas DC-3A-456 Skytrain (C-47A)	'43-48234	14050/25495	43-48234, VH-DMV, VH-CAO, VH-BAB	PVC
☐ Nanchang CJ-6A	VH-XXB	2032016		PVA
☐ North American NA-88 Texan (AT-6C) (Harvard IIA)	VH-XXH	88-13189	41-33716, EX743, NZ1040, ZK-REB	PVA
☐ Panstwowe Zaklady Lotnicze (PZL) 104 Wilga 80	VH-AQX	CF21920938		PVA
☐ Sasin SA-29 Spraymaster (De Havilland D.H.C.1 Chipmunk T.10)	WB601	C1/0042	WB601, VH-BCA	PVA

ZUCCOLI'S CLASSIC AIRCRAFT COLLECTION (AUS72)

Address:	P.O. Box 1214, Toowoomba, Queensland 4350.
Tel:	07-4633-1315
Fax:	aerotec@bigpond.com
Admission:	Monday-Friday 1000-1600.
Location:	In Hangar H on Spitfire Street at Toowoomba Airport which is about 5 km north west of the town.

Guido and Lynette Zuccoli assembled an interesting collection of aircraft over the last few years. The main base is now at Towoomba with a workshop at Darwin in the Northern Territory. The Fiat G.59 was built in 1949 and served with the Italian Air Force until 1953. After a period in store with the Museo Storico dell'Aeronautica Militare Italiana it was sold to Pino Valenti, who has a G.59 flying in Italy. Guido bought G.59 in 1983 and shipped the airframe to Chino for rebuild by Saunders Aircraft. The first flight took place on September 2nd 1987. In 1994 it was rebuilt as a single seater and is now painted in a North African Desert Italian colour scheme. An interesting project is the construction of a sixty five percent scale replica of the Stipa Caproni. The original first flew in 1932 and featured a Gipsy engine mounted inside a large diameter barrel shaped fuselage. The shrouded propeller caused a thrust to emerge at the end of the tube. The Falco was built in Toowoomba in 1992 and the Chipmunk arrived from England. Guido was sadly killed on March 6th 1997 in the crash of a T-6G at R.A.A.F. Tindal. Lynette and her family have continued maintaining this impressive collection.

TYPE	REG/SER	CON. NO.	PI/NOTES	STATUS
☐ Boeing-Stearman A75N1 Kaydet (PT-17)	VH-ZYZ	75-1439	41-7880 – flies as N2S-4 '07880'	PVAX
☐ De Havilland D.H.C.1 Chipmunk 22 (T.10)	VH-ZCM	C1/0530	WG480	PVA
☐ Fiat G.59-4B	VH-LIX	179	MM53772, N59B	PVA
☐ Mignet HM-14 Pou-du-Ciel				RA
☐ New Zealand Aerospace CT/4B Airtrainer	VH-CTZ	CT4-081	NZ1933, ZK-JMN	PVA
☐ North American NA-174 Trojan (T-28A) (AT-28D)	VH-ZUK	174-374	51-7521, 3403 (Laos), VH-DUK – flies as US Navy '7521'	PVA
☐ North American NA-174 Trojan (T-28A) (AT-28D)	VH-ZUC	174-429	51-7576, 3401 (Laos) – flies as '91576/TL-576'	PVAX
☐ North American NA-88 Texan (AT-6D) (Harvard III)	VH-SNJ	88-16324	42-84543, EZ329, NZ1085, ZK-ENM	PVA
☐ Pitts S-1S Special	VH-IGZ	KA-076		PVA
☐ Ryan STA	VH-UVQ	132	VH-UZQ, VH-BWQ	PVA
☐ Sequoia F.8L Falco	VH-LZF	Q-52		PVA
☐ Stipa Caproni (Scale R)	VH-SCZ	SCR-1		PVA
☐ Vultee V-54D Valiant (BT-13)	VH-BTD		(USAAF)	RAC

SOUTH AUSTRALIA

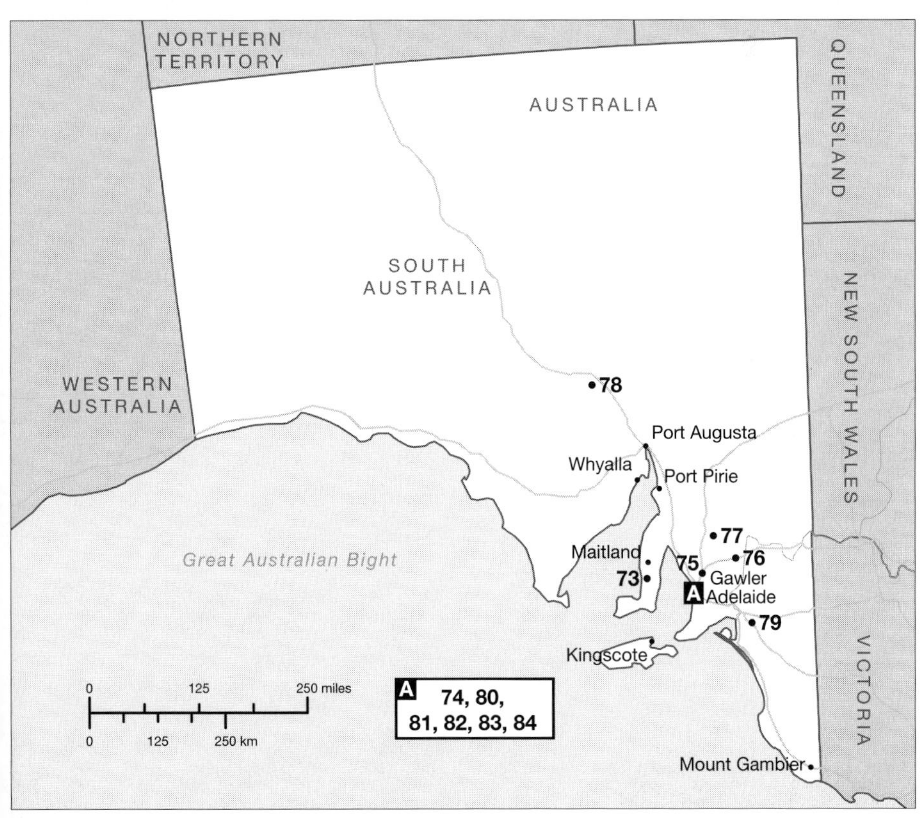

CAPTAIN HARRY BUTLER MEMORIAL (THE) (AUS73)

Address:	P.O. Box 88, Minlaton, South Australia 5575.
Tel:	08-8853-2027
Admission:	Minlaton Museum Tuesday-Friday 0930-1300 Saturday 0930-1600. Aircraft on permanent view.
Location:	In Maitland Road which is in the northern suburbs of the town.

Captain Harry Butler, a native of Minlaton, brought two Bristol M.1Cs to Australia. One arrived with an Avro 504K in July 1919. He flew the M.1C to Minlaton from Adelaide on August 6th 1919 and performed aerobatics over the town. He returned to Adelaide carrying mail five days later. In January 1922 he received serious head injuries whilst flying the Avro 504 and eventually died on July 29th 1923. Before his death he ordered the second M.1C, which disappeared, and a De Havilland Humming Bird which survived in Perth until the 1960s. In 1930 Captain Horrie Miller bought the first M.1C from Butler's estate. The airframe was modified with flat sides to the fuselage and fitted with a Gipsy 1 engine. The aircraft won the 1931 and 1932 Adelaide Aerial Derbies and competed in several other races. The Bristol was removed from the register in 1936 but in 1940 Miller obtained a permit to ferry it from Adelaide to Perth. The aircraft flew twice after World War II and was then placed in store. Captain Miller presented it to the town of Minlaton in 1956. A building to house the aircraft was opened in 1958. The structure was redesigned and rebuilt in 1989 and the aircraft restored to original configuration, with round fuselage and Le Rhone radial engine, by members of the Balaklava Gliding Club. Resplendent in the red colour scheme it wore in 1919, the M.IC is the only original example of its type left. A display of photographs tracing the life of Harry Butler is located in the local history museum.

TYPE	REG/SER	CON. NO.	PI/NOTES	STATUS
☐ Bristol 20 M.1C	C5001	2819	C5001, G-AUCH, VH-UQI	PV

CLASSIC JETS FIGHTER MUSEUM (AUS74)

Address:	Hangar 52, Anderson Drive, Parafield Airport South Australia.
Tel:	08-8258-2277
Fax:	08-8258-1090
Email:	cjfm@chariot.net.au
Admission:	Wednesday-Sunday 1000-1600.
Location:	About 15 km north of Adelaide on the Sturt Highway – Route A20.

Bob Jarrett began collecting aircraft more that ten years ago with the aim of setting up a museum. Plans were realised in July 1996 with the establishment of the collection at Parafield. The Meteor was used by No. 77 Squadron of the Royal Australian Air Force at Kimpo in Korea. This aircraft was stored at the Moorabbin Air Museum until 1992 when it was acquired and restored for display. Under rebuild in the hangar is the Mirage III which made a wheels up landing at Tullamarine Airport in Melbourne in October 1974. The airframe was converted into components for disposa l in 1986. The museum obtained the Mirage in 1992 and has gradually found the parts it needs to restore the delta to pristine condition. The Vampire is painted in the colours of the 1963 'Tel-stars' aerobatic team. The Sea Venom spent a period in the 1970s at the Tuggerah Lakes War Museum and was then in store for many years before this museum purchased it in 1993. Bob Jarrett bought the Sabre in 1985 and the fighter was used as a training airframe at a college in Parafield before the museum opened. The Lightning was recovered from Papua New Guinea in 1997 and is being restored. Also on show are engines, flying suits, photographs and artefacts tracing the development of the jet fighter and trainer.

TYPE	REG/SER	CON. NO.	PI/NOTES	STATUS
☐ Bell 26E Airacobra (P-39Q)	A53-1		41-7119	RAC
☐ British Aircraft Corporation 167 Strikemaster 88	VH-ZEP	EEP/JP/3233	G-27-197, NZ6361	PVA
☐ Commonwealth CA-18 Mustang 21 [North American P-51D] (FSM)			Front fuselage only.	PV
☐ Commonwealth CA-27 Sabre 32 [North American F-86F]	A94-974	CA27-74		PV
☐ Commonwealth CA-29 Mirage IIIO(A) (IIIO(F)) [Dassault Mirage III]	A3-16	CA29-16		PV
☐ Commonwealth CA-30 [Aermacchi MB.326H]	A7-016	CA30-16		RA
☐ Commonwealth CA-30 [Aermacchi MB.326H]	A7-025	CA30-25		RA
☐ Dassault Mirage IIIEO			Cockpit section only.	PV
☐ De Havilland D.H.82A Tiger Moth	VH-ZIS	DHA.215	A17-214, VH-AQF	PVA
☐ De Havilland D.H.112 Sea Venom FAW.53	WZ939	12781	WZ939, N4-939	PV
☐ De Havilland D.H.C.1 Chipmunk 22 (T.10)	WP971/VH-ZIZ	C1/0683	WP791, G-APTS, 'WP976'	PVA
☐ Gloster Meteor F.8	A77-867		WK685	PV
☐ Government Aircraft Factory Jindivik 203B (IIIB)	'WRE 529'		Composite of at least nine.	PVX
☐ Kawasaki Ki-61 Hien			Cockpit section only.	PVD
☐ Lockheed 222-81-20 Lightning (P-38H)	42-66841	222-1352		PV
☐ Nanchang CJ-6A	VH-NNJ	2432070		PVA
☐ North American NA-124 Mustang (P-51D)	44-84832	124-44688	Front fuselage only.	PV
☐ Wytwornia Sprzetu Komunikacyjnego (WSK) SBLim-2 (Lim-1) [MiG-15] [MiG-15UTI]		1A 06-036	636 (Poland), (VH-LKW)	PV

Right: The Beck family have a museum a museum at Mareeba in Queensland. This Bell P-39D is a prized exhibit. (Eric Munk)

Below: The impressive Rohrlach Tecnology and Heritage Centre at Angaston is home to this Fokker Dr I replica.

The Kaufman Glider was built in 1924 and can be seen at Lincoln Nitschke's museum at Greenock.

DAVIS COLLECTION (AUS75)

Address:	P.O. Box 318 Salisbury South Australia 5108.
Admission:	By prior permission only.
Location:	At Gawler Airfield which is about 3 km west of the town.

The stars of this private collection are the two Avro Avians. One is currently in flying condition and the other is under restoration. The history of these Avians is complex. In 1944 A.G. and H.W. Murrell bought VH-UQE and crashed it three years later. Parts of VH-UVX were acquired soon after and a composite rebuild took place. VH-UVX was rebuilt using components from VH-UQE and the biplane flew in 1958 carrying the registration VH-UQE. The rebuild of the genuine VH-UQE then started. VH-UQX now carries its correct registration. The Curtiss Robin is the only example of the classic American monoplane currently in Australia. The Beech 17 was acquired in the auction at Airworld in Wangaratta, VIC.

TYPE	REG/SER	CON. NO.	PI/NOTES	STATUS
☐ Avro 616 Avian IVM	VH-UVX	R3/CN/522	G-ABLF, VH-UVX – contains parts from c/n R3/CN/531 VH-UQE and flew as this for a time.	RAA
☐ Avro 616 Sports Avian	VH-UQE	R3/CN/531	Contains parts from c/n R3/CN/522 G-ABLF, VH-UVX.	RAC
☐ Beech F17D	VH-AME	248	NC19476, VH-ACU, A39-1, VH-ACU	RAA
☐ Boeing-Stearman A75 Kaydet (PT-13B)	VH-HYU	75-0909	41-0849, N58067	RAA
☐ Curtiss 50H Robin J-1 (50 Robin B)	VH-JUV	477	NC364K	RAA
☐ Stampe & Vertongen S.V.4B	VH-LFO	'699299'	(France), N9184R	RAA

KEV ROHRLACH TECHNOLOGY AND HERITAGE CENTRE (AUS76)

Address:	21 Dean Street, Angaston, South Australia 5353.
Tel:	08-8563-3407
Admission:	Monday-Saturday 1100-1600, Sunday and and Public Holidays 1000-1700.
Location:	Between Tanunda and Nuriootpa.

This informative museum has been assembled by Kev Rohrlach and is housed in a purpose built exhibition hall. On show are cars, motor cycles, tractors, military vehicles, home drawn carriages, steam and oil engines, rockets and missiles. There is a section devoted to the settlement of the Barossa Valley region with clothes, memorabilia and artefacts on view. The aviation section includes three scale replicas constructed for film and television use. The Jindivik pilotless aircraft was used in large numbers at Woomera. The Ascender microlight was flown by Kev Rohrlach across the inhospitable Simpson Desert in the 1970s.

TYPE	REG/SER	CON. NO.	PI/NOTES	STATUS
☐ Fokker Dr I (R)	'425/17'		Replica containing many original parts.	PVX
☐ Government Aircraft Factory Jindivik 203B (IIIB)	'WRE 529'		Composite.	PVX
☐ Nieuport 11 (Scale R)				PV
☐ Pterodactyl Ascender				PV
☐ Royal Aircraft Factory S.E.5A (Scale R)				PV

LINCOLN NITSCHKE'S MILITARY AND HISTORICAL AIRCRAFT COLLECTION (AUS77)

Address:	P.O. Box 20, Greenock, South Australia 5360.
Tel:	08-8562-8226
Admission:	Wednesday-Sunday 1000-1600.
Location:	On the Kapunda Road about 3 km north of Greenock.

Lincoln Nitschke has built up this impressive collection over the last quarter of a century. Over fourteen hundred 1/72nd scale models, engines and components are on show in the building. Nearing completion is an Anson fuselage painstakingly rebuilt from parts of derelict airframes. Lincoln has completed a replica cockpit section of a Mosquito B.IV and is currently constructing an FB.40 fuselage using some original components. Two Oxford noses are present and a complete fuselage will be built. Eleven Wirraway fuselage frames can be seen along with the remains of two Edgar Percival E.P.9s. Australian-born Edgar Percival set up a company in England in the 1930s and many successful designs emerged. When this firm was taken over he designed the EP.9 for agricultural work. Two former Royal New Zealand Air Force Devons are in the collection, one of which is believed to have been involved in the smuggling of gold bars out of Kalgoorlie in Western Australia. The British built Canberra was used at Woomera for trials in the Jindivik, Red Top and Blue Steel programmes. The Kaufman Glider is one of a pair built in 1924 in Loxton. The Pascoe Spruce Goose glider dates from 1954. Vast amounts of airframe spares are in store and these will be used in future projects.

TYPE	REG/SER	CON. NO.	PI/NOTES	STATUS
☐ Airspeed AS.10 Oxford I			Front fuselage only.	PV
☐ Airspeed AS.10 Oxford I	V3475		Front fuselage only.	PV
☐ Avro 652A Anson I	W2589		Front fuselage only.	PVD
☐ Avro 652A Anson I	AX350		Fuselage only	PV
☐ Avro 652A Anson I	MG390			PVD
☐ Beech 65 Queen Air			Nose only.	PV
☐ Commonwealth CA-1 Wirraway I [North American NA-33]			Several fuselage frames.	PV
☐ Commonwealth CA-12 Boomerang I			Front fuselage only.	PV
☐ Commonwealth CA-16 Wirraway III [North American NA-33]	A20-408		Front fuselage only.	RA
☐ Commonwealth CA-16 Wirraway III [North American NA-33]	A20-686		Fusealge only.	PV
☐ Commonwealth CA-18 Mustang 23 [North American P-51D] (FSM)	'A68-150'			PVX
☐ De Havilland D.H.98 Mosquito B.IV (R)	'DZ652'		Front fuselage only.	PVX
☐ De Havilland D.H.98 Mosquito FB.40	'A52-28'		Incorporates parts of DZ652.	PVX
☐ De Havilland D.H.104 Devon C.1	NZ1814	04397	NZ1814, VH-CJX	PV
☐ De Havilland D.H.115 Vampire T.35	A79-602	4123	A79-602, N11920	PV
☐ Edgar Percival E.P.9	VH-SSX	27	G-43-6, G-APAD, VH-SSW	PVD
☐ Edgar Percival E.P.9	VH-DAV	46	VH-SSR – fuselage only	PV
☐ English Electric EA.1 Canberra B.2	WH700			PV
☐ Fairey Battle I			Centre section only.	PVD
☐ Pascoe Spruce Goose				PV
☐ Piper PA-23-250 Aztec C	VH-COO	27-2746	N5633Y	PV

LIONS CLUB PARK MISSILE MUSEUM (AUS78)

Address:	P.O. Box 125, Woomera, South Australia 5720.
Tel:	08-8673-7042
Admission:	Daily 1000-1600.
Location:	In the centre of the town at the corner of Banool and Deevrang Avenues.

For over thirty years the site at Woomera was used to develop rockets and missiles. The local branch of the Lions Club has set up the centre in the town to portray this aspect of the history of the region and the development of the base. Three aircraft can be seen. A number of Meteor F.4s and F.8s were converted for use as unmanned target aircraft on the ranges. Piloted versions were also flown on trials. The T.7 on show was, in the 1950s, the personal aircraft of Wing Commander W.H. Garing. The Canberra was delivered to Woomera in 1982 for development work on the Karinga bomb. A number of airframes were used as targets. The pilotless Jindivik was used in large numbers over the years. The work carried out at Woomera was significant in the development of rockets and missiles and it is appropriate that this is honoured in the town.

TYPE	REG/SER	CON. NO.	PI/NOTES	STATUS
☐ Gloster Meteor T.7	A77-701		WA731, A77-229	PV
☐ Government Aircraft Factory Canberra Mk.20 [English Electric EA.1]	A84-241	41		PV
☐ Government Aircraft Factory Jindivik 102A (IIA)	A92-??			PV

MONARTO GLIDING MUSEUM (AUS79)

Address:	Monarto, South Australia 5155.
Tel:	08-85-4-4011
Email:	gliding@emilis.sa.on.net
Admission:	By prior permission only.
Location:	About 10 km north west of Murray Bridge.

Emilis Prelgauskas bought a hundred acre site at Monarto in 1983. After constructing a home he developed an airfield with hangars, workshops and a clubhouse. In 2000 the first museum building was completed and a second is now ready. The South Australian Gliding History Trust has collected a vast amount of material including taped interviews with pioneers. The history of gliding in the region is portrayed in a number of interesting displays. The Hoffman glider dates from 1924 and is one of two built for use by the local Air Scouts. This was a rigid tandem wing hang glider which was based on German designs flow in the pioneering days. There are several Australian designed sailplanes from Edmund Schneider and his son Harry. The set up a factory at Parafield near Adelaide and a series of successful types were sold to clubs and private owners. Their first product in their new home was a variant of the ES-49, one of his last German designs. The Kookaburra made its maiden flight in June 1954 and over twenty were supplied to Australian clubs. The ES.52B version features a longer wing to improve the performance but only four were built. The Kingfisher followed in 1956 and was a single seater intended for cross country soaring. Eight were completed at the factory and three more were amateur built. Schneider built the Schleicher Ka-6 under licence but Australian owners demanded a heavier and stronger machine and in response the Boomerang appeared. The type achieved success in Australian competitions and two flew in the 1965 World Gliding Championships at South Cerney in England. Just over twenty were completed with one exported to the U.S.A. Harry Schneider designed the ES.65 Platypus which used composite construction. A sole prototype was built and this flew successfully at Gawler in August 1984.

TYPE	REG/SER	CON. NO.	PI/NOTES	STATUS
☐ Anselma Sagitta II	VH-GQS	014		RA
☐ Brasov IS-32A	VH-HND	6		RAA
☐ Hoffman Glider				PV
☐ Let L-13 Blanik			Damaged airframe – due soon.	–
☐ Let L-13 Blanik	VH-GYD	174322		RAA
☐ Miller Tern				PV
☐ Polyteknikkojen Ilmailukerho PIK-20			Front fuselage only.	PV
☐ Primary Glider			Major components.	PV
☐ Reich Neumann ULF-1			Due soon.	–
☐ Riverland Glider				PV
☐ Schleicher Ka-6 Rhönsegler	VH-GHA	77		RA
☐ Schneider ES.52 Kookaburra II	VH-GHN	10		RAA
☐ Schneider ES.52 Kookaburra 4				RA
☐ Schneider ES.52B Longwing Kookaburra	VH-GLZ	40		RA
☐ Schneider ES.57 Kingfisher II	VH-GRH	28		RAC
☐ Schneider ES.60 Boomerang	VH-GTI	99		RA
☐ Schneider ES.60 Boomerang AI	VH-GQG	74		RAA
☐ Schneider ES.65 Platypus (FSM)			Front fuselage only.	PV
☐ Start+Flug H-111				PV
☐ Stemme S-10VT	VH-TCP			RAA

ROYAL AUSTRALIAN AIR FORCE BASE EDINBURGH MEMORIAL (AUS80)

Address:	West Avenue, Edinburgh, South Australia 5111.
Tel:	08-8393-2111
Admission:	By prior permission only.
Location:	About 25 km north of Adelaide

This base was built on the site of a wartime munitions factory. An airfield was constructed and the RAAF moved in during 1955. The Mirage is now restored and the Macchi is by the parade ground.

TYPE	REG/SER	CON. NO.	PI/NOTES	STATUS
☐ Commonwealth CA-29 Mirage IIID [Dassault Mirage III]	A3-115	CA29-115		RA
☐ Commonwealth CA-30 [Aermacchi MB.326H]	A7-064	CA30-064		RA

SIR ROSS AND SIR KEITH SMITH WAR MEMORIAL (AUS81)

Address:	Adelaide Airport, 1 James Schofield Drive, Adelaide, South Australia 5950.
Tel:	08-8306-9211
Admission:	On permanent view.
Location:	About 8 km south west of the city centre

In March 1919 the Australian Government offered a prize of £10,000 for the first flight from England to Australia by an Australian crew in a British aircraft. Brothers Captain Ross and Lieutenant Keith Smith entered a Vickers Vimy and, accompanied by two mechanics, Sergeants J.M. Bennett and W.H. Shiers, they left Hounslow on November 12th 1919. The Vimy arrived in Darwin on December 10th, taking one hundred and eighty eight hours and twenty minutes flying time. After a few problems the aircraft reached Sydney on February 14th 1920 and the crew were presented with their prize by the Prime Minister. The Vimy was donated to the Australian Government by Vickers and is now preserved in a specially constructed hall at Adelaide Airport. The brothers were both knighted and in 1922 Ross and Bennett were killed in England while testing a Vickers Viking amphibian which they proposed to use on a round the world flight. Keith served for over thirty years as the Vickers representative in Australia and on the board of Qantas until his death in 1955.

TYPE	REG/SER	CON. NO.	PI/NOTES	STATUS
☐ Vickers FB.27A Vimy IV	G-EAOU		F8630, G-EAOU, A5-1	PV

SOUTH AUSTRALIAN AVIATION MUSEUM (AUS82)

Address:	P.O. Box 150, Lipson Street, Port Adelaide, South Australia 5015.
Tel:	08-8240-1230
Email:	saam@adam.com.au
Admission:	Daily 1030-1630.
Location:	In the centre of the town which is about 10 km north west of Adelaide.

Formed in 1984, the museum first opened in a garage at Glenelg. A move to a former flour mill in Mundy Street Port Adelaide took place in November 1986. In January 1996 the exhibition moved a short distance to a large hangar on Ocean Steamers Road and has now relocated to Lipson Street. In 1990 the museum was provisionally accredited as the State Aviation Museum by the History Trust of South Australia. The following year it took over the State Historical Aviation Collection which had been held by the National Motor Museum at Birdwood. In early 1996 the Government Defence Science and Technology Organisation loaned their rocket collection to the museum. On show are over twenty items including rockets fired from the Woomera range between 1950 and the early 1980s. The history of aviation, since the first flight in South Australia in March 1910 by Bill Wittber in a Blériot XI near Bolivar, is portrayed in detail. Among the items on show are a flying helmet and gloves used by Sir Charles Kingsford Smith and an engine built by Bill Wittber in 1915 to power a biplane he designed More than twenty engines dating from World War I to modern times can also be seen. An interesting homebuilt on show is the parasol monoplane completed in 1938 by Clem Sheppard who had previously constructed a glider. The first aircraft to be acquired by the museum was the Anson EF954 donated by a farmer from Mallala who had bought it in 1947. Under restoration in the hangar is one of the Gipsy Moths moved from Birdwood. This example flew with Guinea Airways until 1942 when it was bought by the School of Mines as an instructional airframe. A workshop and store are located nearby. The museum has made great strides since it was formed.

TYPE	REG/SER	CON. NO.	PI/NOTES	STATUS
☐ Aero Commander 680	VH-PSG	422-96	VH-SMA	PV
☐ Avro 652A Anson I	EF954			PVC
☐ Commonwealth CA-30 [Aermacchi MB.326H]	A7-026	CA30-26		PV
☐ Commonwealth CA-30 [Aermacchi MB.326H]	A7-030	CA30-30		PV
☐ De Havilland D.H.60G Gipsy Moth	VH-ULJ	1074		PVC
☐ De Havilland D.H.60M Moth	VH-ULO	1405	Fuselage frame only	PV
☐ De Havilland D.H.100 Vampire FB.31 (F.30)	A79-202	4039	A79-202, INST.18	PVC
☐ De Havilland D.H.112 Sea Venom FAW.53	WZ931	12773		PVC
☐ De Havilland D.H.C.1 Chipmunk 22 (T.10)	WB587	C1/0039	WB587, VH-UEK	PVD
☐ Douglas DC-3A-467 Skytrain (C-47B) (Dakota IV)	A65-114	16712/33460	44-77128, A65-114/VHRGH, A65-114/VMHJY	PV
☐ English Electric EA.1 Canberra B.2	WK165			PVC
☐ English Electric EA.1 Canberra T.4 (B.2)	WD954	EEP71036	Front fuselage on show – rest of fuselage and other components in store.	PVC
☐ Fairey Battle I	N2188	F3213	Composite involving parts from several other unidentified aircraft.	PVC
☐ Fokker Dr I (Scale R)	'425/17'			PVX
☐ Fokker F.27 Friendship 100	VH-CAT	10132	PH-FAZ	S
☐ Gloster Meteor F.8	A77-851		WK683 – front fuselage and centre section only.	PV
☐ Government Aircraft Factory Jindivik 203B (IIIB)	N11-752			PV
☐ Hornet Ultralight				RA
☐ Mead Rhön Ranger				PV
☐ Schneider ES.54 Gnome				RA
☐ Sheppard CS2				PV
☐ Supermarine 349 Spitfire F.Vc	EE853	WASP/20/484	EE853, A58-146 – on loan from Spitfire Museum.	PV
☐ Terrafly ANO 95-10				PV
☐ Westland-Sikorsky WS-58 Wessex HAS.31B	N7-224	WA.224	WA224	PV

SPITFIRE MUSEUM (THE LANGDON BADGER TRUST) (AUS83)

Address:	26/9-11 Fifth Esplanade, Glenelg, South Australia 5045.
Tel:	08-8294-9796
Admission:	By prior permission only.
Location:	The museum is at Unley Park in the southern suburbs of Adelaide.

Built at Yeovil by Westland Aircraft the Spitfire was stored for over a year before being shipped to Australia in March 1943. The aircraft served with No. 79 Squadron in New Guinea until it crashed on landing at Kiriwina on August 28th 1943. The airframe was taken back to the squadron's base at Goodenough Island and, after removal of useful spares, was abandoned. The wreck was found in 1971 by Langdon Badger. He dismantled the Spitfire and shipped it to Adelaide two years later. A hangar to house the aircraft was built and restoration commenced. Parts from several other Spitfires were used in the rebuild. Also on show in the hangar are engines, documents, propellers and components and the complete collection of No. 79 Squadron photographs from World War II. This fascinating display traces the history of the unit, which was formed at Laverton in April 1943. The squadron was then based on several Pacific islands where it often encountered Japanese aircraft. After a short spell at Darwin No. 79 Squadron was disbanded at Oakey in Queensland on November 12th 1945. The Spitfire has now moved to the South Australian Aviation Museum so that it could be viewed on a regular basis.

TYPE	REG/SER	CON. NO.	PI/NOTES	STATUS
☐ Supermarine 349 Spitfire F.Vc	EE853	WASP/20/484	EE853, A58-146 – on loan to SAAM.	–

WEST TORRENS RAILWAY SIGNAL/ TELEGRAPH AND AVIATION MUSEUM (AUS84)

Address:	112 Marion Road, Brooklyn Park, South Australia 5032.
Tel:	08-8172-2001
Email:	aviat@chariot.net.au
Admission:	Sunday 1300-1630.
Location:	Just north of Adelaide Airport.

This fascinating museum concentrates on transport communications. The railway section has a wide range of signalling equipment showing the development which has taken place over the years. The history of the South Australian railway system is portrayed. The aviation section contains communication equipment from both aircraft, ground stations and airport control towers. A Royal Australian Air Force Memorial Room honours all residents of the state who have given their lives in the service of their country.

TASMANIA

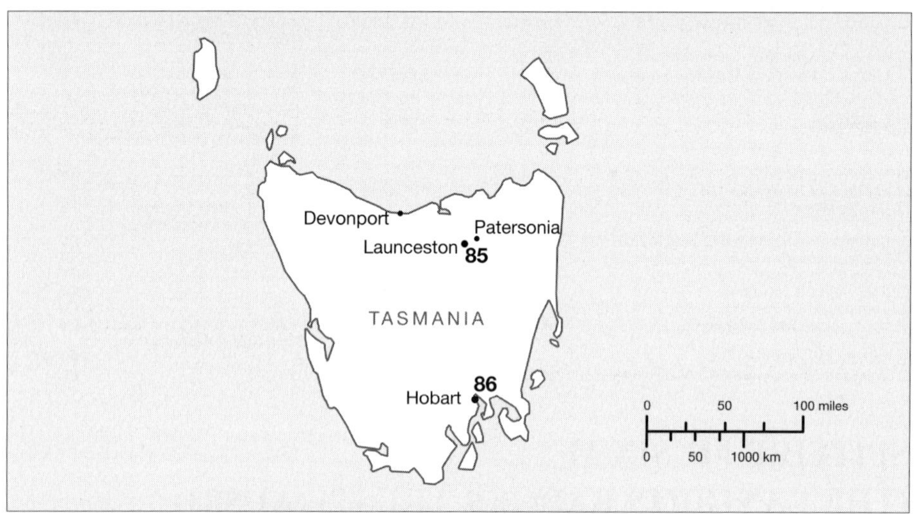

QUEEN VICTORIA MUSEUM AND ART GALLERY (AUS85)

Address:	2 Wellington Street, Launceston, Tasmania 7250.
Tel:	03-6323-3777
Fax:	03-6323-3776
Email:	enquiries@qvmag.tas.gov.au
Location:	Daily 1000-1700.
Admission:	In the centre of the city.

The museum has two sites in the city. These are a purpose-built complex in Royal Park and the former Launceston Railway workshops at Inveresk. Both sites stage interesting and informative exhibitions covering many aspects of art, crafts, Tasmanian history and natural science. There is also a planeterium at Royal Park. The museum has four aircraft which are currently all in store. The Desoutter was bought from Iona Airways in Ireland and flown to Australia between late December 1931 and February 1932. The aircraft flew on a service between Launceston and Whitemark on Flinders Island. These flight involved a hundred mile crossing of the Bass Strait. In 1935 it moved to the Australian mainland and had a number of owners before being withdrawn in the 1950s. The Desoutter eventually returned to Tasmania and for many years was on show in the terminal building at Launceston Airport. The aircraft will form part of a new large history exhibition at the Inveresk site from 2010. Up to then it will be moved to a new storage site. The Blériot replica was built by students at the Technical and Further Education Institute of Tasmania. The museum acquired three Riley Herons a few years ago. One went to the Queensland Aviation Museum and another will be rebuilt with the third being used for spares.

TYPE	REG/SER	CON. NO.	PI/NOTES	STATUS
☐ Blériot XI				PV
☐ Desoutter II	VH-UEE	D.30	G-ABOM, EI-AAD	PV
☐ Riley Heron 2D/A2 (De Havilland D.H.114 Heron 2D)	VH-CLV	14124	CA+002, G-ASCX	RA
☐ Riley Heron 2E/A2 (De Havilland D.H.114 Heron 2)	VH-CLZ	14075	VT-DHJ, VQ-FAC, DQ-FAC	RA

ROYAL AUSTRALIAN AIR FORCE MEMORIAL CENTRE MUSEUM (AUS86)

Address:	61 Davey Street, Hobart, Tasmania 7000.
Tel:	03-6234-3862
Email:	raafatas@netspace.net
Admission:	Wednesday, Friday 1000-1500 or by prior permission only.
Location:	In the centre of the city.

The local branch of the Royal Australian Air Force Association has set up a display of memorabilia at its Hobart premises. On show are medals, photographs, documents, uniforms and badges. The service careers of local people who served with the Air Force are highlighted.

VICTORIA

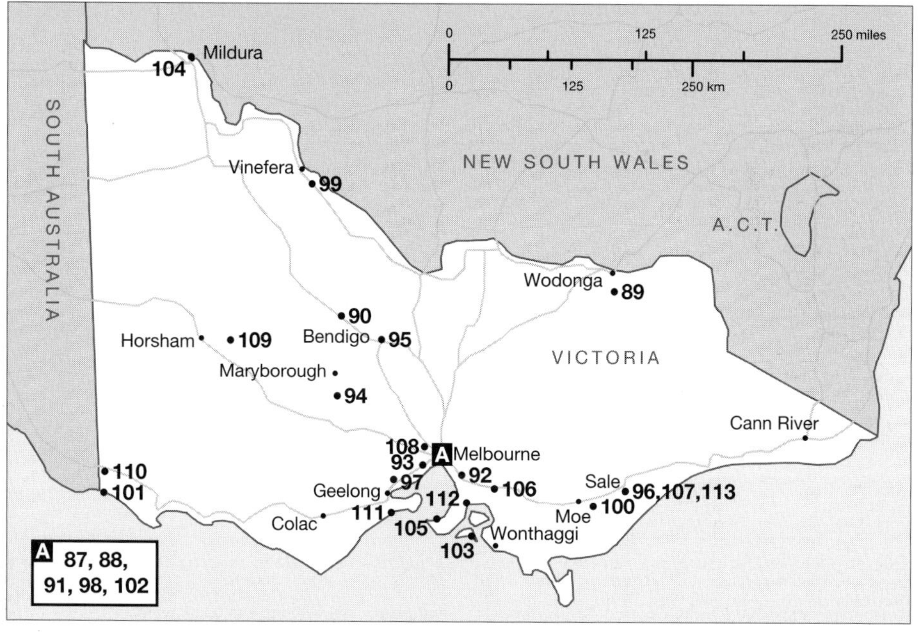

AERONAUTICAL AND MARITIME RESEARCH LABORATORIES DISPLAY (AUS87)

Address:	506 Lorimer Street, Fishermans Bend, Victoria 3207.
Tel:	03-9626-7000
Fax:	03-9626-7999
Email:	information@dsto.defence.gov.au
Admission:	By prior permission only.
Location:	Near Melbourne Port.

The Government Aircraft factory had a major plant at Fishermans Bend during and after World War II. Now the complex houses research establishments. Many aircraft were produced at the site. Two licence built types are preserved by the gate to the laboratories to serve as a reminder of the heritage of the area.

TYPE	REG/SER	CON. NO.	PI/NOTES	STATUS
☐ Commonwealth CA-27 Sabre 31 [North American F-86F]	A94-941	CA27-41		RA
☐ Government Aircraft Factory Canberra Mk.20 [English Electric EA.1]	A84-245	45		RA

AIRWAYS MUSEUM (AUS88)

Address:	Box 5, 250 English Street, Essendon, Victoria 3041
Tel:	03 9374 3905
Email:	cahs@bigpond.com
Admission:	Tuesday 0900-1500 and by appointment.
Location:	Rear of Building 44 at Essendon Airport which is about 10 km north of Melbourne.

Displays at the museum trace the development of airlines in Australia. There is an excellent collection of photographs, models and memorabilia. Radio equipment, airfield lighting and radar consoles can also be seen.

ARMY TRANSPORT MUSEUM (AUS89)

Address:	Gaza Ridge Barracks, P.O. Box 26, MILPO Bandiana, Victoria 3694.
Tel:	02-6055-2525
Fax:	02-6055-2886
Admission:	Daily 0930-1600.
Location:	About 5 km south east of Wodonga off the Kiewa Highway – Route C531.

The museum was established at Puckapunyal several years ago. The displays trace the development of vehicles used by the service. Space was limited and a decision was taken to move the exhibition during 1997. The fuselage of the Caribou and a Bell 47 helicopter are the only aeronautical items on show. There is an excellent collection of tanks, lorries, personnel carriers and items of artillery along with memorabilia.

TYPE	REG/SER	CON. NO.	PI/NOTES	STATUS
☐ Bell 47G-3B-1 Sioux	A1-407	3407		PV
☐ De Havilland D.H.C.4A Caribou	A4-264	264	Fuselage only – identity believed correct.	PV

ARNOLD AIR MUSEUM (AUS90)

Address:	91 Simpsons Creek Lane, Arnold, Victoria 3551.
Email:	arnoldaircraftmuseum@yahoo.com.au
Admission:	By prior permission only.
Location:	Just west of the town.

This privately owned museum is steadily gathering an interesting collection of airframes. Three front fuselages have been acquired from Arizona and transported across the Pacific Ocean. The displays are being developed and more aircraft are expected. Two Doves, one a Riley conversion, can be seen. The aim is to trace the development of aviation in Australia with particular reference to local events.

TYPE	REG/SER	CON. NO.	PI/NOTES	STATUS
☐ Beech 70 Queen Air	VH-CLH	LB-20	N8106R – wings from another aircraft.	PV
☐ Birdman Promotions TL-1 Grasshopper				PV
☐ De Havilland D.H.104 Dove 5	VH-DHN	04486	PH-ION, G-ASMX, I-ALGO, G-ASMX	PV
☐ Douglas DC-3A-456 Skytrain (C-47A)	VH-TAK	13338	42-108949, A65-52/VHCII – front fuselage only.	PV
☐ Fokker F.28-4000 Fellowship	VH-EWD	11208	PH-EXT – fuselage only.	PV
☐ Grumman G-134 Mohawk (OV-1C)			Front fuselage only.	PV
☐ Martin 272E Canberra (B-57E) (EB-57E)	55-4298	400	Front fuselage only.	PV
☐ North American NA-201 Sabre (F-86D) (F-86L)	53-4036	201-570	Front fuselage only.	PV
☐ Riley Dove 400 (De Havilland D.H. 104 Dove 1)	VH-ABM	04097	YI-ABK, TJ-ACA, D-100 (Jordan), G-ATGI, VQ-ZJC, G-ATGI	PV

AUSTRALIAN GLIDING MUSEUM (AUS91)

Address: 2 Birch Street,
Mount Waverley,
Victoria 3129.
Tel: 03-9187-5362
Admission: By prior permission only.
Location: In a number of locations in the Melbourne area.

Gliding started in Australia in 1909 and since then it has been a popular sport with many clubs around the country. A group of enthusiasts is trying to set up a museum and they have already collected several interesting sailplanes. Negotiations for a permanent display site are taking place and hopefully these will come to fruition in the not too distant future. Several unique types have joined the museum. Edmund Schneider was invited to Australia after World War II and with his sons he set up a new company and many original designs appeared. The only ES.50 Club produced has been restored and other products of the firm are being sought. The Slingsby T.35 Austral was developed from the T.31 as a special order for an Australian club. Another rarity is the Dunstable Kestrel designed by Bill Manuel. One was built in England and the example in the collection was constructed at Geelong in Victoria. A number of unique homebuilt types have also been acquired along with several early primary gliders. There is potential for an excellent museum tracing the history of gliding in the country.

TYPE	REG/SER	CON. NO.	PI/NOTES	STATUS
☐ Avionautica M.100S Mesange	VH-GUD	069		RA
☐ Backstrom EPB-1C Flying Plank				RA
☐ Dunstable Kestrel				RA
☐ Elliott AP.5 EoN Olympia 2	VH-GHR	RA12		RA
☐ Hijack Primary Glider				RA
☐ Hütter H 17	VH-GQM	GFA/HB/43	VH-GRG	PV
☐ Lessing Glider				RA
☐ Mead Rhön Ranger				RA
☐ Northrop Primary Glider				RA
☐ Proctor Coogee	VH-GFP	GFA-7		RA
☐ Schleicher Ka-6 Rhönsegler	VH-GRW	55		RA
☐ Schneider ES.49B Wallaby				RA
☐ Schneider ES.50 Club	VH-GHP			RA
☐ Schneider ES.52 Kookaburra I	VH-GFF	9		RA
☐ Schneider Grunau Baby IIIA	VH-GHV	GFA-29		RA
☐ Schreder HP-14T	VH-GIB	32/GFA-72		RA
☐ Schweizer SGS.2-12 (TG-3A)	VH-GDI	G15		RA
☐ Slingsby T.25 Gull 4	VH-GFA	545	BGA.602	RA
☐ Slingsby T.31B Tandem Tutor	VH-GDB	GFA/HB/12		RA
☐ Slingsby T.35 Austral	VH-GFX			RA
☐ Slingsby T.50 Skylark 4	VH-GTB	1382	BGA.1114	RA
☐ Stamer-Lippisch Z-12 Zögling				RA
☐ Szybowcowy Zaklad Doswiadczalny S.Z.D.22C Mucha Standard				RA
☐ Szybowcowy Zaklad Doswiadczalny S.Z.D.9bis Bocian 1D	VH-GPH	F-834		RA
☐ Vögt Lo 150 Zwergreher	VH-GUC	EB 71		RAA

AUSTRALIAN NATIONAL AVIATION MUSEUM (AUS92)

Address: P.O. Box 242.
Mentone,
Victoria 3194.
Tel: 03-9580-7752
Email: Info@aarg.com.au
Admission: Daily 1000-1700.
Location: At Moorabbin Airport which is about 25 km south of Melbourne north of the Nepean Highway.

Run by the Australian Aviation Research Group, the museum opened in 1965. Development of the site has been steady and now the majority of the aircraft are displayed under cover. An addition is the Casey Hangar from the closed Berwick Airfield. The aim of the museum is to trace the history and development of aviation in the country. Over half the aircraft in the collection were designed or built in Australia. The oldest aircraft owned by the museum is the Gipsy Moth which completed two round trips to New Guinea and also made the first aerial delivery of the Herald newspaper in Victoria. A range of aircraft designed by the Commonwealth Aircraft Corporation is one of the highlights of the display. Seven hundred and fifty five Wirraways were built between 1939 and 1946. Based on the North American NA-33, the aircraft was intended to serve in the training role but several were pressed into use as fighters in Malaya and New Guinea. The example on show is the eighth built and the oldest survivor of the type. The Wackett basic trainer was the only wholly Australian design to be produced in World War II and two hundred were made. The Boomerang was conceived, built and flown in just sixteen weeks. The need for a fighter was paramount and the team used the Wirraway as the basis for the aircraft. Two hundred and fifty were constructed. Very few have survived and the example in the collection was found derelict in Queensland in 1986. The Boomerang was restored by Hawker de Havilland and donated to the museum in 1994. Parked outside is a Commonwealth built Sabre. The airframe was extensively modified to accept a Rolls Royce Avon and cannons. The Winjeel replaced the Wirraway as the R.A.A.F. advanced trainer in 1958. The Ceres is an agricultural conversion of the Wirraway and the CA-31 was intended to be a trainer and ground attack aircraft. The Yeoman Cropmaster used the basic Wackett airframe and twenty one were built for top dressing. A unique aircraft is the only Southern Cross SC-1 built. Developed at the Toowoomba Foundry in Queensland, the prototype flew twenty five hours in the early 1960s before the programme was terminated. This aircraft is currently loaned out to the Museum of Army Flying in Queensland. The Heron glider built in the late 1920s was discovered in a shed at Upper Beaconsfield in 1943. The airframe was restored and the glider flew for a number of years. Also on show are light and ultralight aircraft, gliders, airliners and military aircraft which present a comprehensive view of aviation in the country. The main hangar contains many associated displays which enhance this interesting exhibition.

TYPE	REG/SER	CON. NO.	PI/NOTES	STATUS
☐ Auster J/1B Aiglet	VH-ACY	2705		PV
☐ Avro 694 Lincoln B.2	RF342		RF342, G-APRJ, G-29-1, G-36-3, G-APRJ, G-29-1	RA
☐ Beech 65-B80 Queen Air	PK-LEC	LD-157	N6869Q, VH-TGB	PV
☐ Bensen B-8M Gyrocopter				PV
☐ Bristol 170 Freighter 31 (31M)	VH-ADL	13193	G-18-185, S4438 (Pakistan), AP-AMD	PV
☐ Bristol 171 Sycamore 3	A91-1	12894	G-ALSZ, WV695, A91-1, VH-GVR	PV
☐ British Aircraft L.25c Swallow II	VH-UUM	409		RA
☐ Cessna 310	VH-AER	35537	(N5337A), N11B, ZK-BSY, VH-UAL, VH-PRC	PV
☐ Commonwealth CA-1 Wirraway I [North American NA-33]	A20-10	8		PV
☐ Commonwealth CA-6 Wackett Trainer	A3-22	256	A3-22, VH-ALV	PV
☐ Commonwealth CA-12 Boomerang I	A46-25	848		PV
☐ Commonwealth CA-25 Winjeel	A85-418	CA25-18		RA
☐ Commonwealth CA-27 Sabre 32 [North American F-86F]	A94-989	CA27-89	Contains parts of CA-27 Mk.30 A94-906.	PV
☐ Commonwealth CA-28 Ceres C	VH-WOT	CA28-19	VH-WOT – contains parts of c/n CA.28-17 VH-CET, VH-WHY – see Queensland Air Museum.	PV
☐ Commonwealth CA-29 Mirage IIIO(A) (IIIO(F)) [Dassault Mirage III]	'A3-40'	CA29-45	A3-45	PVX
☐ Commonwealth CA-31 (Mock up)				RA
☐ Consolidated 28-5A Catalina (PBY-5A)	A24-88	1714	Bu48352 – fuselage only.	PV
☐ Curtiss 87-B2 Warhawk (P-40E) (Kittyhawk IA)	A29-53	16738	41-13522	PV
☐ De Havilland D.H.60G Gipsy Moth	VH-UKV	1066	VH-UKV, A7-79	PV
☐ De Havilland D.H.82A Tiger Moth	A17-377	DHA.418	A17-377, VH-AQM	PV
☐ De Havilland D.H.100 Vampire FB.52	'A79-417'	V.0683	252 (South Africa), R1382 (Zimbabwe)	PVX
☐ De Havilland D.H.112 Sea Venom FAW.53	N4-901	12758	WZ901	PV
☐ De Havilland D.H.115 Vampire T.35A (T.33)	A79-835	4120	Also reported as 'XA167'	PV
☐ Department of Aircraft Production Beaufighter 21 [Bristol 156]	'A8-39'		A8-328	PVX
☐ Department of Aircraft Production Beaufort IX [Bristol 152]	A9-320		With parts from A9-501.	RAC
☐ Desoutter II	VH-UPR	D.35		RA
☐ Douglas DC-2-112	A30-9	1292	NC13782, A30-9/VHCRK	RA
☐ Douglas DC-3-277D (C-50)	VH-ANH	4120	(NC33657), 41-7698, VHCDJ	PV
☐ Dunstable Kestrel				PV
☐ Enterprise Wings Foil 165 Hang Glider				RA
☐ Fairey Firefly AS.6	WD827	F8655		PV
☐ Fairey Gannet AS.4 (AS.1)	XG789	F9357		PV
☐ Gloster Meteor T.7	A77-707		WH118	PV
☐ Government Aircraft Factory Canberra Mk.20 [English Electric EA.1]	A84-222	22	Front fuselage only.	PV
☐ Government Aircraft Factory Jindivik 102A (IIA)	A92-492			PV
☐ Heath Parasol				RA
☐ Heron Primary Glider				PV
☐ Koltai Ornithopter				RA
☐ Martin 162B Mariner (PBM-3R)	A70-??		(USN) – wings only	PV
☐ Mignet HM-14 Pou-du-Ciel				RAC
☐ Miles M.38 Messenger 2A	VH-AVQ	6373	G-AJKG	RA
☐ Percival P.28B Proctor I	'A75-1'	K.253	P6194, G-AHDI, VH-AUC	PV
☐ Riley Heron 2D/A1 (De Havilland D.H.114 Heron 2D)	VH-CLX	14098	(G-ANPV), G-5-24, G-ANPV	PV
☐ Royal Aircraft Factory B.E.2a			Wings only.	PV

TYPE	REG/SER	CON. NO.	PI/NOTES	STATUS
☐ Sander Veenstra SV5 Thermite	'791'			PV
☐ Skycraft Scout				PV
☐ Skyseeker Ultralight				PV
☐ Southern Cross SC.1	VH-SCA	1	On loan to Flypast Museum, QLD.	–
☐ Transavia PL-12 Airtruk	VH-BOA	G460		RA
☐ Ultralight Industries Wombat				RA
☐ Vickers 816 Viscount (818)	VH-TVR	318	CU-N622, CU-T622, (ZK-CVB)	PV
☐ Victa Airtourer 100	VH-BWI	81	(ZK-CHD), VH-MTB	PV
☐ Volmer Jensen VJ-22 Sportsman				RA
☐ Westland-Sikorsky WS-58 Wessex HAS.31B	N7-204	WA.204	WA204	PV
☐ Yeoman YA-1 Cropmaster 250R	VH-AGL	113	VH-CYY	RAD

B-24 LIBERATOR MEMORIAL FUND (AUS93)

Address: P.O. Box 156,
Werribee,
Victoria 3030.
Tel: 03-9731-1263
Email: kitchengept@bigpond.com
Admission: Tuesday, Thursday and Sunday 0900-1700.
Location: At the first hangar on the Geelong Road which is about 1 km south west of the town.

Two hundred and eighty seven Liberators were used by the R.A.A.F. from February 1944 until the early 1950s. In 1952 over two hundred were scrapped and melted down. In August 1988 a meeting was held at R.A.A.F. Wagga Wagga to examine the possibility of acquiring an example of the B-24 for display in Australia. The fund was set up and the first committee meeting held the following January. The fuselage of a Liberator was obtained from George Toye of Moe in Victoria. The aircraft was struck off charge at East Sale in 1948 and after a short period as an instructional airframe was bought by Mr. Toye who lived in the fuselage while he built a house. The airframe was acquired by the fund in 1995 and moved to one of several World War II hangars surviving on the now disused Werribee airfield. Crash sites have been investigated and a wing and tailplane were acquired from Papua New Guinea and other parts are being sought. The Patron of the Fund is Wing Commander Deryck Kingwell who flew the aircraft during its service days. When complete the B-24 will go on display in a museum in Australia. The group has now acquired a derelict Oxford which will be restored.

TYPE	REG/SER	CON. NO.	PI/NOTES	STATUS
☐ Airspeed AS.10 Oxford II	LX181			RAD
☐ Consolidated 32 Liberator (B-24M)	A72-176	5892	44-41956 – wings from B-24D c/n 2168 42-41091.	PVC

BALLARAT AVIATION MUSEUM (AUS94)

Address: P.O. Box 24,
Ballarat,
Victoria 3353.
Tel: 03-5339-3996
Admission: Saturday-Sunday and Public Holidays 1300-1700.
Location: At Ballarat airfield which is about 8 km north west of the town off the Sunraysia Highway.

In April 1940 No. 1 Wireless Air Gunners School was set up at the airfield. A military training establishment remained in residence until 1961. The field then became the airport for the town. The museum was formed in 1983 by a group of local enthusiasts as the Eureka Aviation Museum before adopting its current name in 1987. The exhibition hall contains a number of airframes as well as displays of engines, components, uniforms, documents, radios, missiles and memorabilia. Among the collection is a thirty foot plus span model of the Hughes 'Spruce Goose' flying boat and photographs depicting its one short flight. The story of the base is portrayed as well as local aviation events. The hall is connected to a World War II hangar where more aircraft can be seen. Some are privately owned and are on loan to the museum to enhance the display. At any time these may be away flying The Demoiselle replica was constructed by Personal Plane Services in England and flown in the film 'Those Magnificent Men in Their Flying Machines'. The front fuselage of the Mariner is a rarity and was found locally. The mock up of the Commonwealth AA-107, a jet which was never built, can also be seen. The Nomad featured a number of times in the television series 'The Flying Doctors'. The diminutive Gere Sport biplane first appeared in the early 1930s. The first example was completed by the designer's father, 'Bud' Gere, who was building the biplane when he fell into the propeller of an ice vehicle and killed. Plans were available to amateur constructors and several were completed before the outbreak of World War II.

TYPE	REG/SER	CON. NO.	PI/NOTES	STATUS
☐ Airborne Windsports Edge	T2-2691	AB/E-198/E-2		PVA
☐ Airborne Windsports Edge	T2-2813	AB/E-244/E-2		PVA
☐ Auster J/1B Aiglet	VH-KAZ	2672		PVA
☐ Auster J/5B Autocar	VH-ASZ	2922	VH-KAX, VH-GVC	PVA
☐ Avro 652A Anson I	LV284		Front fuselage from another aircraft.	RAC
☐ Avro 652A Anson I	W2483		W2483, VH-BEV – front fuselage only.	RA
☐ Cessna 170B	VH-BUX	26854	N2911D, N2861P	PV

TYPE	REG/SER	CON. NO.	PI/NOTES	STATUS
☐ Cessna 180K Skywagon 180	VH-NMM	18053015	N2607K	PVA
☐ Commonwealth CA-9 Wirraway II	A20-502	703		PV
☐ Commonwealth AA-107 (Mock-up)				PV
☐ De Havilland D.H.82A Tiger Moth	VH-CJW	DHA.812	(DX755), A17-662, VH-VJW	PVA
☐ Gere Sport			Incomplete	PV
☐ Government Aircraft Factory N.22B Nomad	VH-MSF	N22B-69		PV
☐ Kennealy Gyrocopter	EG-V001			PV
☐ Martin 162B Mariner (PBM-3R)			Front fuselage only.	PV
☐ Mignet HM-293 Pou-du-Ciel				RA
☐ Piper PA-22-150 Tri-Pacer	VH-GJL	22-4510		PV
☐ Riley Dove 5 (De Havilland D.H. 104 Dove 1B)	VH-ABK	04113	YI-ABL, TJ-ACB, D-101 (Jordan), G-ATGJ – front fuselage only.	PV
☐ Santos-Dumont XX Demoiselle (R)		PPS/DEM/2		PV
☐ Stephens Acro Z Laser	VH-JAD	V-71		PVA

BENDIGO MUSEUM HANGAR (AUS95)

Address:	Bendigo Airport, Victoria 3552.
Tel:	03-5443-8395
Fax:	03-5443-8395
Admission:	By prior permission only.
Location:	In the north eastern suburbs of the town.

A display of photographs and items of memorabilia tracing the history of the airfield have been set up in one of the hangars. There is an active aero club at the field and many privately owned aircraft can be seen.

GIPPSLAND ARMED FORCES MUSEUM (AUS96)

Address:	Punt Lane, P.O. Box 9177, Sale, Victoria 3850.
Tel:	03-5144-5500
Admission:	Monday-Friday 1000-1600.
Location:	In the centre of the town.

The area has a military tradition as many local people have, over the years, served in the armed forces. Since the end of World War II the nearby RAAF Base at East Sale has trained pilots and technical staff. The idea of a museum was put forward and the council gave it full support. The exhibition opened in December 2003. The informative display traces the story of Gippsland people and the local military history. On show are military vehicles, weapons, badges and uniforms. There is an extensive photographic exhibition which includes the actual camera which filmed the landing of cavalry forces at Gallipolli in World War I. Macchi MB.326s were used for a few months in 1968 by the East Sale bases 'Roulettes' aerobatic team. The front fuselage on an Anson has been acquired. Several examples of the type were flown in Australia.

TYPE	REG/SER	CON. NO.	PI/NOTES	STATUS
☐ Avro 652A Anson I	MG872		Front fuselage only.	PV
☐ Commonwealth CA-30 [Aermacchi MB.326H]	A7-015	CA30-15		PV

GOVERNMENT AIRCRAFT FACTORY MEMORIAL (AUS97)

Address:	80 Beach Road, Lara, Victoria 3212.
Tel:	03-5227-9100
Fax:	03-5282-3335
Email:	Avalon.Airport@Linfox.com
Admission:	Aircraft on permanent view.
Location:	About 5 km northwest of Avalon.

The Government Aircraft Factory at Fishermans Bend had produced many aircraft during World War II and in years after. The runway became too short for modern jets so a new airfield was built at Avalon. The first aircraft to land was an Avro Lincoln which made the short flight from Fishermans Bend on April 3rd 1953. The plant produced the licence built Canberras. An example of the jet bomber has been preserved.

TYPE	REG/SER	CON. NO.	PI/NOTES	STATUS
☐ Government Aircraft Factory Canberra Mk.20 [English Electric EA.1]	A84-232	32		PV

KANANA HISTORICAL AIRCRAFT SOCIETY (AUS98)

Address:	12 Glenys Avenue, Airport West, Victoria 3042.
Admission:	By prior permission only.
Location:	At Tullamarine Airport, which is about 15 km north west of Melbourne.

This early DC-3 was delivered to Australian National Airways in October 1938 and given the name 'Kanana'. After a long career with ANA and Ansett Airways the aircraft was withdrawn in 1972. After a period of storage it was restored and flown by the Ansett Historical Aviation Group. The DC-3 has now been registered to the new society who will hopefully continue to fly it to events around the country.

TYPE	REG/SER	CON. NO.	PI/NOTES	STATUS
☐ Douglas DC-3-232A	VH-ABR	2029	VH-ABR, A30-3	RAA

LAKE BOGA FLYING BOAT MUSEUM (AUS99)

Address:	Catalina Park, Lake Boga, Victoria 3584.
Tel:	03-5037-2850
Fax:	03-5037-2860
Admission:	Daily 0930-1600.
Location:	About 16 km south east of Swan Hill just east of the Murray Valley Highway – Route B400.

Lake Boga was the home of No. 1 Flying Boat Repair Unit from July 1942 until March 1946. The site was under Care and Maintenance until disposed of in November 1947. The Royal Australian Air Force operated Catalinas during the conflict with one hundred and sixty examples delivered between 1941 and 1945. A composite airframe has been built up using parts recovered in the area. The aircraft is displayed in a compound close to the former base. The museum is housed in the former communications bunker.

TYPE	REG/SER	CON. NO.	PI/NOTES	STATUS
☐ Consolidated 28-5 Catalina (PBY-5)	'A24-30'	1097	Bu08203, A24-38 – possible identity of rear fuselage.	PVCX

LATROBE FLYING MUSEUM (AUS100)

Address:	Latrobe Valley Airport, Airfield Road, Traralgon, Victoria 3844.
Admission:	By prior permission only.
Location:	About 5 km north east of Morwell.

This private museum currently has three aircraft in flying condition. The Mustang served with the RAAF until 1948 and then spent many years in store. The aircraft, was for a time, on show at the Camden Aviation Museum. One of the Australian built Sabres is being restored and the other airframe is being used for spares. The C-47 served with the RAAF between 1945 and 1954 and during this time had a spell in Malaysia.

TYPE	REG/SER	CON. NO.	PI/NOTES	STATUS
☐ Commonwealth CA-18 Mustang 21 [North American P-51D]	VH-AGJ/A68-118	1443	A68-118, VH-WAS	PVA
☐ Commonwealth CA-25 Winjeel	VH-AGR	CA25-44	A85-444	PVA
☐ Commonwealth CA-27 Sabre 31 (30) [North American F-86F]	A94-907	CA27-7		RA
☐ Commonwealth CA-27 Sabre 32 [North American F-86F]	A94-352	CA27-92		PVC
☐ De Havilland D.H.115 Vampire T.35	A79-659	4181		PV
☐ Douglas DC-3A-467 Skytrain (C-47B)	VH-AGU	15920/32668	44-76336, A65-72/VHCIO	PVA

MCBAIN COLLECTION (AUS101)

Address:	Beach Road, Nelson, Victoria 3292.
Admission:	By prior permission only.
Location:	About 2 km south of the town.

The McBain family and friends have gathered an interesting collection of aircraft at their private airfield. De Havilland types feature prominently including one of the few remaining airworthy Dragons. The Australian branch of the firm built eighty seven examples of the twin engined biplane.

TYPE	REG/SER	CON. NO.	PI/NOTES	STATUS
☐ Boeing-Stearman A75N1 Kaydet (PT-17)			Frame only.	RA
☐ Cessna 172M	VH-WYJ	17266471	(N80244)	RAA
☐ Cessna 175	VH-RFB	55756	N7456M	RAA
☐ De Havilland D.H.82A Tiger Moth	VH-BPU	85639	DE709	RAA
☐ De Havilland D.H.82A Tiger Moth	VH-UJW	DHA.274	A17-255, VH-RAQ	RA
☐ De Havilland D.H.84 Dragon 1	VH-AON	2019	A34-30	RAA
☐ De Havilland D.H.85 Leopard Moth	VH-BAH	7016	G-ACKY, VH-ADV, VH-RSL	RAA
☐ De Havilland D.H.85 Leopard Moth	VH-UUE	7109		RAA
☐ De Havilland D.H.87B Hornet Moth	VH-UXY	8131	G-AEZG, BB830, G-AEZG	RA
☐ De Havilland D.H.A.3 Drover 2	VH-AZS	5018	(VH-DRF)	RAA

MUSEUM OF VICTORIA – SCIENCEWORKS (AUS102)

Address:	2 Booker Street, Spotswood, Melbourne, Victoria 3015.
Tel:	03-9392-4800
Fax:	03-9391-0100
Admission:	Daily 1000-1630.
Location:	In the western suburbs of the city near the Westgate Bridge.

The Museum of Victoria opened its Scienceworks site in 1992. The science and transport sections were formerly housed in the main building in the city centre. The exhibition features many 'hands-on' displays and modern technology is much in evidence. Two aircraft are currently on show. The Duigan Biplane was built by John and Reginald Duigan on their farm and was the first aircraft designed and constructed in Australia. John made the maiden flight on July 16th 1910 and the following year the biplane flew five times at Epsom racecourse in Melbourne achieving a height of sixty feet and travelling three thousand feet. In store is the wooden Millicer Airtourer of 1959. The design was developed into the all metal Victa Airtourer of which one hundred and sixty nine were produced. Manufacturing rights were sold to New Zealand in 1966.

TYPE	REG/SER	CON. NO.	PI/NOTES	STATUS
☐ Commonwealth CA-16 Wirraway III [North American NA-33]	A20-651	1103	On loan to FAA Museum, NSW.	–
☐ Duigan Biplane				PV
☐ Millicer Airtourer	VH-FMM	1		RA
☐ Skycraft Scout				PV

NATIONAL VIETNAM VETERANS MUSEUM (AUS103)

Address:	P.O. Box 318, San Remo, Victoria 3925.
Tel:	03-5956-6400
Fax:	03-5956-6406
Admission:	Daily 1000-1600.
Location:	In Veterans Drive at Newhaven which is about 70 km south of Melbourne.

Australian forces fought in Vietnam from 1962 until 1972. Many people were killed or wounded in the bitter conflict. The museum was opened by the Victoria Premier on March 3rd 2007. The story of Australian involvement in the campaign is portrayed in a number of dioramas and video presentations. The indoor display contains many photographs, documents, uniforms and badges. Tanks and military vehicles have been put on show. The Huey Cobra gunship was flown in support of Australian forces in the war. The Canberra is the oldest surviving example of the classic jet bomber. Built in Preston, it was designated the reserve aircraft RAAF aircraft in the 1953 London-Melbourne Air Race. When it was withdrawn from service it was put on show at No.1 Central Ammunition Depot at Orchard Hills in New South Wales. The aircraft remained here for many years before journeying south to the museum. The Wessex was delivered to the Australian Navy in 1963 and served until 1989. The helicopter was stored behind the museum at Nowra before arriving in Victoria.

TYPE	REG/SER	CON. NO.	PI/NOTES	STATUS
☐ Bell 204 Iroquois (UH-1C)	N9-3103	3103	64-17623, N9-103 – front fuselage only.	RA
☐ Bell 209 Huey Cobra (AH-1G)	68-15092	20626		PV
☐ English Electric EA.1 Canberra Mk.21 (B.2)	A84-307	EEP.71020	WD939	RA
☐ Westland-Sikorsky WS-58 Wessex HAS.31B	N7-210	WA.210	WA210	RAC

This Australian built Beaufighter is on show at the Australian National Aviation Museum at Moorabbin near Melbourne. (Douglas Rough)

Above: This Hawker Demon was found in a derelict state and was rebuilt for the RAAF Museum at Point Cook. (Douglas Rough)

Right: The only aircraft at the Mining Museum in Kalgoorlie is this Auster Autocar. (Douglas Rough)

No. 2 OPERATIONAL TRAINING UNIT MUSEUM (AUS104)

Address:	34 Kavav Avenue, Mildura, Victoria 3500.
Tel:	03-5022-7691
Email:	2oturaaf@ruralnet.net.au
Admission:	Tuesday, Friday, Sunday 1000-1600.
Location:	In the southern part of the town.

This museum, which opened on November 17th 2001, is housed in premises formerly occupied by the unit which was based at Mildura. No. 2 OTU received its first aircraft, Wirraways, in April 1942 and was operational until October 1945. The displays trace the history of the airfield and the OTU with an interesting range of photographs and memorabilia. Future plans envisage the acquisition of types which served at Mildura. In addition to the Wirraway, Boomerangs, Spitfires, Kittyhawks and Mustangs were flown. For many years Pearce Dunn had his 'Warbird Museum' at the airfield. On show were more than twenty aircraft many of them dismantled. Examples of the types sought by the current museum were then present at Mildura.

ORRMAN COLLECTION (AUS105)

Address:	P.O. Box 23, Blairgowrie, Victoria 3942.
Admission:	By prior permission only.
Location:	About 50 km south of Melbourne.

The Orrman family have owned a number of classic aircraft over the years. The star of the fleet is the Gipsy Moth. This aircraft is the eighth of ten built by the Government Aviation Factory at Helsinki in Finland. The biplane was intended for service with the Finnish Air Force but was soon transferred to the Aviation Club of Finland. The Moth was damaged in 1956 and after a period of storage arrived in Australia in the late 1970s.

TYPE	REG/SER	CON. NO.	PI/NOTES	STATUS
☐ De Havilland D.H.60X Moth	VH-SSC	8	MO-103 (Finland), K-SILD, OH-ILD	RAA
☐ De Havilland D.H.82A Tiger Moth	VH-SSB	DHA.1027	A17-592, VH-BBD	RAA
☐ De Havilland D.H.82A Tiger Moth	VH-IAN	DHA.818	(DX761), A17-688, VH-RVO, VH-AMM, VH-RUO	RAA
☐ Piper PA-22-108 Colt	VH-PIF	22-8210		RAA
☐ Piper PA-22-150 Tri-Pacer	VH-SDO	22-4076		RAA

RETURNED AND SERVICES LEAGUE MEMORIAL (AUS106)

Address:	RSL Club, Dandenong, Victoria 3175.
Tel:	03-9792-1535
Admission:	Aircraft on permanent view.
Location:	In the eastern part of the town.

The memorial to the Vietnam War consists of statues and flags set in a landscaped garden. The Iroquois is mounted on a pole. This helicopter is one of a few in Australia which carries the serial of one lost in a pilot rescue mission in Vietnam in 1971. The Huey was delivered in 2003 and then painted at a local Army base before being put on show. The club has acquired at least three composite Aermacchi MB.326 airframes. These are currently in store at a nearby Army depot. The plan is to restore the aircraft and mount them in a spectacular flying pose. One of these was built by the parent company in Italy and then shipped to Australia to serve as a pattern aircraft for the batch produced by the Commonwealth company. Components from several other unidentified aircraft were bought at the sale and these will be used in the restoration programme.

TYPE	REG/SER	CON. NO.	PI/NOTES	STATUS
☐ Aermacchi MB.326H	A7-002	6370	Rear fuselage from CA30-048 A7-048.	RA
☐ Bell 205 Iroquois (UH-1H)	73-21763/'A2-767'	13451		PVX
☐ Commonwealth CA-30 [Aermacchi MB.326H]	A7-014	CA30-014		RA
☐ Commonwealth CA-30 [Aermacchi MB.326H]	A7-075	CA30-075	Rear fuselage fron CA30-011 A7-011	RA
☐ Commonwealth CA-30 [Aermacchi MB.326H]	A7-087	CA30-087	N14-087 – rear fuselage from CA30-083 A7-083.	RA

ROYAL AUSTRALIAN AIR FORCE BASE EAST SALE MEMORIAL (AUS107)

Address:	Aerodrome Road, East Sale, Victoria 3852.
Tel:	03-5146-6111
Admission:	By prior permission only.
Location:	About 5 km east of Sale.

The base is home to a number of training schools. The Commonwealth Winjeel was in RAAF service from 1955 until 1977. An example of the trainer serves as a monument to those who flew the type from East Sale.

TYPE	REG/SER	CON. NO.	PI/NOTES	STATUS
☐ Commonwealth CA-25 Winjeel	A85-405	CA25-05		RA

ROYAL AUSTRALIAN AIR FORCE MUSEUM (AUS108)

Address:	RAAF Williams, Point Cook, Victoria 3027.
Tel:	03-9256-1300
Fax:	03-9256-1692
Email:	museuminfo@defence.gov.au
Admission:	Tuesday-Friday 1000-1500;Saturday-Sunday 1000-1700
Location:	About 8 km south east of Werribee and 25 km south west of Melbourne.

Air Marshal George Jones, then Chief of the Air Staff, submitted the proposal for a museum in 1949. In 1952 the site was chosen as Point Cook which in 1914 saw the first flight of a military aircraft in Australia. The airfield was an active base until recently. The first display opened in a small hut and in 1957 a second was added. In 1971 the collection moved into the old R.A.A.F. College headquarters building and four more huts were renovated in 1975. In 1971 it was decided to add aircraft to the collection and since then examples of most of the types used by the Air Force from the mid-1950s have been collected. Aircraft from earlier periods are slowly being acquired. The main display is now in two interconnected hangars to which an impressive entrance hall has recently been added. The story of military aviation in the country is portrayed in detail with photographs, documents, badges, memorabilia and uniforms on show. The first hangar traces the early history of the service and in the centre of the floor is the Farman which was used at Point Cook in the early days. Nearby is a superbly re stored Hawker Demon. The remains of two examples of the classic biplane were found, one in Tasmania in 1977 and the other soon after in South Australia. Jack MacDonald, then a serving officer, restored one for static display for the museum. The other is now at Calboolture, Queensland (q.v.). In the second hall are examples of classic jets used by the service in the 1950s and 1960s. The Pika is a piloted version of the Jindivik target aircraft and only two were built. The first flew at Woomera in November 1950. The second is on show and this made one hundred and seventy flights totalling seventy one flying hours. Several aircraft are maintained in flying condition and these occasionally take part in shows. and A number of restored aircraft are stored in four hangars close to the main exhibition. Hopefully some way can be devised to enable the visitor to view these. A gallery displaying training types opened in 2001. Hangars on the south side house many airframes awaiting restoration.

TYPE	REG/SER	CON. NO.	PI/NOTES	STATUS
☐ Aermacchi MB.326H	A7-001	6351		PV
☐ Aero Engine Services CT/4A Airtrainer	A19-027	CT4-027	ZK-DZP	PV
☐ Aero Engine Services CT/4A Airtrainer	VH-NZP	CT4-077	ZK-EUZ, A19-077	RAA
☐ Avro 504K (R)	'A3-17'	0015	G-BYKV, 'E3747'	PVX
☐ Avro 643 Cadet II	A6-34	1069	A6-34, VH-BJB, VH-RUO	PV
☐ Avro 652A Anson I	LT710		Fuselage frame only.	RA
☐ Avro 707A	WD280			RA
☐ Avro 748 Series 2/228	A10-601	1601	A10-601, G-AVZD	PV
☐ Bell 204 Iroquois (HU-1B) (UH-1B)	A2-384	384	62-4606	PV
☐ Bell 204 Iroquois (UH-1B)	A2-1020	1020	63-13588 – with tail boom from c/n 389 62-4611, A2-389.	PV
☐ Bell 205 Iroquois (UH-1H)	A2-377	9377	67-17179	PV
☐ Bristol 170 Freighter 21E	A81-1	12799	G-AIMI, WB482, A81-1, VH-SJG	PV
☐ Cessna 305A Bird Dog (L-19A) (O-1A)	VH-OIE	21416	51-14591	RAA
☐ Commonwealth CA-12 Boomerang I	A46-30	853		PV
☐ Commonwealth CA-16 Wirraway III [North American NA-33]	A20-670	1122	Fuselage frame only	RA
☐ Commonwealth CA-16 Wirraway III [North American NA-33]	'A20-561'	1139	A20-687	RAX
☐ Commonwealth CA-18 Mustang 23 [North American P-51D]	A68-137	1462	A68-137, (VH-PPV)	RA
☐ Commonwealth CA-18 Mustang 23 [North American P-51D]	'A68-750'	1495	A68-170, VH-SVU	PVX
☐ Commonwealth CA-22 Winjeel	A85-618	1526		RA
☐ Commonwealth CA-25 Winjeel	A85-401	CA25-01	A85-401, VH-NTY	PV

☐ Commonwealth CA-25 Winjeel	A85-439	CA25-39	A85-439, VH-FTS	RAA
☐ Commonwealth CA-26 Sabre [North [North American F-86E]	A94-101	1428		PV
☐ Commonwealth CA-27 Sabre 30 [North American F-86F]	A94-910	CA27-10		RA
☐ Commonwealth CA-27 Sabre 30 [North American F-86F]	A94-902	CA27-2	Front fuselage only	PV
☐ Commonwealth CA-27 Sabre 32 [North American F-86F]	A94-970	CA27-70		RA
☐ Commonwealth CA-29 Mirage IIIO(A) [Dassault Mirage III]	A3-51	CA29-51		RA
☐ Commonwealth CA-29 Mirage IIIO(A) [Dassault Mirage III]	A3-72	CA29-72	Preserved on base.	RA
☐ Commonwealth CA-29 Mirage IIIO(A) [Dassault Mirage III]	A3-92	CA29-92		PV
☐ Commonwealth CA-30 [Aermacchi MB.326H]	A7-097	CA30-97	Front fusealge only.	RA
☐ Consolidated 28-5A Canso A	'A24-104'	CV 369	11060 (Canada), CF-NJD, N609F, N609FF, VH-EXG	PVX
☐ Curtiss 87-B2 Warhawk (P-40E) (Kittyhawk IA)	A29-28		41-5336	RAC
☐ De Havilland D.H.82A Tiger Moth	VH-AWA	DHA.824	(DX781), A17-692, VH-TWA –	RAA
☐ De Havilland D.H.82A Tiger Moth	A17-711	DHA.843	(DX800), A17-711, VH-BFF, VH-DDW, VH-FHJ, VH-RTB	PV
☐ De Havilland D.H.84 Dragon 1	A34-92	2081	A34-92, (G-AJKF), VH-BDS, VH-AML	PV
☐ De Havilland D.H.98 Mosquito PR.XVI	A52-600		NS631, A52-600, (VH-JUX)	RAC
☐ De Havilland D.H.100 Vampire FB.31 (F.30)	'A79-876'	4011	A79-375 – with booms from c/n 4079 A79-333	PVX
☐ De Havilland D.H.100 Vampire FB.31 (F.30)	A79-178	4051	Front fuselage only – probable identity.	PV
☐ De Havilland D.H.115 Vampire T.35	A79-636	4158	A79-636, VH-HLF	RA
☐ De Havilland D.H.115 Vampire T.35A (T.33)	A79-616	4138	With tail booms from A79-827.	PV
☐ Department of Aircraft Production Beaufighter 21 [Bristol 156]				RA
☐ Deperdussin Monoplane (R)	'CFS.13'			RAX
☐ Douglas DB-7B Boston III	A28-8	3839	AL907, 240 (Netherlands)	PV
☐ Douglas DC-3A-467 Skytrain (C-47B)	A65-78	15929/32677	44-76345, A65-78/VMHJU, A65-98/VMHJQ	RA
☐ Fairey Battle I			Centre section only.	RAD
☐ Farman MF-11 Shorthorn	CFS-20			PV
☐ Gloster Meteor T.7	A77-702		WA732, A77-305	RA
☐ Gloster Meteor T.7	A77-705		WA680	RA
☐ Gloster Meteor F.8	A77-870		WK748	RA
☐ Government Aircraft Factory Canberra Mk.20 [English Electric EA.1]	A84-234	34	Front fuselage only.	RA
☐ Government Aircraft Factory Canberra Mk.20 [English Electric EA.1]	A84-236	36		PV
☐ Government Aircraft Factory Jindivik 102A (IIA)	A92-47	27		PV
☐ Government Aircraft Factory Jindivik 102A (IIA)				RA
☐ Government Aircraft Factory Pika	'C-2'		A93-2	PVX
☐ Hawker Demon I	A1-8	41H/60050		PV
☐ Hunting-Percival P.84 Jet Provost T.2	A99-001	P.84/12	G-AOHD	RA
☐ Lockheed 182-1A Hercules (182-44-03) (C-130A)	A97-214	182-3214	57-0507, (N2268N)	PV
☐ Lockheed 237-27-01 Ventura (PV-1)	'A59-67'	237-5378	Bu33369, 2221 (RCAF), NX1590V, N1590V, N159V, N159U, VH-SFF	RACX
☐ Lockheed 382C-2D Hercules (C-130E)	A97-160	382C-4160	65-12897	PV
☐ Lockheed 414-08-10 Hudson IVA (A-28)	A16-122	414-6051	41-23192, A16-122, VH-AGX – nose from 414-56-03 Hudson III (A-29) c/n 414-6497 41-37008, (FH207), A16-244	RA
☐ Lockheed 426-42-11 Neptune MR.1 (P2V-5)	A89-302	426-5021	Bu133640, A89-595	
☐ Lockheed 726-45-17 Neptune MR.4 (P2V-7) (P2V-7S) (SP-2H)	A89-275	726-7275	Bu149075	PV
☐ McDonnell M.98HO Phantom II (F-4E)	'97208'	2912	67-0237	PVX
☐ North American NA-88 Texan (AT-6C) (Harvard IIA)	'NZ947'	88-12033	41-33562, EX589, NZ1034, INST210	RAX
☐ Royal Aircraft Factory S.E.5A	A2-11		D8474	RAD
☐ Royal Aircraft Factory S.E.5A (R)	'A2-31'			PVX
☐ Sikorsky S-51 Dragonfly	A80-374	5117	G-AJHW, WB220	PV
☐ Sopwith Pup (R)	'D4170'	TSP-1	VH-PSP – On loan	RAAX
☐ Supermarine 236 Walrus I	HD874		Parts from X9516.	PV

SCHNEIDER COLLECTION (AUS109)

Address:	Marnoo Road, Rupanyup, Victoria 3388.
Tel:	03-5385-5228
Admission:	By prior permission only.
Location:	About 30 km east of Horsham.

This private collection of mainly former RAAF aircraft is located on a farm on the outskirts of the town. Aircraft have been purchased in military sales and some of the Aermacchi MB.326s are believed to contain parts from other airframes. The Airtruk is an an unconventional design for agricultural work. Well over one hundred have been completed since the prototype first flew in 1960. Parts of the Vampires have been used in restorations at other museums and the components are stored for a possible composite rebuild.

TYPE	REG/SER	CON. NO.	PI/NOTES	STATUS
☐ Avro 652A Anson I	MG172		Fuselage only.	RA
☐ Commonwealth CA-16 Wirraway III [North American NA-33]			Fuselage frame only.	RAD
☐ Commonwealth CA-25 Winjeel	A85-437	CA25-37		RA
☐ Commonwealth CA-25 Winjeel	A85-462	CA25-62		RA
☐ Commonwealth CA-30 [Aermacchi MB.326H]	A7-010	CA30-10		RA
☐ Commonwealth CA-30 [Aermacchi MB.326H]	A7-028	CA30-28		RA
☐ Commonwealth CA-30 [Aermacchi MB.326H]	A7-089	CA30-89		RA
☐ De Havilland D.H.104 Dove 5 (1)	VH-DHD	04104	VT-CQY, VH-AWA, VH-MMN	RA
☐ De Havilland D.H.115 Vampire T.35	A79-658	4180	Pod only.	RAD
☐ De Havilland D.H.115 Vampire T.35A (T.33)	A79-819	4099	Pod only.	RAD
☐ De Havilland D.H.115 Vampire T.35			Pod only.	RAD
☐ De Havilland D.H.115 Vampire T.35			Pod only.	RA
☐ Douglas DC-3A-467 Skytrain (C-47B) (Dakota IV)	VH-JXD	16549/33297	44-76965, A65-108/VHRGZ, A65-108/VMJMH, A65-108/ VHJRG	RA
☐ Government Aircraft Factory Canberra Mk.20 [English Electric EA.1]	A84-208	8		RA
☐ Transavia PL-12 Airtruk	VH-EVY	1248		RA
☐ Westland-Sikorsky WS-58 Wessex HAS.31B	N7-215	WA.215	WA215	RA
☐ Wytwornia Sprzetu Komunikacyjnego (WSK) SBLim-2 (Lim-1) (MiG-15) [MiG-15UTI]	'102'	1A 12-002	202 (Poland) – in false Soviet markings.	RAX

SIR REGINALD ANSETT TRANSPORT MUSEUM (AUS110)

Address:	P.O. Box 652. Corner Ballarat Road and Riley Street. Hamilton. Victoria 3300.
Tel:	03-5571-2440
Fax:	03-5571-2080
Email:	alkira@ansonic.com.au
Admission:	Daily 1000-1600.
Location:	About 2 km east of the town off the Glenelg Highway – Route B100.

Reginald Ansett, who was later knighted, flew his first service from Hamilton to Melbourne on February 18th 1936 using an American-built Fokker Universal. In 1973 Ansett Airlines bought a Dutch built Fokker F.XI in Austria. The airframe was in a poor condition and was rebuilt by the company at Essendon and placed on show in the Ansett Terminal at Tullarmarine in Melbourne before moving to Mascot in Sydney. The F.XI differs slightly from the Universal but it carries the markings of Ansett's first aircraft. The original hangar at the old airport at Hamilton survived and was moved to a site on the outskirts of the town and refurbished for museum use. The area used for the first flight is now a playing field. The museum opened in February 1991 on the fifty-fifth anniversary of the flight to Melbourne. On December 5th 1931 Ansett drove a Studebaker car from Hamilton to Ballarat and eleven years later the company operated the largest road passenger service in the Commonwealth. The story of Ansett Airlines and Coachlines, from the beginning to the present day is shown with an interesting display of models, photographs, uniforms, vehicles and components.

TYPE	REG/SER	CON. NO.	PI/NOTES	STATUS
☐ Fokker F.XI	'VH-UTO'	5124	CH-188, HB-ALO, OE-DAA	PVX

TIGER MOTH WORLD (AUS111)

Address:	325 Blackgate Road, Torquay. Victoria 3228.
Tel:	03-5261-5100
Fax:	03-5261-5797
Email:	fly@tigermothworld.com
Admission:	Daily 1000-1700.
Location:	About 20 km south of Geelong and east of the Surfcoast Highway.

The organisation was set up in the late 1980s and operates from its own airfield. Two Tiger Moths are used for pleasure flights. A pair of American designed biplanes are also used. The Great Lakes first flew in the 1930s but the type was put back into production in the 1970s. The Grumman Ag-Cat dates from the early 1960s.A museum tracing the story of the de Havilland company has been set up. Photographs, memorabilia and components can be seen. There are plans to construct a new larger facility on the opposite side of the field.

TYPE	REG/SER	CON. NO.	PI/NOTES	STATUS
☐ De Havilland D.H.82A Tiger Moth	VH-DHK	DHA.157	A17-156, VH-ANS, VH-BTF	PVA
☐ De Havilland D.H.82A Tiger Moth	VH-SAC	DHA.1065	A17-734	PVA
☐ Great Lakes 2T-1A-2	VH-LKE	0705		PVA
☐ Grumman G-164A Ag-Cat	VH-ADB	1206	N9685	RAA

TYABB AIRPORT COLLECTION (AUS112)

Address:	c/o The Old Aeroplane Company, Western Port Airfield, Stuart Road, P.O. Box 89, Tyabb, Victoria 3913.
Tel:	03-5977-4539
Admission:	By prior permission only.
Location:	About 1 km west of the town which is about 50 km south of Melbourne.

Tyabb Airfield is home to several classic and warbird aircraft and there are long term plans to build a large hangar to house the majority of these. Housed in the hangars of the firm run by Judy Pay are two fighters. The Curtiss P-40 was recovered from Errumango Island, Vanuatu in 1989. Alongside it in the hangar is a Commonwealth-built Mustang which was displayed outside a garage at Laverton from 1960 to 1964. The fighter was then exhibited at the Moorabbin Air Museum and the R.A.A.F. Museum at Point Cook before moving to Tyabb in 1990 for rebuild. In Graham Hoskin's hangar are a batch of Ryan STM-2s which were once used in the Dutch East Indies. An exchange with the Royal New Zealand Air Force Museum resulted in a Vought Corsair arriving at the field and a Curtiss P-40, also recovered from Errumango, crossing the Tasman Sea to Wigram. The hangars always contain privately owned warbirds arriving for maintenance.

TYPE	REG/SER	CON. NO.	PI/NOTES	STATUS
☐ Canadian Car & Foundry Harvard 4 [North American NA-186 (T-6H-4M)]	VH-USR		(USAF), MM53833, N1363R	RAA
☐ Commonwealth CA-18 Mustang 21 [North American P-51D]	'KH677'	1430	A68-105, VH-JUC	RAAX
☐ Commonwealth CA-25 Winjeel	VH-HOY	CA25-50	A85-450	RAA
☐ Curtiss 87-B3 Warhawk (P-40F)	VH-HWK		41-14112	RAC
☐ De Havilland D.H.82A Tiger Moth	VH-BVB	85829	DE969, G-AMPN, ZK-BBG	RAA
☐ De Havilland D.H.100 Vampire FB.52	R1829	V.0583	216 (South Africa) – in Zimbabwean markings.	RA
☐ De Havilland D.H.100 Vampire FB.52	R1835	V.0659	245 (South Africa) – in Zimbabwean markings.	RA
☐ De Havilland D.H.100 Vampire FB.52	R1378	V.0674	251 (South Africa) – in Zimbabwean markings.	RA
☐ De Havilland D.H.115 Vampire T.55	R2424		(South Africa) – in Zimbabwean markings.	RA
☐ De Havilland D.H.115 Vampire T.55	VH-ZVZ	15392	(South African), R4221 (Zimbabwe), 119	RA
☐ Morane-Saulnier MS.500 Criquet [Fieseler Fi 156 Storch]	VH-FIS	340	340 (France), N45FS	RAA
☐ North American NA-88 Texan (AT-6C) (Harvard IIA)	VH-NZH	88-13908	41-33767, EX794, NZ1051	RAC
☐ North American NA-88 Texan (AT-6C) (Harvard IIA)	VH-NAH	88-14177	41-33800, EX827, NZ1056, ZK-ENL	RAA
☐ North American NA-88 Texan (SNJ-4) (Harvard IIA)	VH-XSA	88-9851	Bu10127, 7667 (South Africa)	RAA
☐ North American NA-200 Trojan (T-28B)	VH-NAW	200-349	Bu138278, N138NA	RAA
☐ North American NA-200 Trojan (T-28B) (AT-28D)	VH-DPT	200-303	Bu138232, 3416 (Laos)	RAA
☐ Piper J-5B Cub Cruiser	VH-FIV	5-1274		RAA
☐ Ryan STM-2	VH-WEB	454	S-18 (Netherlands), A50-27, VH-AGU	RA
☐ Ryan STM-2	VH-AWG	459	S-23 (Netherlands), A50-11, VH-AGD	RAA
☐ Ryan STM-2	VH-CXR	482	S-46 (Netherlands), A50-19	RAC
☐ Vought F4U-5NL Corsair			Bu124493, 608 (Honduras) – composite with parts of several aircraft.	RAC

WELLINGTON SHIRE COUNCIL MEMORIAL (AUS113)

Address:	70 Foster Street, Sale, Victoria 3850.
Tel:	1300-366-244
Admission:	Not applicable.
Location:	Unknown at the present time.

The council has acquired an Australian built Macchi MB.326 to serve as a memorial to local servicemen. The aircraft is currently in store and will be restored for display in the town.

TYPE	REG/SER	CON. NO.	PI/NOTES	STATUS
☐ Commonwealth CA-30 [Aermacchi MB.326H]	A7-014	CA30-014		RA

WESTERN AUSTRALIA

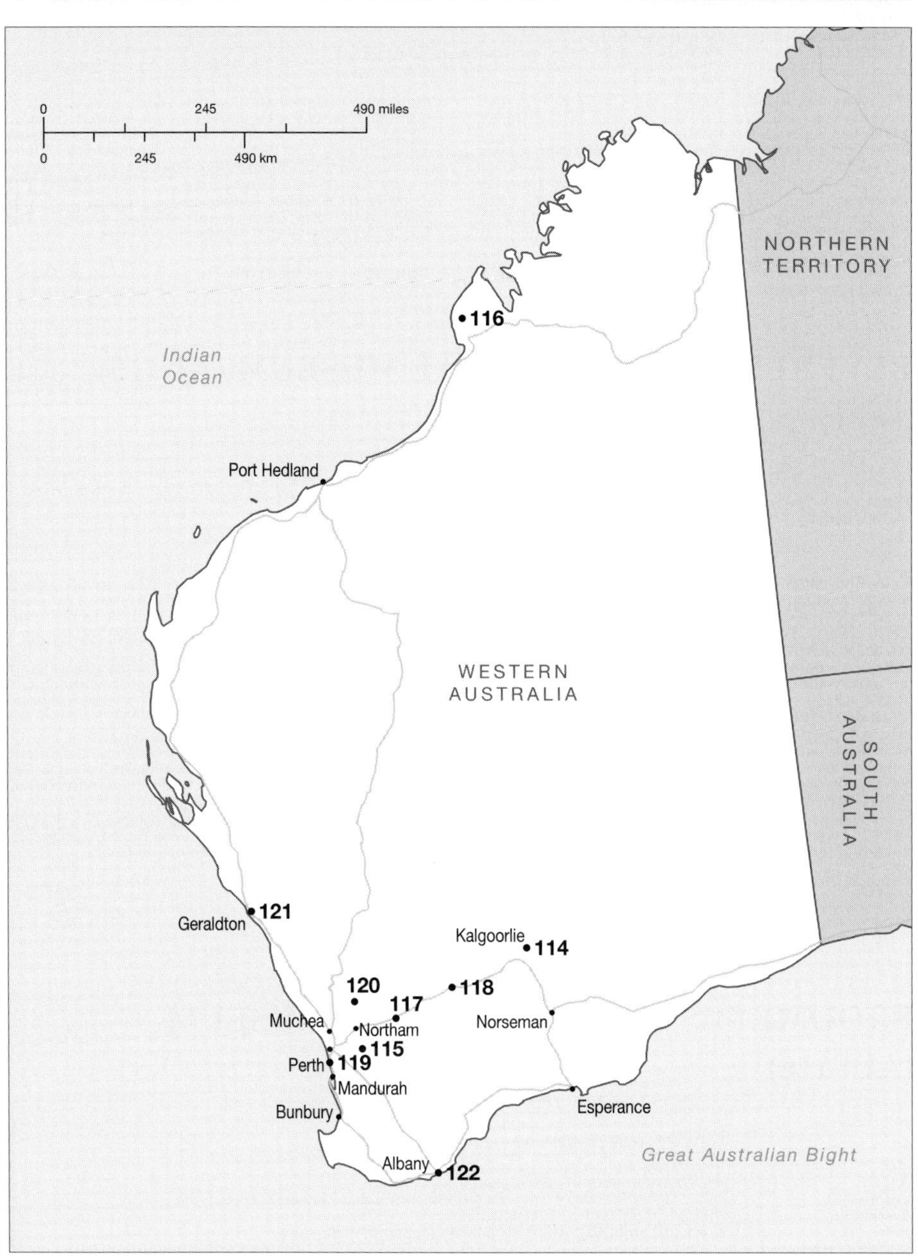

AUSTRALIAN PROSPECTORS AND MINERS HALL OF FAME (AUS114)

Address:	Goldfields Avenue, Kalgooirlie, Western Australia 6430.
Tel:	08-9026-7000
Fax:	08-9091-4075
Email:	enquiries@mininghall.com
Admission:	Daily 0900-1630.
Location:	About 3km north of the town centre off Route 94.

This interactive museum was set up on October 30th 2001 on the site of a former gold mine which opened in the mid-1890s and was last worked in 1952. Visitors can go about one hundred feet down the Hannans North Mine and see the conditions endured by the miners. They can try their hand at panning for gold. The story of prospecting and mining is told in detail with many innovative displays. There is a superb display of minerals which have been extracted from the area. A section of the exhibition is devoted to the laws which were set up to ensure that mining was carried in an ordered fashion. Outside there is an observation deck which gives excellent views over the surrounding countryside. There is also a peaceful Chinese Memorial Garden honouring the many miners who arrived from the Asian country. The sole aircraft on show is the Auster Autocar which is suspended in the 'Business of Mining' Gallery. The aircraft was based in the area for many years.

TYPE	REG/SER	CON. NO.	PI/NOTES	STATUS
☐ Auster J/5P Autocar	VH-KCC	3251		PV

BEVERLEY AERONAUTICAL MUSEUM (AU115)

Address:	P.O.Box 84, Vincent Street, Beverley, Western Australia 6304.
Tel:	08-9646-1555
Fax:	08-9409-6631
Admission:	Daily 0900-1600.
Location:	In the main street of the town which is about 150 km south east of Perth.

Selby Ford operated a powerhouse in the town and in 1928 he drew in chalk on the floor of the building the plans for an aircraft. Assisted by his cousin Tom Shackles he started constructing the airframe. Tom's sister Elsie was persuaded to sew the fabric for the wings and tail surfaces. The initial engine for the biplane was a 25 h.p. Anzani but this was too low powered. A Cirrus motor was obtained from a de Havilland Moth and on July 1st 1930 it was flown for twenty five minutes by Captain C.H. Nesbit. On July 4th 1930 the aircraft was flown to Maylands Aerodrome in Perth. The flight was undertaken to commemorate the centenary of the founding of the city and the biplane was named 'Silver Centenary'. Geoffrey de Havilland and Amy Johnson inspected the aircraft but bad weather prevented them from air testing it. In 1931 a series of flights around the region were carried out but the authorities grounded the aircraft as no plans were ever drawn, apart from those on the floor. The aircraft, which was a delight to fly, was stored in the powerhouse for many years. In 1967 the museum was built in the main street of the town and the aircraft moved the short distance to its new home. The 'Silver Centenary' has now left the exhibition. The biplane was acquired by the grandson of Selby Ford and has been rebuilt to flying condition. The aircraft has now obtained a certificate of airworthiness seventy-seven years after its first flight. Also on show are engines, components and a fascinating display of photographs depicting the early days of flying in Western Australia. One of the Vampires is mounted outside the museum and the other was next to the main north south road on the outskirts of the town. The latter one has been removed and is probably in store. The Mignet Pou-du-Ciel replica was built locally and was constructed to compare the design with that of a conventional biplane.

TYPE	REG/SER	CON. NO.	PI/NOTES	STATUS
☐ De Havilland D.H.115 Vampire T.35	A79-638	4160		PV
☐ De Havilland D.H.115 Vampire T.35	A79-651	4173		RA
☐ Mignet HM-14 Pou-du-Ciel (R)				PV

BROOME HISTORICAL SOCIETY MUSEUM (AUS116)

Address:	P.O. Box 559, Broome, Western Australia 6725.
Tel:	08-9192-2075
Email:	president@broomemuseum.org.au
Admission:	June-October Monday-Friday 1000-1600; November-May daily 1000-1300.
Location:	Museum in the centre of the town. Wreck at Carnot Bay which is about 80 km. north of Broome.

The society maintains a museum tracing the history of the region. The first building used was a former general store and the collection has had several homes before moving into its current location. Many artefacts and photographs from the pioneer days can be seen. On May 3rd 1942 a Dakota piloted by a Russian World War I ace was fleeing from the Japanese invasion of the Dutch East Indies. The aircraft was shot down an force landed at Carnot Bay, about 80 kilometres north of Broome. The wreck was strafed and four people were killed. A flying boat later dropped bombs on the DC-3. The aircraft was carrying a quantity of gold and some of this mysteriously disappeared in the aftermath of the forced landing. The society have recovered small parts from the aircraft and put them on show with a display tracing the history of the flight. Larger components still survive at Carnot Bay.

TYPE	REG/SER	CON. NO.	PI/NOTES	STATUS
☐ Douglas DC-3-194B	PK-AFV	1965	PH-ALP	PVD

CUNDERDIN MUNICIPAL MUSEUM (AUS117)

Address:	100 Forrest Street, Cunderdin, Western Australia 6407.
Tel:	08-9635-1291
Fax:	08-9635-1464
Email:	cmmuseum@wn.com.au
Admission:	Daily 1000-1600.
Location:	In the town off the Great Eastern Highway – Route 94.

Cunderdin was home to No. 9 Elementary Flying Training School from December 1940 to October 1945. Many of the original buildings still survive at the airfield. An interesting museum has been set up in a former powerhouse in the town. All the artefacts and machinery on show have a local connection. The visitor can see the development of the community over the last century. Clothes, furniture and household items are displayed. A large collection of vehicles and agricultural machinery can also be seen and there is a section devoted to the railways of the area. The Tiger Moth hanging from the roof was built in 1941 and was in store at Cunderdin for most of 1945. The biplane was sold to the Royal Aero Club of Western Australia in 1946 and had several other owners in the state before retirement in 1965.

TYPE	REG/SER	CON. NO.	PI/NOTES	STATUS
☐ De Havilland D.H.82A Tiger Moth	'VH-WLQ'	DHA.358	A17-339, VH-AMP	PVX

MERREDIN MILITARY MUSEUM (AUS118)

Address:	P.O. Box 45, Great Eastern Highway, Merredin, Western Australia 6415.
Tel:	08-9041-1505
Fax:	08-9041-4505
Admission:	Friday 1000-1400 and by appointment.
Location:	In the town off the Great Eastern Highway – Route 94.

The area has a rich military tradition and the museum has been set up to honour this. There are many uniforms, documents, badges and photographs to be seen along with weapons and communications equipment. Local servicemen are honoured and many of their personal items are in the exhibition. The largest collection of military vehicles in Western Australia is on the museum inventory. There are jeeps, lorries, personnel carriers, tanks and items of artillery to be seen. The museum is an ideal starting point for touring the military relics in the surrounding countryside. Among those left are the remains of a military hospital, a High Frequency Direction Finding Station and some giant aviation fuel tanks used to supply local airfields.

TYPE	REG/SER	CON. NO.	PI/NOTES	STATUS
☐ Commonwealth CA-30 [Aermacchi MB.326H]	A7-057	CA30-57		RA

ROYAL AUSTRALIAN AIR FORCE ASSOCIATION AVIATION HERITAGE MUSEUM OF WESTERN AUSTRALIA (AUS119)

Address:	Bull Creek Drive, Bull Creek, Western Australia 6149.
Tel:	08-9311-4470
Fax:	08-9311-4445
Email:	alclarke@raafawa.org.au
Admission:	Daily 1000-1600.
Location:	About 10 km south of Perth near the corner of Bull Creek Drive and Leach Highway.

In 1959 the Air Force Association acquired a Spitfire from England and mounted it outside its headquarters. The Lancaster was donated to the Association in 1962 and placed in a compound at Perth Airport. The A.F.A. Historical Group was formed in 1971 with the aim of setting up an aviation museum. Airframes and other items were collected and stored in the area, some in a compound at the A.F.A. estate which was chosen as the site for the museum. Construction started in the late 1970s and the first building opened on November 18th 1979. By this time there were seventeen aircraft, a number of engines and components and items of memorabilia in the collection. The Lancaster was parked outside next to the museum. In 1983 the second hangar was complete and all aircraft could be put under cover. The original hangar, the south wing, traces the history of aviation from the early days and displays civil types. The north wing is dominated by the Lancaster and Dakota and houses military machines. The pioneer days are represented by the Santos-Dumont Demoiselle and World War I by a Sopwith Camel. Both these aircraft are replicas. A rarity is the Kingsford Smith KS-3, an agricultural conversion of the Wackett Trainer. A range of light and ultralight aircraft can also be seen. The prototype Slingsby Gull I is a prized exhibit. The sailplane was imported into Australia in 1939 and heralded a new gliding era in the country. This sailplane was active until 1963. The Backstrom Flying Plank glider is another rarity. The Lancaster was used by the French Navy in New Caledonia before its acquisition by the A.F.A. The Spitfire is now in the hangar and in 1985 was replaced on the pole by a plastic replica. In 1997 the prototype de Havilland Heron I arrived from Jandakot Airport. The airframe had spent many years outside at the field. Restoration has now started and the aircraft will be displayed in a new building to be constructed between the two wings. Nearby is a workshop where the airframes and engines are restored. An excellent, informative and varied display has been developed over the years. There are many photographs, documents, models, uniforms, and items of memorabilia to be seen in both exhibition halls.

TYPE	REG/SER	CON. NO.	PI/NOTES	STATUS
☐ Auster J/5 Adventurer	VH-KAV	2894		PV
☐ Avro 652A Anson I	VH-WAB		MG841, (VH-BKE) – front fuselage and centre section only.	RAD
☐ Avro 652A Anson I	VH-WAC		MG271, (VH-BJY), VH-WAA – front fuselage only.	PV
☐ Avro 652A Anson I	W2121		W2121, VH-BEL	PV
☐ Avro 683 Lancaster MR.VII (B.VII)	NX622		NX622, WU-16 (France)	PV
☐ Backstrom EPB-1A Flying Plank				PV
☐ Bede BD-5				PVC
☐ Bensen B-8M Gyrocopter				PV
☐ Bristol 86 Tourer (R)	'G-AUDK'			PVX
☐ Challenge 503 Gyrocopter				PV
☐ Commonwealth CA-6 Wackett Trainer	VH-AIY	265	A3-31	PV
☐ Commonwealth CA-16 Wirraway III [North American NA-33]	A20-688	1140		PV
☐ Commonwealth CA-30 [Aermacchi MB.326H]	'A7-025'	CA30-66	Composite with fuselage from A7-066.	PVX
☐ Commonwealth CA-30 [Aermacchi MB.326H]	A7-084	CA30-84	N14-084 – front fuselage only.	PV
☐ Consolidated 28-5A Catalina (PBY-5A)	N9502C	1988	Bu46624 – loan for five years.	RA
☐ De Havilland D.H.82A Tiger Moth	A17-161	DHA.162	A17-161, VH-AHP	PV
☐ De Havilland D.H.94 Moth Minor	VH-THT	94076	A21-12, VH-AMI, VH-DDG	PV
☐ De Havilland D.H.114 Heron 1	VH-CJS	10903	G-ALZL, LN-BDH, G-ALZL, OY-DGS	PVC
☐ De Havilland D.H.115 Vampire T.35A (T.33)	A79-821	4101		PV
☐ Delta Hang Glider				PV
☐ Douglas DC-3A-467 Skytrain (C-47B) (Dakota IV)	A65-124	16960/34220	45-957, A65-124/VHRGL, A65-912/VMLBZ, A65-124/ VMLBA	PV
☐ Eagle X-Wing	VH-XEG	E2X-88-1-A-01		PV
☐ Gardan GY-80 Horizon 180	'VH-AMB'	215	F-OCLI, VH-CJZ – less wings.	PVX
☐ Government Aircraft Factory Canberra Mk.20 [English Electric EA.1]	A84-230	30		PV
☐ Hang Glider				PV
☐ Hang Glider				PV
☐ Hang Glider				PV
☐ Heath Parasol				PV
☐ Junkers W 33 c (FSM)	'D-1925'			PVX
☐ Kingsford Smith KS-3	VH-AJH	283	A3-49 – converted from Commonwealth CA-6 Wackett.	PV
☐ Martin 162B Mariner (PBM-3R)	A70-3	3017	Bu6565 – front fuselage only.	PV
☐ Mignet Ultralight	10-0718			PV
☐ Mitchell Wing U-10				PV
☐ Mitsubishi Ki-46			Crash remains	RAD
☐ Percival P.34A Proctor III	VH-BQR	K.392	Z7203, G-ALIS	PVC
☐ Rotorway Scorpion 133		12323?		PV
☐ SantSadlier VX-3				PV
☐ Santos-Dumont XX Demoiselle (R)				PV
☐ Schneider ES.57/III Kingfisher	VH-GRE	42		PV
☐ Sindlinger HH-1 Hurricane	VH-AFW	W140/PFA/ 26-10663	G-BJSH	PV
☐ Slingsby T.12 Gull 1	VH-GHL	293A	BGA.334	PV
☐ Sopwith F.1 Camel (R)	'M6394'			PVX
☐ Spehar Grasshopper Man Powered Aircraft				PV
☐ Supermarine 356 Spitfire F.22	PK481	CBAF-70		PV
☐ Supermarine 361 Spitfire LF.XVIe (FSM)	'TE283'/'TB592'			PVX
☐ Vultee V-72 Vengeance I	A27-41		Parts only	PV
☐ Vultee V-72 Vengeance II	A27-247		AF929	PV
☐ Wheeler Skycraft Scout Mk.1				RA
☐ Winton Grasshopper				PV

ROYAL AUSTRALIAN AIR FORCE BASE PEARCE MEMORIAL (AUS120)

Address:	Great North Highway, Bullsbrook, Western Australia 6084.
Tel:	08-9571-1111
Admission:	By prior permission only.
Location:	In the south western part of the town.

The airfield was built in the 1930s when the threat to the west coast of Australia became apparent. The station opened on February 6th 1939 and was named after Sir George Pearce who served as Minister of Defence for four spells between 1908 and 1934. The airfield now houses a squadron of British Aerospace Hawks which replaced the Aermacchi MB.326H in 2001. A training unit flying Pilatus PC.9s is also in residence along with the Flying Training School of the republic of Singapore Air Force. A Vampire was mounted outside the Station Headquarters but this was taken down and parts are being used in the rebuild of another.

TYPE	REG/SER	CON. NO.	PI/NOTES	STATUS
☐ Commonwealth CA-30 [Aermacchi MB.326H]	A7-027	CA30-27		RA
☐ De Havilland D.H.115 Vampire T.35	A79-620	4142	Composite with parts of c/n 4124 A79-603.	RAC

WESTERN AUSTRALIA MUSEUM (AUS121)

Address:	1 Museum Place, Batavia Coast Marina, Geraldton, Western Australia 6530.
Tel:	08-9921-5080
Fax:	08-9921-5158
Email:	geraldton.museum@museum.wa.gov.au
Admission:	Daily 0930-1600.
Location:	In the town.

The museum was founded in 1891 as the Perth Museum and it now has exhibitions in several towns in the state. Plans have been put forward for a major exhibition complex on the site of the old East Perth Power Station. The display at Geraldton features a shipwreck gallery as well as displays on the history and culture of the area. The Bristol Tourer replica was built for a television series and represents one used in the state in the early 1920s.

TYPE	REG/SER	CON. NO.	PI/NOTES	STATUS
☐ Bristol 47 Tourer (R)	VH-UDC	QA-32-1		PV

WHALEWORLD (AUS122)

Address:	Frenchman Bay Road, Albany, Western Australia 6330.
Tel:	08-9844-4021
Fax:	08-9921-5158
Email:	reception@whaleworld.com
Admission:	Daily 0900-1700.
Location:	About 20 km south west of Albany.

The Cheynes Beach Whaling Company Station at Frenchman Bay closed in 1978. Two years later it was given to the Jaycees Community Foundation. The site is now the largest whaling museum in the world. A new entrance hall and restaurant have been constructed and the remainder of the site is almost as it was when whaling ceased. The Cheynes IV – the last whale chasing boat operated in Australia – is beached on the site. Aircraft were operated by the company for whale spotting and a small airstrip used by the Cessna 172 was located behind the plant. The Cessna 337, which replaced the 172, was flown from the local airport. John Bell, who was killed in the crash of another Cessna 337 in 1995, set up an aviation museum close to the strip. A new hangar was built and the two Cessnas used by the company are on show. For many years a rare Vought Kingfisher was on show The aircraft, lacking one wing, came from the now closed Warbirds Aviation Museum at Mildura in Victoria. Now the airframe is at Wangaratta in New South Wales where it is being rebuilt. The components of two Vultee Vengeances were loaned by the Aviation Heritage Museum in Perth but these have now returned to Bull Creek. One complete aircraft will eventually emerge. The Catalina was also at the Mildura Museum from 1968 to 1989. John Bell started work on the airframe in 1989 and many parts from farms in the Lake Boga area of Victoria were found to assist in the rebuild. This aircraft is currently stored in the hangar.

TYPE	REG/SER	CON. NO.	PI/NOTES	STATUS
☐ Cessna 172C Skyhawk	VH-CBW	17249044	(N1344Y), VH-RWG	PV
☐ Cessna 337B Super Skymaster	VH-CBW	33700583	N5483S	PV
☐ Consolidated 28-5A Catalina (PBY-5A)	A24-46	1166	Bu-08272 – composite.	PV

GUAM

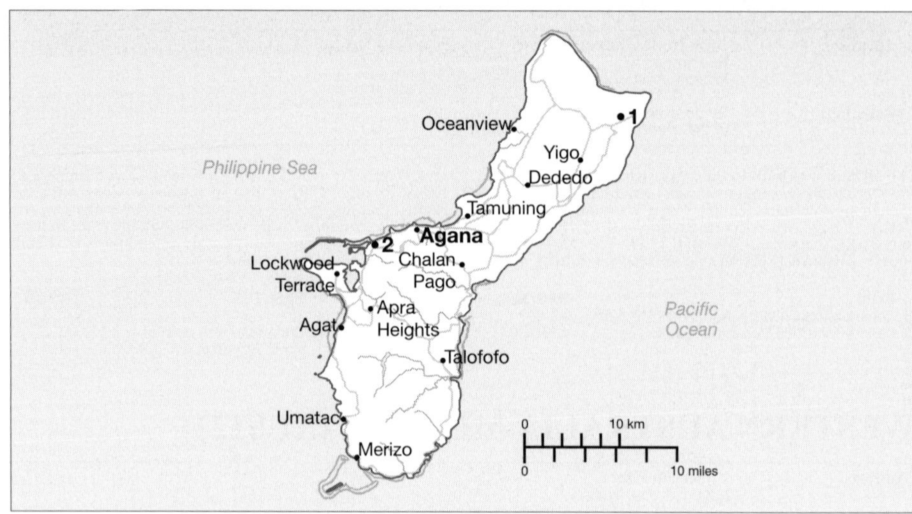

ANDERSEN AIR FORCE BASE (GM1)

Address:	36 Wing PA, Unit 14003, Box 25 Guam 96542-4003.
Tel:	671-366-4202
Email:	webmaster.pa.36WG@andersen.af.mil
Admission:	By prior permission only.
Location:	About 17 miles north of Agana.

The base opened in 1945 and is named after General James Andersen who went missing on a flight between Guam and Hawaii on February 26th 1945. For many years Strategic Air Command bombers were based at the field. No aircraft are currently resident at Anderson but the field has many visitors including those from foreign forces on training exercises. A Phantom has been preserved by the main gate. The B-52 on show has been repainted to represent the aircraft which was the last one to drop bombs on Vietnam. The original was on show for a time but suffered from corrosion and had to be scrapped in the mid-1980s.

TYPE	REG/SER	CON. NO.	PI/NOTES	STATUS
☐ Boeing 464-201-7 Stratofortress (B-52D)			Rear fuselage only.	RAD
☐ Boeing 464-201-7 Stratofortress (B-52D)	'55'-0100'	17269	56-0586	RAX
☐ McDonnell M.98HO Phantom II (F-4E)	71-1392	4270		RA

MARIANAS MILITARY MUSEUM (GM2)

Address:	PSC455, Box 152 Guam 96540-1000.
Tel:	671-339-3319
Fax:	671-339-8194
Email:	milmuseum@kuentos.guam.net
Admission:	Monday-Friday 0900-1700; Saturday 1000-1700 with prior permission.
Location:	About 5 km south west of Piti.

The main exhibition is located in buildings on the U.S. Navy base. The displays trace the military history of the area with a series of informative exhibits. The aviation section includes photographs of Pan-American Airways flying boat operations in the 1930s and extensive coverage of World War II. There is a designated walk around the base where many historic sites can be seen. The wreck of the Corsair is located in the jungle by a former U.S. Marines airstrip. Under the sea are a number of Japanese aircraft and nearby is a midget submarine. There are many derelict buildings and gun emplacements around the large area.

TYPE	REG/SER	CON. NO.	PI/NOTES	STATUS
☐ Vought F4U-4 Corsair				RAD

NEW ZEALAND

NORTH ISLAND

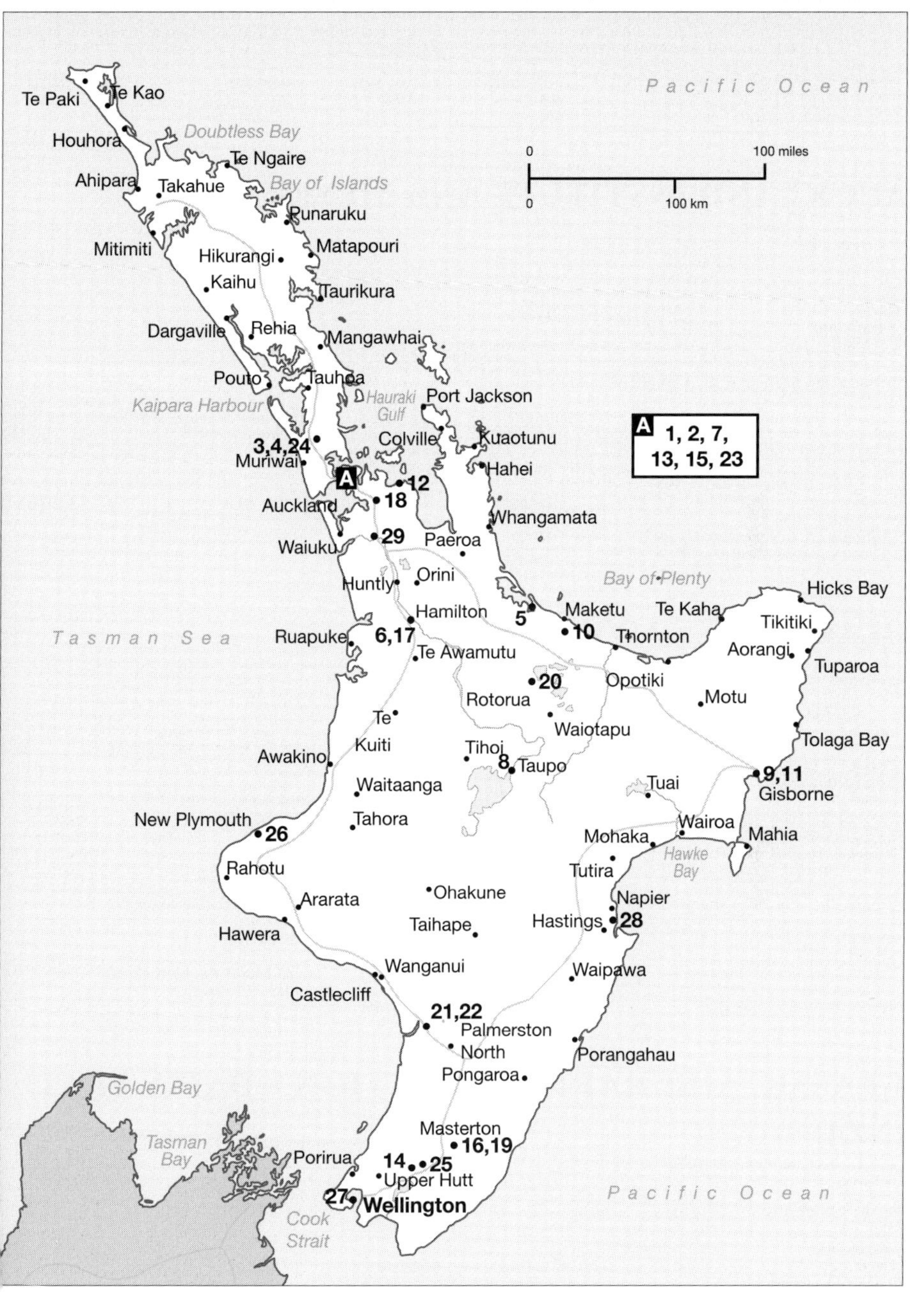

AIRCRAFT RESTORATION SOCIETY (NZ1)

Address: Auckland.
Admission: By prior permission only.
Location: In private workshops.

Two Tiger Moths are being restored to flying condition by members of the society. One is British built and was delivered to the Royal New Zealand Air Force in the early 1940s. The second aircraft was constructed at Bankstown in Australia and after military service was sold on the civilian market in 1946. After a short period in use with Kingsford Smith Aviation at Mascot it arrived in New Zealand in 1951.

TYPE	REG/SER	CON. NO.	PI/NOTES	STATUS
☐ De Havilland D.H.82A Tiger Moth	ZK-AII	83468	T5759, NZ669	RAC
☐ De Havilland D.H.82A Tiger Moth	ZK-AVA	DHA.235	A17-234, VH-BKW	RAC

AUCKLAND INSTITUTE AND MUSEUM (NZ2)

Address: Private Bag 92018,
Parnell,
Auckland.
Tel: 09-309-0443
Email: info@aucklandmuseum.com
Admission: Daily 1000-1700.
Location: In Auckland Domain which is about 3 km east of the city centre.

The Auckland Institute was set up in 1867 and took over the museum the following year. The War Memorial building opened in 1929 and was enlarged in 1956. The impressive displays trace the history of New Zealand's contribution to the two World Wars and of subsequent conflicts in which their forces have been involved. In mid-1991 the aircraft were restored and placed on show in newly refurbished galleries. The Spitfire was donated to the museum in 1951 at the request of Air Chief Marshal Sir Keith Park who commanded No. 11 Group in 1940. The Zero was captured at Kara and flew a few times in New Zealand before being presented to the museum.

TYPE	REG/SER	CON. NO.	PI/NOTES	STATUS
☐ Fieseler Fi 103A-1				PV
☐ Mitsubishi A6M3 Zero Sen Model 22	'2-152'	3844	2-182, NZ6000, INST113	PVX
☐ Supermarine 361 Spitfire LF.XVIe	TE456	CBAF-IX-4590		PV

BLACK SHEEP WING (NZ3)

Address: P.O. Box 35-411,
Browns Bay
Auckland.
Tel: 09-426-3751
Fax: 09-424-8723
Email: info@northcross.co.nz
Admission: Saturday 1000-1700.
Location: At North Shore Airfield which is about 25 km north of Auckland and east of Route 1.

The sixteenth wing incorporated in then Confederate Air Force was formed in 1979. This was the first outside the U.S.A. A hangar, workshops, offices and social club were built at North Shore Airfield. The new organisation took over the fleet in 2003 and it is named after the famous VMF-214 Squadron of the U.S. Marines. The Beech 18 is a regular visitor to air shows. The twin is painted in the colours of one used by the American Chief of Staff in the Pacific during World War II. The Texan was rebuilt in the workshops and is in period Marine colours.

TYPE	REG/SER	CON. NO.	PI/NOTES	STATUS
☐ Beech D18S	ZK-TEX	A-989	N1182T, N11821, N1182F	PVA
☐ North American NA-88 Texan (AT-6D) (Harvard III)	ZK-USM	88-16143	42-84362, EZ299, NZ1082, INST175, ZK-ELN	PVA
☐ Piper PA-18-95 Super Cub	ZK-BTQ	18-6165		PVA

CLASSIC AIRCRAFT COLLECTION – DAIRY FLAT (NZ4)

Address: P.O. Box 71,
Silverdale,
Auckland.
Tel: 09-426-5183
Admission: By prior permission only.
Location: About 25 km north of Auckland west of Route 1.

Don Subritzky and his son Mike are restoring a number of classic aircraft in their workshops. Recently they acquired an Airspeed Oxford which had been in store near Wanganui for fifty years. The airframe had been cut into sections and these are being joined together to produce a static exhibit. The Spitfire was obtained in 1974 and is being rebuilt to flying condition. The aircraft crashed in the Solomon Islands in January 1945 and was recovered many years later. Sixty three Hawker Hinds were supplied to New Zealand under the British Commonwealth Air Training Plan. The remains of four are in store and one will eventually go to M.O.T.A.T. in Auckland when complete. The Meteor arrived from the closed Warbirds Museum at Mildura in Australia.

TYPE	REG/SER	CON. NO.	PI/NOTES	STATUS
☐ Airspeed AS.10 Oxford II	NZ1332	PAC.228	AP414	RAC
☐ Avro 652A Anson I	NZ412		DG701	RA
☐ De Havilland D.H.82A Tiger Moth	ZK-BKF	83740	T7399, G-ANSK	RA
☐ Fletcher FU-24	ZK-BYC	78	(ZK-BPA)	RA
☐ Gloster Meteor TT.20 (NF.11)	WD767			RA
☐ Hawker Hind	NZ1528		L7184	RAD
☐ Hawker Hind	NZ1535		K6721, INST45	RAD
☐ Hawker Hind	NZ1544		K6703	RAD
☐ Hawker Hind	NZ1554		K5465, INST46	RAC
☐ Percival P.56 Provost T.1	ZK-JOT	P.56/183	WV666, 7925M, N2416R, G-BTDH	RAA
☐ Supermarine 361 Spitfire LF.XVIe	TE330	CBAF-11446	TE330, 7449M, N75460	RAC
☐ Vickers 266 Vincent	NZ311		K6357	RAC
☐ Westland Wasp HAS.1	XS532	F9559		RA
☐ Westland Wasp HAS.1	XS566	F9577		RA
☐ Westland Wasp HAS.1	NZ3901	F9678		RA

CLASSIC FLYERS MUSEUM (NZ5)

Address:	8 Jean Batten Drive, Tauranga, Mount Maungaiui.
Tel:	07-572-4000
Admission:	Daily 1000-1600.
Location:	At the airport which is about 3 km east of Tauranga

This collection has been assembled by a group of private owners. The aircraft are displayed in a hangar at the airfield. Among the New Zealand built types is one of the one hundred and eight one Tiger Moths built in the country. The Fletcher FU-24 was designed in America and put into production in New Zealand for the agricultural market. Over four hundred have now been built in different versions. The CT-4 has its origins in the Australian Victa Airtourer. The design was sold to New Zealand in 1967 and piston and turbo-prop engined models have been sold both to civilian and military owners. A large collection of military memorabilia, engines, models and photographs are also on show. In addition there are several vintage motor cycles and military vehicles to be seen. Flights are available in a number of types.

TYPE	REG/SER	CON. NO.	PI/NOTES	STATUS
☐ Bell 205 Iroquois (UH-1H)	69-15616	11904	Cabin only.	PV
☐ Bell 47G				PVA
☐ Boeing-Stearman E75 Kaydet (PT-13D)	ZK-RTA	75-5907	42-17744, N5312N, N1628T	PVA
☐ Cessna 150	'21765'			PV
☐ Cessna 150M	ZK-TAE	15078198		PVA
☐ Cessna 318E Dragonfly (A-37B)			Due soon.	–
☐ Consolidated 28-5A Catalina (PBY-5A)			Front fuselage only.	PV
☐ De Havilland D.H.82A Tiger Moth	ZK-BJQ	83454	T5819, G-AMFN	PVA
☐ De Havilland D.H.82A Tiger Moth	ZK-AVJ	DHA.401	A17-366, VH-AQN	PVA
☐ De Havilland D.H.82A Tiger Moth	ZK-BRL	DHNZ.123	NZ1443	PVA
☐ De Havilland D.H.104 Devon C.1	ZK-UFO	04169	NZ1802- right half on wall.	PV
☐ De Havilland D.H.104 Devon C.1	ZK-UCO	04322	NZ1812	PVD
☐ De Havilland D.H.114 Heron 1B	ZK-BBM	14011	ZK-BBM, VQ-FAY, DQ-FAY, ZK-EEX	RAC
☐ Delore Skytrike	ZK-EXM	MAANZ/166		PV
☐ Ercoupe 415D	ZK-EXC	4811		PVA
☐ Fletcher FU-24-300	'ZK-BDS'	124	ZK-CRY	PVX
☐ Grumman G-164A Ag-Cat	ZK-RTA	441		PVA
☐ Hall Cherokee II	ZK-GBT	G1		RA
☐ Hawker P.1099 Hunter FR.74A (F.6)	ZK-JIL	41H/688080	XJ689, G-9-327, 517 (Singapore)	PV
☐ Hawker P.1101 Hunter T.75 (P.1067 Hunter F.4)	'500'	HABL 003007	XE664, 516 (Singapore)	PVX
☐ New Zealand Aerospace CT/4B Airtrainer	ZK-JMV	CT4-083	NZ1935	PVA
☐ North American NA-88 Texan (AT-6D) (Harvard III)	ZK-ENB	88-15871	41-34117, EZ244, NZ1076	RAA
☐ North American NA-88 Texan (AT-6D) (Harvard III)	ZK-ENC	88-16505	42-84724, EZ360, NZ1091 – often at Dairy Flat.	RAA
☐ North American NA-88 Texan (AT-6D) (Harvard III)	ZK-END	88-17004	42-85223, EZ449, NZ1096	PVA
☐ North American NA-88 Texan (AT-6D) (Harvard III)	ZK-ENJ	88-17010	42-85229, EZ455, NZ1098	PVA
☐ North American NA-176 Sabre (F-86F)	'12910'	176-427	55-51-13496, 284 (Ethiopia)	PVX
☐ Piper PA-18-150 Super Cub	ZK-TOW	18-6726		PVA
☐ Piper PA-23-250 Aztec	ZK-CEU	27-217	N4688P	PVD
☐ Pitts S-1 Special	ZK-JNW	DMS-1		PV
☐ Pitts S-1C Special	N7BH	BH-1-PS1C		PVA

TYPE	REG/SER	CON. NO.	PI/NOTES	STATUS
☐ Supermarine 349 Spitfire F.V (R)	'LJ3'			PVX
☐ Ultraflight Mirage	ZK-WYE			PV
☐ War Aircraft Fw 190	ZK-FWI	AACA/330		PVA

CLYDESDALE AGRICULTURAL MUSEUM (NZ6)

Address:	Mystery Creek Gate 3, Mystery Creek, Hamilton.
Tel:	07-843-7990
Admission:	0900-1630 Daily.
Location:	About 2 km south of Hamilton Airport and about 10 km south of the town off Route 3.

This large site is the home of the National Agricultural Heritage Centre which holds shows and conferences. The National Dairy Museum, a heritage village, a display of fire engines and a number of farm animals are among the attractions. The Clydesdale Agricultural Museum traces the history of farming and its associated industries in the country. The Dakota was used for agricultural work by James Aviation for many years.

TYPE	REG/SER	CON. NO.	PI/NOTES	STATUS
☐ Douglas DC-3A-467 Skytrain (C-47B) (Dakota IV)	'ZK-SAL'	16568/33316	44-76984, NZ3545, ZK-AZL	PVX
☐ Fletcher FU-1060	ZK-CTZ	1001	At airport gate.	PV
☐ Supermarine 361 Spitfire LF.XVIe (FSM)	'TE288'		In nearby park.	PVX

DARBY COLLECTION (NZ7)

Address:	P.O. Box 58036 East Tamaki Auckland.
Tel:	09-274-8400
Admission:	By prior permission only.
Location:	In the south eastern suburbs of the city

Charles Darby has made many expeditions to the Pacific Islands recording and recovering wrecked aircraft He has also acquired several rare types over the years. Forty Fairey Gordon bombers were delivered to New Zealand in 1939 to serve as trainers. A further one was assembled in the country probably using components from crashed machines. The sole survivor has been moved into the works at Pacific Aircraft to commence a painstaking rebuild. Twenty nine Black-burn Baffins arrived in New Zealand in 1937 and served until 1941.

TYPE	REG/SER	CON. NO.	PI/NOTES	STATUS
☐ Blackburn Baffin	NZ152	2690/7	S1430 – major components.	RAD
☐ Curtiss 87V Warhawk (P-40N) (Kittyhawk IV)	ZK-CAG	28492	42-104730, A29-448 – registered with NZ Warbirds.	RAA
☐ Fairey Gordon I	ZK-TLA	F1886	K2759, NZ629	RA

DEER WORLD NEW ZEALAND (NZ8)

Address:	State Highway 1, Taupo.
Tel:	07-374-8053
Admission:	Daily 1000-1700.
Location:	Just north of the town.

Deer farming is widespread in the country and all aspects of this work are highlighted at the centre. The use of helicopters for hunting and capturing deer was pioneered in New Zealand. The Hughes 500, displayed on a pole, was used in this Work. Wild animals were recovered by the dropping of weighted nets over them.

TYPE	REG/SER	CON. NO.	PI/NOTES	STATUS
☐ Hughes 500				PV

EAST COAST MUSEUM OF TECHNOLOGY (NZ9)

Address:	Main Road, P.O. Box 971, Makaraka, Gisborne.
Tel:	06-868-9284
Email:	info@ecmot.8.com
Admission:	Daily 0900-1630.
Location:	About 5 km north west of the town on Route 35.

The museum has on show items from most forms of transport as well as agricultural and industrial machinery. The Hatfield built Tiger Moth is being restored to top dressing configuration in a private hangar at the nearby airport. The first parts completed were the front fuselage and engine which has now moved to the museum. The volunteer crew are slowly continuing work on the remainder of the airframe.

TYPE	REG/SER	CON. NO.	PI/NOTES	STATUS
☐ De Havilland D.H.82A Tiger Moth	ZK-AWA	83186	T5461, VH-ATG	PV/RAC

GALPIN COLLECTION (NZ10)

Address: 216 Pongakawa Station Road,
RD6,
Pongakawa,
Te Puke.
Tel: 07-533-3859
Admission: By prior permission only.
Location: At private premises in the area.

John Galpin has four aircraft in store at his premises. They include the first production de Havilland Moth Minor which was intended for Australia but was delivered to New Zealand. The aircraft was impressed during World War II but returned to civil use after the end of hostilities. The Rearwin 9000 also arrived in the country in the late 1930s and was impressed as was the Hatfield built Tiger Moth.

TYPE	REG/SER	CON. NO.	PI/NOTES	STATUS
☐ De Havilland D.H.82A Tiger Moth	ZK-AFO	3630	ZK-AFO, NZ720, ZK-ASA	RA
☐ De Havilland D.H.82A Tiger Moth	ZK-AJQ	DHA.502	NZ1416	RA
☐ De Havilland D.H.94 Moth Minor	ZK-ALN	94001	G-AFRD, (VH-AAQ), ZK-AHI, NZ596	RA
☐ Rearwin 9000L	ZK-ALF	613D	ZK-AGQ, NZ599	RA

GISBORNE AVIATION PRESERVATION SOCIETY (NZ11)

Address: P.O. Box 491,
Gisborne.
Tel: 06-867-9815
Fax: 06-867-9815
Email: av8or@ihug.co.nz
Admission: By prior permission only.
Location: At Gisborne Airport which is in the western suburbs of the town.

The first aircraft flew into Gisborne in 1920 and ten years later the airfield opened an aero club was formed. Scheduled airline services soon followed. In 1949 the first New Zealand company for top dressing work was formed at Gisborne. In 1974 a Lockheed Lodestar, formerly used in the area for this task, was mounted on poles at the entrance to the airport. Local enthusiasts became concerned at its condition and formed the society in 1995. Funds were raised and a hangar/workshop was constructed. The Lodestar was taken down, dismantled and moved inside. Restoration to flying condition is proceeding with a team of volunteers. The second acquisition was the Grumman Avenger which is on loan from the Air Force Museum.The aircraft was the first of its type in New Zealand and was based at Gisborne during World War II. The C-47 was used for crop-dressing duties in the are before being retired in 1981. The aircraft was preserved in Wellington and on poles by the military airfield of Ohakea before arriving at Gisborne in 2000. The Fletcher represents the modern face of agricultural flying in the country.

TYPE	REG/SER	CON. NO.	PI/NOTES	STATUS
☐ De Havilland D.H.82A Tiger Moth	ZK-BAL	82793	R4876, G-AMMG	RAA
☐ Douglas DC-3A-456 Skytrain (C-47A)	'NZ3547'	20051	43-15585, NC65393, ZK-BYF	RAX
☐ Fletcher FU-24-950M	ZK-BWV	72	(ZK-BOU)	RA
☐ Grumman G-40 Avenger (TBF-1)	NZ2505	5220	Bu24377 – on loan from AF World.	RAC
☐ Lockheed 18-56-23 Lodestar IA (18-07-23) (C-59)	ZK-BUV	18-2152	41-29631, EW981, EC-22 (Spain), N9930F	RAC

HARNISH COLLECTION (NZ12)

Address: 155 Trig Road,
Whitford,
Auckland.
Tel: 09-530-8456
Admission: By prior permission only.
Location: About 20 km south east of the city.

The delightful Grumman Widgeon first flew in 1940 and two hundred and seventy six were produced by the company for civil and military use. In addition forty one were built in France between 1949 and 1952. Mount Cook Airlines operated a small fleet of Widgeons until the mid-1977 when they sold their water borne services to See Bee Air based at Mechanics Bay in Auckland. Owen Harnish has now acquired four Widgeons.

TYPE	REG/SER	CON. NO.	PI/NOTES	STATUS
☐ Grumman G-44A Widgeon	ZK-BPX	1432	NC86606, LV-NCG, N4262A	RA
☐ Grumman G-44A Widgeon	ZK-CFA	1439	NC86613, CU-P346, CU-346, N9096R	RA
☐ Grumman G-44A Widgeon	ZK-AVM	1466	NC86640, VH-AZO, ZK-AVM, VH-WET, P2-WET	RA
☐ Grumman G-44A Widgeon (J4F-2)	ZK-CHG	1356	Bu37726, N97102	RA

JEAN BATTEN MEMORIAL (NZ13)

Address:	Terminal Building, Auckland International Airport, Manakau 2150.
Tel:	09-275-0789
Fax:	09-275-5835
Email:	Admin@akl-airport.co.nz
Admission:	On permanent view.
Location:	About 20 km south of the city centre off Route 20A.

On November 11th 1935 Jean Batten took off from Lympne in Kent and two days later landed at Natal in Brazil, thus completing the first flight across the South Atlantic by a woman. She also beat the England to South America time set by Jim Mollison two years earlier and was awarded the Britannia Trophy. On October 5th 1936 she again left Lympne in the Gull and arrived at Darwin in the record time of five days, twenty-one hours and three minutes. She later lowered the time for a crossing of the Tasman Sea and made the first ever flight from England to New Zealand. The Gull was impressed in England during World War II and survived to be bought by Percival Aircraft in 1946. The famous aircraft was donated to the Shuttleworth Collection on April 25th 1961. In 1990 the aircraft was loaned to Auckland Airport for eight months. The airport purchased the historic Gull in the autumn of 1994 and it was air freighted to New Zealand in February 1996. The aircraft was flown for the last time on the sixtieth anniversary of Jean Batten's arrival in New Zealand. The historic machine is now exhibited in the terminal building along with a display of photographs and memorabilia.

TYPE	REG/SER	CON. NO.	PI/NOTES	STATUS
☐ Percival D.3 Gull Six	G-ADPR	D.55	G-ADPR, AX866, G-ADPR, (ZK-DPR)	PV

MUSEUM OF AVIATION (KAPITI) (NZ14)

Address:	P.O. Box 2005, Raumati Beach, Paraparaumu.
Tel:	04-299-4660
Email:	rogernewth@paradise.net.nz
Admission:	Saturday-Sunday 1400-1600.
Location:	At Paraparaumu Airport which is just north west of the town.

This interesting collection of artefacts is housed in the old Meteorological building next to the original 1942 airport control tower. The display opened in January 1995.and has on show documents, artefacts, models and aviation clothing. Paraparaumu opened in 1939 and for many years was the main airport for Wellington although it is about fifty kilometres from the city. Passenger and freight services operated from the site until Wellington International opened in 1959. The history of the airport through this period is highlighted in the displays. From 1947 until 1991 the New Zealand Airfield Calibration Flight had its headquarters at the field and their work is portrayed. At the current time the airfield is a thriving general aviation centre and this aspect of flying features prominently. Another area is devoted to the work of New Zealand's aviation pioneers. Models and photographs of their aircraft can be seen. The Wellington Gliding Club history is also traced.

MUSEUM OF TRANSPORT, TECHNOLOGY AND SOCIAL HISTORY (NZ15)

Address:	P.O. Box 44144, Point Chevalier, Auckland.
Tel:	09-846-5800
Fax:	09-846-4242
Email:	enquiries@motat.org.nz
Admission:	Daily 1000-1700.
Location:	About 5 km west of the city centre.

On June 5th 1960 a meeting was organised by the Old Time Transport Preservation League of Matakohe, The Royal Aeronautical Society (New Zealand Division) and the Historic Auckland Society. The aim of the gathering was to bring together a number of groups which were interested in the preservation of transport and technological material. The idea of a museum was put forward and in October 1964 the collection opened on a site at Western Springs. Over the last three decades this site has been steadily developed and halls devoted to all forms of transport have been erected. In addition there is a pioneer village. On show are many historic vehicles, railway engines and carriages. Historic buildings have been moved to this area of the museum and aspects of life in the 1840–1890 period are vividly portrayed. In 1977 Jean Batten opened the Pioneers of New Zealand Aviation Pavilion. Around the walls of this building are photographs, models and documents tracing the story of flying in the country in the early days. Richard Pearse was born in 1877 and began his aeronautical work in 1899. His aircraft hopped in 1901 and apparently flew a distance of about fifty yards, possibly on March 31st 1903. The remains of the original engine are on show in the pavilion along with a replica of the aircraft. In the late 1920s and early 1930s Pearse built another aircraft which incorporated a number of revolutionary features including a variable pitch propeller which could be controlled from the cabin, a self designed engine which could be tilted for hovering and leading edge flaps. This unique machine was restored in the early 1970s and can be seen in the pavilion. In 1978 a nearby site was opened and named the Sir Keith Park Memorial Airfield in honour of one of the New Zealand's World War II heroes. Buildings were constructed but for many years the majority of the larger aircraft had to be parked outside. In 1987 the first stage of a large exhibition hangar was opened and three years later this was enlarged. At the current time only the Sunderland, which has recently been repainted, and the Lodestar are exposed to the elements but these will soon be inside. The centre of the hall is dominated by a Lancaster and a Solent. The Lancaster honours two aircraft flown by New Zealand crew members in World War II. The Solent was purchased by T.E.A.L. in 1949 and flown from Mechanics Bay in the city until the early 1960s. A replica Fairey Swordfish has been constructed as part of a display on the Fleet Air Arm. A range of military and civil aircraft complete this interesting exhibition. In a smaller hangar are a number of other airframes, all of which will be restored by the largely volunteer A large new hangar is nearing completion and this will enable more of the collection to be put under cover and exhibit some of the aircraft which are either in cramped conditions or in store.

TYPE	REG/SER	CON. NO.	PI/NOTES	STATUS
☐ Adams Ornithopter	ZK-MPF			PV
☐ Aero Engine Services Airtourer 115	ZK-CXU	521		PV
☐ Auster J/1B Aiglet	'NZ1708'	3103	ZK-BBY, ZK-BWH	PVX
☐ Avro 683 Lancaster MR.VII (B.VII)	'ND752'		NX665, WU-13 (France) – parts of NX666, WU-05 (France) – marked as 'PB457' on one side.	PVX
☐ Beech C18S Kansan (AT-11)	ZK-AHO	3691	42-37208	RA
☐ Cessna A188 Agwagon	ZK-COO	1880054	N9804V	RAD
☐ Commonwealth CA-28 Ceres	ZK-BPU	CA28-4	VH-CED	RA
☐ Curtiss 87-A4 Warhawk (P-40E) (Kittyhawk IA)	'NZ3039'		41-36385, EV131	PVX
☐ De Havilland D.H.82A Tiger Moth	'ZK-AIN'	84648	T6200, G-AMNF, ZK-BAD	PVX
☐ De Havilland D.H.82A Tiger Moth	NZ775	DHNZ.25	NZ775, ZK-AIN	PV
☐ De Havilland D.H.83C Fox Moth (R)	'ZK-AEK'	'FM.48'	'ZK-APT'	RAX
☐ De Havilland D.H.89 Dragon Rapide	ZK-AHS	6423	ZK-AGT, NZ558	PV
☐ De Havilland D.H.98 Mosquito T.43 (FB.40)	NZ2305		(A52-19), A52-1053	RA
☐ De Havilland D.H.100 Vampire FB.9	WR202	V.1043	WR202, NZ1717, INST171	PV
☐ Douglas DC-3A-467 Skytrain (C-47B) (Dakota IV)	ZK-BQK	16567/33315	44-76983, NZ3544, ZK-BQK, 5W-FAH	PV
☐ Everson Autogyro				PV
☐ Fairey Swordfish II (FSM)	'DK791'			PVX
☐ Flaglor Sky Scooter	ZK-EYL	AACA/367		PV
☐ Fletcher FU-24	ZK-BXQ	75		RAD
☐ Gere Sport				PV
☐ Grumman G-40 Avenger (TBF-1C)	NZ2527	5625	Bu47859, NZ2527, ZK-CBO	PV
☐ Handley Page H.P.95 Hastings C.3	NZ5801	127	Nose only.	PV
☐ Hang Glider				PV
☐ Hawker Hind	NZ1518		K6717 – currently with Classic Aircraft Collection.	–
☐ Hawker Hurricane I (FSM)	'P3854'		'P3350'	PVX
☐ Lockheed 10-A Electra	ZK-AFD	1095		RA
☐ Lockheed 10-A Electra	'ZK-AFD'	1138	NC21735, N21735, N10Y, ZK-BUT	PVX
☐ Lockheed 137-27-02 Ventura IIA (B-34)	NZ4600	137-4773	41-38117, (FD665)	RA
☐ Lockheed 18-08-01 Lodestar (18-10-01) (C-56D)	ZK-BVE	18-2020	NC25630, 42-53504, AX756, G-AGCN, AX756, (Spanish AF), EC-A??, N9933F	PV
☐ Lockheed 414-56-03 Hudson III	NZ2031	414-3854	AE499	RA
☐ Mignet HM-14 Pou-du-Ciel	ZM-AAA			PV
☐ Miles M.14A Hawk Trainer 3 (Magister)	L8353	779	L8353, G-AMMC, ZK-AYW	PV
☐ Miles M.65 Gemini 1A	ZK-ANT	6322		PV
☐ North American NA-66 Harvard II	NZ944	66-2757	AH195, NZ944, INST153	RA
☐ North Tui' Sports			Fuselage from a Lincoln Sports.	RAC
☐ Pearse Monoplane (R)				PV
☐ Pearse Monoplane 2 (R)				PV
☐ Pearse Utility Monoplane				PV
☐ Ryan STM-2	ZK-BEM	489	S.53 (Netherlands), A50-13, VH-AGS – with a N.Z. Warbirds Syndicate at Ardmore.	–
☐ Schneider ESG 31 Grunau Baby II (D.F.S. 108-49)	ZK-GDG	107	SE-SPH/SE-SDH	PV
☐ Short S.25 Sunderland MR.V	NZ4115	SH.1552	SZ584, G-AHJR, SZ.584	PV
☐ Short S.45 Solent 4	ZK-AMO	SH.1559		PV
☐ Transavia PL-12 Airtruk	ZK-CVB	706		PV
☐ Westland Wasp HAS.1	NZ3902	F9679	On loan to Navy Museum.	–

NEW ZEALAND SPORT AND VINTAGE AVIATION SOCIETY (NZ16)

Address: P.O.Box 669, Masterton.
Tel: 06-377-3466
Email: info@svas.org.nz
Admission: By prior permission only.
Location: At Hood Airport which is just south of the town off Route 2.

Formed more than a decade ago with the aim of keeping vintage aircraft in flying condition, the society now occupies two hangars at Hood Airfield. One of the handful of still airworthy Proctors is a rarity. In the late 1940s a small number of new Proctor 5s were delivered to the country and the majority are still in existence. Two Chrislea Super Aces were bought by New Zealand owners in the same period and one is undergoing a complete rebuild in the group's workshops. The Rearwin Sportster owned by the society was originally delivered to Australia and crossed the Tasman Sea in 1941. After a brief period in civilian ownership the aircraft was impressed in 1942 and operated by the military for four years. The homebuilt glider was built by a local resident and dates from the inter-war period. This airframe is in poor condition.

TYPE	REG/SER	CON. NO.	PI/NOTES	STATUS
☐ Chrislea C.H.3 Super Ace Series 2	ZK-ASI	128		RAC
☐ De Havilland D.H.82A Tiger Moth	ZK-BAT	82139	G-AFSH, X5106, G-AFSH	RAA
☐ De Havilland D.H.82A Tiger Moth	ZK-ANL	82512	N9458, NZ861	RAA
☐ De Havilland D.H.82A Tiger Moth	ZK-BLK	82812	R4895, G-AOAF	RAA
☐ De Havilland D.H.82A Tiger Moth	ZK-BEX	83829	T7302, G-ANGT	RAA
☐ De Havilland D.H.82A Tiger Moth	ZK-BLV	85071	T6802, G-ANSJ	RAA
☐ De Havilland D.H.82A Tiger Moth	ZK-BTR	85768	DE883, G-ANSU, ZK-BGY, ZK-BVN	RAA
☐ De Havilland D.H.82A Tiger Moth	ZK-BCZ	DHNZ.155	NZ1475	RA
☐ De Havilland D.H.C.1 Chipmunk 22 (T.10)	ZK-SKH	C1/0547	WK511, G-BVBT	RAA
☐ Douglas DC-3A-467 Skytrain (C-47B) (Dakota IV)	ZK-APB	15945/32693	44-76361, NZ3534 – front fuselage only.	RA
☐ Homebuilt Glider				RAD
☐ Macchi MB.308	ZK-MDF	5852/79	I-AHDF	RAA
☐ North American NA-88 Texan (AT-6C) (Harvard IIA)	ZK-SGQ	88-12032	41-33561, EX588, NZ1033	RAA
☐ Percival P.44 Proctor 5	ZK-AQZ	Ae.143	Also registered with NZ Warbirds.	RAA
☐ Piper J-3C-50 Cub	ZK-AHD	2707		RAA
☐ Rearwin 9000KR Sportster	ZK-AKA	656D	VH-ADL, ZK-AHN, NZ569	RAC

NEW ZEALAND VINTAGE AERO CLUB (NZ17)

Address: P.O. Box 4306, Hamilton East.
Tel: 07-856-9097
Admission: By prior permission only.
Location: On the north side of Hamilton Airport which is about 8 km south of the town on Route 3.

Originally based in the Auckland area, the club moved to Hamilton in the mid-1980s. Members of the group restored the first hangar to be built at the field when it opened in the 1930s. The Autocrat was operated by Aeroplane magazine in England from 1946 until 1950. During this period it became the first British civil aircraft to land on an aircraft carrier when it alighted on H.M.S. Illustrious on October 16th 1946. In May 1948 the Autocrat landed on the Canadian carrier H.M.C.S. Magnificent. These two feats are commemorated on the cowling. Unfortunately the aircraft crashed at Mangaatawhiri on January 16th 2001 and was badly damaged.

TYPE	REG/SER	CON. NO.	PI/NOTES	STATUS
☐ Auster J/1 Autocrat	ZK-AUX	1994/2	G-AHHE, G-AERO	RAD
☐ Cessna 120	ZK-FFK	11102	NC76662, N76662	RAC
☐ Piper J-3C-90 Cub (J3C-65) (L-4B)	ZK-ATU	9707	43-0846, VQ-FAG	RAA
☐ Slingsby T.42B Eagle 3	ZK-GBG	1091	BGA.787	RAC

NEW ZEALAND WARBIRDS ASSOCIATION (NZ18)

Address: Private Bag 14, 700 Harvard Lane, Ardmore Airfield, Papakura, Auckland.
Tel: 09-298-9207
Fax: 09-298-9210
Email: nzwarbirds@paradise.net.org
Admission: By prior permission only.
Location: About 6 km north east of Papakura and 25 km south east of Auckland.

The organisation was formed in the late 1970s to encourage members to preserve and restore former military aircraft to flying condition. All the machines are owned by individuals or syndicates. A large hangar at Ardmore houses many of the aircraft and several more are in other buildings on the field. The ultimate aim of the organisation is to construct a large purpose-built museum. Over two hundred Harvards were flown by the Royal New Zealand Air Force. In 1977 nineteen airworthy examples were put up for tender and a large proportion of these were bought by New Zealand owners. Several are now based in the hangar at Ardmore in a variety of colour schemes used by the Air Force over the years. A Mustang is painted in the markings of one flown by Squadron Leader Ray Archibald when he commanded No. 3 Squadron. The Fury is one of a batch of twenty-seven imported into the U.S.A. from Iran in the late 1970s. Jets are being added to the inventory with a Vampire and a Venom in flying condition. The Cessna Dragonfly acquired from Vietnam is now airworthy. Training and communications aircraft are not forgotten and two examples of the indigenous Airtrainer are based at Ardmore. With the current worldwide interest in warbirds it is likely that the list of aircraft owned by members will continue to grow. Several aircraft are based with their owners at other airfields around the country.

TYPE	REG/SER	CON. NO.	PI/NOTES	STATUS
☐ Aero Engine Services CT/4A Airtrainer	ZK-LJH	CT4-042	ZK-EAE, A19-042, VH-JDN	RAA
☐ Akrotec G202	ZK-NUT	G202028		RAA
☐ Beech D17S	ZK-AMU	203	CF-CCA	RAA
☐ Boeing-Stearman A75N1 Kaydet (PT-17)	ZK-RRR	75-1965	41-8406, N53314, N9163R	RAA
☐ Boeing-Stearman E75 Kaydet (PT-13D)	ZK-JID	75-5064	42-16901, PI-C543, RP-C543, N4036	RAA
☐ Cessna 305A Bird Dog (L-19A) (O-1A)	ZK-FYA	22737	51-16903, (South Vietnam	RAA
☐ Cessna 305A Bird Dog (L-19A) (O-1A)	ZK-OIG	22975	51-12520, 3-04126 (Vietnam)	RA
☐ Cessna 318E Dragonfly (A-37B)	ZK-JTL	43392	71-0854, 854 (Vietnam)	RAA
☐ Consolidated 28-5A Canso A	ZK-PBY	CV 357	11054 (Canada), CF-JCV, C-FJCV, Z-CAT	RAA
☐ Curtiss 87V Warhawk (P-40N) (Kittyhawk IV)	ZK-CAG	28492	42-104730, A29-448 – Darby Collection aircraft.	RAA
☐ De Havilland D.H.82A Tiger Moth	ZK-BEC	83626	T7167, G-ANBT	RAA
☐ De Havilland D.H.82A Tiger Moth	ZK-BEN	84671	T6245, G-AMVH	RAA
☐ De Havilland D.H.82A Tiger Moth	ZK-BSN	DHA.501	NZ1415	RAA
☐ De Havilland D.H.82A Tiger Moth	ZK-ALM	DHNZ.91	NZ841	RAA
☐ De Havilland D.H.82A Tiger Moth	ZK-BLI	DHNZ.128	NZ1448 – based at Craigmore.	RAA
☐ De Havilland D.H.82A Tiger Moth	ZK-CYC	DHNZ.133	NZ1453, INST168	RAA
☐ De Havilland D.H.82A Tiger Moth	ZK-BRM	DHNZ.152	NZ1472	RAA
☐ De Havilland D.H.89B Dragon Rapide (Dominie I)	ZK-AKU	6662	HG663, NZ528 – based at Dairy Flat.	RA
☐ De Havilland D.H.98 Mosquito T.43	NZ2308		A52-20	RAC
☐ De Havilland D.H.104 Devon C.1	ZK-KTT	04324	NZ1808	RAA
☐ De Havilland D.H.112 Venom FB.4	ZK-VNM	969	J-1799 (Switzerland), G-BLIC, N502DM	RAA
☐ De Havilland D.H.115 Vampire T.55	ZK-RVM	985	U-1225 (Switzerland), HB-RVM	RAA
☐ De Havilland D.H.C.1 Chipmunk 22 (T.10)	ZK-RFS	C1/0141	WB693	RAA
☐ De Havilland D.H.C.1 Chipmunk 22 (T.10)	ZK-UAS	C1/0633	WK621, G-BDBL	RAA
☐ De Havilland D.H.C.1 Chipmunk 22 (T.10)	ZK-TAZ	C1/0840	WP974	RAA
☐ De Havilland D.H.C.2 Beaver	'NZ6001'	25	ZS-DCG, G-ARTR, ZK-CKH	RAAX
☐ Douglas DC-3A-467 Skytrain (C-47B)	ZK-DAK	15035/26480	43-49219, PI-C-486, VH-PNM, VH-SBT	RAA
☐ Hawker P.1099 Hunter FR.74A (F.6)	ZK-JIL	41H/688080	XJ689, G-9-327, 517 (Singapore) – based at Tauranga.	RAA
☐ Isaacs Fury II	'K1790'	AACA/179/1	ZK-DMN	RAAX
☐ Luscombe 8E Silvaire	N35CB			RAA
☐ Nanchang CJ-6A	ZK-STP	1232011	76 (China) – at Omaka.	RAA
☐ Nanchang CJ-6A	ZK-OII	1582004	26 (China)	RAA
☐ Nanchang CJ-6A	ZK-WOK	2132042	46 (China)	RAA
☐ Nanchang CJ-6A	ZK-FRU	2132048	24 (China), VH-NNA	RAA
☐ New Zealand Aerospace CT/4B Airtrainer	ZK-DGY	CT4-001		RAA
☐ Nord N.1002 Pingouin II [Messerschmitt Bf 108B]	ZK-WFI	103	103 (France), OO-NET, N109H, ZS-WFI	RAA
☐ North American NA-122 Mustang (P-51D)	'NZ2415'	122-41369	44-74829, 9265 (Canada), N8675E, N169MD, N769MD, ZK-TAF	RAAX
☐ North American NA-226 Trojan (T-28C)	ZK-JGS	226-140	Bu140563, N563GH	RAA
☐ North American NA-78 Texan (AT-6A)	ZK-XSA	78-6647	41-16269, 7660 (South Africa)	RAA
☐ North American NA-88 Texan (AT-6C) (Harvard IIA)	ZK-SGQ	88-12032	41-33561, EX588, NZ1033	RAA
☐ North American NA-88 Texan (AT-6C) (Harvard IIA)	ZK-MJN	88-13909	41-33768, EX795, NZ1052	RAA
☐ North American NA-88 Texan (AT-6C) (Harvard IIA)	ZK-JJA	88-13910	41-33769, EX796, NZ1053	RAA
☐ North American NA-88 Texan (AT-6D) (Harvard III)	ZK-TVI	88-14178	41-33801, EX828, NZ1057	RAA
☐ North American NA-88 Texan (AT-6D) (Harvard III)	ZK-ENF	88-14889	41-33917, EX944, NZ1065	RAA
☐ North American NA-88 Texan (AT-6D) (Harvard III)	ZK-ENG	88-15873	41-34119, EZ246, NZ1078	RAA
☐ North American NA-88 Texan (AT-6D) (Harvard III)	ZK-WAR	88-16506	42-84725, EZ361, NZ1092	RAA
☐ North American NA-88 Texan (AT-6D) (Harvard III)	ZK-END	88-17004	42-85223, EZ449, NZ1096 – based at Tauranga.	RAA
☐ North American NA-88 Texan (AT-6D) (Harvard III)	ZK-ENJ	88-17010	42-85229, EZ455, NZ1098	RAA

TYPE	REG/SER	CON. NO.	PI/NOTES	STATUS
☐ Papa51 Thunder Mustang	ZK-TMG	18	ZU-TMG	RAA
☐ Percival P.44 Proctor 5	ZK-AQZ	Ae.143	NZ Sport and Vintage Ass. aircraft.	RAC
☐ Pitts S-2B Special	ZK-MAD	5087	N260J	RAA
☐ Ryan ST-3KR Recruit (PT-22)	ZK-RYN	2062	41-20853, N57913, N579S	
☐ Ryan STM-2	ZK-BEM	489	S-53 (Netherlands), A50-13, VH-AGS – MOTAT aircraft.	RAC
☐ Victa Airtourer 115	ZK-CLD	130	(ZK-CLH)	RAA
☐ Yakovlev Yak-3U (Let C.11)	ZK-YYY	1701231	(Egypt), (France), NX11SN, (G-BUXZ), G-BWOE	RAA
☐ Yakovlev Yak-52	ZK-PNN	800807	(DOSAAF), LY-ANL	RAA
☐ Yakovlev Yak-52	ZK-KGB	866909	105 (DOSAAF), LY-AOF, ZK-LJH	RAA
☐ Yakovlev Yak-52	ZK-ZAY	9111602	67 (DOSAAF), LY-ANH, ZK-YAQ	RAA
☐ Yakovlev Yak-52	ZK-YAK	9712002	(DOSAAF), LY-AFL, ZK-YAQ	RAA

OLD STICK AND RUDDER COMPANY COLLECTION (NZ19)

Address:	Hangar 14, Hood Aerodrome, Masterton.
Tel:	02-137-1958
Email:	info@oldstickand rudder.com
Admission:	By prior permission only.
Location:	At Hood Airport which is just south of the town off Route 2.

This collection of warbirds was established with the aim of portraying the aviation heritage of the country. The First World War period is represented by four aircraft. The Bristol Fighter includes the fuselage of one rescued from the famous barn at Weston-on-the-Green in England. The biplane was built by Skysport Engineering and spent some time at Duxford before being exported to New Zealand. Close connections exist between this collection and the museum at Omaka and aircraft often move to the South Island airfield. The Avro 504 was also built in England by Skysport Engineering and made its maiden flight in the mid-1990s. The Royal New Zealand Air Force operated just under three hundred Curtiss P-40s. They were used across the Pacific theatre of operations from 1942 until 1944, claiming around one hundred Japanese aircraft shot down. Most of the survivors were scrapped in 1948 but fortunately a handful escaped the axe. The Americans were impressed with the performance of the New Zealand pilots in the P-40 and decided to allocate over four hundred Corsairs to the country, although by the time they arrived there were virtually no Japanese aircraft left in the region. Also located on the airfield is the New Zealand Sport and Vintage Aviation Society.

TYPE	REG/SER	CON. NO.	PI/NOTES	STATUS
☐ Avro 504K (R)	'D8781'	14	G-ECKE, ZK-EHB	RAAX
☐ Boeing 235 (F4B-4) (R)				RAX
☐ Bristol 14 F.2B Fighter	'D8084'		G-ACAA, ZK-BRI – built from components.	RAAX
☐ Curtiss 87-A4 Warhawk (P-40E) (Kittyhawk IA)	ZK-RMH	19669	41-25158, ET942, NZ3009, ZK-RMH, G-CCBE	RAA
☐ De Havilland D.H.C.1 Chipmunk 22 (T.10)	ZK-SKH	C1/0547	WK511, G-BVBT	RAA
☐ De Havilland D.H.C.1 Chipmunk 22 (T.10)	N861WP	C1/0748	WP861, N67273	RAA
☐ Percival P.56 Provost T.1	ZK-SGN	P.56/226	WW397, 8060M, G-BKHP, VH-OIL	RAA
☐ Royal Aircraft Factory S.E.5A (R)	'F5690'	WA.19	ZK-SEV	RAAX
☐ Sopwith F.1 Camel (R)	'B6289'			RAAX
☐ Vought FG-1D Corsair	ZK-COR	3205	Bu88391, NZ5648, 'NZ5611', NX55JP, G-BXUL	PVA

RAINBOW SPRINGS AND FARM (NZ20)

Address:	P.O. Box 25, Fairy Springs Road, Rotorua.
Tel:	07-347-9301
Admission:	Daily 0800-1700.
Location:	About 5 km north of the town on Route 5.

At Rainbow Springs the visitor can view a wide range of indigenous animals and plants. At the Farm demonstrations of working animals are regularly held. Agricultural machinery and implements are also on view. A programme of conservation of the Kiwi was initiated and now over five hundred birds have been hatched. The Tiger Moth is displayed in the farm shop to honour the top dressing work carried out by the type over many years. The aircraft was built from spares by Colin Sutherland at Rotorua Airport.

TYPE	REG/SER	CON. NO.	PI/NOTES	STATUS
☐ De Havilland D.H.82A Tiger Moth	'ZK-AVJ'		Composite built from spares.	PVX

Jean Batten's famous Percival Gull is preserved in the terminal building at Auckland Airport.

The Vickers 22 was designed before World War I but was not built until the late 1950s. The aircraft survives in the Southward Museum.

This Mosquito is awaiting restoration at the Ferrymead complex on the outskirts of Christchurch. (John Mounce)

ROYAL NEW ZEALAND AIR FORCE HISTORIC FLIGHT (NZ21)

Address:	RNZAF Ohakea, Palmerston North.
Tel:	06-551-5168
Admission:	By prior permission only.
Location:	About 25 km north west of Palmerston North on Route 1.

Established in 1985 at Wigram, the flight moved to Ohakea in 1994 soon after the Central Flying School transferred to the North Island field. Two aircraft, the Tiger Moth and the Harvard are currently airworthy with a spare Harvard in store. The Air Force acquired Hatfield-built Tiger Moth in 1985 and restored it to the colours it wore in service at No. 2 EFTS at Ashburton. Star of the fleet is the only surviving Avro 626. This machine is currently on show in the museum at Wigram and rarely flies. Four 626s were delivered in 1936 and the flight's example served until 1943 when it was allocated to an A.T.C. unit at Hastings. J.R. Frogley of Havelock North bought the biplane in the late 1940s and flew it occasionally until it was acquired by the R.N.Z.A.F. Museum trustees in 1980. Restored at Ohakea over a five year period, the 626 flew again in July 1985.

TYPE	REG/SER	CON. NO.	PI/NOTES	STATUS
☐ Avro 626	NZ203	811	NZ203, INST90, ZK-APC – at RNZAF Museum.	–
☐ De Havilland D.H.82A Tiger Moth	NZ662	83492	T5763, NZ662, ZK-AIE, VQ-FAG, DQ-FAG	RAA
☐ North American NA-88 Texan (AT-6C) (Harvard IIA)	NZ1015	88-9272	41-33166, EX193	RAA
☐ North American NA-88 Texan (AT-6D) (Harvard III)	NZ1083	88-16144	42-84363, EZ300, NZ1083, INST212	RA

ROYAL NEW ZEALAND AIR FORCE MUSEUM – OHAKEA WING (NZ22)

Address:	Private Bag 11033 RNZAF Ohakea Palmerston North.
Tel:	06-351-5020
Fax:	06-351-5020
Email:	afx@xtra.co.nz
Admission:	Temporarily closed.
Location:	About 25 km north west of Palmerston North on Route 1.

Ohakea was constructed in the late 1930s and was until recently a front line strike base operating Douglas A-4K Skyhawks and Macchi MB.339Cs. With the closure of Wigram as an active station the Central Flying School moved in with its CT-4 Airtrainers. The museum opened in 1993 and its imaginative displays trace the history of the base, the units which have flown from the field and military flying in New Zealand. On show are photographs, models, documents, uniforms, components and memorabilia. Sixteen Strikemasters were delivered between 1972 and 1975 to equip No. 14 Squadron. Visitors can view the operational flying from the museum cafeteria which overlooks the field. At the current time the museum is closed whilst new hangars are constructed for the NH-90 helicopter fleet. All the aircraft and artefacts are in store and a new exhibition is planned.

TYPE	REG/SER	CON. NO.	PI/NOTES	STATUS
☐ Aermacchi MB.339CB			Front fuselage only.	RA
☐ Aermacchi MB.339CB	NZ6465	6795/169		RA
☐ British Aircraft Corporation 167 Strikemaster 88	NZ6374	344	G27-343	RA
☐ De Havilland D.H.100 Vampire FB.5	NZ5767		WA374, NZ5767, INST202	RA
☐ De Havilland D.H.100 Vampire FB.5	NZ5772		WA452, NZ5772, INST203	RA
☐ Douglas A-4K Skyhawk			Front fuselage only.	RA
☐ Douglas A-4L Skyhawk	'NZ6257'		Built from components.	RAX
☐ Lockheed 414-56-03 Hudson III			Fuselage section.	RAD
☐ North American NA-88 Texan (AT-6C) (Harvard IIA)	NZ1009	88-9266	41-33160, EX187, NZ1009, INST211	RA

ROYAL NEW ZEALAND NAVAL MUSEUM (NZ23)

Address:	HMNZS Taranaki, Box 32901, Devonport, Auckland.
Tel:	09-445-5186
Fax:	09-445-5046
Admission:	Daily 1000-1630.
Location:	In the north eastern part of the city.

The displays trace the naval history of the country in peace and war. On show are documents, photographs, models and uniforms. A small number of Wasp helicopters were flown from ships.

TYPE	REG/SER	CON. NO.	PI/NOTES	STATUS
☐ Sopwith Pup (R)				RAC
☐ Westland Wasp HAS.1	NZ3902	F9679	On loan from MoTaT.	PV

SMITH COLLECTION (NZ24)

Address: North Shore Airfield, Postmans Road RD.4, Albany, Auckland.
Tel: 09-426-3435
Admission: By prior permission only.
Location: About 25 km north of Auckland and east of Route 1.

Stan Smith runs a restoration and overhaul facility at North Shore Airfield. He has also collected a number of vintage aircraft which will all eventually be rebuilt to fly. The Australian built Dragon, which last flew in 1967, has recently undergone a complete restoration and is now active. This biplane is painted in the colours of East Coast Airways to honour the company which was the first licensed airline in the country and the first to operate the Dragon.

TYPE	REG/SER	CON. NO.	PI/NOTES	STATUS
☐ Auster J/1B Aiglet	ZK-AXE	2673		RA
☐ Auster J/5 Adventurer	ZK-DBU	2095	NZ1702	RA
☐ Champion 7GCAA	ZK-FSC	265-73	N57466	RAA
☐ De Havilland D.H.60MIII Moth (D.H.82A)	ZK-AQA	82355	N9254, NZ863	RAC
☐ De Havilland D.H.83C Fox Moth	ZK-APT	FM.48		RAC
☐ De Havilland D.H.84 Dragon 1	ZK-AXI	2057	A34-68, VH-AEF	RAA
☐ De Havilland D.H.94 Moth Minor	ZK-AKM	94012	G-AFON, ZK-AHK, NZ597	RAA
☐ Miles M.14A Hawk Trainer 3	ZK-ALO	332	G-AETL, ZK-AEY, NZ586	RAD
☐ Miles M.65 Gemini 1A	ZK-KHW	6524	G-AKHW	RA
☐ Percival P.44 Proctor 5	ZK-ARP	Ae.97	G-AIEO	RAA
☐ Piper J-3C-65 Cub (O-59A) (L-4A)	ZK-AIR	9024	42-38455, NC62052, N62052	RAA
☐ Savage SAS Monoplane	ZK-BUD	1	ZK-ALV	RA
☐ Yakovlev Yak-52	ZK-YAX	811811	(Romania), (ZK-LIZ)	RAA

SOUTHWARD MUSEUM TRUST (NZ25)

Address: Otaihanga Road, Paraparamu.
Tel: 04-297-1075
Fax: 04-297-0503
Email: southward@kapiti.co.nz
Admission: Daily 1000-1630.
Location: About 3 km north of Paraparamu off Route 1 about 55 km north east of Wellington.

The Trust was established in 1972 with the main aim of preserving one of the largest private collections of motor vehicles in the Southern Hemisphere. Sir Len Southward entered the motor industry in 1919 and later set up a number of companies. He acquired a Model T Ford in 1956 and the collection, now numbering over two hundred and fifty vehicles, was started. The purpose-built museum and conference centre opened in December 1979. Len Southward was also well known as a powerboat racer and his 'Redhead' speedboat, in which he won many championships, is on view. The Vickers 22 design was conceived as an improvement on the Blériot Monoplane before the outbreak of World War I. The type was intended for use with the Vickers Flying School. In the late 1905's Doug and Tony Bianchi of Personal Plane Services in England, built the 'prototype'.

TYPE	REG/SER	CON. NO.	PI/NOTES	STATUS
☐ De Havilland D.H.100 Vampire FB.5	NZ5770		WA444, NZ5770, INST198	PV
☐ De Havilland D.H.82A Tiger Moth	ZK-AOX	DHA.503	NZ1417	PV
☐ Vickers 22		PPS/REP/1		PV

TARANAKI AVIATION, TRANSPORT AND TECHNOLOGY MUSEUM (NZ26)

Address: P.O. Box 4135, New Plymouth.
Tel: 06-752-2845
Email: tatatm@xxtra.co.nz
Admission: Sunday 1000-1630
Location: At the corner of Main and Kent Roads south of the city off Route 3.

Four aircraft are displayed at this museum which also has on show many vehicles and items of agricultural and industrial machinery. Just over two hundred Harvards served with distinction with the Air Force from 1942 until the late 1970s. The composite Cessna is slowly being rebuilt.

TYPE	REG/SER	CON. NO.	PI/NOTES	STATUS
☐ Airspeed AS.10 Oxford I	NZ277	499	P2030 – possible identity – components from crash site.	PVD
☐ Brewsters Flying Flea				PV
☐ Cessna 170B	ZK-BJT	26671	(N4327B) – fuselage only – parts from Cessna 180 c/n 50819 ZK-BWY and wings from Cessna 172 c/n 49521 ZK-CCE	PVC
☐ North American NA-88 Texan (AT-6D) (Harvard III)	NZ1089	88-16328	42-84547, EZ333, NZ1089, INST177 – wings from c/n 88-17010 42-85229, EZ455, NZ1098	PVC

TE PAPA NATIONAL MUSEUM (NZ27)

Address: Cable Street, Wellington 6001.
Tel: 04-3851-7000
Admission: On the waterfront.
Location: In the centre of the city.

The museum which traces the history and culture of the country closed its old exhibition site in April 1996. A new building was constructed and this was ready in 1998. The Tiger Moth has been loaned to the collection by James Aviation and is exhibited in top dressing configuration in the agricultural section of the museum. The company operated the aircraft in this role for a decade from 1949.

TYPE	REG/SER	CON. NO.	PI/NOTES	STATUS
☐ De Havilland D.H.82A Tiger Moth	ZK-AJO	DHA.489	NZ1403	PV

VINTAGE AVIATION HAWKE'S BAY CHARITABLE TRUST (NZ28)

Address: P.O. Box 944, Hawke's Bay.
Tel: 06-843-7883
Fax: 06-843-7871
Email: gcangencies@xtra.co.nz
Admission: By prior permission only
Location: At a private building in the area.

The group is raising funds for a display which will trace the history of flying in the area. Interviews with pilots have been recorded and items of memorabilia have been collected and stored.

WARD COLLECTION (NZ29)

Address: P.O. Box 136, Pokeno.
Admission: By prior permission only.
Location: The airfield is about 5 km east of the town.

This interesting collection of aircraft imported from the United States currently has several in airworthy condition with the remainder in store in the area. The Travel Air 4000 first flew in 1926 and about six hundred were built. Several versions, powered by a variety of engines, appeared in the late 1920s. The all metal Luscombe Silvaire made its maiden flight in 1937 and the type remained in production until 1961 by which time over six thousand had been sold. In the 1960s several Stampe S.V.4s were shipped to the U.S.A. from France.

TYPE	REG/SER	CON. NO.	PI/NOTES	STATUS
☐ Luscombe 8A Silvaire	N45856	2383	NC45856	RAA
☐ Luscombe 8E Silvaire	N1757K	4484	NC1757K	RAA
☐ Luscombe 8E Silvaire				RA
☐ Stampe & Vertongen S.V.4C	N419W	219	F-BFZS, N62447	RAA
☐ Taylorcraft BC-12D	N44022	9822	NC44022	RAA
☐ Travel Air 4000	N901	181	NC901	RA
☐ Travel Air 4000	N1592	196	NC1592	RA
☐ Travel Air 4000	N8192	894	NC8192	RAA
☐ Travel Air 4000	N8134	895	NC8134	RAA

SOUTH ISLAND

AEROVIEW MUSEUM (NZ30)

Address:	39 Morris Road, Fairton, Ashburton
Tel:	03-307-2376
Admission:	By prior permission only.
Location:	About 5 km west of the town.

This private museum also contains a number of vehicles including a 1957 Bedford Fire Engine. The Friendship which flew on National Airways Corporation services for over three decades was towed to the nearby Ashburton Aviation Museum in March 2008 to coincide with the airline's sixtieth anniversary tour of New Zealand airfields. The Air Force ordered thirty de Havilland Devons with the first arriving in the country 1948. The example in the collection was intended for the Lebanese Air Force but was diverted to New Zealand. The aircraft served as a radio navigational trainer and spent many years at Wigram. Before moving to Ashburton it was on show at the Wanaka Transport and Toy Museum. The early Harvard is being restored.

TYPE	REG/SER	CON. NO.	PI/NOTES	STATUS
☐ De Havilland D.H.104 Devon C.1	NZ1804	04304	(LR-M-109), NZ1804, INST214	RA
☐ Fokker F.27 Friendship 100	ZK-BXG	10189	PH-FDD – on loan to Ashburton AM.	–
☐ North American NA-66 Harvard II	NZ948	66-2761		RAC

AIR FORCE WORLD – ROYAL NEW ZEALAND AIR FORCE MUSEUM (NZ31)

Address:	Air Force World, Private Bag, Christchurch.
Tel:	03-343-9532
Fax:	03-343-9533
Email:	info@afw.co.nz
Admission:	Daily 1000-1700.
Location:	At RNZAF Wigram which is in the south western sububs of Christchurch on Route 74.

The first military aircraft to arrive in the country was a two seat Blériot XI presented to the country by the Imperial Air Fleet Committee. During World War I two commercial organisations trained pilots for the Royal Flying Corps and the Royal Naval Air Service. At the end of hostilities a small number of aircraft were donated to the country by Britain. The Air Force Reserve was formed in 1922 and the Permanent Air Force was established the following year. In the inter-war period development was limited until the country saw the need for a larger modernised force as tension increased in Europe. Newer types arrived and large numbers of pilots were trained under the British Commonwealth Air Training Plan. During the conflict New Zealand personnel served with distinction in many theatres. The service was cut back at the end of hostilities and until recently maintained an effective force for the defence of the country. Flying started at Sockburn (re-named Wigram in 1923) in 1917 and the base was in operational use until 1993. The museum was set up in 1979 and opened to the public in 1987. A new entrance hall was added to the front of one of the hangars. Four aircraft including a replica of the Blériot XI-2 and a Tiger Moth are displayed here. Before reaching the main display hangar the visitor passes through a superb exhibition tracing the history of the Air Force. Aircraft on view in the main hall include a Dakota in VIP configuration, the only surviving Avro 626 which is part of the R.N.Z.A.F. Historic Flight, and a Douglas Dauntless displayed in the condition it was found on Espiritu Santu Island in the Pacific over forty years after crashing. The Auster Antartic was delivered to New Zealand in 1956 and flew in the South Polar region for seven years. The aircraft crashed in 1966 and has been rebuilt to its Antartic configuration. New Zealand was a major operator of the rugged Bristol 170 and the Air Force ordered a dozen for transport duties. Many others flew in a civilian role. Two more hangars are now in use. One is a workshop and under a painstaking rebuild is a Curtiss P-40F which is being modified to the P-40E model which was flown by the Air Force. The Airspeed Consul which is on long term loan from the Canada Aviation Museum will be restored to represent one of the almost three hundred Oxfords flown by the service from between 1938 and 1954. The New Zealand Air Force acquired ten former Royal Air Force Andovers in the mid-1970s and they flew on UN duties in the Middle East and Africa as well as disaster work in the Pacific. The second hangar houses many restored aircraft for which there is no room in the main hall. A storage site a short distance away is home to more aircraft, components and engines. The remains of a number of Vickers Vildbeeste and Vincent airframes are here. These were obtained from M.O.T.A.T. in Auckland in return for rebuilding a Mosquito wing. Work will soon start on a composite rebuild of one of these Vickers biplanes. This excellent collection presents a comprehensive picture of military aviation in the country over the last ninety years.

TYPE	REG/SER	CON. NO.	PI/NOTES	STATUS
☐ Airspeed AS.10 Oxford II	NZ1229	2638	P6844	RAC
☐ Airspeed AS.65 Consul (A.S.10 Oxford I)	G-AIKR	4338	PK286 – On loan from Canada AM, ON.	RAC
☐ Auster C.4 Antarctic (T.7)	NZ1707		WE563	PV
☐ Avro 626	NZ203	811	NZ203, INST90, ZK-APC – RNZAF Historic Flight aircraft.	PV
☐ Avro 652A Anson I	'NZ406'		LT376, NZ415 – composite with parts of DG695, NZ410, INST152, ZK-BCL; NZ422, LT447 and wings from VL352.	PVX
☐ Avro 748 Andover C.1	NZ7621	7	XS600	PV

☐ Bell 205 Iroquois (UH-1H)	NZ3800	12213	69-15923	PV
☐ Blériot XI-2 (R)				PV
☐ Bristol 170 Freighter 31E (31M)	NZ5903	12834	G-18-100, G-AINT	RA
☐ British Aircraft Corporation 167 Strikemaster 88	NZ6373	343	G-27-242	PV
☐ Cessna 337M Super Skymaster (O-2A)	69-7639	337M0437		PV
☐ Consolidated 28-5A Catalina (PBY-5A) (OA-10A)	'NZ7624'	CV 592	(Bu68045), 44-34081, VR-HDH, VH-SBV – parts from c/n 21986 9757 (Canada), CF-SAT, C-FSAT.	PVCX
☐ Curtiss 87-B3 Warhawk (P-40F)	'NZ3024'		To be rebuilt as a P-40E. May be 41-14205	PVC
☐ De Havilland D.H.82A Tiger Moth	'NZ825'	DHNZ.161	NZ1481, INST150	PVX
☐ De Havilland D.H.98 Mosquito FB.VI	NZ2355		TE863 – parts only.	RA
☐ De Havilland D.H.98 Mosquito FB.VI	ZK-BCU	983103	RF597, NZ2383	RAD
☐ De Havilland D.H.100 Vampire FB.5	NZ5757		WA311, NZ5757, INST193	PV
☐ De Havilland D.H.100 Vampire FB.5	NZ5765		WA314, NZ5765, INST201 – on loan to NZ Fighter Pilot's Mus.	–
☐ De Havilland D.H.100 Vampire FB.52	NZ5735	V.0575	NZ5735, INST186	RA
☐ De Havilland D.H.104 Devon C.1	NZ1803	04294		PV
☐ De Havilland D.H.104 Devon C.1	NZ1827	04425		RA
☐ De Havilland D.H.115 Vampire T.11	NZ5710	15691	XH317, NZ5710, INST205	PV
☐ De Havilland D.H.115 Vampire T.11	NZ5711	15761	XH366, NZ5711, INST206	RA
☐ De Havilland D.H.115 Vampire T.55	NZ5701	15009	Wings and tail booms only.	RAD
☐ De Havilland D.H.115 Vampire T.55	NZ5704	15026	NZ5704, INST187	PV
☐ De Havilland D.H.C.2 Beaver	'NZ6001'	1084	VH-AAL, ZK-CMW	PVX
☐ Douglas A-4L Skyhawk (A4D-2N) (A-4C)	'NZ6207'	12841	Bu149516, N402FS	PVX
☐ Douglas DC-3A-456 Skytrain (C-47A) (Dakota III)	NZ3503	9420	42-23558 – front fuselage only.	PV
☐ Douglas DC-3A-467 Skytrain (C-47B) (Dakota IV)	NZ3551	16963/34223	45-0960	PV
☐ Douglas SBD-4 Dauntless	NZ5037	1858	Bu06953	PVD
☐ English Electric EA.1 Canberra B(I).8	WT346	EEP71506	8197M	RA
☐ Government Aircraft Factory Canberra Mk.20 [English Electric EA.1]	A84-240	40		PV
☐ Grumman G-40 Avenger (TBF-1C)	'NZ2521'	5219	Bu24336, NZ2504, INST182, NZ2504	PVX
☐ Grumman G-40 Avenger (TBF-1C)	NZ2505	5220	Bu24377 – on loan to Gisborne APS.	–
☐ Kaman K-20 Seasprite (SH-2F)	NZ3442	236	Bu162585	PVC
☐ Lockheed 414-56-03 Hudson III	NZ2013	414-3826	V9241 – fuselage only.	PV
☐ New Zealand Aerospace CT/4B Airtrainer	NZ1948	CT4-096		PV
☐ North American NA-88 Texan (AT-6C) (Harvard IIA)	NZ1050	88-13907	41-33766, EX793, NZ1050, INST207	PV
☐ North American NA-88 Texan (AT-6D) (Harvard III)	'NZ948'	88-16326	42-84545, EZ331, NZ1087, INST213	PVX
☐ North American NA-122 Mustang (P-51D)	'NZ2410'	122-41367	44-74827, 72-1541, F-367 (Indonesia)	PVX
☐ Pearse Monoplane (R)				PV
☐ Schleicher Ka-4 Rhönlerche II	ZK-GBQ	392/58		RA
☐ Sopwith Pup (R)	'N6160'	EMK/001	G-BIAT	PVCX
☐ Supermarine 361 Spitfire LF.XVIe	TE288	CBAF-11414	TE288, 7287M, 'AR251'	PV
☐ Vickers 266 Vincent	NZ355		K6351	RAD
☐ Vickers 266 Vincent	NZ357		K6353	RAD
☐ Vickers 277 Vildebeest III	NZ102		Fuselage only.	PVD
☐ Vickers 277 Vildebeest III	NZ105			RAD
☐ Vickers 286 Vildebeest IV				RAD
☐ Vickers 286 Vildebeest IV	NZ124		K8080	RAD
☐ Westland Wasp HAS.1	NZ3906	F9570	XS543	RA
☐ Wright Flyer (R)				RA

ARGOSY TRUST (NZ32)

Address:	P.O. Box 38, Renwick, Marlborough.
Tel:	03-572-9723
Fax:	03-572-9722
Email:	info@argosy.org.nz
Admission:	By prior permission only.
Location:	At Woodbourne Airfield which is about 10 km west of Blenheim on Route 6.

British European Airways bought six Argosy 200s for freight services in 1965/6 and flew them until 1970 when the five survivors were sold to Transair in Canada. Safe Air acquired two in 1973/4 and for many years they were a familiar sight around New Zealand. The Argosy Trust was formed in 1991 to preserve an example of the type and to raise funds for the construction of a museum. The complete aircraft has been restored and is now displayed outside a café on the road which passes Woodbourne Air Force Base. The fuselage of the other is in store.

TYPE	REG/SER	CON. NO.	PI/NOTES	STATUS
☐ Armstrong Whitworth A.W.650 Argosy 222	ZK-SAF	6801	G-ASXM, CF-TAG, EI-AVJ, CF-TAG – fuselage only.	RA
☐ Armstrong Whitworth A.W.650 Argosy 222	ZK-SAE	6802	G-ASXN, CF-TAJ	PV

ASHBURTON AVIATION MUSEUM (NZ33)

Address:	No 3 RD, Ashburton.
Tel:	03-302-6820
Fax:	03-308-3082
Email:	neil.stuckey@xtra.co.nz
Admission:	Saturday 0900-1600; First Sunday in month 1330-1630.
Location:	At Ashburton Airfield which is about 5 km east of the town.

From 1942 to 1944 Ashburton was home to No. 2 Elementary Flying Training School which flew Tiger Moths. The large grass field is now the airport for this rural town. In 1978 a Harvard was purchased from the Air Force and plans were put forward to house it in a display building. The idea of a museum grew out of this and opened on April 6th 1991 in a hangar built by society members. The adjoining hangar has recently been bought and this will serve as a workshop. Around the edges of the exhibition hall are a number of interesting displays. The history of the field in World War II is highlighted and a large model of the site during this period has been built. Photographs and memorabilia depicting both local and national events can also be seen. A prized exhibit is a 'Space Ball' from the Soviet Probe Cosmos 482, which broke up over South Island on April 2nd 1972. A collection of engines and airframe components can also be seen. The Devon was recovered from a Canterbury farm in 1990 and has only seventeen flying hours in its log book; the airframe was stored during most of its military life. The Porterfield 35 is the only one of its type in the country. Several years ago it was restored in its impressment colours. The museum plans to repaint the aircraft in its original civil scheme. Only twenty one Yeoman Cropmasters were built in Australia and six were exported to New Zealand. The YA-1 on show is the only complete example surviving. (a damaged airframe is in store with the Australian National Aviation Museum at Moorabbin in Victoria). Gliding is a popular sport in the country and a number of classic designs are on show. The Hughes 269 was used for agricultural work and for rounding up deer. The plan is to restore it in the latter configuration. A range of homebuilt types is being acquired. Only a few Mignet HM-14s were constructed in New Zealand one was found locally. All the museum exhibits are under cover, (except the loaned F.27) and this policy will continue in order to keep them in excellent condition.

TYPE	REG/SER	CON. NO.	PI/NOTES	STATUS
☐ Auster J/5C (AOP.5)	ZK-AZF	1272	TJ187, G-ALKI	PV
☐ Bede BD-5B			Incomplete.	PV
☐ Bensen B-8 Gyroglider			On loan from NZ Helicopter HM.	PV
☐ De Havilland D.H.82A Tiger Moth	ZK-CDU	3581	L6926, G-ALAD, ZK-BAW	PV
☐ De Havilland D.H.100 Vampire FB.5	NZ5769		WA306, NZ5769, INST197	PVC
☐ De Havilland D.H.104 Devon C.1	NZ1829	04427		PV
☐ De Havilland D.H.115 Vampire T.11	NZ5707	15579	XH265 – on loan from Burns Collection.	PV
☐ Elliott AP.5 EoN Olympia 2	ZK-GAT	3059/SCGC/1	On loan from Burns Collection.	PV
☐ English Electric EA.1 Canberra B.2	WH734	EEP.71218 (?)	Front fuselage only.	PV
☐ Fokker F.27 Friendship 100	ZK-BXG	10189	PH-FDD – on loan from Aeroview Museum.	PV
☐ Hawker-Siddeley P.1127 Harrier GR.3	XZ129	41H/712188	XZ129, A2602	PV
☐ Hughes 269C	ZK-HHY	44-0293	On loan from NZ Helicopter HM.	PV
☐ Jacobs Weihe (D.F.S. 108-68)	ZK-GAE	535	BGA.433, G-ALKG – in Christchurch.	RAC
☐ Light Miniature LM-1	ZK-FWB	627-02-A/ MAANZ/442	(ZK-SVU)	PV
☐ Mignet HM-14 Pou-du-Ciel (R)	'ZM-AAM'			PVX
☐ North American NA-88 Texan (AT-6C) (Harvard IIA)	NZ1012	88-9269	41-33163, EX190	PV
☐ Porterfield 35W	NZ598	316	ZK-AFT, NZ581, ZK-AHJ, NZ598, ZK-APJ	PVA
☐ Scheibe Bergfalke II/55	ZK-GAZ	353		PVC
☐ Slingsby T.31B Tandem Tutor	ZK-GAL	MAC/1		PVC
☐ Transavia PL-12U Airtruk	ZK-DMZ	G356	On loan.	PV
☐ Yeoman YA-1 Cropmaster 250R Series 2	ZK-CPW	119	VH-TPM – on loan.	PV

BRODIE COLLECTION (NZ34)

Address:	1 Brodie Road, RD 26, Rangitata Island.
Tel:	03-693-8675
Admission:	By prior permission only.
Location:	About 20 km north east of Temuka.

Four de Havilland types are in this collection with the New Zealand built Tiger Moth under restoration to flying condition. The three Hornet Moths were all delivered new to Australia in the late 1930s. Two are of the early pointed wing tip version – the D.H.87A. All were withdrawn from use in the 1960s and stored.

TYPE	REG/SER	CON. NO.	PI/NOTES	STATUS
☐ De Havilland D.H.82A Tiger Moth	ZK-ALX	DHNZ.70	NZ820	RA
☐ De Havilland D.H.87A Hornet Moth	ZK-APR	8036	VH-UUD	RA
☐ De Havilland D.H.87A Hornet Moth	ZK-AUR	8041	VH-UUW	RA
☐ De Havilland D.H.87B Hornet Moth	ZK-AZK	8139	VH-UYX	RA

Two Simmonds Spartan biplanes exist in New Zealand and this example is at the Geraldine Vintage Car and Machinery Museum.

Above: The enthusiasts at the Gore Air Force Museum own this Cessna Ag-Wagon

Right: Mounted outside the J.K. McCarthy Museum in Goroka is this restored Bell P-39N Airacobra. (J.K. McCarthy Museum)

BURNS COLLECTION (NZ35)

Address:	Irvine Road, Dunsandel.
Tel:	03-325-4255
Admission:	By prior permission only.
Location:	About 1 km east of the town which is about 35 km south west of Christchurch on Route 1.

Philip Burns has acquired a number of airframes over recent years. He is a member of the Ashburton Aviation Museum and part of his collection is on show in their display hangars. The Olympia glider was developed from the successful Hans Jacobs designed Meise by Elliotts of Newbury in England in the late 1940s. The example on show at Ashburton was built in New Zealand using a kit supplied by Elliotts. The R.N.Z.A.F. bought six Vampire T.55s in 1952 and these were later joined by five T.11s originally intended for the R.A.F.

TYPE	REG/SER	CON. NO.	PI/NOTES	STATUS
☐ Airspeed AS.10 Oxford I	NZ2144	3765	NM630 – nose and other parts.	RA
☐ De Havilland D.H.115 Vampire T.11	NZ5707	15579	XH265 – on loan to Ashburton AM.	–
☐ De Havilland D.H.115 Vampire T.55	NZ5702	15010	Front fuselage only.	RAD
☐ De Havilland D.H.115 Vampire T.55	NZ5703	15021	Front fuselage only.	RAD
☐ Elliott AP.5 EoN Olympia 2	ZK-GAT	3059/SCGC/1	On loan to Ashburton AM.	–
☐ Percival P.44 Proctor 5	ZK-AQK	Ae.79		RA
☐ Percival P.44 Proctor 5	ZK-APH	Ae.126		RAD

CROYDON AVIATION HERITAGE TRUST (NZ36)

Address:	R.D.6, Gore.
Tel:	03-208-9755
Fax:	03-208-4288
Email:	croydonaircraft@esi.co.nz
Admission:	Daily 0900-1700.
Location:	At Mandeville Airfield which is about 15 km north west of Gore on Route 94.

Colin Smith set up the Croydon Aircraft Company in the mid-1980s. Over the last decade the firm has come well known for its authentic restorations of vintage aircraft, especially de Havilland types. The hangars and workshops have been steadily extended and at the present time many airframes are stored off site waiting their turn in the rebuilding queue. A restaurant and clubhouse has opened in the late 1990s and regular functions are held here. The Trust has been formed to raise funds for a large museum hall and this was completed in 2006. Several private owners now base their aircraft at Mandeville and some of those under rebuild will stay. The hangars and workshops contain one of the most comprehensive range of de Havilland types anywhere in the world. Two metal fuselage Moths are in residence. The American built one arrived in the United Kingdom in 1987 and was badly damaged by fire following a force landing two years later. The first production Puss Moth is being rebuilt. This aircraft was shipped to Australia in 1930 and without authorisation was flown across the Tasman Sea to New Zealand in 1934. One of the Fox Moths and the Dragonfly have recently been bought from Brian Woodford in England. The Leopard Moth is nearing the end of its rebuild. A replica of the famous Comet racer is well advanced and hopefully this will be airworthy in the not too distant future. One Dragon Rapide one other retrieved in 1995 from a mountain near Arrowtown where it had remained since crashing in 1965, is in store. Very few Dragonfly biplanes have survived and the example in the collection has seen service in the United Kingdom, Australia and the United States. Three Moth Minors are being rebuilt and a recent arrival is one of a batch of Canadian built Chipmunks bought in India. Herbert Pither built a Blériot style monoplane and there are unsubstantiated claims that he flew at Oreti Beach on July 5th 1910. A replica of his design was built and flew at Mandeville in February 2003. Passenger flights are available in a number of types.

TYPE	REG/SER	CON. NO.	PI/NOTES	STATUS
☐ Auster J/5B Autocar	ZK-AYN	2943		PV
☐ Cessna U206A Super Skywagon	ZK-DIB	U2060598	N4898F	PV
☐ De Havilland D.H.60GM Moth	G-AANF	49	NC237K, N237K, N298M	RAD
☐ De Havilland D.H.60M Moth	ZK-ACE	1561	ZK-ACE, NZ509	PVC
☐ De Havilland D.H.80A Puss Moth	ZK-AEV	2125	G-ABHC, 2125 (New Zealand), ZK-AEV, NZ590	RA
☐ De Havilland D.H.80A Puss Moth	ZK-ACX	2204	ZK-ACX, NZ593, NZ567, ZK-AJN	PVC
☐ De Havilland D.H.82A Tiger Moth	ZK-ALK	3795	ZK-AGZ, NZ704	PVA
☐ De Havilland D.H.82A Tiger Moth	ZK-AYY	82521	N9494, G-AMMK	RA
☐ De Havilland D.H.82A Tiger Moth	ZK-ARZ	82899	R4989, NZ888	PVA
☐ De Havilland D.H.82A Tiger Moth	ZK-BFH	83343	T7035, G-ANDB	PVA
☐ De Havilland D.H.82A Tiger Moth	ZK-AJC	83463	T5754, NZ655	RA
☐ De Havilland D.H.82A Tiger Moth	ZK-BAH	83589	T5853, ZK-BAH, G-ALZA	PVA
☐ De Havilland D.H.82A Tiger Moth	ZK-AZO	84013	T7611, G-ALZI	RA
☐ De Havilland D.H.82A Tiger Moth	ZK-BDH	DHA.320	A17-301, VH-BDW	RA
☐ De Havilland D.H.82A Tiger Moth	ZK-AVK	DHA.425	A17-384, VH-AXZ	RA
☐ De Havilland D.H.82A Tiger Moth	ZK-ASV	DHNZ.36	NZ786	RAA
☐ De Havilland D.H.82A Tiger Moth	ZK-AIB	DHNZ.75	NZ825	PVC
☐ De Havilland D.H.82A Tiger Moth	ZK-BJR	DHNZ.105	NZ1425	RAD
☐ De Havilland D.H.82A Tiger Moth	NZ1427	DHNZ.107		RA
☐ De Havilland D.H.82A Tiger Moth	ZK-BRC	DHNZ.115	NZ1435	PVA

TYPE	REG/SER	CON. NO.	PI/NOTES	STATUS
☐ De Havilland D.H.82A Tiger Moth	ZK-ARK	DHNZ.140	NZ1460	RA
☐ De Havilland D.H.83 Fox Moth	ZK-ADI	4097	NZ566, ZK-ADI, N83DH	PVC
☐ De Havilland D.H.83C Fox Moth	ZK-AQB	FM.49		PVC
☐ De Havilland D.H.85 Leopard Moth	ZK-ARG	7007	CH-366, HB-OTA, G-ATFU	PVC
☐ De Havilland D.H.87B Hornet Moth	ZK-AHR	8038	HB-OBE, F-AQBY, G-ADRH	PVC
☐ De Havilland D.H.88 Comet (R)				RA
☐ De Havilland D.H.89B Dragon Rapide (Dominie I)	ZK-AKS	6647	HG648, NZ523	RAD
☐ De Havilland D.H.89B Dragon Rapide (Dominie I)	ZK-AKY	6653	HG654, NZ525	PVA
☐ De Havilland D.H.90 Dragonfly	ZK-AYR	7508	G-AEDT, (VH-ABM), G-AEDT, VH-AAD, G-AEDT, N2034, G-AEDT	PVA
☐ De Havilland D.H.94 Moth Minor	ZK-AJN	94031	G-AFPR, X5122, G-AFPR	PVC
☐ De Havilland D.H.94 Moth Minor	ZK-AJX	94071	NZ592	PVC
☐ De Havilland D.H.94 Moth Minor	ZK-AJR	94084	(G-AFUU), A21-20, VH-AGA	RA
☐ De Havilland D.H.C.1 Chipmunk 1A-2	ZK-CVR	39	VT-CVR	PVC
☐ Hindustan HAOP-27 Krishnak 2				RA
☐ Percival P.28B Proctor I	ZK-DPP	K.305	P6271, G-AHTV, VH-BCX	RAC
☐ Pither Monoplane (R)				PVA
☐ Taylorcraft BC-12D	ZK-BSW	7512	NC43853, N43853	PVA

FERRYMEAD AERONAUTICAL SOCIETY (NZ37)

Address:	P.O. Box 25-044, Victoria Street, Christchurch.
Tel:	03-384-1970
Email:	info@ferrymead.org.nz
Admission:	Daily 1000-1630.
Location:	About 10 km east of the city centre off Ferry Road.

The large Ferrymead Historic Park has many buildings on show depicting life from earlier days. A tram runs from the main entrance around the town. Working railway engines, fire engines, cars and commercial vehicles are maintained by associated societies. The Ferrymead Aeronautical Society was formed in 1972 and has a large workshop in the southern part of the park. A hangar was built and other exhibition areas are planned. The C-47 was donated to the city of Christchurch by the U.S. Navy in 1969. A base is still maintained at the local airport for Antarctic projects and the C-47 served in this role for many years. Components from crop dusting aircraft are being collected and the society plans to construct a hall tracing the important story of agricultural flying in the country. Several types specifically designed for this work have been collected.

TYPE	REG/SER	CON. NO.	PI/NOTES	STATUS
☐ Bristol 170 Freighter 31 (21)	ZK-AYG	12826	G-AINK, G-18-92, G-AINK, WH575 – front fuselage only.	PV
☐ Bristol 170 Freighter 31E (31M)	ZK-CRK	13159	G-18-151, S4406 (Pakistan) – front fuselage only.	PV
☐ Callair B-1	ZK-CRC	10006		RAD
☐ Cessna A188 Agwagon	ZK-CQY	A1880167	N9717V – fuselage frame only.	RA
☐ De Havilland D.H.98 Mosquito FB.VI	NZ2328		TE758 – composite with parts of HR339, NZ2382	PVC
☐ De Havilland D.H.100 Vampire FB.5	NZ5753		WA379 – wings only.	RA
☐ De Havilland D.H.100 Vampire FB.5	NZ5758	V.0460	VZ838, NZ5758, INST196 – composite with parts of NZ5775.	PV
☐ Douglas DC-3A-456 Skytrain (C-47A) (R4D-5) (LC-47H)	Bu17221	13319	42-93410	PV
☐ Hiller UH12E	ZK-HKU	3067	N167HA	PV
☐ Hughes 369				PV
☐ Lockheed 414-56-03 Hudson III	NZ2035	414-3858	AE503	PV
☐ Lockheed 414-56-03 Hudson IIIA (A-29A)	NZ2084	414-6725	41-37236, (FH435)	PV
☐ North American NA-88 Texan (AT-6D) (Harvard III)	NZ1058	88-14491	41-33838, EX865	PV
☐ Piper PA-23-150 Apache	ZK-BLO	23-446	Fuselage only	PVD
☐ Piper PA-23-160 Apache	ZK-CHU	23-1529	N4052P	PVD
☐ Piper PA-25-235 Pawnee	ZK-BZK	25-2337		PV
☐ Short S.25 Sunderland MR.V	NZ4112		VB881 – sections only	PVD
☐ Transavia PL-12 Airtruk	ZK-DMX	G352		PVD
☐ Vickers 807 Viscount	ZK-BRF	283		PV
☐ Westland-Sikorsky WS-58 Wessex 60 Series 1	'ZK-IDL'	WA.740	G-AZBY, 5N-ALR, G-AZBY, G-17-5, G-AZBY	PVX

FOUNDERS PARK (NZ38)

Address:	87 Atawhai Drive, Nelson.
Tel:	03-548-2649
Email:	elspeth.mceachan@ncc.gov.nz
Admission:	Daily 1000-1630.
Location:	In the north eastern suburbs of the city off Route 6.

The park contains many historic buildings which have been moved to the site as well as a number of replicas. Displays trace the development of cultural and social history over the years. Examples of vintage vehicles, trains and agricultural machinery are also on view. The Bristol Freighter was originally delivered to the Pakistan Air Force in 1953 and bought by the Woodbourne based Straits Air Freighter Express in 1966. The Bell helicopter served in the agricultural role in the region for several years.

TYPE	REG/SER	CON. NO.	PI/NOTES	STATUS
☐ Bell 47G-2A	ZK-HCB	2673	N8477E, ZK-HAX, N8477E	PV
☐ Bristol 170 Freighter 31E (31M)	ZK-CLU	13156	G-18-148, S4403 (Pakistan) – rebuilt with parts of c/n 13170 G-18-162, S4421 (Pakistan) ZK-CRM.	PV

GERALDINE VINTAGE CAR AND MACHINERY MUSEUM (NZ39)

Address:	Talbot Street, Geraldine.
Tel:	03-693-8700
Fax:	03-693-1006
Email:	geraldinevintage@extra.co.nz
Admission:	October-June daily 1000-1200 1330-1600; July-November Saturday-Sunday 1000-1200 1330-1600.
Location:	In the southern part of the town on Route 79 and about 120 km south west of Christchurch.

The South Canterbury Vintage Club was formed in May 1967 and two years later it acquired premises in the country town of Geraldine. J.L. Morrison purchased a saw mill and coal yard where he constructed a building to house his collection of vintage cars. He donated the remainder of the site to the club which in 1971 changed its name to the Geraldine Vintage Machinery Club. The society opened its first premises in 1974. Unfortunately Mr. Morrison's building burned down in 1979. With the help of the town, the club constructed the hall which now serves as the car museum. The site includes a new tractor shed, opened in 1995, and a workshop. On show is a superb collection of over thirty cars dating from 1905, ninety tractors, including the oldest working one in the country, and farm equipment. The only aircraft displayed is a 1929 Simmonds Spartan biplane built at Weston near Southampton in England. Five were imported into the country and the one in the museum is the only complete surviving example. In the Christchurch area another example is being rebuilt to fly.

TYPE	REG/SER	CON. NO.	PI/NOTES	STATUS
☐ Simmonds Spartan	ZK-ABZ	43		PV

GORE AIR FORCE MUSEUM (NZ40)

Address:	43 Maitland Street, East Gore.
Tel:	03-208-5354
Fax:	03-208-5354
Admission:	Most days by prior permission.
Location:	In the northern suburbs of the town north of Route 1.

Roy Richardson has been acquiring aviation memorabilia for many years. He has constructed an exhibition building and a clubhouse at the rear of his home. A museum group has been formed; this holds regular meetings and members carry out rebuilding work. The Tiger Moth, painted in the famous yellow military training colours, often taxies up and down the field adjacent to the museum. The Evans VP-2 was acquired in the late 1990s from a local constructor. This low wing two seater is also able to taxy around. On show in the building are Dakota, Harvard, Mosquito and Piper Cub components plus an interesting collection of memorabilia, photographs, documents and uniforms. The history of flying in the area is also portrayed.

TYPE	REG/SER	CON. NO.	PI/NOTES	STATUS
☐ Cessna A188 Agwagon	ZK-CQZ	1880171	(N9721V)	PV
☐ De Havilland D.H.82A Tiger Moth	ZK-BLM	DHNZ.164	NZ1484	PV
☐ Evans VP-2	ZK-EEN	AACA/314		PV
☐ Hughes 269B				PV

GORE HISTORICAL MUSEUM (NZ41)

Address:	Hokonui Drive, P.O. Box 305, Gore.
Tel:	03-208-7032
Email:	heritage@goredc.govt.nz
Admission:	Monday-Friday 0930-1630; Saturday-Sunday 0930-1530 (Opens at 1300 at weekends in winter)
Location:	In the town.

This local history museum opened in 1999 in the Honokui Heritage Centre. The building also houses the Honokui Moonshine Museum. Prohibition was introduced in the area in 1902 and for over half a century there was a flourishing illegal industry in the countryside around the town. The only aircraft in the collection is the Ladybird. This original design flew in the early 1930s and crashed in 1933. The remains were stored in the area for many years. A few small parts are owned by the Southland Museum in Invercargill.

TYPE	REG/SER	CON. NO.	PI/NOTES	STATUS
☐ Cross Ladybird				PVD

NEW ZEALAND FIGHTER PILOTS MUSEUM/ ALPINE FIGHTER COLLECTION (NZ42)

Address:	P.O. Box 218, Wanaka Airport, Wanaka, New Zealand.
Tel:	03-443-7010
Fax:	03-443-7011
Email:	ibrodie@nzfpm.co.nz
Admission:	Daily 0930-1600 (closes at 1800 December 27-January 27).
Location:	About 8 km east of the town on Route 6.

The Alpine Fighter Collection began in 1984 when a Mustang was bought in the U.S.A. This aircraft was sold in 1986 in order to assist with the purchase of the Spitfire XVI. The collection grew steadily and the museum opened at Easter 1993. Displays in the building honour the contribution of New Zealanders during the wars in which their fighter aircraft have served. Seven hundred and eighty fighter pilots from the country lost their lives in the two World Wars and all are named in the Roll of Honour. The ninety five aces, those who shot down more than five enemy aircraft in air to air combat, are portrayed around the walls of the exhibition hangar. The replica S.E.5A hangs in the entrance hall. Close by is a large hangar where the visitor can view the rest of the collection from an upstairs balcony. The founder of the Alpine Fighter Collection, Sir Tim Wallis, suffered major injuries when he crashed a Spitfire on January 2nd 1996 but fortunately he recovered. Five Polikarpov I-16s arrived from Russia along with three I-153 biplanes. Certification was carried out at Wanaka near Christchurch. The collection has been run down over the last few years with aircraft sold to collectors and museums around the world. Every two years an airshow is held at the airfield, which is surrounded by a spectacular backdrop of mountains.

TYPE	REG/SER	CON. NO.	PI/NOTES	STATUS
☐ De Havilland D.H.82A Tiger Moth	ZK-BRB	DHNZ.139	NZ1459, ZK-BRD	RAA
☐ De Havilland D.H.100 Vampire FB.5	NZ5765		WA314, NZ5765, INST201 – on loan from Air Force World.	PV
☐ De Havilland D.H.C.1 Chipmunk 21	'WB568'	C1/0834	G-AMUH, ZK-MUH	RAAX
☐ Hawker Hurricane IIB	ZK-TPL		P3351	RAC
☐ North American NA-88 Texan (AT-6D) (Harvard III)	ZK-ENE	88-14672	41-33878, EX905, NZ1066	RAA
☐ Polikarpov I-153	ZK-JJB	6326	10	RA
☐ Polikarpov I-153	ZK-JKM	7027	'75'	RAA
☐ Polikarpov I-16 tip 24	ZK-JIO	2421234	4	RAA
☐ Polikarpov I-16 tip 24 (tip 18)	ZK-JIN	2421319	9	RAA
☐ Royal Aircraft Factory S.E.5A (R)	'F5459'			PVX

NEW ZEALAND HELICOPTER HERITAGE MUSEUM (NZ43)

Address:	80 Harpers Road, Eyreton, RD2 Kaiapoi.
Tel:	03-312-6334
Email:	Helicopterheritage@xtra.co.nz
Admission:	Not yet open
Location:	At a number of sites in the area.

The museum was formed in 1999 with the aim of collecting helicopters which have flown in the country. Construction of a permanent building started in 2006 but at the present time the aircraft are stored in around the Canterbury area. Photographs, documents, videos and items of memorabilia have also been acquired.

TYPE	REG/SER	CON. NO.	PI/NOTES	STATUS
☐ Aérospatiale AS.350B Ecureuil	ZK-HGV	2507		RA
☐ Bell 47G-3B-2A	ZK-HRD	6350		RA
☐ Bell 47G-3B-2A	ZK-HFU	6863		RA
☐ Bell 206A Jet Ranger	ZK-HVH	423	N1495W	RAC
☐ Bell 206B Jet Ranger	ZK-HUV	297	HI-155, N128GW	RAC
☐ Bensen B-8 Gyroglider			At Ashburton AM	–

☐ Hiller UH12E	ZK-HGN	HA3002R	N102HA	PV
☐ Hughes 269C	ZK-HHY	44-0293	At Ashburton AM.	–
☐ Hughes 269C	ZK-HEI	52-0141R		RA
☐ Hughes 269C Osage (TH-55A)		111-0029		RA
☐ Hughes 369HS	ZK-HLY	33-04595	N9134F	RA
☐ Robinson R-22 Alpha	ZK-IMG	0455	N8556Z, G-BPRZ, ZK-HLZ	RA

OMAKA AVIATION HERITAGE CENTRE (NZ44)

Address:	P.O. Box 641, Blenheim, Marlborough.
Tel:	03-579-1305
Fax:	03-579-1306
Email:	info@omaka.org.nz
Admission:	Daily 1000-1600.
Location:	At Omaka Airport which is about 3 km west of the town and south of Route 6.

Omaka airfield opened in 1921 and many well known aviators flew into and from the site. During World War II it was occupied by the Royal New Zealand Air Force. Owners of vintage aircraft in the Marlborough area met on March 27th 1997 to discuss a proposal to set up a museum at Omaka airfield. The decision to go ahead was taken and plans to construct display hangars were put forward. Founding members of the museum own several interesting aircraft. A biennial air show was initiated in 2001 to raise funds for the project. The first stage of the exhibition called 'Knights of the Sky' opened on December 9th 2006. This phase highlights the World War I period. There is a superb collection of memorabilia from famous pilots of the period including von Richthofen, Immelman, Udet Rickenbacker, Boelcke and Fonck. Dioramas containing full size replicas and some original aircraft are positioned in typical Western Front scenes. These machines have been obtained from many countries and Omaka now hosts one of the largest collections in the world of aircraft from the conflict. A rarity is the genuine Caproni Ca 22 obtained in Italy from the designer's children. The collection can mount a spectacular display of airworthy Fokker Triplane replicas painted in typical colours. Funds are being raised to exhibition halls to house the civil aircraft from the inter-war period and also World War II combat types. Several classic American types have arrived at the airfield and these include the Ryan STM-2, the Porterfield 35/70 and the Fairchild 24 C8C. When the next phases of building are complete a magnificent exhibition will be staged.

TYPE	REG/SER	CON. NO.	PI/NOTES	STATUS
☐ Aeronca 7AC Champion	ZK-KCO	7AC-5384	NC1817E, N1817E, CF-BMQ, C-FBMQ, VH-UMN	RAA
☐ Aeronca K	VH-ACK	K.162	NC18888	RA
☐ Albatros B II	'23.02'			PVX
☐ Andrews A-1	ZK-BLU	1		RAA
☐ Avro 504K	ZK-ACU		A202	RAC
☐ Blériot XI (R)				RA
☐ Boeing-Stearman E75 Kaydet (PT-13D) (N2S-5)	ZK-AZR	75-5236	42-17073, Bu61114, N1300V, C-GPDR	RAA
☐ Breguet 14A2 (R)				PV
☐ Bristol 14 F.2B Fighter				RAC
☐ Bristol 14 F.2B Fighter (R)	'J7624'		N624, ZK-JNU	RAAX
☐ Bristol 170 Freighter 31E	ZK-CPT	13126	(G-AMRR), (G-18-127), EC-WHI, EC-AHI	PV
☐ Caproni Ca.22				PV
☐ Culver V Satellite	N8442B	V-98	NC8442B	RA
☐ Curtiss 75A Hawk	CU-554	13659	In Finnish markings.	RAC
☐ Curtiss 87-A4 Warhawk (P-40E) (Kittyhawk IA)				RAC
☐ Curtiss 87-B3 Warhawk (P-40K) (Kittyhawk III)	A29-183	21562	42-10178	RAC
☐ Curtiss 49 (F8C) (R)				RA
☐ De Havilland D.H.2 (R)	ZK-JOJ/'7855'	100	N5496	PVA
☐ De Havilland D.H.5 (R)	ZK-JOQ/'A9242'	A9507	N950JS	PVA
☐ De Havilland D.H.82A Tiger Moth	ZK-AZQ	3985	N6712, G-AMMV	RA
☐ De Havilland D.H.82A Tiger Moth	ZK-AJH	82887	R4977, NZ885	RA
☐ De Havilland D.H.82A Tiger Moth	ZK-BER	DHA.844	(DX801), A17-712, VH-BEX	RA
☐ De Havilland D.H.82A Tiger Moth	ZK-BMY	DHNZ.101	NZ1421	RA
☐ De Havilland DH-4M	'AS63786'	652	NC489	RA
☐ Etrich Taube D2 (R)	D-ETRI	1913		RAA
☐ Fairchild 24 C8C	N18617	2605	NC18617	RA
☐ Fairchild 24W41A Forwarder (C-61) (UC-61) (Argus II)	VH-EMP	W41A-837	43-14873, HB600, G-AJSG, VH-DDG, VH-EMF	RAC
☐ Fleet 16B Finch II	ZK-AGC	668	NC128H, N128H	RAA
☐ Fokker D IV (R)	N4200S	CS008		PVA
☐ Fokker Dr I (R)				RAX
☐ Fokker Dr I (R)	ZK-FOC	112		PVA
☐ Fokker Dr I (R)	ZK-JOC	143	N4203K	RAA
☐ Fokker Dr I (R)	ZK-JOG	1823	N91065	RAA
☐ Fokker Dr I (R)	ZK-JOK	2009	N112DR	RAA
☐ Fokker Dr I (R)	ZK-FOK	AACA/266/2		RAA
☐ Fokker Dr I (R)	ZK-JOB	TCS-1	N240TS	RAA
☐ Fokker E III (R)	'105/15'			PVX
☐ Halberstadt D IV (R)	ZK-JOW	S-11	N1388J	RAA
☐ Hawker Hurricane I (FSM)	'P3854'			PVX
☐ Helio H-250 Super Courier	ZK-TCE	2503	N5446E, T-110 (Bophutaswana), ZS-ELJ	RA

TYPE	REG/SER	CON. NO.	PI/NOTES	STATUS
☐ Junkers Ju 87B (FSM)	'TG+M'			RAX
☐ Let C-11 [Yakovlev Yak-11]		172212		RA
☐ Lincoln Sport	ZK-BMV	1		RA
☐ Lockheed 12-A Electra Junior	NC14999	1252	NC18996, N18996, N200E, N4105B – contains parts from c/n 1217 NC17373, N17373, N12AT, N17373, N12AT	RAA
☐ Morane-Saulnier BB	'A301'			PV
☐ Nanchang CJ-6A	ZK-STP	1232011	76 (China)	RAA
☐ Nanchang CJ-6A		1832041	(China)	RAC
☐ Nanchang CJ-6A	ZK-WOK	2132042	46 (China)	RAA
☐ Nanchang CJ-6A	ZK-JQS	3832020	(China)	RAA
☐ Nanchang CJ-6A		4432032	(China)	RAC
☐ Nieuport 27 (R)	'B2812'			PVX
☐ North American NA-66 Harvard II	NZ906	66-2699	Front fuselage only.	RAD
☐ North American NA-88 Texan (AT-6C) (Harvard IIA)	NZ1041	88-13190	41-33717, EX744	RAC
☐ Parnell Penguin				RA
☐ Pfalz D III (R)	ZK-JPI	PT.16	G-ATIJ, EI-ARD, N905AC	PV
☐ Piper PA-18-95 Super Cub	ZK-BTP	18-6114		RAA
☐ Piper PA-18-95 Super Cub (L-18C)	ZK-KEZ	18-1628	51-15628, 51-15628 (France), OO-SPL, (G-BKEZ)	RAA
☐ Piper PA-18-150 Super Cub	ZK-BVJ	18-6180	N8475D	RAA
☐ Piper PA-22-150 Tri-Pacer	ZK-BLA	22-3347		RAA
☐ Porterfield 35/70	NC14480	137	NC14480, N14480	RA
☐ Royal Aircraft Factory B.E.2e	G-BVGR		A1325, 37 (Norway), 133 (Norway)	RAC
☐ Royal Aircraft Factory R.E.8 (R)	'A4397'			PVX
☐ Royal Aircraft Factory S.E.5A (R)	'D6864'			PVX
☐ Ryan STM-2				RA
☐ Siemens-Schuckert D IV (R)	N2160F/ 'D1031/18'	HW003		PVA
☐ Sopwith F.1 Camel (R)	'B3889'		N4463, ZK-JMU	RAAX
☐ Stinson HW-75				RA
☐ Stinson V-74 Vigilant (O-49) (L-1) (L-1C)	40-283			RAD
☐ Yakovlev Yak-3UA	N47FT	407106		RAA

PEARSE MEMORIAL (NZ45)

Address:	Upper Waitohi Road, Waitohi Valley.
Admission:	On permanent view.
Location:	About 8 km north west of Pleasant Point.

Richard Pearse carried out short hops in his first aircraft in 1901 and it is possible that on March 31st 1903 he flew for about fifty yards before landing in a gorse hedge. This date, based on circumstantial evidence from local people, is almost nine months before the Wright Brothers' flight. A replica of has aircraft has been mounted on a pylon close to the spot where he crash landed. The original aircraft was powered by an engine Pearse designed and constructed using lengths of steel irrigation pipes for the cylinders.

TYPE	REG/SER	CON. NO.	PI/NOTES	STATUS
☐ Pearse Monoplane (FSM)				PV

SMITH COLLECTION (NZ46)

Address:	Gardeners Valley, RD 1, Upper Moutere, Nelson.
Admission:	By prior permission only.
Location:	About 20 km west of Nelson off Route 60.

In the 1950s many military aircraft were withdrawn by the Air Force and the majority were scrapped. John Smith decided to try to save some from this fate. Large numbers of Mosquitos ended their days at Woodbourne and the example in the collection came from this airfield. Most of the type saw little service and spent most of their military life in store. Over the last forty years the airframe has slowly been restored and the engines are run occasionally. The Mosquito is now housed in a large building with the other aircraft in the collection stored around it. The P-40N saw service in the Pacific claiming 2 1/2 Japanese aircraft destroyed. The Mustang flew for only two hundred and sixty one hours and was used by No.1 Squadron R.N.Z.A.F. The Vampire 1 was delivered to New Zealand in the 1950s for instructional purposes. John is to be congratulated for possessing the foresight to collect the aircraft when most people at that time were not interested in preserving their aviation heritage.

TYPE	REG/SER	CON. NO.	PI/NOTES	STATUS
☐ Curtiss 87-A4 Warhawk (P-40E) (Kittyhawk IA)	NZ3043	18931	41-36410, EV156	RAD
☐ Curtiss 87V Warhawk (P-40N) (Kittyhawk IV)	NZ3220	30901	43-22962	RAD

TYPE	REG/SER	CON. NO.	PI/NOTES	STATUS
☐ De Havilland D.H.100 Vampire F.1	INST166		TG443 – possible identity – incomplete.	RA
☐ De Havilland D.H.100 Vampire FB.9			Incomplete.	RA
☐ De Havilland D.H.82A Tiger Moth	ZK-BQB	DHNZ.147	NZ1467	RA
☐ De Havilland D.H.98 Mosquito FB.VI	NZ2336		TE910	RAC
☐ Lockheed 414-56-03 Hudson IIIA (A-29A)	NZ2049	414-6465	41-36976, (FH175)	RA
☐ North American NA-66 Harvard II	NZ909	66-2702		RA
☐ North American NA-88 Texan (AT-6D) (Harvard III)	NZ1068	88-14674	41-33880, EX907, NZ1068, INST172	RA
☐ North American NA-124 Mustang (P-51D)	NZ2423	124-48266	45-11513	RA

SOUTH CANTERBURY AVIATION HERITAGE CENTRE (NZ47)

Address:	Old Control Tower, Richard Pearse Airport, Timaru.
Tel:	03-684-3641
Email:	jackaud@farmside.co.nz
Admission:	Tuesday-Friday 1000-1630, Saturday- Sunday 1330-1630.
Location:	In the southern part of the town centre.

Displays at this interesting museum trace local, natural and human history from Maori times. The settlement of the area by European immigrants is portrayed in detail. An exhibition tracing Timaru's whaling days can be seen. A replica of Richard Pearse's 1903 aircraft has been constructed.

TYPE	REG/SER	CON. NO.	PI/NOTES	STATUS
☐ Pearse Monoplane (R)				PV
☐ Stamer-Lippisch Z-12 Zögling (R)				RAC

SOUTHLAND MUSEUM AND GALLERY (NZ48)

Address:	108 Gala Street, Invercargill
Tel:	03-219-9069
Email:	office@southlandmuseum.co.nz
Admission:	Monday-Friday 0900-1700; Saturday-Sunday 1000-1700.
Location:	In the town.

This local history museum has in its collection a few small parts of the 1930s homebuilt the Cross Ladybird. The remainder of the aircraft, which crashed in 1933, is at the Gore Historical Museum.

TYPE	REG/SER	CON. NO.	PI/NOTES	STATUS
☐ Cross Ladybird			Small parts only	PVD

WANAKA TRANSPORT AND TOY MUSEUM (NZ49)

Address:	State Highway, RD.2, Wanaka.
Tel:	03-443-8765
Fax:	03-443-8750
Email:	wanaka-transport-museum@xtra.co.nz
Admission:	Daily 0830-1700
Location:	Close to Wanaka Airport which is about 8 km east of the town on Route 6.

This museum opened in 1996 and displays items collected over many years by Gerald Rhodes. On show in the main building are vintage and classic cam, motor cycles, mowers, stationary engines, boat engines and a large collection of models. The exhibition is well laid out and almost all the items exhibited are informatively labelled and details of their history are given. The only aircraft on show in this section is the Pou-du-Ciel built in Oamuru in 1936/7 by W.L. Notman. Powered by a Scott Squirrel engine the aircraft flew successfully for a short time. The Pou was exhibited at Ferrymead for a period before moving to Wanaka. The large outside park displays the Hudson and the Australian built Canberra as well as a large number of military and agricultural vehicles. The remainder of the aircraft are on view in a hangar which is dominated by the Lithuanian registered Antonov An-2. A comparative rarity is the only Percival Prentice in the country.

TYPE	REG/SER	CON. NO.	PI/NOTES	STATUS
☐ Antonov An-2T	LY-AKH	1G 160-37	(DOSAAF)	PV
☐ Auster J/1 Autocrat	ZK-BJL	2327	G-AJEC	PVA
☐ Beagle A.61 Terrier 2 (Auster Q T.7)	ZK-CDG	B.625	WE542, G-35-11	RA

TYPE	REG/SER	CON. NO.	PI/NOTES	STATUS
☐ De Havilland D.H.104 Devon C.1	ZK-RNG	04323	NZ1807	PVA
☐ Government Aircraft Factory Canberra Mk.20 [English Electric EA.1]	A84-207	7		PV
☐ Lockheed 18-56-23 Lodestar (C-60A)	VH-XUS	18-2388	42-55951, NC17615, N17615, XA-SAX, N56LH	PV
☐ Mignet HM-14 Pou-du-Ciel	ZM-AAC			PV
☐ Mikoyan-Gurevich MiG-21US	5141	01685141	In Polish markings.	PV
☐ Percival P.40 Prentice T.1	ZK-DJC	PAC/252	VS316, G-AOMF – registered with c/n 5820/1	PVA
☐ Replica Plans S.E.5A	ZK-TOM	AACA/352	ZK-EHV – also carries 'B4863'	PVA
☐ Team Minimax 103R	ZK-JDW	736		PV
☐ Victa Airtourer 115	ZK-CLF	121		RAA
☐ Victa Airtourer 115	ZK-COW	166		PV

YALDHURST MUSEUM OF TRANSPORT AND SCIENCE (NZ50)

Address:	School Road, RD.6, Yaldhurst.
Tel:	03-342-7914
Fax:	03-342-7916
Email:	enquiries@yaldhurstmuseum.co.nz
Admission:	July-May 1000-1700.
Location:	About 10 km west of Christchurch off Route 73.

Opened in 1968 this museum has on show vintage and racing cars, motor cycles, horse drawn carriages, fire engines and farm machinery. Military equipment and a replica newspaper Print shop can also be seen. The exhibits are displayed in a number of buildings on the pleasant site. The Tiger Moth is exhibited as a bare frame.

TYPE	REG/SER	CON. NO.	PI/NOTES	STATUS
☐ De Havilland D.H.82A Tiger Moth				PVD

PAPUA-NEW GUINEA

ADMIRAL YAMAMOTO AIRCRAFT WRECK (PG1)

Address:	Near Aku Village, Bougainville.
Admission:	Monday and Friday by appointment. Tour starts at 0800.
Location:	About 25 km south of Buin.

On April 18th.1943 Admiral Yamamoto the Commander-in-Chief of the Combined Fleet took off front Rabaul in the twin engined 'Betty'. The aircraft was escorted by Zero fighters. The Japanese were not aware that their code had been broken. A flight of Lockheed Lightnings intercepted the 'Betty' and it was shot down with the loss of all on board. In addition to the Admiral, the crew of four and four senior officers perished. Local entrepreneurs have cut a track one kilometre long through the jungle to the crash site.

TYPE	REG/SER	CON. NO.	PI/NOTES	STATUS
☐ Mitsubishi G4M1	T1-323	2656		PVD

AIR NUIGINI COLLECTION (PG2)

Address:	Air Nuigini House, Jackson Airport, Port Moresby.
Admission:	On permanent view.
Location:	About 12 km north west of the city.

The airline has mounted a Dakota outside its headquarters at the airport. A collection of photographs and memorabilia tracing the history of the company can be seen in the offices. The aircraft on show was delivered to Trans Australian Airlines – New Guinea in 1970 and transferred to Air Niugini. The company was set up when the country became independent in 1973. The Dakota was withdrawn from use in 1977.

TYPE	REG/SER	CON. NO.	PI/NOTES	STATUS
☐ Douglas DC-3A-467 Skytrain (C-47B) (Dakota IV)	P2-ANQ	15665/27110	43-49849, KN241, G-AMZH, VH-SBW, P2-SBW	PV

J.K.McCARTHY MUSEUM (PG3)

Address:	Box 132, Goroka, E.H.P.
Tel:	0732-1502
Admission:	Monday-Friday 0800-1600;Saturday 1400-1600;Sunday 1000-1200.
Location:	In the Goroka Showgrounds Complex in West Goroka which is about 400 km north of Port Moresby.

Named after one of the pioneers of the area, the museum displays trace the history and culture of the country. There is an excellent collection of photographs showing the development which has occurred over the years. A number of war relics, including helmets, guns, cartridge cases etc. found in the area can also be seen. Mounted behind the building is the restored P-39 which was abandoned at Tadji at the end of World War II. Between January and June 1944 Lieutenant Charles W. Borders piloted the aircraft on fifty six combat missions. The P-39 flew from airstrip at Dodobura, Finschafen and Siador in Papua New Guinea and Owi and Biak in West Irian.

TYPE	REG/SER	CON. NO.	PI/NOTES	STATUS
☐ Bell 26C Airacobra (P-39N)	42-19039			PV

KOKOPO WAR AND CULTURAL MUSEUM (PG4)

Address:	P.O. Box 1879, Rabaul, East New Britain.
Tel:	0982-8453
Fax:	0982-8439
Admission:	Monday-Friday 0800-1200 1300-1600; Saturday-Sunday 1300-1700.
Location:	About 25 km south east of Rabaul.

The museum was set up in the early 1980s at the 'Yamamoto Bunker' near Rabaul. As the collection grew larger it moved to Kokopo. The displays trace the history and cultureof the region through the early period, German colonisation and Japanese occupation There are several Japanese military, vehicles, guns and tanks to be seen along with a narrow gauge railway engine used in airfield construction. A number of the aircraft wrecks were displayed at other locations before the establishment of the museum. The Zero spent many years in the yard of the Rabaul Technical College before joining the exhibition in 1985. The Wirraway is one of eight that was scrambled from Vunakanu airfield on January 20th 1942 to try and repel an attacking force of one hundred and eight Japanese aircraft. Engines and propellers recovered from the jungle can also be seen. It is expected that more aircraft components will be recovered from the jungle and put on show in due course.

TYPE	REG/SER	CON. NO.	PI/NOTES	STATUS
☐ Boeing 299-O Fortress (B-17E)	41-2429	2240	Small components.	PVD
☐ Boeing 299-O Fortress (B-17E)	41-2430	2241	Large components.	PVD
☐ Commonwealth CA-1 Wirraway I [North American NA-33]			Fuselage frame and other parts.	PVD
☐ Mitsubishi A6M2 Zero Sen Model 21				PVD
☐ North American NA-96 Mitchell (B-25C)	42-64570	96-16449	Small components.	PVD
☐ Vought F4U-1A Corsair	Bu02566			PVD

PAPUA NEW GUINEA NATIONAL MUSEUM AND ART GALLERY (PG5)

Address:	Modern History Department, P.O. Box 5560, Boroko, NCD.
Tel:	0325-2422
Admission:	Monday-Friday 0900-1500;Saturday 1400- 1700.
Location:	In Ahuia Street, Hohola which is about 8 km west of Port Moresby.

In 1978 the privately run Air Museum of Papua New Guinea was taken over by the National Museum. The Aviation, Maritime and War Branch was set up and in 1984 it was renamed the Department of Modern History. The main museum building located in Waigani displays local artefacts tracing the history and development of the country. There are plans to construct a new Constitutional and Heritage Facility which will be able to house all the collection. Records and documents from the World War II period have been gathered and further research is proceeding. The aviation section contains many components and engines recovered from wrecks which are plentiful in inhospitable regions of the country. Some of the aircraft are currently on display at other locations. The ninth B-25C built acts as a memorial to all who served in the Sepik River regions. The Ford Trimotor was used by Guinea Airways in 1935 assisting the gold dredging work in Morobe. This aircraft was impressed by the Royal Australian Air Force and used as an air ambulance. The Ford crashed on November 24th 1942 at Myola and was taken to the museum in early 1980. A team at R.A.A.F. Amberley in Queensland completed the restoration of a Douglas A-20G Havoc which crashed near the Gogol River on April 16th 1944. A Canberra at Amberley has alsobeen allocated to the museum. These two airframes will be shipped to the country when the new exhibition area is ready. The Bell Airacobra force landed near the Lakekamu River in August 1943 and was recovered with one other airframe by a Chinook helicopter of the R.A.A.F. in 1984. Several aircraft wrecks previously under the care of the museum were exported to Australia without their knowledge.

TYPE	REG/SER	CON. NO.	PI/NOTES	STATUS
☐ Bell 14 Airacobra (P-400)	AP347		At the Aero Club.	PVD
☐ Cessna 140A			Fuselage only.	RA
☐ Commonwealth CA-1 Wirraway I [North American NA-33]	'A20-19'	11	A20-13	RA
☐ Douglas A-20G Havoc	42-86786		At RAAF Amberley, QLD, Australia	–
☐ Ford 5-AT-C	VH-UBI	5-AT-60	NC401H, G-ABHO, VH-UBI, A45-1 – fuselage and other parts from 5-AT-B c/n 5-AT-41 NC9686.	PV
☐ Government Aircraft Factory Canberra Mk.21 (Mk.20) [English Electric EA.1]	A84-203	3	At RAAF Amberley, QLD, Australia	–
☐ Junkers W 33 c	VH-UIW	2575		RAC
☐ Lockheed 222-60-12 Lightning (P-38F)	42-12647	222-7081		PV
☐ Lockheed 222-68-18 Lightning (F-5A)	42-13084	222-7518		PVD
☐ North American NA-82 Mitchell (B-25C)	41-12442	82-5077	Tail from 41-30074 – at Aitape	PV
☐ North American NA-98 Mitchell (B-25H)	43-4450	98-21451	At Popondetta	PV
☐ Piper PA-23-250 Aztec	P2-CSA	27-221	N4692P, VH-CSA	PV
☐ Republic P-47D Thunderbolt	42-27609		At Popondetta	PVD

PAPUA-NEW GUINEA DEFENCE FORCE DISPLAY (PG6)

Address:	Headquarters Building, Jackson Field, Port Moresby.
Admission:	By prior permission only.
Location:	About 12 km north west of the city.

The force was set up in 1975 and four Dakotas were delivered from Australia. One has been retained by the service and is currently parked on the military apron at Port Moresby. A collection of documents, photographs and memorabilia has been assembled and some items are on show in the headquarters building.

TYPE	REG/SER	CON. NO.	PI/NOTES	STATUS
☐ Douglas DC-3A-467 Skytrain (C-47B) (Dakota IV)	P-002	16129/32877	44-76545, A65-84, P65-002	RA

WAR MEMORIAL PARK (PG7)

Address:	Kieta.
Admission:	
Location:	On the east coast of Bougainville Island

The park contains a Japanese medium tank and a field gun along with the wreckage of the Zero. There is also a war memorial consisting of a large obelisk surrounded by flag poles.

TYPE	REG/SER	CON. NO.	PI/NOTES	STATUS
☐ Mitsubishi A6M2 Zero Sen Model 21		3412		PV

SOLOMON ISLANDS

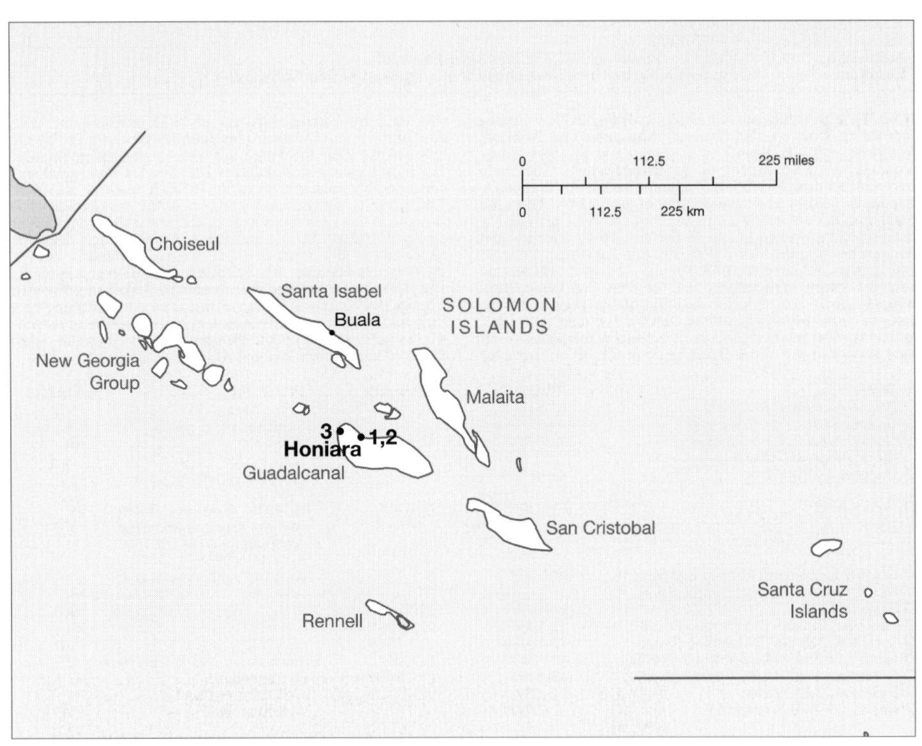

BETIKAMA HIGH SCHOOL WAR MUSEUM (SO1)

Address:	P.O. Box 516, Betikama, Honiara.
Tel:	0677-30223
Admission:	Monday-Thursday 0800-1700,Friday and Sunday 0800-1200.
Location:	Opposite Henderson Airport on the Honiara side of the Lungga River.

The school has collected a number of relics from the World War II period and placed them on display. The Airacobra was flown by the 67th Pursuit Squadron of the U.S.A.A.F. and recovered from Henderson Field in 1974. Also on show are weapons, military vehicles and components. Many fierce battles were fought on Guadalcanal during World War II and the story of these is portrayed in the museum.

TYPE	REG/SER	CON. NO.	PI/NOTES	STATUS
☐ Bell 14 Airacobra (P-400)	BW157			PVD
☐ Douglas SBD-3 Dauntless	Bu06662	1477		PVD
☐ Grumman G-36 Wildcat (F4F-3)			Crash remains.	PVD

SOLOMON ISLANDS NATIONAL MUSEUM (SO2)

Address:	Honiara.
Admission:	Daily 1000-1600.
Location:	In the centre of the town.

The National Museum was set up to portray the history and culture of the islands. There are many interesting items to be seen in the exhibition halls. A new project was initiated a few years ago and this is to have a display dedicated to World War II. There are many relics still left in the jungle but these are deteriorating and others were damaged in a local storm. Some wrecked aircraft have been recovered and put in store. These will be restored when funds become available. There are plans to retrieve more airframes in the near future.

TYPE	REG/SER	CON. NO.	PI/NOTES	STATUS
☐ Aichi B3A2				RAD
☐ Mitsubishi A6M5 Zero Sen Model 52				RAD
☐ Mitsubishi F1M2				RAD
☐ Mitsubishi G4M1				RAD

VILU CULTURAL VILLAGE AND WAR MUSEUM (SO3)

Address:	C/o The Post Office, Honiara.
Admission:	0900-1700 daily.
Location:	About 25 km west of Honiara.

The late Fred Kona set up the museum in the 1980s and the work is continued by his family. A typical rural village has been constructed on the site. Crash locations in the area were investigated and several wrecks and aircraft abandoned on airstrips were recovered. Also on show are several pieces of artillery, military vehicles and armaments. There are many small items to be seen including helmets, rifles, uniforms, personal equipment and items of memorabilia. The folding wing mechanism on the Wildcat is still in working order. This U.S. Marines aircraft was damaged at Henderson Field on March 14th 1943 and after thirty years was taken to the museum. The Grumman Duck is now a rarity with only about a dozen surviving from the almost six hundred and fifty examples of the amphibian produced. A machine gun is still in place in the wing of the Corsair. Displays tracing the conflicts in the area have been staged.

TYPE	REG/SER	CON. NO.	PI/NOTES	STATUS
☐ Bell 14 Airacobra (P-400)				PVD
☐ Boeing 299-O Fortress (B-17G)			Wing sections only	PVD
☐ Consolidated 28-5A Catalina (PBY-5A)			Major components	PVD
☐ Douglas SBD-5 Dauntless				PVD
☐ Douglas SBD-5 Dauntless				PVD
☐ Grumman G-15 Duck (J2F-5)			Fuselage only.	PVD
☐ Grumman G-36 Wildcat (F4F-1)			Wings only.	PVD
☐ Grumman G-36 Wildcat (F4F-4)	Bu12068	3763		PVD
☐ Grumman G-40 Avenger (TBF-1C)			Wings only.	PVD
☐ Lockheed 222-60-15 Lightning (P-38F-1)				PVD
☐ Mitsubishi G4M3	357	1350	Front fuselage and wing only.	PVD
☐ Vought V-166B Corsair (F4U-1)				PVD
☐ Vought V-310 Kingfisher (OS2U-3)			Major components.	PVD

The remains of this Douglas Dauntless are in the grounds of the Betikama High School War Museum. (Charles Darby)

INDEX

All aircraft are listed alphabetically by manufacturer or designer (in the case of some gliders and homebuilt aircraft) followed by the type. Each country is denoted by a two/three letter code and each museum/collection a number e.g. NZ36 is thirty sixth museum/collection in alphabetical order in New Zealand.

Country codes are as follows:-
AUS Australia; **GM** Guam; **NZ** New Zealand; **PG** Papua New Guinea; **SO** Solomon Islands.

This Lockheed Neptune is preserved at RAAF Townsville in Queensland. (Nigel Hitchman)

Bristol Freighters served for many years in New Zealand. This example is in Founders Park in Nelson.

CENTRAL AMERICA AND THE CARIBBEAN

UNITED STATES
North Atlantic Ocean
MEXICO
Gulf of Mexico
BAHAMAS
North Pacific Ocean
CUBA
PUERTO RICO
HAITI
DOM. REP.
BELIZE
JAMAICA
ANTIGUA & BARBUDA
ST KITTS & NEVIS
DOMINICA
HONDURAS
Caribbean Sea
ST VINCENT & THE GRENADINES
ST LUCIA
GUATEMALA
NICARAGUA
BARBADOS
EL SALVADOR
GRENADA
TRINIDAD & TOBAGO
PANAMA
COSTA RICA
FRENCH GUIANA
VENEZUELA
SURINAME
COLOMBIA
GUYANA
ECUADOR
South Pacific Ocean
BRAZIL
PERU

ARUBA

WAR MEMORIAL (ARU1)

Address:	L.G. Smith Boulevard, Oranjestad.
Admission:	On permanent view.
Location:	Just north of Queen Beatrix International Airport.

Over the years several aircraft, including a number of DC-3s, have been abandoned at the airport possibly after drug flights. A C-47 can now be seen as a memorial to those who lost their lives. The transport is parked in a pleasant garden close to the main entrance to the airfield. The identity is possibly the one listed.

TYPE	REG/SER	CON. NO.	PI/NOTES	STATUS
☐ Douglas DC-3A-456 Skytrain (C-47A)			Possibly c/n 19778 43-15312, NC54099, PP-SQO, PT-KUD, (N301AK), PT-KUD	PV

BARBADOS

CONCORDE EXPERIENCE (BAR1)

Address:	Grantley Adams International Airport, Christ Church.
Tel:	246-253-6257
Fax:	246-426-7332
Email:	info@barbadosconcorde.com
Admission:	Daily 0900-1800.
Location:	About 12 km east of Bridgetown.

Concorde was a regular visitor to the airport during its time with British Airways. When the type was withdrawn from service G-BOAE made its last flight to the island on November 17th 2003 after almost twenty four thousand flying hours. The exhibition opened to the public on April 16th 2007. The visitor can experience a simulated flight in the supersonic airliner starting from a replica departure lounge. Modern audio and visual techniques have been used to enhance the informative displays. The history of the type can be followed. Also to be seen is a Thorp T-18 which is one of the small number of homebuilt aircraft constructed in Barbados.

TYPE	REG/SER	CON. NO.	PI/NOTES	STATUS
☐ Aérospatiale / British Aircraft Corporation Concorde 102	G-BOAE	100-012	G-BOAE, N94AE	PV
☐ Thorp T-18	8P-BGB			PV

COSTA RICA

MUSEO DE AVIACIÓN (COS1)

Address:	Restaurant La Candela, San Jose International Airport.
Tel:	506-440-8989
Admission:	Daily 1000-2300.
Location:	About 25 km west of the city.

A display has been set up alongside this restaurant which overlooks the main runway at the airport Three aircraft are currently on show and these include a former United States Air Force Caribou which was used by the Costa Rica Security Police. The Hughes served on similar duties and was damaged in a crash in August 1996. The Cherokee was delivered to Costa Rica in 1969 and subsequently flew with a number of private owners. Also displayed are small components from airliners including a Boeing 727 and a Convair 340.

TYPE	REG/SER	CON. NO.	PI/NOTES	STATUS
☐ De Havilland D.H.C.4A Caribou (CV-2B) (C-7B)	MSP010	81	62-4146	PV
☐ Hughes 369D	MSP010	0081E		PV
☐ Piper PA-28-235C Cherokee	TI-ACV	28-11215	TI-465L	

MUSEO DE LOS NIÑOS (COS2)

Address:	Calle 4, Al Norte de Avenida 9, San Jose.
Tel:	506-233-2734
Email:	info@museocr.com
Admission:	Tuesday-Sunday 0900-1200 1400-1700.
Location:	In the northern part of the city centre.

The displays at this innovative museum, located in a former prison and barracks, are designed to interest children in many aspects of natural history, science, technology and transport. The Sikorsky S-55 is painted in an all yellow scheme and this is outside along with the Commander. The DC-6 nose is believed to be in store at the museum. Also to be seen are several cars, bicycles and a railway engine.

TYPE	REG/SER	CON. NO.	PI/NOTES	STATUS
☐ Aero Commander RC680	MSP001		'TG-EOE' – possible identity.	PV
☐ Douglas DC-6BF (DC-6B) (DC-6A)	N59050	44429	N91307, TI-1080C – front fuselage only – may be here.	–
☐ Sikorsky S-55D Chickasaw (H-19B) (UH-19B)	MSP-100			PV

CUBA

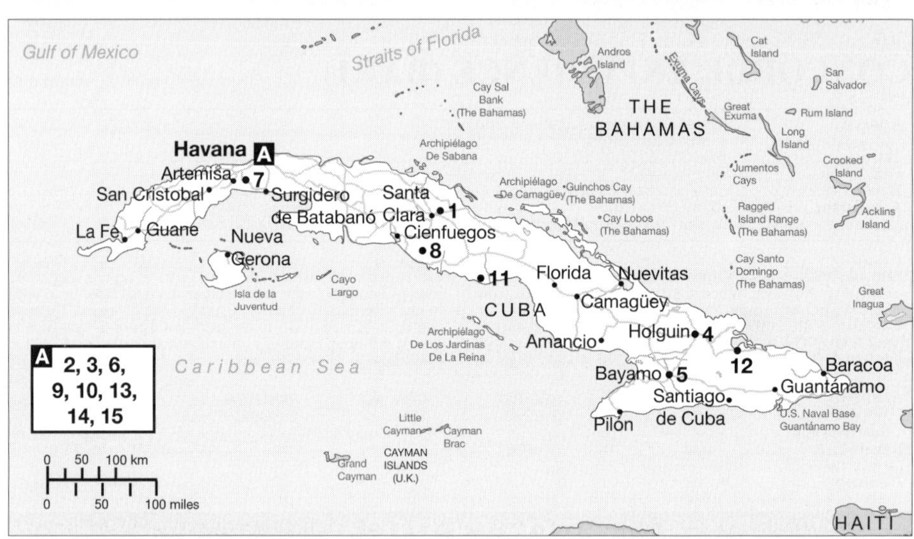

COLECCIÓN DE LA BASE AÉREA DE SANTA CLARA (CU1)

Address:	Santa Clara.
Admission:	By prior permission only.
Location:	Just north east of the town.

This base is home to squadrons operating Mil Mi-8s, Mil-17s, Mi-24s and Mi-35s. There is a collection of preserved aircraft outside some buildings on the opposite side of the road to the airfield.

TYPE	REG/SER	CON. NO.	PI/NOTES	STATUS
☐ Aero L-39C Albatros				RA
☐ Mikoyan-Gurevich MiG-17F	230		At local school.	RA
☐ Mikoyan-Gurevich MiG-21MF				RA
☐ Mikoyan-Gurevich MiG-23MF				RA
☐ Mil Mi-4				RA
☐ Mil Mi-8T				RA
☐ Mil Mi-8T				RA
☐ Mil Mi-24				RA

COLECCIÓN DEL INSTITUTO TECNICO MILITAR (CU2)

Address:	Calle 45/66A, Marianao, Havana.
Admission:	By prior permission only.
Location:	In the western suburbs of the city.

The college was a private school for many years and took up its current role and title in 1967. The impressive buildings were constructed in the late 1920s.The aircraft are displayed in a courtyard and are also used for instruction. Students follow courses in a variety of subjects leading to service in the armed forces. The aircraft are all of eastern European origin and reflect the types used in recent years.

TYPE	REG/SER	CON. NO.	PI/NOTES	STATUS
☐ Aero L-39C Albatros	12			RA
☐ Antonov An-2				RA
☐ Mikoyan-Gurevich MiG-21bis	637			RA
☐ Mikoyan-Gurevich MiG-23ML	232			RA
☐ Mil Mi-17	103			RA

MONUMENTO DE LA BASE AÉREA DE CIUDAD LIBERTAD (CU3)

Address:	Ciudad Libertad, Havana.
Admission:	By prior permission only.
Location:	In the western suburbs of the city.

This former fighter base now houses a maintenance and repair facility. The MiG-15 which was flown by front line units for many years is parked inside the main gate. Recently helicopter squadrons and a pilot training school were both based at the field but they have moved out and no operational aircraft are in residence.

TYPE	REG/SER	CON. NO.	PI/NOTES	STATUS
☐ Mikoyan-Gurevich MiG-15bis	50			RA

MONUMENTO DE ESCUELA MILITAR DE HOLGUIN (CU4)

Address:	Holguin 80700.
Admission:	By prior permission only.
Location:	In the north eastern part of the town.

The airfield at Holguin housed weapons during the 1962 Cuban Missile Crisis. The base is now home to squadrons operating MiG-21s and MiG-23s. The nearby military school has a MiG-17F as a monument. This type was formerly used by the resident squadrons and served as a front line fighter for many years.

TYPE	REG/SER	CON. NO.	PI/NOTES	STATUS
☐ Mikoyan-Gurevich MiG-17F	215			RA
☐ Mikoyan-Gurevich MiG-23ML	240		At airfield.	RA

MUSEO DE COMMANDANCIA LA PLATA (CU5)

Address:	Sierra
Tel:	023-2504
Admission	Unknown.
Location:	In the mountains south of Bayamo.

In the 1950s Fidel Castro and his followers set up a base in the remote Sierra Madera mountains south of Bayamo. Here his forces lived in a number of wooden huts and they broadcast to the country on their radio station. The site has been preserved and is reached by a walk through the forest. A number of components from an Invader, shot down during the April 1961 Bay of Pigs invasion, can be seen.

TYPE	REG/SER	CON. NO.	PI/NOTES	STATUS
☐ Douglas A-26B Invader				PVD

MUSEO DE LA REVOLUCIÓN (CU6)

Address:	Calle Refugio 1, 10600 Havana.
Tel:	07-624091
Admission:	Tuesday-Saturday 1300-1800; Sunday 1000-1300
Location:	In the city centre close to Avenue de Belgica.

Displays at this museum trace the story of the struggle by the Castro forces to win control of the island. The building was constructed in 1920 and was the Presidential Palace for forty years. In March 1957 it was the site of an unsuccessful assassination attempt on Fulgenio Batista and bullet holes can still be seen on the outside walls. Hawker Furies were used by both sides in the conflict. The Mustang, now on show at the Air Force Museum, was displayed here for many years. Cuba received a small number of Vought Kingfishers in 1942 and the example in the collection is exhibited as a landplane in Navy markings. The prototype Kingfisher first flew in May 1938 with the OS2U-3 version appearing two years later. Just over one thousand were produced. The U-2 was brought down on one of the many spying missions flown over the country by the U.S.A.

TYPE	REG/SER	CON. NO.	PI/NOTES	STATUS
☐ Hawker Sea Fury FB.11	542			PV
☐ Lockheed U-2C			Tail section only.	PV
☐ Vought V-310 Kingfisher (OS2U-3)	'50'		Bu5933, 31	PVX

MUSEO DE LA BASE AÉREA SAN ANTOÑIO DE LOS BANOS (CU7)

Address:	21 Grupo de Caza, Base Aérea San Antonio de los Banos, San Antonio de los Banos.
Admission:	By prior permission only.
Location:	In the southern suburbs of the town.

The airfield was built in the early 1940s and has been developed so that modern combat types can operate from its runways. The base is now home to squadrons flying MiG-21s, MiG-23s, MiG-29s, Zlin 142s and the L-39C Albatros. In addition there is a small number of helicopters on detachment from Santa Clara based at the site. Several MiGs are stored around the base both in hard shelters and in the open. A collection of preserved aircraft can clearly be seen on satellite photos; however, a visitor to the airfield was told that there was not a museum on the airfield. Several types have been identified but only two serials have been obtained. Any detailed information would be most welcome. Thirty Aero L-39Cs were delivered in the early 1980s and used for training and ground attack duties. Mil helicopters have seen wide use in Cuba and two types are in the collection.

TYPE	REG/SER	CON. NO.	PI/NOTES	STATUS
☐ Aero L-39C Albatros				RA
☐ Douglas A-26B Invader				RA
☐ Lockheed 580 (T-33A)				RA
☐ Mikoyan-Gurevich MiG-15				RA
☐ Mikoyan-Gurevich MiG-19P				RA
☐ Mikoyan-Gurevich MiG-21bis	1779			RA
☐ Mikoyan-Gurevich MiG-23ML	215			RA
☐ Mikoyan-Gurevich MiG-29				RA
☐ Mil Mi-8				RA
☐ Mil Mi-24				RA

MUSEO DE PLAYA GIRÓN (CU8)

Address:	Cienaga de Zapata, Matanzas, Playa Giron.
Tel:	045-98-4122
Admission:	Wednesday-Sunday 0900-1800.
Location:	In the centre of the town which is about 150 km south east of Havana.

In 1961 the C.I.A. backed, but then withdrew its support, for an attack on Cuba by expatriates opposed to the Castro regime. The operation was a disaster for the invaders who were easily defeated. Furies were flown by the Air Force against the rebels and this was the last time the type was used in combat. Fifteen single seat and a pair of two seat Furies were bought by the Batista regime in 1958 and the survivors were taken over by the Castro forces the following year. The wreck of a Douglas Invader shot down in the raid has been placed on show. This bomber was also used the Castro side and several were painted in false Cuban colours. The museum displays portray the abortive invasion in great detail. There are several tanks and weapons on show.

TYPE	REG/SER	CON. NO.	PI/NOTES	STATUS
☐ Douglas A-26B Invader				PVD
☐ Hawker Sea Fury FB.11	541			PV

MUSEO DEL AIRE (CU9)

Address:	Avenue 212/ 22 y 31 Rpto, La Coronela, La Lisa.
Tel:	07-271-6632
Admission:	Tuesday-Saturday 1000-1700.
Location:	In the southern suburbs of Havana near the outer ring road.

In 1913 a Morane monoplane was imported into Cuba and this led to the idea of the formation of a military air service but it was not until 1919 that the first unit was activated. Training of pilots took place in the U.S.A. and six Curtiss Jenny biplanes were purchased by the Cuban Government. Progress was slow over the next twenty years and only a small number of aircraft were acquired. In 1947 Cuba signed the Rio Pact and became eligible for the delivery of U.S. aircraft. For the first time truly combat types were delivered including Mitchell bombers and Mustang fighters. The first jets supplied were Lockheed T-33s, some of which were fitted with weapons. Just before Fidel Castro gained control in 1959, eighteen Invaders were purchased. Six of these flew in the Bay of Pigs operation against C.I.A.-supplied Invaders wearing false Cuban colours. During the 1960s Castro turned to the Soviet Union for military hardware and many aircraft were delivered. The museum was set up on April 17th 1986 and over the last two decades the display has grown considerably. The Mustang was formerly on show at the Museo de la Revolucion in the centre of Havana. The Cessna 310 was used by the Castro forces in the latter stages of their conflict against the Batista Government. The aircraft later served as the personal transport of 'Che' Guervara. The Mil Mi-4 was presented to Castro by the Soviet Union when he became president of the country. There is an extensive display of anti-aircraft guns, radar equipment and missiles. The indoor displays trace the history of the service from its early days. A prized exhibit is the suit worn by the first Cuban astronaut, Arnaldo Tamayo-Mendez who flew on Soyuz 38 in September 1980.

TYPE	REG/SER	CON. NO.	PI/NOTES	STATUS
☐ Aero L-39C Albatros	16	232342	(Czechoslovakia)	PV
☐ Antonov An-2		1G 177-33	I-40 (Angola)	PV
☐ Antonov An-26		7106	CCCP-47412, CU-T-1453, T-53	PV
☐ Canadian Car & Foundry Harvard 4 [North American NA-186 (T-6J)]	'116'	CCF4-497	52-8576, AA+697, 1783 (Portugal)	PVX
☐ Cessna 310C	58		N66938	PV
☐ Douglas A-26B Invader	'937'	27814	44-34535, N8020E, 7101 (Portugal), '933'	PVX
☐ Douglas DC-8-43	CU-T1201	45611	CF-TJI – small parts only – possible identity.	PVD
☐ Ilyushin Il-14	CU-T825			PV
☐ Lockheed 580 (T-33A)	'703'		(USAF), 701	PVX
☐ Lockheed U-2C	56-6676	343		PVD
☐ Mikoyan-Gurevich MiG-15UTI	02	110211		PV
☐ Mikoyan-Gurevich MiG-17F	237			PV
☐ Mikoyan-Gurevich MiG-19P	88			PV
☐ Mikoyan-Gurevich MiG-21F-13	411	1405		PV
☐ Mikoyan-Gurevich MiG-21MF	111	031017		PV
☐ Mikoyan-Gurevich MiG-21PF	'1006'	1911		PVX
☐ Mikoyan-Gurevich MiG-21UM	502	09695152		PV
☐ Mikoyan-Gurevich MiG-23BN	711	0393209121		PV
☐ Mikoyan-Gurevich MiG-23MF	822	0390213710		PV
☐ Mikoyan-Gurevich MiG-23ML	'223'	0390310703	223 (Angola) – in false Cuban markings.	PVX
☐ Mikoyan-Gurevich MiG-23UB	'706'	A1038407	708	PVX
☐ Mikoyan-Gurevich MiG-29UB	901	50903014717	May have left the exhibition in early 2008.	–
☐ Mil Mi-4P	H-100			PV
☐ Mil Mi-8T	H-02	31202	(Angola)	PV
☐ Mil Mi-8TB	H-85	40711		PV
☐ Mil Mi-17	101	407M01		PV
☐ Mil Mi-24D	12			PV
☐ North American NA-122 Mustang (P-51D) (Mustang IV)	401	122-41045	44-74505, 9233 (Canada), N3990A, N68DR	PV
☐ North American NA-174 Trojan (T-28A)	121	174-609	51-7756	PV
☐ Yakovlev Yak-40	FAR 14-41	9631049	12-41, CU-T1441	PV

MUSEO DEL MINISTÉRIO DEL INTERIOR (CU10)

Address:	Avenue 5 / Calle 14, Havana.
Tel:	07-301556
Admission:	Tuesday-Saturday 0900-1700.
Location:	In Miramar suburb of the city.

The Ministry of the Interior has operated a number of helicopters on official duties and a Mi-2 was on show in the forecourt of the building along with a patrol boat. The indoor displays highlight the history of the organisation.

TYPE	REG/SER	CON. NO.	PI/NOTES	STATUS
☐ Mil Mi-2	6001	5310042027		RA

MUSEO HISTORICO MUNICIPAL TRINIDAD (CU11)

Address:	Calle Simon Bolivar 423, Trinidad.
Tel:	041-9-4460
Admission:	Saturday-Thursday 0900-1700.
Location:	In the centre of the town. The airport is about 5 km west of the town.

The museum is located in a former palace built by the owner of a number of sugarcane plantations. The history and cultural development of the region is portrayed in the displays. A major section is devoted to the slave era and the abolition of the practice. The three wars against Spain fought in the nineteenth century in order to gain independence also feature prominently. Maps, documents, photographs and personal items can be seen. There are small parts of a shot down U-2 to be seen. The Yak-18T is parked at the local airport.

TYPE	REG/SER	CON. NO.	PI/NOTES	STATUS
☐ Lockheed U-2C	56-6676	343	Parts only.	PVD
☐ Yakovlev Yak-18T	CU-T1508	50217 (?)	At airport.	PV

MUSEO MUNICIPAL 'FRANK PAIS GARCIA' (CU12)

Address:	Avenue de los Martires, Mayari Ariba.
Tel:	25749
Admission:	Daily 0730-1200, 1330-1700.
Location:	In the town.

This local history museum has sections devoted to all aspects of local life. The transport section has a number of vehicles on show. In 2001 sections devoted to military operations were opened. There are many models and documents on show along with the aircraft. The Kingfisher carries the same number as the one on show in Havana but is a different aircraft. Further information on this collection would be most welcome.

TYPE	REG/SER	CON. NO.	PI/NOTES	STATUS
☐ Douglas DC-3A-456 Skytrain (C-47A)				PV
☐ North American NA-122 Mustang (P-51D)			Less outer wings.	PV
☐ North American NA-159 Trojan (T-28A)				PV
☐ Vought V-310 Kingfisher (OS2U-3)	'50'			PVX

PALÁCIO CENTRAL DE PIONEROS ERNESTO GUEVARA (CU13)

Address:	Arroyo Noraijo, Havana.
Admission:	Unknown.
Location:	In the southern suburbs of the city.

Ernesto 'Che' Guevara was to the forefront in the Castro take over of Cuba. There are many museums in the country devoted to his exploits. The story of his life before he joined the Cuban movement is portrayed. His work with Castro features prominently as does his later life up to his death in Bolivia in 1967. The ubiquitous Antonov An-2 has seen wide use in Cuba in both civilian and military roles.

TYPE	REG/SER	CON. NO.	PI/NOTES	STATUS
☐ Antonov An-2	CU-A595			PV

PALÁCIO DE PIONEROS (CU14)

Address:	Avenida Manduley, Calle 11, Santiago de Cuba.
Admission:	Daily 0900-1600.
Location:	In the centre of the city.

There are many exhibitions in the country highlighting the contribution of locals to the development of the country since the Castro take-over. The MiG-15 is in the garden area which also includes a playground.

TYPE	REG/SER	CON. NO.	PI/NOTES	STATUS
☐ Mikoyan-Gurevich MiG-15UTI	26			PV

This MiG-15UTI is outside the Pioneers Palace in Santiago de Cuba (Phil Dunnington)

This former Swedish Vampire is on show outside the Headquarters of the Dominican Air Force in Santo Domingo.

Several Dassault Ouragans are preserved at the Museo Nacional de Aviacion at Ilopango. (Paul Seymour)

PARQUE LENIN (CU15)

Address:	Calzada de Bejucal, Arroyo Noraijo, Havana.
Admission:	On permanent view.
Location:	In the southern suburbs of the city.

This vast park on the outskirts of the city has exhibitions devoted to various forms of transport and includes a number of steam trains. Several military aircraft were once on show but these moved to the Air Force Museum.

TYPE	REG/SER	CON. NO.	PI/NOTES	STATUS
☐ Antonov An-2M	CU-T973			PV
☐ Antonov An-24B	CU-T880	67302502		PV
☐ Mil Mi-8T	83			PV
☐ Yakovlev Yak-18T	CU-T1509			PV

DOMINICAN REPUBLIC

COLECCIÓN DE LA FUERZA AÉREA DOMINICANA (DO1)

Address:	Cuartel General, Fuerza Aérea Dominicana, Santo Domingo.
Admission:	By prior permission only
Location:	At the Headquarters in Santo Domingo (1) At San Isidro AFB which about 10 km east of the city (2)

During the 1930s a number of former United States civil aircraft were flown in the country by military personnel. Development was slow and although a few types were supplied under Lend-Lease it was not until the late 1940s that the force became modernised. In the 1950s a batch of over thirty Mustangs was acquired from Sweden who later supplied about forty Vampires. Seven OH-6s and two Sikorsky S-55Cs were operated by the Air Force.

TYPE	REG/SER	CON. NO.	PI/NOTES	STATUS
☐ Beech D45 Mentor (T-34B)				PV.1
☐ Cessna 318E Dragonfly (A-37B) (OA-37B)	3705	43296	70-1281	PV.1
☐ Cessna 318E Dragonfly (A-37B) (OA-37B)	3702	43326	70-1311	RA.1
☐ Cessna 337M Super Skymaster (O-2A)	1702	337M0156	68-6867	PV.2
☐ De Havilland D.H.100 Vampire F.1	2714		Fv28042	PV.1
☐ De Havilland D.H.100 Vampire FB.50	2741	V.0864	Fv28408	PV.2
☐ Douglas DC-3A-467 Skytrain (C-47B)	3404	14085/25530	43-48269	PV.2
☐ Hughes 369M (OH-6A)		701079		PV.1
☐ North American NA-88 Texan (AT-6D)	1031		(USAF)	PV.2
☐ North American NA-122 Mustang (P-51D)	1914	122-31982	44-72123, Fv26092	PV.1
☐ Sikorsky S-55C	3003	55-1156	May be c/n 55-1174 3004.	PV.1

MUSEO DE LA SECRETARÍA DE LAS FUERZAS ARMAS (DO2)

Address:	Avenida 27 de Febrero, Santo Domingo.
Admission:	Tuesday-Sunday 1000-1600.
Location:	In the centre of the city.

Two Curtiss-Wright CW-19R light attack aircraft were bought in 1937. The example on show is the second of the pair and was delivered in August 1937. On November 12th 1937 the aircraft, crewed by Major Frank Feliz Maranda and Sergeant Major Ernesto Tejeda, took part in a goodwill flight through Central and South America. The CW-19R, named 'Colon', was accompanied by two Cuban Stinson Reliants which managed to collide with each other in Colombia on December 29th 1937. The aircraft was formerly on show at the Museo del Hombre Dominicano and has recently moved to this exhibition. The displays trace tine history of all branches of military forces in the country which finally gained its independence in 1844. Also to be seen are a number of dioramas portraying significant military events in the turbulent history of the region

TYPE	REG/SER	CON. NO.	PI/NOTES	STATUS
☐ Curtiss-Wright CW-19R-12	7	19R-11	7, 9, (Civil) – temporarily in store.	RA

EL SALVADOR

MUSEO MILITAR DE FUERZA ARMADA (EL1)

Address:	10 Avenue Captain Albero Sanchez, San Salvador.
Tel:	503-250-0100 ext 8800
Fax:	503-250-0100 ext 8801
Admission:	Monday-Saturday 0800-1700.
Location:	In the centre of the city.

This impressive museum is housed in the former presidential palace. Inside are ten rooms tracing the military history of the country and its forces. On show are photographs, documents, weapons and uniforms. Outside is a collection of military vehicles. The Bell Iroquois has been operated by Army units around the country.

TYPE	REG/SER	CON. NO.	PI/NOTES	STATUS
☐ Bell 204 Iroquois (UH-1C) (UH-1M)	231	1356	65-9456	PV
☐ Bell 205 Iroquois (UH-1H)	249	10012	67-17814	PV

MUSEO NACIONAL DE AVIACIÓN (EL2)

Address:	Boulevard del Ejercito, Km 9 1/2, Aeropuerto Internacional de Ilopango, Ilopango, San Salvador.
Tel:	503-250-0070 ext 1119
Email:	museo_aviacion@fas.gds.sv
Admission:	Monday-Tuesday; Thursday-Saturday 0900-1200 1400-1630.
Location:	In the eastern suburbs of the city.

A Military Aviation Service was formed in 1922 and over the years has operated a variety of types. At the main base at Ilopango a collection of withdrawn types was assembled. This collection has developed into the museum now housed in the former terminal building. The informative displays trace the history of aviation in the country. Many photographs, documents, uniforms and personal items can be seen. Eighteen former Israeli Ouragans were acquired in 1973 and six of these were destroyed in a terrorist attack at Ilopango in January 1982. Some of the preserved examples are with the museum and others can be found nearby. Six Invaders arrived in the country in the late 1960s and were in service for just over ten years. The country has experienced many problems with insurgents and with its neighbours and the Magister, Dragonfly and Rallye have seen used in the ground attack role. Civil types are joining the display and the immaculate Bellanca Crusair Senior was one of the first privately owned aircraft in the country after World War II.

TYPE	REG/SER	CON. NO.	PI/NOTES	STATUS
☐ Bell 204 Iroquois (UH-1C) (UH-1M)	320	1626	66-0644	PV
☐ Bell 204 Iroquois (UH-1C) (UH-1M)	230	1764	66-15036 – preserved on base.	RA
☐ Bell 205 Iroquois (UH-1D) (UH-1H)	209	5888	66-16194 – front fuselage only.	PV
☐ Bell 205 Iroquois (UH-1H)	260	13151	71-20327	PV
☐ Bellanca 14-13-3 Crusair Senior	YS-64P	1626		PV
☐ Cessna 172F Mescalero (T-41A)				PV
☐ Dassault MD-450 Ouragan	705		(France), (Israel) – front fuselage only.	PV
☐ Dassault MD-450 Ouragan	706		(France), (Israel)	PV
☐ Dassault MD-450 Ouragan	709		(France), (Israel) – preserved on base.	RA
☐ Dassault MD-450 Ouragan	713		(France), (Israel)	PV
☐ Dassault MD-450 Ouragan	716		(France), (Israel) – preserved at CAA Headquarters.	RA
☐ Douglas A-26B Invader	'601'		422	PVX
☐ Douglas DC-3A-456 Skytrain (C-47A)	114			PV
☐ Douglas DC-3A-456 Skytrain (C-47A)	106			PV
☐ Douglas DC-3A-456 Skytrain (C-47A)			Front fuselage only.	PV
☐ Douglas DC-3A-467 Skytrain (TC-47B)	109	15962/32710	44-76378	PV
☐ Douglas DC-6A (DC-6B)	301	45078	CF-CZQ, OD-ADP, CF-CZQ, G-ARZO, CF-CZQ, N122M, YS-32C, 302	PV
☐ Fairchild 473 Provider (205) (C-123B) (C-123J) (C-123K) (UC-123K) (VC-123K)	122	20259	56-4375	RA
☐ Fouga CM.170R Magister	510	43	43 (France)	RAA
☐ Fouga CM.170R Magister	500		(Israel)	PV
☐ Fouga CM.170R Magister	505			PV
☐ North American NA-88 Texan (AT-6C)				RA
☐ Piper PA-23-250 Apache	YS-02N			PV
☐ Société de Constructions D'Avions de Tourisme et D'Affaires (SOCATA) Rallye 235GT	58	13275		RA

GUATEMALA

COLECCIÓN DE LA FUERZA AÉREA GUATEMALTECA (GU1)

Address:	Cuartel General, Fuerza Aérea Guatemalteca, Avenida Hincapie, Guatemala City,
Admission:	By prior permission only.
Location:	At La Aurora Air Force Base which is about 15 km south west of the city.

Military aviation arrived in the country in 1918 when a French air mission brought three Breguet 14s. The instructor died before the aircraft were unpacked and the group returned home. A second mission arrived in 1923 but progress over the next few years was slow. In the mid-1930s several Waco biplanes were bought and these were followed by seven Boeing P-26As and twelve Ryan STM-2s. More American aircraft were supplied under Lend-Lease and in 1945 a group from the U.S.A. was given the task of re-organising the force. The air force has a collection of aircraft preserved at is main base. The star is the Waco VPF-7, which until recently was maintained in flying condition. Six were bought in 1937 and used as fighter trainers. The aircraft is now stored in a hangar awaiting a major rebuild. Over two dozen Mustangs were acquired in the 1950s and these gave excellent service for over two decades. Eight Invaders served with the Air Force and were normally based at La Aurora. Six Kansans arrived in the country in 1947 and they were initially used as light bombers. There is the potential for a museum at the base as items of memorabilia, uniforms and documents have been saved.

TYPE	REG/SER	CON. NO.	PI/NOTES	STATUS
☐ Beech C18S Kansan (AT-11)			(USAAF)	RA
☐ Douglas DC-3A-467 Skytrain (C-47B)	540	13980/25425	43-48164,	RA
☐ Douglas A-26B Invader	404	27899 (?)	44-35620 -possible identity.	RA
☐ Lockheed 580 (T-33A)	'735'	580-1012	56-1662	RAX
☐ North American NA-122 Mustang (P-51D)	'336'		(USAAF), 360	PVX
☐ North American NA-168 Texan (T-6G)	209	168-316	49-3212	RA
☐ Sikorsky S-55D Chickasaw (H-19B) (UH-19B)	110		51-3905	PVX
☐ Waco VPF-7	21			RA

MUSEO HERÁLDICO Y DE ARMAS DEL EJÉRCITO DE GUATEMALA (GU2)

Address:	24 Calle 3-81, Zona 1, Cuidad de Guatemala.
Tel:	502-253-5286
Admission:	Monday-Saturday 0900-1600.
Location:	In the centre of the city.

This museum is located in the remaining tower of a nineteenth century fort. The buildings were badly damaged in an earthquake in 1917 and abandoned. Most of the complex was destroyed in an uprising in 1994. The displays trace the history of the army from its early days. On show is an excellent collection of photographs, documents, weapons and uniforms. The Iroquois is one of the batch built in Taiwan by AIDC.

TYPE	REG/SER	CON. NO.	PI/NOTES	STATUS
☐ Bell 205 Iroquois (UH-1H)	H-113	18032	332 (Taiwan)	PV

HONDURAS

COLECCIÓN DE LA BASE AÉREA SAN PEDRO SULA (HO1)

Address:	Grupo Tactico 1, Base Aerea San Pedro Sula
Admission:	By prior permission only.
Location:	About 10 km south east of the town.

This airfield is one of the main bases in the country and houses fighter and liaison aircraft. Currently in use are Cessna A-37B Dragonflies flown in combat and ground attack duties. The airfield also serves as the main civil airport for the region. Three aircraft have been preserved at the site. Eight former Yugoslav Canadair Sabres were acquired in the late 1970s. These aircraft were refurbished in Miami and served for many years.

TYPE	REG/SER	CON. NO.	PI/NOTES	STATUS
☐ Canadair CL-13 Sabre 4 [North American F-86E]	3008	581	19681, XB827, 11079 (Yugoslavia)	RA
☐ Lockheed 580 (T-33A)			(USAF)	RA
☐ North American NA-232 Sabre (F-86K)	1101	232-139	55-4899, (Germany), (Venezuela)	RA

FUNDACIÓN MUSEO DEL AIRE (HO2)

Address:	Base Aerea Teniente-Colonel Herman Acosta Mejian, Toncontin, Tegucigalpa.
Tel:	0233-4623
Admission:	Saturday-Sunday 10001-1700.
Location:	About 5 km north of the city.

Ivan Lamb, a Canadian mercenary, brought a Bristol Fighter to the country in 1921 and was made a General and Director of Aviation. Over the next two decades a few more aircraft were imported and a Military Aviation School established. American types were acquired after 1944. In the post-war years there have been a number of conflicts with neighbouring countries. After a series of football matches with El Salvador in 1969 war broke out. Taking part in the operations were Vought Corsairs of the Honduran forces, one of which downed three Salvadorian machines – two Corsairs and one Mustang. This historic aircraft has been preserved and was one of the first to join the museum. The Kaydet is sometimes flown on special occasions and the Kingcobra, one of five delivered in 1947, is mounted outside the Officers Club. Three North American NA-16s were bought in 1938 and two survived until recently. One has now joined the collection. This type was the forerunner of the famous Texan/Harvard series of trainers and the prototype made its maiden flight in the spring of 1934. In the mid-1970s just over twenty Super Mystères were acquired from Israel. Israeli Aircraft Industries re-engined the supersonic fighters with Pratt and Whitney J-52s and the aircraft gave excellent service for a number of years. The F-86K is one of four that were bought from Venezuela. These former Luftwaffe fighters were not assembled in Venezuela after being shipped from Germany and the Honduran engineers managed to make two airworthy. The Commando was seized by Nicaraguan officers and their families in 1979. They used the aircraft to escape from the Sandanista forces who were winning the battle to overthrow the dictator Anasastasio Somoza. One of the C-47s has been painted in the colours of the airline TACA. The identity of this transport is not known for certain. There are several other aircraft stored around the airfield and some of these may eventually join the exhibition.

TYPE	REG/SER	CON. NO.	PI/NOTES	STATUS
☐ Beech C18S Kansan (AT-11)	105		(USAAF)	PV
☐ Bell 33 Kingcobra (P-63E)	'401'		43-11730, 403, (N9001R). '402', '214' – preserved on base by Officers Club.	RAX
☐ Bell 47G-3B-1	910	2814		PV
☐ Bell 204 Iroquois (UH-1B)	927	963	63-8738	RA
☐ Bell 204 Iroquois (UH-1B)	934	1114	64-13990	PV
☐ Bell 204 Iroquois (UH-1B)	921		Preserved at military gate.	RA
☐ Bellanca 14-13-3 Crusair Senior				RA
☐ Boeing-Stearman A75N1 Kaydet (PT-17)	'42'		(USAAF), 46	RACX
☐ Canadair CL-13 Sabre 4 [North American F-86E]	3006	721	19821, XB958, XB934, 06-147 (Yugoslavia), 11-106 (Yugoslavia)	PV
☐ Cessna R172F Mescalero (T-41D)	225	R1720612		PV
☐ Cessna 185B Skywagon (U-17A)	111	1850632	63-13135	RA
☐ Cessna 206	HR-IAD			PV
☐ Cessna 318E Dragonfly (A-37B) (OA-37B)	1018	43414	71-1414	PV
☐ Cessna 337 Super Skymaster	HR-HCM			PV
☐ Curtiss-Wright CW-20B-2 Commando (C-46D)	AN-BRX	22531	44-78708, N1668M, JY-ABY, N9900F, CX-BAH	PV
☐ Dassault Super Mystère B2	2009	25 (?)	25 (France), (Israel)	PV
☐ Douglas DC-3A-456 Skytrain (C-47A)	306	13642	42-93701	PV
☐ Douglas DC-3A-456 Skytrain (C-47A)	'XH-TAZ'		(USAAF), 312,'315'	PVX
☐ Douglas DC-3A-467 Skytrain (C-47B)	307	15320/26765	43-49504	RA
☐ Douglas DC-6A Liftmaster (C-118A) (R6D-1) (C-118B)	N203CM	44627	53--3256, Bu152688	PV
☐ Hughes 269A	915	980971		PV
☐ Lockheed 580 (T-33A)	1200	580-5860	51-6528, M-51 (Netherlands), N650, 222	PV
☐ North American NA-16A-2A	21	42-692	21, '20'	PV
☐ North American NA-88 Texan (SNJ-4)	205	88-9549	Bu09990, 205-C	PV
☐ North American NA-200 Trojan (T-28B)	'EAN 214'	200-380	Bu138309, 230	PVX
☐ North American NA-221 Sabre (F-86K)	'1000'	221-144	55-4904, (Germany), (Venezuela), 1102	PVX
☐ Piper PA-25-235 Pawnee				RA
☐ Sikorsky S-55D Chickasaw (H-19B) (UH-19B)				PVD
☐ Stinson 108-3 Voyager				RA
☐ Vought F4U-5N Corsair	609		Bu124715	PV
☐ Vultee V-54D Valiant (BT-13)	60			PV

MEXICO

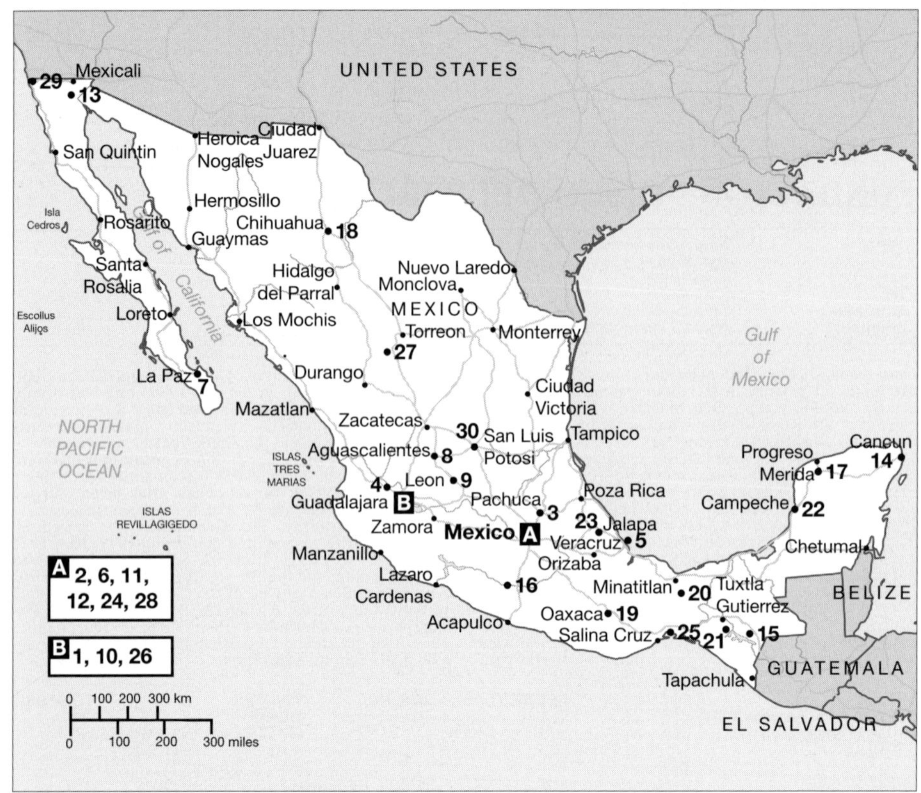

CENTRO DE CIENCIA Y TECNOLOGÍA PLANETARIO (MEX1)

Address:	Anillo Periferico Manuel Gómez Morìn 401, Huentitan el Alto, 44390 Guadalajara,
Tel:	033-3674-4106
Email:	directorplanetario@prodigy.net.mx
Admission:	Tuesday-Sunday 1000-1700.
Location:	In the centre of the city.

The complex, which opened in 1982, is named after the famous scientist is Severo Dias Saavedro. An aviation display has been set up at the planetarium. A replica of the Government Aircraft Factory Series C biplane has been built by Arturo de la Torre. The original Series C was designed by Francisco Santarini and Guillermo Villasarna and emerged from the works in 1918. This biplane fighter was powered by a 150 hp Hispano-Suiza engine. The Thunderchief, which was flown by the New Jersey Air National Guard, is exhibited in a 'lizard' colour scheme used in Vietnam. Visitors can sit in the cockpits of this pair and handle the controls. The Monnett Monerai powered glider was built from a kit. The type is also available as a pure sailplane. A Link Trainer acquired from the Air Force College is also on display. Astronomy enthusiasts can observe the stars every Friday from 8pm and take part in a workshop to construct a working telescope. The museum has a Newtonian telescope of 11 inches diameter with a 100-inch focal length. There are many interactive exhibitions of different aspects of science and technology, including biology, engineering, physics, chemistry and maths.

TYPE	REG/SER	CON. NO.	PI/NOTES	STATUS
☐ Boeing 707			Nose only.	PV
☐ Monnett Monerai P				PV
☐ Republic F-105B Thunderchief	57-5784	B-21		PV
☐ Talleres Nacionales de Construcciones Aeronáuticas 1C31 (R)				PV

CENTRO DE DESSAROLLO INFANTIL 'TIAZUCHIUALPILLI' (MEX2)

Address:	Tulyehualco, Mexico City.
Admission:	By prior permission only.
Location:	In the southern suburbs of the city.

This centre for disadvantaged children has set up a display in is grounds. This is dominated by the DC-3 which was delivered to the United States Army Air Force in October 1943 and served with them for two and a half years. Use as a cargo aircraft with National Skyway Freight and Flying Tiger Lines in California followed. The C-47 made the short journey across the border in 1949 and then served with on airline duties with Mexicana until 1975. The aircraft was stored for a period before being transported to the centre.

TYPE	REG/SER	CON. NO.	PI/NOTES	STATUS
☐ Douglas DC-3A-456 Skytrain (C-47A)	XA-REX	13818	43-30667, NC63363, XA-JAO	RA

COLECCIÓN DE LA BASE AÉREA 1 (MEX3)

Address:	Avenida Santa Lucia Modua, 55640 Los Reyes Acozac. Edo. de Mexico.
Tel:	059-5924-1315
Admission:	By prior permission only.
Location:	About 40 km north of Mexico City.

This important base houses fighter and transport wings operating a variety of types including a few C-47s. Mexico obtained twenty five Thunderbolts in early 1945 and the newly formed 201st Combat Squadron served in the Philippines. Almost eight hundred ground attack missions were flown. The last Thunderbolts were withdrawn in 1962. The Call brothers flew their low wing model A in 1940 and over the next few years they developed the design. The A-9 appeared in the mid-1960s and the company was later sold to the Rockwell Corporation. In 1971 the design rights and all components and tooling was sold to AAMSA in Pasteje, Mexico. The A-9B was built in Laredo, Texas but most of the production aircraft were sold to Mexican owners.

TYPE	REG/SER	CON. NO.	PI/NOTES	STATUS
☐ Aeronautica Agricola Mexicana A-9B Quail [Rockwell A-9B Quail Commander]	EPA-1			RA
☐ Beech A23-19 Musketeer	EMB-01	MB-461	EBP-301	RA
☐ Beech A23-19 Musketeer	EMB-04	MB-464	EBP-304	RA
☐ Beech C90A King Air	5206		ETE-1344	RA
☐ Convair 580 (440-3)	3907	37 (455)	N910BS, N812PS, N123MH, N123RP, N153WC, N318CP, N333TN, HK-3635, TE-003	RA
☐ Douglas DC-3A-456 Skytrain (C-47A)	ETM-6046	12647	42-92806, G-AJTO, VH-INF, VH-AKR, VH-MAN, P2-MAN, P2-ANY, N55892	RA
☐ Douglas DC-6A	ETP-10018	45226	OD-ADC, F-BKBQ, 45226 (France), N72532	RA
☐ Lockheed 182-1A Hercules (182-44-03) (C-130A)	3606	182-3116	56-0508, 10606	RA
☐ Lockheed 580 (T-33A)	JE-006	580-6980	51-9196	RA
☐ Lockheed 580 (T-33A)	JE-039		(USAF)	RA
☐ Lockheed 580 (T-33A)	JE-042		(USAF)	RA
☐ Lockheed-Azcarate LASA-60 Santa Maria	BRL-1018	1018	FAM-1018	PV
☐ North American NA-174 Trojan (T-28A)				RA
☐ Republic P-47D Thunderbolt	'PZT-1003'		(USAF)	PVX
☐ Sikorsky VS-316B Hoverfly II	'FAM-10'			RAX
☐ Stinson V-76 Sentinel (L-5E)	502		In Air Force College.	RA
☐ Sud-Est SE.3130 Alouette II	1102	1895	HBRA-1102	RA
☐ Volpar Super Turbo 18 [Beech D18S Expeditor (C-45G)]	ETL-1319		(USAF)	RA
☐ Volpar Super Turbo 18 [Beech D18S Expeditor (C-45G)]	ETL-1320		(USAF)	RA
☐ Vought V-310 Kingfisher (OS2U-3)			Fuselage only.	RA

COLECCIÓN DE LA BASE AÉREA 5 (MEX4)

Address:	R/R Colonel Unidad, Habitacional Militar, 44008 Zapopan,
Tel:	0333-624-1401
Admission:	By prior permission only.
Location:	About 30 km north west of Guadalajara.

Zapopan is the site of the Military Aviation School comprising the Air College and the Air Force Specialists School. The college units are divided into three squadrons covering elementary, primary and advanced flying. Types used are the Boeing-Stearman Kaydet, the Maule MX-7, the Beech F.33 Bonanza and the Pilatus PC-7. The display of static aircraft includes three Texans. Over eighty were delivered to Mexico and about twenty were still being flown in the early 1980s. The Vampire, the first jet type to be flown by the Air Force, is one of a batch of fifteen bought from Canada in 1960. The aircraft were refurbished before being ferried across the United States to Mexico. In the college there is an exhibition of memorabilia and photographs.

TYPE	REG/SER	CON. NO.	PI/NOTES	STATUS
☐ Beech A23-19 Musketeer	EBM-015	MB-475	EBP-315	RA
☐ Beech C18S Kansan (AT-11)	BHB-1525	1254	41-27409	RA
☐ Bell 206B Jet Ranger	1162	1039	EBRE-1162	RA
☐ Boeing-Stearman A75N1 Kaydet (PT-17)	EPS-101		(USAAF)	RA
☐ De Havilland D.H.100 Vampire F.3	13	EEP42304	17012 (Canada), N6882D	RA
☐ Lockheed 580 (T-33A)	JE-047		(USAF)	RA
☐ Lockheed-Azcarate LASA-60 Santa Maria				RA
☐ North American NA-88 Texan (AT-6C)	EAN-735			RA
☐ North American NA-88 Texan (AT-6C)	EAN-796			RA
☐ North American NA-88 Texan (AT-6C)	EAN-808			RA
☐ North American NA-174 Trojan (T-28A)	945		(USAF)	RA
☐ Pilatus PC.7	523	208		RA

COLECCIÓN DE LA BASE AVIACIÓN NAVAL DE VERA CRUZ (MEX5)

Address:	Avenue CTAT, Las Badajas, 91726 Vera Cruz.
Tel:	0229-921-9812
Admission:	By prior permission only.
Location:	In the south western suburbs of the city.

In 1919 a locally built floatplane was flown from the port but naval flying did not really start until World War II. A small number of Vought Kingfishers were operated. Now many types are flown from bases around the country. Vera Cruz is home to a maintenance unit and a transport squadron. For many years a flying training school was based at the field. Two of the aircraft are preserved at a school in the main navy base in the city. The Mexican Navy operated a small fleet of DC-3s on transport duties from the late 1960s until the early 1980s.

TYPE	REG/SER	CON. NO.	PI/NOTES	STATUS
☐ Aero Commander 695	MP-301			RA
☐ Beech D18S Expeditor (C-45G)			At Naval School.	RA
☐ Douglas DC-3A-467 Skytrain (C-47B)	MT-104		(USAAF)	RA
☐ Grumman G-111 Albatross (UF-2S) (HU-16D)	MP-102			RA
☐ Grumman G-111 Albatross (UF-2S) (HU-16D)	MP-504		At Naval School.	RA

COLECCIÓN DEL CUARTEL GENERAL DE LA FUERZA AÉREA MEXICANA (MEX6)

Address:	Comandancia de la Fuerza Aerea Mexicana, Mexico D.F.
Admission:	By prior permission only.
Location:	In the suburbs of the city.

The Air Force has a number of aircraft stored and displayed at several locations in the city and there are long term plans for a new museum. The National Aircraft Manufacturing Workshops were set up at Balbuena in November 1915. In store at the Air Force Base at the city airport is the fuselage of the Azcarate OE-1. The prototype of this design made a circuit of the country in 1928. A large collection of photographs, documents, engines and components has been gathered over the years.

TYPE	REG/SER	CON. NO.	PI/NOTES	STATUS
☐ Aerocurvo Ventosa 1				RA
☐ Azacarate OE-1			Fuselage only – at the Air Force Logistics Base.	RA
☐ Boeing-Stearman A75N1 Kaydet (PT-17)	EPS-84		(USAAF)	RA
☐ Boeing-Stearman A75N1 Kaydet (PT-17)			(USAAF)	RA
☐ De Havilland D.H.100 Vampire F.3	1	EEP42308	(VP689), 17016 (Canada), N6870D	RA
☐ De Havilland D.H.100 Vampire F.3	15			RA
☐ Douglas DC-3A-456 Skytrain (C-47A)			Front fuselage only.	RA
☐ Sud-Ouest SO.1221S Djinn				RA
☐ Talleres Nacionales de Construcciones Aeronáuticas Quetzalcoalt A10 (Scale R)				RA

This Waco VPF-7 is part of the museum collection at La Aurora. The biplane is awaiting restoration. (Rod Simpson)

This locally produced A-9B Quail is preserved at the base at Santa Lucia. (Tim Spearman)

The Mexican Navy preserves several aircraft at its Vera Cruz Base. A C-47 is shown here. (Iván Nesbit)

COLECCIÓN ESCUELA DE AVIACIÓN NAVAL / BASE AÉREA 9 (MEX7)

Address:	Al Aeropuerto, 23000 La Paz.
Tel:	0612-124-6764
Admission:	By prior permission only.
Location:	About 5 km west of the town.

The basic flying training school for helicopter pilots is located at this airfield. A variety of types are in use and fixed wing training is carried out on Zlin Z.242s. Transport aircraft are also in residence. The Grumman Albatross amphibian served with the navy from the mid-1970s. Four former Canadian aircraft arrived in 1974 and a batch of ex-United States Navy machines followed a few years later. The type was normally based at La Paz. The Air Force also has a base on the field and the two Trojans are preserved in their area.

TYPE	REG/SER	CON. NO.	PI/NOTES	STATUS
☐ Beech F33A Bonanza	MP-23	CE-1031	ME-038	RA
☐ Cessna 404 Titan	MP-508			RA
☐ Cessna 441 Conquest II	AME-1000			RA
☐ Grumman G-111 Albatross (G-64) (SA-16B) (UF-1G) (UF-2G) (HU-16E)	MP-429	G-246	51-7188, 7188 (USCG), N118DB	RA
☐ Hiller UH12E3	ME-009	5082	HME-009	RA
☐ North American NA-159 Trojan (T-28A)	974	159-222	49-1710 – at Air Force Base.	RA
☐ North American NA-174 Trojan (T-28A)	966		(USAF) – at Air Force Base.	RA

DESCUBRE, MUSEO INTERACTIVO DE CI NCIA Y TECNOLOGÍA (MEX8)

Address:	Avenida San Miguel, Col. Jardines de Parque, 20270 Aguascalientes.
Tel:	044-9913-7012
Fax:	044-9913-6752
Email:	elopez@descubre.org.mx
Admission:	Tuesday-Sunday 1000-1800.
Location:	In the southern part of the town

The exhibition is located in a modern building surrounded by a large park. The displays cover many aspects of science and technology and there is a planetarium. The two aircraft are parked on either side of the entrance. The Mexican Air Force operated Kansans on a variety of training duties and the one on show was moved from the collection at Santa Lucia Air Base. The Piper Navajo is believed to be a former civil registered aircraft.

TYPE	REG/SER	CON. NO.	PI/NOTES	STATUS
☐ Beech C18S Kansan (AT-11)	BHB-1531	3518	42-37138	RA
☐ Piper PA-31-350 Navajo				PV

EXPLORA CENTRO DE CIÊNCAS (MEX9)

Address:	Boulevard Francisco Villa 202, Col La Martinica C.P., 37500 Léon.
Tel:	047-7711-6711
Email:	explora@explora.edu.mex
Admission:	Tuesday-Friday 0900-2100; Saturday-Sunday 1000-2100
Location:	In the south eastern part of the city.

Three aircraft are displayed at this science museum which concentrates on explaining topics so that they can be understood by children. An IMAX theatre has been constructed at the site. Many aspects of technology are explored and there are a number of 'hands-on' displays. The Commando was delivered in late 1944 to Karachi where it was flown by the USAAF. In 1946 the aircraft was sold to the Florida Leasing Company and was then used by a number of cargo airlines. After a period in store it was flown to Mexico. The C-46 flew in the country for several years before being withdrawn from use in 1989 and then stored for many years at Mexico City. The Commando was subsequently dismantled and transported to the museum. The Alouette was flown on Government duties for two decades. The Wright Flyer replica was built locally and resides in the foyer of the building. This aircraft honours the contribution of the brothers and was completed for the centenary of powered flight.

TYPE	REG/SER	CON. NO.	PI/NOTES	STATUS
☐ Curtiss-Wright CW-20B-2 Commando (C-46D)	TE-6047	30686	42-101231, N5131B	PV
☐ Sud SA.319B Alouette III	XC-FUO	2036		PV
☐ Wright Flyer (R)				PV

GLOBO MUSEO DEL NIÑO (MEX10)

Address:	Calle Analco y 5 Febrero, 44460 Guadalajara.
Tel:	033-3369-1381
Email:	globo@guadalajara.gob.mx
Admission:	Tuesday-Friday 0900-1700; Saturday-Sunday 1000-1800.
Location:	In the centre of the city.

The museum has many hands on exhibitions so that children can learn about aspects of science, technology and natural history. During the school holidays and at weekends and in the evenings many experimental sessions are held for people between three and eight years old. A former Air Force LASA-60 is the only aircraft on view. A number of bicycles and motor vehicles are also in the transport section.

TYPE	REG/SER	CON. NO.	PI/NOTES	STATUS
☐ Lockheed-Azcarate LASA-60 Santa Maria	BRL-1034	1034	FAM-1034	PV

HANGARES PRESIDENCIALES (MEX11)

Address:	Estado Mayor Presidencial, Aeropuerto Internacional de la Ciudad de Mexico.
Admission:	By prior permission only.
Location:	In the southern suburbs of the city.

The C-47 was the first presidential aircraft in the country and carried out this role from 1947 until 1978. The aircraft is mounted outside the hangar and inside there is a display of memorabilia. The aircraft served with the United States Army Air Force and was then transferred to the Royal Air Force for duties in India and Burma where it crashed in 1944. The C-47 was transported back to the U.S.A. and was rebuilt and upgraded.

TYPE	REG/SER	CON. NO.	PI/NOTES	STATUS
☐ Douglas DC-3C (DC-3A-456 Skytrain (C-47A) (Dakota III)	TP-0202	43083	Original c/n 9869 42-24007, FD948, XB-FAB, XC-PAB, AP/TP-0202	RA

MONUMENTO DE HERÓICO COLEGIO MILITAR (MEX12)

Address:	Cuauhtemoc, Mexico City.
Tel:	0155-5553-3289
Admission:	By prior permission only.
Location:	In the southern suburbs of the city.

There are several military schools around the country which bear the same name. Located in the southern part of the Mexico City conurbation this school has been in existence for many years. Students are trained in all aspects of military life and specialist subjects are also taught. A display of military equipment has been set up in the grounds and there are also several memorials. The only aircraft preserved is a former Air Force C-47. The first example of the type was delivered to the Mexican Air Force in December 1945 and small numbers are still in use. The code 'TED' signifies that this aircraft served as an executive transport.

TYPE	REG/SER	CON. NO.	PI/NOTES	STATUS
☐ Douglas DC-3A-456 Skytrain (C-47A)	TED-6022			RA

MONUMENTO DE LA BASE AÉREA 3 (MEX13)

Address:	22710 El Cipres, Ensenada Baja California.
Admission:	By prior permission only.
Location:	Just north of the town.

The base now houses a liaison and communications unit flying Cessna 182s. Two trainers also used for ground attack work have been preserved as monuments. Both types have given long and distinguished service in Mexico and were highly thought of by their pilots. The field is home to a number of general aviation companies and also serves as a port of entry into Mexico for flights from the southern U.S.A.

TYPE	REG/SER	CON. NO.	PI/NOTES	STATUS
☐ North American NA-88 Texan (AT-6C)	EAN-795		(USAAF)	RA
☐ North American NA-174 Trojan (T-28A)	T-28-924		(USAF)	RA

MONUMENTO DE LA BASE AÉREA 4 (MEX14)

Address:	77600 Cozumel, Quintana Roo.
Admission:	By prior permission only.
Location:	Just north east of the town.

The base has been home to training squadrons for many years and the Swiss designed Pilatus PC-7 is currently in use. Two former residents have been preserved as monuments to all who served at the field.

TYPE	REG/SER	CON. NO.	PI/NOTES	STATUS
☐ North American NA-174 Trojan (T-28A)	T-28-972		(USAF)	RA
☐ North American NA-174 Trojan (T-28A)	T-28-973		(USAF)	RA

MONUMENTO DE LA BASE AÉREA 6 (MEX15)

Address:	30700 Tuxtla Gutierrez, Chiapas.
Admission:	By prior permission only.
Location:	In the western suburbs of the town.

This base is home to a squadron flying the Pilatus PC-7. Aircraft and helicopters operated by the Federal Police are also in residence. A T-33 has been preserved as a monument to pilots who have lost their lives.

TYPE	REG/SER	CON. NO.	PI/NOTES	STATUS
☐ Lockheed 580 (T-33A)				RA

MONUMENTO DE LA BASE AÉREA 7 (MEX16)

Address:	39900 Pie de la Cuesta, Guerrero.
Admission:	By prior permission only.
Location:	About 5 km north west of the town.

Helicopter units operating Bell 206s and Bell 212s are in residence along with a number of Pilatus PC-7s. North American T-28s once flew from the field and one has been preserved as a monument.

TYPE	REG/SER	CON. NO.	PI/NOTES	STATUS
☐ North American NA-174 Trojan (T-28A)	'T-28-917'		(USAF)	RAX

MONUMENTO DE LA BASE AÉREA 8 (MEX17)

Address:	97127 Merida, Yucatan.
Admission:	By prior permission only.
Location:	In the south western suburbs of the town.

Bell 206 Jet Rangers and Bell 212 helicopters operate from this base. A unit flying Cessna 210s is also in residence. A T-33A is mounted as a monument to those who have served at the field.

TYPE	REG/SER	CON. NO.	PI/NOTES	STATUS
☐ Lockheed 580 (T-33A)	'JE-011'		(USAF)	RAX

MONUMENTO DE LA BASE AÉREA 13 (MEX18)

Address:	32000 Chihuahua.
Admission:	By prior permission only.
Location:	About 5 km south of the town.

A communications and liaison squadron flying Cessna 182s operates from the base. A T-33A painted with a false serial is preserved as a monument. The field also serves as the civil airport for the city and several airlines operate services. Executive aircraft and general aviation types are also in residence.

TYPE	REG/SER	CON. NO.	PI/NOTES	STATUS
☐ Lockheed 580 (T-33A)	'JE-4013'		(USAF)	RAX

MONUMENTO DE LA BASE AÉREA 15 (MEX19)

Address:	San Juan Buutista La Raya, Oaxaca.
Admission:	By prior permission only.
Location:	In the south eastern suburbs of the town.

Bell 212 helicopters are based at the field. The Mexican Air Force ordered several examples of the type and they entered service in the late 1980s. A T-33A is preserved as a memorial to former pilots.

TYPE	REG/SER	CON. NO.	PI/NOTES	STATUS
☐ Lockheed 580 (T-33A)	JE-045		(USAF)	RA

MONUMENTO DE LA BASE AÉREA 16 (MEX20)

Address:	86140 Ciudad Pemex, Tabasco.
Admission:	By prior permission only.
Location:	In the south eastern suburbs of the town.

The base is currently held in reserve and no operational units are in residence. One of the many T-33s operated by the Mexican Air Force has been preserved as a monument to those who have served at the field.

TYPE	REG/SER	CON. NO.	PI/NOTES	STATUS
☐ Lockheed 580 (T-33A)			(USAF)	RA

MONUMENTO DE LA BASE AÉREA 17 (MEX21)

Address:	Copalar, Chiapas.
Admission:	By prior permission only.
Location:	About 10 km south east of Comitan.

This base is currently held in reserve but sees occasional flights and detachments from other fields. A T-33 is preserved as a monument. Civil aircraft also use the site and several reside at the field.

TYPE	REG/SER	CON. NO.	PI/NOTES	STATUS
☐ Lockheed 580 (T-33A)			(USAF)	RA

MONUMENTO DE LA BASE AERONAVAL DE CAMPECHE (MEX22)

Address:	24079 Campeche.
Admission:	By prior permission only.
Location:	Just south east of the town.

The Mexican Navy operates a number of types on patrol and communications mission from their base on the field. A Grumman Albatross, formerly used on these duties, serves as a monument.

TYPE	REG/SER	CON. NO.	PI/NOTES	STATUS
☐ Grumman G-111 Albatross (UF-2S) (HU-16D)	MP-506			RA
☐ Grumman G-111 Albatross (UF-2S) (HU-16D)	MP-507		By civil terminal	PV

MUSEO DE CIENCAS Y TECNOLOGIA (MEX23)

Address:	Avenida Rafael Morillo, 91070 Xalapa.
Tel:	052-2812-5110
Admission:	Tuesday-Friday 0900-1700; Saturday-Sunday 1000-1800.
Location:	About 2 km west of the city which is about 100 km north west of Vera Cruz.

Displays at this museum trace the rapid advances which have been made in recent years in all aspects of technology. The aviation section includes models, photographs and documents. The Reliant was used by Aeronaves de Mexico in the 1930s. The DC-7 was delivered to United Airlines in 1958 and operated for six years. Over the next two decades it was used by several travel clubs in the U.S.A. The Mexican Navy acquired nine ex-U.S. Navy HU-16Cs in the late 1970s to supplement the four former Canadian examples delivered four years earlier. The Albatross on show was operated by 5 Squadron of the Mexican Navy at Campeche. The Wright Flyer replica was built to commemorate the centenary of powered flight. The collection has recently moved to an improved site on the outskirts of the town. Exhibition halls have been constructed and there is an outside park where the larger aircraft and several vehicles reside.

TYPE	REG/SER	CON. NO.	PI/NOTES	STATUS
☐ Bell 206 Jet Ranger				PV
☐ Douglas DC-7	'XA-VER'	45490	N6357C	PVX
☐ Grumman G-231 Albatross (CSR-110)	MP-503	G-454	9306 (Canada), N9387	PV
☐ Lockheed 1329 JetStar 8				PV
☐ Lockheed 580 (T-33A)	JE-018	580-6544	51-8760, M-53 (Netherlands), N647	PV
☐ North American NA-174 Trojan (T-28A)	964		(USAF)	PV
☐ Stinson SR-5C	XB-AJI	9276		PV
☐ Sud-Est SE.3130 Alouette II	XC-HAJ			PV
☐ Wright Flyer (R)				PV

MUSEO DE COMPANIA MEXICANA DE AVIACIÓN (MEX24)

Address:	Avenida Base de Mantenimento, Colonel Juan de Aragua Unidad, 09000 Mexico DF.
Tel:	055-5784-0812
Admission:	By prior permission only.
Location:	At the airport which is in the north eastern suburbs of the city.

The airline was founded in 1921 and the first aircraft flown was a Lincoln Sport. A faithful replica of the type has been built and flown. Over the years the company has operated a variety of types on both international and domestic services. A display of models, photographs and memorabilia has been put on show at their main base at the international airport. The Lincoln has been shown at exhibitions around the country.

TYPE	REG/SER	CON. NO.	PI/NOTES	STATUS
☐ Lincoln Standard (R)				RAA

MUSEO DE LA BASE AÉREA 2 (MEX25)

Address:	Inf Disponsible S/N, Colonel El Espanol, 70110 Ixtepec.
Tel:	097-1281-8001
Admission:	By prior permission only.
Location:	About 15 km south west of the town.

Two fighter squadrons of the 10th. Group are in residence at this field. The T-33 has been flown in this role for many years and four have been preserved along with the two North American designed trainers. The aircraft are parked at a number of locations around the field. The base has set up a museum in a building on the site. The history of the airfield, its units, aircraft and personnel are highlighted. On show are models, badges, components, documents, photographs and uniforms along with a collection off memorabilia.

TYPE	REG/SER	CON. NO.	PI/NOTES	STATUS
☐ Lockheed 580 (T-33A)	JE-051	580-1090	56-1740	RA
☐ Lockheed 580 (T-33A)	JE-006	580-6980	51-9196	RA
☐ Lockheed 580 (T-33A)	JE-007	580-7051	51-9267	RA
☐ Lockheed 580 (T-33A)	JE-024		(USAF)	RA
☐ Lockheed 580 (T-33A)	JE-048		(USAF)	RA
☐ Lockheed 580 (T-33A)	JE-057		(USAF)	RA
☐ North American NA-174 Trojan (T-28A)	'910'	174-100	51-3562, T28-929 (Mexico), N5206V, N128DR	RAX

MUSEO DEL EJÉRCITO Y FUERZA AÉREA MEXICANOS (MEX26)

Address:	Valentin Gomez 600, 44450 Guadalajara.
Tel:	033-3618-3974
Admission:	Tuesday-Saturday 1000-1800.
Location:	In the centre of the city.

The museum opened in June 1999 and the displays trace the military history of the country. There are many photographs, models, uniforms, documents and trophies in the halls. There is a section devoted to the development of weapons. Featured prominently are the pre-Hispanic period, the War of Independence and the 1910 Revolution. The Pietenpol was built in 1936 by a pilot with only four hours of flying instruction. He flew the aircraft from Morelia to Mexico City and was promptly accepted into the military aviation school. Bernard Pietenpol designed the Aircamper in the 1930s with the idea that it could be built by the 'average American'. Powered by a Ford engine, the parasol wing monoplane was a success and plans appeared in a number of engineering and flying magazines. Modern versions are still being built by amateur constructors as are a few single seat Sky Scouts. The military aircraft represent types flown by the Air Force in recent years and include a classic P-47 Thunderbolt. Mexican pilots flew the type in the Pacific area on combat duties against the Japanese. At the end of the conflict the aircraft were left behind but the United States donated another twenty five to equip fighter units. They gave excellent service for many years until replaced by jets such as the Vampire. The Stearman Kaydet was used to train pilots in many countries and Mexico was no exception.

TYPE	REG/SER	CON. NO.	PI/NOTES	STATUS
□ Bell 205A-1	1500	30124	HBR-1153	PV
□ Boeing-Stearman A75N1 Kaydet (PT-17)	EPS-6086		(USAAF), EPS-86	PV
□ De Havilland D.H.100 Vampire F.3	5	EEP42346	(VP729), 17040 (Canada), N6875D	PV
□ Lockheed 580 (T-33A)	JE-002	580-5858	51-6526 – front fuselage only.	PV
□ Lockheed 580 (T-33A)	JE-011	580-8628	53-5289	PV
□ North American NA-88 Texan (AT-6C)	EAN-757			PV
□ North American NA-174 Trojan (T-28A)	931		(USAF)	PV
□ Pietenpol B4-A Aircamper				RA
□ Republic P-47D Thunderbolt	'PZT-1016'		44-90205, PZT-1012	PVX
□ Talleres Nacionales de Construcciones Aeronáuticas H	12H67			PV

MUSEO FRANCISCO SARABIA (MEX27)

Address:	Boulevard Miguel Aleman, 35150 Ciudad Lerdo.
Admission:	By prior permission only.
Location:	In the town which is about 250 km north east of Durango.

The Granville brothers were famous in the 1930s for their racing aircraft and at the current time several replicas of their designs are flying in the U.S.A. Their last model, the Q.E.D., was constructed for Jackie Cochrane to fly in the 1934 race from Mildenhall in England to Melbourne in Australia. The aircraft was flown in the 1934 Bendix Trophy but did not do well and in the race to Australia it got as far as Bucharest in Romania. However on its return to the U.S.A. it took part in a number of races but completed none of them. Francisco Sarabia bought the Q.E.D. in 1939, named it 'Conquistador del Cielo', and seemed to have broken the jinx. He set a record for a non-stop flight from Mexico City to New York on May 24th 1939. On the return trip, starting from Washington D.C., the Q.E.D. crashed into the Potomac River, killing Sarabia. The engine failed on take off due to a rag left in the cowling being sucked into the carburettor. The remains of the aircraft were salvaged and restored for static display by the Sarabia family. They constructed a purpose built museum on their property in Ciudad Lerdo to house the aircraft. Around the walls are photographs of the flights and items of memorabilia.

TYPE	REG/SER	CON. NO.	PI/NOTES	STATUS
□ Granville Gee Bee R-6H Q.E.D.	XB-AKM	1	NR14307, NX14307	PV

MUSEO TECNOLOGICO DE LA COMISION FEDERAL DE ELECTRICIDAD (MEX28)

Address:	Segunda Seccion Bosque de Chapultepec, 11580 Mexico D.F.
Tel:	055-5272-6378
Admission:	Tuesday-Saturday 0900-1700.
Location:	In the western part of the city.

The area of Chapultec Park houses the city zoo and a number of museums covering many aspects of history and culture. Displays at this museum, set up by the national electricity commission, deal with many fields of technology. The generation and distribution of electricity is featured in a number of innovative displays. The contribution of industry to the development of the country is also portrayed. There are many 'hands-on' exhibits in all sections of the museum. The aircraft are parked outside the building. The Mitchell was flown for a short time at Greenville in South Carolina before being put into storage in Texas. The aircraft was sold to Canada in 1952 where it was operated for a decade. It was used as a civil machine in the U.S.A. from 1961 until 1970 and it appeared at this museum two years later. The twin engined bomber is mounted on a pole and is in civil colours. The C-47 is now painted in the colours of one of five flown by the Mexican Navy. The aircraft was originally delivered to the United States Navy in the spring of 1942 and operated at a number of bases in California. The Fairchild Engine and Airplane Company purchased it in 1946 and after a period of private use it arrived in Mexico in December 1971. Two helicopters which have flown with the commission can be seen. Visitors can view the cabin of the Puma. These have been used for inspecting overhead power cables and transporting heavy equipment and people to remote sites. The exhibitions cover all field of transport and several public service vehicles used in the city can be seen. These includes, buses, lorries and railway engines.

TYPE	REG/SER	CON. NO.	PI/NOTES	STATUS
☐ Aero Commander 680F				PV
☐ Bell 47G-3B-1	XC-DAL	2931		PV
☐ Douglas DC-3A-360 Skytrain (R4D-1)	'MT-203'	4282	Bu3142, NC41046, XC-CTM	PVX
☐ North American NA-108 Mitchell (B-25J) (TB-25J) (Mitchell III)	N92872	108-32403	44-29128, 5236 (RCAF)	PV
☐ Sud SA.330J Puma	XC-GEH	1649		PV

PARQUE MUNICIPAL FUERZA AÉREA MEXICANA (MEX29)

Address:	Colonia 70/76, 22300 Tijuana
Admission:	On permanent view.
Location:	In the centre of the city.

A display honouring the Mexican Air Force has been set up in the municipal park in the city. The only aircraft on show is a North American Trojan. This trainer was the first of eighty acquired by the service and was used for engine test work by the 3rd Maintenance Squadron based at the nearby military airfield.

TYPE	REG/SER	CON. NO.	PI/NOTES	STATUS
☐ North American NA-159 Trojan (T-28A)	'1900'	159-205	49-1693, '1'	PVX

PARQUE TANGAMANGA I (MEX30)

Address:	San Luis Potosi.
Admission:	On permanent view.
Location:	In the south western suburbs of the town.

There are a number of attractions in this large park which has two separate sections. There are areas devoted to sport and recreation. Two large lakes are surrounded by pleasant gardens and wooded areas. These are used for fishing and boating. There are two aircraft and a number of vehicles on show. The colourful C-47 also serves as a cinema for children and their parents. The Aero Commander is parked nearby and has its markings erased. A motor racing circuit is in the other section of the park and regular meetings are held.

TYPE	REG/SER	CON. NO.	PI/NOTES	STATUS
☐ Aero Commander				PV
☐ Douglas DC-3A-456 Skytrain (C-47A)	'XPT-I-06'			PVX

NICARAGUA

MUSEO AERONAUTICO DE LA FUERZA AÉREA DE NICARAGUA (NIC1)

Address:	Base Aerea Augusto Cesar Sandino, Pista Pedro Joaquin Chamoro, Managua.
Admission:	By prior permission only.
Location:	About 10 km east of the city.

In the early 1920s an America presented the Nicaraguan Army with four Curtiss Jenny trainers and a small number of U.S. built DH-4s. Progress was slow and over the next few years a few more aircraft arrived. During World War II an aviation school was established at Managua using PT-13s, PT-19s and AT-6s. At the end of the conflict P-38 Lightnings were obtained along with P-47 Thunderbolts and P-51 Mustangs. Transports and trainers were also acquired. In recent years there have been a number of conflicts between government and rebel forces. Currently the Air Force operates a number of transports, light aircraft and helicopters. On show in the building are photographs, models, uniforms and documents. The three preserved aircraft are displayed around the base with the Mil-24 by the main gate and the Twin Bonanza in the recreational area. The first Mi-24 was delivered to Nicaragua in 1986 and several have been lost in conflicts with rebel forces.

TYPE	REG/SER	CON. NO.	PI/NOTES	STATUS
☐ Beech D50B Twin Bonanza	YN-CBQ	DH-214		RA
☐ Mil Mi-2	YN-CCI	563227123		RA
☐ Mil Mi-24	361			RA

Above: This P-47D Thunderbolt is preserved at the Mexican Air Force Museum in Guadalajara. (Iván Nesbit)

Right: Francisco Sarabia's Granville Q.E.D. is on show in his home town of Ciudad Lerdo. (Source Unknown)

This Mil Mi-24 is preserved at Managua. (Paul Seymour)

PANAMA

MONUMENTO DE BASE AEREA DE TOCUMEN (PAN1)

Address:	Tocumen, Panama City.
Admission:	By prior permission only.
Location:	About 10 km east of the city.

The Panamanian Air Force operates a variety of helicopters and light aircraft from their base at the main international airport. A Bell Iroquois is mounted by the entrance to their area.

TYPE	REG/SER	CON. NO.	PI/NOTES	STATUS
□ Bell 205 Iroquois (UH-1H)	SAN-101			RA

PUERTO RICO

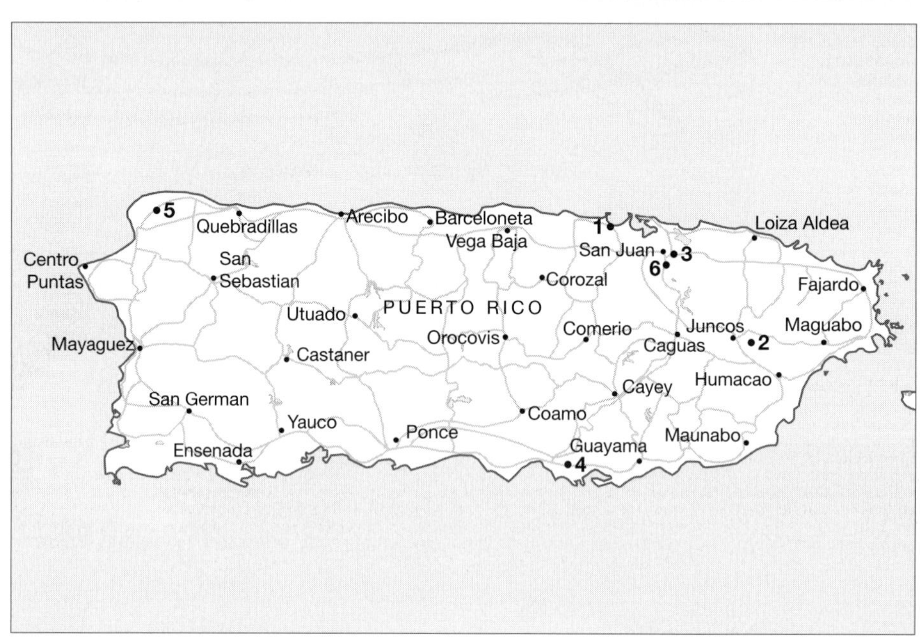

DORADO AIR NATIONAL GUARD MONUMENT (PR1)

Address:	Parque Dorado
Admission:	On permanent view.
Location:	In the south eastern part of the town.

The Vought Corsair served with the local Air National Guard from 1975 until 1993. One has been preserved in the park as a memorial to local people who have served with the 198th Squadron.

TYPE	REG/SER	CON. NO.	PI/NOTES	STATUS
□ Vought A-7D Corsair II	70-0995	D-141		PV

LAS PIEDRAS AIR NATIONAL GUARD MONUMENT (PR2)

Address:	Las Piedras.
Admission:	By prior permission only.
Location:	In the town.

Many local people have served with the Puerto Rico Air National Guard. The Corsair was flown for many years and one formerly flown has been preserved as a monument in a local park.

TYPE	REG/SER	CON. NO.	PI/NOTES	STATUS
☐ Vought A-7D Corsair II	72-0212	D-334		PV

MUNIZ AIR NATIONAL GUARD BASE MONUMENT (PR3)

Address:	200 Jose A. Santana Avenue, Carolina, Puerto Rico 00979-1514.
Tel:	787-253-7502
Fax:	787-253-2513
Email:	starbase@prsanj.ang.af.mil
Admission:	By prior permission only.
Location:	In the eastern part of San Juan.

The airfield has been home to the Puerto Rico Air National Guard for more than half a century. An example of the Corsair is preserved just inside the main gate. A Starfighter is parked near the ramp.

TYPE	REG/SER	CON. NO.	PI/NOTES	STATUS
☐ Lockheed 383-04-05 Starfighter (F-104C)				RA
☐ Vought A-7D Corsair II	69-6202	D-32		RA

PUERTO RICO NATIONAL GUARD MUSEUM (PR4)

Address:	Camp Santiago, Salinas 00751.
Tel:	787-289-1675
Admission:	Daily 1000-1600.
Location:	About 2 km north of the town.

This large site opened in 1940 as a training centre for members of the local guard. In 1975 it was renamed Camp Santiago after Specialist Fourth Class Hector Santiago-Colon who sacrificed his life in Vietnam to save his colleagues. He won both the Purple Heart and the Medal of Honor. The flying unit of the Puerto Rico Air National Guard was formed in November 1947 at Isla Grande Airport. A move to the International Airport took place in May 1956. The initial equipment consisted of P-47N Thunderbolts. Since then Sabre and Starfighter variants were operated along with A-7 Corsairs and F-16s. The museum has been set up to trace the history of all branches of the guard and on view are uniforms, weapons, vehicles, documents and photographs. A display of military vehicles including lorries, tanks and armoured personnel carriers is on view. There are several items from the Spanish era to be seen. Five aircraft are currently on show with more expected.

TYPE	REG/SER	CON. NO.	PI/NOTES	STATUS
☐ Bell 47G-2 Sioux (H-13H) (OH-13H)				PV
☐ Bell 209 Huey Cobra (AH-1G)				PV
☐ De Havilland D.H.C.4A Caribou (CV-2B) (C-7A)	63-9747	201		PV
☐ General Dynamics 401 Fighting Falcon (F-16A)	80-0612	61-333		PV
☐ Vought A-7D Corsair II	74-1760	D-435		PV

RAMEY AIR FORCE BASE HISTORICAL SOCIETY (PR5)

Address:	P.O. Box 250165, Aguadilla, Puerto Rico 00604.
Email:	webmaster@rameyafb.org
Admission:	By prior permission only.
Location:	About 5 km north of Borinquen.

Borinquen Army Airfield opened on appropriated land in late 1939. The first occupants were nine Douglas B-18As which arrived from Langley Air Force Base in Virginia. Over the next few years the field was home to a variety of types. Strategic Air Command took over the base in 1952 and B-36s moved in. Later B-52s were flown before the U.S.A.F. moved out in 1973. In September 1948 the site was named after Brigadier General Howard K. Ramey who was killed in the South Pacific. Today the field is used for general aviation and a unit of the U.S. Coast Guard is in residence. The society was formed to preserve the heritage of the base and has members across the United States. Memorabilia has been collected and regular events are held. Volunteers are working on the restoration of the Super Constellation which has been at the airport since it was struck on the ground by a DC-4 in February 1992. Hopefully this will lead to the setting up of a museum at the field.

TYPE	REG/SER	CON. NO.	PI/NOTES	STATUS
☐ Lockheed 1049H/01-03-148 Super Constellation (1049H/01-03-143)	HI-542CT	1049H-4825	N6922C, CF-BFN, N6922C, 'EC-ARN', N6922C	RAC

UNIVERSITY OF PUERTO RICO – SAN JUAN MONUMENT (PR6)

Address: Rio Pedras Barrio, San Juan 00931-3343.
Tel: 787-764-4063
Email: esantiago@upr.edu
Admission: By prior permission only.
Location: In the southern part of the city.

Starfighters operated with the local Air National Guard from the International Airport from the summer of 1967 until mid-1975. Many university students served with the unit and the aircraft preserved is a reminder of this. The educational establishment has several campuses around the island where different courses are offered. This aircraft may have moved to Muniz Air National Guard Base.

TYPE	REG/SER	CON. NO.	PI/NOTES	STATUS
☐ Lockheed 383-04-05 Starfighter (F-104C)	57-0929	383-1246		RA

TRINIDAD AND TOBAGO

CHAGUARAMAS MILITARY HISTORY AND AEROSPACE MUSEUM (TR1)

Address: Western Main Road, Chaguaramas, Trinidad.
Tel: 808-634-4391
Fax: 808-634-2012
Email: cmham@carib-link.net
Admission: Daily 0900-1700.
Location: In the western part of the city.

The area was taken over by the Americans as a naval base in early 1941 and the station opened on June 1st that year. During World War II many ships used the port and the base was one of the most important in the Caribbean. The run down of the facilities began in 1956 and the Americans returned the peninsula to Trinidad in 1963. This museum was set up by Gaylord Kelshall, a former Trinidad Coast Guard officer. The exhibition covers the five hundred year military history of the islands and there are several early weapons on show. The era when pirates sailed the local waters is portrayed in a series of paintings. A number of impressive displays have been set up including a reconstruction of a World War I trench and a German World War II bunker. The contribution of local soldiers to wars abroad is featured The site is dominated by the Lockheed TriStar. An exhibition tracing the history of British West Indies Airways is being set up in the fuselage. Light aircraft including parts from a crashed Gipsy Moth, are being added to the displays. The Bensen gyrocopter was built locally.

TYPE	REG/SER	CON. NO.	PI/NOTES	STATUS
☐ Bensen B-8M Gyrocopter				PV
☐ Cessna 150				PVX
☐ De Havilland D.H.60G Gipsy Moth	VP-TAA	859	G-CAVW – parts from crash.	PVD
☐ Lockheed L-1011-500 TriStar	9Y-TGN	1191		PV
☐ Sud SA.341G Gazelle	9Y-TFO	1029	F-WTNS, NS-1, TTDF-2	PVD

INDEX

All aircraft are listed alphabetically by manufacturer or designer (in the case of some gliders and homebuilt aircraft) followed by the type. Each country is denoted by a two/three letter code and each museum/collection a number e.g. CU10 is tenth museum/collection in alphabetical order in Cuba.

Country codes are as follows:-
ARU Aruba; **BAR** Barbados; **COS** Costa Rica; **CU** Cuba; **DO** Dominican Republic; **EL** El Salvador; **GU** Guatemala; **HO** Honduras; **MEX** Mexico; **NIC** Nicaragua: **PAN** Panama; **PR** Puerto Rico; **TR** Trinidad and Tobago.

This Convair 580 is preserved at Santa Lucia Air Base in Mexico. (Iván Nesbit)

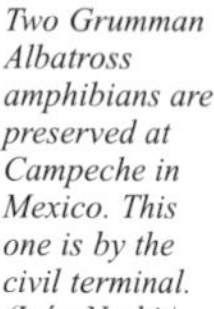

Two Grumman Albatross amphibians are preserved at Campeche in Mexico. This one is by the civil terminal. (Iván Nesbit)

SOUTH AMERICA

Caribbean Sea
Atlantic Ocean
GUYANA
VENEZUELA
SURINAME
FRENCH GUIANA
COLOMBIA
ECUADOR
BRAZIL
PERU
BOLIVIA
PARAGUAY
Pacific Ocean
CHILE
ARGENTINA
URUGUAY
Atlantic Ocean
FALKLAND ISLANDS
SOUTH GEORGIA

ARGENTINA

BOLIVIA
CHILE
PARAGUAY
BRAZIL
URUGUAY
ARGENTINA
South Pacific Ocean
South Atlantic Ocean
FALKLAND ISLANDS
Salta
Formosa
San Miguel de Tucuman
Santiago del Estero
Resistencia
Posadas
Catamarca
La Ribja
Santo Tome
Curuzu Cuatia
Cordoba
San Juan
Parana
Mendoza
Mercedes
San Rafael
Buenos Aires
Telen
Santa Rosa
Mar del Plata
Necochea
Neuquen
Zapala
Viedma
San Carlos de Bariloche
Esquel
Rawson
Comodoro Rivadavia
Las Heras
Puerto Deseado
Gobernador Gregores
Puerto Santa Cruz
Rio Gallegos
A 11, 12, 13, 46, 49, 56, 57, 59, 65
0 100 200 300 km
0 100 200 300 miles

COLECCIÓN COBREROS (ARG1)

Address: Sierra de los Padres.
Admission: By prior permission only.
Location: About 15 km north west of Mar del Plata.

A group of enthusiasts near Bahia Blanca stored the majority of the airframes in the collection for a proposed museum devoted to light civil aircraft. Hopefully the project will come to fruition one day. Some years ago the aircraft were moved to their current location. Several have suffered from years of exposure to the elements. The wings of the Macchi are from one of the batch of forty six built in Argentina in the late 1950s and early 1960s. The Nord Norécrin emerged as the winner of a competition for a touring aircraft. The type was put into production for French aeroclubs. Many were exported and Argentina received considerable numbers.

TYPE	REG/SER	CON. NO.	PI/NOTES	STATUS
☐ Aero 45	LV-FJW	03001		RAD
☐ Aeronca C-3				RAD
☐ Aeronca 7AC Champion				RAD
☐ Auster J/1 Autocrat			Possible type.	RAD
☐ Champion 7EC Traveler	LV-FMI	7EC-599		RAD
☐ Ercoupe 415C	'LV-XUV'			RADX
☐ Macchi MB.308G			Wings only.	RAD
☐ Nord N.1203-III Norécrin (1203-II)	LV-FDI	277	LQ-FDI	RAD
☐ Piper J-3C-65 Cub (L-4J)	LV-NHN	12420	44-80124	RAD
☐ Piper J-5A Cub Cruiser	LV-NCM	5-3012		RAD
☐ Republic RC-3 Seabee				RAD

COLECCIÓN DE LA BASE AÉREA CÓRDOBA (ARG2)

Address: Escuela de Aviación Militar/Esceula de Suboficiales
Avenue Forca Aérea Km 6 1/2,
Base Aerea Córdoba.
Tel: 0351-433-3942
Email: incorporacion@eam.iua.edu.ar
Admission: By prior permission only.
Location: About 6 km west of the city on Route 20.

There are two training establishments at this base. One (EAM) is the main pilot training school of the Air Force. On the other side of the road from the airfield is the ESFA. The preserved aircraft at both locations have been assembled to show the recruits the history and traditions of the service. Personnel from the base have restored several airframes for the National Aviation Museum at Morón. The collection includes a number of indigenous designs. The Mirage IIICJ is mounted in the town as a memorial to Air Force personnel.

TYPE	REG/SER	CON. NO.	PI/NOTES	STATUS
☐ Beech B45 Mentor (T-34A)	E-025	CG-189		RA
☐ Cessna 320D SkyKnight	PG-387	0089	N5789X, LV-PQZ, LV-HOB, LV-LCD – at Sub-Officers School.	RA
☐ Dassault Mirage IIICJ			Nearby in town.	PV
☐ Dassault Mirage IIIEA			At Sub-Officers School	RA
☐ Douglas A-4B Skyhawk (A4D-2)	C-225	11865	Bu142803 – at Sub-Officers School	RA
☐ English Electric EA.1 Canberra B.62 (B.2)	B-101	HP.183B	WJ616, G-AYHO, G-27-111	RA
☐ Fabrica Militar de Aviones IA.50A Guarani II	LV-MBS	24	At Sub-Officers School	RA
☐ Fabrica Militar de Aviones IA.50A Guarani II	T-114	6	At Sub-Officers School	RA
☐ Fabrica Militar de Aviones IA.58 Pucará	A-501	001	At Sub-Officers School	RA
☐ Fabrica Militar de Aviones IA.58A Pucará	A-559	060		RA
☐ Gloster Meteor F.4	C-025		EE532, G-5-125, I-025	PV
☐ Hiller UH12L4	H-03	3546	N86687, LV-JAO – at Sub-Officers School	RA
☐ Hughes 369HM	'H-33'	490048M	H-29 – at Sub-Officers School	RAX
☐ Morane-Saulnier MS.760A Paris I	E-226	A-14		RA
☐ North American NA-174 Trojan (T-28A)	E-641			RA
☐ North American NA-191 Sabre (F-86F)	'C-111'	191-658	52-4962, C-124	RA

COLECCIÓN DE BASE AÉREA MILITAR MAR DEL PLATA (ARG3)

Address: Ruta 2 Km 400.
7600 Mar del Plata.
Admission: On permanent view.
Location: About 5 km north of the town.

The Air Force maintains a base at the airfield which also serves as the civil airport for the town. Two aircraft are parked by the military gate. The identity of the Meteor is in some doubt because C-071 is also reported to be the aircraft marked as 'C-073' at the Jorge Newbery Technical School. The Skyhawk is parked by the aero club buildings and carries the markings of one lost in the Falklands conflict in 1982.

TYPE	REG/SER	CON. NO.	PI/NOTES	STATUS
☐ Douglas A-4Q Skyhawk (A4D-2) (A-4B)	'0667'	12244	Bu144988, 0661 – at aero club.	PVX
☐ English Electric EA.1 Canberra B.62 (B.2)	B-105		WH702, G-27-127 – at military gate.	PV
☐ Gloster Meteor F.4	C-071		I-071 – possibly a different aircraft.	PV

COLECCIÓN DE LA BASE AÉRONAVAL DE PUNTA INDIO (ARG4)

Address:	Fuerza Aéronaval 1, Punta Indio.
Admission:	By prior permission only.
Location:	About 10 km south west of the town.

The base is home to the main pilot training school of the Navy. The current equipment is the Beech Turbo Mentor which replaced the Sud Fennec in 1978. Sixty of the French conversions of the T-28 were acquired in the late 1960s. Earlier more than thirty examples of the classic T-6 Texan had been used. Twenty Panthers and a pair of Cougar trainers served at Punta Indio from the late 1950s until the early 1970s when replaced by the MB.326.

TYPE	REG/SER	CON. NO.	PI/NOTES	STATUS
☐ Grumman G-79 Panther (F9F-2)	0452/3-A-111		(USN)	PV
☐ North American NA-88 Texan (AT-6D) (SNJ-5)	'0375'/EAN-001		(USAAF), (USN), 0355	PVX
☐ Sud Fennec [North American NA-174 Trojan (T-28A)]	'1-A-251'			PVX

COLECCIÓN DE LA ESCUELA DE EDUCACIÓN TÉCNICA 8 JORGE NEWBERY (ARG5)

Address:	Almafuerte 17, Villa Luzuriaga, San Justo, Buenos Aires.
Tel:	011-4659-1833
Fax:	011-4659-1859
Admission:	By prior permission only.
Location:	About 16 km west of the city.

This long established school has a number of airframes in its workshops. The Fairchild FH-227 airliner arrived on the premises in 2005. The type is derived from the successful Dutch designed Fokker Friendship. One of the few surviving Percival Prentices in Argentina has been at the site for several years.

TYPE	REG/SER	CON. NO.	PI/NOTES	STATUS
☐ Beech D18S Expeditor (C-45H)	0531	AF-561	52-10631	RA
☐ Douglas A-4Q Skyhawk (A4D-2) (A-4B)	0654	12118	Bu144872	RA
☐ Fairchild-Hiller FH-227J	LV-PAD	065	N150L, N750L, 5T-CJU, N4798W, N280PH, LV-AZW	RA
☐ Gloster Meteor F.4	'C-073'		I-071, C-071	RAX
☐ North American NA-174 Trojan (T-28E) (T-28A) [Sud Fennec]	0553	174-493	51-7640, 137 (France)	RA
☐ Percival P.40 Prentice T.1	E-350	PAC/202		RA
☐ Schneider ESG 31 Grunau Baby IIA	LV-ECU	11		RA
☐ Schneider ESG 31 Grunau Baby IIA				RA

COLECCIÓN DE LA ESCUELA DE EDUCACIÓN TÉCNICA QUILMES (ARG6)

Address:	Avenida Otamendi Quilmes 1878.
Tel:	011-4254-1512
Admission:	Monday-Friday 0900-1400.
Location:	In the north western suburbs of the town.

This airfield houses a unit responsible for the overhaul of helicopters and liaison aircraft. An original 1920s hangar built for the airline Aéropostale survives. The school, which was established in March 1957, is located on the civil side of the site. A number of interesting airframes are in the workshops.

TYPE	REG/SER	CON. NO.	PI/NOTES	STATUS
☐ Aero Commander 500U	T-143	1770-53		RA
☐ Cessna 336 Skymaster	PG-391		TS-02	RA
☐ Gloster Meteor F.4	C-010		RA393, G-5-110, I-010	RA
☐ Hughes 369HM	H-24	390034M	At military gate.	RA
☐ Hughes 369HM	H-25	390035M	At military gate.	RA
☐ Morane-Saulnier MS.760A Paris I	E-225	A-13		RA
☐ Sikorsky S-55D Chickasaw (H-19B) (UH-19B)	H-08			RA
☐ Sikorsky S-62A	ZS-HCW	62003	JA9010	RA
☐ Sud-Est SE.3130 Alouette II	ZS-HIS	1974		RA

COLECCIÓN DE LA II BRIGADA AÉREA (ARG7)

Address:	Avenida Rivadavia 170, Paraná 3100.
Tel:	0343-422-3553
Admission:	By prior permission only.
Location:	In the south eastern suburbs of the town.

This base now houses squadrons operating transport aircraft. The collection of preserved aircraft includes two locally designed types. One of the Canberras serves as a monument and is located by the river in the town.

TYPE	REG/SER	CON. NO.	PI/NOTES	STATUS
☐ English Electric EA.1 Canberra T.64 (T.4)	B-112	EEP.71371	WJ875, G-27-122 – monument in town.	PV
☐ English Electric EA.1 Canberra T.64 (T.4)	B-111	EEP.71416	WT476, G-27-121	RA
☐ Fabrica Militar de Aviones IA.35-1b Huanquero	A-320			RA
☐ Fabrica Militar de Aviones IA.50A Guarani II	T-110	20		RA
☐ Fabrica Militar de Aviones IA.50A Guarani II	F-35	34		RA

COLECCIÓN DE LA III BRIGADA AÉREA (ARG8)

Address:	Ruta Nacional 11, Reconquista 3560.
Tel:	03482-427525
Admission:	By prior permission only.
Location:	About 5 km south of the town.

Squadrons flying the Pucará fly from this base along with a number of liaison aircraft. The preserved example of the type has been painted in the markings of one shot down near Port Stanley in 1982. The Huanquero light transport was the first DINFIA (later FMA) type to be put into production and around fifty were completed.

TYPE	REG/SER	CON. NO.	PI/NOTES	STATUS
☐ Fabrica Militar de Aviones IA.35-1b Huanquero	A-305			PV
☐ Fabrica Militar de Aviones IA.58 Pucará	AX-02		Front fuselage only.	RA
☐ Fabrica Militar de Aviones IA.58 Pucará	'A-514'	005	A-505 with parts of c/n 073 A-573.	RAX

COLECCIÓN DE LA VII BRIGADA AÉREA (ARG9)

Address:	Base Aérea Mariano Moreno, Ruta 11 s/n, Sauce Viejo 2242.
Tel:	0342-499-5061
Admission:	By prior permission only.
Location:	About 17 km south west of Santa Fe.

The base is currently home to units flying a variety of helicopters on a number of tasks. The Meteor is mounted by the main gate to the airfield and serves as a memorial to those who have been killed while flying from the field. The Air Force operated small numbers of Hughes 369s and 500s. Some examples were built under licence in Argentina. One has been preserved on the airfield. A Bell UH-1H has recently joined the collection.

TYPE	REG/SER	CON. NO.	PI/NOTES	STATUS
☐ Bell 205 Iroquois (UH-1H)			(USAF)	RA
☐ Gloster Meteor F.4	C-099		I-099	RA
☐ Hughes 500D	H-37	1190621D		RA
☐ North American NA-174 Trojan (T-28A)	E-610		(USAF) – at aero club.	RA

COLECCIÓN ESTANCIA SANTA ROMANA (ARG10)

Address:	Ruta Nacional 7 Km 680, Justo Daract.
Tel:	054-2657-480707
Admission:	By prior permission only.
Location:	About 20 km south west of Mercedes.

The owner of this ranch, wild animal park and hotel is collecting aircraft for his new museum. A large hangar and display area has been built to house former Air Force types. He has started planning for similar exhibitions of Army and Naval aircraft. He has acquired a large section of the flight deck of the carrier 'Vientinco de Mayo'.

TYPE	REG/SER	CON. NO.	PI/NOTES	STATUS
□ Aero Commander 500U	T-131	1742-38		RA
□ Dassault Etendard IV			Due soon.	-
□ Dassault Mirage IIIBJ	'21'	BJ2/237	C-721	RAX
□ Dassault Mirage IIICJ	'C-701'	CJ-66	C-718	RAX
□ Douglas A-4F Skyhawk	'C-937'		Composite – mocked up as A-4AR.	RA
□ Douglas A-4F Skyhawk	Bu154173	13630		RA
□ Douglas A-4P Skyhawk (A4D-2) (A-4B)	'22'	11811	Bu142749, C-232	RA
□ Douglas DC-3A-456 Skytrain (C-47A) (Dakota III)	T-104	13373	42-93459, KG614, LV-ACE, VR-14	RA
□ Fabrica Militar de Aviones IA.50A Guarani II	T-129	22		RA
□ Fabrica Militar de Aviones IA.58A Pucará	A-590	090		RA
□ Gloster Meteor F.4	C-027		EE527, G-5-127, I-027	RA
□ Grumman G-121 Tracker (S-2E)	0862	324C	Bu153568	RA
□ Grumman G-134 Mohawk (OV-1C) (OV-1D)	AE-035	99C	67-18898 – possible identity.	RA
□ Grumman G-134 Mohawk (OV-1C) (OV-1D)	AE-037	119C	67-18918	PV
□ Mil Mi-2	SP-SCL	529614016		RA
□ Morane-Saulnier MS.760A Paris I	E-224	A-12		RA
□ North American NA-174 Trojan (T-28A)	E-608	174-112	51-3574 – on loan from MNA.	RA
□ North American NA-191 Sabre (F-86F)	'C-113'		Composite with parts from C-105 and C-121.	RAX
□ Piper PA-23-250 Aztec E	LV-JXF	27-4641	LV-PQU	RAX
□ Sikorsky S-61D-4 Sea King	0696/2-H-235	61779		RA

COMPLEJO MUSEOGRÁFICO ENRIQUE UDAONDO (ARG11)

Address:	Lezica y Torrezouri 917, Luján 6700.
Tel:	02323-420245
Admission:	Thursday-Friday 1200-1730; Saturday-Sunday 1000-1730.
Location:	In the centre of the town which is about 70 km west of Buenos Aires.

The site is one of the largest museum complexes in the country. The transport area houses an excellent display of horse-drawn carriages, a collection of motor vehicles and railway engines and rolling stock. The only surviving example of the famous Dornier Wal flying boat is the star exhibit. The aircraft was built at Marina di Pisa in Italy in 1925. On January 22nd 1926, piloted by Ramon Franco, the Wal left Spain and flew to Buenos Aires alighting on the River Plate on February 10th. Two weeks later the aircraft was presented to the Argentinean Government and it then served with the Navy at Puerto Belgrano. In 1936 the Wal was donated to the museum which was then named Museo Colonial e Historico. In 1968 the aircraft went to Spain for an exhibition before returning to Argentina. A second trip across the Atlantic Ocean took place in 1985. C.A.S.A., who had built several Wals at Cadiz in the 1930s, completely rebuilt this historic flying boat to its original configuration.

TYPE	REG/SER	CON. NO.	PI/NOTES	STATUS
□ Dornier J Wal	M-MWAL	23	W-12	PV

EDIFICIO CÓNDOR (ARG12)

Address:	Avenida Comodoro Pedro Zanni 250, Buenos Aires.
Tel:	011-4317-6148
Admission:	On permanent view.
Location:	In the city.

The building houses the headquarters of the Air Force and inside are several small displays tracing the history and development of the service. The Meteor is mounted in the grounds surrounding the office block.

TYPE	REG/SER	CON. NO.	PI/NOTES	STATUS
□ Gloster Meteor F.4	C-095		I-095	PV

EDIFICIO LIBERTAD (ARG13)

Address:	Comodoro Py 2055, Buenos Aires.
Tel:	011-4503-9629
Admission:	On permanent view.
Location:	In the centre of the city.

The headquarters of the Navy are located in these buildings. Inside there is a collection of memorabilia and photographs tracing the history of the service from its early days. The site has a helipad and rotary wing aircraft are frequent visitors. A Skyhawk which served in the Falklands is preserved at the site. The type entered Argentinean service in the autumn of 1966 and served with squadrons based at Mendoza and Villa Reynolds for many years. Several examples were lost in the 1982 Falklands War.

TYPE	REG/SER	CON. NO.	PI/NOTES	STATUS
☐ Douglas A-4Q Skyhawk (A4D-2) (A-4B)	0657/3-A-304	12161	Bu144915	PV

MONUMENTO DE AEROCLUB ARGENTINO (ARG14)

Address:	Avenida JMD Rojas S/n, San Justo 1754.
Tel:	011-4467-1757
Admission:	On permanent view.
Location:	Just north east of the town

The club was formed in January 1908 and its first activities were mainly in the field of hot air ballooning. The centenary was celebrated with a fly-in which attracted large numbers of visiting aircraft to the airfield. The Guarani which was used by as a transport for the Aerial Operations squadron has been put on show by the club buildings. There are several vintage and classic aircraft based at San Justo.

TYPE	REG/SER	CON. NO.	PI/NOTES	STATUS
☐ Fabrica Militar de Aviones IA.50B Guarani II	T-122	14		RA

MONUMENTO DE AEROCLUB BELL VILLE (ARG15)

Address:	Ruta Provincial 3, Bell Ville.
Tel:	03534-426746
Admission:	By prior permission only.
Location:	Just south of the town.

The club offers flying training and has an active parachute school. There are several privately owned classic types based at the field. The Argentinean Air Force ordered one hundred examples of the Percival Prentice and one of the few survivors acts as a monument. The type flew as a trainer for many years.

TYPE	REG/SER	CON. NO.	PI/NOTES	STATUS
☐ Percival P.40 Prentice T.1	E-372	PAC.249		RA

MONUMENTO DE AEROCLUB CARLOS CASARES (ARG16)

Address:	Avenue 9 de Julio 88, Carlos Caseres 6500.
Tel:	02396-1562-4782
Email:	aeroclubcc@intercaseres.com.ar
Admission:	By prior permission only.
Location:	Just south of the town

This small club has just three aircraft in its fleet including a 1947 Piper J-3C Cub which is still used for pilot training. One of the batch of Trojans used by the Air Force serves as a monument.

TYPE	REG/SER	CON. NO.	PI/NOTES	STATUS
☐ North American NA-174 Trojan (T-28A)	E-636		(USAF)	RA

The Argentine Air Force flew a number of Canberras and this one serves as a monument at Mar del Plata. (Nigel Hitchman)

The collection at the Air Force Base at Reconquista includes this Huanquero. (Tim Spearman)

The only surviving genuine Dornier Wal can be seen in the museum complex at Luján. (Nigel Hitchman)

MONUMENTO DE AEROCLUB CHIVILCOY (ARG17)

Address:	Ruta Nacional 5, Chivilcoy.
Tel:	02346-432011
Email:	aerochiy@hotmail.com
Admission:	By prior permission only.
Location:	About 5 km south west of the town.

This thriving club has a fleet of training and touring aircraft. The Argentinean Air Force operated one hundred Meteor F.4's with the first arriving in 1948 and the type was withdrawn in the second half of 1971.

TYPE	REG/SER	CON. NO.	PI/NOTES	STATUS
☐ Gloster Meteor F.4	C-088		I-088	RA

MONUMENTO DE AEROCLUB COLON (ARG18)

Address:	Edijo Colon, Colon 3280,
Tel:	03447-492004
Email:	aeroclubcolon@colon.co.ar
Admission:	On permanent view.
Location:	Just south of the town.

One of two surviving General Aircraft Cygnets is mounted at the gate as a memorial. The aircraft flew in the Tierra del Fuego for many years and was damaged on landing at Colon. The all metal Cygnet made its maiden flight at Hanworth in 1937. The prototype was built in Slough by C. W. Aircraft and had a tailwheel undercarriage. The company went into liquidation and General Aircraft at Hanworth took over the design.

TYPE	REG/SER	CON. NO.	PI/NOTES	STATUS
☐ General Aircraft GAL.42 Cygnet	LV-FAH	117	G-AGAS	PV

MONUMENTO DE AEROCLUB CORONEL PRINGLES (ARG19)

Address:	Aerodrómo Coronel Pringles, Avenida 25 de Mayo Ruta 5, Coronel Pringles 7530.
Tel:	02922-462488
Admission:	By prior permission only.
Location:	In the south eastern suburbs of the town.

Juan Pascal Pringles fought against the Spanish in the struggle to gain Argentina's independence. A former Navy Texan is preserved at the airfield to serve as a memorial to local aviators.

TYPE	REG/SER	CON. NO.	PI/NOTES	STATUS
☐ North American NA-78 Texan (AT-6A)	0208/4-G-78			RA

MONUMENTO DE AEROCLUB CORONEL SUÁREZ (ARG20)

Address:	Aerodrómo Coronel Suárez, Mitre S/N. Coronel Suárez 7540.
Tel:	02426-431811
Admission:	By prior permission only.
Location:	Just east of the town.

Manuel Isidoro Suárez fought in the conflicts again Spain and then led the Colombian and Peruvian infantry in similar struggles. After World War II several Texans were supplied to train naval pilots.

TYPE	REG/SER	CON. NO.	PI/NOTES	STATUS
☐ North American NA-88 Texan (AT-6D) (SNJ-5C)	'0462/4-G-78'		See MUAN.	RAX

MONUMENTO DE AEROCLUB JUNIN (ARG21)

Address:	Sin Sombre S/N, Aeroparque Municipal, Junin 5585.
Tel:	02362-444175
Admission:	By prior permission only.
Location:	In the north eastern suburbs of the town

The Gloster Meteor F.4 served as a frontline fighter in the Argentinean Air Force from the late 1940s until the arrival of the Dassault Mirage III in 1971. The preserved Meteor, at this club, which operates both powered aircraft and gliders, is mounted on a plinth in a landscaped garden on the approach road to the hangar area.

TYPE	REG/SER	CON. NO.	PI/NOTES	STATUS
☐ Gloster Meteor F.4	C-038		EE587, I-038	RA

MONUMENTO DE AEROCLUB LAS PAREJAS (ARG22)

Address:	Aerodrómo Las Parejas, Las Parejas 2525.
Admission:	By prior permission only.
Location:	Just north of the town.

Argentina acquired large numbers of British built aircraft in the late 1940s. The country was the first overseas purchaser of the Meteor F.4 and it was the first jet fighter to serve with the Air Force. The aircraft were initially flown by Fighter Bomber Groups 2 and 3 then based at Morón. The Meteors flew missions for both sides in the 1955 revolution and a number of aircraft were damaged or destroyed. The Sabre was wanted as a replacement for the elderly jets but a lack of finance resulted in the Meteor soldiering on for several years.

TYPE	REG/SER	CON. NO.	PI/NOTES	STATUS
☐ Gloster Meteor F.4	C-031		EE588, I-031	RA

MONUMENTO DE AEROCLUB NEUQUÉN (ARG23)

Address:	Aeropuerto Internacional Neuquén, Neuquen.
Tel:	0299-444-0246
Email:	acn@aeroclubneuquen.org.ar
Admission:	By prior permission only.
Location:	Just north of the town.

The Meteor is preserved as a monument to local aviators at the airport which is named after former President Juan Perón. This aircraft was one of the second batch of fifty ordered by Argentina and was a new build machine. About forty Doves were delivered to the Argentine Civil Aeronautics Board in 1948/49. They were used on a variety of duties and some were later transferred to the Air Force. An example has been restored and put on show. In addition to the powered aircraft there is also a gliding club with several interesting types.

TYPE	REG/SER	CON. NO.	PI/NOTES	STATUS
☐ De Havilland D.H.104 Dove 1	LV-XZX	04143	LV-XZX, LQ-XZX	RA
☐ Gloster Meteor F.4	C-093		I-093	RA

MONUMENTO DE AEROCLUB RAFAELA (ARG24)

Address:	Aerodrómo, Rafaela.
Admission:	By prior permission only.
Location	About 2 km south of the town.

A Lockheed Lodestar has been preserved at this airfield. The aircraft was damaged on landing some years ago. Members of the club have restored it and painted it in the national colours of blue and white. The airframe is mounted on pylons and a stairs have been fitted to enable visitors to view the interior. A number of Lodestars have flown in Argentina and most were cancelled from the civil register in the early 1960s. The example on show has been given the false markings 'LV-ACR' representing the title of the club.

TYPE	REG/SER	CON. NO.	PI/NOTES	STATUS
☐ Lockheed 18-56-23 Lodestar (C-60A)	'LV-ACR'			RAX

MONUMENTO DE AEROCLUB SAN ANTONIO (ARG25)

Address:	Aerodrómo, San Antonio de Areco 2760.
Admission:	By prior permission only.
Location:	About 3 km north east of the town

The club has restored a Dove for display at its picturesque grass airfield. The aircraft was delivered to Argentina in the summer of 1948 and later served with the Ministry of Agriculture as a staff transport. The prototype Dove made its maiden flight at Hatfield in September 1945. The type proved popular with both military and civilian operators. When production ceased in 1967 five hundred and forty two had been built.

TYPE	REG/SER	CON. NO.	PI/NOTES	STATUS
☐ De Havilland D.H.104 Dove 1	LV-YAO	04181	LV-YAO, LQ-YAO	RA

MONUMENTO DE AEROCLUB SAN FRANCISCO (ARG26)

Address:	Ruta Nacional 19 Km 135, San Francisco 2400.
Tel:	03664-422871
Admission:	By prior permission only.
Location:	About 5 km south east of the town

The club operates a small fleet of training and touring aircraft from its airfield. The Guarani which once served with Group 1 at El Palomar has been put on show as a memorial to local aviators. The Guarani II prototype was shipped to France and exhibited at the 1965 Paris Air Show. The aircraft was the taken to the test centre at Istres and evaluated for over two hundred flying hours. When it flew back to Argentina in February 1966 it became the first Latin American designed type to fly across the Atlantic Ocean.

TYPE	REG/SER	CON. NO.	PI/NOTES	STATUS
☐ Fabrica Militar de Aviones IA.50A Guarani II	T-117	9		RA

MONUMENTO DE AEROCLUB TOLOSA (ARG27)

Address:	Aerodrómo, Tolosa 1900.
Admission:	By prior permission only.
Location:	Just north of the town.

The Dove, which is on show at the airfield, was delivered to Argentina in January 1949 and later joined the Air Force, and reported written off. The airframe was derelict at La Plata in 2005 and it is now restored for display. The aircraft is painted in the white colours with yellow trim of its last civilian owner. The club operates a fleet of Cessnas for training and pleasure flying. In addition they own a Piper PA-11 Cub Special.

TYPE	REG/SER	CON. NO.	PI/NOTES	STATUS
☐ De Havilland D.H.104 Dove 1	LV-LES	04237	LV-YBJ, T-82	RA

MONUMENTO DE AEROCLUB USHUAIA (ARG28)

Address:	CC22, Aeropuerto Ushuaia, Ushuaia 9410.
Tel:	02901-421717
Email:	aeroclubushuaia@speedy.com.ar
Admission:	By prior permission only.
Location:	In the southern suburbs of the town.

The club, formed in 1954, has the most southerly location in the world. Members of the club have restored the C-47 for display. The airframe is now resplendent with a polished metal wings and fuselage. The wing tips and tail are red and the national colours adorn the tail. The Skytrain was one of the first to join the Argentinean Navy when it arrived in the country in December 1946. A display of photographs is in the clubhouse.

TYPE	REG/SER	CON. NO.	PI/NOTES	STATUS
☐ Douglas DC-3A-456 Skytrain (C-47A)	'5-T-22'	9578	42-23716, 0172,	PVX

MONUMENTO DE AEROPUERTO EL CALAFATE (ARG29)

Address:	Sec Fuerza, Aeropuerto El Calafate, El Calafate 9405.
Tel:	02902-49-1912
Admission:	On permanent view.
Location:	About 25 km east of the town.

The airport opened in 2000 to replace the one located in the eastern suburbs of the town. The DC-3 has been moved from at Rio Cuarto and will be restored to represent the use of the old site by Air Force transports.

TYPE	REG/SER	CON. NO.	PI/NOTES	STATUS
☐ Douglas DC-3A-456 Skytrain (C-47A) (Dakota III)	T-101	14010/25455	43-48194, KG778, LV-ACF, LQ-ACF, LV-ACF, TS-03	PV

MONUMENTO DE CENTRO UNIVERSITARIO DE AVIACIÓN (ARG30)

Address:	Aerodromo, La Matanza 1754.
Tel:	011-4693-1724
Admission:	By prior permission only.
Location:	Just south west of the town.

The group operates a pair of Piper PA-11 Cub Specials along with a number of more modern types. The Czechoslovakian designed Morava has been pole mounted near the hangars.

TYPE	REG/SER	CON. NO.	PI/NOTES	STATUS
☐ Let L-200A Morava	'LV-CUA'	170711	LV-HRE	RAX

MONUMENTO DE CLUB AEROMODELISTA RIO DE LA PLATA (ARG31)

Address:	Campo Ernesto Columbo, Ezpeleta.
Tel:	011-4240-7166
Email:	info@ezpeletac.com.ar
Admission:	By prior permission only.
Location:	In the northern suburbs of the town.

The club was originally based at the military airfield at Quilmes. A move to the current site took place in the 1970s. A former Air Force C-47 has been preserved as a reminder of its military links. The aircraft served in Hawaii with the USAAF from 1944 until 1947. Its first civilian owner was the Hughes Tool Company who flew it for a year. Airline service followed before the C-47 moved south to Argentina in 1960. The aircraft was based at Paraná until the late 1980s when it was put into store at Quilmes before moving the short distance to the club.

TYPE	REG/SER	CON. NO.	PI/NOTES	STATUS
☐ Douglas DC-3A-456 Skytrain (C-47A)	TC-34	12792	42-92936, NC63400, N91229, N149A, T-34	RA

MONUMENTO DE COMODORO RIVADAVIA (ARG32)

Address:	Comodoro Rivadavia 9000.
Admission:	On permanent view.
Location:	In the town.

The Argentine Air Force purchased thirty Fiat G.46s in the late 1940s and they operated in the training role for several years. One of the few survivors has been preserved as a monument to local aviators.

TYPE	REG/SER	CON. NO.	PI/NOTES	STATUS
☐ Fiat G.46-5B	Ea-445			PV

MONUMENTO DE CRESPO (ARG33)

Address: Crespo 3116.
Admission: On permanent view.
Location: In the town.

The Guarani light transport served with the Air Force for several years. An example of the type is preserved in the town as a monument to the residents of the town who have served with the military.

TYPE	REG/SER	CON. NO.	PI/NOTES	STATUS
☐ Fabrica Militar de Aviones IA.50A Guarani II	T-118	10		PV

MONUMENTO DE DIAMANTE (ARG34)

Address: Diamante 3105
Admission: On permanent view.
Location: In the town.

This important port located on the River Paraná has been given an example of the Guarani transport too serve as a monument to local servicemen who have lost their lives in service of their country.

TYPE	REG/SER	CON. NO.	PI/NOTES	STATUS
☐ Fabrica Militar de Aviones IA.50B Guarani II	T-126	26		PV

MONUMENTO DE GOYA (ARG35)

Address: Goya 3450.
Admission: On permanent view.
Location: In the town.

This former Royal Air Force Meteor, which was part of the first batch of fifty delivered by sea to Argentina in the late 1940s, has been preserved as a monument to local military aviators. The town has a long military tradition and there are other memorials with guns and military vehicles to be seen.

TYPE	REG/SER	CON. NO.	PI/NOTES	STATUS
☐ Gloster Meteor F.4	C-014		EE575, I-014	PV

MONUMENTO DE GRUPO 1 DE VIGILANCIA (ARG36)

Address: Ruta 200 S/N,
Merlo 1722.
Tel: 0220-483-0470
Admission: On permanent view.
Location: In the south eastern part of the town.

The organisation was set up in December 1952 to control flights in Argentinean airspace. The headquarters are at Merlo and there are tracking stations around the country. When the group was set up the defence of the Buenos Aires region was in the hands of Meteor squadrons. One example is preserved outside the buildings and the other is located in a nearby park. These early jet fighters were in service in the country from 1948 until the early 1970s. Both have been designated as monuments to personnel killed on service duties.

TYPE	REG/SER	CON. NO.	PI/NOTES	STATUS
☐ Gloster Meteor F.4	'C-051'		RA-386, I-002, C-002 – in nearby park.	PVX
☐ Gloster Meteor F.4	'C-091'		I-094,C-094	PVX

MONUMENTO DE GUERRA DE MALVINAS – RIO GRANDE (ARG37)

Address: Plaza Malvinas,
Rio Grande 9420.
Admission: On permanent view.
Location: In the town.

The airport was used as a military base during the Falklands conflict. British aircraft attacked the site but failed to destroy the parked machines. Among the types operated were Air Force IAI Daggers and Skyhawks and Navy Dassault Super Etendards. A memorial to those who lost their lives has been erected in the town. The Argentinean Navy flew eight Italian built Macchi MB.326GBs and in the early 1990s eleven built under licence in Brazil arrived. The type is still in use with a squadron at Punta Indio. Designed as a trainer with the capability of being modified to carry weapons the prototype first flew in Italy in 1957.

TYPE	REG/SER	CON. NO.	PI/NOTES	STATUS
☐ Embraer EMB.326GB Xavante [Aermacchi MB.326) (AT-26)	0647/4-A-108	6540		PV

MONUMENTO DE LA VI BRIGADA AÉREA (ARG38)

Address:	Secc Chacras, Tandil 7000.
Tel:	02293-446240
Admission:	By prior permission only.
Location:	About 5 km north west of the town.

Tandil has been an important fighter base for many years and aircraft from the field took part in the 1955 Revolution. At the time squadrons of Meteor F.4s were in residence. The North American Sabre replaced the early British jet and was flown by based units for many years. At the current time Dassault Mirage IIIs and IAI Fingers equip the squadrons. In addition a liaison flight is based at Tandil. The aircraft have been preserved in the markings of the local unit and are memorials to all who have lost their lives whilst flying from the base.

TYPE	REG/SER	CON. NO.	PI/NOTES	STATUS
☐ Dassault Mirage IIICJ	C-711	CJ-34 or CJ-36	725 (Israel)	RA
☐ Gloster Meteor F.4	I-057		I-057, C-057	RA

MONUMENTO DE ORO VERDE (ARG39)

Address:	Universidad del Littoral, Oro Verde 3100.
Admission:	On permanent view.
Location:	In southern part of the town.

The Guarani is mounted outside the university which has an engineering faculty. Many graduates have served with Air Force and the base at Paraná is nearby. The aircraft came from this airfield. The local Group II operated the type on general transport duties and some examples were fitted with cameras for survey work.

TYPE	REG/SER	CON. NO.	PI/NOTES	STATUS
☐ Fabrica Militar de Aviones IA.50A Guarani II	T-116	8		PV

MONUMENTO DE RESISTENCIA (ARG40)

Address:	Resistencia 3500.
Admission:	On permanent view
Location:	In the town.

The Meteor has been preserved as a memorial to local aviators. Over the years the active local aero club has trained many pilots who have subsequently joined the Army, Air Force or Navy.

TYPE	REG/SER	CON. NO.	PI/NOTES	STATUS
☐ Gloster Meteor F.4	C-084		I-084	PV

MONUMENTO DE RIO TERCERO (ARG41)

Address:	Rio Tercero 5850.
Admission:	On permanent view.
Location:	In the city.

The Pucará ground attack aircraft first flew in prototype form in late 1969. The production version was ready a few years later and the type entered service with III Brigade at Reconquista in 1975. The Argentinean Air Force operated the Pucará in the Falklands War. Several were captured and shipped to the United Kingdom.

TYPE	REG/SER	CON. NO.	PI/NOTES	STATUS
☐ Fabrica Militar de Aviones IA.58 Pucará	'A-537'		AX-04	PVX

MONUMENTO DE SALTA (ARG42)

Address: Salta 4400.
Admission: On permanent view
Location: In the town.

The Meteor is on show in a park in the town along with a Sherman tank, weapons and flags. The display has been set up to remind the residents of the contribution of the military in the development of the country.

TYPE	REG/SER	CON. NO.	PI/NOTES	STATUS
☐ Gloster Meteor F.4	C-090		I-090	PV

MONUMENTO DE SAN LORENZO (ARG43)

Address: San Lorenzo 3545.
Admission: On permanent view.
Location: In the town.

Argentina has operated several versions of the French fighter. Nineteen former Israeli Air Force IIICJ's were supplied in the mid-1980s and one has recently been put on show in the town. This version saw combat duties in Israel and achieved several 'kills' in the Six Day War and other local conflicts. The monument honours the local aviators who were killed or wounded in the Falklands war and other conflicts.

TYPE	REG/SER	CON. NO.	PI/NOTES	STATUS
☐ Dassault Mirage IIICJ			(Israel)	RA

MONUMENTO DE SANTA ROSA (ARG44)

Address: Santa Rosa 6300.
Admission: On permanent view.
Location: In the town.

The historic city is home to many picturesque parks and a number of museums. This memorial is dedicated to local aviators who have been killed or injured in the service of Argentina and is located in a park in the town. The Meteor was a familiar sight in local skies for almost a quarter of a century.

TYPE	REG/SER	CON. NO.	PI/NOTES	STATUS
☐ Gloster Meteor F.4	C-019		EE553, I-019	PV

MONUMENTO DE TANCACHA (ARG45)

Address: Ruta Provincial 6,
Tancacha 5933.
Admission: On permanent view
Location: In the centre of the town.

The Guarani I light transport first flew in 1962 and the production Guarani II was ready the following year. Just over thirty were completed with the last being withdrawn in 2006. One has been placed on show in a park in the town. The aircraft is positioned by the main road and can be seen by most people passing through.

TYPE	REG/SER	CON. NO.	PI/NOTES	STATUS
☐ Fabrica Militar de Aviones IA.50A Guarani II	TX-01	01		PV

MONUMENTO DE VILLA LUGANO (ARG46)

Address: Plaza Fuerza Aérea Argentina
Villa Lugano 1440.
Admission: On permanent view.
Location: In the south western suburbs of Buenos Aires.

This former Israeli Mirage has been erected in the town as a memorial to those who have served in the Air Force. Villa Lugano was the site of one of the earliest airfields in the country. Many pioneering aviators flew from the field and a number of record breaking journeys took off or landed at the site.

TYPE	REG/SER	CON. NO.	PI/NOTES	STATUS
☐ Dassault Mirage IIICJ	C-706		(Israel)	PV

Very few General Aircraft Cygnets have survived and this example is at Colon. (Nigel Hitchman)

The aero club at Tolosa have preserved this Dove. (Nigel Hitchman)

This Morava is preserved at La Matanza. (Nigel Hitchman)

MUSEO AÉRONAUTICO DEL AEROCLUB BARADERO (ARG47)

Address:	Avenue Jorge Newbery 1450, Baradero 2942.
Tel:	03329-484540
Email:	info@aeroclub-baradero.com.ar
Admission:	By prior permission only.
Location:	In the north western part of the town.

The club was formed in 1946 and has operated a wide range of types over the last half century. The museum was established in 1995 and currently has three aircraft on show with more being sought. The trio all gave excellent service in Argentina and all three types were used in considerable numbers.

TYPE	REG/SER	CON. NO.	PI/NOTES	STATUS
☐ De Havilland D.H.104 Dove 1	LV-LER	04042	LV-XWL, T-57, T-83	PV
☐ Douglas DC-3A-456 Skytrain (C-47A)	'TC-35'	20093	43-15627, NC67776, LV-XEP, T-151, T-174, T-17, T-31, TC-31	PVX
☐ Gloster Meteor F.4	'C-002'		G-5-151, I-051, C-051	PVX

MUSEO AÉROPOSTAL (ARG48)

Address:	General Pacheco 1610.
Admission:	Unknown.
Location:	In the town.

A report has been received that this early DC-3 has been allocated to the museum. The aircraft was delivered to the United States Navy in 1942 and served at Cherry Point in North Carolina. Airline service in Brazil, between 1948 and 1953 followed before it journey south to the Argentinean Air Force. The aircraft was withdrawn from use and stored at Quilmes for several years. Further details would be most welcome.

TYPE	REG/SER	CON. NO.	PI/NOTES	STATUS
☐ Douglas DC-3A-360 Skytrain (R4D-1)	TC-27	4280	Bu3140, PP-KAA, PP-ANS, T-38, TC-38, LQ-IPC	RA

MUSEO DE AVIACIÓN DEL EJÉRCITO ARGENTINO (ARG49)

Address:	Agrupcion de Aviacion de Ejercito 601, Campo de Mayo, Buenos Aires.
Admission:	By prior permission only.
Location:	In the western suburbs of the city.

On January 4th 1945 the Argentinean Air Force became autonomous after being under Army control for over forty years. In 1951 a new Army Aviation Command was set up using mainly light aircraft and helicopters for liaison and transport duties. The main base is at Campo de Mayo where the museum has been established. Army aircraft operate from many unprepared airstrips throughout the vast country. Three Bell 47s were acquired from the U.S.A. and one is on show. Most of the aircraft bought have come from the U.S.A. but in the early 1980s French and Italian designs were ordered. The displays trace the history of army flying in Argentina. Hopefully more types will be added to the display when their flying days are over. The airfield is now home to the main helicopter attack squadrons of the Army and fixed wing units operating a variety of types.

TYPE	REG/SER	CON. NO.	PI/NOTES	STATUS
☐ Bell 47G-3B-1 Sioux (TH-13T)	AE-392	3484	65-8051	PV
☐ Cessna 185B Skywagon	AE-205	1850643		PV
☐ Grumman G-134 Mohawk (OV-1D)	AE-036	37D	69-17026	PV

MUSEO DE LA AVIACIÓN NAVAL (ARG50)

Address:	Base Aeronavale Comandante Espora, 8107 Puerto Belgrano, Bahia Blanca.
Tel:	0291-4810-510
Fax:	0291-487992
Admission:	Monday-Friday 1000-1600; Sunday 1500-1900.
Location:	About 10 km south west of the city which is about 550 km south west of Buenos Aires.

In 1921 a flying boat unit was established at Puerto Belgrano. Six Curtiss PN-5s were used for operational duties and a training school was also set up with two Curtiss HS.2Ls which were soon joined by fourteen floatplane Avro 552s. Since these humble beginnings the air arm of the Argentinean Navy has been to the forefront in the defence of the country. The airfield currently houses both fixed and rotary wing units. Historic aircraft were preserved by the Navy over the years and the decision was taken to set up a museum. Two early types are the Curtiss-Wright CW-16E and the Vought V.65 Corsair. A small number of CW-16 biplanes were delivered in the 1930s and used for training. Fifteen V.65F biplanes were ordered in 1933. Powered by the Pratt and Whitney Hornet radial, eleven were used as landplanes and the other four were operated on floats. An example of the second Vought design to bear the name Corsair, the famous gull-wing F4U, can also be seen. Efforts are being made to acquire examples of as many types as possible. Eight former Royal Air Force Neptunes were bought in 1958 and were later joined by a similar number of ex-United States Navy machines. The example in the collection was used in an attack on H.M.S. Sheffield in the Falklands conflict and carries a 'kill' marking on its nose. Argentina was the only country, apart from the U.S.A, to operate the Grumman Panther. Three Electras were delivered in 1973 and converted for maritime patrol duties. Several versions of the versatile Alouette have served with the Navy for more than a quarter of a century. Ten Macchi MB.339AAs were acquired in 1981 and operated from Punta Indio. A number of aircraft are under restoration and these should soon be put on display. Dassault Super Etendards were delivered in 1980 after the United States refused to supply parts for the Skyhawks. The French design flew almost six hundred operations in the Falklands war and there were no losses. The history of naval aviation in Argentina is portrayed in a series of informative displays. On show are photographs, documents, models, uniforms, badges, engines and instruments.

TYPE	REG/SER	CON. NO.	PI/NOTES	STATUS
☐ Aermacchi MB.326GB	0618/4-A-106	6459/200		PV
☐ Aermacchi MB.339AA	0768/4-A-117	6631/026		PV
☐ Aérospatiale AS.555N (FSM)				PV
☐ Bell 47D Sioux	0834/2-HE-3	75		PV
☐ Boeing-Stearman E75 Kaydet (PT-13D) (N2S-5)	0308/1-E-31	75-5273	42-17110, Bu61151, 1E-57, 3-G-1, LV-GFY, LQ-ZKY	PV
☐ Curtiss-Wright CW-16E Light Sport	0032/1-N-3	3549	0032, LV-ZIB, LV-FIB	PV
☐ Dassault Super Etendard	0752	51	Front fuselage only.	RA
☐ Douglas DC-3A-360 Skytrain (C-47)	0296/CTA-15	4664	41-18539, VH-CCL, VH-CFD, NC68180, 'CTA-15'	PV
☐ Douglas A-4Q Skyhawk (A4D-2) (A-4B)	0655/3-A-302	12128	Bu144882	PV
☐ Grumman G-79 Panther (F9F-2)	0425/3-A-113	K-665	Bu127207	PV
☐ Grumman G-89 Tracker (S2F-1) (S-2A)	0510/2-G-52	173	Bu133202	PV
☐ Grumman G-89 Tracker (S2F-1) (S-2A)	0511/2-G-51	220	Bu133249	PV
☐ Grumman G-89 Tracker (S2F-1) (S-2A)	0512/2-G-53	228	Bu133257	PV
☐ Grumman G-105 Cougar (F9F-8T) (TF-9J)	0516/3-A-151	27	Bu142463	PV
☐ Grumman G-111 Albatross (G-64) (SA-16A) (SA-16B) (HU-16B)	BS-03/4-BS-3	G-109	51-0034	RA
☐ Lockheed 188EK Electra (188A) (188PF)	0692/6-P-106	188-1120	N6129A	PV
☐ Lockheed 188EW Electra (188A) (188PF)	0793	188-1072	N6118A, N5534	RA
☐ Lockheed 188PF Electra (188C)	0792	188-1071	N5536, N511PS – fuselage only.	PV
☐ Lockheed 726-45-17 Neptune (P2V-7) (P2V-7S) (SP-2H)	0708/2-P-112	726-7283	Bu150280	PV
☐ Luscombe 8E Silvaire	'3-E-1'	5922	0269, LV-JXI	PVX
☐ Nord N.1203-II Norécrin	LV-FEJ	289		RA
☐ North American NA-88 Texan (SNJ-4)	0503/1-E-225	88-13081	Bu27625, N1624M, Fv16221	PV
☐ North American NA-88 Texan (AT-6D) (SNJ-5)	0462/2-A-304	88-17660	42-85879, Bu90662	PV
☐ Sikorsky S-55B Chickasaw (H-19C) (UH-19C)	0371/4-H-12	55633	51-14298	RA
☐ Sud Fennec [North American NA-174 Trojan (T-28A)]	0624/3-A-204	174-333	51-3795, 109 (France)	PV
☐ Sud Fennec [North American NA-174 Trojan (T-28A)]	0582/3-A-333	174-670	51-7817, 17 (France)	PV
☐ Sud SA.319B Alouette III	0735/3-H-112	2346	F-WTNJ – Boom from c/n 1851 0681.	PV
☐ Vought V-65F Corsair	0011/3-O-3	1026		PV
☐ Vought F4U-5 Corsair	0391/3-A-211		Bu121928	PV
☐ Vultee V-74 Valiant (BT-13A)		74-6847	41-22709	RA

MUSEO DE LA INDUSTRIA (ARG51)

Address:	Parque General Paz, Boulevard General Paz, Cordóba.
Tel:	0351-433-1613
Admission:	Tuesday-Saturday 0900-1330 1500-1900; Sunday 1500-1900
Location:	In the city.

The Military Aircraft Factory was set up at Cordóba in 1927 and over the years has produced a range of designs which have seen both military and civilian use in the country. The museum displays trace all aspects of local industry and many cars, motor cycles and commercial vehicles are on show. The aviation section has models and photographs of all types produced by the factory. About Guarani II twin turboprops were produced and served in a number of roles with the Air Force and Navy. The prototype flew in 1963 and the example on show is a transport version. The IAe.34M glider designed by Reimar Horten is slowly being rebuilt.

TYPE	REG/SER	CON. NO.	PI/NOTES	STATUS
☐ Fabrica Militar de Aviones IAe.34M				RAC
☐ Fabrica Militar de Aviones IA.50B Guarani II	T-121	13 (P-1)	Fuselage only.	PVD

MUSEO DE LA IV BRIGADA AÉREA (ARG52)

Address:	BAM El Plumerillo, Mendoza.
Tel:	0448-7128 ext. 111
Admission:	Monday-Friday 0800-1300 by prior permission.
Location:	About 8 km north of the city.

The airfield is currently home to combat units and the aerobatic squadron of the air force. The museum has been set up to trace the history of the base and the units which have flown from the field. The pioneer aviator Benjamin Matienzo was killed in an airship crash in 1919 and parts of this machine have been retrieved.

TYPE	REG/SER	CON. NO.	PI/NOTES	STATUS
☐ Dassault Mirage IIICJ	C-713	CJ-42		RA
☐ Dassault Mirage IIICJ	C-716	CJ-64		RA
☐ Douglas A-4C Skyhawk (A4D-2N)	'C-301'		(USN)	RAX
☐ Douglas A-4C Skyhawk (A4D-2N)	C-314	12889	Bu149564	RA
☐ Morane-Saulnier MS.760A Paris I	E-201	003	A-01	RA
☐ Morane-Saulnier MS.760A Paris I	E-219	A-7	In nearby town.	PV
☐ Morane-Saulnier MS.760A Paris I	E-233	A-21		RA
☐ North American NA-191 Sabre (F-86F)	C-124	191-670	52-4974	RA

MUSEO DE LA V BRIGADA AÉREA (ARG53)

Address:	Jorge Newbery S/N, Villa Reynolds
Tel:	02657-423576
Admission:	Monday-Friday 0900-1200 by appointment.
Location:	About 15 km south east of Mercedes.

The museum at this historic base opened on August 10th 2000. The indoor exhibition is housed in three halls of the basement of the Brigade Headquarters. On show in this area are photographs, armaments, flags, equipment and components. The Lincoln, one of thirty acquired in the late1940s, has now been repainted in its correct markings.

TYPE	REG/SER	CON. NO.	PI/NOTES	STATUS
☐ Avro 694 Lincoln B.2	B-016	1492	B-016, 'B-017'	PV
☐ Douglas A-4M Skyhawk	C-906	14239	Bu158417 – major components.	PV
☐ Douglas A-4P Skyhawk (A4D-2) (A-4B)	C-221	11362	Bu142108	RA
☐ Douglas A-4P Skyhawk (A4D-2) (A-4B)	C-214	11363	Bu142109	RA
☐ Douglas A-4P Skyhawk (A4D-2) (A-4B)	C-231	11810	Bu142748	PV

MUSEO HISTORICO Y TRADICIONALISTA FUERTE INDEPENDENCIA (ARG54)

Address:	4 Avenida Abril 851, Tandil.
Tel:	02993-435573
Fax:	02993-424025
Admission:	Tuesday-Sunday 1600-2000.
Location:	In the centre of the town which is about 300 km south of Buenos Aires.

A military outpost, Fuerte Independencia, was established in 1823 and the settlement grew into the town of Tandil. Displays at this museum, which opened in 1955, trace the military and cultural development of the region. There are three halls dealing with military matters including the Falklands conflict. The local Air Force Base features in the exhibition. The Meteor is preserved in the courtyard area of the buildings.

TYPE	REG/SER	CON. NO.	PI/NOTES	STATUS
☐ Gloster Meteor F.4	C-005		RA390, G-5-105, I-005	PV

MUSEO HISTORICO DE LA PREFECTURA NAVAL ARGENTINA (ARG55)

Address:	Liniers 1264, Tigre 1648.
Tel:	01-749-6161
Admission:	Wednesday-Sunday 1000-1800.
Location:	In the centre of the town which is about 30 km north west of Buenos Aires.

The Coast Guard operates both fixed and rotary wing aircraft along with a large fleet of patrol boats. The museum, which opened on October 25th 1985, traces the history and traditions of the force. On show are documents, uniforms, models and artefacts. The aeronautical section has scale models of types used by the Guard. These include a Grumman Goose which served from 1947 to 1957, a Dakota used from 1963 to 1971 and a Short Skyvan. Five Skyvans were delivered in 1971 and one was destroyed at Pebble Island in 1982. The type was withdrawn from use in 1985. The first helicopter operated by the service was a Sikorsky S-51 used for beach rescue at Mar del Plata. The sole aircraft on show is one of six Hughes 369s used.

TYPE	REG/SER	CON. NO.	PI/NOTES	STATUS
☐ Hughes 369HM	PA-30	110290		PV

MUSEO HISTORICO DEL EJÉRCITO (ARG56)

Address:	Carlos Pellegrini y Padre Elizalde, Ciudadela.
Tel:	011-4653-1818
Fax:	011-4653-1774
Email:	museodelejercito@ejercito.mil.ar
Admission:	Tuesday-Friday 1000-1700; Saturday-Sunday 1400-1600.
Location:	In the north eastern suburbs of Buenos Aires.

This museum tracing the history of the Army is housed in a former logistics facility on the outskirts of the city. On display are tanks, military vehicles and armaments. There are pavilions devoted to the major campaigns in which the service has fought. Here the history of these conflicts is portrayed with photographs, documents and items of memorabilia. The aircraft are exhibited in the grounds surrounding the museum.

TYPE	REG/SER	CON. NO.	PI/NOTES	STATUS
☐ Bell 47G-2 Sioux (H-13H) (OH-13H)	AE-396	1660	55-4631	PV
☐ Grumman G-134 Mohawk (OV-1C) (OV-1D)	AE-021	136C	68-15932	PV

MUSEO NACIONAL DE AERÓNAUTICA (ARG57)

Address:	Eva Perón 2200, Morón 1808.
Tel:	011-4514-1615
Fax:	011-4514-4268
Email:	mna@uolsinectis.com.ar
Admission:	Tuesday-Friday 0900-1300; Saturday-Sunday 1000-1800.
Location:	In the south western suburbs of Buenos Aires.

In 1912 a Military Aviation School was established at El Palomar near Buenos Aires using Blériot, Farman and Morane-Saulnier aircraft. After World War I French and Italian air missions provided support and aircraft. In October 1927 the Fabrica Militar de Aviones was set up at Córdoba. and the first aircraft produced were thirty two Dewoitine D.21s, forty Bristol F.2Bs and one hundred Avro 504Rs. Original designs soon followed and the company is still producing successful and innovative products. Both the Army and Navy purchased aircraft from abroad in the 1930s. During World War II the country remained neutral so did not qualify for American Lend-Lease. At the end of the conflict Argentina bought surplus U.S. types including Beech Kansans, Douglas C-47s and C-54s. Large orders were also placed for British aircraft. Fifteen Lancasters, thirty Lincolns, one hundred Meteors, one hundred Prentices, forty four Doves and smaller numbers of Vikings and Bristol Freighters were supplied to modernise the Air Force which was established in its own right in 1945. Over recent years orders have been placed with several European countries as well with the United States. The first airline in the country was formed in 1919 and civil flying has flourished ever since. In 1960 a decision was made to set up a National Aviation Museum and this first opened on May 27th 1962 at the Aeroparque Airport located north east of the city. A small building was constructed and on show here are models, photographs, documents and memorabilia tracing the rich aeronautical traditions of the country. A small hangar was completed in 2000 but most of the aircraft were in an outside park. A decision was made to move the collection to Morón. The operational aircraft had moved out and the Civil Aviation Institute remained with a fleet of light aircraft. Hangars were refurbished and displays set up. Aircraft which were located at other Air Force bases were transported to their new home. After World War II the famous Focke-Wulf designer Kurt Tank joined the staff of the Instituto Aerotecnico (the name adopted by F.M.A. for a period). Two jet prototypes soon appeared – the Pulqui designed by Emile Dewoitine and the Pulqui II designed by Tank. Both of these unique aircraft are on show along with other products from the factory. The Stieglitz was built under licence in the military factory at Córdoba and was used by the aviation school at the nearby base. Until recently it was kept in airworthy condition at Córdoba. The IAe.22DL trainer first flew in 1943 and over two hundred were built. The sole survivor is on show in the halls. The twin engined Huanquero has served in a number of roles including primary training, crew training, ambulance work, and photographic surveying. The Pucará came to prominence in the Falklands conflict and the prototype is on show at the museum. The French airline Aéropostale was founded by Pierre Latécoère in 1918 with the aim of connecting France with South America. Subsidiary companies were set up in a number of countries including Argentina. The Latécoère 25 is one of the aircraft used by the pioneering French airline. The prototype Latécoère 25.1.R later converted to a 25.3.R was restored at Quilmes. This historic machine is the sole survivor of a fleet of eleven which flew services to Chile, Paraguay and Patagonia in the south of the country. The Fairchild 82D served in the 1930s before being sold for mapping work. British aircraft feature prominently in the display and one of the few surviving Lincolns in the world can be seen (one other is also preserved in Argentina). The Beaver is one of six used in the Antarctic. Two examples of Reimar Horten's flying wing gliders are on view. The history of aviation in the country is portrayed in detail and new displays are being added. As types are withdrawn from use examples will join the collection.

	TYPE	REG/SER	CON. NO.	PI/NOTES	STATUS
☐	Aero Commander 500U	T-137	1749-44		RA
☐	Avro 694 Lincoln B.2	'B-010'	1408	RE351, B-004	PVX
☐	Beech C18S Kansan (AT-11)	E-110	3495	42-37115, E-110, LV-XHM, Ea-17	PV
☐	Bell 205 Iroquois (UH-1H)	H-19	9701	67-17503	PV
☐	Blériot XI				PV
☐	Bristol 170 Freighter 1A	TC-330	12751	G-AICH, LV-XIM, LV-AEY, T-30, T-330	PV
☐	British Aircraft Corporation 1-11 Series 515FB	'LV-MHT'	187	D-ALAT, G-AZPY, D-AMAS, LV-PEW, LV-MZM	PVX
☐	Cierva C.30A (Avro 671)	LV-FBL	1031	R 340, LV-CEA	PV
☐	Dassault Mirage IIICJ	C-712	CJ-40	(Israel)	PV
☐	De Havilland D.H.104 Dove 1	F-12	04156	LV-YAI, T-90, F-5	PV
☐	De Havilland D.H.C.2 Beaver	P-05	1506		PV
☐	Dinfia I.Ae 22DL	Ea-701	728		PV
☐	Dinfia I.Ae 27 Pulqui I	C-001			PV
☐	Dinfia I.Ae 33 Pulqui II	IA-X-33			PV
☐	Dittmar Condor IV	LV-EGG	7		RA
☐	Douglas DC-3A-360 Skytrain (R4D-1)	TA-05	19965	43-15499, NC65283, LV-ABF, T-05, TC-05	PV
☐	Douglas DC-4 Skymaster (C-54D)	TC-45		(USAAF), T-45 – front fuselage only.	PV
☐	English Electric EA.1 Canberra B.62 (B.2)	B-109	SH.1632	WH875, G-27-163	PV
☐	Douglas A-4C Skyhawk (A4D-2N)	C-322	12839	Bu149514	PV
☐	Douglas A-4P Skyhawk (A4D-2) (A-4B)	C-207	11750	Bu142688	PV
☐	Douglas A-4P Skyhawk (A4D-2) (A-4B)	C-240	11917	Bu142855	PV
☐	Douglas A-4P Skyhawk (A4D-2) (A-4B)	'C-200'		(USN) – front fuselage only.	PVX
☐	Fabrica Militar de Aviones IA.35-1b Huanquero	A-316			PV
☐	Fabrica Militar de Aviones IA.41 Urubu [Horten XVc]		01		PV
☐	Fabrica Militar de Aviones IA.50B Guarani II	F-31	06		PV
☐	Fabrica Militar de Aviones IA.50B Guarani II	LQ-JXY	21	LQ-JXY, LV-JXY	RA
☐	Fabrica Militar de Aviones IA.53 Mamboreta	PGX-01		LV-X33, PG-01	PV
☐	Fabrica Militar de Aviones IA.58 Pucará	AX-01		A-X2	PV
☐	Fabrica Militar de Aviones IA.63 Pampa (FSM)	'FX-03'			PVX
☐	Fairchild 82D	LV-FHZ	66	F-152	PV
☐	Farman HF-7 (R)				PV
☐	Fiat G.46-5B	Ea-441	76		PV
☐	Focke-Wulf Fw 44J Stieglitz	'Ee-122'	119	E.e-119, PG-396	PVX
☐	Fokker F.27 Friendship 600 (400)	T-42	10346	PH-FLS, T-80	PV
☐	Gloster Meteor F.4	C-041	G5/141 (?)	EE586, G-5-141, I-041	PV
☐	Grumman G-111 Albatross (G-64) (SA-16A) (SA-16B) (HU-16B)	BS-02	G-70	50-0181	PV
☐	Hiller UH12E	LV-HEN	2087		PV
☐	Horten Ho Xb Piernifero 2				PV
☐	Hughes 369HE	'PGH-05'	890107E	H-20	PVX
☐	Iriate Monoplane	LV-X-114			PV
☐	Junkers Ju 52/3mge	'T-158'	4043	D-3356, D-ABIS, PP-CAX, LQ-ZBD, 'T-149'	PVX
☐	Latécoère 25-3R (25-1R)	F-AIEH	603	F-AIEH, R 211, LV-EAB	PV
☐	Luscombe 8A Silvaire	LV-NMQ	4237		PV
☐	Max Holste MH.1521C Broussard	PG-336	24C	LQ-FZL	PV
☐	Morane-Saulnier MS.502 Criquet [Fieseler Fi 156 Storch]	LV-ZIV	681	681 (France)	PV
☐	Morane-Saulnier MS.760A Paris I	E-207	15		PV
☐	Morane-Saulnier MS.760A Paris I	'E-218'	A-35/015	A-07, E-247	PVX
☐	Nieuport 28C.1		N6993		RA
☐	North American NA-174 Trojan (T-28A)	E-608	174-112	51-3574 – on loan to Col Estancia Santa Romana.	–
☐	North American NA-191 Sabre (F-86F)	C-122	191-669	52-4973	PV
☐	North American NA-191 Sabre (F-86F)			Front fuselage only.	PV
☐	Percival P.40 Prentice T.1	E-390	PAC/280		PV
☐	Sikorsky S-51	LV-XXS	5165	Front fuselage only.	RAD
☐	Sikorsky S-55B Chickasaw (H-19A) (UH-19A)	H-04		51-3886, H-4,	PV
☐	Sikorsky S-61R	H-02	61763		PV
☐	Vickers 615 Viking 1B	T-9	163	LV-XET, T-9, T-09	PV
☐	Wright Flyer (R)				PV

MUSEO NACIONAL MALVINAS (ARG58)

Address:	Ruta Nacional 9, Oliva 5940.
Tel:	03522-422291
Email:	museomalvinas@coop-oliva.com
Admission:	Daily 0900-1230 1600-2100
Location:	In the centre of the town.

The museum traces the history of the islands. The territory has had a complex history with several nations including France and Spain claiming them in the eighteen century. Britain took over the area in 1883 but the now independent Argentina continued to assert that they were part of their country. In 1982 Argentina invaded the Falklands and after a forty five day conflict Britain regained control The exhibitions cover all aspects of this complex history. There are memorials to the Argentineans who were killed and a display of militaria.

TYPE	REG/SER	CON. NO.	PI/NOTES	STATUS
☐ Douglas A-4C Skyhawk (A4D-2N)	C-302	12631	Bu148438	PV
☐ English Electric EA.1 Canberra B.62 (B.2)	B-102	EEP.71234	WJ714, G-27-112, G-AYHP	PV
☐ Fabrica Militar de Aviones IA.58A Pucará	A-581	082	Wings from AX-06 and parts from c/n 051 A-550.	PV

MUSEO NAVAL DE LA NACION (ARG59)

Address:	Paseo Victoria 602, Tigre 1648.
Tel:	011-4749-0608
Admission:	Monday-Friday 0830 – 1730; Saturday-Sunday.1030-1830.
Location:	In the centre of the town which is about 30 km north west of Buenos Aires.

The displays trace the maritime history of the country. On show are many models of ships, uniforms, badges, documents and memorabilia. Outside are a number of boats and guns from ships. The Comando de Aviación Naval Argentina was formed in October 1919 and has played a major put in the defence of the country ever since. The three aircraft are on show in the outdoor park. Over thirty Texans were acquired by the Navy, one batch in 1948 and the other in 1959. A few flew from the Independicia. Twenty Grumman Panthers were delivered in 1957/8 and served at Punta Indio. Sixteen Skyhawks were initially purchased and flown from the shore base at Puerto Belgrano as well as from the carrier 25 de Mayo. The example on show carries the markings of one lost in the Falklands conflict. One of the halls has an excellent display of wooden ships.

TYPE	REG/SER	CON. NO.	PI/NOTES	STATUS
☐ Douglas A-4Q Skyhawk (A4D-2) (A-4B)	'0667'/3-A-112	112296	Bu145050	PVX
☐ Grumman G-79 Panther (F9F-2)	0453/3-A-118		(USN)	PV
☐ North American NA-88 Texan (SNJ-4)	0442/4-G-75	88-11825	Bu26966	PV

MUSEO NAVAL FUERTE BARRAGAN (ARG60)

Address:	Constanca a Punta Lara y Arroyo Dona Flora, Ensenada 1925.
Admission:	Daily 0900-1600.
Location:	In the centre of the town.

This historic fort was started in 1800 and has been used for a number of purposes over the years. The Navy once had offices at the site and a museum has been set up. The only aircraft is an ex-Navy Texan.

TYPE	REG/SER	CON. NO.	PI/NOTES	STATUS
☐ North American NA-88 Texan (SNJ-4)	'EAN-003'	88-12618	Bu27382 – may be c/n 88-13275 Bu27719 – or a composite.	PVX

MUSEO TÉCHNOLOGICO AEROESPACIAL (ARG61)

Address:	Ruta 158 Km 182, Area de Material, Las Higueras.
Tel:	0358-497642
Fax:	0358-497642
Email:	museofaa@arnet.com
Admission:	Tuesday,Thursday,Friday 0900 -1400; Wednesday 0900-1700; Sunday 1500-1900.
Location:	In the north eastern suburbs of the town.

The museum opened on November 26th 1999 in the Material Sector of the Air Force. This unit was set up in 1945 and its history is traced in a series of informative displays. The development of flight and space travel is also portrayed. The Pampa Aeromodelling Society has its headquarters at the museum and many models can be seen. The aircraft collection is growing steadily and a number of interesting machines will soon be on display. The base workshops have been responsible for the overhaul of many types over the last sixty years.

TYPE	REG/SER	CON. NO.	PI/NOTES	STATUS
☐ Aero Commander 500U	T-134	1745-41		RA
☐ Aero Commander 680	LV-FYF	537-206	N6268D, LV-PFM	PV
☐ Dassault Mirage IIIBJ	'C-721'	239/BJ4	C-722	PVX
☐ Douglas A-4B Skyhawk (A4D-2)	'C-204'	11835	Bu142773, C-212	PVX
☐ Douglas A-4P Skyhawk (A4D-2) (A-4B)	C-222	11814	Bu142752	PV
☐ Douglas DC-3A-456 Skytrain (C-47A)	TC-37	20007	43-15541, TA-07	PV
☐ Fabrica Militar de Aviones IA.58C Pucará	AX-06	039	Composite.	PV
☐ Israeli Aircraft Industries M5 Finger [Dassault Mirage IIBJ]	C-418	S-46		PV
☐ Morane-Saulnier MS.760A Paris I	'E-235'			PVX

PARQUE DE AVIACIÓN DEL EJÉRCITO (ARG62)

Address:	Malvinas Argentinas, Buenos Aires 1613.
Admission:	On permanent view.
Location:	In the area.

This park is dedicated to the Argentinean Army and one of the nine Puma helicopters used by the service has been put on show. Several examples of the type were destroyed in the 1982 conflict. The type served with 601 Squadron at Campo de Mayo. This unit is the main helicopter attack squadron in the Army.

TYPE	REG/SER	CON. NO.	PI/NOTES	STATUS
☐ Sud SA.330L Puma	AE-506	1556		PV

PLAZA AERÓNAUTICA (ARG63)

Address:	El Palomar 1684.
Admission:	On permanent view.
Location:	In the centre of the town.

The park is located near the Headquarters of the First Air Brigade and is a monument to local aviators who have flown from the military airfield. The Fiat G.46 trainer is mounted on a pylon.

TYPE	REG/SER	CON. NO.	PI/NOTES	STATUS
☐ Fiat G.46-5B	Ea-434			PV

PLAZA DE FUERZA AÉREA ARGENTINA (ARG64)

Address:	Loreto 4208.
Admission:	On permanent view.
Location:	In the town.

Two aircraft are on show in this park which is dedicated to members of the Air Force. The Commando was damaged in a forced landing near to the town in September 1964. This was caused by an engine fire and the aircraft hit a horse whilst attempting to land. The undercarriage collapsed and parts of the airframe were burnt. The aircraft was moved to the park where it has remained for the last forty years. More than twenty five examples of the C-46 were used by airlines in Argentina for passenger and freight work.

TYPE	REG/SER	CON. NO.	PI/NOTES	STATUS
☐ Curtiss-Wright CW-20B-2 Commando (C-46D)	LQ-IYV	30391	42-96729, N9342R, (PP-NMJ), CX-BCN	PV
☐ Gloster Meteor F.4	C-057		I-057 – away for restoration.	RA

PLAZA DE HEROES DE MALVINAS – LANUS (ARG65)

Address:	Lanus 1824.
Admission:	On permanent view.
Location:	In the town.

The Argentinean Air Force operated Sabres from 1960 until the mid-1980s. The survivors were withdrawn from front line service in 1976 but a few were subsequently used as operational trainers. During the 1982 Falklands conflict they were used on home defence duties. The one on show is dedicated to this use.

TYPE	REG/SER	CON. NO.	PI/NOTES	STATUS
☐ North American NA-191 Sabre (F-86F)	C-104	191-842	52-5146	PV

PLAZA DE HEROES DE MALVINAS – PUERTO SAN JULIÁN (ARG66)

Address:	Puerto San Julián 2840.
Admission:	On permanent view.
Location:	In the town.

During the 1982 Falklands War the airfield was used by Argentinean aircraft as the field was the closest to the Islands. One hundred and forty nine sorties were flown by Douglas Skyhawks and IAI Daggers in 1980. Eleven Daggers were lost during the war and the majority of the survivors were later upgraded.

TYPE	REG/SER	CON. NO.	PI/NOTES	STATUS
☐ Israeli Aircraft Industries M5 Dagger A (Nesher)	'C-421'		C-424	PVX

BOLIVIA

COLECCIÓN DE BASE AÉREA COCHABAMBA (BO1)

Address:	Brigada Aérea II, Base Aérea Jorge Wilsterman, Cochabamba.
Admission:	By prior permission only.
Location:	In the south western suburbs of the city.

Military aviation started in Bolivia in 1917 when three officers were sent to Argentina for pilot training. The base at Cochabamba is named after Jorge Wilsterman who was one of the pioneers of Bolivian aviation. The field is currently home to training aircraft and helicopters and also serves as the civil airport for the city. Three aircraft are preserved. The T-6 is located at the main Air Force Technical School which is a short distance away. The Bolivian Air Force operated Trojans on training and ground attack duties and one is located in the main base. The 1947 Rio Pact resulted in a number of B-25 Mitchells arriving in Bolivia. One has been restored in period Air Force colours and has been placed in the centre of a roundabout a short distance from the airfield.

TYPE	REG/SER	CON. NO.	PI/NOTES	STATUS
☐ North American NA-88 Texan (AT-6D)			At FAB Technical School.	RA
☐ North American NA-108 Mitchell (B-25J)	FAB-542		(USAAF) – displayed on roundabout near base.	PV
☐ North American NA-159 Trojan (T-28A) (AT-28D)	FAB-411	174-399	51-7546	RA

COLECCIÓN DE BASE AÉREA SANTA CRUZ (BO2)

Address:	Brigada Aérea III, Base Aérea El Trompillo, Santa Cruz.
Admission:	By prior permission only.
Location:	About 5 km south west of the city.

For many years the base was home to the Air Force College which operated a range of training aircraft. About twenty Kaydets, including six former Argentinean Navy aircraft, were flown. These rugged biplanes were in use for many years and many pilots made their first solo in the type. One of the preserved pair is airworthy and flown on special occasions. At the present time the base is home to training squadrons, helicopter units and a detachment of Canadair Silver Stars. The Brazilian designed Uirapuru entered Bolivian service in 1974 and is still used for primary training at El Trompillo. The Iroquois is also flown from the field.

TYPE	REG/SER	CON. NO.	PI/NOTES	STATUS
☐ Aerotec A.122A Uirapuru	FAB-169	085		RA
☐ Aerotec A.122A Uirapuru	FAB-183	090		RA
☐ Bell 205 Iroquois (UH-1H)	FAB-700			RA
☐ Bell 205 Iroquois (UH-1H)	FAB-720			RA
☐ Boeing-Stearman A75N1 Kaydet (PT-17)	'FAB15'		(USAAF), FAB007	RAX
☐ Boeing-Stearman A75N1 Kaydet (PT-17)	FAB16		(USAAF)	RAA

COLECCIÓN DE BASE AÉREA LA PAZ (BO3)

Address:	Brigada Aérea I, Base Aérea El Alto, La Paz.
Admission:	By prior permission only.
Location:	In the south western suburbs of the city

The headquarters of the Transporte Aereo Militar is located at the base. The unit operates freight services on charter to civilian operators as well as carrying out its military duties. The DC-3 was originally delivered to Trans World Air Lines in June 1937, impressed in 1942, returned to the airline when hostilities ceased and then soon sold. Purchased by Bolivia in the mid-1950s the aircraft was damaged at La Paz in 1972 and after a period in store was restored for display. The aircraft carries the markings of the first used by TAM. This example was preserved for several years but suffered with major corrosion problems in the harsh climate and was relegated to the dump before being scrapped. For several years one of the DC-4s flown by T.A.M. was parked close to the C-47 but this also succumbed to corrosion and was scrapped. Over eighty Texans have been operated by the Air Force with many being fitted with armaments. The example on show, in a yellow colours scheme, is mounted on a pylon outside Air Force offices near to the main gate. Fifteen Canadair built T-33s were acquired in 1973/4. A further five arrived in 1977 as part of a deal which resulted in the six surviving Mustangs going to Northwest Industries. The T-33 is still in service with the Bolivian Air Force.

TYPE	REG/SER	CON. NO.	PI/NOTES	STATUS
☐ Canadair CL-30 Silver Star 3 (CT-133) [Lockheed 580 (T-33AN)]	FAB-602	T33-492	21492, 133492	RA
☐ Douglas DC-3A-467 Skytrain (C-47B)	'TAM-01'	15221/26666	43-49405, TAM-16	PV
☐ North American NA-88 Texan (AT-6D)	FAB-362		(USAAF)	PV

BRAZIL

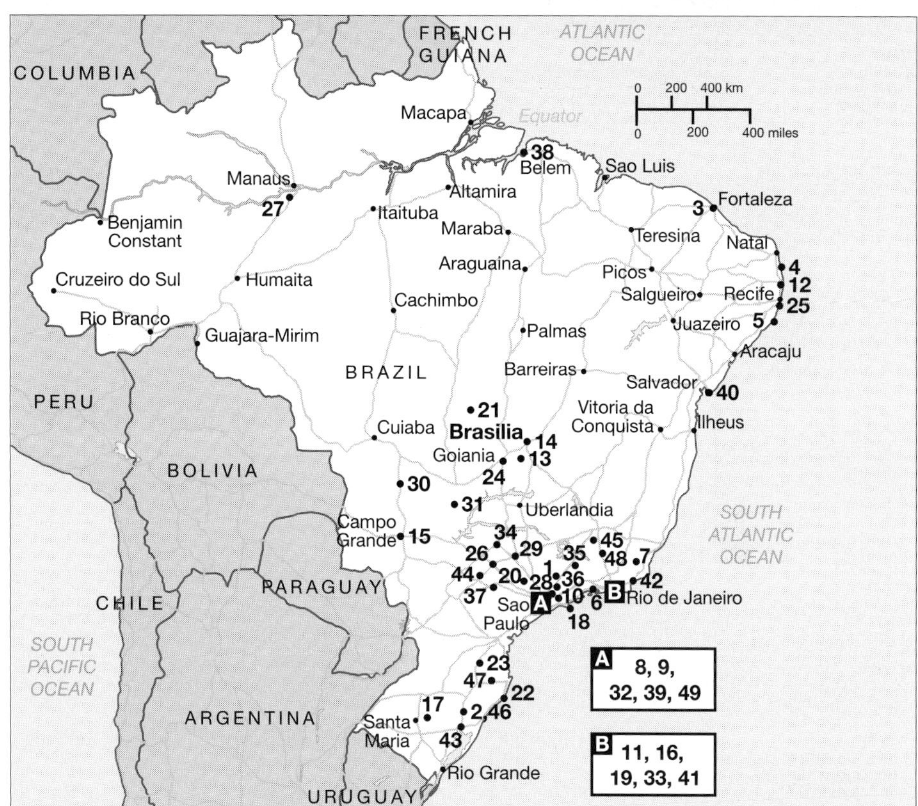

COLEÇÃO DA ACADEMIA DA FORÇA AÉREA (BR1)

Address:	Academia da Força Aérea, Fontenelle 21500, Pirassununga 13630-000.
Tel:	019-561-3909
Admission:	By prior permission only.
Location:	About 10 km south east of Sao Paolo.

Officers receive their pilot training at the Academy. The current types in use are the Embraer Tucano and the Neiva Universal. The field is also home to the military gliding club and the official Air Force acrobatic team 'Esquadrilha da Fumaça' which flies Tucanos. A small exhibition room was opened on October 9th 1967 to enlighten cadets on the history and traditions of the Air Force and to portray the history of the Academy. Over the years a number of aircraft have been preserved and others are in store awaiting restoration. Well over four hundred Texans have been used by the service including eighty-one assembled at Lagoa Santa.

TYPE	REG/SER	CON. NO.	PI/NOTES	STATUS
☐ Aerotec A.122A Uirapuru (T-23)	T23-1737	071		RA
☐ Embraer EMB.326GB Xavante [Aermacchi MB.326) (AT-26)	AT26-4598	78143386		RA
☐ Fairchild M-62A Cornell (PT-19)	0222		42-33679	RA
☐ Gloster Meteor F.8	F8-4413	G5-453708		RA
☐ Lockheed 580 (T-33A) (AT-33A)	TF33A-4328	580-7497	52-9387	RA
☐ Neiva N.561 Universal (T-25A)	T25A-1870	1040		RA
☐ Neiva N.621 Universal (T-25)	'T25-1932'			RAX
☐ North American NA-88 Texan (AT-6D)	T6D-1647	88-17583	42-85802	RA
☐ North American NA-121 Texan (AT-6F) (SNJ-6)	SNJ6-1718	121-43133	44-82411, Bu112230	RA
☐ Vultee V-74A Valiant (BT-15)	1137	74A-10006	42-41773	RA

COLEÇÃO DA BASE AÉREA DE CANOAS (BR2)

Address:	Rua Augusto Severo 1700, Nossa Senhora das Graças, Canoas 92110-290.
Tel:	051-462-5165
Email:	comsocal@baco.aer.mil.br
Admission:	By prior permission only.
Location:	About 10 km north of Porto Alegre.

The base is currently the home of the 14th Fighter Group which operates the Northrop F-5 and the Embraer Tucano.. There is also a transport unit in residence flying the Embraer Bandeirante. This historic field first came into use in the 1930s and during the latter stages of World War II Douglas A-20 Havocs and Curtiss P-40 Warhawks were used by the squadrons. The P-40 on show in the Museu Aeroespacial is painted in the markings of the group which was the last unit in Brazil to operate the type. Meteors flew with the group for several years and most fighter squadrons had a few T-33s allocated for training and liaison duties.

TYPE	REG/SER	CON. NO.	PI/NOTES	STATUS
☐ Gloster Meteor F.8	F8-4433	G5-453781		RA
☐ Gloster Meteor F.8	F8-4448	G5-453818		RA
☐ Gloster Meteor F.8	F8-4439	G5-454076	On show in town.	PV
☐ Lockheed 580 (T-33A) (AT-33A)	AT33A-4336	580-7346	52-9280	RA

COLEÇÃO DA BASE AÉREA DE FORTALEZA (BR3)

Address:	Avenida Borges de Melo s/n, Alto da Balança, Fortaleza 60415-510.
Tel:	085-3216-3000
Admission:	By prior permission only.
Location:	In the southern part of the city.

The base was operational in World War II and housed American units operating Curtiss P-36A Hawks and North American B-25B Mitchells. Missions were flown against German U-boats in the South Atlantic. The Brazilian Air Force was also in residence with Mitchells and Lockheed A-28 Hudsons. For many years both bomber and fighter units flew from the field but at the current time it is home to a Bandeirante transport squadron. Just over thirty Lockheed Shooting Stars were flown by the Brazilian Air Force. The type entered service in 1959 and the last were withdrawn in the early 1970s. The F-80 served at Fortaleza as did the Embraer Xavante. The example in the collection carries a serial never allocated to the type.

TYPE	REG/SER	CON. NO.	PI/NOTES	STATUS
☐ Embraer EMB.326GB Xavante [Aermacchi MB.326) (AT-26)	'AT26-4460'			RAX
☐ Lockheed 080 Shooting Star (P-80C) (F-80C)	F80C-4225	080-2575	49-0287	RA
☐ Lockheed 580 (T-33A) (AT-33A)	TF33A-4325	580-7359	52-9293	RA
☐ Lockheed 580 (T-33A) (AT-33A)	TF33A-4327	580-7558	52-9448	RA

COLEÇÃO DA BASE AÉREA DE NATAL (BR4)

Address:	Base Aérea de Natal, Estrada de Bant s/n Emaus, 59048-900 Parnamirim.
Tel:	084-4008-7533
Email:	chscs@bant.aer.mil.br
Admission:	By prior permission only.
Location:	About 20 km south of the town which is about 300 km north of Recife.

Pilot training is carried out at this base using Embraer Tucanos and Xavantes. The latter is a licence built version of the Macchi MB.326 and more than one hundred and eighty were built in Brazil. The collection of preserved aircraft has been assembled to remind students of their heritage. The Invader and Mitchell were on show for many years at the Air Force Academy at Pirrassununga. Both types gave excellent service in Brazil and equipped several squadrons at bases across the country. Over seventy Aerotec Uirapuru low wing primary trainers were ordered by the Air Force in the late 1960s and early 1970s.

TYPE	REG/SER	CON. NO.	PI/NOTES	STATUS
☐ Aerotec A.122B Uirapuru (T-23A)	T23-0948	012		RA
☐ Douglas A-26C Invader	B26B-5156	28865	44-35586	RA
☐ Embraer EMB.326GB Xavante [Aermacchi MB.326) (AT-26)	AT26-4487	72026269		RA
☐ Embraer EMB.326GB Xavante [Aermacchi MB.326) (AT-26)	AT26-4577	77119362		RA
☐ North American NA-108 Mitchell (B-25J)	B25J-5133		(USAAF) – also reported as B25J-5123.	RA

COLEÇÃO DA BASE AÉREA DE RECIFE (BR5)

Address:	Avenida Maria Irene, Jordao, Recife 51250-020
Tel:	081-3461-7400
Email:	barf@barf.aer.mil.br
Admission:	By prior permission only.
Location:	In the southern western suburbs of the city.

The base is home to a maintenance unit, a transport flight and a communications squadron. An air park is being set up at the airfield. The B-17 arrived in Brazil in the early 1950s and served on search and rescue duties at Recife until October 1968. Since then the Boeing classic has been displayed close to the main gate where it has been joined by a T-33. Five Xavantes have been preserved and these are at a number of locations on the base.

TYPE	REG/SER	CON. NO.	PI/NOTES	STATUS
☐ Boeing 299-O Fortress (B-17G) (TB-17H) (SB-17G)	B17-5402	8492	44-85583	RA
☐ Embraer EMB.326GB Xavante [Aermacchi MB.326) (AT-26)	'AT26-4462'		Composite.	RAX
☐ Embraer EMB.326GB Xavante [Aermacchi MB.326) (AT-26)	AT26-4466	71005248		RA
☐ Embraer EMB.326GB Xavante [Aermacchi MB.326) (AT-26)RA	AT26-4523	74062305		
☐ Embraer EMB.326GB Xavante [Aermacchi MB.326) (AT-26)	AT26-4535	75074317		RA
☐ Embraer EMB.326GB Xavante [Aermacchi MB.326) (AT-26)	AT26-4548	75087330		RA
☐ Lockheed 580 (T-33A) (AT-33A)	TF33A-4322	580-7514	52-9404	RA

COLEÇÃO DA BASE AÉREA DE SANTA CRUZ (BR6)

Address:	Rua do Imperio s/n, Santa Cruz, 23555-020 Rio de Janiero
Tel:	021-3078-0302
Email:	ocsbasc@basc.aer.mil.be
Admission:	By prior permission only.
Location:	About 40 km west of Rio de Janiero.

Santa Cruz is an important fighter base housing squadrons flying the Northrop F-5 and the joint Brazilian-Italian developed AMX attack aircraft. A maritime patrol unit is also in residence. The Air Force used Thunderbolts as the main fighter aircraft until they were progressively replaced by Meteors from 1953 although the last were not withdrawn until 1960. Brazil ordered sixty single seat Meteor F.8s and ten two seat T.7s. Twenty Grumman Trackers served with the Air Force and the first entered service in 1961. Three of the earlier S-2A version were later converted to serve as staff transports. The collection of preserved aircraft represents types previously flown from the field and more airframes are being sought.

TYPE	REG/SER	CON. NO.	PI/NOTES	STATUS
☐ Embraer EMB.326GB Xavante [Aermacchi MB.326) (AT-26)	'AT26-4458'			RAX
☐ Gloster Meteor F.8	F8-4430	G5-453761		RA
☐ Gloster Meteor F.8	F8-4441	G5-453797		RA
☐ Grumman G-121 Tracker (S-2E)	P16E-7032	243C	Bu152356	RA
☐ Lockheed 580 (T-33A) (AT-33A)	TF33A-4348	580-8569	53-5230	RA
☐ Republic P-47D Thunderbolt	'419660'		42-26757, 4107	RAX

COLEÇÃO DA ESCUELA PREPATORIA DE CADETES DO AR (BR7)

Address:	Rua Santos Dumont, Bairro São José, Barbacena 36205-058.
Tel:	032-339-4000
Email:	epcar@barbacena.com.br
Admission:	By prior permission only.
Location:	In the north eastern part of the town.

The college was originally set up in the late 1940s at Campo dos Afonsos, now the site of the Museu Aeroespacial. In 1949 after combining with other Air Force educational institutions it took up its current name. A site at Barbacena was constructed and students are educated in aspects of military life and receive specialist training. Four aircraft are preserved in the pleasant grounds of the school. All types have given excellent service to the Brazilian Air Force and are a reminder of the traditions of the service.

TYPE	REG/SER	CON. NO.	PI/NOTES	STATUS
☐ Aerotec A.122A Uirapuru (T-23)	'T23-4948'			RAX
☐ Gloster Meteor F.8	'F8-4406'			RAX
☐ Lockheed 580 (T-33A) (AT-33A)	TF33A-4342	580-4717	52-9163	RA
☐ North American NA-84 Texan (AT-6B)	T6B-1223	84-7453	41-17075, FAB 21	RA

ESQUADRILHA OI (BR8)

Address: T.R. Silva Braga 415, Hangar 38, Aeroporto de Amarais, Campinas.
Email: circo@extremeairtaxiaero.com.br
Location: About 10 km north west of the town..

The group operates three Texans painted in a distinctive red scheme and they are frequent performers at air shows in the region. The Air Force flew over four hundred T-6s and their official aerobatic team 'Esquadrilha da Fumaça' used the type from 1952 to 1968 and from the early 1970s to 1977. The NA-119 version was only delivered to Brazil. The Beech 18 and Bandeirante are used as a support aircraft to the team.

TYPE	REG/SER	CON. NO.	PI/NOTES	STATUS
☐ Beech E18S	PT-DHI	BA-401	N5661D, N151G	RAA
☐ Cessna 170A	PT-AGB	19734		RAA
☐ Embraer EMB.110C Bandeirante	PT-EDO	110016	PP-SBD	RAA
☐ North American NA-84 Texan (AT-6B)	PT-LDQ	84-7505	41-17127	RAA
☐ North American NA-88 Texan (AT-6D) (SNJ-5)	PT-KRC	88-17199	42-85418, Bu85038, N9821C, SNJ5-1706	RAA
☐ North American NA-119 Texan (AT-6D)	PT-LDO	119-40147	T6D-????	RAA

FUNDAÇÃO MUSEU DE TECNOLOGIA DE SÃO PAULO (BR9)

Address: 526 Avenida Billin, Jaguare, São Paulo 05321-010.
Tel: 011-3768-5785
Fax: 011-5718-0160
Email: museutec@uol.com.br
Admission: Tuesday-Sunday 1000-1600.
Location: In the northern suburbs of the city.

Displays at this museum cover many aspects of science, engineering and technology. The Dakota flew with VASP and was operated from 1946 until 1975. After a four year spell with Projecto Rondon, who organised flights across the country for students, the aircraft was acquired by the museum in November 1979 and is now parked in front of the building. A Viscount was on show but this was scrapped several years ago.

TYPE	REG/SER	CON. NO.	PI/NOTES	STATUS
☐ Douglas DC-3A-467 Skytrain (C-47B)	PT-KUB	17021/34285	45-1018, PP-SPO	PV

MEMORIAL AEROESPACIAL BRASILEIRO (BR10)

Address: Embraer, Avenida Brigadeiro Faria Lima 2.170, São José,de Campos.
Tel: 012-3927-6177
Fax: 012-3927-1610
Email: adriana.shoshan@embraer.com.br
Admission: By prior permission only.
Location: The factory is about 2 km south east of the town. The park is in the northern part of town.

The Embraer company was formed in 1969 with government investment. Its first product was the Bandeirante turpoprop, designed by Max Holste, and this soon entered production and over five hundred were completed over the next two decades. Other successful designs followed including the Tucano trainer which has been exported to many countries. The Xavante is a licence built version of the widely used Aermacchi MB.326. The company has developed a range of jet commuter airliners which are in production for airlines around the world. Several gliders and light aircraft have also been produced. On August 20th 2007 the company opened an exhibition tracing its history. This is located in a building in the grounds of its factory. On show are photographs, documents, models and components. Outside is a small collection of aircraft including one of the prototype Bandeirantes. There is a spectacular monument to aviation nearby. Three more aircraft are in Santos Dumont Park which honours the Brazilian pioneer aviator.

TYPE	REG/SER	CON. NO.	PI/NOTES	STATUS
☐ Aeritalia AMX (YA-1)	YA1-4200	A4/BP001		RA
☐ Aerotec Urubu	PP-ZUR			RA
☐ Embraer EMB.100 Bandeirante	PP-ZDF	03	PP-ZCN	RA
☐ Embraer EMB.110 Bandeirante	PP-SBI		In nearby park.	PV
☐ Embraer EMB.110 Bandeirante (C-95)	C95-2132	110001	2133	PV
☐ Embraer EMB.312 Tucano (YT-27)	'1300'			RAX
☐ Embraer EMB.326GB Xavante [Aermacchi MB.326) (AT-26)	AT26-4478	72017260		RA
☐ Lockheed 580 (T-33A) (AT-33A)	TF33A-4363	580-5189	53-5189 – in nearby park.	PV
☐ Santos-Dumont 14bis (R)			In nearby park.	PV

MONUMENTO DA 26 BATALHÃO DE INFANTERIA PARA-QUEDISTA (BR11)

Address: Avenida Benedito de Silveira,
Vila Militar,
Campo dos Afonsos,
Rio de Janeiro 21605-220.
Admission: By prior permission only.
Location: Just north of the airfield.

The unit has preserved an example of the thirteen C-119Gs delivered to Brazil in the early 1960s. The type, which operated from Campo dos Afonsos, was withdrawn from service in the mid-1970s. Many paratroopers carried out their training jumps using the ubiquitous Flying Boxcar.

TYPE	REG/SER	CON. NO.	PI/NOTES	STATUS
☐ Fairchild 110 Flying Boxcar (C-119G)	C119G-2304	10968	51-8074	RA

MONUMENTO DA ASSOCICÃO DE ENSINO SUPERIOR DE OLINDA (BR12)

Address: Avenida Transamazonica 405,
Olinda 53300-240.
Tel: 081-3426-9797
Admission: By prior permission only.
Location: In the north western part of the town.

The DC-3 was delivered to American Airlines in July 1940 and flew on their routes for almost nine years. The aircraft was sold by Island Air Ferries to VASP in 1951 but was never delivered. Three years later the airliner travelled south to Brazil and was operated by REAL. Several private owners followed before the DC-3 was withdrawn from use in the mid-1980s. The airliner, painted in a psychedelic scheme by artist Romero Britto, is now mounted on pylons outside one of the buildings at the university. Many former students have gone on to serve in the military forces of Brazil and the aircraft now reminds the present student population of this.

TYPE	REG/SER	CON. NO.	PI/NOTES	STATUS
☐ Douglas DC-3-277C		2248	NC15592, (PP-SQL), PP-YQO, PT-BFU	RA

MONUMENTO DA BASE AÉREA DE ANÁPOLIS (BR13)

Address: Rodovia BR 414,
Anápolis 75000-000.
Tel: 062-3310-4000
Admission: By prior permission only.
Location: About 10 km north of the town.

The base is home to fighter and transport units. Currently flown are Dassault Mirage 2000s along with Embraer Tucanos and Xavantes. Two Mirage III's have been preserved. One is at the airfield and the other in the town. Twelve single seaters and a pair of two seaters were ordered in mid-1970. The aircraft were handed over at Bordeaux in 1972 and Brazilian Air Force pilots were sent to Dijon for training on them. The Mirages were based at the then new airfield at Anápolis. A few more aircraft were later acquired.

TYPE	REG/SER	CON. NO.	PI/NOTES	STATUS
☐ Dassault Mirage IIIEBR	F103E-4910			RA
☐ Dassault Mirage IIIEBR	F103E-4919		In town	PV

MONUMENTO DA BASE AÉREA DE BRASILIA (BR14)

Address:	Area Miliata do Aeroporto Internacional de Brasilia, Brasilia 71607-900.
Tel:	061-3364-8000.
Admission:	By prior permission only.
Location:	In the south eastern part of the city.

Construction of the new capital of the country began in the late 1950s and the government moved from Rio de Janiero in 1960. The airfield which also serves as the main airport for the city houses transport aircraft and helicopters as well as the Presidential Flight. Two aircraft have been preserved in the area. The Uirapuru is at the Air Force Headquarters and the Mirage at the local Air Command building on the base.

TYPE	REG/SER	CON. NO.	PI/NOTES	STATUS
☐ Aerotec A.122A Uirapuru (T-23)	PP-???			RA
☐ Dassault Mirage IIIEBR	F103E-4916			RA

MONUMENTO DA BASE AÉREA DE CAMPO GRANDE (BR15)

Address:	Avenida Duque de Caxias 2905 Bairro Santo Antonio, Campo Grande 79101-001.
Tel:	067-3368-3000
Admission:	By prior permission only.
Location:	About 10 km south west of the town.

Units at the base currently operate Tucano and Super Tucano aircraft along with Bell UH-1s and Bandeirante transports. The Texan is located by the main gate and serves as a monument to personnel who have lost their lives flying from the airfield. The aircraft is in a camouflage scheme and is fitted with underwing bombs. Over four hundred Texans served with the Air Force from 1942 and the last few were withdrawn in the 1970s.

TYPE	REG/SER	CON. NO.	PI/NOTES	STATUS
☐ North American NA-78 Texan (SNJ-3)	SNJ3-1415	1415	Bu6895	PV

MONUMENTO DA BASE AÉREA GALEÃO (BR16)

Address:	Estrado do Galeão, Ilha do Governador, Rio de Janiero 21941-005.
Email:	infobagl@aer.mil.br
Admission:	By prior permission only.
Location:	In the northern part of the city.

The airfield is located on an island and is the main airport for the city. Many airlines operate flights from around the world. The Air Force has a base on the south side of the field. Types in use include the Lockheed C-130 Hercules, Embraer Bandeirantes and EMB-145. A unit flying the Boeing KC-137 tanker is also in residence. Brazil ordered twelve Avro 748s with the first entering service in early 1963. The first six were used mainly as passenger aircraft but the second half dozen were fitted with large freight doors. The type was first based with the Special Transport unit at Brasilia but all later moved to Galeão. One of the passenger versions has been preserved as a monument to the crews who flew the 748 around the country.

TYPE	REG/SER	CON. NO.	PI/NOTES	STATUS
☐ Avro 748 Series 2/205 (C-91)	C91-2502	1552		RA

MONUMENTO DA BASE AÉREA SANTA MARIA (BR17)

Address:	RSC Km 240, Camoba, Santa Maria 97105
Tel:	055-3220-3300.
Admission:	By prior permission only.
Location:	About 15 km east of the town.

Units flying the join Brazilian Italian AMX combat jet are in residence. Helicopters and liaison types are also based at the field. An Embraer Xavante has been preserved in the colours of the local unit.

TYPE	REG/SER	CON. NO.	PI/NOTES	STATUS
☐ Embraer EMB.326GB Xavante [Aermacchi MB.326) (AT-26)	'4'			PVX

MONUMENTO DA BASE AÉREA SANTOS (BR18)

Address: Avenida Presidente Castelo Branco s/n, Santos, Guaruja 11450-010
Tel: 013-3341-7113
Email: scs.bast@maerj.gov.br
Admission: By prior permission only.
Location: In the north eastern part of the town.

This base houses helicopter units operating the Helibras HB-350B helicopter. This is a licence built Brazilian version of the Aérospatiale AS.350 Ecureuil. A Bell 47G has been preserved as a monument. The first Bell 47Ds were delivered to the Air Force in 1953 and were the first helicopter used by the service. Forty eight of the improved G model arrived in the late 1950s/early 1960s and remained in service for many years.

TYPE	REG/SER	CON. NO.	PI/NOTES	STATUS
☐ Bell 47G-2 Sioux (H-13H)	H13H-8600	1946	56-2234	RA

MONUMENTO DA VARIG (BR19)

Address: Avenida Vinte de Janeiro, Aeroporto Antonio Carlos Jobim, Galeão 21942-900.
Tel: 021-403-7000
Admission: By prior permission only.
Location: In the northern part of the city.

Varig was founded in 1927 and operates both domestic and international services. The airline operated almost fifty DC-3s between with the last being retired in 1971. The aircraft preserved was located in a park in Rio from 1971. After damage by vandals it was moved to Galeão and restored for display.

TYPE	REG/SER	CON. NO.	PI/NOTES	STATUS
☐ Douglas DC-3A-456 Skytrain (C-47A)	PP-VBF	10156	42-24294, (NC95473), NC68358	RA

MONUMENTO DE CAMPINAS (BR20)

Address: Parque Portugal, Avenida Heitor Penteanda 1671, Campinas.
Admission: On permanent view.
Location: In the centre of the town.

There are many attractions in this large park. The Air Force operated over one hundred and twenty BT-13s between 1942 and 1956. One, in civilian markings, is preserved as a monument. The type was used for primary training and many of the survivors were sold to aero clubs and private owners.

TYPE	REG/SER	CON. NO.	PI/NOTES	STATUS
☐ Vultee V-74A Valiant (BT-15)	PP-GRK		(USAAF)	PV

MONUMENTO DE CANARANA (BR21)

Address: Canarana 78640-000
Admission: On permanent view.
Location: In the town.

In the 1980s the aircraft was donated to the town by the Coopercol company. The C-47 had been rotting away at the local airport and the mayor agreed to it being mounted as a monument in a garden in the town. The airliner was dismantled, towed to its new home, restored and re-painted in VACA colours.

TYPE	REG/SER	CON. NO.	PI/NOTES	STATUS
☐ Douglas DC-3A-456 Skytrain (C-47A) (Dakota III)	PP-YPU	12303	42-92496, FZ697, PP-JAB	PV

MONUMENTO DE CLUB DE AEROMODELISMO ASAS DO VALE (BR22)

Address:	Rodovia Jorge Lacarda, Gaspar.
Tel:	047-3332-1564
Email:	emwolff@terra.com.br
Admission:	On permanent view.
Location:	About 5 km north east of the town.

The club has its home at a purpose built complex. There is a runway for radio-controlled models, a circle for control line work and a helipad. The Neiva Universal is mounted by the main entrance.

TYPE	REG/SER	CON. NO.	PI/NOTES	STATUS
☐ Neiva N.621 Universal (T-25)	T25-1841	1012		PV

MONUMENTO DE ERICHEM (BR23)

Address:	Avenida Sete de Septembro, Erechim.
Admission:	On public view.
Location:	In the southern part of the city.

The American built Texan has been erected as a monument to local Air Force personnel who have been killed on duty. The aircraft mounted in a square and painted in standard training colours.

TYPE	REG/SER	CON. NO.	PI/NOTES	STATUS
☐ North American NA-88 Texan (AT-6C)	T6C-1259	88-12144	42-4065, FAB 37	PV

MONUMENTO DE GOIÃNIA (BR24)

Address:	Goiania.
Admission:	On permanent view.
Location:	In the town.

Brazil ordered ten two seat Meteor T.7s and sixty F.8s to equip its fighter squadrons. The first were delivered in April 1953 and all had arrived by the end of the year. One is preserved in the town as a memorial.

TYPE	REG/SER	CON. NO.	PI/NOTES	STATUS
☐ Gloster Meteor F.8	F8-4411	G5-454009		PV

MONUMENTO DE JOÃO PESSOA (BR25)

Address:	Joao Pessoa.
Admission:	On permanent view.
Location:	In the town.

Sixteen examples of the tricycle undercarriage version of the popular Beech 18 were flown on transport and training duties between 1964 and 1977. One has been restored to its original colours and placed on show.

TYPE	REG/SER	CON. NO.	PI/NOTES	STATUS
☐ Beech H18S	TC45T-2888	BA-675	2888, PT-KXQ	PV

MONUMENTO DE LENÇOIS PAULISTA (BR26)

Address:	Lencois Paulista.
Admission:	On permanent view.
Location:	In the town.

The Lockheed T-33 first served with the Air Force in 1956 and was in service for two decades. The type was flown for advanced training and attack roles. One is on show in the town as a monument.

TYPE	REG/SER	CON. NO.	PI/NOTES	STATUS
☐ Lockheed 580 (T-33A) (AT-33A)	TF33A-4313			PV

MONUMENTO DE MANAUS (BR27)

Address: Manaus 69035-460.
Admission: On permanent view.
Location: At a number of locations.

Two aircraft are on show in the town. The Xavante is at the local Air Traffic Control Centre. The two seat Meteor can be seen in a square in the town. A Cruziero DC-3 has disappeared from its place in another square.

TYPE	REG/SER	CON. NO.	PI/NOTES	STATUS
☐ Embraer EMB.326GB Xavante [Aermacchi MB.326) (AT-26)	'AT26-4948'		At CINDACTA IV.	RAX
☐ Gloster Meteor T.7	TF7-4308	G5-453721	WS150	PV

MONUMENTO DE NOVA IGUAÇU (BR28)

Address: Nova Iguacu.
Admission: On permanent view.
Location: In the town.

The Brazilian Air Force operated several versions of the Beech 18. The C-45F was in service between 1944 and 1976 and the last of twenty two delivered can be seen preserved in this town.

TYPE	REG/SER	CON. NO.	PI/NOTES	STATUS
☐ Beech C18S Expeditor (C-45F) (UC-45F)	UC45-2875		44-47672	PV

MONUMENTO DE PARAGUAÇU (BR29)

Address: Paraguacu.
Admission: On permanent view.
Location: In the town.

Many local pilots carried out their training on the Texan. The type served with the Brazilian Air Force for more than three decades and several were fitted with guns and bomb racks. One example is on show in this town.

TYPE	REG/SER	CON. NO.	PI/NOTES	STATUS
☐ North American NA-88 Texan (AT-6C)	T6C-1260	88-12145	42-4066, FAB38	PV

MONUMENTO DE RIO NEGRO (BR30)

Address: Rio Negro.
Admission: On permanent view.
Location: In the town.

The first Texans were delivered to the Air Force in 1942 and several were converted for ground attack duties. In addition they were used by the official aerobatic team. The one on show is in standard training colours.

TYPE	REG/SER	CON. NO.	PI/NOTES	STATUS
☐ North American NA-88 Texan (AT-6C)	T6C-1287	88-13813	42-44150, FAB 65	PV

MONUMENTO DO PARQUE DE MATERIAL AERONÁUTICA – LAGOA SANTA (BR31)

Address: Lagoa Santa 33500-900.
Email: administrator@pamals.mil.br
Admission: On permanent view.
Location: About 5 km south of the town.

The factory was established more than half a century ago and over the years has been responsible for the overhaul of many Air Force aircraft. More than eighty T-6s were assembled at the site and delivered to the Air Force. One of these has been preserved and is displayed near the main gate as a memorial.

TYPE	REG/SER	CON. NO.	PI/NOTES	STATUS
☐ North American NA-119 Texan (T-6D)	T6D-1378	LS-006/1		PV

MONUMENTO DO PARQUE DE MATERIAL AERONÁUTICA – SÃO PAULO (BR32)

Address:	Avenida Bras Leme, São Paulo 02022-901
Tel:	011-2281-4000
Fax:	011-2221-5552
Email:	Informatica@pamasp.aer.mil.br
Admission:	By prior permission only.
Location:	About 6 km north of the city centre.

The airfield was constructed in 1919 and for almost twenty years was the main airport for the city. The factory was set up to carry out major overhauls on Air Force aircraft. A Tracker is preserved at the gate.

TYPE	REG/SER	CON. NO.	PI/NOTES	STATUS
☐ Grumman G-89 Tracker (S-2B) (US-2B)	UP16-7021	750		RA

MUSEU AEROESPACIAL (BR33)

Address:	Avenue Mal Fontenelle 2000, Campo do Afonsos, Rio de Janiero 21331-700..
Tel:	021-3357-5212
Fax:	021-3357-5873
Admission:	Tuesday-Friday 0900-1600 Saturday-Sunday 0930-1600.
Location:	About 25 km west of the city centre.

Alberto Santos-Dumont became famous in the first decade of the twentieth century and although most of his work was done in France he put Brazil firmly on the aviation map. He arrived in Europe in 1898 and built a series of airships. His first powered aircraft was the 14bis which made a series of hops at Bagatelle in late 1906. These were the first flights in Europe with an aircraft taking off under its own power. The successful Demoiselle appeared in November 1907 and around thirty were built. In 1913 a naval seaplane school was set up in Brazil and the army established its own the next year. One of the earliest bases in the country was at Campo dos Afonsos which became the site of the Air Academy in 1914. The country has a rich aviation heritage and aircraft have been bought from many countries for both military and civilian use. In addition numerous indigenous designs have given excellent service and in recent years Embraer has exported aircraft around the world. A decision to set up a museum was taken in the early 1970s and it opened at Campo dos Afonsos on October 18th 1976. A two storey building and five hangars incorporate the exhibition and workshop areas. The history of aviation in the country is traced with many photographs, documents and models on show. The collection now numbers over one hundred machines with many rarities in the hangars. A propeller from the Graf Zeppelin is a prized exhibit. The airship suffered engine vibrations whilst in Rio and the propeller was removed. The large airscrew was spirited away by one of the German engineers who subsequently took up residence in the country. A major restoration has taken place on the sole surviving Focke-Wulf Weihe. Considerable numbers of this light twin were built in Germany in the late 1930s and early 1940s. Licence production was undertaken in Brazil and Hungary. On show is a Curtiss Fledgling painted to represent the aircraft which inaugurated the Army Air Mail Service in 1931. Parked nearby is a colourful Waco CPF-5 which took over the routes the following year. The Stearman A76 was used for armament training and is the only known survivor of its type. One hangar is devoted to the Brazilian aircraft industry. The Muniz M-7 biplane was the first Brazilian type to enter production and eleven were delivered to the Army in the late 1930s. One of the almost eight hundred CAP-4's built can be seen along with the first prototype of the successful Bandeirante. Two Neiva prototypes and two production models are also on view. Several other indigenous designs are being restored and should enhance this area in the future. The Douglas Havoc in the collection was found derelict in a children's playground and the museum staff took four years to restore it to the markings it carried in 1952. The Caudron G.3 was restored in France by Jean Salis in the 1960s. The Nieuport 21 was used for training in the 1920s and a faithful replica is on display. Some of the aircraft noted as in store may have left.

TYPE	REG/SER	CON. NO.	PI/NOTES	STATUS
☐ Aeritalia AMX (YA-1)	YA1-4201	A06/BP002		PV
☐ Aerotec A.122 Uirapuru	PP-ZTT	002		PV
☐ Aerotec A.122A Uirapuru (T-23)	PP-HKS	018	T23-0954	RAA
☐ Aerotec A.122A Uirapuru (T-23)	PT-LGV	068	T23-1734	RA
☐ Aerotec A.122B Uirapuru	PP-KBB	109		RAC
☐ Avro 748 Series 2/205 (C-91)	C91-2504	1554		PV
☐ Beech C18S Kansan (AT-11)	T11-1371	4615	42-37619	PV
☐ Beech D17S (UC-43)	UC43 2778	6691	44-67714, (Bu23679), 2778, PT-CVC	PV
☐ Beech D18S (UC-45)	UC45-2856	A-517		PV
☐ Beech D18S Expeditor (C-45H)	491	AF-784	52-10854, N9137Z – in Chilean markings.	RA
☐ Beech H18S	PT-KXM	BA-684	H18S-2897	RA
☐ Bell 206B Jet Ranger (UH-4)	VH4 8571	169		PV
☐ Bell 47G-2 (H-13)	H13H-8524	2470		RA
☐ Bell 47G-2 Sioux (H-13H) (OH-13H)	H13H-8611	2324	58-5311	RA
☐ Bell 47G-2 (H-13)			Composite.	PV
☐ Bell 47J (H-13)	H13J-8510	1746	(YV-E-DPY)	PV
☐ Bensen B-8M Gyrocopter	PP-ZWR			PV
☐ Boeing 299-O Fortress (B-17G) (TB-17H) (SB-17G)	SB17G-5408	32359	44-83718 Also quoted as c/n 32103 44-83462.	RA

☐ Boeing-Stearman A75J1 Kaydet (PT-18)	PT-ABY	75-476	40-1919	RAA
☐ Boeing-Stearman A75L3 Kaydet	K132	75-611	K-132, 13, 0053, PP-GFI	PV
☐ Boeing-Stearman A76C3	K210	76-023	K-210, 10, 1016, PP-GGI	PV
☐ Bücker Bü 131D-2 Jungmann	'FAB-07'	908	PP-TFM	PVX
☐ Caudron G.3		640	F-WYSL, F-PYSL, F-AZBB	PV
☐ Cessna 305A Bird Dog (L-19A) (O-1A)	PP-EKN	21972	51-5067, 5067	RA
☐ Cessna 305A Bird Dog (L-19A) (O-1A)	PP-GYV	23409	53-7998, L19E-3067	RA
☐ Cessna 305A Bird Dog (L-19A) (O-1A)	PP-EKO		(USAF)	RA
☐ Cessna 305C Bird Dog (L-19E) (O-1E)	L19E-3155	23692	56-2570 – may be c/n 23712 56-2590.	PV
☐ Cessna 318C Tweety Bird (T-37C)	T37C 0922	41212	N5423M	PV
☐ Cessna T-50 Bobcat (AT-17B) (UC-78B)	'22'	3505	42-39296, N75609, 'PP-LDQ'	PVX
☐ Companhia Nacional de Navegacao Aerea – Henrique Lage HL-6B Caure	PP-RHW	BL-220		PV
☐ Consolidated 28-5A Canso A	C10A-6527	21981	9752 (RCAF)	PV
☐ Curtiss 51 Fledgling	'K-263'	B-40	NC263H, N263H	PVX
☐ Curtiss 87V Warhawk (P-40N)	P40N-4064	33440	44-7700, 46	PV
☐ Curtiss-Wright CW-20B Commando (C-46A) (R5C-1)	C46-2058	155	43-47084, Bu50711, PP-XBR, C46-2058, PP-ZBE, PT-LBP	PV
☐ Dassault Mirage IIIEBR	F103E-4913			PV
☐ De Havilland D.H.125-3A/RA (C-93)	C93-2113	25136	G-AVHB, N501W, N506N, N505W, N605W, N700RG, N700RD, N700RG, N125HS	PV
☐ De Havilland D.H.82A Tiger Moth	12HI-105	3329	12HI-105, 02, MT0014, PP-DLL,	PV
☐ De Havilland D.H.82A Tiger Moth				RAD
☐ De Havilland D.H.89A Dragon Rapide (D.H.89B Dominie I)	'PP-VAN'	6900	NR836, CS-ADJ, CR-SAD, CR-LKR	PVX
☐ De Havilland D.H.C.5 Buffalo (C-115)	C115-2371	41		PV
☐ Douglas A-20K Havoc	A20K-6085	23762	44-0539, 40539, 25	PV
☐ Douglas A-26C Invader (A-26B)	A26-5159	7001	41-39288	PV
☐ Douglas DC-3A-456 Skytrain (C-47A)	TC-21	19961	43-15495, NC86547, LV-AET – in Argentinean markings.	RAA
☐ Douglas DC-3A-456 Skytrain (C-47A)	'PP-AVJ'	20555	43-16089, C47-2024, N4946F	PVX
☐ Douglas DC-3A-467 Skytrain (C-47B)	C47-2009	14234/25679	43-48418, FAB 01	PV
☐ Douglas DC-3A-467 Skytrain (C-47B)	C47-2015	14240/25685	43-48424, FAB 07	PV
☐ Eipper MX-2 Quicksilver	U-001			RA
☐ Eipper MXL Quicksilver				PV
☐ Embraer EMB.100 Bandeirante (YC-95)	YC95-2130	001		PV
☐ Embraer EMB.200	PP-ZIP	001		RAD
☐ Embraer EMB.312 Tucano (YT-27)	YT27-1300	312001		PV
☐ Embraer EMB.326GB Xavante [Aermacchi MB.326) (AT-26)	AT26-4525	74064307		PV
☐ Embraer EMB.400 Urapema	PP-ZPD			RA
☐ Embraer EMB.400 Urapema	PP-ZTU	9	PT-PDS	RA
☐ Embraer EMB.720D Minuano [Piper PA-32-301 Saratoga]	PT-EAP	720-006	May be c/n 720-132 PT-FAP	RA
☐ Empresa Aeronáutica Ypiranga CAP-4	PP-TJR	04		PV
☐ Fabrica do Galeao 3FG [Fairchild M-62 Cornell]	PP-HQE	3FG-184	PT19-0450	RA
☐ Fabrica do Galeao 3FG [Fairchild M-62 Cornell]	PP-HNU	3FG-234		RA
☐ Fabrica do Galeao 3FG [Fairchild M-62 Cornell]	PP-GEX	3FG-244	PT19-0511	RA
☐ Fabrica do Galeao 3FG [Fairchild M-62 Cornell]	'0500'	3FG-255	PT19-0522, PP-HOA	PVX
☐ Fairchild 22 C7G	PP-TBD	1801	NC14785	PV
☐ Fairchild 24W41	UC61A-2683	W41-121	PT-CHF	PV
☐ Fairchild M-62A Cornell (PT-19B)	PT19-0310	T43-5809	42-83222, 283222, FAB140	RA
☐ Fairchild 78 Packet (C-82A)	PP-CEL	10153	45-57783, N7855B – at Manaus.	RA
☐ Fairchild 78 Packet (C-82A)	C82-2202	10220	48-0585	RA
☐ Fairchild 110 Flying Boxcar (C-119G)	C119G-2305	10970	51-8076	PV
☐ Fairchild-Hiller FH-1100	PP-EFN	252		PV
☐ Focke-Wulf Fw 44J Stieglitz	'I1AvN-161	174	(Argentina), LV-XX?, 4243	PVX
☐ Focke-Wulf Fw 58B-2 Weihe	'AT-Fw-1530'	1016	V2AvN-215, AT-Fw-1184, PP-FDE c/n also quoted as 215.	PVX
☐ Fokker S.11.4 Instructor (T-21)	T21-0789	085		PV
☐ Fokker S.12.2 (T-22)	T22-0811	012		PV
☐ Fouga CM.170R Magister	'T24-1720'	196	196 (France)	PVX
☐ Gloster Meteor T.7	TF7F-4300	G5-444838	(WS142)	RAC
☐ Gloster Meteor T.7	TF7F-4309	G5-453729	(WS151)	PV
☐ Gloster Meteor F.8	'F8-4460'	G5-361700	F8-4399	PVX
☐ Gloster Meteor F.8	F8-4438	G5-453792	On loan.	RA
☐ Gloster Meteor F.8	F8-4453	G5-453824		RA
☐ Grumman G-44A Widgeon (J4F-2)	FAB-14	1290	Bu34585, FAB-14, 2680, (PP-HPU), PP-GQV	PV
☐ Grumman G-64 Albatross (SA-16A) (HU-16A)	'SA16-6529'	G-37	49-0079, SA16-6534	PVX
☐ Grumman G-89 Tracker (S2F-1) (S-2A) (P-16)	P16A-7016	745	Bu149039	PV
☐ Grumman G-121 Tracker (S-2E)	P16E-7037	314C	Bu152845	PV
☐ Instituto de Pesquisas Tecnologicas IPT-02b Nhapecan	PT-ZBN	002	PP-ZQN	RA
☐ Instituto de Pesquisas Tecnologicas IPT-16 Surubim	PP-ZDB			RA
☐ Instituto de Pesquisas Tecnologicas IPT-O-B Bichinho	PT-KYL	3	PP-ECM	RA
☐ Lippisch Hols der Teufel				PV
☐ Lockheed 18-56-23 Lodestar (C-60A)	C60A-2006	18-2368	42-55931, 16, FAB-07	PV
☐ Lockheed 080 Shooting Star (P-80C) (CC)	F80C-4201	080-2181	49-0433	PV

□ Lockheed 188A Electra	PP-VJM	188-1025	N6104A	PV
□ Lockheed 237-27-01 Ventura (PV-1)	N165H	237-5890	Bu48654, 2262 (Canada), N3949C, N165H, (N367)	PV
□ Lockheed 426-42-11 Neptune MR.1 (P2V-5)	P2E-7010	426-5157	51-15952, WX529, 51-15952	PV
□ Lockheed 580 (T-33A) (AT-33A)	TF33A-4364	580-8294	53-4955	PV
□ Lockheed 683-10-19 Starfighter (F-104S) (F-104S/ASA) (F-104S/ASAM)	MM6890	683-6890	In Italian markings.	PV
□ Microlight	U4175			RA
□ Morane-Saulnier MS.760A Paris I (C-41)	C41-2932	76		PV
□ Muniz M-7	13	13	PP-TEN	PV
□ Neiss 5FG	PP-GLZ			RA
□ Neiss 5FG	PP-GNH	49		RA
□ Neiva 56B Paulistinha (L-6)	L6-3095	1016		PV
□ Neiva 56C	PP-GTP	1058		PV
□ Neiva N.591 Regente (YL-42) (L-42)	YL42-3120	3501		PV
□ Neiva N.591-290 Regente	PP-HRT	3001	PT-BZA	RA
□ Neiva N.591-290 Regente (C-42)	PP-GYY	2075	C42-2234	RA
□ Neiva N.592 Regente (L-42)	L42-3225	5067		PV
□ Neiva N.621 Universal (YT-25)	YT25-1830	1001	PP-ZTW	PV
□ Nieuport 21E.1 (R)	'N2102'			PVX
□ North American NA-84 Texan (AT-6B)	PT-KTG	84-7571	41-17193, T6B-1484	RA
□ North American NA-88 Texan (AT-6C)	T6C-1262	88-12147	42-4068, (40?)	RAA
□ North American NA-88 Texan (AT-6D)	T6D-1617	88-18266	42-86485	PV
□ North American NA-108 Mitchell (B-25J)	B25J-5127	108-33344	44-30069	PV
□ North American NA-119 Texan (AT-6D)	T6D-1559	LS-008/05		PV
□ North American NA-121 Texan (AT-6D)	PT-TRB	121-42286	44-81564, T6D-1643	RA
□ North American NA-171 Trojan (T-28A) (T-28R-1)	N-703	171-8	50-0202, N9104Z, N-703, 0862	PV
□ North American NA-221 Sabre (F-86K)	0014	221-151	55-4911, JD+109, JD+101, JD+301 – in Venezuelan markings.	PV
□ Northrop N-156B Freedom Fighter(F-5B)	F5B-4800	X.1001	74-1576	PV
□ Pilatus P.3-04 (L-3) (O-3)	O3-3182	333	HB-HOC, N-503	PV
□ Pilatus P.3-04 (L-3) (O-3)	O3-3183	335	HB-HOE, N-505	RA
□ Piper J-3F-65 Cub	PP-TUF	9065		RA
□ Piper J-4A Cub Coupe	'1'	4-454	PP-TEX	PVX
□ Piper J-5A Cub Cruiser	PP-TTU	5-1332		RA
□ Pitts S-2A Special	PT-ZMM			PV
□ Republic P-47D Thunderbolt	'44-19662'		44-20339, 420339, P47-4184	PVX
□ Republic P-47D Thunderbolt	'420339'	399-55690	45-49151, P47-4120	PVX
□ Republic RC-3 Seabee	PP-DLV	1044	NC6756K, N6756K	RA
□ Republic RC-3 Seabee	PP-???	189		RA
□ Republic RC-3 Seabee	CX-AID	410		RAD
□ Santos-Dumont 14bis (R)				PV
□ Santos-Dumont XX Demoiselle (R)				PV
□ Stinson SR-10D Reliant	UCSR10-2653	5917	NC?????, PP-TFQ, PP-IFY	PVX
□ Vickers 789D Viscount (C-90)	VC90-2101	345		RA
□ Vultee V-74A Valiant (BT-15)	BT15-1137	74A-10006	42-41773, 241773, 83	RA
□ Vultee V-74A Valiant (BT-15)	BT15-1072	74A-3240	41-10373, 110373	PV
□ Waco CJC	'C66'		Converted from a UIC	PVX
□ Waco CPF-5	C80	4354	C-80, 2560, PP-RAE	PV
□ Waco CSO	F154	1544		PV
□ Waco RNF	'K162'	3633	LV-GBA	PVX
□ Westland Wasp HAS.1	N-7039	F9603	XT433, G-17-6	PV

MUSEU ASAS DE UM SONHO (BR34)

Address:	Caixa Postal 358, Centro Tecnológico da TAM, 13560-970, São Carlos.
Tel:	016-3362-1500
Email:	museu@tam.com.br
Admission:	Daily 1000-1600.
Location:	At São Carlos which is about 250 km from São Paulo.

Rolim and João Amaro formed an air taxi service in the late 1950s and this has now grown into TAM (Taxi Aereo Marilia) which is the second largest airline in the country. The brothers started collecting and restoring vintage and classic aircraft when they acquired a derelict Cessna 195 in the early 1990s. Other types were acquired and this led to the idea of a museum. Sadly Rolim was killed in a helicopter crash in 2001 but the plans continued. A former agricultural vehicle factory close to an airfield was converted into display halls and an aircraft maintenance area for the airline's fleet. The first phase of the exhibition opened in November 2006. The oldest aircraft in the collection is the 1928 Curtiss Robin which was bought in Argentina in 1996 and flew again the following year. Another type from this era is the Fleet 2 biplane which was also found in Argentina. Only two RWD.13 high wing monoplanes are known to exist. The three student designers built their first aircraft in 1928 and the type was steadily improved. A company was set up and it became one of the leading producers of light aircraft in Poland. The RWD.13 first flew in 1935 and soon entered production. By the outbreak of World War II over one hundred had been completed. Six examples were delivered to Brazil in the late 1930s and some were still flying in the mid-1950s. Another rarity is the Miles Hawk Major which has been completely restored to its original British markings. The aircraft was bought at Woodley in 1936 by a representative of the Madrid government. Along with a Miles Falcon and a Monospar ST-25 it was flown to Spain and served with the Republican side. The Hawk survived the conflict and moved to Uruguay in 1938. Found in a derelict condition in the 1990s it was eventually purchased for the collection. A fairly new arrival is the rare Lippisch Professor glider. This intermediate sailplane made its maiden flight at the famous Wasserkupe site in Germany in May 1928. A few examples are known to have been built in Brazil so the example in store is probably one of these. The hangar is dominated by the Constellation rescued from Paraguay and restored in Panair do Brasil colours. Between 1946 and 1956 the airline operated fourteen examples of the Lockheed airliner on its trans-Atlantic services. .Several airframes have arrived on loan from the Santos Dumont collection. The only surviving twin-hulled Savoia-Marchetti SM.55A flying boat is now in the workshops and will be restored to its former glory.

TYPE	REG/SER	CON. NO.	PI/NOTES	STATUS
☐ Aeronca C-3	NC14630	A-516	NC14630, N14630	PVA
☐ Aeronca 7AC Champion	LV-FRC	7AC-446		RAA
☐ Aeronca 11AC Chief	LV-NXN	11AC-1827		RA
☐ Beech V35 Bonanza	PT-IKN	D-9417	Private aircraft of museum owner.	RAA
☐ Boeing-Stearman B75N1 Kaydet (N2S-3)	LV-FGD	75-7631	Bu38010	PVA
☐ Cessna 140				RA
☐ Cessna 140	PT-ADV	15496	On loan from F Santos Dumont.	PVC
☐ Cessna 140A	PP-DYX	15281	N9640A	PVA
☐ Cessna 150J	PT-BKW	15070815	(N61122)	RAA
☐ Cessna 150J	PT-AKY	69369	(N50523)	RAA
☐ Cessna 170B	PT-BDE	25060	N8208A	RAA
☐ Cessna 172 Skyhawk	PT-CPS	36425	N8725B, PT-AZM, PP-MGE	RA
☐ Cessna 180F	PT-BXZ	18051249	N2149Z	PVA
☐ Cessna A185F Skywagon 185	PT-KJM	18502466	(N1746R)	PVC
☐ Cessna 195B	PT-LDK	16096	(N2111C), N11B, PP-FVF, PT-DGA	PVA
☐ Cessna 206				RA
☐ Cessna 305A Bird Dog (L-19A) (O-1A)	'72774'	21959	51-5054, PP-EKF	PVAX
☐ Cessna 305A Bird Dog (L-19A) (O-1A)	'62612'	22841	51-12415, PP-EKJ	PVAX
☐ Cessna 305A Bird Dog (L-19A) (O-1A)	'54736'	22850	51-16968, PP-EKI	PVAX
☐ Cessna 337 Super Skymaster				RA
☐ Construcciones Aeronáuticas (CASA) 1.131E [Bücker Bü 131 Jungmann]	E.3B-595		E.3B-595, (Paraguay), N46926, NX595BJ	PV
☐ Construcciones Aeronáuticas (CASA) 1.131H [Bücker Bü 131 Jungmann]	EC-BKA	1081	E.3B-370	RAA
☐ Convair 105 (L-13A) (L-13B)	N4236K	286	47-0406	RAA
☐ Convair 440-79 Samaritan (C-131D)	2001	322	55-0297, 2001(Paraguay), N6168R	RA
☐ Curtiss 50C Robin C-2				RA
☐ Curtiss-Wright CW-16E Light Sport	K178	3530	On loan from F Santos-Dumont.	RA
☐ De Havilland D.H.C.1 Chipmunk 22	LV-MAI	C1/0952	E-602 (Uruguay), CX-BBG	RAA
☐ Douglas DC-3A-456 Skytrain (C-47A)			Front fuselage only.	PV
☐ Douglas DC-3A-456 Skytrain (C-47A)	N101KC	11639	42-68712, NC45375	RAA
☐ Embraer EMB.110C Bandeirante	PP-SBA	110009	PP-SSA – Fuselage only.	RA
☐ Embraer EMB.110C Bandeirante	PP-SBG	110024		RA
☐ Embraer EMB.312 Tucano (T-27)				RA
☐ Embraer EMB.326GB Xavante [Aermacchi MB.326) (AT-26)	AT26-4566	76105348		RA
☐ Embraer EMB.326GB Xavante [Aermacchi MB.326) (AT-26)				RA
☐ Embraer EMB.400 Urapema	PT-PDO	4		PV
☐ Embraer EMB.712 Tupi	PT-NXW	712046		RA
☐ Empresa Aeronáutica EAY-201 Ypiranga	PP-TBF	01	On loan from F. Santos Dumont.	PV
☐ Empresa Aeronáutica Ypiranga CAP-4		01		RA
☐ Empresa Aeronáutica Ypiranga CAP-4A	'N-505'	320	PP-RSV	PVX
☐ Fabrica do Galeao 3FG [Fairchild M-62 Cornell]	PP-GAY	260A	(Brazilian AF), PP-GUG, PP-FDU	PV
☐ Fairchild 24R (24 C8C)	UC61A-2687	2687	FAB-04	PV
☐ Fleet 2	LV-ZCE	50	PT-???.LV-DBC	RA
☐ Flug Werk FW 190A-8/N		990012		RAA
☐ Focke-Wulf Fw 44J Stieglitz	LV-ZAS	149		RA
☐ Fokker 100	PT-MRL	11441	PH-LXS	RA
☐ Fokker F.27 Friendship			Front fuselage only.	RA
☐ Ganota WR-II Gyrocopter	PU-WME	EA-01/94		RA
☐ Gloster Meteor F.8	F8-4440	G5-453795	On loan from F. Santos Dumont.	PV
☐ Grumman G-121 Tracker (S-2E)				RA
☐ Grumman G-121 Tracker (S-2E)	P16E-7034	296C	Bu152827	RA
☐ Grumman G-164 Ag-Cat	PP-XDI	CPSJ-01		RAA
☐ Ikarus C42B	PU-CCE	3116577		RA
☐ Industria Paranese de Estruturas KW.1	PT-PEI	4		PV
☐ Industria Paranese de Estruturas KW.1	PT-PFJ	027		PV
☐ Lippisch Professor				RA
☐ Lockheed 049-46-59 Constellation (049-51-26)	'PP-PDD'	049-2071	PH-TAX, PH-TDA, N86533	PVX
☐ Lockheed 580 (T-33A)				RA
☐ Messerschmitt Bf 109G-2	'12456'			PVX
☐ Microleve				RA
☐ Mikoyan-Gurevich MiG-21MF	'17'	968703	8703 (Poland), 03 (Poland) – in false Soviet markings,	PVX
☐ Miles M.2H Hawk Major	G-ADAS	138	G-ADAS, CX-ACT	PVAX
☐ Montalva AC-4	PT-ZGE	950215		RA
☐ Neiva P-56 (R)	PT-ZGY	SDSPG-001/98		RA
☐ Nord N.1203-II Norécrin	PP-EBE	210	PT-AJF, PT-ABJ	PVA
☐ North American NA-168 Texan (T-6G)	PT-KVF	168-306	49-3202, T6G-1658	RAA
☐ Piper PA-12 Super Cruiser				PVA
☐ Pitts S-1S Special	PT-ZML	M-00-45-1		RA
☐ Rearwin 9000L Sportster	LV-MEA	588D		RAA
☐ Rearwin 9000L Sportster	PT-TEE	606D		RA

TYPE	REG/SER	CON. NO.	PI/NOTES	STATUS
☐ Republic P-47D Thunderbolt	'229265/B5'		42-26760, P47-4109 – on loan from F Santos Dumont.	PVX
☐ Riley Dove 400 [De Havilland D.H.104 Dove 6 (2A)]	PT-KUG	04334	PT-AMP, PP-FVD	RA
☐ Rogalski, Wigura, Drzewiecki R.W.D.13	PT-LFY	286	PP-TGJ, PP-ZDM	RAA
☐ Rutan 33 Vari-Eze				RA
☐ Santos-Dumont 14bis (R)				PV
☐ Santos-Dumont XX Demoiselle (R)				PV
☐ Savoia-Marchetti SM.55A	I-BAUQ	10509	I-SAAV – on loan from F. Santos Dumont.	RAC
☐ Schneider ESG 31 Grunau Baby II (D.F.S. 108-49)				PV
☐ Sikorsky S-61D-3 Sea King (SH-3D)				RA
☐ Stinson V-77 Reliant (AT-19)	PP-RZI	77-360	43-44070, FB632, Bu11626	RA
☐ Stinson 108-3 Voyager	PP-DOZ	108-4440	NC6440M	RA
☐ Supermarine 361 Spitfire HF.IXe	'EN398'		MA793, 5601 (SAAF), 'PT672', N930LB	PVAX
☐ Svenska Aeroplan Aktiebolaget (SAAB) 91A Safir	LV-RIG	91115	SE-AZK	RAA
☐ Taylorcraft BC-12D	PU-RYS	7740	Privately owned.	PVA
☐ Universal Aircraft Company American Flea Ship	PP-TKX	60		PV
☐ Vought F4U-1A Corsair	'17-F-13'	4078	Bu17995, N90285, ZK-FUI, 'NZ5201'	PVAX
☐ Waco CSO				RA
☐ Wytwornia Sprzetu Komunikacyjnego (WSK) SBLim-2 [MiG-15UTI]	6247	622047	6247 (Poland), G-OMIG, LV-X216	PVA
☐ Wytwornia Sprzetu Komunikacyjnego (WSK) Lim-5 [Mikoyan-Gurevich MiG-17F]	'23'	1C 13-05	1305 (Poland) – in false Soviet markings.	PVX
☐ Yakovlev Yak-40				RA

MUSEU CASA SANTOS DUMONT (BR35)

Address: Rue do Encato 22, Petropolis.
Tel: 024-2247-3158
Admission: Daily 1000-1600.
Location: In the town.

The house was bought as a summer home by the aviation pioneer and inventor. The exhibition traces his life and highlights his work. There are photographs, models and personal items to be seen along with videos.

MUSEU DA ACADEMIA MILITAR DAS AGULHAS NEGRAS (BR36)

Address: Resende 27500-000.
Tel: 024-3358-4500
Email: pr@aman.ensino.eb.br
Admission: By prior permission only.
Location: In the northern part of the town.

The first military academy in the country was set up in Rio de Janeiro in the late eighteenth century. A move was made to Resende and a museum tracing the history of the college has been set up. The display opened in 1947 and there are many uniforms, photographs and documents on show. In the grounds are tanks, guns and the Meteor.

TYPE	REG/SER	CON. NO.	PI/NOTES	STATUS
☐ Gloster Meteor F.8	F8-4401	G-453691		RA

MUSEU DA AERONÁUTICA DA FUNDAÇÃO SANTOS DUMONT (BR37)

Address: Rua Mesopotâmia, s/n – Pavilhão 2, Centro Municipal de Campismo, Cotia.
Tel: 011- 4702-8072
Admission: Not open at the present time.
Location On the outskirts of the town.

Work on a building for the museum started in 1959. The display grew steadily for the first few years and exhibits were transferred from the Ypiranga Museum. The historic material collected in 1956 for the São Paulo Aeronautical Exhibition celebrating the fiftieth anniversary of Santos-Dumont's flight was also donated. The collection was forced to close in 1986 when the municipal authorities declared the building unsafe. In 1999 some of the collection moved to Cotia. The rarest aircraft is the Savoia-Marchetti SM.55A twin hulled flying boat. This aircraft was built at Sesto Calende in 1925 and in the October of that year took off on a flight to Buenos-Aires which it was forced to abandon at Casablanca. The SM.55A returned and was extensively modified. On October 13th 1926, piloted by the Brazilian Joao Ribeiro de Barros, it took off for São Paolo, finally arriving at its destination on April 28th 1927. Named 'Jahu' after the city where Barros was born the aircraft was first donated to the Ypiranga Museum joining the collection

TYPE	REG/SER	CON. NO.	PI/NOTES	STATUS
☐ Cessna 140A	PT-ADV	15496	On loan to Museu Asas.	–
☐ Curtiss-Wright CW-16E Light Sport	K178	3530	On loan to Museu Asas	–
☐ Embraer EMB.100 Bandeirante (YC-95)	YC95-2131	02		RA
☐ Empresa Aeronáutica EAY-201 Ypiranga	PP-TBF	01	On loan to Museu Asas	–
☐ Empresa Aeronáutica EAY-201 Ypiranga	PP-TLS	02		RA
☐ Fabrica do Galeao 3FG [Fairchild M-62 Cornell]	PT19-0509	3FG-242		RA
☐ Fokker S.11.4 Instructor (T-21)	T21-0774	070		RA
☐ Gloster Meteor F.8	F8-4440	G5-453795	On loan to Museo Asas.	–
☐ Instituto de Pesquisas Tecnologicas IPT-6 Stratus				RA
☐ Instituto de Pesquisas Tecnologicas IPT-12A Cabore	PP-PBT	01		RA
☐ Muniz M-7	PP-TEN	013		RA
☐ North American NA-119 Texan (AT-6D)	T6D-1390	LS-005/2	On loan to SP Base Museum.	–
☐ Republic P-47D Thunderbolt	'229265/B5'		42-26760, P47-4109 – on loan to Museu Asas.	–
☐ Santos-Dumont 14bis (R)				RA
☐ Savoia-Marchetti SM.55A	I-BAUQ	10509	I-SAAV – on loan to Museu Asas	–
☐ Szybowcowe Zaklad Doswiadczalny S.Z.D.48-1 Jantar Standard 2	PT-PIS	B-1240		RA
☐ Waco CSO	UCCSO-2516		3???, C-29	RA

MUSEU DA AERONÁUTICA DE BELEM (BR38)

Address:	Rodovia Arthur Bernandes, s/n Val de Cans, 66115-000 Belem.
Tel:	091-257-0088
Admission:	Not yet open.
Location:	In the northern suburbs of the city.

The Catalina is on display at the Air Force Base in the city. The type had given sterling service in the region for many years.. There are plans to construct a museum in the city with the Catalina as the centrepiece of the display.

TYPE	REG/SER	CON. NO.	PI/NOTES	STATUS
☐ Bell 205 Iroquois (UH-1H)	UH1H-8655	13487	73-21799 – possible identity.	RA
☐ Cessna 305C Bird Dog (L-19E) (O-1E)	L19E-3165			RA
☐ Consolidated 28-6A Catalina (PBY-6A)	C10A-6552	2007	Bu46643, N9556C, 6552, PT-BBQ, PP-PEB	RA
☐ Douglas DC-3A-456 Skytrain (C-47A)	C47-2032	20414	43-15948	RA

MUSEU DA BASE AÉREA DE SÃO PAULO (BR39)

Address:	Avenida Monteiro Lobato 6365, Cumbica 07184-000.
Tel:	011-6465-2000
Admission:	By prior permission only.
Location:	About 6 km north of the city centre.

A museum is being set up to trace the history of the airfield which opened in 1919. Items of memorabilia, photographs and documents are being gathered. The aircraft are currently stored in a hangar.

TYPE	REG/SER	CON. NO.	PI/NOTES	STATUS
☐ De Havilland D.H.82A Tiger Moth	PP-TEN			RA
☐ Fabrica do Galeao 3FG [Fairchild M-62 Cornell]	PT19-0508	3FG-241		RA
☐ North American NA-88 Texan (SNJ-4)	SNJ4-1478	88-12428	Bu27328	RA
☐ North American NA-119 Texan (AT-6D)	T6-1390	LS-005/2	On loan from F. Santos Dumont.	RA

MUSEU DA BASE AÉREA DE SALVADOR (BR40)

Address:	Aeroporto Internacional Luis Eduardo Magalhaes, 41510 Salvador.
Tel:	071-3377-8219
Admission:	By prior permission only.
Location:	About 10 km east of the town.

This base was home to Neptune squadrons from 1958 until the type was withdrawn in 1976. A small museum has been set up at the field to trace the history of the site, its aircraft and its units.

TYPE	REG/SER	CON. NO.	PI/NOTES	STATUS
☐ Gloster Meteor F.8	F8-4004	G5-453693		RA
☐ Lockheed 426-42-11 Neptune MR.1 (P2V-5)	P2E-7009	426-5153	51-15948, WX544	RA

MUSEU DA BRIGADA DE INFANTERIA PARA-QUEDISTA (BR41)

Address:	Avenida General de Silveira, Campo dos Afonsos.
Admission:	By prior permission only.
Location:	Just north of the airfield.

The unit has set up a small museum at its headquarters. The history of the brigade and the development of paratroop forces is portrayed. The C-47 has been painted in false Air Force colours.

TYPE	REG/SER	CON. NO.	PI/NOTES	STATUS
☐ Douglas DC-3A-456 Skytrain (C-47A)	'C47-2017'	20193	43-15727, NC53594, N4908V, PP-AOA, PP-AKA	RAX

MUSEU DA MARINHA (BR42)

Address:	Base Aeronaval, São Pedro da Aldeia
Admission:	By prior permission only.
Location:	Just north of the town

The Navy is setting up a museum at its São Pedro base. A naval aviation school was set up in 1916 and this became the Navy Aviation Corps in 1931. This was incorporated into the National Air Force in 1941 and it was not until 1958 that an independent Naval Air Arm was established again. The Curtiss company sent a representative to Brazil in 1916 and this led to the purchase of three Curtiss F flying boats. The example in the collection is probably a replica incorporating some original parts but this has not been confirmed. Seventeen Tiger Moths were flown between 1933 and 1941. The history of naval aviation in the country is portrayed in the displays.

TYPE	REG/SER	CON. NO.	PI/NOTES	STATUS
☐ Curtiss F			Possibly a partial replica.	RA
☐ De Havilland D.H.82A Tiger Moth				RAA
☐ De Havilland D.H.82A Tiger Moth (R)	'2-1'2'			RA
☐ Pilatus P.3-04	N-506	336	HB-HOF, N-306, 3180	RA
☐ Sikorsky S-61D-3 Sea King (SH-3D)	'N-3009'		Outside base.	PVX
☐ Westland Wasp HAS.1	N-7040	F9557	XS530, G-17-7	RA
☐ Westland Wasp HAS.1	N-7016	F9615		RA
☐ Westland-Sikorsky WS-51 Widgeon Series 2	N-7001	WA/H/142	H-4001, HU-1	RA
☐ Westland-Sikorsky WS-55 Whirlwind Series 3	N-7024	WA.692	G-17-1, PT-HQK	RA

MUSEU DA VARIG (BR43)

Address:	Rue Agusta Severo 851, Porto Alegre 90240.
Tel:	051-357-7000 ext 7419.
Admission:	Tuesday-Friday 0900-1130 1400-1630; Saturday 0900-1100.
Location:	At the VARIG maintenance base at the airport in the southern suburbs of the city.

VARIG was founded on May 7th. 1927 and its first aircraft were single examples of the Dornier Wal and Merkur. In the 1930s the fleet comprised mainly of German types. In 1971 the airline established a museum at its Porto Alegre base. The displays trace the development of the company and of commercial flying. On show are models, uniforms, airline menus, engines, propellers, photographs, documents and an Airbus flight simulator. In 1937 employees of the airline formed a flying club, Varig Aerosporte, and one of the first gliders used was a Goppingen Wolf. The DC-3 on show is the first built and was delivered to American Airlines in August 1936. The aircraft was first bought by VASP in 1951 and later damaged in a collision with a C-46.

TYPE	REG/SER	CON. NO.	PI/NOTES	STATUS
☐ Douglas DC-3-178	'PP-VRG'	1545	NC16009, PP-SQH, PP-ANU – with rear fuselage of DC-3A (C-47B) c/n 17028/34293 45-1025, PP-ATH, PP-ANI	PVX
☐ Göppingen Gö 1 Wolf (D.F.S. 108-58)	PT-PAQ		PP-10, PP-PAQ	PV

The only complete Focke Wulf Weihe is a prized exhibit at the Museu Aeroespacial. (John Mounce)

This Miles Hawk Major was found in Uruguay and restored in Brazil for the Museu Asas de um Sonho. (Renato Spillimbergo)

The last surviving SAAB Scandia can be seen in the museum at Bebeduoro. (Renato Spillimbergo)

MUSEU DE ARMAS,VEICULOS MOTORIZADOS E AVIOES ANTIGOS' EDUARDO ANDRÉ MATARAZZO' (BR44)

Address:	Praca Santos Dumont. Bebeduoro
Tel:	017-3342-2255
Email:	matarazzo@matazzaro.org
Admission:	Thursday, Saturday, Sunday 0900-1700.
Location:	In the centre of the town which is about 350 km north west of Sao Paulo.

Between 1904 and 1974 Eduardo Matarazzo bought eighty two cars for his personal use. These vehicles formed the basis of the collection and over the years commercial vehicles, steam and diesel locomotives, railway carriages and military equipment have been added. Now over two hundred vehicles can be seen along with motor cycles and associated equipment. The sole surviving SAAB Scandia is a prized exhibit. Only eighteen examples of the twin engined airliner were built been 1948 and 1954 in both Sweden and Holland. Scandinavian Airlines System operated eight and the remainder were delivered to Brazil. The airline VASP, based at São Paulo, eventually bought all the eighteen built and flew them until the early 1970s. The example on show was used by VASP from 1955 to 1969 and then spent five years in store before joining the museum. The former British European Airways Viscount was also operated by VASP. The HL-1B high wing two seater, resembling a Piper Cub was produced in the early 1940s and was used by several aero clubs and evaluated by the Air Force. Another high wing design is the EAY-201. The type was in essence an unlicenced copy of the American Taylor Cub. Only five were built before the company was taken over and the Ypiranga was developed into Paulista CAP-4 with a 65 hp. Franklin engine. Well over eight hundred were built for both military and civil use. Also on show in the main halls are several aero-engines, propellers, instruments and components.

TYPE	REG/SER	CON. NO.	PI/NOTES	STATUS
☐ Beech D18S	UC45-2850	A-448		PV
☐ Companhia Nacional de Navegacao Aerea – Henrique Lage HL-1B	PP-TVX	39		PV
☐ Convair 240-2	PP-VDG	67	N74667, NC90666, N90666, (PP-VCP)	PV
☐ Curtiss-Wright CW-20B Commando (C-46A)	PP-VCE	30656	42-101201, XB-JAP, XA-HAM	PV
☐ Douglas A-26B Invader	A26-5176	27413	44-34134, N4974N, N115RG	PV
☐ Douglas DC-3A-467 Skytrain (C-47B)	PP-VBK	15378/26823	43-49562, NC79020	PV
☐ Douglas DC-6A	PP-LFB	45528		PV
☐ Empresa Aeronáutica EAY-201 Ypiranga				PV
☐ Gloster Meteor F.8	F8-4409	G5-453704		PV
☐ Gloster Meteor F.8	F8-4442	G5-453798		PV
☐ Lockheed 18-56-23 Lodestar (C-60)	PT-CGV	18-2190	42-32170, NC74659, N74659, TI-1030, ZP-CBU	PV
☐ Lockheed 580 (T-33A) (AT-33A)	TF33A-4323	580-7528	52-9418	PV
☐ North American NA-108 Mitchell (B-25J) (CB-25J)V	B25J-5097		(USAAF)	P
☐ North American NA-88 Texan (AT-6D)	T6D-1575	S7-04 (?)		PV
☐ North American NA-121 Texan (AT-6D)	T6D-1339	121-41713	44-80991, FAB 117	PV
☐ Svenska Aeroplan Aktiebolaget (SAAB) 90-A2 Scandia	PP-SQR	90-15		PV
☐ Vickers 701C Viscount	PP-SRO	64	G-ANHD	PV
☐ Westland-Sikorsky WS-51 Dragonfly 1B	PT-HAL	WA/H/30	G-AMHB, OO-CWA, XB-JUQ	PV

MUSEU DE CABANGU – SANTOS DUMONT (BR45)

Address:	Cabangu, Santos Dumont.
Admission:	Daily 1000-1600.
Location:	About 15 km north west of the town.

The city of Palmira was renamed after the Brazilian aviation pioneer Alberto Santos Dumont. He was born on a farm in the village of Cabangu on July 20th 1873. This house has now been converted into a museum tracing his life and achievements. The family moved to France in 1891 and he became fascinated by flight. He designed the first successful dirigible balloons and in October 1901 flew around the Eiffel Tower. He made the first public in flight in Europe in October 1906 in his 14bis. His final design was the Demoiselle which was produced in some numbers in several versions. His last flight was in 1910 as he had contacted Multiple Sclerosis. He returned to his native country where he died in 1932. A scale replica of his 14bis is mounted in the grounds along with a Neiva Uirapuru trainer. The Shooting Star is preserved nearby. The T-33 is in a square in Santos Dumont where it honours the work of the aviator. Parts of the house have been restored to its nineteenth century condition. Other rooms house collections of models, photographs and items of memorabilia.

TYPE	REG/SER	CON. NO.	PI/NOTES	STATUS
☐ Aerotec A.122A Uirapuru (T-23)				PV
☐ Lockheed 080 Shooting Star (P-80C) (F-80C)	F80C-4220	080-2467	49-0719.	PV
☐ Lockheed 580 (T-33A) (AT-33A)	T33-4350	580-8886	53-5547 – in square in Santos Dumont.	PV
☐ Santos-Dumont 14bis (Scale R)				PV

MUSEU DE TECNOLOGIA DA ULBRA (BR46)

Address:	Avenue Farroupilha 8000, Bairro São José, Canoas 92450-900.
Tel:	051-3477-4000
Fax:	051-3477-1313
Email:	museu@ulbra.br
Admission:	Tuesday-Sunday 1000-1700.
Location:	In the northern part of the city.

This modern museum has been set up by the Lutheran University. The history of the Brazilian motor industry is portrayed with over three hundred cars on show. The career of Emerson Fittipaldi is also highlighted The development of communications is also followed. The Xavante is parked outside the building.

TYPE	REG/SER	CON. NO.	PI/NOTES	STATUS
☐ Embraer EMB.326GB Xavante [Aermacchi MB.326) (AT-26)	AT26-4508	73047290		PV

MUSEU DO EXPEDICIONARIO (BR47)

Address:	S/N P.C. Expedicionario, Curitiba.
Tel:	041-264-3931
Admission:	Tuesday-Sunday 1000-1600.
Location:	In the town which is about 300 km south west of Sao Paolo.

In January 1944 Brazilian aircrews were sent to the U.S.A. for training. The 1st Grupo de Caca of the Força Expedicionaria Brasiliera was formed, posted to Italy, and equipped with Republic P-47Ds. Allocated to the 350th Fighter Group of the Twelfth Air Force, the unit arrived at Tarquinia in October 1944 and when fully operational transferred to Pisa-San Giusto in December 1944. Overtwo and a half thousand missions were flown with the loss of seventeen aircraft and five pilots. At the end of the conflict the group returned to Brazil and was based at Curitiba. This museum has been set up to honour the exploits of the Group. On show are photos, documents and memorabilia tracing the history of the unit during its time in the U.S.A. and Italy. The Thunderbolt, which spent many years on display at the airfield, is mounted outside the building. Also on show is an example of the Meteor F.8s which served with the Brazilian Air Force for more than two decades.

TYPE	REG/SER	CON. NO.	PI/NOTES	STATUS
☐ Gloster Meteor F.8	F8-4452	G5-453825		PV
☐ Republic P-47D Thunderbolt	'226756'		44-26762, P47-4110	PVX

MUSEU MARIANO PROCOPIO (BR48)

Address:	Rue Dom Pedro II, Bairro Mariano Procopio, Juiz de Fora 36035-090.
Tel:	032-3211-1145
Admission:	Tuesday-Sunday.1200-1800.
Location:	In the centre of the town which is about 150 km north of Rio de Janiero.

Set in a pleasant park, the museum houses artefacts and works of art from the period of Portuguese rule up to modern times. The Porterfield CP-50 appeared in 1939 and about sixty were built at Kansas City.

TYPE	REG/SER	CON. NO.	PI/NOTES	STATUS
☐ Porterfield CP-50	PP-GAN	619		PV

SUBMARINO MUSEU RIACHUELO (BR49)

Address:	Cais do Espaco, Avenue Alfredo Agache, Rio de Janiero.
Tel:	021-2216-6814
Admission:	Tuesday-Sunday 1200-1700.
Location:	In the harbour area of the city.

The submarine entered service in January 1977 and is the seventh ship to carry the name of the famous battle. Visitors can tour the majority of the vessel and the Sea King is parked on the nearby quay.

TYPE	REG/SER	CON. NO.	PI/NOTES	STATUS
☐ Sikorsky S-61B Sea King (SH-3D)	N-3018	61397	Bu154107	PV

CHILE

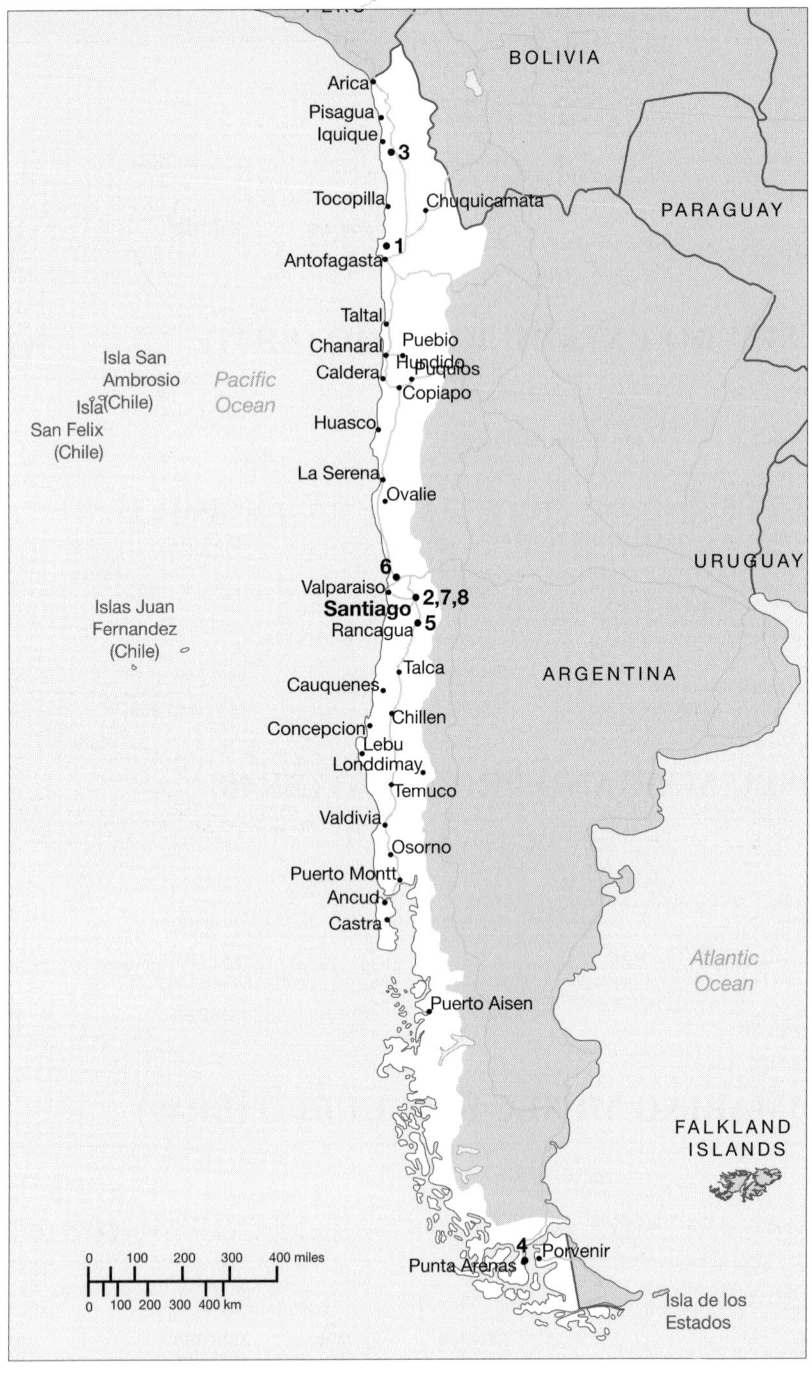
BOLIVIA
PARAGUAY
URUGUAY
ARGENTINA
Pacific Ocean
Atlantic Ocean
FALKLAND ISLANDS
Arica
Pisagua
Iquique
3
Tocopilla
Chuquicamata
1
Antofagasta
Taltal
Chanaral
Puebio Hundido
Puquios
Caldera
Copiapo
Huasco
La Serena
Ovalie
6
Valparaiso
2,7,8
Santiago
5
Rancagua
Talca
Cauquenes
Chillen
Concepcion
Lebu
Londdimay
Temuco
Valdivia
Osorno
Puerto Montt
Ancud
Castra
Puerto Aisen
4
Porvenir
Punta Arenas
Isla de los Estados
Isla San Ambrosio (Chile)
Isla San Felix (Chile)
Islas Juan Fernandez (Chile)
0 100 200 300 400 miles
0 100 200 300 400 km

COLECCIÓN DE BASE AÉREA ANTOFAGASTA (CH1)

Address: Brigada Aérea V HQ,
Cerro Moreno.
Antofagasta.
Tel: 0552-209781
Fax: 0552-209502
Admission: By prior permission only.
Location: About 10 km north of the town.

In 1995 Brigada Aérea V was formed and this is the main fighter unit in the country. The wing currently operates the Northrop F-5E and the General Dynamics F-16. The airfield also serves as the airport for the area. Six aircraft have been preserved around the site. Chile ordered over fifty Hunters which were delivered between 1967 and 1982. The last were withdrawn from use in 1995. The Chilean Air Force was the largest operator of Invaders in South America and the first ten delivered in 1954/5 were based at Antofagasta.

TYPE	REG/SER	CON. NO.	PI/NOTES	STATUS
☐ Dassault Mirage 5BD	725	212	BD-12 (Belgium)	RA
☐ De Havilland D.H.115 Sea Vampire T.22	J-304			RA
☐ Douglas A-26C Invader	'863'	29032	44-35753, 824 – probable identity.	RAX
☐ Hawker P.1099 Hunter FGA.9 (F.6)	749	41H/688139	XK137, J-749	RA
☐ Hawker P.1099 Hunter FGA.71 (F.6)	727	41H/679932	XE557, G-9-319	RA
☐ Lockheed 580 (T-33A)	J-324		(USAF)	RA

COLECCIÓN DE BASE AÉREA EL BOSQUE (CH2)

Address: Vulcan Osman,
El Bosque,
Santiago.
Tel: 02-420-1765
Admission: By prior permission only.
Location: In the southern suburbs of the city.

This historic airfield opened in 1913 when pilot training for the Chilean Military Aviation Service was transferred from Lo Espejo. Among the types used was the Blériot XI. On January 1st 1915 the first flying display in South America was held at the site with fourteen aircraft taking part. A flying school remained at El Bosque for many years and a technical training centre was also in residence. At the current time maintenance work is carried out of the Air Force training gliders and their tugs. A collection of preserved aircraft is being assembled at the field. Two types, including a Blériot XI replica, have moved the short distance from the museum at Los Cerrilos. Also on show are two products of the local aviation industry. The Pillan is derived from the Piper PA-28 Arrow. Two prototypes were built in Florida in the early 1980s. Kits for the production aircraft were shipped to Chile and the type was exported to other Latin American countries and Spain. The Ñamcu is a side-by-side low wing monoplane suitable for training. The prototype of this composite design made its maiden flight in April 1989 but only a few were completed before development was halted.

TYPE	REG/SER	CON. NO.	PI/NOTES	STATUS
☐ Beech B45 Mentor (T-34A)	147	CG-204		RA
☐ Bell 205 Iroquois (UH-1H)	H-91	11465	69-15177	RA
☐ Blériot XI (R)	'13'		On loan from MNA.	RAX
☐ Cessna 318B Tweety Bird (T-37B)	375	40609	60-0126, J-375	RA
☐ Cessna 318B Tweety Bird (T-37B)	'398'			RA
☐ Dassault Mirage 5BR	721	313	BR-13 (Belgium)	RA
☐ Empresa Nacional de Aeronáutica de Chile (ENAER) Ñamcu	CC-007			RA
☐ Empresa Nacional de Aeronáutica de Chile (ENAER) T-35 Pillan [Piper PA-28R-300]	120	170		RA
☐ Fairchild M-62A Cornell (PT-19)	'50'	2674	43-33769 – on loan from MNA.	RAX
☐ Hawker P.1099 Hunter FGA.71 (F.6)	712	8871	N-232 (Netherlands), G-9-221, J-712	RA
☐ Hawker P.1099 Hunter FGA.71 (P.1067 Hunter F.4)	731	41H/670744	WT801, 7789M, G-9-379	RA
☐ North American NA-78 Texan (AT-6A) (SNJ-3)	285	78-7160	41-16782, Bu01931	RA

COLECCIÓN DE BASE AÉREA LOS CONDORES (CH3)

Address: Avenida Diego Portales 1805,
Iquique.
Tel: 057-431433
Admission : By prior permission only.
Location: About 20 km south of the town.

This important fighter base is home to squadrons flying the F-16 and the A-36. The latter type is a Chilean built version of the Spanish CASA C-101 Aviojet. The collection of preserved types includes some previously flown from the airfield. The Texan has been assembled from components of several aircraft.

TYPE	REG/SER	CON. NO.	PI/NOTES	STATUS
☐ Cessna 318C Tweety Bird (T-37C)				RA
☐ De Havilland D.H.115 Sea Vampire T.22	J-302			RA
☐ Hawker P.1099 Hunter FGA.71 (F.6)	J-729	41H/679963	XE625, G-9-331	RA
☐ North American NA-88 Texan (AT-6C)	'264'		Composite.	RAX

COLECCIÓN DE BASE AÉREA PUNTA ARENAS (CH4)

Address:	Brigada Aérea 'Carlos Ibanez', Avenida Espana 01574, Chabunco, Punta Arenas.
Tel:	061-219969
Admission:	By prior permission only.
Location:	About 5 km north of the town.

This important base covers the defence of the south of the country and fighter, ground attack and special operations squadrons are based at the site. One of the T-33s is in the town and the other aircraft are inside the camp.

TYPE	REG/SER	CON. NO.	PI/NOTES	STATUS
☐ Atlas Cheetah E (Dassault Mirage IIIEZ)	'500'		(South Africa)	RAX
☐ Beech D18S Expeditor (C-45H)	481	AF-781	52-10851, N9136Z, N1050	RA
☐ Lockheed 080 Shooting Star (P-80C) (F-80C)	333		(USAF), J-333	RA
☐ Lockheed 580 (T-33A)	317		(USAF), J-317	RA
☐ Lockheed 580 (T-33A)	323		(USAF), J-323 – in town.	PV

COLECCIÓN DE REGIMENTO DE AVIACIÓN DE EJÉRCITO (CH5)

Address:	Regimento No 1 Independencia, Rancagua.
Admission:	By prior permission only.
Location:	In the western suburbs of the town.

In 1970 Army aviation was again established as an independent service. The headquarters were at Rancagua and the unit controls all bases throughout the country. At each site there are normally helicopters and fixed wing types. Four aircraft are preserved at the base. The Puma has been assembled from components of crashed and withdrawn machines. Fifteen Enstrom 280FX helicopters were delivered in 1989. The Piper Super Cruiser has been painted in period camouflage markings but its true identity has not been established.

TYPE	REG/SER	CON. NO.	PI/NOTES	STATUS
☐ Construcciones Aeronáuticas (CASA) C-212A-100 Aviocar	215	126		RA
☐ Enstrom F.280FX	173	2034	H-173	RA
☐ Piper PA-12 Super Cruiser	'E100'			RAX
☐ Sud SA.330 Puma	'H1185'		Composite.	RAX

MUSEO DE LA AVIACIÓN NAVAL (CH6)

Address:	Base Aéronaval, Vina del Mar, Torquemada.
Tel:	032-268-3408
Admission:	By prior permission only.
Location:	About 5 km east of Concon.

Founded in 1919 the Chilean Naval Air Service initially flew five floatplanes, three Avro 504s and two Sopwith Babies. In 1930 the service was merged with the Military Air Service to create the Chilean Air Force. In 1954 a new naval air arm was established flying a small number of helicopters. The service now operates transport, training and patrol aircraft in addition to its rotary wing fleet. The first helicopter used by the service was the Bell 47. A small number of C-47s was flown until the mid-1970s. The Pilatus PC-7 is a recent addition to the display Two examples of the Brazilian designed Bandeirante are in the collection. The collection of preserved aircraft is steadily increasing and hopefully others will be added as types are withdrawn from use. Two aircraft are mounted on pylons outside the Naval Headquarters in the town.

TYPE	REG/SER	CON. NO.	PI/NOTES	STATUS
☐ Beech D18S	104	A-1027	A-104	RA
☐ Beech A45 Mentor (T-34A)	201	G-3		RA
☐ Bell 47G	N-01	1289	May be H-01 c/n 630.	RA
☐ Bell 206 Jet Ranger	'38'		At HQ in town.	PVX
☐ Cessna 337 Super Skymaster (O-2A)	'338'		At HQ in town.	PVX
☐ Douglas DC-3A-456 Skytrain (C-47A) (R4D-5)	121	13009	42-93131, Bu17198	RA
☐ Embraer EMB.110CN Bandeirante	107	110101	PT-GKF	RA
☐ Embraer EMB.111A(N) Bandeirante	261	110147		RA
☐ Lockheed 185 Orion (P3V-1) (P-3A) (UP-3A)	401	185-5044	Bu150518	RA
☐ Pilatus PC.7	214	234		RA

MUSEO HISTÓRICO DE CARABINEROS DE CHILE (CH7)

Address:	1505 Avenue Antonio Varias, Providencia.
Tel:	02-2250922
Admission:	Monday-Friday 1000-1300 1500-1700.
Location:	In the north eastern suburbs of Santiago.

The first 'police' in the country were locally employed night watchmen. In the early 1800s several cities established forces and there was also a network of local police. In 1927 all the law enforcement agencies in the country were incorporated into the Carabineros. The force also controls the customs agency and provides the Presidential Guard. The Air Police have flown a number of of fixed and rotary wing types in recent years. The museum has been set up to trace the history and work of the service since its formation. On show are uniforms, vehicles and items of equipment. Two aircraft are currently on show.

TYPE	REG/SER	CON. NO.	PI/NOTES	STATUS
☐ Aeronca 7AC Champion	'CC-EPA'			PVX
☐ Hughes 269B	CC-KKO	690420	C-03	PV

MUSEO NACIONAL DE AÉRONAUTICA DE CHILE (CH8)

Address:	Avenida Pedro Aguirre Cerda 5100, Los Cerillos, Santiago.
Tel:	02-538-1919
Fax:	02-557-0344
Email:	museo@dgac.cl
Admission:	Tuesday-Sunday 1000-1700.
Location:	At the closed Los Cerillos Airport which is in the western suburbs of the city.

Chile has had a long aviation tradition and the first balloon flight took place in the country in 1785, thirty five years before independence from Spain. A Military Aviation School was set up at El Bosque in early 1913 using French aircraft. In 1918/19 twelve Bristol M.1Cs were bought and one, flown by Lieutenant Dagoberto Fuenteabla, made the first aerial crossing of the Andes between El Bosque and Mendoza in Argentina on December 12th 1918. A Central Workshops, which later became the National Aircraft Factory, was established at El Bosque and in 1921 a British Air Mission arrived in the country. This was soon followed by one from Germany and purchases of aircraft were also made in Canada and the United States. During World War II Lend-Lease resulted in over two hundred aircraft arriving in Chile. The first jets to be acquired were five Vampire T.55s in 1954. Over the last forty years mainly American types have been used but a number of British and French jets have also seen service. The museum was set up in 1944 and for the first few years occupied rooms in three different buildings in Santiago. No full size aircraft were on show but the collection of models and memorabilia was started. The situation changed in 1968 when the museum moved into the Paris Pavilion in the city. Space was still limited but an interesting display was staged. One of the sixty four de Havilland Moths operated by the military and one of the few surviving Miles Hawk Majors could be seen. The Gipsy Moth has recently been rebuilt for the exhibition. During the work it became apparent that it was probably assembled in Chile from spares and was not a genuine factory built machine as had previously been thought. This exhibition closed in 1991. In the early 1990s a new complex was started at Los Cerillos Airport and the museum moved there in 1992. On show in this building are models, photographs, engines, components and memorabilia. Halls are devoted to 'The Dream of Flight', 'The Pioneers' and 'Space Flight'. Future plans include a display featuring the aerial operations following the 1960 earthquake which devastated a large area of the country and another showing navigation using satellites. Several replica aircraft have been acquired with some being built in England. These include a Bristol M.1C, the type used by Fuenteabla on his historic flight. A second static M.1C has been constructed by the museum staff. Military machines from other countries are also on view. The Pitts Specials were flown by an Air Force aerobatic team. The unit now operates the Walter Extra and an example of this monoplane has joined the exhibition. A recent arrival is the wreck of a licence built Fairchild FC-2. The aircraft disappeared on a flight in 1939 and the remains were located in 2006 in the Atacama Desert. A recovery operation was mounted and the airframe is now at the museum. The then commander of the Army Air Service founded an airline known as Linea Aérea Santiago-Arica and it flew its first service in March 1929. A change of name to Lineas Aérea Nacional took place in 1932 and the company was government owned until 1989. In the mid-1960s two dozen Sabres were due to arrive under the MDAP scheme to replace a squadron of Lockheed F-80 Shooting Stars. The fighters did not reach Chile and the museum has a Canadian built former Honduran example in the exhibition. Chile purchased two dozen former Belgian Air Force Mirage Vs in the mid-1990s. Several of these were upgraded to Elkan standard in the SABCA factory at Gosselies before making the long journey across the South Atlantic. The museum also has on its inventory a number of former Air Force aircraft which are exhibited around the country.

TYPE	REG/SER	CON. NO.	PI/NOTES	STATUS
☐ Aeronca 65TC Grasshopper (O-58B) (L-3B)	CC-SHA	9563	43-26819, CC-XAR/35, CC-KHA, CC-SHA, CC-DMH	PV
☐ ALA Delta Saphir	128			PV
☐ Atlas Cheetah E (Dassault Mirage IIIEZ)	833	464		PV
☐ Avro 504K (R)	'78'			RAX
☐ Beech D18S Expeditor (TC-45G)	CC-CDR	AF-121	51-11564, N9127Z, 489 – possible identity.	RAD
☐ Beech D18S Expeditor (C-45H)	465	AF-495	52-10565, N9132Z – also reported as c/n A-1024.	PV
☐ Beech D18S Expeditor (C-45H)	493	AF-882	52-10952, N9140Z – at Victor Lafón Aerodrome, San Felipe.	PV
☐ Beech D18S Expeditor (C-45H)	484		(USAF) – at Chilean Army Special Forces School at Peldehue.	RA
☐ Beech B45 Mentor (T-34A)	'133'	CG-17	113	PVX
☐ Beech B45 Mentor (T-34A)	134	CG-142		PV
☐ Beech B45 Mentor (T-34A)	138	CG-146	180, 138, CC-DMJ	PVA
☐ Beech C50 Twin Bonanza	481	CH-358		RA
☐ Beech 65TC Baron	CC-CKZ	TG-61	471, A-2	RA
☐ Beech 90 King Air				RA
☐ Bell 47D-1	H-02	631	At Group 9 Headquarters in Santiago.	RA
☐ Bell 47D-1	H-03	637	Previously reported as c/n 655	PV
☐ Bell 205 Iroquois (UH-1H)	H-88	12805	68-16517 – parts only.	RA
☐ Blériot XI (R)				PV
☐ Boeing 707-330B	CC-CCG	18462	D-ABOS, D-ABOV	RA
☐ Boeing 737-200			Due soon.	–
☐ Boeing-Stearman A75N1 Kaydet (PT-17)	CC-DMG	75-1880	41-8321, 661, CC-PYA	PVA
☐ Bölkow BO 105LSA	C-19	S-655	CC-CKC	RA
☐ Bristol 20 M.1C (R)	'C4987'			PV
☐ Bristol 20 M.1C (R)	'C4988'	AJD-01	G-BPLT, CC-DMA	PVAX
☐ British Aircraft Corporation 1-11 Series 207AJ	CC-CYM	039	VP-YXA, (9J-RCH), G-ATTP, 9J-RCH, 7Q-YKE, 9J-RCH, G-ATTP	RA
☐ British Aircraft Corporation 1-11 Series 207AJ	CC-CYL	040	VP-YXB, 9J-RCI, G-ATVH, 9J-RCI, G-ATVH	RA
☐ Canadair CL-13 Sabre 4 [North American F-86E]	'FAH-3006'	721	XB958, XB934, 06-147 (Yugoslavia), 11-106 (Yugoslavia), FAH-3001 (?) – in Honduran markings.	PVX
☐ Cessna 150A	CC-KQZ	15059104	N7004X, CC-KSV, CC-KZB, CC-SFC	RA
☐ Cessna 195 (190)	CC-FCC	7672	N1060D, CC-FCC, CC-ECC	PV
☐ Cessna 310B	'CC-CDR'	35559	N5359A, YV-C-BAH, N6849D, CC-CFI	RACX
☐ Cessna 318B Tweety Bird (T-37B)	371	40317	58-1892, J-371	RA
☐ Cessna 318B Tweety Bird (T-37B)	392	40584	60-0102, J-392 – on show in San Felipe town.	PV
☐ Cessna 318B Tweety Bird (T-37B)	372	40649	60-0157, J-372	PV
☐ Cessna 318B Tweety Bird (T-37B)	396	40681	60-0184, J-396	PV
☐ Cessna 318E Dragonfly (A-37B)			Due soon.	RA
☐ Cessna 337 Super Skymaster	CC-CFN	33700087	N2187X	PV
☐ Consolidated 28-5A Catalina (PBV-1A) (OA-10A)	'405'	CV 520	Bu67973, 44-34009, N62043, CF-IHC F-WMKR, F-BMKR, 20/F-YEIA (France), CC-CDU, CC-CGY	PVX
☐ Construcciones Aeronáuticas (CASA) 1.131E [Bücker Bü 131 Jungmann]	CC-DMD	2223	E.3B-623	PVA
☐ Culver LFA Cadet	CC-PDB	LFA-445		PV
☐ Dassault Mystère IVA			29 (Israel)	PV
☐ Dassault Mirage 5BR	722	325	BR-25 (Belgium)	PV
☐ Dassault Mirage M5MA Elkan (5BA)	701	01	BA-01 (Belgium)	PV
☐ Dassault Mirage M5MA Elkan (5BA)	'725'		Composite – at War Academy in Santiago.	RA
☐ Dassault Mirage 50CN Pantera (Mirage 5F)	503	5	5 (France)	PV
☐ De Havilland D.H.60G Gipsy Moth	'32'		CC-PFN, CC-FNG, 67, 'G.35' – possibly built in Chile from spares.	PVX
☐ De Havilland D.H.82A Tiger Moth	CC-DMC	85879	DF130, F-BDOB, G-BACK	PVA
☐ De Havilland D.H.115 Sea Vampire T.22	'J-01'		Assembled from spares.	PVX
☐ De Havilland D.H.115 Sea Vampire T.22	J-310	15205	XA107	RA
☐ De Havilland D.H.115 Sea Vampire T.22	J-307	15508	XA166	RA
☐ De Havilland D.H.115 Sea Vampire T.22	J-306	15652	XG777	RA
☐ Douglas DC-3A-456 Skytrain (C-47A)	961	12937	42-93067, 961 (Chile), '963'	PV
☐ Douglas DC-3A-456 Skytrain (C-47A)	CC-CBX	13296	42-93390, CA-39, XT-T31, N8326C, N4660V, CC-CBJ, CC-CLDT	PV
☐ Douglas DC-3A-456 Skytrain (C-47A)	CC-CLK	20158	43-15692, NC60942, LV-ADF, TC-20 (Argentina)	PV

This Cessna T-37 is on show at El Bosque Air Force base. (Álvaro Romero)

This is one of two Bristol M.1C replicas in the Chilean National Aeronautical Museum. (Álvaro Romero)

A recent arrival at the Chilean National Aeronautical Museum is this Mirage Pantera. (Álvaro Romero)

☐ Douglas DC-3A-467 Skytrain (C-47B)	CC-CBW	15259/26704	43-49443, XT-T32, N8330C, N4661V, CC-CBI, CC-CLDS, CC-PQG	RA
☐ Douglas DC-6B			(Switzerland) – front fuselage only.	PV
☐ Douglas A-26C Invader	840	7250	41-39537	PV
☐ Douglas TB-26D Invader (A-26B) (TB-26B)	848	28020	44-34741 – at Mejillones.	PV
☐ Druine D.31 Turbulent	XX-03			RA
☐ Empresa Nacional de Aeronáutica de Chile (ENAER) Ñamcu	CC-PZC	001		PV
☐ Empresa Nacional de Aeronáutica de Chile (ENAER) T-35S Pillán (T-35A) [Piper PA-28R-300]	CC-PZB	101-82	101	PV
☐ English Electric EA.1 Canberra PR.9	341	SH.1730	XH166	RA
☐ English Electric EA.1 Canberra PR.9	343	SH.1737	XH173	RA
☐ Fabrica do Galeao 3FG [Fairchild M-62 Cornell]	'64'	3FG-188	PT19-0454 (Brazil), PP-HNQ, CC-DMF – parts from 3FG-275 PT19-0542 (Brazil), PP-HNV	RAAX
☐ Fairchild M-62A Cornell (PT-19)	'50'	2674	43-33769 – on loan to El Bosque AFB.	–
☐ Fairchild F-27F Friendship (F-27A)	CC-CBS	37	N146L, N746L, CC-CBS, CC-PKA	RA
☐ Fokker Dr I (R)	CC-DMB	2009	'1425/17'	PVAX
☐ Göppingen Gö 3 Minimoa	CC-PIA	3	D-CHEMNITZZ III, D-ARGENTINA	RA
☐ Grumman G-111 Albatross (G-64) (SA-16A) (SA-16B) (HU-16B)	570	G-98	51-0024 – this aircraft also reported in Taiwan.	RA
☐ Hawker P.1099 Hunter FGA.9 (F.6)	744	41H/680020	XE546, J-744 – original c/n 41H/677921 – front fuselage of c/n 41H/680020 XG195, G-9-453.	PV
☐ Hawker P.1099 Hunter FGA.9 (F.6)	750	41H/688140	XK138.J-750	PV
☐ Hawker P.1099 Hunter FGA.9 (F.6)	752		XG291, J-752- at Mejillones.	PV
☐ Hawker P.1099 Hunter FGA.71 (F.6)	726	41H/679936	XE561, G-9-318, J-726 – at Puerto Montt.	PV
☐ Hawker P.1099 Hunter FGA.71 (F.6)	724	41H/680024	XG199, G-9-312, J-724	RA
☐ Hawker P.1099 Hunter FGA.71 (F.6)	722	41H/688088	XJ713, G-9-298, J-722 – at Quintero AFB.	RA
☐ Hawker P.1099 Hunter FGA.71 (F.6)	702	8878	IF-108 (Belgium), G-9-105, J-702 – at Air Force Logistics Headquarters in Santiago.	RA
☐ Hawker P.1099 Hunter FGA.71 (F.6)	725	S 4U 3358	XF512, G-9-313, J-725 – at War Academy in Santiago.	RA
☐ Hawker P.1099 Hunter FGA.71 (P.1067 Hunter F.4)	735	41H/670800	WV326, 7669M, G-9-396, J-735	RA
☐ Hawker P.1099 Hunter FR.71A (P.1067 Hunter F.4)	734	HABL 003078	XF317, 7773M, G-9-383, J-734	RA
☐ Hawker P.1101 Hunter T.72 (66A)	718	8763	G-APUX, J-718 – centre and rear fuselage of Belgian F.6 IF-19, 567 (Iraq), G-APUX, L-581(Lebanon), G-APUX, G-9-232 – nose from Indian T.66 35369.	RA
☐ Hawker-Siddeley P.1127 Harrier GR.3	XZ970	41H/712206		RA
☐ Hiller UH12L4	H-72	2524	Parts only.	RAD
☐ Kunzemüller Hang Glider				PV
☐ Let L-13 Blanik	CC-K7W	171921	(Chilean AF)	RA
☐ Lineas Aérea Nacional de Chile Tipo Fairchild	CC-LAN-18			RAD
☐ Lockheed 080 Shooting Star (P-80C) (F-80C)	J-342	080-2535	49-0787	PV
☐ Lockheed 282-1B Hercules (C-130B)	997	282-3551	58-0752	PV
☐ Lockheed 580 (T-33A)	J-314	580-9894	55-4450	PV
☐ McDonnell M.98DE Phantom II (F-4C)	63-7683	811		RA
☐ Miles M.2R Hawk Major	CC-FBB	257	CC-FBB, CC-PFB	PV
☐ Naval Aircraft Factory N3N-1	CC-DME		Bu0719, 500, 001	RAA
☐ North American NA-88 Texan (AT-6D) (SNJ-5)	CC-DMI	88-16308	42-84527, Bu43966, C.6-127 (Spain), '237'	RAA
☐ North American NA-88 Texan (AT-6D)	273		Possibly ex 42-43966	RA
☐ Piper PA-28R-300XBT Pillán	'YBT'	28R-300-02	N48098, CC-PZA	PV
☐ Piper PA-38-112 Tomahawk	CC-CRM	38-78A-0673		RAD
☐ Pitts S-2A Special	1	2220		PV
☐ Pitts S-2A Special	4	2271		PV
☐ Pitts S-2S Special	7	3003		RA
☐ Pterodactyl Ascender II (Fledgling)				RA
☐ Republic P-47D Thunderbolt	750	399-55758	45-49219 – possible identity.	PV
☐ Royal Aircraft Factory S.E.5A (R)	'66'	R 004		PVX
☐ Rutan 61 Long Ez	CC-PVS		Parts only.	PV
☐ Scheibe 138 Specht	CC-K9W	809	D-8097	RA
☐ Schneider ESG 29 Grunau 9 (D.F.S. 108-10)	'CC-AAA'		CC-SXV	RAX
☐ Sikorsky S-55T (S-55C)	H-55	551274	H-55, CC-DMK	PVA
☐ Sikorsky S-58 Seabat (HSS-1N) (SH-34J)	N-51	581623	Bu150730	PV
☐ Supermarine Spitfire (Scale R)				PV
☐ Universidad Nacional Cormorán	ULM-168			PV
☐ Vought V-310 Kingfisher (OS2U-3)	314		Bu59??	PV
☐ Vultee V-74 Valiant (BT-13A)	'164'	74-4895 (?)	(USAAF), CC-PBG	RA
☐ Walter Extra 300	4			PV
☐ Wright Flyer (R)				PV

COLOMBIA

0 100 200 km
0 100 200 miles
Caribbean Sea
Pacific Ocean
Aruba (Neth.)
Curacao
Bonaire
Netherlands Antilles (Neth.)
Golfo de Venezuela
A 6, 7, 9, 10, 12
Puerto Bolivar
Riohacha
Santa Marta
Barranquilla
Cartagena
Valledupar
Covenas
Sincelejo
PANAMA
Monteria
Turbo
Careoa
VENEZUELA
Cucuta
Barrancabermeja
Bucaramanga
Arauca
Puerto Berrio
8 Medellin
Puerto Carreno
Paz de Rio
Quibdo
1 Puerto Salgar
Tunja
Yopal
Manizales
Pereira
4
A Bogota
Santa Rita
Ibaque
3
Villavicencio
Tulua
Buenaventura
2 COLOMBIA
Puerto Inirida
Barrancomina
Cali 5,11
Neiva
Popayan
San Vicente del Caguan
San Jose del Guaviare
maco
Calamar
Florencia
Pasto
Mocoa
Larandia
Mitu
Ipiales
Santa Ana
Tres Esquinas
San Miguel
Puerto Asis
La Tagua
Puerto Leguizamo
ECUADOR
BRAZIL
Puerto Santander
La Pedrera
El Encanto
PERU
Leticia

COLECCIÓN DE LA BASE AÉREA GERMAN OLANO (COL1)

Address:	Comando Aéreo de Combate 1, Base Aerea Militar 2, Palanquero, Puerto Salgar.
Tel:	096-839-8520
Email:	accionintegralcacom1@fac.mil.co
Admission:	By prior permission only.
Location:	About 5 km north of La Dorada.

Comando Aéreo de Combate I is in residence at this important base. Types currently flown by the squadrons include the Mirage and Kfir. A small number of AC-47 gunships are also based at the field along with some light aircraft and helicopters. The Venezuelan Air Force donated the F-86F.

TYPE	REG/SER	CON. NO.	PI/NOTES	STATUS
☐ Boeing-Stearman A75N1 Kaydet (PT-17)	FAC1995	A75-1995	(USAAF)	RAA
☐ Lockheed 580 (T-33A)	FAC2006		(USAF)	RA
☐ North American NA-242 Sabre (F-86F)	'FAC2022'	242-38	56-4153, JE+113, JD+113, JD+313, 1135 (Venezuela)	RA

COLECCIÓN DE LA BASE AÉREA LUIS F. GOMEZ NINO (COL2)

Address:	Comando Aéreo de Combate 2, Base Aérea Militar, Via Puerto Lopez, Apiay.
Tel:	06-698720
Email:	accionintegralcacom2@fac.mil.co
Admission:	By prior permission only.
Location:	About 5 km north of La Balsa.

Among the units at the field is a special operations squadron (No. 311) currently flying the Bronco. These aircraft, used in the war against the drug producers, are scheduled to be withdrawn in the near future. The Tucanos of No. 312 Squadron are used for advanced training and light attack and No. 313 flies helicopters.

TYPE	REG/SER	CON. NO.	PI/NOTES	STATUS
☐ Douglas A-26C Invader	FAC2504	28787	44-35508	RA
☐ Douglas DC-3A-456 Skytrain (C-47A) (Dakota III)	FAC1676	9108	42-32882, 652 (Canada), A509 (Canada), N45F, CF-ITQ, 6Y-JJQ, 676	RAD
☐ Lockheed 580 (T-33A)	FAC2018			RA
☐ Lockheed 580 (T-33A)	FAC2030	580-1635	58-0586	RA
☐ North American NA-305 Bronco (OV-10A)	FAC2224	305-59	Bu155448	RA

COLECCIÓN DE LA BASE AÉREA LUIS F. PINTO (COL3)

Address:	Comando Aéreo de Combate 4, Kilimetro 1 Via Panamericana Melgar-Bogota, Melgar, Tolima.
Tel:	098-2450551
Email:	accionintegralcacom4@fac.mil.co
Admission:	By prior permission only.
Location:	In the north eastern suburbs of the town.

The base is hone to Comando Aéreo de Tacito 4 which operates mainly helicopters. More than thirty Bell 47s have been used by the Air Force. One has been maintained in an airworthy state and the other is mounted the base gate. Considerable numbers of the Iroquois series have been operated.

TYPE	REG/SER	CON. NO.	PI/NOTES	STATUS
☐ Bell 205 Iroquois (UH-1H)	FAC4412			RA
☐ Bell 47G-2 Sioux (H-13H) (OH-13H)	FAC4226		(USAF)	RA
☐ Bell 47G-3B Sioux (OH-13S)	FAC4214	3919	67-15870, 214 (Colombia)	RAA
☐ North American NA-88 Texan (AT-6D)	FAC791			RA

COLECCIÓN DE LA BASE AÉREA MADRID (COL4)

Address: Carrera 5 2-91,
Madrid,
Cundiamarca.
Tel: 08-209108
Email: accionintegralcaman@fac.mil.co
Admission: By prior permission only.
Location: About 15 km north west of Bogota.

Madrid is the location of the maintenance command headquarters and the presidential flight. Four aircraft are preserved at the airfield. The tricycle undercarriage Beech 18 and the Texan are on show at the main gate. The T-33 and Cessna T-37B are located in the base. Fifty two T-33s have been operated by the Air Force and some were used in the close support role. The first was delivered in 1954 and the last in 1978.

TYPE	REG/SER	CON. NO.	PI/NOTES	STATUS
☐ Beech H18S	FAC5779		Also reported as 5579.	PV
☐ Cessna 318B Tweety Bird (T-37B)	FAC2122	41161	68-8066	RA
☐ Lockheed 580 (T-33A)	FAC2020		(USAF)	RA
☐ North American NA-88 Texan (AT-6D)	FAC720		(USAAF)	PV

COLECCIÓN DE LA BASE AÉREA MARCO FIDEL SUAREZ (COL5)

Address: Escuela Militar de Aviación,
Carrara 8 58-67,
Santiago de Cali,
Valle del Cauca.
Tel: 092-488-1000
Email: emayu@emavi.edu.co
Admission: By prior permission only.
Location: About 5 km north west of the city.

Located at the base is the Military Aviation School which operates both fixed and rotary wing types. Four trainers have been preserved. Sixty Stearman Kaydets were delivered in the early 1940s under the Lend-Lease plan and in return the United States obtained military bases m the country. The first Texans arrived in Colombia in 1942 and eventually ninety nine were flown by the Air Force. Six Canadair built Sabres were delivered in 1956.

TYPE	REG/SER	CON. NO.	PI/NOTES	STATUS
☐ Beech D45 Mentor (T-34B)	FAC2301	BG-19	Bu140685, 301A	RA
☐ Bell 205 Iroquois (UH-1H)	FAC4216			RA
☐ Boeing-Stearman A75N1 Kaydet (PT-17)	62		(USAAF)	RAA
☐ Canadair CL-13B Sabre 6 [North American F-86E]	FAC2024	1456		RA
☐ Caudron G.3 (R)				RA
☐ Cessna 318E Dragonfly (A-37B) (OA-37B)	FAC2170	43322	70-1307	RA
☐ Cessna R172F Mescalero (T-41D)	FAC2408	R1720343	408	RA
☐ Glider				RA
☐ North American NA-88 Texan (AT-6D)	'796'		(USAAF), 798	PVX
☐ Wright Flyer (R)				RA

MUSEO AEROESPECIAL COLOMBIANA (COL6)

Address: Basa Aérea Catam,
El Dorado,
Bogota.
Tel: 01-439-7800
Email: museofac@fac.mil.co
Admission: Monday-Friday 0800-1530: Saturday 1400-1630 by prior permission.
Location: On the east side of El Dorado Airport which is about 5 km south west of the city.

In early 1922 a Military Aviation School was formed at Flandes Airfield using eleven aircraft supplied by France, three Caudron G3s, four Caudron G4s and four Nieuport 17s. Financial difficulties caused it to close two years later. A second attempt was made in 1925 at Cundinamarca using three Swiss Wild WT-3s. The development which occurred in the next few years was partly due to the assistance provided by SCADTA – a joint Colombian-German airline. Junkers F 13s, W 33s and W 34s were used on services around the country. In the 1930s the force used both German and American aircraft. The museum has been set up in the military area of El Dorado airfield on the outskirts of Bogota. The main transport unit of the Air Force is based at the field. In addition SATENA (the military airline) has its headquarters there. Displays in the museum building trace the development of military flying in the country with models, uniforms, photographs and documents on show. The outside aircraft park contains a number of interesting types. The star is the float mounted Junkers W 34. Nine examples of the type were acquired by SCADTA in 1932 and the last was withdrawn in 1952. Like the W 34, the Ju 52 on show was shared between SCADTA and the Aviación Militar. The tri-motor was one of five delivered in 1933 and also served until the early 1950s. Thirty five Thunderbolts were supplied in 1947 and the last was retired in 1956. Several P-47s were dumped in the Magdalena River which runs close to Palanquero. More than forty C-47s and sixteen C-54s have been used by the Air Force and SATENA. The C-54 on show is a former Scandinavian Airlines Systems aircraft. Delivered to Colombia in 1954, it served as the presidential transport for many years. The museum was officially opened on March 25th 1967 at Madrid Air Force base and moved to its present site in the early 1970s. There is a possibility that a move to Cali will soon take place.

TYPE	REG/SER	CON. NO.	PI/NOTES	STATUS
Beech A45 Mentor (T-34A)	FAC318			PV
Beech C18S Kansan (AT-11)	902		(USAAF)	PV
Bell 204 Iroquois (HU-1B) (UH-1B)	FAC4272	461	62-1941 – may be c/n 885 63-8660.	PV
Bell 47G-2	FAC206	718		PV
Canadair CL-13B Sabre 6 [North American F-86E]	FAC2023	1455		PV
Cessna 318C Tweety Bird (T-37C)	FAC2112			PV
Cessna 318E Dragonfly (A-37B) (OA-37B)	FAC2164	43113	68-7966	PV
Cessna R172F Mescalero (T-41D)	FAC2425	R1720360	425	RA
De Havilland D.H.C.2 Beaver	'FAC108'		HK-108X, 120 – possible identity.	PVX
Douglas A-26C Invader	FAC2519	29057	44-35778	PV
Douglas DC-3A-456 Skytrain (C-47A)	FAC667		(USAAF)	PV
Douglas DC-4-1009 Skymaster	FAC690	42926	SE-BBC, OY-DFY, FAC690, FAC1690	PV
Fabrica Militar de Aviones IA.58A Pucará				PV
Gavilán 358M	FAC5062			PV
Hiller UH12B Raven (H-23B) (OH-23B)	FAC220		C/n is 670, 671 or 672 – also reported as c/n 0423.	PV
Hughes 500M	FAC4251	480043M		PV
Junkers Ju 52/3mg4e	625			PV
Junkers W 34h	407	2823		PV
Lockheed 080 Shooting Star (P-80C) (F-80C)	FAC2061		(USAF)	PV
Lockheed 237-27-01 Ventura (PV-1)	'FAC654'	237-5599	Bu34709, 2244 (Canada), N1206, N5034F, N1970H, N197RD, N100LR, YV-183CP – conv to BACC BA-400 when as N5034F.	PVX
Lockheed 282-1B Hercules (C-130B)	'FAC1011'	282-3575	60-5451, 10302 (Canada), N4653, FAC1001	PVX
Lockheed 580 (T-33A)	FAC2033	580-1755	58-706 – with parts from FAC2024A and FAC2015A.	PV
North American NA-305 Bronco (OV-10A)	FAC2223	305-49	Bu155348	PV
North American NA-88 Texan (AT-6D)	772		(USAAF)	PV
Republic P-47D Thunderbolt	FAC861	399-55641	45-49102	PV
Swearingen SA226 Metro	FAC1240			PV

MUSEO DE LOS NIÑOS (COL7)

Address:	Carrera 48 63-97 Bogota.
Tel:	01-225-7687
Fax:	01-225-9579
Admission:	Wednesday-Friday 1400-1700; Saturday-Sunday 0900-1230 1400-1800.
Location:	In the centre of the city.

This delightful children's museum features many 'hands-on' exhibits designed to interest young people in natural history, science, transport and recreation. The only aircraft on show is the Boeing 720 which was originally delivered to Lufthansa in January 1962. Pan American purchased the aircraft in December 1965 and flew it until November 1972 when it was sold to Avianca. The airliner was withdrawn in 1982 and stored at Bogota for a time before being transferred to the museum. There are also motor vehicles and trains to be seen.

TYPE	REG/SER	CON. NO.	PI/NOTES	STATUS
Boeing 720-030B	HK-749	18248	D-ABON, N786PA	PV

MUSEO DEL AIRE – MEDELLIN (COL8)

Address:	Parque del Norte, Medellin.
Admission:	By prior permission only.
Location:	In the northern part of the city.

A group of local enthusiasts is working to set up a museum. They have acquired a collection of memorabilia and artefacts. A Boeing 727, which was parked at the airport for some time, is their only aircraft.

TYPE	REG/SER	CON. NO.	PI/NOTES	STATUS
Boeing 727-25	HK-2541	18281	N8130N	PV

MUSEO HISTORICO PALACIO DE POLICIA (COL9)

Address:	Calle 9 9-27, Bogota.
Tel:	01-233-5911
Admission:	Tuesday-Saturday 0800-1200 1400-1700.
Location:	In the city.

The collection was started in 1973 and and the museum opened in the former Police Palace in 1984. The displays trace the history of police work in the country. There are uniforms and items of equipment to be seen.

TYPE	REG/SER	CON. NO.	PI/NOTES	STATUS
☐ Bell 205 Iroquois (UH-1H)	PNC-128			PV

MUSEO MILITAR (COL10)

Address:	Calle 10 4-92, Bogota.
Tel:	01-281-3131
Admission:	Daily 1000-1700.
Location:	In the centre of the city.

The displays at this museum trace the military history of the country from the early days. The period of Spanish rule is highlighted. There are many uniforms, weapons, military vehicles in the exhibition.

TYPE	REG/SER	CON. NO.	PI/NOTES	STATUS
☐ Bell 47D-1	204			PV
☐ Cessna 318E Dragonfly (A-37B) (OA-37B)	FAC2171	43405	71-0870	PV
☐ Lockheed 580 (T-33A)	FAC2008		(USAF)	PV

MUSEO NACIONAL DE TRANSPORTE (COL11)

Address:	Aeropuerto Alfonso Bonilla Aragon, Cali.
Tel:	057-6511154
Admission:	Monday-Friday 0800-1600; Saturday-Sunday 1000-1700.
Location:	At the International Airport

The National Transportation Museum Foundation was set up in March 1998 by the local Aero Club Pacifico, a railway group and the Antique and Classic Auto Club of Columbia. Later the Colombian IPMS joined the organisation. A building was constructed near to the airport at Cali and in addition to the aircraft there are railway engines and rolling stock and many cars to be seen along with cars and motor cycles.

TYPE	REG/SER	CON. NO.	PI/NOTES	STATUS
☐ Air and Space 18A	N6132S	18-39		PVA
☐ Beech D18S Expeditor (C-45H)	HK-1086-P	AF-741	52-10811, N86472, HK1086G	PVA
☐ Bell 47G				PV
☐ Bell 205 Iroquois (UH-1H)	FAC287			PV
☐ Boeing-Stearman A75N1 Kaydet (PT-17)	HK-3149-P	75-4886	42-16723, (Colombia)	PVA
☐ Cessna 140A	HK-41-P	15465	(N9455A)	PVA
☐ Cessna 195A	HK-273-P	7753	(N1531D)	PVA
☐ Cessna 318E Dragonfly (A-37B)				PV
☐ Cessna R172F Mescalero (T-41D)				PVD
☐ Douglas DC-3A-467 Skytrain (C-47B)	HK-3993P	14898/26343	43-49082, PP-SPS, PP-FOZ, PT-KTZ	PV
☐ Grumman G-21A Goose	HK-2058-P	1084	NC28635, VP-BAL, VP-BBI, N86639	PV
☐ Lake LA-4-200 Buccaneer				PVA
☐ Microlight				PV
☐ North American NA-88 Texan (AT-6D) (SNJ-5)	HK-2049-P	88-16469	42-84688, Bu44017, 777	PVA
☐ Piper PA-18-135 Super Cub	HK-470-P	18-3256		PVA
☐ Pitts S-1C Special				PV
☐ Wright Flyer (R)				PV

PARQUE JAIME DUQUE (COL12)

Address:	Autopista Nord Km 34, Bogota.
Tel:	01-611-0945/091-857-4233
Fax:	01-611-2677
Admission:	Monday-Friday 0900-1700; Saturday-Sunday 1000-1830.
Location:	About 34 km north of the city.

This large park opened in February 1898 and its attractions include a fun fair and a zoo. Replicas of famous buildings have been built and there are attractive landscaped gardens. The transport section includes boats moored on a lake and railway engines. Three aircraft are on show. The early DC-3 served with the U.S.A.A.F. until 1945 and it then flew with Resort Airlines before moving to Brazil for use by VASP. After its military days were over the DC-4 was sold to Pan American Airways who immediately transferred it to Avianca who operated it for many years. The aircraft was used by a number of local airlines before joining the display.

TYPE	REG/SER	CON. NO.	PI/NOTES	STATUS
☐ Beech E18S	N8627A	BA-283	N23R, N86HA	PV
☐ Douglas DC-3A-360 Skytrain (C-47)	PT-KUC	4347	41-7848, NC18639, PP-SQK	PV
☐ Douglas DC-4 Skymaster (C-54A)	HK-136	10407	42-72302, N88929, C-136	PV

ECUADOR

COLECCIÓN DE LA BASE AÉREA GUAYAQUIL (EC1)

Address:	II Zona Aérea Headquarters, Base Aérea Simón Bolivar, Guayaquil.
Admission:	By prior permission only.
Location:	On the east side of the town.

In the mid-1930s Guayaquil was the site of the main flying school for the Air Force. Six Curtiss-Wright 16E biplanes were in use. The commander of the unit was American and the instructors were local pilots. The airfield is now home to a combat wing operating helicopters and fixed wing support types. Units of the Army are also in residence and squadrons flying helicopters and transport types use the field. In addition therc is a pilot training school using Beech T-34Cs. The Navy has a facility on the field with helicopters, trainers and liaison aircraft. A small collection of preserved aircraft has been assembled. Approximately twenty North American Trojans were delivered, about half of these were converted to T-28D standard, and were withdrawn from use in the late 1970s. A Piper Comanche is now in the collection but its origins are unknown. The C-47 has suffered from the elements but it may be restored for the display. The base is named after the revolutionary Simón Bolivar who freed Ecuador from Spanish rule in May 1822.

TYPE	REG/SER	CON. NO.	PI/NOTES	STATUS
☐ Douglas DC-3A-467 Skytrain (C-47B)	49875	15601/27046	43-49785, HC-AUP	RAD
☐ Gloster Meteor FR.9	'091'		WH540, 706, FF-116	RAX
☐ Lockheed 580 (T-33A) (AT-33A)	FAE702			PV
☐ North American NA-174 Trojan (T-28A) (AT-28D)	TB-572	174-110	51-3572	RA
☐ Piper PA-24-180 Comanche	E-160			RA
☐ Sikorsky S-55D Chickasaw (H-19B) (UH-19B)				RA

COLECCIÓN DE LA BASE AÉREA MANTA (EC2)

Address:	Ala de Combate 23, Base Aérea Eloy Alfaro. Manta.
Admission:	By prior permission only.
Location:	About 10 km east of the town.

The airfield opened in October 1978 and the first residents were eight Strikemasters which flew in from Taura. Over the years more examples of the type arrived including some from an embargoed Sudanese order. Squadron 2323 still flies a few of the type and these are the last operational ones in the world. Also in residence is a squadron of Cessna Dragonflies and a small number of helicopters. Three aircraft are preserved at this field. A unit flying Lockheed AT-33s was based at Eloy Alfaro until 1977. The base is named after Eloy Alfaro Delgado who was president of the country from 1895 to 1901 and 1906-1911. He separated the state from the church and introduced many civil reforms. He was murdered by an enraged mob in Quito in 1912.

TYPE	REG/SER	CON. NO.	PI/NOTES	STATUS
☐ Cessna 318B Tweety Bird (T-37B)				RA
☐ Lockheed 580 (T-33A) (AT-33A)	FAE621		(USAF)	RA
☐ Lockheed 580 (T-33A) (AT-33A)	FAE624			RA

COLECCIÓN DE LA BASE AÉREA SALINAS (EC3)

Address:	Escuela Superior Militar de Aviación, Base Aérea General Ulpiano Paez, Salinas
Tel:	04-277-2400
Admission:	By prior permission only.
Location:	In the northern part of the town.

The airfield was constructed in the late 1930s and for several years housed combat units. The base is named after General Ulpiano Paez and is home to the Air Academy and the pilot training squadron. The Academy bears the name of Cosme Renella. He was one of the first military pilots in the country and fought in Europe during World War I. He is credited with shooting down seventeen enemy aircraft. Examples of trainers used in recent years have been preserved around the site to remind cadets of the traditions of the force. The Academy was formed at Manta in the early 1920, moved to Guayaquil in 1931 and relocated to Salinas in 1942. Ecuador signed the Rio Pact of Mutual Defense in 1947 and America began supplying modern types. In the main building there is a collection of memorabilia, photographs, models and trophies.

TYPE	REG/SER	CON. NO.	PI/NOTES	STATUS
☐ Lockheed 580 (T-33A) (AT-33A)	FAE536			PV
☐ North American NA-88 Texan (AT-6D)	111			RA
☐ North American NA-88 Texan (AT-6D)	TB-102		(USAAF), TB-109	PV
☐ North American NA-171 Trojan (T-28A) (AT-28D)	TB-229	171-35	50-0229	RA

COLECCIÓN DE LA BASE AÉREA TAURA (EC4)

Address:	Ala de Combate 21, Grupo 211, Base Aérea Taura, Taura.
Admission:	By prior permission only.
Location:	About 20 km south east of Guayaquil on the road to Machala.

The airfield was constructed in 1947 and over the years has steadily been improved. The base is home to first line fighter squadrons flying Mirages and Kfirs. Ecuador ordered sixteen Mirage F.1JAs and two F.1JEs to equip 2112 Squadron. The type entered service in 1979 and two years later was in combat with Peruvian aircraft. Troubles flared again in 1995 and in both conflicts the Mirages shot down a number of aircraft. Ten single seat Kfir C.2s and a pair of two seat TC.2s were refurbished in Israel and delivered to Ecuador in 1982/3. These also fought against Peru in 1995. Additional Kfirs have been acquired and the majority of these have been upgraded to CE standard. A collection of preserved fighters and armed conversions of trainers is located around the site. Ecuador acquired former twelve Royal Air Force Meteor FR.9s in 1954/5 and they flew from Taura with 21 Wing until the early 1970s. Sixteen Lockheed F-80 Shooting Stars were also flown from the field. Units flying the joint British/French Jaguar operated from Taura. Ten single seaters and a pair of the two seat version were ordered in 1974. A few are stored at Taura and one may possibly be allocated for preservation.

TYPE	REG/SER	CON. NO.	PI/NOTES	STATUS
☐ Gloster Meteor FR.9	FF-118		WH549, 708	RA
☐ Gloster Meteor FR.9				RA
☐ Lockheed 080 Shooting Star (P-80C) (F-80C)	FT-714	080-2461 (?)		RA
☐ Lockheed 580 (T-33A) (AT-33A)	FAE803		(USAF)	RA
☐ North American NA-159 Trojan (T-28A) (AT-28D)				RA
☐ North American NA-159 Trojan (T-28A) (AT-28D)				RA

COLECCIÓN DE LA BRIGADA DE FUERZAS ESPECIALES 9 (EC5)

Address:	Brigada 9, Fort Patria, Route 35, Latacunga.
Admission:	By prior permission only.
Location:	About 5 km north of the town

This special forces unit has four aircraft preserved at its barracks. Among the tasks carried out is parachute training. The two C-47s have not been positively identified. The Ecuadorian Air Force operated fourteen examples of the type and paratroopers would have made many drops from the type. The pair on show are probably from this source or from T.A.M.E. the airline operated by the military on uneconomic services. Several T-33s are stored at Manta and one has been moved to the camp. Ground attack duties in support of the army was one of the tasks carried out by the jet. The French designed and built Gazelle is still in service with army units around the country. Inside the base there is a collection of preserved military vehicles, tanks and guns.

TYPE	REG/SER	CON. NO.	PI/NOTES	STATUS
☐ Douglas DC-3A-456 Skytrain (C-47A)	'CA-47'			RAX
☐ Douglas DC-3A-456 Skytrain (C-47A)				RA
☐ Lockheed 580 (T-33A) (AT-33A)				RA
☐ Sud SA.342L Gazelle	340			RA

MONUMENTO DE LA BASE AÉREA DEL EJÉRCITO PORTOVIEJO (EC6)

Address:	Grupo Aérea 43, Fuerte Militar Ortiz, Portoviejo
Admission:	By prior permission only.
Location:	In the town.

Army aviation in Ecuador started in 1954 with the formation of the Servicio Aérea del Ejército. Since then a variety of fixed and rotary wing types have been flown from bases around the country. Aircraft and helicopters have participated in a number of local conflicts including attacks on rebel forces. Brigade status was later granted and in 1996 it became a full arm of the Army. Units at the fort operate Sud Gazelles and Aérospatiale Ecureuils. Over thirty Gazelles were ordered and one has been preserved as a monument.

TYPE	REG/SER	CON. NO.	PI/NOTES	STATUS
☐ Sud SA.342L Gazelle	369	5025		RA

MONUMENTO DE LA BASE AÉREA DEL EJÉRCITO SANGOLQUÍ (EC7)

Address:	Brigada de Aviacion 15, Campo Militar General Marco Zubia, Sangolqui.
Admission:	By prior permission only.
Location:	In the town.

Units in the Brigade currently operate Gazelle, Puma, Ecureuil and Mil Mi-17 helicopters. The two preserved airframes are position close to the main gate to the camp. Both are damaged possibly as a result of crashes.

TYPE	REG/SER	CON. NO.	PI/NOTES	STATUS
☐ Sud SA.315B Lama	'673'			RA
☐ Sud SA.342L Gazelle	'365'			RAX

MONUMENTO DE LA FUERZA AÉREA ECUATORIANA (EC8)

Address:	Parque La Acacia, Manta.
Admission:	On permanent view.
Location:	In the southern part of the town

Ecuador flew about fifty T-33s with the last retiring from active service in the mid-1990s. One was put on show in this park as a memorial to Air Force personnel who had lost their lives flying from the nearby airfield. There have been no recent reports of the aircraft but it was still there a few years ago. An update would be welcome.

TYPE	REG/SER	CON. NO.	PI/NOTES	STATUS
☐ Lockheed 580 (T-33A)	FAE635	580-1120	56-1770	PV

MUSEO AÉRONAUTICO DE LA FUERZA AÉREA ECUATORIANA (EC9)

Address:	Avenue de la Prensa 3570, Quito.
Tel:	0593-445046
Admission:	Monday-Friday 0800-1600.
Location:	In the military part of the airport which is about 8 km west the city.

Military aviation began in the country when an Italian air mission set up a flying school near Guayaquil in 1920. Little progress was made in the next ten years due to a shortage of funds. In 1935 an American instructor was put in charge of the school, pilots were sent to the U.S.A. for training, more modern aircraft were ordered and a few more airfields were built. The American influence remained for several years and when the country signed the Rio Pact in 1947 more modern types were acquired. The Air Force became a separate service in 1947. Ecuador was the second South American country to order jet aircraft and six English Electric Canberra B.6s and twelve Gloster Meteor FR.9s were delivered in 1954. The British connection has continued in recent years with Jaguars and Strikemasters joining the force. American types acquired since the 1950s include P-80 Shooting Stars, T-33s, A-37s and C-130s. Kfirs have been bought from Israel and Mirages from France. The museum is located on the military side of the main airport for Quito. A hall has recently been built and houses a comprehensive display of models, uniforms, components and memorabilia. The history of aviation in the country is portrayed and famous pilots are honoured. The development of the Air Force and airlines in the country can be traced. The oldest aircraft on show is a Macchi built Hanriot HD-1 biplane in which Captain E. Liut made a flight across the Andes. On November 26th 1920 he flew from Riobamba in Brazil to Quito. Over twelve hundred examples of the biplane fighter were built and the type achieved success in World War I. The Italian factory completed more than eight hundred of the total. The Stinson Reliant was flown from San Diego in California by Teodoro Gildred and arrived at the museum in 1981. This aircraft served with the Royal Navy in England during the latter part of World War II. The preserved Meteor is exhibited in the colours of No. 2111 Squadron. At the end of its flying career the fighter was used for aerobatic training. Transportes Aéreos Militares Ecuatorianos has its main base at the field and several aircraft formerly used by the organisation are on show. This military run airline was set up in the early 1960s and initially flew a route from Quito to Guayaquil and a few other provincial airports. The C-47 was the first type used by T.A.M.E. and later six DC-4s were flown. Three Catalinas were used by the Air Force and in addition to patrol duties flew T.A.M.E. missions to the Galapagos Islands. The identity of the example in the collection is not known. The Mitchell, painted in military markings, was impounded at Quito in 1970. This aircraft first appeared on display in the late 1970s and probably saw no military use in Ecuador. In 1941 a United States Air Mission arrived in Ecuador and land was allocated for the construction of the airfield at Punta Arenas. A small number of Fairchild M-62s and North American NA-16s arrived. The Brazilian built Fairchild Cornell was presented to the F.A.E. in 1947 as the type was one of the first to serve in the country. The Air Force operated a small number from Quito with the first arriving in the country in the late 1970s. Only a few Douglas Dragons have survived. This twin engined bomber made its maiden flight in July 1939 and only thirty eight were completed. And twelve were converted for transport duties and glider towing. After a number of civilian owners in the U.S.A. the example in the collection flew with the local airline Ecuatoriana from 1968 to 1982. Beech 18s have flown in Ecuador but no examples were saved for preservation. The Chilean Air Force has donated one of their retired C-45s and this is currently stored on the base. The Texan was used for pilot training for many years and was replaced by the Beech Mentor. Five Avro 748s were ordered for use by the Air Force and T.A.M.E. Two were fitted with large freight doors and one was a convertible V.I.P. version for presidential use. One airframe is currently on show and another is stored on the base. Four C-130B Hercules were operated and one of these has now joined the exhibition. Two Cessnas used for communications and training duties can be seen. Examples of types currently in use will join this interesting display as they are withdrawn from service. Several aircraft are preserved by the main gate to the Air Force Base and others are in store on the airfield awaiting preservation.

TYPE	REG/SER	CON. NO.	PI/NOTES	STATUS
☐ Avro 748 Series 2A/246	HC-AUD	1682	FAE682 – stored on base.	RA
☐ Avro 748 Series 2A/285	FAE738	1738	FAE738, HC-BAZ	PV
☐ Beech D18S Expeditor (C-45G)	465		(USAF) – in Chilean markings – preserved on base.	RA
☐ Beech A45 Mentor (T-34A)	TH-344	G-105	53-3344	PV
☐ Cessna A150L Aerobat	00506	A1500506		PV
☐ Cessna 172F	FAE835	17252835		PV
☐ Cessna T337D Super Skymaster	FAE162	1162	HC-GYA – preserved on base.	PV
☐ Consolidated 28-5A Catalina (PBY-5A)	53602		(USN)	PV
☐ Douglas DC-3A-467 Skytrain (C-47B)	77164	16748/33496	44-77164, 77164/HC-AUT, CA164	PV
☐ Douglas DC-6B	HC-AVH/FAE691	44691	CC-CLDB, CC-CCE, 44691	PV
☐ Douglas UC-67 Dragon (B-23)	'TH-344'	2717	39-031, NC51436, N400W, N4000W, HC-APV	PVX
☐ English Electric EA.1 Canberra B.6	FAE405	EEP.71405	804, BE-804, 71405/BE-405 – stored on base.	RA
☐ English Electric EA.1 Canberra B.6	FAE509	EEP.71409	806, BE-806, 71509/BE-509, PV71409/BE409	
☐ English Electric EA.1 Canberra B.6	FAE411	EEP.71411	805, BE-805, 71411/BE-411 – stored on base.	RA
☐ Fabrica do Galeao 3FG [Fairchild M-62 Cornell]	PP-GZN	3FG-190	PT19-0456 (Brazil)	PV
☐ Gloster Meteor FR.9	'FF-123'		VW366, 703, FF-113	PVX
☐ Hanriot HD-1				PV
☐ Lockheed 282-1B Hercules (C-130B)	FAE896	282-3528	58-0733	PV
☐ Lockheed 580 (T-33A)	FAE663	580-1508	58-0459	PV
☐ Lockheed 580 (T-33A)	TD-945	580-8091	52-9945	PV
☐ Lockheed 580 (T-33A) (AT-33A)	FAE633	580-8433	53-5094 – preserved on base.	RA
☐ North American NA-88 Texan (AT-6C)	43233		(USAAF) – preserved on base.	PV
☐ North American NA-108 Mitchell (B-25J) (TB-25J)	B-N9069Z	108-47620	44-86866, N9069Z	PV
☐ North American NA-159 Trojan (T-28A) (AT-28D)	49-1545	159-57	49-1545, N6514C	PV
☐ North American NA-159 Trojan (T-28A) (AT-28D)	91647	159-159	49-1647, N9859C	PV
☐ North American NA-168 Texan (T-6G)	20310		(USAF)	PV
☐ Sikorsky S-55D Chickasaw (H-19B) (UH-19B)	527536		52-7536	PV
☐ Stinson V-77 Reliant (AT-19)	NC731M	77-73	42-46712, FK886, Bu11646, N9369H	PV

MUSEO DE LA BASE AÉREA LATACUNGA – COTOPAXI (EC10)

Address:	Ala 12, Base Aérea Cotopaxi, Latacunga.
Admission:	By prior permission only.
Location:	About 5 km north of the town.

The base is named after the active volcano which is located close by. The airfield opened in 1929 and for years the field was used by combat units and the preserved aircraft reflect this role. Maintenance work and training of engine and airframe fitters is now carried out at the site. Twelve former Royal Air Force Meteor FR.9s were delivered in 1954 and served with No. 2111 Squadron. Six Canberras were acquired at the same time making Ecuador the second South American country to possess a tactical jet force. Twelve Cessna A-37s were operated by No. 2112 Squadron from 1976. In 1989/90 a further nine were purchased and the majority remain in service with No. 2311 Squadron at Manta. A number of Dakotas have been used for transport duties giving excellent service over the rugged terrain. The example in the collection saw airline service in Brazil before moving across the Andes. The Mentor is still used for training by the Air Force Academy at Salinas and by the Navy at Guayaquil. The Engineering School at the base has set up a small museum tracing the history of the field and its units. The exhibition includes engines, documents, items of memorabilia and photographs.

TYPE	REG/SER	CON. NO.	PI/NOTES	STATUS
☐ Beech D45 Mentor (T-34C-1)	0025	GM-25		RA
☐ Cessna 318E Dragonfly (A-37B)	FAE387		(USAF)	RA
☐ Douglas DC-3A-457 Skytrooper (C-53D)	CA747	11747	42-68820, PP-PBS, PP-AKI, FAE11747, 11747/HC-AUY	RA
☐ Gloster Meteor FR.9	FF-112		WH547, 702	RA
☐ Gloster Meteor FR.9	FF-114		WB136, 704	PV

This locally built Gavilan 358M has recently joined the Colombian museum in Bogota. (Mike Nelson)

This former Royal Air Force Phantom is preserved at Mount Pleasant. (Douglas Rough)

This Faucett-Stinson F.19 is preserved at the airport at Arequipa. (Eduardo Cardenas)

MUSEO DE LOS NIÑOS (EC11)

Address:	Parque de las Carolinas, Quito.
Tel:	0244-9824 (Science Museum)
Admission:	Daily 1000-1700 (Park)
Location:	In the north eastern part of the city.

This vast park houses a botanical garden and has many sports and recreational facilities. There are designated walks around the site which has a number of lakes within its boundaries. The Museum of Natural Sciences is also located here. The displays at this museum are designed to all people in aspects of science, technology and transport. A former Air Force DC-6 was moved from Quito Air Force Base to the park in the late 1990s. The aircraft was delivered to Western Air Lines in 1956, bought by Braniff two years later. The airliner was sold to LAN in Chile in 1965 and arrived in Ecuador in 1971. After being withdrawn in 1976 it spent over twenty years in store. Around the aircraft are several attractions for children. Regular film shows take place in the fuselage, where there is a display tracing the history of the airliner, and outside is a theatre and an area for puppet shows.

TYPE	REG/SER	CON. NO.	PI/NOTES	STATUS
□ Douglas DC-6B	063	45063	N91311, CC-CCG, HC-AVI	PV

FALKLAND ISLANDS

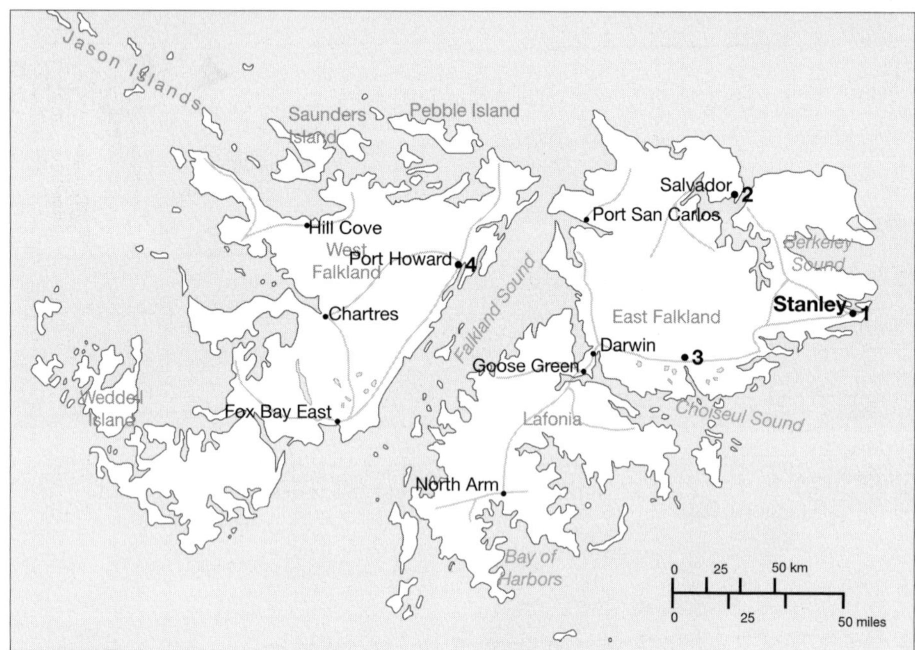

FALKLANDS ISLANDS MUSEUM AND NATIONAL TRUST (FI1)

Address:	Britannia House, Holdfast Road, Stanley FIQQ 1ZZ.
Tel:	500-27428
Fax:	500-22727
Email:	falklands.museum@horizon.co.fk
Admission:	November-March Monday-Friday 0930-1600; Saturday-Sunday 1400-1600. (Hours may be extended to cover cruise ship visits): April-October Monday-Friday 0930-1200 1330-1600; Saturday-Sunday 1400-1600
Location:	Near the centre of the town.

The building was constructed in 1980 for the Argentinean Air Force who, at the time, ran a twice weekly air service to the islands. From 1982 until 1985 it was used by Commanders of the British Forces and took up its present name. The museum was founded by local historian John Smith who started collecting items tracing the history of the islands. The museum was opened in Britannia House on February 13th 1989 by the former Governor Sir Rex Hunt. The displays have been steadily improved and a comprehensive history of the islands is portrayed. The trust is responsible for several historic buildings and wrecks both on the land and off the coast. A new facility is being built at the Government Dockyard and when completed in a few years time will provide a much larger exhibition space. Tourists visiting the islands on cruise ships usually include a visit to the museum on their itinerary. Two aircraft left behind after the 1982 conflict were saved and stored at Mount Pleasant Airport but the Pucará was scrapped in 1999 and the fate of the Iroquois is unknown. The aviation section includes display boards showing the use of aircraft in the islands. A propeller from Noorduyn Norseman VP-FAD can also be seen. The Everett Gyroplane was donated in 2007 and is currently in store.

TYPE	REG/SER	CON. NO.	PI/NOTES	STATUS
☐ Everett Gyroplane Series 4	VP-FBS	014	G-BOVC	RA

GIBRALTAR STATION (FI2)

Address:	Salvador House, Gibraltar Station, Salvador, East Falkland FIQQ 1ZZ.
Tel:	500-31199
Fax:	500-31194
Email:	rmp.jep@horizon.co.fk
Admission:	By prior permission only.
Location:	About 30 miles north west of Stanley.

The owner of the house has preserved the Whirlwind as reminder of the association of HMS Endurance with the islands. In December 1969 the helicopter ditched into a creek close to Gibraltar Station after running short of fuel. The owner of the house, Robin Pitaluga, towed it to the beach and later to the house. Royal Navy Whirlwinds were allocated to many ships and served in a number of roles including search and rescue.

TYPE	REG/SER	CON. NO.	PI/NOTES	STATUS
☐ Westland-Sikorsky WS-55 Whirlwind HAR.9 (HAS.7)	XM666	WA.527		PVD

MOUNT PLEASANT COMPLEX (FI3)

Address:	British Forces South Atlantic Islands, BFPO655, East Falkland FIQQ 1ZZ.
Tel:	500-74204
Admission:	On permanent view.
Location:	About 30 miles south west of Stanley.

In June 1992 1435 Flight relinquished its four Phantoms and Tornado F.3s arrived. One of the quartet has been saved and preserved outside the passenger terminal. The Phantom provided Air Defence cover in the islands from October 1982 until April 1985 at R.A.F. Stanley until the newly built Mount Pleasant was completed. The new airfield is equipped with the facilities to operate most modern combat types.

TYPE	REG/SER	CON. NO.	PI/NOTES	STATUS
☐ McDonnell M.98 Phantom FGR.2	XV409	2955	XV409, 9160M	RA

PORT HOWARD WAR MUSEUM (FI4)

Address:	Port Howard Lodge, Port Howard, West Falkland FIQQ 1ZZ.
Tel:	500-42187
Email:	porthowardlodge@horizon.co.fk
Admission:	By prior permission only.
Location:	By the airstrip which is about 60 miles west of Stanley

The museum was set up shortly after the 1982 conflict and houses an interesting collection of relics. The starboard wing and other parts from an Argentine Air Force Dagger which was shot down on May 21st 1982 by a missile fired from a Sea Harrier can be seen. Also on view are small components from an A-4B Skyhawk, C-215, and the helmet from of the pilot of Dagger C-403 which was downed on the same day as C-404.

TYPE	REG/SER	CON. NO.	PI/NOTES	STATUS
☐ Israeli Aircraft Industries M5 Dagger A (Nesher)	C-404	S12	Wing and other parts.	PVD

PARAGUAY

COLECCIÓN DE LA BASE AÉREA DE CAMPO GRANDE (PAR1)

Address:	Campo Grande, Asunción. IAP.
Admission:	By prior permission only.
Location:	In the northern suburbs of the city.

This Air Force base houses transports and combat types. A collection of preserved aircraft has been assembled by the military gate. The sole Piper Lance acquired by the Air Force has now joined the collection. Two PZL Wilgas were bought and one of these has been preserved. The Fokker is located at the nearby Civil Aviation Institute. A few of the batch of Lockheed AT-33As are still flown by the based combat squadron.

TYPE	REG/SER	CON. NO.	PI/NOTES	STATUS
☐ Bell 204 Iroquois (UH-1B)				RA
☐ Fokker S.11.1 Instructor (S.11)	ZP-EAC		At nearby Institute.	RA
☐ Lockheed 580 (T-33A) (AT-33A)				RA
☐ Lockheed 580 (T-33A) (AT-33A)				RA
☐ North American NA-88 Texan (AT-6D) (Harvard III)	0119	88-10647	41-33525, EX552, 7229 (South Africa), N3173R – possible identities.	RA
☐ Panstwowe Zaklady Lotnicze (PZL) 104 Wilga 80				RA
☐ Piper PA-32R Lance	0214	7880027		RA

COLECCIÓN DE LA BASE AÉREA NU GUAZU (PAR2)

Address:	Villa Militar Nu Guazu,, Asunción.
Tel:	021-670552
Admission:	By prior permission only.
Location:	At the south east corner of the International Airport which is in the northern suburbs of the city.

The Fuerzas Aéreas del Ejército Nacional Paraguayo was formed as part of the Army in 1927 and became an independent air force in 1946. This airfield with a grass runway houses all training units and a helicopter group. Paraguay was supplied with fourteen Uirapiru and five Neiva Universals from Brazil. These types were used for training and communications duties. The C-47 was painted with a false serial and has not been identified.

TYPE	REG/SER	CON. NO.	PI/NOTES	STATUS
☐ Aerotec A.122B Uirapuru (T-23A)	0012	056	T23-0992 (Brazil)	RA
☐ Bell 204 Iroquois (UH-1B)	PR-H-005	426	62-1906	RA
☐ Cessna U206G Stationair 6	0210	U20605365		RA
☐ Cessna 210 Centurion	0218	21069780		RA
☐ Douglas DC-3A-467 Skytrain (C-47B)	'T-22'			RAX
☐ Lockheed 580 (T-33A)	1022	580-1276	57-0547 – with tail from c/n 580-1418 57-0689	RA
☐ Neiva N.621 Universal (T-25)	0125	135		RA
☐ North American NA-88 Texan (SNJ-4)	0129	88-9747	Bu10063, 1398 (Brazil)	RA

COLECCIÓN DE TRANSPORTES AÉREOS DEL MERCOSUR (PAR3)

Address:	Instituto Paraguayo de Historica Aeronautica, Asunción.
Admission:	By prior permission only.

The company, with the assistance of the institute, is planning to set up a collection of historic piston engined airliners at Asunción. Over the years large numbers of propliners have been flown on services in the land locked country. The first member of the fleet, an early Convair 240, served in Argentina before coming to Paraguay.

TYPE	REG/SER	CON. NO.	PI/NOTES	STATUS
☐ Convair 240-6	ZP-CDO	62	LV-ADO	PVC

MONUMENTO DE ACADEMIA MILITAR (PAR4)

Address:	Capiatá.
Admission:	By prior permission only.
Location:	In the eastern suburbs of Ascuncion.

The grounds of this academy contain a number of military vehicles and weapons. The only aircraft on show is a Brazilian built Texan, one of several supplied to the country for training duties.

TYPE	REG/SER	CON. NO.	PI/NOTES	STATUS
☐ North American NA-119 Texan (AT-6D)	0105		(Brazil)	RA

PERÚ

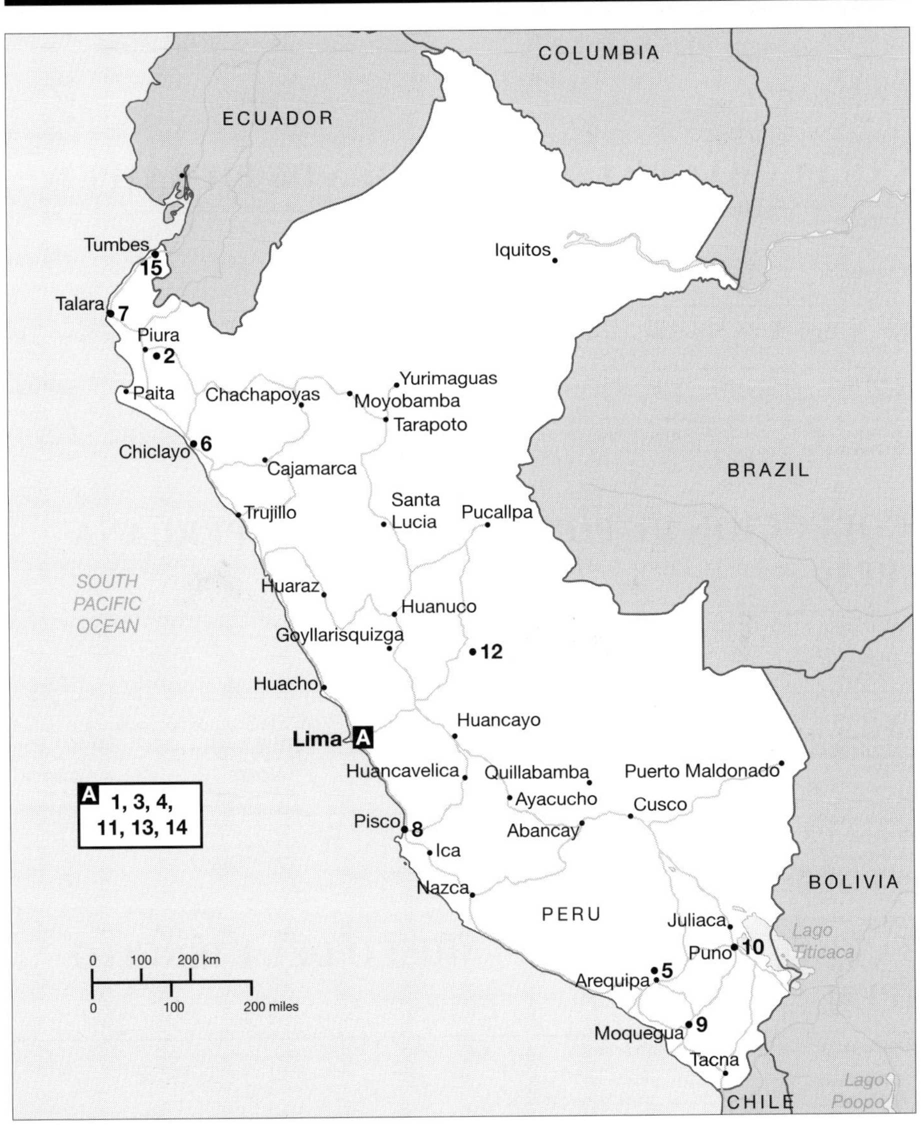

COLECCIÓN DE LA BASE AÉREA DE LIMA-CALLAO (PE1)

Address:	Grupo Aereo 8, Base Aérea Jorge Chavez, Callao, Lima.
Admission:	By prior permission only.
Location:	In the north western suburbs of the city.

The group operates a fleet of transport aircraft from the airport and the Presidential Flight is also in residence. A collection of preserved aircraft is being assembled. The types include several flown by the organisation.

TYPE	REG/SER	CON. NO.	PI/NOTES	STATUS
☐ Antonov An-32	363/OB-1380	0910		RA
☐ De Havilland D.H.C.5D Buffalo	328	51		RA
☐ Douglas DC-6	381	42866	N37501, N375ED, N19544, N117PM, CP-2110, CP-2250, 381, PNP-236	RA
☐ Mil Mi-8	678			RA
☐ Stinson-Faucett F-19	OA-BBQ	8	OB-PAJ-143	RA

COLECCIÓN DE LA BASE AÉREA DE PIURA (PE2)

Address:	Grupo Aéreo 7, Base Aérea Capitan Concha, Piura.
Admission:	By prior permission only.
Location:	In the south eastern part of the town.

Piura is home to two squadrons operating the Cessna Dragonfly. Three complete aircraft are preserved around the base. The front fuselage and wings of another are mounted in a wall near the Officers quarters.

TYPE	REG/SER	CON. NO.	PI/NOTES	STATUS
☐ Cessna 318E Dragonfly (A-37B)	121	43466	74-1700	RA
☐ Cessna 318E Dragonfly (A-37B)	123	43470	74-1702	RA
☐ Cessna 318E Dragonfly (A-37B)			Less rear fuselage and tail.	RA
☐ Cessna 318E Dragonfly (A-37B)				RA

COLECCIÓN DE POLICIA NACIONAL PERUANA (PE3)

Address:	Aeropuerto Jorge Chavez, Lima.
Admission:	By prior permission only.
Location:	In the north western suburbs of the city.

The Peruvian National Police operate a fleet of helicopters and fixed wing aircraft from bases around the country. Two aircraft are preserved outside their headquarters which is located near the airport.

TYPE	REG/SER	CON. NO.	PI/NOTES	STATUS
☐ Bell 47G-3B-1			At Headquarters.	RA
☐ Bell 47G-3B-1	PNP-102	6856	At airport.	RA
☐ Bell 47G-3B-1	PNP-103			RA
☐ Cessna 172	PNP-201		At airport.	RA
☐ Cessna 172	PNP-204		At headquarters.	RA
☐ Hughes 500D	PNP-101	1000822D	At airport.	RA

FUERTE REAL FELIPE – MUSEO DEL EJÉRCITO (PE4)

Address:	Plaza Indepenencia, Callao.
Admission:	Daily 1000-1700.
Location:	In the centre of the town.

This vast fort was built by the Spanish between 1747 and 1776 to protect the port and the town. With a perimeter of more than one and a half kilometres the walled compound contains two forts and many other buildings. The whole site is in a remarkable state of preservation. The Army maintains a small presence in the fort and a museum tracing their history has been set up. There are many weapons, uniforms, flags and items of memorabilia on show. In the courtyards are original cannons, military vehicles and tanks.

TYPE	REG/SER	CON. NO.	PI/NOTES	STATUS
□ Sud-Est SE.3130 Alouette II				PV

MONUMENTO DE ALA AÉREA 3 (PE5)

Address:	Aeropuerto Alfredo Rodriguez Balón, Arequipa.
Tel:	044-4564
Email:	sptaqp@tsi.com.pe
Admission:	On permanent view.
Location:	About 5 km north west of the town.

The airfield is the headquarters of the 3rd. Air Wing which controls squadrons at three bases in the region. The Sukhoi Su-22 in false markings is mounted on a pylon at the airport. The serial '003' refers to the number of the Wing. Forty Su-22s have been flown by the Air Force. The Sabre is at a park in the nearby town.

TYPE	REG/SER	CON. NO.	PI/NOTES	STATUS
□ North American NA-191 Sabre (F-86F)	176		(USAF) – in park in town.	PV
□ Stinson-Fawcett F-19	'110'			PVX
□ Sukhoi Su-22	'003'			PVX

MONUMENTO DE BASE AÉREA DE CHICLAYO (PE6)

Address:	Grupo Aéreo 6, Aeropuerto Jose A. Quinones Gonzaléz, Chiclayo.
Admission:	By prior permission only.
Location:	In the south eastern suburbs of the town.

The base houses squadrons operating the Mirage 5 and MiG-29. The Hunter was ordered by Peru in the mid-1950s and served for many years. An example has been preserved as a monument.

TYPE	REG/SER	CON. NO.	PI/NOTES	STATUS
□ Hawker P.1067 Hunter F.52 (F.4)	632		WW662	RA

MONUMENTO DE LA BASE AÉREA DE EL PATO (PE7)

Address:	Base Aerea Capitan Montes, Talara.
Admission:	By prior permission only.
Location:	Just east of the town.

The base is home to squadrons fling Sukhoi Su-22s. Peru was the only South American country to order the jet and a two seat version has been preserved as a monument along with a Lockheed Shooting Star. This early combat jet was supplied to a number of South American countries as it was replaced in American service.

TYPE	REG/SER	CON. NO.	PI/NOTES	STATUS
□ Lockheed 080 Shooting Star (P-80C) (F-80C)				RA
□ Sukhoi Su-22U	008			RA

MONUMENTO DE BASE AÉREA DE PISCO (PE8)

Address:	Grupo Aéreo 9, Base Aerea Capitan Renan Elias Oliviera, Pisco.
Admission:	By prior permission only.
Location:	Just south of the town.

Peru ordered its first Canberras in late 1955 and subsequently more were delivered. In all almost forty were operated and the type has recently been withdrawn. One has been preserved as a monument.

TYPE	REG/SER	CON. NO.	PI/NOTES	STATUS
☐ Douglas A-26C Invader	226		(USAAF)	RA
☐ English Electric EA.1 Canberra B.56 (B.2)	240	EEP.71265	WJ757, G-27-97	RA

MONUMENTO DE BASE DE EJÉRCITO DE MOQUEGA (PE9)

Address:	Brigada Blindada 3, Moquega.
Admission:	By prior permission only.
Location:	In the northern part of the town.

The Army has an attack regiment based at these barracks. Eleven Enstrom F.280C helicopters were delivered for basic pilot training. One is preserved near to the main gate of the camp along with items of artillery.

TYPE	REG/SER	CON. NO.	PI/NOTES	STATUS
☐ Enstrom F.280C	EP-908	779		RA

MONUMENTO DE BASE DE EJÉRCITO DE PUNO (PE10)

Address:	Brigada Tapapaca de Montana 4, Puno.
Admission:	By prior permission only.
Location:	In the town.

The Peruvian Army operates Mil Mi-8s, 17s, 25s and 26s from bases around the country. All have proved their worth in the harsh terrain. An example of the Mi-17 has been preserved near the gate to the barracks.

TYPE	REG/SER	CON. NO.	PI/NOTES	STATUS
☐ Mil Mi-17	EP-631			RA

MONUMENTO DE LA BASE NAVAL DE CALLAO (PE11)

Address:	Callao.
Admission:	By prior permission only.
Location:	By the port.

The Peruvian Navy operated ten Grumman Trackers on coastal patrol duties from its base at Callao. One has been moved to the naval docks in the centre of the town and preserved as a monument.

TYPE	REG/SER	CON. NO.	PI/NOTES	STATUS
☐ Grumman G-121 Tracker (S2F-3) (S-2E)				RA

MONUMENTO DE SAN RAMON (PE12)

Address:	San Ramon.
Admission:	On permanent view.
Location:	In the town.

Elmer Faucett, and a group of local businessmen set up Faucett Airlines in 1928. In the early 1930s the company built a larger version of the Stinson SM.6B known as the Stinson-Faucett F.19. The prototype flew in September 1934 and over the next twelve years thirty six were built in the company workshops at Lima for both airline and military use. One of surviving F.19s has been mounted as a monument in the town

TYPE	REG/SER	CON. NO.	PI/NOTES	STATUS
☐ Stinson-Faucett F-19	OB-R-140	25	OB-PAH-140	PV

Right: The Peruvian Air Force flew Sukhoi Su-22s and one is preserved at Arequipa. (Eduardo Cardenas)

Below: The base at Chiclayo has this Hunter as a monument. (Eduardo Cardenas)

On show in the Peruvian Aeronautical Museum at Las Palmas is this Ansaldo SVA 5. (Eduardo Cardenas)

MUSEO AERONÁUTICA DEL PERÚ (PE13)

Address:	Las Palmas, Surco, Lima.
Tel:	01-247-5893
Email:	musarperu@hotmail.com
Admission:	Monday-Friday 0800-1600 – by prior permission only.
Location:	In the southern suburbs of the city.

Formed in January 1919, the Peruvian Army Air Service was helped by a French air mission which brought with it a small number of training types. A British mission replaced the French and twelve Avro 504s, three Bristol Fighters and a Blackburn Kangaroo arrived in the country. The third nation to send a mission to Peru was the United States which came in 1924 and over the next decade a number of American types were acquired. A border dispute with Colombia occurred in 1933 and when it was realised that the United States was supplying aircraft to both sides Peru bought a dozen aircraft from Fairey in Britain. In 1939 an agreement was made with Italy and a number of Caproni aircraft were acquired and licence built examples were constructed in Peru. These aircraft were not a success and Peru turned again to America. Among the types purchased were seven North American NA-50A fighters and ten Douglas DB-8A-3P attack bombers. These aircraft were used in further local conflicts including an invasion of Ecuador in 1941. At the end of World War II Peru signed the 1947 Rio Pact and larger numbers of American types arrived. In recent years purchases have been made from Britain, the Soviet Union, France and Italy in addition to the U.S.A. With this rich and diverse aeronautical history there is potential for an excellent museum. The exhibition has been set up at Surco on the outskirts of Lima but the base is due to close and be replaced by housing. Hopefully the museum can remain on part of the site or be found a new location. The indoor display, in a typical 1930s terminal building, features models, uniforms, photographs and documents. The star aircraft exhibits are a North American NA-50A and a Douglas DB-8A-3P. Both these are mounted on pylons near the main gate to the base and are the only known survivors of their respective types. A Catalina is due to join the display. An early Ansaldo biplane is also of great interest. This Italian company built a series of successful biplane fighters in the World War I period and several export orders were received. The first jet fighters to arrive in the country were fifteen Sabres supplied by the U.S.A. in 1955 and these replaced the fifty seven Thunderbolts which served from 1948 to 1959. Sixteen examples of the Buffalo were ordered in the early 1970s and operated by 8 Group at Callao. In recent years Peru has ordered Russian types and two Su-22s are on view.

TYPE	REG/SER	CON. NO.	PI/NOTES	STATUS
☐ Aermacchi MB.339AP	479	6653/055		PV
☐ Aermacchi MB.339AP	485	6658/061		PV
☐ Ansaldo SVA 5				PV
☐ Beech 65-A80 Queen Air	732	LD-247		PV
☐ Bell 212	'660'	30644	612, OB-1517, 612	PVX
☐ Bensen B-8 Gyroglider	OB-V-1046			PV
☐ Blériot XI (R)				PV
☐ Boeing-Stearman A75N1 Kaydet (N2S-5)	126	75-8502	Bu43408, OB-I-835	PV
☐ Boeing-Stearman A75N1 Kaydet (PT-17)	168		(USAAF) – at Air Force Academy.	RA
☐ Cessna 318B Tweety Bird (T-37B)	'447'	40660	60-0164, 474	PVX
☐ Cessna 318E Dragonfly (A-37B)				RA
☐ Cessna 318E Dragonfly (A-37B)				RA
☐ Consolidated 28-5A Catalina (PBY-5A)				RA
☐ De Havilland D.H.C.5D Buffalo	322	45		PV
☐ Douglas A-26C Invader	227		(USAAF)	PV
☐ Douglas DB-8A-3P	XXXI-1			PV
☐ Douglas DC-3A-456 Skytrain (C-47A)	357	13828/25273	43-48012, 62-357	PV
☐ Hawker P.1067 Hunter F.52 (F.4)	137	41H/670731	WT774, 637 (Peru)	PV
☐ Lockheed 18-56-23 Lodestar (C-60A)	'512'	18-2576	42-56083, NC13K, N13K, N1929, N1846, N1846G	PVX
☐ Lockheed 182-1A Hercules (182-44-03) (C-130A)			Front fuselage only – on base.	RA
☐ Lockheed 580 (T-33A) (AT-33A)	455		(USAF)	PV
☐ Mil Mi-8T	EP-519		In nearby barracks.	RA
☐ North American NA-50	XXI-41-3		251	RA
☐ North American NA-88 Texan (AT-6C)	194		(USAAF) – at Air Force Academy.	RA
☐ North American NA-88 Texan (AT-6C)	455		(USAAF)	PV
☐ North American NA-191 Sabre (F-86F)	180			PV
☐ Stinson-Faucett F-19	OB-R-143	27	OB-PAJ-143	PV
☐ Sukhoi Su-22	163			PV
☐ Sukhoi Su-22	005	34817	Also quoted as c/n 34919.	RA

MUSEO DEL FUERZA DE AVIACIÓN NAVAL DEL PERÚ (PE14)

Address:	Servicio Aéronaval de la Marina Peruana, Avenue Faucett, Lima-Callao.
Tel:	01-575-1097
Admission:	By prior permission only.
Location:	In the north western suburbs of the city.

The first Peruvian Naval Air Service amalgamated with the Army in 1929 after a decade of independence. A few Curtiss Seagulls and de Havilland D.H.9s were flown in this period. The force became autonomous again in the early 1960s. A variety of fixed and rotary wing types are currently in service. A museum tracing the history of the service is being set up at Callao. In the building is the first aircraft flown by the new service. This Bell 47 was delivered in 1962. Outside is a later model of the successful helicopter. This one was flown by the national police and has been preserved since the late 1990s. The Tracker served in the patrol, anti-submarine and search and rescue roles for many years. The Beech T-34C Turbo Mentor is now used by the Navy for pilot training and counter insurgency work. Small numbers of the earlier piston engined version were also used.

TYPE	REG/SER	CON. NO.	PI/NOTES	STATUS
☐ Beech A45 Mentor (T-34A)	AI-503		On base gate.	RA
☐ Bell 47G-2A	401	2728		RA
☐ Bell 47G-3	PNP-100	3388		RA
☐ Grumman G-121 Tracker (S2F-3) (S-2E)	AA-548	256C	Bu152369 – on base gate.	RA

PARCO HISTÓRICO (PE15)

Address: Tumbés.
Admission: On permanent view.
Location: In the centre of the town.

The park honours all three branches of the services. On show are military vehicles, plaques and flags. The only aircraft is a Cessna Dragonfly. The Peruvian Air Force has operated over forty examples of this ground attack design based on the T-37 Tweety Bird trainer. The A-37 still serves with two squadrons at Piura. The aircraft was preserved by the main gate at Piura for several years but it moved to the park in the early 2000s.

TYPE	REG/SER	CON. NO.	PI/NOTES	STATUS
☐ Cessna 318E Dragonfly (A-37B)	132		(USAF)	PV

URUGUAY

COLECCIÓN DE ESCUELA TÉCNICA AERONÁUTICA (UR1)

Address:	Ruta 101 KM 31.500, Base Aérea General Artigas, Pando Taledo Sur.
Tel:	02-288-5070
Email:	bedeliaema@adinet.com.uy
Admission:	By prior permission only.
Location:	About 5 km south of the town.

The school was set up in October 1946 and since then has trained many airframe and engine fitters in a variety of trades. Four types used have been preserved to remind students of the traditions of the service. The three trainers were used for the instruction of many pilots and the Aero Commander flew on communication duties. There are also engines, components, photographs and instruments on show in the workshops.

TYPE	REG/SER	CON. NO.	PI/NOTES	STATUS
☐ Aero Commander RC680	501	499-169		RA
☐ Beech D45 Mentor (T-34B)	669	BG-224	Bu140890	RA
☐ Lockheed 580 (T-33A) (AT-33A)	201	580-9887	55-4443	RA
☐ North American NA-88 Texan (AT-6C)	'340'	88-14295	42-44392, 350	RAX

COLECCIÓN DE LA BASE AÉREA 1 CARRASCO – CANELONES (UR2)

Address:	Base Aérea 1, Montevideo-Carrasco.
Admission:	By prior permission only.
Location:	About 15 km east of the city centre.

Transport aircraft and helicopters are based at the field which is also home to the headquarters of Brigada Aérea I. The DC-3 was the mainstay of airline services in the country for many years and two have been preserved. The Mentor served in the communications role with the maintenance command at the base. The T-33s are from the batch of several modified for attack duties. They were replaced in this role by the Pucará and Cessna Dragonfly. Uruguay ordered a small number of Westland Wessex helicopters and in the late 1990s these were supplemented by five former Royal Air Force examples. Three FH-227s were flown on transport duties. There is also an Air Force technical training school near the base and one of the T-33s and the T-6 are here.

TYPE	REG/SER	CON. NO.	PI/NOTES	STATUS
☐ Beech A45 Mentor (T-34A)				RA
☐ Bell 205 Iroquois (UH-1H)	'069'			RAX
☐ Douglas DC-3A-456 Skytrain (C-47A)	T-510	19021	42-100558, CX-BJG	RA
☐ Douglas DC-3A-467 Skytrain (C-47B)	T-514	20604	43-16138, 514, CX-AKH	RA
☐ Fairchild-Hiller FH-227D	572	574	N2785R, CX-BIM	RA
☐ Lockheed 580 (T-33A) (AT-33A)	205	580-9301	53-5860	RA
☐ Lockheed 580 (T-33A) (AT-33A)	201	580-9887	55-4441	RA
☐ North American NA-182 Texan (T-6G)	'350'			RAX
☐ Westland-Sikorsky WS-58 Wessex HC.2	070	WA.137	XR515	RA
☐ Westland-Sikorsky WS-58 Wessex HC.2	072	WA.532	XT605	RA

COLECCIÓN DE LA BASE AÉREA NAVAL 'CAPITAN CURBELO' (UR3)

Address:	Laguna del Sauce.
Admission:	By prior permission only.
Location:	On the south side of the lake.

Uruguayan naval aviation started in the early 1930s and a small number of Italian C.A.N.T aircraft were operated. Expansion of the service occurred in the latter stages of World War II and American trainers, fighters and patrol types were supplied. The base at Laguna del Sauce is now the only airfield where naval aircraft are normally based. Helicopters, transport and patrol types are operated. A museum is being developed at the site and items of memorabilia, documents, photographs and uniforms have been collected. Three aircraft have been preserved with the Texan parked near the Headquarters building and the other two near the main gate.

TYPE	REG/SER	CON. NO.	PI/NOTES	STATUS
☐ Grumman G-89 Tracker (S2F-1) (S-2A)	851	186	Bu133215, A-851	RA
☐ North American NA-88 Texan (SNJ-4)	'258'		(USN), A-256, 256	RAX
☐ Westland-Sikorsky WS-58 Wessex 60	063	WA.504	G-631 (Ghana), G-BGWT, N250HL, A-063	RA

The Peruvian Aeronautical Museum at Las Palmas owns this rare North American NA-50. (Eduardo Cardenas)

The small museum at Durazno Air Base contains this Lockheed F-80C Shooting Star. (Gerry Manning)

This Mitchell is preserved at Barquisimeto Air Base. (Iván Nesbit)

MUSEO AERONÁUTICO (UR4)

Address:	Avenida Larranagna, San Gabriel 4004, Montevideo.
Tel:	02-2152039
Email:	aamaneregalli@adinet.co.ur
Admission:	Friday-Sunday 1430-1730.
Location:	In the northern suburbs of the city.

The first flight in Uruguay took place in 1911 and in the following year a Naval officer Ensign Atilio Frigerio obtained his pilots licence in Italy. He proposed that a flying school should be set up and this came about on November 20th 1916. Five monoplanes designed by Pablo Castaibert and built in Argentina were the initial equipment. Two Henri Farman biplanes, also constructed in Argentina, soon joined the fleet. Over the next two decades aircraft were bought from Britain, France and Italy and a few from the United States. In 1940 Uruguay let America use some bases in the country and in return a number of training machines were supplied. Since then the majority of the military aircraft delivered have come from the U.S.A. The idea of a museum was put forward in 1956 but it was ten years before it opened to the public. An interesting display was set up with many unique exhibits. In December 1997 a disastrous fire destroyed many airframes and others were badly damaged. Among those lost were the last surviving Potez 25. In 1929 seven Potez 25 A-2 general purpose biplanes were purchased and they served until the 1940s. The Neybar, the only indigenous Uruguayan aircraft, designed by Vladimir Neyeloff and Fernando Barrandeguy, flew in January 1947. The four seat high wing monoplane was withdrawn in 1962 after fifteen hundred flying hours and presented to the museum. This historic machine also perished. Two de Havilland types lost were a Morane-Saulnier built Moth and a former PLUNA Dragonfy. The twin engined Dragonfly first flew in 1935 and only sixty seven were completed. After this disaster the dedicated staff and a team of volunteers set about rebuilding the display. A Mustang was saved for the collection but this was eventually sold to the U.S.A. and replaced by a replica which unfortunately was destroyed. The building was cleaned up and new aircraft and other items arrived. Pablo Castaibert was a Frenchman living in Argentina and between 1910 and 1915 he designed and built seven similar types. Uruguay ordered small numbers and two were preserved. Both were damaged in the fire and one has been completely restored for the exhibition. Rebuilding of the earlier IV is planned for the near future. Seven Curtiss-Wright Falcons were supplied in 1942 and served at Durazno and Pando. The survivor of this batch suffered in the fire but has now been rebuilt to pristine condition. Ten Chipmunks were bought in the 1950s but they saw only limited military use before being sold on the civil market. The civilian example on show was used by the Director General of Civil Aviation in Montevideo. This has replaced a victim of the fire. Uruguay operated several B-25 Mitchells but unfortunately none survived. The gap was filled several years ago with the arrival of a former Brazilian Air Force machine. The Shooting Star was the first jet type to be operated by the Air Force and the one in the display made the last flight by the type in the country on August 12th 1969. The Argentinean built primary glider owes its origins to the successful German designs which appeared in the inter-war period. A range of civilian types used by private owners and local aero clubs is being acquired. Three classic American designs from the post-World War II period are the Beech Bonanza, the Ryan Navion and the Stinson Voyager. The associated displays portray an excellent record of aviation in the country. On show are engines, components, documents, photographs and uniforms. This excellent exhibition reminds all visitors of what can be achieved in a comparatively short time after a major disaster. Over the next few years more aircraft should join the collection.

TYPE	REG/SER	CON. NO.	PI/NOTES	STATUS
☐ Beech C18S Kansan (AT-11)	101		(USAAF)	PV
☐ Beech 35 Bonanza	CX-BDF	D-950	NC3968N, LV-ZIJ	RAD
☐ Beech D45 Mentor (T-34B)	675	BG-222	Bu140888	PV
☐ Bell 204 Iroquois (HU-1B) (UH-1B)	061	283	61-0703	PV
☐ Bell 205 Iroquois (UH-1H)	'050'	9282	66-17088	PVX
☐ Bell 205 Iroquois (UH-1H)	'052'	13282	72-21583	PVX
☐ Castaibert IV				PVD
☐ Castaibert VI				PV
☐ Cessna 318E Dragonfly (A-37B)	284	43274	69-6429 – also reported as c/n 43276.	PV
☐ Curtiss-Wright CW-22B Falcon	G2-205			RAC
☐ De Havilland D.H.82A Tiger Moth	F2			RAC
☐ De Havilland D.H.C.1 Chipmunk 21	G-ANOW	C1/0972	G-ANOW, CX-BGH	PV
☐ De Havilland D.H.C.1 Chipmunk 21	CX-AVA	C1/0978	E-607	RAD
☐ Douglas DC-3A-456 Skytrain (C-47A)	T-521	19231	42-100768, 521, CX-BHR – front fuselage only.	PV
☐ Douglas DC-3A-467 Skytrain (C-47B) (Dakota IV)	CX-BDB	16644/33392	44-77060, KN682, G-AMNL, I-TAVO	PV
☐ Fabrica Argentina de Aeronidos Primary Glider				PV
☐ Fairchild M-62A Cornell (PT-19B)	634	T43-5670	42-83084, CX-BBH – possible identity.	PVD
☐ Fairchild M-62A-4 Cornell (PT-26)			Quoted as 24-444/A36 6069.	RAD
☐ Fairchild M-62A-4 Cornell (PT-26)		T42-4124 (?)	FH775	RAD
☐ Globo Truffi AX-7	CX-BPH			RA
☐ Hiller UH12E-4 Raven (H-23F) (OH-23F)	'026'	2297	64-14850, 026, CX-BNR	PVX
☐ Lockheed 18-56-23 Lodestar (C-60A)	N69415	18-2349	42-32215, NC69415	PV
☐ Lockheed 080 Shooting Star (P-80C) (F-80C)	213	080-1966	47-0205	PV
☐ Lockheed 580 (T-33A)	203	580-9889	55-4445	PV
☐ Lockheed-Kaiser CL-400-2	LV-GOL	3001		RA
☐ North American NA-88 Texan (AT-6D)	373		(USAAF)	PV
☐ North American NA-108 Mitchell (B-25J)	'156'	108-34860	43-27847, 5087 (Brazil)	PVX
☐ Piper J-3C-65 Cub	503			PV
☐ Ryan Navion A	CX-AJT	NAV-4-1119	NC4119K	PV
☐ Stinson 108-3 Voyager	CX-ALL	108-5225	NC4225C	PV
☐ Westland-Sikorsky WS-58 Wessex HC.2	071	WA.144	XR522	PV

MUSEO DE LA BASE AÉREA DURAZNO (UR5)

Address:	Brigada Aérea 2, Teniente Segundo Mario Walter Parallada, Aeropuerto Santa Bernadina, Durazno.
Admission:	By prior permission only.
Location:	In the eastern suburbs of the town.

The Air Force has set up a museum at the base which is home to a training unit. The five aircraft are displayed outside. Just under twenty Lockheed Shooting Stars were delivered in the late 1950s and served until 1971. The T-33 is one of five acquired from the U.S.A. in 1990 to provide spares for those flown by No. 2 Group at Carrasco. The aircraft is now painted in the markings of one which crashed. Over forty Beech T-34s have been used in the training role. Eight A-37s were acquired in the 1970s and used by No. 2 Group. Several Cessna types have been flown on communications, liaison and training duties. A Skywagon has now joined the collection.

TYPE	REG/SER	CON. NO.	PI/NOTES	STATUS
☐ Beech D45 Mentor (T-34B)	685	BG-289	204 (Chile)	RA
☐ Cessna 185B Skywagon (U-17A)	755	1851020	66-8033	RA
☐ Cessna 318E Dragonfly (A-37B)	279	43304	70-1289	RA
☐ Lockheed 080 Shooting Star (P-80C) (F-80C)	210	080-1963	47-0202	RA
☐ Lockheed 580 (T-33A)	'202'	580-9936	56-1586, 206	RAX

VENEZUELA

COLECCIÓN DE LA BASE AÉREA MARISCAL SUCRE (VE1)

Address:	Grupo Aéreo de Entrenamiento, Base Aérea Marischal Sucre, Boca del Rio, Aragua.
Admission:	By prior permission only.
Location:	In the western suburbs of Maracay.

Located at the base is the elementary training unit of the Military Aviation School. A number of aircraft have been preserved around the field so that students are reminded of the traditions of the service. The first Texans were delivered in the 1940s and served for many years. Twenty four Vampire FB.5s were bought in 1952 and some flew with the Air Force aerobatic team 'Las Panteras'. Later acquisitions from Britain were fifteen Jet Provosts some of which served until the mid-1980s. Twenty-two F-86F Sabres were bought from the U.S.A. Later fifty-one former Luftwaffe F-86Ks were acquired but not all were operated.

TYPE	REG/SER	CON. NO.	PI/NOTES	STATUS
☐ Beech C18S Kansan (AT-11)	2506		May be an AT-10.	RA
☐ Hunting-Percival P.84 Jet Provost T.52	5324			RA
☐ North American NA-182 Texan (T-6G)	2506			RA
☐ North American NA-221 Sabre (F-86K)	0019	221-152	55-4912, JE+103, JD+124, JD+324	RA
☐ North American NA-221 Sabre (F-86K)	7881	221-154	55-4914	RA
☐ North American NA-242 Sabre (F-86K)	0597	242-16	56-4131, JE+238, JD+238, JD+338	RA
☐ North American NA-242 Sabre (F-86K)	0881	242-22	56-4137, JE+234, JD+234, JD+334	RA
☐ North American NA-242 Sabre (F-86K)	0931	242-25	56-4140, BB+701, JE+106, JD+106, JD+306	RA
☐ North American NA-242 Sabre (F-86K)	5610	242-41	56-4156, JE+117, JD+117	RA
☐ North American NA-398 Buckeye (T-2D)	'9187'	398-10	Bu160237, 4150	RAX

ESCUADRON LEGENDARIO (VE2)

Address:	Base Aérea El Libertador, Palo Negro, Aragua.
Admission:	By prior permission only.
Location:	About 15 km south east of Maracay.

In the mid-1980s the Air Force decided to set up an historic flight. A Caudron G.3, which incorporates some original parts, was built by Salis Aviation in France and arrived in the country as part of an exchange deal which took a P-47 Thunderbolt to La Ferté Alais. This aircraft has now returned to the museum in Maracay. Three Morane-Saulnier MS.230s were bought in 1935 and it is believed that the aircraft used by the flight is not from the original trio but one obtained from Jean Salis in 1984. Fifteen Jet Provosts were acquired from Britain and remained in service for over twenty years with the last being replaced by Embraer Tucanos in the mid-1980s. Hopefully more aircraft win be added to the flight as they are withdrawn from active service. Two aircraft are preserved on the base. Twenty four former United States Navy North American Buckeye trainers were delivered to Venezuela in the mid 1970s.

TYPE	REG/SER	CON. NO.	PI/NOTES	STATUS
☐ Cessna 310B	9531		Preserved on base.	RA
☐ Dassault Mirage 5V	1225		1506 – preserved on base.	RA
☐ De Havilland D.H.112 Venom FB.52	8176			RA
☐ Douglas DC-3A-456 Skytrain (C-47A) (Dakota III)	1840	12386	42-92571, KG377, G-AJAV, N19E, N70 N70F, N40G, YV-P-EPO, YV-T-RTC, '5984'	RA
☐ Hunting-Percival P.84 Jet Provost T.52	9415			RAA
☐ Morane-Saulnier MS.230	012			RAA
☐ North American NA-182 Texan (T-6G)			(USAF), N20240	RAA
☐ North American NA-358 Buckeye (T-2D)	9187	358-12	Bu 159341 – preserved on base.	RA
☐ Sud-Est SE.3160 Alouette III	1325	1349		RA

MONUMENTO DE BASE AÉREA DE BARCELONA (VE3)

Address:	Base Teniente Luis del Valle Garcia, Barcelona.
Admission:	By prior permission only.
Location:	In the southern suburbs of the town.

The base is currently home to units operating the Sukhoi Su-30. This type replaced the North American T-2 Buckeye. Two aircraft are preserved with the Canberra parked by the main gate to the airfield. The Sabre is in a town square which is dedicated to the Air Force and serves as a memorial to local servicemen.

TYPE	REG/SER	CON. NO.	PI/NOTES	STATUS
□ English Electric EA.1 Canberra B(I).8	'1511'	EEP.71565	4B-39, G-27-160, 4B-39, G-27-308, 0923	RAX
□ North American NA-242 Sabre (F-86K)	4341	242-40	56-4155, JE+115, JD+115, JD+355 – at Plaza FAV in town.	PV

MONUMENTO DE BASE AÉREA DE BARQUISIMETO (VE4)

Address:	Base Teniente Vicente Landaeta Gil, Barquisimeto.
Admission:	By prior permission only.
Location:	In the south western suburbs of the town.

The base is home to Air Force squadrons flying the Canadian built VF-5 fighter. Army helicopter units are also in residence. Two aircraft are preserved at the site. Mitchell bombers were supplied in the late 1940s after Venezuela signed the Rio Pact. Some later had their armaments removed and served in the transport role.

TYPE	REG/SER	CON. NO.	PI/NOTES	STATUS
□ North American NA-108 Mitchell (B-25J)	4B40	108-33906	44-30631	RA
□ North American NA-242 Sabre (F-86K)	5627	242-43	56-4158, JE+249, JD+249, JE+349	RA

MONUMENTO DE BASE AÉREA DE LA CARLOTA (VE5)

Address:	Base Generalissimo Francisco de Miranda, Caracas.
Admission:	By prior permission only.
Location:	In the eastern suburbs of the city.

This base near the capital city houses Air Force, Army and National Guard units operating both fixed and rotary wing types. The Queen Air, painted in false markings, is located by the Air Force gate.

TYPE	REG/SER	CON. NO.	PI/NOTES	STATUS
□ Beech 65 Queen Air	'0001'	LC-105	YV-1032P	RAX

MONUMENTO DE BASE AÉRONAVAL DE PUERTO CABELLO (VE6)

Address:	Puerto Cabello.
Admission:	By prior permission only.
Location:	In the western part of the town.

The field is the only shore base of the Navy. A variety of fixed and rotary wing types are in residence. The service operates a small fleet of ships which can take helicopters and they receive major maintenance at the base. Trackers were flown on coastal patrol missions and one, serving as a memorial, is parked by the main gate.

TYPE	REG/SER	CON. NO.	PI/NOTES	STATUS
□ Grumman G-121 Tracker (S2F-3S) (S-2E)	ARV-0105	150C	Bu149875	RA

MONUMENTO DE BASE EJÉRCITO DE SAN FELIPE (VE7)

Address:	Base Teniente Nestor Arias. San Felipe.
Admission:	By prior permission only.
Location:	About 10 km south of the town.

Several Sabres are preserved at Marischal Sucre Air Base. One is pictured here. (Iván Nesbit)

Above: This Mirage 5V can be seen at El Libertador Air Base on the outskirts of Maracay. (Iván Nesbit)

Left: The exhibits at the Venezuelan Air Force Museum in Maracay include this Caudron G.3 (Iván Nesbit)

The Venezuelan Army has bases around the country. In service are helicopters and a small number of fixed wing aircraft. An Agusta A.109 is mounted on a pole as a memorial to Army crews.

TYPE	REG/SER	CON. NO.	PI/NOTES	STATUS
☐ Agusta A.109A	EV-8334	7241		RA

MUSEO AERONÁUTICO DE LA FUERZA AÉREA VENEZOLANA (VE8)

Address:	Avenida Las Delicas, Cruce Con Aveida 19 de Abril, Maracay.
Tel:	043-333812
Admission:	Saturday-Sunday and Holidays 0900-1800.
Location:	In the suburbs of the city.

Aviation came to the country on September 29th 1912 when Frank Boland flew at Caracas but it was not until December 1920 that an Air Academy opened at Maracay. A French air mission arrived in Venezuela in January 1921 and stayed for just over two years. The first aircraft, Caudron G.3s and G.4s along with four Farman biplanes, were delivered in 1921. Over the next few years the majority of the types used were bought from France. In the late 1930s an Italian air mission came to tin country bringing with it three Fiat CR.32s and a BR.20. When war broke out in Europe the Italians left and the United States provided assistance. Aircraft were supplied under Lend-Lease in exchange for defence facilities. Since the end of World War II aircraft have been bought from Canada, France, Great Britain, Italy and the United States. The then chief of the Maintenance Service, Colonel Luis Hernan Paredes, was concerned about the destruction of historic material and he suggested that a museum should be formed. The Academy airfield at Maracay closed in 1960 and on December 10th 1963, forty three years to the day after it opened, the museum was set up in some of the original buildings. Colonel Paredes became the director in 1964. The exhibition halls display many interesting items including a section devoted to the first civil pilot in the country. On show are photographs, documents, uniforms, engines, components and instruments. The history of the Air Force is told in the informative displays. The aircraft collection contains many rare types. Three Morane-Saulnier MS.147 trainers were bought in 1935. The Breguet 273 is the only surviving example of its type in the world. Nine were acquired in the mid-1930s. The aircraft has been removed from the display and is believed to under restoration in an Air Force workshop. Venezuela bought three Fleet 10Bs and three 10Ds in 1937 and these were used by the Academy at Maracay. Replicas of early types have been built and modern aircraft are being added to the collection, as they are withdrawn from service. The museum was closed for restoration from January 1990 until November 1995 and during that time the display was enlarged. Several fairly modern types were added and more are expected in the near future.

TYPE	REG/SER	CON. NO.	PI/NOTES	STATUS
☐ Aeronca 7AC Champion				RA
☐ Beech C18S Navigator (AT-7C)	6BR1	2257	(USAAF)	PV
☐ Beech D18S	5AR1	A-839	2228	PV
☐ Beech A45 Mentor (T-34A)				RA
☐ Beech 65-B80 Queen Air	8720	LD-283		PV
☐ Beech 65-B80 Queen Air	3168	LD-444		RA
☐ Beech 200C Super King Air	3240	BL-19		PV
☐ Bell 47J	6HR1	1782		PV
☐ Bell 204 Iroquois (UH-1B)	8519	1070	64-13946	PV
☐ Bensen B-8M Gyrocopter	1XDT			PV
☐ Boeing-Stearman A75N1 Kaydet (PT-17)	1	75-1447	41-7888, N?????, N14RL	PV
☐ Boeing-Stearman A75N1 Kaydet (PT-17)	2			RA
☐ Breguet 273		6		RA
☐ Caudron G.3			F-AZBB	PV
☐ Cessna 185 Skywagon	GN-6708			PV
☐ Champion 7EC Traveler	YV-E-MR20	7EC-346	On loan from Museo del Trans.	PV
☐ Dassault Mirage 5E			Due soon.	–
☐ De Havilland D.H.100 Vampire FB.5	3C35		0003, 6C35	PV
☐ De Havilland D.H.104 Dove 2A	2531	04382	(N4281C), G-AMXS, YV-T-FTQ, 3C-R1	PV
☐ De Havilland D.H.112 Venom FB.54	3B34		8C34	PV
☐ De Havilland D.H.115 Vampire T.55	1E35	15060	1E35, 2A36, 0023	PV
☐ Douglas DC-3-455 (C-49K)	4AT1	4984	NC34975, 43-1997, NC20751, N207U, 4984	PV
☐ Douglas DC-3A-360 Skytrain (C-47)	YV-C-AKE	4705	41-18580, YV-AKE	PV
☐ Douglas DC-3D	YV-C-ANI	42960	NC37470, YV-ANI – nose only	PV
☐ Douglas DC-4 Skymaster (C-54A)	7AT1	10287	42-72182, NC51877	PV
☐ English Electric EA.1 Canberra B(I).88 (B(I).58)	0453	EEP71602	4C-39, G-27-311	PV
☐ English Electric EA.1 Canberra B.82 (B.2)	2A39	EEP71176	WH709, 2A39, 6315, G-27-159, G-27-303	PV
☐ Fairchild 24R			Fuselage frame only.	RA
☐ Fairchild M-62A Cornell (PT-19A)		8623AE	43-31424, YV-E-MR-21, YV-T-VTB	RA
☐ Fairchild M-62A Cornell (PT-19B)	0271	T43-5129	42-34463, PT19-0271, PP-HNL – in Brazilian markings.	PV
☐ Fairchild 205 Provider (C-123B)	1673	20295	57-6199, 3CT-2	PV
☐ Flamingo G-2-W (R)	'NC9487'			RAX
☐ Fleet 10D	1			PV
☐ Grumman G-121 Tracker (S2F-3S) (S-2E)			Due soon.	–

TYPE	REG/SER	CON. NO.	PI/NOTES	STATUS
☐ Hanriot HD-1 (R)				PV
☐ Hunting-Percival P.84 Jet Provost T.52			Front fuselage only.	RA
☐ Hunting-Percival P.84 Jet Provost T.52	6780			PV
☐ Hunting-Percival P.84 Jet Provost T.52	E040		G-23-1	PV
☐ Morane-Saulnier MS.147	2			PV
☐ Morane-Saulnier MS.147 (FSM)				RA
☐ North American NA-78 Texan (AT-6A)	E-45	78-6445	41-16107	PV
☐ North American NA-81 Harvard II	E96	81-4128	3837 (Canadian)	PV
☐ North American NA-108 Mitchell (B-25J)	2B40	108-35109	43-28096, 5B40	PV
☐ North American NA-122 Mustang (P-51D) (FSM)	'413926'			PVX
☐ North American NA-191 Sabre (F-86F)	1A36		(USAF)	PV
☐ North American NA-242 Sabre (F-86K)			Front fuselage only.	RA
☐ North American NA-354 Bronco (OV-10E)	2641	354-2	Bu159058	PV
☐ North American NA-398 Buckeye (T-2D)	3861	398-9	Bu160236	RA
☐ Rans S-6 Coyote II	1052			RA
☐ Republic P-47D Thunderbolt	10B36	195-3770	44-32809, 10B36	PV
☐ Republic P-47D Thunderbolt	8A36	399-53775	44-32814	RA
☐ Scheibe 138 Specht				PV
☐ Sikorsky S-55D Chickasaw (H-19B) (UH-19B)	4AHR1	55911	52-7578, 4BHR1	PV
☐ Sud-Est SE.3160 Alouette III	2112			PV
☐ Vultee V-74A Valiant (BT-15)	E-26		42-33300, YV-E-MR-??, ET-4	PV
☐ Westland-Sikorsky WS-51 Dragonfly HR.5	1HR1	WA/H/56	WG725	PVX

MUSEO CIUDAD BOLIVAR (VE9)

Address:	Aeropuerto Ciudad Bolivar, Avenida Jesus Soto, Ciudad Bolivar.
Tel:	085-26-279
Admission:	Aircraft on permanent view.
Location:	At the airport which is just south of the town.

In 1937 Jimmy Angel carried out a search for Paul Redfern's aircraft which was lost ten years earlier. Piloting a Flamingo he discovered the world's highest waterfall, now named Angel Falls, plunging some three thousand feet. On September 9th 1937 he landed at the base of the falls near Auyantepuy and abandoned the aircraft after it became stuck in the soggy ground. The crew of three trekked through the jungle for two weeks before reaching their camp. The Flamingo, named 'El Rio Caroni', was recovered by the Air Force in 1970 and rebuilt for display. Just over twenty examples of the Flamingo G-2 were built at Cincinnati in 1929/30.

TYPE	REG/SER	CON. NO.	PI/NOTES	STATUS
☐ Flamingo G-2-W	NC9487	11		PV

MUSEO DEL TRANSPORTE 'GUILLERMO J. SCHAEL' (VE10)

Address:	Avenida Francisco de Miranda, Parque Nacional del Este, Caracas.
Tel:	0212-224-2234
Email:	museotransporte@cantv.net
Admission:	Wednesday-Friday 0800-1600; Saturday-Sunday 0900-1700.
Location:	On the east side of the city close to the airport.

Displays of all forms of transport can be seen in this museum which opened in October 1970. On show are cars, commercial vehicles, railway engines, rolling stock and boats. Some of these are in working order. Scale models showing the city as it was a century ago are of particular interest. The Aeronca Champion, now at the Air Force Museum, the Dakota and the Skyvan were all used by the Ministry of Communications before being donated to the museum. The Skyvan, a recent arrival, is one of four bought by the Ministry in 1976/7. Two former Air Force aircraft are also on show. The Cornell spent some time in private hands when its military days were over. The local aero club and private owners often put park their aircraft near the hangar. There is a possibility that the museum may move to another site.

TYPE	REG/SER	CON. NO.	PI/NOTES	STATUS
☐ Balloon				PV
☐ Beech D18S	YV-521C		GN-5210	PV
☐ Beech D50 Twin Bonanza				PV
☐ Beech 65-B80 Queen Air	YV-130P	LD-455		PV
☐ Beech 65-B80 Queen Air	YV-700P	LD-476	YV-TAFV	PV
☐ Beech 95-B55 Baron	YV-348P	TC-826	YV-T-LTA	PV
☐ Champion 7EC Traveler	YV-E-MR20	7EC-346	On loan to Mus. Aer. FAV	–
☐ Douglas DC-3A-456 Skytrain (C-47A)	YV-O-MC1	19335	42-100872, YV-O-MC	PV
☐ Fairchild M-62A Cornell (PT-19A)	YV-T-NTR	T43-7257	43-33672	PV
☐ Microlight				PV
☐ North American NA-88 Texan (AT-6C)	E-98		(USAAF) – at nearby garage.	PV
☐ Piper PA-23-150 Apache	YV-T-JTQ	23-834	C-FYZZ, N879	PV

TYPE	REG/SER	CON. NO.	PI/NOTES	STATUS
☐ Short SC.7 Skyvan 3-100	YV-O-MTC-9	SH.1949	G-14-117, G-BDVO, YV-O-MC-9, YV-O-MTC-9, YV-O-MC-9	PV

MUSEO HISTÓRICO MILITAR (VE11)

Address:	Colina Cajigal, Parque El Calvario, La Planicie, Caracas 1010.
Tel:	0212-484-5175
Admission:	Wednesday-Sunday 0930-1700.
Location:	In the centre of the city.

This museum, which opened in March 1979, is housed in the former Military School and Ministry of Defence buildings. The military history of the country is traced in a series of imaginative displays. There are sections devoted to the struggle for independence and the local conflicts which have since occurred. On show are weapons, uniforms, photographs, documents and vehicles. The only aircraft is the former Luftwaffe Sabre.

TYPE	REG/SER	CON. NO.	PI/NOTES	STATUS
☐ North American NA-242 Sabre (F-86K)	0984	242-31	56-4146, JE+243, JD+243, JD+343	PV

PARQUE RECREACIONAL DE EJÉRCITO (VE12)

Address:	Fuerte Tiuna, Caracas.
Admission:	By prior permission only.
Location:	In the southern suburbs of the city.

This large army base in the city houses a number of units. Helicopters are frequent visitors to the site. The Military Academy is located within its boundaries. A large tree lined avenue has been constructed and along this are monuments honouring the National Heros of Venezuela. Three aircraft have been preserved in the recreational area of the site. In 1972 Venezuela obtained sixteen Canadian built Northrop Freedom Fighters.

TYPE	REG/SER	CON. NO.	PI/NOTES	STATUS
☐ Canadair CL-219 Freedom Fighter (CF-5A) (CF-116) [Northrop N-156A]	7200	1073	116773	RA
☐ North American NA-221 Sabre (F-86K)	0002	221-135	55-4895, JD+253, JD+353 – probably a composite with c/n 242-20 56-4135, JE+232, JD+232, JD+332	RA
☐ North American NA-242 Sabre (F-86K)	0178	242-11	56-4126, JE+122, JD+122, JD+332	RA

The Venezuelan Ministry of Transport operated this Short Skyvan. The aircraft is now at the Transport Museum in Caracas. (Mike Nelson)

INDEX

All aircraft are listed alphabetically by manufacturer or designer (in the case of some gliders and homebuilt aircraft) followed by the type. Each country is denoted by a two/three letter code and each museum/collection a number e.g. CU10 is tenth museum/collection in alphabetical order in Cuba.

Country codes are as follows:-
ARG Argentina; **BO** Bolivia; **BR** Brazil; **CH** Chile; **COL** Colombia; **EC** Ecuador; **FI** Falklands Islands; **PAR** Paraguay; **PE** Peru; **UR** Uruguay; **VE** Venezuela:

The Argentine National Aviation Museum is home to this Fairchild 82D (Nigel Hitchman)